MONOGRAPHS IN CONTACT ALLERGY

Series Editor: Anton C. de Groot

Monographs in Contact Allergy, Volume 1: Non-Fragrance Allergens in Cosmetics
(Part 1 and Part 2)

MONOGRAPHS IN CONTACT ALLERGY
VOLUME 1, PART 1

NON-FRAGRANCE ALLERGENS IN COSMETICS

MONOGRAPHS IN CONTACT ALLERGY
VOLUME 1, PART 1

NON-FRAGRANCE ALLERGENS IN COSMETICS

Anton C. de Groot

With the help of Heleen de Jong in drawing the structural formulas

CRC Press
Taylor & Francis Group
Boca Raton London New York

CRC Press is an imprint of the
Taylor & Francis Group, an **informa** business

CRC Press
Taylor & Francis Group
6000 Broken Sound Parkway NW, Suite 300
Boca Raton, FL 33487-2742

© 2018 by Taylor & Francis Group, LLC
CRC Press is an imprint of Taylor & Francis Group, an Informa business

First issued in paperback 2021

No claim to original U.S. Government works

ISBN 13: 978-1-03-207886-1 (pbk)(set)
ISBN 13: 978-1-03-207868-7 (pbk)(part 1)
ISBN 13: 978-1-03-207872-4 (pbk)(part 2)
ISBN 13: 978-1-138-56113-7 (hbk)(set),
ISBN 13: 978-1-138-57325-3 (hbk)(part 1)
ISBN 13: 978-1-138-57338-3 (hbk)(part 2)

Visit the Taylor & Francis Web site at
http://www.taylorandfrancis.com

and the CRC Press Web site at
http://www.crcpress.com

Publisher's Note
The publisher has gone to great lengths to ensure the quality of this reprint but points out that some imperfections in the original copies may be apparent.

Contents

PART 1   2.279   Lonicera japonica (honeysuckle) flower extract..732
               2.280   Macadamia ternifolia seed oil...733
               2.281   Magnolia grandiflora bark extract...734
               2.282   Magnolia officinalis bark extract..735
               2.283   Maleated soybean oil..736
               2.284   Mandelic acid..737
               2.285   Menthoxypropanediol...738
               2.286   Methenamine...739
               2.287   Methoxy PEG-17 dodecyl glycol copolymer..742

PART 2

               2.288   Methoxy PEG-22 dodecyl glycol copolymer.. 745
               2.289   Methyl acrylate 747
               2.290   p-Methylaminophenol...749
               2.291   4-Methylbenzylidene camphor..751
               2.292   Methylchloroisothiazolinone (and) methylisothiazolinone..............................757
               2.293   Methyldibromo glutaronitrile..791
               2.294   Methyldibromo glutaronitrile/phenoxyethanol... 804
               2.295   Methyl dihydroxybenzoate... 812
               2.296   Methylene bis-benzotriazolyl tetramethylbutylphenol................................... 813
               2.297   Methyl glucose dioleate... 815
               2.298   Methyl glucose sesquistearate... 817
               2.299   Methylisothiazolinone... 818
               2.300   Methyl methacrylate.. 839
               2.301   Methyl nicotinate.. 843
               2.302   Methylparaben.. 845
               2.303   Miscellaneous cosmetic ingredients.. 850
                        2.303.1   Aluminum compounds (unspecified).................................... 850
                        2.303.2   Botanical products (miscellaneous) 850
                        2.303.3   CI 15880 (D&C red no. 34) 850
                        2.303.4   Euphorbia extract (unspecified) 850
                        2.303.5   α-Glycerol ester of o-amino-m-(2,3-dihydroxypropoxy)benzoic acid........... 851
                        2.303.6   Labilin® 851
                        2.303.7   Lipacide-cas.. 851
                        2.303.8   Mercury.. 852
                        2.303.9   Miranol® MSA..852
                        2.303.10   Polyester resin (trimellitic anhydride, adipic acid, neopentyl glycol and
                                    cyclohexanedimethanol) 852
                        2.303.11   Procaine... 852
                        2.303.12   Sodium dihydroxycetyl phosphate isopropyl hydroxycetyl ether...............853
                        2.303.13   Zirconium compounds.. 853
               2.304   Monobenzone.. 855
               2.305   Myristic acid... 858
               2.306   Myristyl alcohol... 859
               2.307   Myristyl glucoside..861
               2.308   2,7-Naphthalenediol.. 863
               2.309   Neopentyl glycol diisooctanoate... 865
               2.310   Nickel..866
               2.311   Nitrocellulose.. 869
               2.312   3-Nitro-p-hydroxyethylaminophenol.. 870
               2.313   2-Nitro-p-phenylenediamine... 872
               2.314   Nordihydroguaiaretic acid.. 875
               2.315   Octocrylene.. 876
               2.316   Octyldodecanol... 882
               2.317   Octyldodecyl xyloside.. 884
               2.318   Olaflur.. 885

PREFACE

Cosmetics (which include 'toiletries' such as soap, shampoo, toothpaste *et cetera*) are used by virtually everyone and most people have contact with cosmetic products on a daily base, often more than once a day and with several such products. Therefore, it can hardly come as a surprise that some consumers will develop contact allergy to and allergic contact dermatitis from one or more cosmetics. Related to their extremely widespread use, contact allergic reactions to them are not very frequent. Nevertheless, in several investigations in the general population of some European countries, estimations of the prevalence of sensitization to non-fragrance chemicals used in cosmetics were up to 0.5% for parabens, 0.9% for methylchloroisothiazolinone (and) methylisothiazolinone, 1.4% for colophonium, 1.4% for lanolin alcohol and 1.6% for *p*-phenylenediamine. This does not mean that all these individuals suffer or have suffered from allergic cosmetic dermatitis, but they do have the potential to develop allergic reactions to cosmetic products. In patients seen by dermatologists for suspected contact dermatitis, however, reactions to cosmetics are frequent, with prevalences ranging from 5% in general dermatology practices to 20% in specialized clinics.

Therefore, it is important that dermatologists, allergists and other professionals performing patch tests should have (access to) sufficient knowledge of the ingredients of cosmetics causing allergic contact dermatitis, both to provide optimal diagnostic services and to be able to properly counsel patients after the diagnosis of allergic contact dermatitis from an ingredient of a cosmetic product has been made. In all recent textbooks on contact dermatitis, chapters are devoted to cosmetic allergy and to allergenic components, e.g., fragrances, preservatives and hair dyes. However, there is not a single book providing in-depth reviews of cosmetic allergens. In scientific journals, several articles have reviewed the subject of 'contact allergy to cosmetics' or have discussed groups of allergenic cosmetic ingredients or individual ones. Although such articles are useful, many are – inevitably – rather superficial, others are incomplete or getting (somewhat) older, so that their information is not up-to-date anymore. In fact, the great majority of cosmetic allergens have not been (properly) reviewed and relevant information, if searched for, has to be obtained from many different sources.

Therefore, the author, who has been interested in contact allergy to cosmetics since the early 1980s, decided to create an all-encompassing reference work covering the full spectrum of chemicals and substances that have caused contact allergy by their presence in cosmetic products. In this book, *non-fragrance* allergens in cosmetics are discussed. A total of 497 ingredients in cosmetics that have caused contact allergy/allergic contact dermatitis are presented in Monographs. The information provided for each allergen includes a thorough identification with INCI name, chemical/IUPAC name, other names (synonyms), CAS registry number, EC (European Community) number(s), and their molecular and structural formulas (where applicable). Also, a general description/definition of the compounds is provided, the chemical class(es) to which they belong, and whether and where more information can be found in reviews and monographs published by CIR (Cosmetic Ingredient Review), the Merck Index and European Union SCCS/SCCP/SCCFNP Opinions, and in addition EU cosmetic restrictions. The functions of the chemicals in cosmetics, both in the EU and the USA are mentioned and an advice on patch test concentration and vehicle is shown.

The information provided is not limited to cosmetic allergy but includes – where applicable and available - the results of studies performing patch testing in (subgroups of) the general population, in groups of consecutive patients suspected of contact dermatitis (routine testing) and in groups of selected patients, case reports and case series of cosmetic allergy, case reports and case series of allergy to the chemical in non-cosmetic products, cross-reactions, reports of patch test sensitization, their presence in cosmetic products and chemical analyses, results of ROATs and serial dilution testing, other side effects such as irritant contact dermatitis, photosensitivity, immediate-type reactions, other non-eczematous reactions, systemic side effects from percutaneous absorption and any other information found in literature considered by the author to be relevant to the readers. For each allergen, for example, data on their use in cosmetics in the USA from FDA's Voluntary Cosmetic Registration Program are given. There are additional chapters presenting alphabetical lists of all synonyms indicating their INCI names and lists of all functional groups (antioxidants, preservatives, artificial nail building, emollients, hair dyeing, hair colorants etc.) in both the EU and the USA formats with all chemicals in these groups that have caused cosmetic allergy.

'Monographs in Contact Allergy I' presents detailed information on allergic reactions to ingredients of cosmetics and many other data, of which a substantial part which will not be found by searching in PubMed and other medical and chemical databases. The two-part book gives full coverage of all aspects of non-fragrance allergens in cosmetics not only for dermatologists and allergists to improve levels of medical knowledge and quality of patient care, but also for the benefit of professionals beyond clinical study and practice, such as cosmetic chemists and other researchers developing and marketing cosmetic products, as well as legislators.

This is the first volume in a planned series of Monographs in Contact Allergy. In a second volume, fragrances will be presented and in a third, contact allergy to topical and systemic drugs is planned to be reviewed in-depth.

Anton de Groot, MD, PhD
Wapserveen, The Netherlands, September 2017

ACKNOWLEDGMENTS

The author is very grateful to the following organizations and individuals:

- to the U.S. Food and Drug Administration (FDA) for providing data on the frequency of use of cosmetic ingredients from FDA's Voluntary Cosmetic Registration Program (VCRP)

- to the Personal Care Products Council for permission to use many data of their Personal Care Products Council Ingredient Database in the Identification section of each Monograph, including Description/definition, Chemical class(es), INCI name, Function(s) in cosmetics and sometimes the Structural formulas

- to ACS Publications for permission to use copyrighted data in Chapter 2.408 Shellac

- to dr. ir. Dirk van Aken, chemist, who gave me much useful chemistry information where my knowledge on the subject was insufficient

- and to Heleen de Jong BSc, who spent much time in meticulously drawing the beautiful structural formulas shown in this book

ABOUT THE AUTHOR

Anton C. de Groot, MD, PhD (1951) received his medical and specialist training at the University of Groningen, The Netherlands. In 1980, he started his career as dermatologist in private practice in 's-Hertogenbosch. At that time, he had already become interested in contact allergy and in side effects of drugs by writing the chapter 'Drugs used on the skin' with his mentor prof. Johan Nater, for the famous 'Meyler's Side Effects of Drugs' series. Soon, the subject of this chapter in new Editions and the yearly 'Side Effects of Drugs Annuals' would be expanded to include oral drugs used in dermatology and cosmetics (1980-2000). Contact allergy to cosmetics would become de Groot's main area of interest and expertise and in 1988, he received his PhD degree on his Thesis entitled 'Adverse Reactions to Cosmetics', supervised by prof. Nater (see the back cover).

Frustrated by the lack of easily accessible information on the ingredients of cosmetic products, and convinced that compulsory ingredient labeling of cosmetics (which at that time was already implemented in the USA) would benefit both consumers and allergic patients and would lead to only slight and temporary disadvantages to the cosmetics industry, De Groot approached the newly founded European Society of Contact Dermatitis and became Chairman of the Working Party European Community Affairs. The European Commission and its committees, elected legislators, national trade, health departments and the cosmetics industries were extensively lobbied. This resulted in new legislation by the Commission of the European Communities in 1991, making ingredient labeling mandatory for all cosmetic products sold in EC Member States by December 31, 1997.

Anton has been the chairman of the 'Contact Dermatitis Group' of the Dutch Society for Dermatology and Venereology from 1984 to 1998. In 1990, he was one of the founders of the Nederlands Tijdschrift voor Dermatologie en Venereologie (Dutch Journal of Dermatology and Venereology) and was Editor of this scientific journal for 20 years, of which he served 10 years as Editor-in-chief.

De Groot has authored thirteen books, nine of which – all co-authored by Johan Toonstra MD, PhD – are general dermatology books in Dutch for medical students, general practitioners, 'skin therapists' (huidtherapeuten, a paramedical profession largely restricted to The Netherlands) and pedicures and podotherapists; in addition, he wrote a booklet 'Living with Eczema' for patients with atopic eczema and their parents. Anton also authored three international books, of which two have had three Editions: 'Unwanted Effects of Cosmetics and Drugs used in Dermatology' (first Edition 1983, second 1985, third 1994) and 'Patch Testing' (first Edition 1986, second 1994, third 2008) (www.patchtesting.info); the 4th Edition of 'Patch Testing' is planned for 2018.

His most recent international book 'Essential Oils: Contact Allergy and Chemical Composition', that he wrote with Erich Schmidt, appeared in 2016 and was very well received by dermatologists, the essential oils and fragrance industries and other disciplines. In addition, Anton has written over 60 book chapters (mostly in international books), over 125 articles in international journals and some 240 articles in Dutch medical and paramedical journals. He served as board member of several journals including 'Dermatosen' and is currently member of the Editorial Advisory Board of the Journal 'Dermatitis'. His most recent project is writing the second volume of the 'Monographs in Contact Allergy' series: 'Fragrance Allergens and Essential Oils'.

Since 2012, De Groot has been consulting dermatologist and participant in CESES (Consumer Exposure Skin Effects and Surveillance), a Dutch Cosmetovigilance system monitoring side effects of cosmetics in The Netherland, performed by the National Institute for Public Health and the Environment by order of the Netherlands Food and Consumer Product Safety Authority.

Anton de Groot has retired from dermatology practice, but since 2008 regularly teaches general dermatology to junior medical doctors at the University of Groningen. He and his wife Janny have two daughters, both lawyers.

CHAPTER 1   INTRODUCTION

1.1 WHY A BOOK WITH MONOGRAPHS OF NON-FRAGRANCE ALLERGENS IN COSMETICS?

Allergic contact dermatitis from cosmetics is common. In a tertiary referral center in Valencia, Spain, for example, in the period 1996-2013, nearly 12% of 5419 patch tested patients had allergic contact dermatitis to cosmetics (1). In Leuven, Belgium, in a clinic with special interest in cosmetic allergy, 1055 of 6596 (16%) patch tested patients suffered from adverse reactions to cosmetics in the period 1990-2000, which had increased to 1296 of 6234 (21%) tested in the following decade (2000-2010) (73).

Therefore, it is important that dermatologists, allergists and other professionals performing patch tests should have a thorough knowledge of the ingredients of cosmetics causing allergic contact dermatitis, both to provide optimal diagnostic services and to be able to properly counsel patients after the diagnosis of allergic contact dermatitis from an ingredient of a cosmetic product has been made.

In all recent textbooks on contact dermatitis, several chapters are devoted to cosmetic allergy and to allergenic components, e.g., fragrances, preservatives, hair dyes, and/or the allergens in the European baseline series which may cause cosmetic contact dermatitis: *p*-phenylenediamine, colophonium, parabens, lanolin alcohol, formaldehyde, quaternium-15, methylchloroisothiazolinone (and) methylisothiazolinone, methylisothiazolinone, methyldibromo glutaronitrile and the fragrance mix(es) (3,4,5,6). However, only one book appears to have presented a large number of monographs on contact allergens (2). Unfortunately, this 1992 loose-leaf book was in German only and on the current website of the Publisher, the title cannot be found, so it may be assumed that it is no longer available (https://www.ecomed-storck.de).

In scientific journals, in the period 2004-2017, several articles have reviewed the subject of 'contact allergy to cosmetics' (32,51,53,59,63,64,65,81) or have discussed groups of allergenic cosmetic ingredients such as alkyl glucosides (17), allergens in nail cosmetics (mostly [meth]acrylates in artificial nails [14]), benzophenones (25), copolymers (62), fragrances (29,55,56,65,66), gallate esters (16), parabens (48), plants extracts in cosmetics (54,65), preservatives (30,31,49), sunscreens (24,26,27,28 [28 = photocontact allergy]), tocopherol and its derivatives (42), and new, emergent and unusual allergens (33,44,58). Other authors have reviewed specific allergens in cosmetics: cocamidopropyl betaine (60,61), lanolin (46), methyldibromo glutaronitrile/phenoxyethanol (43), methyl-chloroisothiazolinone (and) methylisothiazolinone (52), methylisothiazolinone (38,39,40,41,52), *Myroxylon pereirae* resin (Balsam of Peru [34]), propolis (47), *p*-phenylenediamine (45), and sodium metabisulfite (57).

The author of this book has written general reviews of formaldehyde and formaldehyde-releasers in cosmetics (7,8,9) and in-depths reviews of contact allergy to octocrylene (10), propolis (11,12), henna (including black henna, not a cosmetic, but used for cosmetic purposes and containing *p*-phenylenediamine, a very important cosmetic allergen in hair dyes) (13), ingredients of toothpastes (15), and essential oils (18,19,20,21,22,23). Contact urticaria from cosmetic ingredients was recently reviewed (50) and this also applies to type-I reactions to chlorhexidine, which are, however, never caused by cosmetic products (35,36,37).

Although all articles are useful, some are rather superficial (which is in the case of 'allergy to cosmetics' of course unavoidable), others are incomplete (especially the larger groups of ingredients of which much literature is available), or are getting somewhat older, so that their information is not up-to-date anymore. Most cosmetic allergens have not been (properly) reviewed and relevant information, if searched for, has to be obtained from many different sources.

Therefore, the author, who has been interested in contact allergy to and other side effects of cosmetics since the early 1980s (67,68,69,70), decided to create an all-encompassing reference work covering the full spectrum of chemicals/substances that have caused contact allergy by their presence in cosmetic products. In this first volume, **non-fragrance** allergens in cosmetics are discussed. In the second volume, fragrances, and possibly essential oils, will be presented.

The author is aware that the terms 'allergen' and 'allergens' are *sensu stricto* not correct and should read 'hapten' and 'haptens'. However, in scientific journals dedicated to contact dermatitis and contact allergy such as *Contact Dermatitis* and *Dermatitis* the term allergen is still often used and is also familiar to physicians, who are not experts in the field and to non-physicians. Therefore, the term allergen is used throughout this book.

1.2 DATA PROVIDED IN THIS BOOK

SCOPE AND DATA COLLECTING

This book provides monographs on all chemicals/substances that have caused contact allergy to / allergic contact dermatitis from their presence in cosmetic products (Chapter 2). In addition, cosmetic ingredients that have caused immediate-type reactions (e.g., contact urticaria), but *not* contact allergy (Chapter 3) or photocontact allergy but *not* contact allergy (Chapter 4) were included.

The main sources of information were:
- the journals *Contact Dermatitis* and *Dermatitis*, that were fully screened from their start in 1975 resp. 1990 through September 2017 (Contact Dermatitis 2017;66:issue 3) and July/August 2017 (Dermatitis 2017;28:issue 4);
- the author's 1988 PhD Thesis *Adverse reactions to cosmetics*, in which all previous literature on cosmetic allergy has been presented (or at least cited);
- the author's books *Unwanted Effects of Cosmetics and Drugs used in Dermatology* (67,68,69) and other reference works: several editions of *Fisher's Contact Dermatitis* (6) and Etain Cronin's 1980 book *Contact Dermatitis* (71);
- relevant articles found in literature lists of journal publications used for the book; most of these could be accessed on-line through the Medical Library of the University of Groningen; important articles that were not accessible on-line were requested from the library and obtained digitally;
- all journals available on-line through the Medical Library of the University of Groningen; before finishing a monograph (in the period January - August 2017), the ingredient name was searched for in PubMed and any additional relevant articles and data were added;
- the new journal *Cosmetics* (not indexed in NLM-catalog).

Sometimes, relevant articles could neither be accessed on-line nor were they requested. If some relevant information was available, e.g., from the Abstract or from being cited in other sources, it was included, in the latter situation mentioning that the information was cited in another article. If data from such articles were missing, this is indicated with 'data missing / specific data unknown, article not read' in the Monograph text.

CRITERIA FOR INCLUSION
To be included in this book, chemicals/substances had to meet one or more of the following criteria:
- they were presented in a case report as causing contact allergy / allergic contact dermatitis and/or immediate-type reactions and/or photosensitivity from their presence in cosmetic products;
- the chemical/substance was mentioned in a list of chemicals that had caused contact allergy to cosmetics (1,72,73 74,75,76,77);
- the chemical was mentioned in a list of allergens found in a group of patients exclusively caused by cosmetics, where it was implied that it was the cause of allergic contact dermatitis (78);
- they were presented in a case report of an allergic reaction to products which are strictly speaking not cosmetic products but which are used for cosmetic purposes or can be considered to be cosmeceuticals (e.g., hair stimulant lotions, diaper rash products);
- when a positive patch test to a chemical/substance was specifically stated to the cause of cosmetic allergy by the author(s);
- all other situations where contact allergy / immediate-type reaction / photosensitivity was not proven but considered to be very likely by the investigators and/or the author; this applies to, for example, newer UV-filters that have caused contact allergy and/or photocontact allergy in groups of patients suspected of photosensitivity or photocontact dermatitis, but where the relevance of these reactions was not specifically stated (e.g., ref. 79).

For historical reasons, the colors that may have caused many cases of pigmented cosmetic dermatitis in Japan in the 1970s were included, although their presence in the products used by these individuals was probably not ascertained. Ingredients of cosmetics that are prohibited in the EU or are mentioned neither in the EU nor in the USA INCI nomenclature (in which case it is highly unlikely that they are used in cosmetics in the EU or the USA) were still included if they met one or more criteria mentioned above. In a number of these (and other) articles, the author had doubts about their validity and conclusions drawn; this is always mentioned in the text.

SEARCH RESULTS
The search resulted in the identification of 497 non-fragrance ingredients in cosmetics that have caused contact allergy / allergic contact dermatitis; these are all presented as monographs in Chapter 2. Eight-two of these cosmetic allergens had also caused immediate-type reactions, either from their presence in cosmetics or in non-cosmetic products (Chapter 3, table 3.2). Sixty-five of the 497 had also caused photosensitivity reactions, mostly photocontact allergy or photoallergic contact dermatitis, virtually always from their presence in sunscreen products and other cosmetics (Chapter 4, table 4.1).
Eighteen chemicals/substances caused immediate-type reactions to cosmetics but *not* contact allergy and five caused photosensitivity but *not* contact allergy; these are presented as monographs in Chapter 3 (Immediate-type reactions) and Chapter 4 (Photosensitivity).

DATA PROVIDED IN MONOGRAPHS
For each chemical/substance that was included, the data shown in table 1.1 – when available and relevant - were searched for. It shows that the information provided is – with few exceptions - not limited to effects and data directly related to cosmetic products. For most chemicals, is has been attempted to provide a full (medical) literature

review. Where this was virtually impossible because of the extensiveness of available published documentation (e.g., *p*-phenylenediamine, propolis, colophonium), this is stated in the Monograph.

Table 1.1 Information provided (when available) in each monograph

IDENTIFICATION	CONTACT ALLERGY
Description/definition	Patch testing in groups of patients
Chemical class(es)	Case reports and case series
INCI name USA	Contact allergy in non-cosmetic products
Chemical/IUPAC name	Cross-reactions, pseudo-cross-reactions and co-reactions
Other names	
CAS registry number (s)	Patch test sensitization
EC number(s)	Presence in cosmetic products and chemical analyses
CIR review(s)	Other information
SCCS/SCCP/SCCFNP opinion(s)	**OTHER SIDE EFFECTS**
Merck Index monograph	Irritant contact dermatitis
Function(s) in cosmetics (EU, USA)	Photosensitivity
EU cosmetic restrictions	Immediate-type reactions
Patch testing	Other non-eczematous contact reactions
Molecular formula	Systemic side effects
Structural formula	Miscellaneous side effects
	OTHER INFORMATION

IDENTIFICATION

In the section **IDENTIFICATION** the chemicals are identified by INCI name (EU name; USA name is mentioned only when different from EU name), chemical/IUPAC (International Union of Pure and Applied Chemistry) name, other names (synonyms), CAS (Chemical Abstract Service) registry (www.cas.org) number(s), EC (European Community) (formerly: EINECS [European Inventory of Existing Commercial Chemical Substances]) number(s), and their molecular and structural formulas (where applicable). Also, a general description/definition of the compounds is provided, the chemical class(es) to which they belong, and whether and where more information can be found in reviews and monographs published by CIR (Cosmetic Ingredient Review), and in the Merck Index. Reference is made to any published European Union SCCS (Scientific Committee on Consumer Safety), SCCP (Scientific Committee on Consumer Products) or SCCFNP (Scientific Committee on Cosmetic Products and Non-Food Products Intended for Consumers) Opinions (back to June 1997) and EU cosmetic restrictions. The functions of the chemicals in cosmetics, both in the EU and the USA are mentioned and an advice on how to patch test the chemical/substance is provided in each Monograph.

For this section, the extremely useful Personal Care Products Council (formerly Cosmetic, Toiletry and Fragrance Association) on-line database has been consulted heavily and the Council's permission to use and publish these data is gratefully acknowledged. The sources of data provided in the section **IDENTIFICATION** are shown below.

IDENTIFICATION	Sources
Description/definition	1, sometimes 2
Chemical class(es)	1
INCI name USA	1
Chemical/IUPAC name	1,2,3,4,5,6,7; 4 (IUPAC name)
Other names	1,3,4,5,6,7, sometimes 2
CAS registry number (s)	1,2,3,4,5,6,7
EC number(s)	1,2,11
CIR review(s)	8
SCCS/SCCP/SCCFNP opinion(s)	2,12
Merck Index monograph	9
Function(s) in cosmetics (EU, USA)	2 (EU), 1 (USA)
EU cosmetic restrictions	2
Patch testing	10
Molecular formula	1,3,4,5,6,7
Structural formula	1,3,4,5,6,7 (all structural formulas have been drawn by Heleen de Jong BSc)

Sources

1   The Personal Care Products Council (formerly Cosmetic, Toiletry and Fragrance Association) on-line ingredient database: http://online.personalcarecouncil.org/jsp/Home.jsp (choose Ingredient database) (subscription only); when no description was available (with chemicals not mentioned in the database, ergo no USA INCI name available), the description and chemical classes were assigned by dr. ir. Dirk van Aken, chemist

2   The European Commission database with information on cosmetic substances and ingredients CosIng: http://ec. europa. eu/growth/tools-databases/cosing/

3   United States National Library of Medicine ChemIDPlus Advanced database: http://chem.sis.nlm.nih.gov/chemid plus/

4   PubChem: http://pubchem.ncbi.nlm.nih.gov/

5   ChemicalBook Inc.: www.chemicalbook.com

6   Chemspider: www.chemspider.com

7   Miscellaneous databases and websites found through Google search

8   Cosmetic Ingredient Review: http://www.cir-safety.org/

9   The Merck Index online: https://www.rsc.org/merck-index

10 Providers of patch test allergens: Chemotechnique Diagnostics (www.chemotechnique.se), SmartPractice EUROPE (www.smartpracticeeurope.com) and SmartPractice CANADA (www.smartpracticecanada.com). If not available from these suppliers, the test concentration(s) as used in the publication(s) was mentioned. If no patch test concentration/vehicle was given in the article (e.g., the name was mentioned in a list of allergens that had been found in cosmetics without giving specifics), a or the test concentration as given in the author's book 'Patch Testing', 3rd Edition, is mentioned (80)

11 ECHA European Chemicals Agency, EC Inventory: https://echa.europa.eu/information-on-chemicals/ec-inventory

12 European Commission Health and Food Safety Scientific Committees: https://ec.europa.eu/health/scientific_committees/consumer_safety/opinions_en

CONTACT ALLERGY AND ALL OTHER DATA

Patch testing in groups of patients

This section shows the results of studies performing patch testing in (subgroups of) the general population, in groups of consecutive patients suspected of contact dermatitis (routine testing) and in groups of selected patients, e.g., patients suspected of cosmetic allergy, patients with leg ulcers, hairdressers with occupational contact dermatitis, or children with suspected contact dermatitis. Data provided include country/countries of the study, period of study, patch test concentration and vehicle used, number of patients tested, number of patients and percentage with positive patch tests, mode of selection, relevance (both percentage and products), other relevant information (in the Comment section) and literature references.

Case reports and case series

Case reports are mostly the description of one, two or three patients with allergic cosmetic dermatitis. Clinical descriptions are given when only one or a few case reports for a particular chemical/substance have been published. The more case reports were found in literature, the less information is provided (usually limited to number of patients, causative products and sometimes localization of dermatitis). Case series are mostly series of 4 or more patients, but far more often the number of patients in lists of causative ingredients in patients with certain or very probable allergic cosmetic dermatitis (1,72,73,74,75,76,77,78).

Contact allergy in non-cosmetic products

Case reports and case series of allergic contact dermatitis from the presence of the chemical/substance in any non-cosmetic product are presented here. Sometimes, only one or a few cases of cosmetic allergy have been described, but many reactions to the allergen in non-cosmetic products have been reported, e.g., in the case of colophonium, benzalkonium chloride and thimerosal; these are all presented in this section of each Monograph.

Cross-reactions, pseudo-cross-reactions and co-reactions

It is often very difficult, if not impossible, to determine whether co-reactions (concomitant positive patch tests) to other chemicals are the result of cross-reactivity (contact allergic reaction to a molecularly similar chemical to which the individual has not yet been exposed), of pseudo-cross-reactions (the index chemical and the co-reacting chemical have the same allergenic constituent, contaminant, metabolite or oxidant product) or (simply) co-reactions, independent of each other. The archetype of cross-reactions are *p*-phenylenediamine and other substituted para-amino compounds, including *p*-aminophenol and toluene-2,5-diamine. A reaction to *p*-aminophenol in a patient sensitized to *p*-phenylenediamine may be the result of cross-reactivity, but can also result from concomitant or successive sensitization in the same or other product(s). Examples of pseudo-cross-reactions are positive patch tests to one or more formaldehyde-releasers such as quaternium-15, diazolidinyl urea, methenamine and imidazolidinyl urea in patients sensitized to formaldehyde. Co-reactions may be the result of sensitization to two or more molecularly unrelated substances appearing simultaneously, but can also indicate concomitant or successive sensitization to structurally similar chemicals.

In this section, chemicals are identified that are certainly or likely able to cross-react or pseudo-cross-react to the monographed chemical/substance. In addition, reactions to compounds that are chemically unrelated but appear statistically more often than in patients not allergic to the index chemical are mentioned. This has been observed especially in patients allergic to methylisothiazolinone and/or methyl(chloro)isothiazolinone, who frequently have concomitant positive reactions to the fragrance mixes I and II and to other preservatives, notably formaldehyde and formaldehyde-releasers. These combined positive patch test reactions are from concomitant or successive sensitization in the same or other (cosmetic) products rather than from cross-reactivity.

Patch test sensitization
Late reactions (>7 days) are accepted as patch test sensitization and presented in the section only, when the patient has been retested and in the second patch test session had a positive patch test after 2-4 days.

Presence in cosmetic products and chemical analyses
Next to data from published studies, information on the frequency of use of chemicals in cosmetics in the USA is presented, based on FDA's Voluntary Cosmetic Registration Program (data obtained from FDA, May 2017) and from EWG's Skin Deep Cosmetics Database, USA (http://www.ewg.org/skindeep/).

Other information
This may include results of Repeated Open Application tests, other provocation tests, serial dilution testing or any other subject related to contact allergy which is not discussed elsewhere.

OTHER SIDE EFFECTS

Irritant contact dermatitis
Irritant contact dermatitis may infrequently be caused by products containing a high concentration of a known irritant, e.g., benzalkonium chloride. Of course, the causal role of the chemical *per se* in the product is hardly ever proven.

Photosensitivity
Photosensitivity reactions include photocontact allergy (causing photoallergic contact dermatitis), phototoxicity (causing phototoxic dermatitis) and combined photocontact allergy and contact allergy, causing photoaggravated allergic contact dermatitis. Because it can easily be avoided, phototoxicity is rare. Most photosensitivity reactions from chemicals used in cosmetics are photocontact allergic.

This section shows the results of studies performing photopatch testing in groups of selected patients, usually individuals suspected of photosensitivity, photocontact allergy or reactions to sunscreen products. Data provided include country/countries of the study, period of study, photopatch test concentration and vehicle used, number of patients tested, number of patients and percentage with positive patch tests, mode of selection, relevance (both percentage and products), other relevant information (in the Comment section) and literature references. Monographed chemicals that have caused photoallergic contact dermatitis (virtually always from their presence in cosmetics, notably sunscreens) can be found in Chapter 4.

Immediate-type reactions
Cases of immediate-type reactions, either from the presence of the chemical in cosmetics or in other products, are presented in this section. Possible symptoms (single or in combination) of such reactions include localized erythema, itching or tingling, localized urticaria, angioedema, generalized urticaria, respiratory symptoms (wheezing, dyspnea, asthma, rhinitis, nasal discharge), cardiac problems (hypotension, bradycardia, ventricular fibrillation or cardiac arrest), gastrointestinal symptoms (abdominal pain, diarrhea, nausea, vomiting) or even anaphylactic shock, which may be life-threatening in some patients and proved fatal in exceptional cases. Monographed chemicals that have caused immediate-type reactions from their presence in cosmetics or other products can be found in Chapter 3.

Other non-eczematous contact reactions
Examples of other non-eczematous reactions are discoloration of the skin, hair or nails, hypopigmentation, depigmentation (chemical leukoderma), hyperpigmentation and onycholysis (sometimes mentioned under 'Miscellaneous side effects').

Systemic side effects
Systemic side effects are caused by percutaneous resorption of chemicals. These are rarely caused by the use of cosmetics products. Examples of chemicals which have induced systemic side effects from their presence in non-cosmetic products include hexachlorophene, *p*-phenylenediamine, and resorcinol.

Miscellaneous side effects
Examples of side effects presented here are asthma (several chemicals), xanthelasmata palpebrarum and hair loss (*p*-phenylenediamine)

OTHER INFORMATION
This section may contain any relevant data on the monographed chemical not related to contact allergy and not discussed elsewhere.

Nearly all Monographs have this standardized format. Some are slightly different, mostly those chemicals of which the author has previously written review articles, which were subsequently used in the preparation of the Monographs. These include formaldehyde, black henna, octocrylene, propolis, methylchloroisothiazolinone (and) methylisothiazolinone and – no review article published - cocamidopropyl betaine and methylisothiazolinone.

REFERENCES
1   Zaragoza-Ninet V, Blasco Encinas R, Vilata-Corell JJ, Pérez-Ferriols A, Sierra-Talamantes C, Esteve-Martínez A, de la Cuadra-Oyanguren J. Allergic contact dermatitis due to cosmetics: A clinical and epidemiological study in a tertiary hospital. Actas Dermosifiliogr 2016;107:329-336

2   Hausen BM, Brinkmann J, Dohn W. Lexicon der Kontaktallergene. Landsberg am Lech: Ecomed Fachverlag, 1992

3   Johansen JD, Frosch PJ, lepoittevin J-P, Eds. Contact Dermatitis, 5th Edition. Berlin Heidelberg: Springer-Verlag, 2011

4   Rustemeyer T, Elsner P, John SM, Maibach HI, Eds. Kanerva's Occupational Dermatology, 2nd Edition. Berlin Heidelberg: Springer-Verlag, 2012

5   Johansen JD, Lepoittevin J-P, Thyssen JP, Eds. Quick guide to contact dermatitis. Berlin Heidelberg: Springer-Verlag, 2016

6   Rietschel RL, Fowler JF Jr, Eds. Fisher's Contact Dermatitis, 6th Edition. Hamilton, USA: BC Decker Inc., 2008

7   De Groot AC, White IR, Flyvholm M-A, Lensen G, Coenraads P-J. Formaldehyde-releasers in cosmetics: relationship to formaldehyde contact allergy. Part 2. Patch test relationship to formaldehyde contact allergy, experimental provocation tests, amount of formaldehyde released and assessment of risk to consumers allergic to formaldehyde. Contact Dermatitis 2010;62:18-31

8   De Groot AC, Flyvholm M-A, Lensen G, Menné T, Coenraads P-J. Formaldehyde-releasers: relationship to formaldehyde contact allergy. Contact allergy to formaldehyde and inventory of formaldehyde-releasers. Contact Dermatitis 2009;61:63-85

9   De Groot AC, White IR, Flyvholm M-A, Lensen G, Coenraads P-J. Formaldehyde-releasers: relationship to formaldehyde contact allergy. II. Formaldehyde-releasers used in cosmetics. Part 1. Characterization, frequency and relevance of sensitization, and frequency of use in cosmetics. Contact Dermatitis 2010;62:2-17

10   De Groot AC, Roberts DW. Contact and photocontact allergy to octocrylene: a review. Contact Dermatitis 2014;70:193-204

11   De Groot AC. Propolis: a review of properties, applications, chemical composition, contact allergy, and other adverse effects. Dermatitis 2013;24:263-282

12   De Groot AC, Popova MP, Bankova VS. An update on the constituents of poplar-type propolis. Wapserveen, The Netherlands: acdegroot publishing, 2014. ISBN/EAN: 978-90-813233-0-7 (pdf booklet). Available at: https://www.researchgate.net/profile/Anton_De_Groot2

13   De Groot AC. Side-effects of henna and semi-permanent 'black henna' tattoos: a full review. Contact Dermatitis 2013;69:1-25

14   Chou M, Dhingra N, Strugar TL. Contact sensitization to allergens in nail cosmetics. Dermatitis 2017;28:231-240

15   De Groot AC. Contact allergy to (ingredients of) toothpastes. Dermatitis 2017;28:95-114

16   Holcomb ZE, Van Noord MG, Atwater AR. Gallate contact dermatitis: product update and systematic review. Dermatitis 2017;28:115-127

17   Loranger C, Alfalah M, Ferrier Le Bouedec M-C, Sasseville Denis. Alkyl glucosides in contact dermatitis: a systematic review. Dermatitis 2017;28:5-13

18   De Groot AC, Schmidt E. Essential oils: contact allergy and chemical composition. Boca Raton, Fl., USA: CRC Press, Taylor and Francis Group, 2016 (ISBN 9781482246407)

19   De Groot AC, Schmidt E. Tea tree oil: contact allergy and chemical composition. Contact Dermatitis 2016;75:129-143

20 De Groot AC, Schmidt E. Essential Oils, Part V: Peppermint oil, lavender oil, and lemongrass oil. Dermatitis 2016; 27:325-332

21 De Groot AC, Schmidt E. Essential Oils, Part III: Chemical composition. Dermatitis 2016;27:161-169

22 De Groot AC, Schmidt E. Essential oils, Part IV: Contact allergy. Dermatitis 2016;27:170-175

23 De Groot AC, Schmidt E. Essential oils, Part VI: Sandalwood oil, ylang-ylang oil, and jasmine absolute. Dermatitis 2017;28:14-21

24 Heurung AR, Raju SI, Warshaw EM. Adverse reactions to sunscreen agents: epidemiology, responsible irritants and allergens, clinical characteristics, and management. Dermatitis 2014;25:289-326

25 Heurung AR, Raju SI, Warshaw EM. Contact allergen of the year. Benzophenones. Dermatitis 2014;25:3-10 (contains many mistakes; Erratum in Dermatitis 2014;25:92-95)

26 Avenel-Audran M. Sunscreen products: finding the allergen. Eur J Dermatol 2010;20:161-166

27 Scheuer E, Warshaw E. Sunscreen allergy: a review of epidemiology, clinical characteristics, and responsible allergens. Dermatitis 2006;17:3-11

28 Shaw T, Simpson B, Wilson B, Oostman H, Rainey D, Storrs F. True photoallergy to sunscreens is rare despite popular belief. Dermatitis 2010;21:185-198

29 Cheng J, Zug KA. Fragrance allergic contact dermatitis. Dermatitis 2014;25:232-245

30 Yim E, Baquerizo Nole KL, Tosti A. Contact dermatitis caused by preservatives. Dermatitis 2014;25:215-231

31 Sasseville D. Hypersensitivity to preservatives. Dermatol Ther 2004;17:251-263

32 Alani JI, Davis MDP, Yiannias JA. Allergy to cosmetics: A literature review. Dermatitis 2013;24:283-290

33 Goossens A. New cosmetic contact allergens. Cosmetics 2015, 2, 22-32; doi:10.3390/cosmetics2010022

34 Scheman A, Rakowski EM, Chou V, et al. Balsam of Peru: Past and future. Dermatitis 2013;24:153-160

35 Sharp G, Green S, Rose M. Chlorhexidine-induced anaphylaxis in surgical patients: a review of the literature. ANZ J Surg 2016;86:237-243

36 Silvestri DL, McEnery-Stonelake M. Chlorhexidine: uses and adverse reactions. Dermatitis 2013;24:112-118

37 Odedra KM, Farooque S. Chlorhexidine: an unrecognised cause of anaphylaxis. Postgrad Med J 2014;90:709-714

38 Lundov MD, Krongaard T, Menné TL, Johansen JD. Methylisothiazolinone contact allergy: a review. Br J Dermatol 2011;165:1178-1182

39 Bruze M, Engfeldt M, Gonçalo M, Goossens A. Recommendation to include methylisothiazolinone in the European baseline patch test series – on behalf of the European Society of Contact Dermatitis and the European Environmental and Contact Dermatitis Research Group. Contact Dermatitis 2013;69:263-270

40 Castanedo-Tardana M, Zug K. Methylisothiazolinone. Dermatitis 2013;24:2-6

41 Latheef F, Wilkinson SM. Methylisothiazolinone outbreak in the European Union. Curr Opin Allergy Clin Immunol 2015;15:461-466

42 Kosari P, Alikhan A, Sockolov M, Feldman SR. Vitamin E and allergic contact dermatitis. Dermatitis 2010;21:148-153

43 Aakhus AE, Warshaw EM. Allergy to methyldibromoglutaronitrile/phenoxyethanol (Euxyl K 400): Regulatory issues, epidemiology, clinical characteristics, and management. Dermatitis 2011;22:127-140

44 Pascoe D, Moreau L, Sasseville D. Emergent and unusual allergens in cosmetics. Dermatitis 2010;21:127-137

45 Krasteva M, Bons B, Ryan C, Gerberick FG. Consumer allergy to oxidative hair coloring products: epidemiologic data in the literature. Dermatitis 2009;20:123-141

46 Lee B, Warshaw E. Lanolin allergy: History, epidemiology, responsible allergens, and management. Dermatitis 2008;19:63-72

47 Walgrave SE, Warshaw EM, Glesne LA. Allergic contact dermatitis from propolis. Dermatitis 2005;16:209-215

48 Cashman AL, Warshaw EM. Parabens: A review of epidemiology, structure, allergenicity, and hormonal properties. Dermatitis 2005;16:57-66

49 Deza G, Giménez-Arnau AM. Allergic contact dermatitis in preservatives: current standing and future options. Curr Opin Allergy Clin Immunol 2017;17:263-268

50 Verhulst L, Goossens A. Cosmetic components causing contact urticaria: a review and update. Contact Dermatitis 2016;75:333-344

51 González-Muñoz P, Conde-Salazar L, Vañó-Galván S. Allergic contact dermatitis caused by cosmetic products. Actas Dermosifiliogr 2014;105:822-832

52 Leiva-Salinas M, Francés L, Silvestre JF. Update on allergic contact dermatitis due to methylchloroisothiazolinone/methylisothiazolinone and methylisothiazolinone. Actas Dermosifiliogr 2014;105:840-846

53 Park ME, Zippin JH. Allergic contact dermatitis to cosmetics. Dermatol Clin 2014;32:1-11

54 Jack AR, Norris PL, Storrs FJ. Allergic contact dermatitis to plant extracts in cosmetics. Semin Cutan Med Surg 2013;32:140-146

55 Arribas MP, Soro P, Silvestre JF. Allergic contact dermatitis to fragrances. Part 1. Actas Dermosifiliogr 2012;103:874-879

56 Arribas MP, Soro P, Silvestre JF. Allergic contact dermatitis to fragrances: Part 2. Actas Dermosifiliogr 2013;104:29-37

57 García-Gavín J, Parente J, Goossens A. Allergic contact dermatitis caused by sodium metabisulfite: a challenging allergen: a case series and literature review. Contact Dermatitis 2012;67:260-269

58 Davies RF, Johnston GA. New and emerging cosmetic allergens. Clin Dermatol 2011;29:311-315

59 Castanedo-Tardan MP, Zug KA. Patterns of cosmetic contact allergy. Dermatol Clin 2009;27:265-280

60 Jacob SE, Amini S. Cocamidopropyl betaine. Dermatitis 2008;19:157-160

61 Schnuch A, Lessmann H, Geier J, Uter W. Is cocamidopropyl betaine a contact allergen? Analysis of network data and short review of the literature. Contact Dermatitis 2011;64:203-211

62 Quartier S, Garmyn M, Becart S, Goossens A. Allergic contact dermatitis to copolymers in cosmetics--case report and review of the literature. Contact Dermatitis 2006;55:257-267

63 Biebl KA, Warshaw EM. Allergic contact dermatitis to cosmetics. Dermatol Clin 2006;24:215-232

64 Orton DI, Wilkinson JD. Cosmetic allergy: incidence, diagnosis, and management. Am J Clin Dermatol 2004;5:327-337

65 Ortiz KJ, Yiannias JA. Contact dermatitis to cosmetics, fragrances, and botanicals. Dermatol Ther 2004;17:264-271

66 Johansen JD. Fragrance contact allergy: a clinical review. Am J Clin Dermatol 2003;4:789-798

67 Nater JP, De Groot AC. Unwanted effects of cosmetics and drugs used in dermatology. Amsterdam: Excerpta Medica, 1983

68 Nater JP, De Groot AC. Unwanted effects of cosmetics and drugs used in dermatology, 2nd Edition. Amsterdam: Elsevier Science Publishers, 1985

69 De Groot AC, Nater JP, Weijland JW. Unwanted effects of cosmetics and drugs used in dermatology, 3rd Edition. Amsterdam: Elsevier Science, 1994

70 De Groot AC. Adverse reactions to cosmetics. PhD thesis, University of Groningen, The Netherlands, 1988

71 Cronin E. Contact Dermatitis. Edinburgh London New York: Churchill Livingstone, 1980

72 Goossens A. Cosmetic contact allergens. Cosmetics 2016, 3, 5; doi:10.3390/cosmetics3010005

73 Travassos AR, Claes L, Boey L, Drieghe J, Goossens A. Non-fragrance allergens in specific cosmetic products. Contact Dermatitis 2011;65:276-285

74 De Groot AC, Bruynzeel DP, Bos JD, van der Meeren HL, van Joost T, Jagtman BA, Weyland JW. The allergens in cosmetics. Arch Dermatol 1988;124:1525-1529

75 De Groot AC. Contact allergy to cosmetics: Causative ingredients. Contact Dermatitis 1987;17:26-34

76 Adams RM, Maibach HI, Clendenning WE, Fisher AA, Jordan WJ, Kanof N, et al. A five-year study of cosmetic reactions. J Am Acad Dermatol 1985;13:1062-1069

77 Laguna C, de la Cuadra J, Martín-González B, Zaragoza V, Martínez-Casimiro L, Alegre V. Allergic contact dermatitis to cosmetics. Actas Dermosifiliogr 2009;100:53-60

78 Dooms-Goossens A, de Boulle K, Dooms M, Degreef H. Imidazolidinyl urea dermatitis. Contact Dermatitis 1986;14:322-324

79 The European Multicentre Photopatch Test Study (EMCPPTS) Taskforce. A European multicentre photopatch test study. Br J Dermatol 2012;166:1002-1009

80 De Groot AC, Patch Testing, 3rd Edition. Wapserveen, The Netherlands, acdegroot publishing, 2008

81 Goossens A. Contact-allergic reactions to cosmetics. J Allergy 2011, 2011, doi:10.1155/2011/467071

CHAPTER 2 MONOGRAPHS OF CHEMICALS AND SUBSTANCES IN COSMETICS THAT HAVE CAUSED ALLERGIC CONTACT DERMATITIS

2.0 INTRODUCTION

In this chapter, Monographs are presented of all non-fragrance chemicals and substances that have, by their presence in cosmetic products, caused allergic contact dermatitis. The mode of data collecting and criteria for inclusion have been discussed in Chapter 1. The literature search has resulted in the identification of 497 non-fragrance ingredients in cosmetics that have caused contact allergy / allergic contact dermatitis. Eight-two of these cosmetic allergens have also caused immediate-type reactions, either from their presence in cosmetics or in non-cosmetic products (Chapter 3, table 3.2). Sixty-five of the 497 have also caused photosensitivity reactions, mostly photocontact allergy or photoallergic contact dermatitis, virtually always from their presence in sunscreen products and other cosmetics (Chapter 4, table 4.1).

The format of the Monographs and explanation of their content and sources can be found in Chapter 1. Table 2.0.1 lists alphabetically the names (INCI names when available) of all Monographed cosmetic allergens.

Table 2.0.1 Alphabetical list of 497 chemicals/substances that have caused allergic cosmetic dermatitis

Acetarsone	Benzophenone-2
Acetylated lanolin	Benzophenone-3
Achillea millefolium extract	Benzophenone-4
C18-36 Acid triglyceride	Benzophenone-8
Alcohol	Benzophenone-10
C12-15 Alkyl benzoate	Benzoxonium chloride
Allantoin	Benzoyl peroxide
Alpha-glucan oligosaccharide	Benzylhemiformal
Alumina	Betula alba (birch) bark extract
Aluminum chloride	BHA
Aluminum chlorohydrate	BHT
Aluminum compounds (unspecified)	Biosaccharide gum-4
4-Aminoazobenzene	Bisabolol
4-Amino-*m*-cresol	Bithionol
2-Amino-4-hydroxyethylaminoanisole sulfate	Bornelone
4-Amino-2-hydroxytoluene	Botanical products (miscellaneous)
2-Aminomethyl-*p*-aminophenol HCl	5-Bromo-5-nitro-1,3-dioxane
4-Amino-3-nitrophenol	2-Bromo-2-nitropropane-1,3-diol
m-Aminophenol	4-Butanediol dimethacrylate
p-Aminophenol 1	Butyl acrylate
Ammoniated mercury	*t*-Butyl alcohol
Ammonium bisulfite	Butylene glycol
Ammonium persulfate	di-*t*-Butylhydroquinone
Ammonium thioglycolate	Butyl methacrylate
Ammonium thiolactate	Butyl methoxydibenzoylmethane
Anthemis nobilis flower extract	Butylparaben
Arachidyl glucoside	4-*tert*-Butylphenol
Arbutin	Butyrospermum parkii (shea) butter
Argania spinosa (argan) kernel oil	Calcium lithol red
Arnica montana extract	Calendula officinalis extract
Ascorbic acid	Candelilla cera
Ascorbyl tetraisopalmitate	Caprylhydroxamic acid
Avena sativa (oat) bran extract	Caprylic/capric triglyceride
Azulene	Capryloyl salicylic acid
Basic blue 99	Caprylyl gallate
Basic red 2	Captan
Basic red 22	Cera alba
Basic violet 10	Cera microcristallina
Benzalkonium chloride	Ceresin
Benzethonium chloride	Cetalkonium chloride
Benzisothiazolinone	Ceteareth-2
Benzoic acid	

Table 2.0.1 Alphabetical list of 497 chemicals/substances that have caused allergic cosmetic dermatitis (*cont'd*)

Ceteareth-3	Diazolidinyl urea
Cetearyl alcohol	4',5-Dibromosalicylanilide
Cetearyl ethylhexanoate	Dibutyl phthalate
Cetearyl glucoside	Dicaprylyl maleate
Cetearyl isononanoate	Dichlorobenzyl alcohol
Cetrimonium bromide	Dichlorodifluoromethane
Cetyl alcohol	Dichlorophene
Chamomilla recutita (matricaria) extract	Didecyldimonium chloride
Chitosan gluconate	Diethylamino hydroxybenzoyl hexyl benzoate
Chlorhexidine digluconate	Diethylene glycol dimethacrylate
Chloroacetamide	Diethyl sebacate
p-Chloro-m-cresol	Diethylstilbestrol
2-Chloro-p-phenylenediamine	bis-Diglyceryl polyacyladipate-2
Chloroxylenol	Diglyceryl sebacate/isopalmitate
Chlorphenesin	Di-HEMA trimethylhexyl dicarbamate
CI 11680	Dihydroxyacetone
CI 12010	Diisopropanolamine
CI 12055	Diisostearyl malate
CI 12085	Dimethyl oxazolidine
CI 12120	Dipentaerythrityl hexahydroxystearate/hexastea-rate/hexarosinate
CI 12150	
CI 15800	Dipotassium glycyrrhizate
CI 15880	Dipropylene glycol
CI 26100	Disodium EDTA
CI 45380	Disodium lauroamphodiacetate
CI 47000	Disodium oleamido MEA-sulfosuccinate
CI 69825	Disodium phenyl dibenzimidazole tetrasulfonate
CI 75470	Disodium ricinoleamido MEA-sulfosuccinate
CI 77163	Disperse blue 85
CI 77288	Disperse blue 106
CI 77289	Disperse yellow 3
Cinoxate	Distearyl phthalic acid amide
CI Pigment red 53:1	Ditrimethylpropane triethylhexanoate
Coal tar	DMDM hydantoin
Cobalt	Dodecyl gallate
Cocamide	Drometrizole
Cocamide DEA	Drometrizole trisiloxane
Cocamidopropylamine oxide	EDTA
Cocamidopropyl betaine	Equae lac
Cocamidopropyl dimethylamine	Ethoxydiglycol
Cocamidopropyl hydroxysultaine	Ethyl acrylate
Cocamidopropyl PG-dimonium chloride phosphate	3-o-Ethyl ascorbic acid
	Ethyl cyanoacrylate
Coco-betaine	Ethylhexyl dimethyl PABA
Coco-glucoside	Ethylhexylglycerin
Cod liver oil	Ethylhexyl methoxycinnamate
Colophonium	bis-Ethylexyloxyphenol methoxyphenyl triazine
Commiphora mukul resin extract	Ethylhexyl salicylate
Copernicia cerifera (carnauba) wax	Ethylhexyl triazone
Cucumis sativus (cucumber) extract	Ethyl methacrylate
Cyclomethicone	Ethyl methoxycinnamate
Cystamine bis-lactamide	Ethylparaben
Cysteamine HCl	Euphorbia extract (unspecified)
D&C red no. 34	Formaldehyde
DEA-dihydroxypalmityl phosphate	Fructooligosaccharides
Decyl glucoside	Glucosamine HCl
Decyl oleate	Glutaraldehyde
2,4-Diaminophenoxyethanol HCl	Glycerin

Table 2.0.1 Alphabetical list of 497 chemicals/substances that have caused allergic cosmetic dermatitis (*cont'd*)

α-Glycerol ester of *o*-amino-*m*-(2,3-dihydroxy-propoxy)benzoic acid	Iodopropynyl butylcarbamate
Glyceryl abietate	Iron oxides
Glyceryl caprylate	Isoamyl *p*-methoxycinnamate
Glyceryl diisostearate	Isobutyl methacrylate
Glyceryl hydrogenated rosinate	Isobutyl PABA
Glyceryl isostearate	Isohexadecane
Glyceryl isostearate/myristate	Isononyl isononanoate
Glyceryl PABA	Isopropyl alcohol
Glyceryl ricinoleate	Isopropyl dibenzoylmethane
Glyceryl rosinate	Isopropyl hydroxypalmityl ether
Glyceryl stearate	Isopropyl myristate
Glyceryl thioglycolate	Isostearamidopropyl morpholine lactate
Glycidyl methacrylate	Isostearyl alcohol
Glycine soja seed extract	Kojic acid
Glycol HEMA-methacrylate	Labilin®
Glycyrrhetinic acid	Lanolin
Glycyrrhiza glabra (licorice) root extract	Lanolin alcohol
Glycyrrhiza inflata root extract	Lanolin alcohol (and) paraffinum liquidum
Glycyrrhizic acid	Lanolin oil
Guaiazulene	Lauramide DEA
Guanine	Lauramine oxide
Guar hydroxypropyltrimonium chloride	Laureth-2
Hamamelis virginiana (witch hazel) bark/leaf/twig extract	Laureth-4
HC blue no. 7	Laureth-7
HC red no. 7	Laureth-9
HC yellow no. 7	Laureth-12
Helichrysum italicum flower extract	Lauroyl collagen amino acids
HEMA	Laurus nobilis leaf extract
Henna, black	Lauryl alcohol
Henna, red	Lauryl glucoside
Hesperidin methyl chalcone	Laurylpyridinium chloride
Hexachlorophene	Lawsone
Hexamidine	Lead acetate
Hexamidine diisethionate	Lipacide-cas
1,6-Hexanediol diacrylate	Lonicera japonica (honeysuckle) flower extract
Hexyldecanoic acid	Macadamia ternifolia seed oil
Hexylene glycol	Magnolia grandiflora bark extract
Hexylresorcinol	Magnolia officinalis bark extract
Hinokitiol	Maleated soybean oil
Homosalate	Mandelic acid
Hydroabietyl alcohol	Menthoxypropanediol
Hydrogenated castor oil	Mercury
Hydrogen peroxide	Methenamine
Hydrolyzed collagen	Methoxy PEG-17 dodecyl glycol copolymer
Hydrolyzed wheat protein	Methoxy PEG-22 dodecyl glycol copolymer
Hydrophilized ceramide	Methyl acrylate
Hydroquinone	*p*-Methylaminophenol
Hydroxydecyl ubiquinone	4-Methylbenzylidene camphor
Hydroxyethyl acrylate	Methylchloroisothiazolinone (and) methylisothiazolinone
2-Hydroxyethylamino-5-nitroanisole	Methyldibromo glutaronitrile
N,N-bis(2-Hydroxyethyl)-*p*-phenylenediamine sulfate	Methyldibromo glutaronitrile/phenoxyethanol
Hydroxypropyl methacrylate	Methyl dihydroxybenzoate
Hydroxypropyl tetrahydropyrantriol	Methylene bis-benzotriazolyl tetramethylbutylphenol
Hydroxystearic acid	Methyl glucose dioleate
Imidazolidinyl urea	Methyl glucose sesquistearate
	Methylisothiazolinone

Table 2.0.1 Alphabetical list of 497 chemicals/substances that have caused allergic cosmetic dermatitis (*cont'd*)

Methyl methacrylate
Methyl nicotinate
Methylparaben
Miranol® MSA Myristyl alcohol
Monobenzone
Myristic acid
Myristyl glucoside
2,7-Naphthalenediol
Neopentyl glycol diisooctanoate
Nickel
Nitrocellulose
3-Nitro-*p*-hydroxyethylaminophenol
2-Nitro-*p*-phenylenediamine
Nordihydroguaiaretic acid
Octocrylene
Octyldodecanol
Octyldodecyl xyloside
Olaflur
Oleamide DEA
Oleamidopropyl dimethylamine
C30-38 Olefin/isopropyl maleate/MA copolymer
Oleth-3 phosphate
Oleth-5
Oleyl alcohol
Osmaron B
Oxyquinoline
PABA
Palmitoyl collagen amino acids
Palmitoyl hydrolyzed milk protein
Palmitoyl hydrolyzed wheat protein
Panthenol
Panthenyl ethyl ether
Parabens, unspecified
Paraffinum liquidum
Paraformaldehyde
PEG-4 dilaurate
PEG-4 dimethacrylate
PEG-4 rapeseedamide
PEG-5 lanolate
PEG-5 soy sterol
PEG-6
PEG-7 hydrogenated castor oil
PEG-7 oleate
PEG-22/dodecyl glycol copolymer
PEG-32 stearate
PEG-40 sorbitan lanolate
Pentaerythrityl rosinate
Pentaerythrityl tetracaprylate/tetracaprate
Pentaerythrityl triacrylate
Pentyl dimethyl PABA
Pentylene glycol
Pentyl rhamnoside
Persea gratissima (avocado) oil
Petrolatum
Phenethyl resorcinol
Phenoxyethanol
Phenylbenzimidazole sulfonic acid
Phenyl dimethicone

p-Phenylenediamine
o-Phenylphenol
N-Phenyl-*p*-phenylenediamine
Phenyl salicylate
Phthalic anhydride/trimellitic anhydride/glycols copolymer
Phytantriol
Phytonadione
Phytonadione epoxide
Pigment orange 5
Pigment red 57:1
Pigment red 172 aluminum lake
Pigment yellow 12
Polyaminopropyl biguanide
Polyester-8
Polyester resin (trimellitic anhydride, adipic acid, neopentyl glycol and cyclohexanedimethanol)
Polyethylene
Polyglyceryl-10 laurate
Polyquaternium-7
Polysilicone-15
Polysorbate 40
Polysorbate 80
Potassium cocoyl hydrolyzed collagen
Potassium persulfate
Potassium sorbate
PPG-1-PEG-9 lauryl glycol ether
PPG-2-ceteareth-9
Procaine
Propantheline bromide
Propolis
Propylene glycol
Propylene glycol ricinoleate
Propyl gallate
Propylparaben
Prunus avium (sweet cherry) seed oil
Pyridoxine dioctenoate
Pyrocatechol
Pyrogallol
Quaternium-15
Quaternium-22
Quinine
Resorcinol
Resveratrol
Retinol
Retinyl palmitate
Ricinoleic acid
Ricinus communis (castor) seed oil
Ruscogenin
Salvia officinalis (sage) extract
Scutellaria baicalensis extract
Selenium sulfide
Sesamum indicum (sesame) seed oil
Shellac
Simmondsia chinensis (jojoba) seed oil
Simmondsia chinensis (jojoba) seed powder
Sodium benzoate
Sodium bisulfite

Table 2.0.1 Alphabetical list of 497 chemicals/substances that have caused allergic cosmetic dermatitis (*cont'd*)

Sodium chondroitin sulfate	Thimerosal
Sodium cocoamphoacetate	2,2'-Thiobis(4-chlorophenol)
Sodium cocoamphopropionate	Thioctic acid
Sodium dihydroxycetyl phosphate	Thioglycerin
Sodium dihydroxycetyl phosphate isopropyl hydroxyl-cetyl ether	Thiolactic acid
	Tinosorb® M
Sodium hydroxymethylglycinate	Tioxolone
Sodium laureth sulfate	Tocopherol
Sodium lauroamphoacetate	Tocopheryl acetate
Sodium lauroyl sarcosinate	Tocopheryl linoleate
Sodium lauryl sulfate	Tocopheryl nicotinate
Sodium metabisulfite	Toluene-2,5-diamine
Sodium myristoyl sarcosinate	Toluene-2,5-diamine sulfate
Sodium PCA	Tosylamide/formaldehyde resin
Sodium pyrithione	Triacontanyl PVP
Sodium stearate	Tribromosalicylanilide
Sodium stearoyl lactylate	Triceteareth-4 phosphate
Sodium sulfite	Trichlorofluoromethane
Solvent yellow 44	Triclocarban
Sorbic acid	Triclosan
Sorbitan oleate	Trideceth-2 carboxamide MEA
Sorbitan sesquioleate	Triethanolamine
Sorbitan tristearate	Triethylene glycol diacrylate
Sorbitol	Triethylene glycol dimethacrylate
Stannous fluoride	Triethylene glycol hydrogenated rosinate
Stearamidoethyl diethylamine phosphate	Trilaureth-4 phosphate
Steareth-10	Trimethylolpropane triacrylate
Stearic acid	Trioleyl phosphate
Stearyl alcohol	Tripropylene glycol diacrylate
Styrax benzoin gum	Tris(*N*-hydroxyethyl)hexahydrotriazine
Sulfated castor oil	Trisodium EDTA
Sulfiram	Trisodium hydroxyethyl ethylenediamine triacetate
Tanacetum parthenium (feverfew) extract	Tromethamine
Tanacetum vulgate (tansy) extract	Undecylenamide DEA
TBHQ	Urethane acrylates
TEA-cocoyl hydrolyzed collagen	Urethane diacrylate
TEA-PEG-3 cocamide sulfate	VP/eicosene copolymer
TEA-stearate	VP/hexadecene copolymer
Terephthalylidene dicamphor sulfonic acid	Witisol
Tetrachlorosalicylanilides	Xanthan gum
Tetrahydrocurcumin	Zinc pyrithione
Tetrahydromagnolol	Zinc ricinoleate
Tetrahydroxypropyl ethylenediamine	Zirconium compounds
Tetrasodium EDTA	

2.1 ACETARSONE*

* Not an INCI name

IDENTIFICATION

Description/definition	: Acetarsone is the aromatic arsonic acid that conforms to the structural formula shown below
Chemical class(es)	: Organometallic compounds; aromatic compounds; amides
INCI name USA	: Neither in CosIng nor in the Personal Care Products Council Ingredient database
Chemical/IUPAC name	: (3-Acetamido-4-hydroxyphenyl)arsonic acid
Other names	: Acetarsol
CAS registry number (s)	: 97-44-9
EC number(s)	: 202-582-3
Merck Index monograph	: 1321
Patch testing	: 1%-5% pet. (2)
Molecular formula	: $C_8H_{10}AsNO_5$

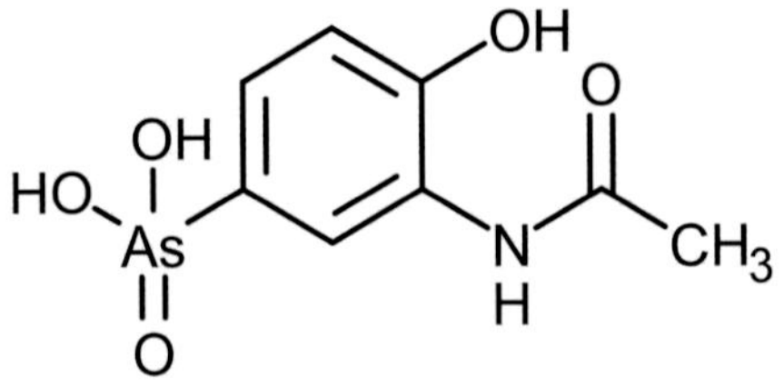

GENERAL

Acetarsone is an organic pentavalent arsenical. In the form of pessaries, powder, or vaginal tablets, it used to be commonly employed in the treatment of vaginitis due to *Trichomonas vaginalis* and *Candida albicans* infections.

As acetarsone is mentioned neither in CosIng nor in the Personal Care Products Council Ingredient Database and – being an arsenical – will currently not be used in cosmetics (or any other product, for that matter), discussion of this chemical is limited to allergic contact dermatitis from its presence in cosmetic products and topical pharmaceuticals.

CONTACT ALLERGY

Case reports and case series

One patient had (a history of) allergy to toothpastes containing acetarsone. She presented with acute dermatitis of the inner thighs from vaginal tablets containing acetarsone. Patch tests were strongly positive to the vaginal tablets, to the toothpaste containing acetarsone and to acetarsone itself. At that time (1978), acetarsone was still present in France in various vaginal products, toothpastes, mouth washes and nasal drops (1).

Contact allergy to acetarsone in non-cosmetic products

A woman complained of vaginal discharge of 16 weeks' duration. During treatment for gonococcal urethritis, *Trichomonas vaginalis* parasites were demonstrated in the vaginal discharge. Acetarsone pessaries were prescribed, to be inserted twice daily. This therapy was continued for 2 months and then reduced to one pessary on alternate days. Five days later the patient returned to the clinic complaining of vulval irritation and of a rash on the backs of the hands, legs, and trunk of 3 days' duration. The rash, which caused moderate irritation especially at night, consisted of a symmetrical erythematous and vesicular eruption involving the back of the hands, both axillae, cubital fossae, dorsal aspects of the feet, and the vulva. A tentative diagnosis of acetarsone sensitivity was made and the pessaries discontinued. Calamine lotion was prescribed and Phenergan, one 25 mg tablet twice daily, was given orally. As the condition was not severe the patient was requested to attend on the following day for further observation of the rash, but she did not return until 9 days later, when she stated that 4 days previously her eyes had become swollen up, and almost completely closed, so that she could barely see, hence her inability to report. Now there was edema of the eyelids and a generalized exfoliative dermatitis especially marked on the face, scalp, dorsal aspects of hands and feet, cubital fossae, and axillae. After healing, a patch test using an acetarsone pessary dissolved in distilled water gave a strongly positive reaction within 24 hours, whereas a control using distilled water only was negative (10).

A woman had allergic contact dermatitis and systemic contact dermatitis from acetarsone vaginal tablets used to treat trichomoniasis vaginalis. She had positive patch tests to the vaginal tablets and its ingredient acetarsone (2).

A woman, known to be allergic to neoarsphenamine (Neosalvarsan, a trivalent arsenical compound), was treated with a pessary containing acetarsone for leucorrhea. Some days later, she developed a generalized erythema with edema of the eyelids. Later, a patch test to the pessary was positive (3).

In early literature, there have been several other reports of female patients with local skin and mucous membrane reactions and often generalized dermatitis after the use of acetarsone in the form of vaginal powder, tablets or pessaries (4,5,6,7,8,9). However, in these cases, either no patch tests were performed (4,5,6,7,8,9), or they were negative (one patient [4]). Interestingly, in some patients, dermatitis appeared in the antecubital fossae and/or or the axillae and/or hands, suggesting systemic allergic contact dermatitis (4,6,10). In a number of cases, the patients had previously had generalized rashes from treatment of syphilis with the trivalent arsenic compound neoarsphenamine (3,5), again suggesting systemic allergic contact dermatitis from absorption or arsenic from the vagina mucosa.

Presence in cosmetic products and chemical analyses

In May 2017, acetarsone was present in zero of 66,975 cosmetic products of which the composition is known in EWG's Skin Deep Cosmetics Database, USA (http://www.ewg.org/skindeep/).In the USA, in April 2017, acetarsone was present in zero of 56,714 cosmetic products of which the composition is known in FDA's Voluntary Cosmetic Registration Program (VCRP) (data obtained from FDA, May 2017).

LITERATURE
1   Robin J. Contact dermatitis to acetarsol. Contact Dermatitis 1978;4:309-310
2   Sasseville D, Carey WD, Singer MI. Generalized contact dermatitis from acetarsone. Contact Dermatitis 1995;33:431-432
3   Orchard WE. Dermatitis after use of pentavalent arsenicals per vaginam. Br Med J 1951;2(4745):1444
4   Kesten BM. Arsenical dermatitis produced in treatment of trichomonas vaginitis. Report of five cases. Arch Derm Syphilol 1938;38:198-199
5   Campbell CHG. Arsenical intolerance and the treatment of Trichomonas vaginalis infection. Lancet 1937;2(5951):688-689
6   Peck BJ. Exfoliative dermatitis after acetarsol vaginal pessaries. Brit Med J 1954;2:850-851
7   White A. Acute systemic reaction to acetarsol. Br Med J 1956;29:2(5008):1528-1529
8   Crosswell HD. Jaundice following acetarsol pessaries. Br J Vener Dis 1951;27:150-153
9   Long MCW. Arsenical intolerance and the treatment of *Trichomonas vaginalis* infection (Letter). Lancet 1937: 2(5953):828.
10 Doyle JO. Acetarsol pessary dermatitis. Brit J Vener Dis 1952;28:210-212

2.2   ACETYLATED LANOLIN

IDENTIFICATION

Description/definition	: Acetylated lanolin is the acetyl ester of lanolin
Chemical class(es)	: Lanolin and lanolin derivatives
Other names	: Lanolin acetate(s)
CAS registry number (s)	: 61788-48-5
EC number(s)	: 262-979-2
CIR review(s)	: J Environ Pathol Toxicol 1980;4:63-92 (access: www.cir-safety.org/ingredients)
Merck Index monograph	: 6679 (lanolin)
Function(s) in cosmetics	: EU: antistatic; emollient; emulsifying; hair conditioning; skin conditioning. USA: hair conditioning agents; skin-conditioning agents - emollient; skin-conditioning agents – occlusive
Patch testing	: Unknown; suggestion: 30% pet.

GENERAL

When lanolin is reacted with acetic anhydride, the hydroxyl groups on the hydroxyl-esters of lanolin are replaced with acetate groups. The acetylated lanolin becomes more hydrophobic as indicated by its failure to form water-in-oil emulsions, and by its solubility in cold mineral oil. As a result of acetylation, the hydroxyl number drops. This process virtually ties up most of the free alcohols of lanolin (5). Acetylated lanolin, therefore, usually gives a negative patch test in lanolin-sensitive individuals (5).

CONTACT ALLERGY

Testing in groups of patients: Selected patient groups
In a group of patients with a history of hypersensitivity to lanolin, 12% reacted to acetylated lanolin (probably tested pure) versus 61% for hydrogenated lanolin and 71% for wool alcohols (4).

Case reports and case series
In a group of 119 patients with allergic contact dermatitis from cosmetics, investigated in The Netherlands in 1986-1987, one case was caused by acetylated lanolin in a lipstick (1,2).

Presence in cosmetic products and chemical analyses
In the USA, in April 2017, acetylated lanolin alcohol was present in 401 of 56,714 cosmetic products of which the composition is known in FDA's Voluntary Cosmetic Registration Program (VCRP) (data obtained from FDA, May 2017). In March 2017, acetylated lanolin was present in 173 of 64,983 cosmetic products of which the composition is known in EWG's Skin Deep Cosmetics Database, USA (http://www.ewg.org/skindeep/).

Other non-eczematous contact reactions
In (somewhat) older literature, acetylated lanolin has been suspected of being comedogenic in 'people with more sensitive complexions or acne-prone problems', based on rabbit ear assays (3).

LITERATURE

1   De Groot AC, Bruynzeel DP, Bos JD, van der Meeren HL, van Joost T, Jagtman BA, Weyland JW. The allergens in cosmetics. Arch Dermatol 1988;124:1525-1529
2   De Groot AC. Adverse reactions to cosmetics. PhD Thesis, University of Groningen, The Netherlands: 1988, chapter 3.4, pp.105-113
3   Fulton JE Jr, Pay SR, Fulton JE 3rd. Comedogenicity of current therapeutic products, cosmetics, and ingredients in the rabbit ear. J Am Acad Dermatol 1984;10:96-105
4   Clark EW, Cronin E, Wilkinson DS. Lanolin with reduced sensitizing potential A preliminary note. Contact Dermatitis 1977;3:69-74
5   Schlossman ML, McCarthy JP. Lanolin and derivatives chemistry: Relationship to allergic contact dermatitis. Contact Dermatitis 1979;5:65-72

2.3 ACHILLEA MILLEFOLIUM EXTRACT

IDENTIFICATION

Description/definition	: Achillea millefolium extract is an extract of the leaves and flowers (INCI USA: of the whole plant) of the yarrow, *Achillea millefolium* L., Asteraceae
INCI name USA	: Botanical products and botanical derivatives
Other names	: Yarrow extract; milfoil extract
CAS registry number (s)	: 84082-83-7
EC number(s)	: 282-030-6
CIR review(s)	: Int J Toxicol 2001;20(Suppl.2):79-84; Final report 2014 (access: www.cir-safety.org/ingredients)
Merck Index monograph	: 105
Function(s) in cosmetics	: EU: antidandruff; cleansing; masking; refreshing; skin conditioning; soothing; tonic. USA: fragrance ingredients; skin-conditioning agents - miscellaneous
Patch testing	: 1.0% pet. (Chemotechnique); also present in the Compositae mix II (Chemotechnique)

GENERAL

Yarrow (synonym: milfoil) is a common weed native to Europe, western Asia, the Caucasus, and northern Iran, and is naturalized as far away as Australia, New Zealand, and North America (1). It is an old medicinal plant and the whole plant (Herba millefolii) as well as the flowers (Flores millefolii) are officinal (8,9). The Community herbal monographs allow the use of both the herb and the flower for the treatment of small superficial wounds (10,11). Traditionally, yarrow preparations have been used both externally and internally: the names knight's milfoil and soldier's wound-wort refer to the perceived wound-healing effects of the plant. The tea is recommended for wounds while a decoction has been used as a compress in skin diseases. Because of a spasmolytic effect, the drug is used for indigestion and liver diseases besides a variety of other conditions in traditional medicine. Furthermore, yarrow extracts are employed 'natural' cosmetics as a 'biological additive' (8). The main sesquiterpene lactone allergen in yarrow is said to be α-peroxyachifolid, which is a strong sensitizer (3).

In this chapter, with the exception of patch testing in groups of patients, only those articles are presented that mention extracts and products containing them as causes of reactions to *Achillea millefolium*.

CONTACT ALLERGY

Patch testing in groups of patients

Achillea millefolium extract has not been patch tested in consecutive patients suspected of contact dermatitis (routine testing). Results of testing in groups of *selected* patients are shown in table 2.3.1. All studies but one have tested Achillea millefolium extract in patients sensitized to the Compositae mix, of which it is a component. Frequencies of sensitization in these populations have ranged from 31% to 53%. In a very small study testing yarrow extract in 27 patients suspected of cosmetic dermatitis, only one reacted (5) as did one patient in a group of 122 with self-declared adverse reactions to botanical products (15). In most studies, no data on relevance were provided and relevance in others related to the Compositae mix, never to the yarrow extract itself. In one investigation, however, in florists selling ornamental flowers, all reactions to yarrow were considered to be cross-sensitivities, ergo not relevant (12).

Case reports and case series

Achillea millefolium extract was responsible for 1 out of 959 cases of non-fragrance cosmetic allergy where the causal allergen was identified, Belgium, 2000-2010 (4). In a German study performed between 1985 and 1990, a group of 118 patients reacted to the Compositae mix consisting of five ingredients: arnica (*Arnica montana* L.), German chamomile (*Chamomilla recutita*), feverfew (*Tanacetum parthenium*), tansy (*Tanacetum vulgare*) and yarrow (*Achillea millefolium*). In 4 patients, the sensitization was caused by 'natural cosmetics', in 3 by 'natural ointments', in one by a 'herbal' massage oil and in one (probably) by a 'herbal' shampoo, soap and ointment. However, it was not specified, which of the 5 plant extracts was/were the actual sensitizer(s) in these products (6).

Cross-reactions, pseudo-cross-reactions and co-reactions

Cross-reactions and pseudo-cross-reactions to other Compositae plants and extracts are common (7). Many positive reactions to yarrow may result from primary *Chrysanthemum* sensitization (16).

Provocation tests

In 20 patients previously reacting to the sesquiterpene lactone mix, 12 (60%) had positive patch test reactions to tea made of *Achillea millefolium* (14).

Table 2.3.1 Patch testing in groups of patients: Selected patient groups

Years and Country	Test conc. & vehicle	Number of patients tested | positive (%)		Selection of patients (S); Relevance (R); Comments (C)	Ref.
2011-2012 Italy	1% pet.	122	1 (0.8%)	S: patients tested with a botanical series, who declared having had adverse reactions to 'botanical' products (cosmetics, detergents, pharmaceutical ointments): R: the reaction was considered to be relevant	15
2006-2011 Denmark	1% pet.	29	10 (34%)	S: patients reacting to the Compositae mix 5% (Chemotechnique); R: 100% of positive reactions to all components of the mix together were considered to be relevant (current or past)	1
2000-2004 Denmark	1% pet.	76	35 (46%)	S: patients reacting to the Compositae mix 6% (Trolab); R: 80% of positive reactions to all components of the mix together were considered to be relevant (current or past)	1
1996-1999 Germany		39	12 (31%)	C: article not read, data missing, cited in ref. 1	2
1990-1998 Denmark	1% pet.	129	53 (41%)	S: patients reacting to the Compositae mix; R: not stated	7
1996-1997 UK	1% pet.	27	1 (4%)	S: patients suspected of cosmetic dermatitis; R: not specified	5
1990 Denmark	1% pet.	24	8 (33%)	S: patients reacting to the Compositae mix; R: 75% for 32 patients sensitized to the Compositae mix, not specified for its ingredients including yarrow	13
1985-1990 Germany	1% pet.	85	45 (53%)	S: patients reacting to the Compositae mix; R: nearly all reactions to the Compositae mix were relevant and were most often caused by contact with plants, some by 'natural' cosmetics; thirty-three (28%) patients were occupationally sensitized (e.g., florists, gardeners) and 11 (9.3%) had airborne allergic contact dermatitis. The relevance of the reactions to the individual ingredients of the Compositae mix including yarrow was not specified	6
<1988 Germany	?	56	20 (36%)	S: florists selling ornamental flowers in a large flower market; R: none; C: the reactions were considered to be cross-sensitivities (article not read, data cited in ref. 9).	12

Presence in cosmetic products and chemical analyses

In the USA, in April 2017, Achillea millefolium (yarrow) extract was present in 193 of 56,714 cosmetic products of which the composition is known in FDA's Voluntary Cosmetic Registration Program (VCRP) (data obtained from FDA, May 2017). In January 2017, Achillea millefolium extract was present in 149 of 64,475 cosmetic products of which the composition is known in EWG's Skin Deep Cosmetics Database, USA (http://www.ewg.org/skindeep/).

LITERATURE

1   Paulsen E, Andersen KE. Patch testing with constituents of Compositae mixes. Contact Dermatitis 2012;66:241-246

2   Geier J, Hausen BM. Epikutantesting mit dem Kompositen-mix. Allergologie 2000;23:334-341

3   Hausen BM, Breuer J, Weglewski J, Rücker G. α-Peroxyachifolid and other new sensitizing sesquiterpene lactones from yarrow (*Achillea millefolium* L., Compositae). Contact Dermatitis 1991;24:274-280

4   Travassos AR, Claes L, Boey L, Drieghe J, Goossens A. Non-fragrance allergens in specific cosmetic products. Contact Dermatitis 2011;65:276-285

5   Thomson KF, Wilkinson SM. Allergic contact dermatitis to plant extracts in patients with cosmetic dermatitis. Br J Dermatol 2000;142:84-88

6   Hausen BM. A 6-year experience with Compositae mix. Am J Contact Dermatitis 1996;7:94-99

7   Paulsen E, Andersen KE, Hausen BM. Sensitization and cross-reaction patterns in Danish Compositae-allergic patients. Contact Dermatitis 2001;45:197-204

8   Paulsen E. Contact sensitization from Compositae-containing herbal remedies and cosmetics. Contact Dermatitis 2002;47:189-198

9   Calapai G, Miroddi M, Minciullo PL, Caputi AP, Gangemi S, Schmidt RJ. Contact dermatitis as an adverse reaction to some topically used European herbal medicinal products - part 1: *Achillea millefolium-Curcuma longa*. Contact Dermatitis 2014;71:1-12

10 Community herbal monograph on *Achillea millefolium* L., herba, EMA/HMPC/290284/2009

11 Community herbal monograph on *Achillea millefolium* L., flos, EMA/HMPC/143949/2010

12 Hausen BM, Oestmann G. The incidence of occupationally-induced allergic skin diseases in a large flower market. Derm Beruf Umwelt 1988;36:117-124 (article in German; data cited in ref. 9)

13 Paulsen E, Andersen KE, Hausen BM. Compositae dermatitis in a Danish dermatology department in one year. Contact Dermatitis 1993;29:6-10

14 Lundh K, Hindsén M, Gruvberger B, Möller H, Svensson A, Bruze M. Contact allergy to herbal teas derived from Asteraceae plants. Contact Dermatitis 2006;54:196-201

15 Corazza M, Borghi A, Gallo R, Schena D, Pigatto P, Lauriola MM, et al. Topical botanically derived products: use, skin reactions, and usefulness of patch tests. A multicentre Italian study. Contact Dermatitis 2014;70:90-97

16 Hausen BM. The sensitizing capacity of Compositae plants. III. Test results and cross-reactions in Compositae-sensitive patients. Dermatologica 1979;159:1-11

2.4   C18-36 ACID TRIGLYCERIDE

IDENTIFICATION

Description/definition	: C18-36 acid triglyceride is the triester of glycerin and C18-36 acid, which conforms to the formula shown below, where x has a value between 16 and 34
Chemical class(es)	: Glyceryl esters and derivatives
Other names	: Glycerides, C18-36
CAS registry number (s)	: 91052-08-3
EC number(s)	: 293-165-5
Function(s) in cosmetics	: EU: emollient; skin conditioning. USA: skin-conditioning agents - occlusive
Patch testing	: 10% pet. (1)

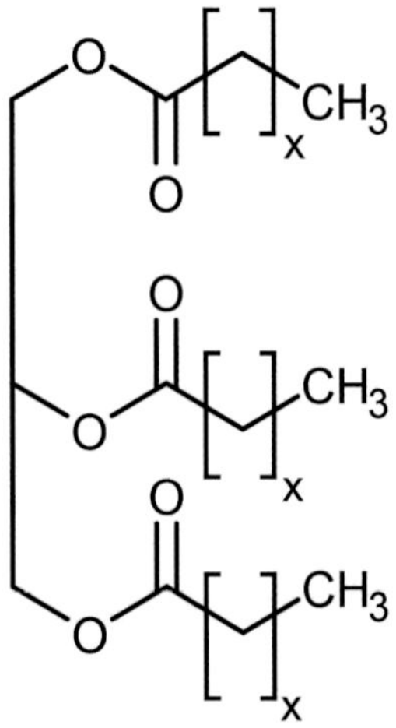

GENERAL

C18-36 acid triglyceride is the triester of glycerin and C18-36 acid. It is used as an alternative to natural wax to provide stable and uniform properties in lipsticks and emulsions (1).

CONTACT ALLERGY

Case reports and case series

A woman was seen with pruritic edematous erythema and scaling on her lips, which had developed 3 months earlier. In the preceding 6 months, she had started using about 30 new cosmetic products. When patch tested, the patient reacted to three of her lip glosses, tested 'as is'. Later, she was patch tested with 21 ingredients of these lip glosses. There was a positive reaction to C18-36 acid triglyceride 10% pet. only. All three products contained this substance. Six control patients showed no positive reactions to C18-36 acid triglyceride 10% pet. (1).

Presence in cosmetic products and chemical analyses

In the USA, in April 2017, C18-36 acid triglyceride was present in 216 of 56,714 cosmetic products of which the composition is known in FDA's Voluntary Cosmetic Registration Program (VCRP) (data obtained from FDA, May 2017). In April 2017, C18-36 acid triglyceride was present in 78 of 65,521 cosmetic products of which the composition is known in EWG's Skin Deep Cosmetics Database, USA (http://www.ewg.org/skindeep/).

LITERATURE

1   Kimura M, Kawada A, Ogino M, Murayama Y. Simultaneous contact sensitivity to hydroxystearic acid and C18-36 acid triglyceride in lip glosses. Contact Dermatitis 2002;47:115

2.5 ALCOHOL

IDENTIFICATION

Description/definition : Alcohol is undenatured ethyl alcohol that conforms to the formula shown below
Chemical class(es) : Alcohols
Chemical/IUPAC name : Ethanol
Other names : Ethyl alcohol
CAS registry number (s) : 64-17-5
EC number(s) : 200-578-6
CIR Review(s) : Int J Toxicol 2008;27(Suppl.1):1-43 (access: www.cir-safety.org/ingredients)
Merck Index monograph : 5084
Function(s) in cosmetics : EU: antifoaming; antimicrobial; adstringent; masking; solvent; viscosity controlling. USA: antifoaming agents; antimicrobial agents; cosmetic adstringents; fragrance ingredients; solvents; viscosity decreasing agents
Patch testing : 70% water (34); the patch with alcohol should be applied immediately after preparation in order to avoid false-negative reactions from the evaporation of the alcohol (13)
Molecular formula : C_2H_6O

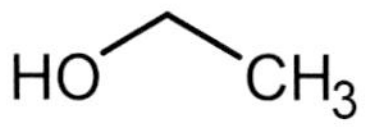

GENERAL

Although it has been shown that alcohol contact sensitivity can be induced under certain conditions (21), allergic contact dermatitis from alcohol is very infrequent and is usually caused by disinfectants containing a high percentage of alcohol (2,3,11,12,13) or from prolonged applications, such as in transdermal patches (7,13,20). When individuals with type IV allergy to alcohol drink alcoholic beverages, this may result in a (generalized) macular erythema or a flare of dermatitis: alcohol-induced systemic contact dermatitis (4,5,6,9,24,25,30). Erythema, aphthous ulcer-like lesions and a burning sensation of the oral mucosa may also occur (5). *Cosmetic* allergy from alcohol appears to be exceedingly rare, although alcohol was found to be present in nearly 20% of facial wipes in the USA in 2016 (18) and its use in (other) cosmetic is not rare (see 'Presence in cosmetic products and chemical analyses' below). In fact, no well-documented cases of allergic contact dermatitis from alcohol in cosmetics have been reported, only positive patch test reactions ascribed to cosmetic allergy (1) and one reaction to alcohol in a group of 475 patients with contact allergy to 'cosmetic ingredients', of which the relevance was not mentioned (14).

Ethyl alcohol is enzymatically degraded, via the intermediate compounds acetaldehyde and acetic acid, to water and carbon dioxide. Genetic defects in alcohol degradation (especially in Oriental people), or acquired inhibition of alcohol metabolizing enzymes by drugs, may lead to accumulation of one of these compounds and associated intolerance syndromes such as the 'Oriental flushing syndrome' or the disulfiram effect, respectively (17,26). Contact urticaria to alcohol is reported occasionally, but may be underreported or go unrecognized, as 13 patients having contact urticaria to alcohol were seen in a 3-year-period in Thailand (16). Immediate-type reactions (sometimes accompanied by a late-phase reaction [8,9]) can lead to generalized urticaria and anaphylactoid reactions with angioedema, asthma, throat constriction, gastrointestinal symptoms and even shock (28,36) when patients drink alcoholic beverages (2,9,16,26,27,28,29,32,35). It is assumed that both non-immunologic and immunologic mechanisms (e.g., positive Prausnitz-Küstner reaction [8,32]) may be involved and some authors assume a role for acetic acid, as many patients also reacted to vinegar and had positive prick tests to acetic acid but not to alcohol (26,27,28,29,35).

This chapter only discusses contact allergic reactions to alcohol and other side effects caused by alcohol *in cosmetic products* (15). The literature on allergic contact dermatitis and contact urticaria up to 1994 has been reviewed (19).

CONTACT ALLERGY

Case reports and case series

Two positive patch test reactions to alcohol were ascribed to cosmetic allergy in a study from Belgium (1). In a 4-month-period in 1996, 475 patients with contact allergy to 'cosmetic ingredients' were collected in 5 centers in Belgium, UK and Germany. There was one reaction to alcohol; relevance was not mentioned (14).

Contact allergy to alcohol in non-cosmetic products

Disinfectants
One patient had allergic contact dermatitis from alcohol used for disinfecting the skin for blood collection. The patient always had generalized flushing and palpitations after drinking alcohol (3). One individual developed ACD from denatured alcohol and alcohol-containing disinfectants (11). A woman had allergic contact dermatitis from alcohol used as disinfectant and would develop a widespread papular rash after drinking alcoholic drinks (25). Two patients (34) and one more (12) had contact allergy to alcohol used as disinfectant (12). A nurse had occupational ACD from alcohol in hand sanitizers and contact allergy to alcohol in perfumes (2). Two patients developed allergic contact dermatitis of the eyelids from the application of rubbing alcohol as an antiseptic (23).

Transdermal therapeutic systems
A woman had allergic contact dermatitis from alcohol in a transdermal estradiol patch. She reacted to 20% alcohol in water, to which 20 control patients were negative (20). Two other patients were also reported to have ACD from alcohol in estradiol transdermal systems; both women reacted to 'ethanol HP', but, quite curiously, not to 70% ethyl alcohol (7). In this article (7), a similar case from France was cited (22). One patient reacted to alcohol in an antiseptic and in pharmaceutical transdermal patches with fentanyl (13). Two women had contact dermatitis from allergy to alcohol contained in the reservoir of a transdermal transfer system with estrogens (34). A woman developed allergic contact dermatitis to alcohol in an estrogen patch. The day after drinking two alcoholic drinks, which she had tolerated well before, she suffered a systemic reaction with facial edema, reddening, generalized itching, and a fine macular rash, mainly on her face and upper trunk as well as reactivation of local dermatitis at previous sites of patch application. Oral challenge with alcohol reproduced the systemic reaction (30).

Other products
A furniture restorer had occupational allergic contact dermatitis from alcohol (4). A pathological technician was seen with contact dermatitis of the neck, wrist and axilla due to a splash with alcohol at work. The patient stated she had been sensitive to all alcohols including scent, deodorants and alcoholic drinks (contact, no abnormal effects from drinking) for four years. She had positive patch tests to alcohol 1-10% in water (33). Another patient had contact allergy to alcohol in a topical antifungal preparation (10). A woman noted itching and redness of the hands and fingers on the morning after drinking small amounts of alcoholic beverages the previous evening on several occasions for 16 years. When 70 per cent alcohol was used to cleanse the skin for a venepuncture, an erythematous reaction at the contact site appeared after 20 hours. When patch tested, the patient reacted to ethyl alcohol and to amyl, butyl, isopropyl and methyl alcohol (9). A provocation test with oral alcohol resulted in intense pruritus and erythema over the arms, hands, anterior chest, neck and thighs. She also had an early reaction after 2-3 hours with itching and mild erythema of the hands (9). Four patients had allergic contact dermatitis from alcohol; in all of them, an eruption developed or was aggravated after drinking alcoholic beverages (5). One individual presented with hand eczema from contact allergy to alcohol (24).

Cross-reactions, pseudo-cross-reactions and co-reactions
Amyl alcohol (9); 2-butanol (5); butyl alcohol (9); isopropyl alcohol (9); methyl alcohol (3,9,12,24); 1-pentanol (5); 1-propanol (12,24); 2-propanol (5); multiple primary alcohols and 4 aldehydes (31).

Presence in cosmetic products and chemical analyses
In July 2017, alcohol was present in 941 of 69,729 cosmetic products of which the composition is known in EWG's Skin Deep Cosmetics Database, USA (http://www.ewg.org/skindeep/). In the USA, in April 2017, alcohol was present in 5326 of 56,714 cosmetic products of which the composition is known in FDA's Voluntary Cosmetic Registration Program (VCRP) (data obtained from FDA, May 2017). Alcohol was present in 33 (19%) of 178 facial wipes for which ingredient information was obtained online and from retail stores, USA, 2016 (18).

Systemic side effects
Percutaneous absorption of alcohol from a beer-containing shampoo may have caused an Antabuse (disulfiram) effect in a patient taking disulfiram for alcoholism (15).

LITERATURE
1   Kohl L, Blondeel A, Song M. Allergic contact dermatitis from cosmetics: retrospective analysis of 819 patch-tested patients. Dermatology 2002;204:334-337
2   Wong JW, Harris K, Powell D. Alcohol urticaria syndrome. Dermatitis 2011;22:352-353
3   Okazawa H, Aihara M, Nagatani T, Nakajima H. Allergic contact dermatitis due to ethyl alcohol. Contact Dermatitis 1998;38:233

4   Patruno C, Suppa F, Sarracco G, Balato N. Allergic contact dermatitis due to ethyl alcohol. Contact Dermatitis 1994;31:124

5   Fregert S, Groth O, Hjorth N, Magnusson B, Rorsman H, Ovrum P. Alcohol dermatitis. Acta Derm Venereol 1969;49:493-497

6   Fisher AA. Topically applied alcohol as a cause of contact dermatitis. Cutis 1983;31:588, 592, 600.

7   Pecquet C, Pradalier A, Dry J. Allergic contact dermatitis from ethanol in a transdermal estradiol patch. Contact Dermatitis 1992;27:275

8   Kanzaki T, Hori H. Late phase allergic reaction of the skin to ethyl alcohol. Contact Dermatitis 1991;25:252-253

9   Drevets CC, Seebohm PM. Dermatitis from alcohol. J Allergy 1961;32:277-282

10 Ishiguro N, Kawashima M. Contact dermatitis from impurities in alcohol. Contact Dermatitis 1991;25:257

11 Melli MC, Giorgini S, Sertoli A. Sensitization from contact with ethyl alcohol. Contact Dermatitis 1986;14:315

12 van Ketel WG, Tan-Lim KN. Contact dermatitis from ethanol. Contact Dermatitis 1975;1:7-10

13 Pitarch G, de la Cuadra Précis J. Patch testing with ethyl alcohol. Dermatitis 2010;21:120-121

14 Goossens A, Beck MH, Haneke E, McFadden JP, Nolting S, Durupt G, Ries G. Adverse cutaneous reactions to cosmetic allergens. Contact Dermatitis 1999;40:112-113

15 Stoll D, King LE Jr. Disulfiram-alcohol skin reaction to beer-containing shampoo. JAMA 1980;244:2045

16 Chularojanamontri L, Tuchinda P, Pongparit K, Pinkaew S, Nuchkull P, Kulthanan K. Contact urticaria caused by alcohol: Clinical characteristics and cross-reactions. Ann Allergy Asthma Immunol 2016;117:721-723

17 Wilkin JK, Fortner G. Ethnic contact urticaria to alcohol. Contact Dermatitis 1985;12:118-120

18 Aschenbeck KA, Warshaw EM. Allergenic ingredients in facial wet wipes. Dermatitis 2017 Mar 23. doi: 10.1097/DER.0000000000000268. [Epub ahead of print]

19 Ophaswongse S, Maibach HI. Alcohol dermatitis: allergic contact dermatitis and contact urticaria syndrome. Contact Dermatitis 1994;30:1-6

20 Gata I, Bravo García B, Pichardo Rodríguez A, Resina Ortega M, Camacho F. Allergic contact dermatitis to ethanol in a transdermal estradiol patch. Am J Cont Dermat 1994;5:221-222

21 Scotts J, Ely WJ. Induction of human skin sensitization to ethanol. J Invest Dermatol 1977;69:209-222

22 Ducros B, Bonnin JP, Nayarrane A, Colomb D. Eczéma de contact a l'éthanol contenu dans une pastille d'oestradiol transdermique (Estraderm TIS 50). Nouv Dermatol 1989;8:21-22 (cited in ref. 7)

23 Baer HL. Dermatitis of the eyelids due to alcohol. Arch Derm Syph 1937;35:291

24 Haxthausen H. Allergic eczema caused by ethyl alcohol, elicited both by epicutaneous and by internal application. Acta Dermato-venereologica 1944;25:527-528

25 Chu GJ, Murad A. A case of ethanol-induced systemic allergic dermatitis. Contact Dermatitis 2017;76:182-184

26 Sticherling M, Brasch J, Brüning H, Christophers E. Urticarial and anaphylactoid reactions following ethanol intake. Br J Dermatol 1995;132:464-467

27 Fernando SL, Clarke LR. Two case reports of life-threatening ethanol-induced anaphylaxis. Case Rep Dermatol 2009;1:1-6

28 Boehnck WH, Gall H. Ethanol metabolite acetic acid as causative agent for type-I hypersensitivity-like reactions to alcohol beverages. Clin Exp Allergy 1996;26:1089-1091

29 Nakagawa Y, Sumikawa Y, Nakamura T, Itami S, Katayama I, Aoki T. Urticarial reaction caused by ethanol. Allergol Int 2006;55:411-414

30 Grebe SK, Adams JD, Feek CM. Systemic sensitization to ethanol by transdermal estrogen patches. Arch Dermatol 1993;129:379-380

31 Fregert S, Hakanson R, Rosman H, Tryding N, Ovrum P. Dermatitis from alcohols. J Allergy 1963;34:404-408

32 Rilliet A, Hunziker N, Brun R. Alcohol contact urticaria syndrome (immediate-type hypersensitivity). Case report. Dermatologica 1980;161:361-364

33 Martin-Scott I. Contact dermatitis from alcohol. Br J Derm 1960;72:372-373

34 Barbaud A, Trechot P, Reichert-Penetrat S, Schmutz J. Contact dermatitis due to ethyl alcohol: how to perform patch tests? Ann Dermatol Venereol 2000;127:484-487 (article in French)

35 Emonet S, Hogendijk S, Voegeli J, Eigenmann PA, Roux N, Hauser C. Ethanol-induced urticaria: elevated tryptase levels after double-blind, placebo-controlled challenge. Dermatology 1998;197:181-182

36 Pérez Martín J. Anaphylactic shock caused by ethyl alcohol ingestion. Rev Alerg Mex 1997;44:124-127 (article in Spanish)

2.6 C12-C15 ALKYL BENZOATE

IDENTIFICATION

Description/definition : C12-15 Alkyl benzoate is the ester of benzoic acid and C12-15 alcohols , which conforms
to the formula shown below, where R represents the C12-15 alkyl group
Chemical class(es) : Esters
Other names : Benzoic acid, C12-15 alkyl esters
CAS registry number (s) : 68411-27-8
EC number(s) : 270-112-4
CIR review(s) : Int J Toxicol 2012;31(Suppl.3):342-372 (access: www.cir-safety.org/ingredients)
Function(s) in cosmetics : EU: antimicrobial; emollient; skin conditioning. USA: skin conditioning agents - emollient
Patch test allergens : 5% pet. (1)

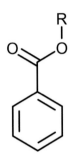

GENERAL

C12–15 alkyl benzoate is a mixture of benzoic acid alkyl esters with carbon chain lengths from 12 to 15 that are
claimed to have antimicrobial, emollient and skin conditioning properties (1).

CONTACT ALLERGY

Case reports and case series

C12-15 Alkyl benzoate was stated to be the (or an) allergen in 2 patients in a group of 603 individuals suffering from
cosmetic dermatitis, seen in the period 2010-2015 in Leuven, Belgium (2).

A man was seen with an itchy skin rash on the neck, arms, armpits, knee folds, and eyelids. This had appeared
following the application of sunscreen products and exposure to sunlight; however, he had no lesions on his legs or
trunk, to which he had applied the same products. Application of mineral sunscreens was well tolerated. A repeated
open application test on his forearm with the sunscreen products had produced a skin reaction. Patch testing and
photopatch testing was performed with the European baseline series, cosmetic and sunscreen series and the
patient's own products (deodorant and sunscreens tested 'as is'). Positive reactions were observed to C12-15 alkyl
benzoate 5% pet., and to the three cosmetics, which all contained C12-15 alkyl benzoate. The patient also had
positive reactions to benzyl benzoate and benzyl salicylate, fragrance ingredients which were present in one of the
sunscreen products. The patch test reactions were positive on both the UV-exposed side and the non-exposed side,
confirming allergic contact dermatitis. Seventy-five control subjects had negative results to C12-15 alkyl benzoate 5%
pet. (1).

Cross-reactions, pseudo-cross-reactions and co-reactions

Possibly to benzyl benzoate and benzyl salicylate (1).

Presence in cosmetic products and chemical analyses

In the USA, in April 2017, C12-15 alkyl benzoate was present in 1503 of 56,714 cosmetic products of which the
composition is known in FDA's Voluntary Cosmetic Registration Program (VCRP) (data obtained from FDA, May
2017). In March 2017, C12-15 alkyl benzoate was present in 1227 of 64,983 cosmetic products of which the
composition is known in EWG's Skin Deep Cosmetics Database, USA (http://www.ewg.org/skindeep/).

LITERATURE

1   Werbrouck J, Lambrecht C, Goossens A. C12–15 alkyl benzoate: a new cosmetic allergen? Contact Dermatitis
2015;73:249-250
2   Goossens A. Cosmetic contact allergens. Cosmetics 2016, 3, 5; doi:10.3390/cosmetics3010005

2.7 ALLANTOIN

IDENTIFICATION

Description/definition : Allantoin is a heterocyclic organic compound that conforms to the formula shown below
Chemical class(es) : Heterocyclic compounds
Chemical/IUPAC name : (2,5-Dioxoimidazolidin-4-yl)urea
Other names : 5-Ureidohydantoin
CAS registry number (s) : 97-59-6
EC number(s) : 202-592-8
CIR review(s) : Int J Toxicol 2010;29(Suppl.2):84-97 (access: www.cir-safety.org/ingredients)
Merck Index monograph : 1520
Function(s) in cosmetics : EU: skin conditioning; skin protecting; soothing. USA: skin protecting agents; skin-conditioning agents - miscellaneous
Patch testing : 5% pet. (4); 1% physiologic saline for immediate open testing (3)
Molecular formula : $C_4H_6N_4O_3$

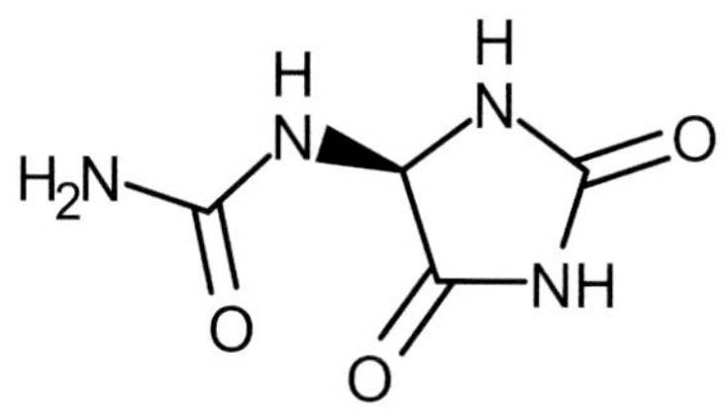

GENERAL

Allantoin is present in botanical extracts of the comfrey plant (*Symphytum officinale* L.) and in urine from cows and most mammals. Animals and plants convert allantoin to glyoxylic acid and urea via allantoic acid. Allantoin is said to have numerous pharmacological uses, including wound healing, anti-irritation, hydration, regeneration of tissue, and cell proliferation, as well as having analgesic and keratolytic effects (5).

CONTACT ALLERGY

Case reports and case series
Allantoin was responsible for 2 out of 399 cases of cosmetic allergy where the causal allergen was identified in a study of the NACDG, USA, 1977-1983 (1). One positive patch test reactions to allantoin was ascribed to cosmetic allergy (2).

Presence in cosmetic products and chemical analyses
In the USA, in April 2017, allantoin was present in 3010 of 56,714 cosmetic products of which the composition is known in FDA's Voluntary Cosmetic Registration Program (VCRP) (data obtained from FDA, May 2017). In January 2017, allantoin was present in 1302 of 64,480 cosmetic products of which the composition is known in EWG's Skin Deep Cosmetics Database, USA (http://www.ewg.org/skindeep/).

OTHER SIDE EFFECTS

Immediate-type reactions
A woman applied a cosmetic skin mask formulation to her face and noted rapid onset of transient rash, burning, stinging and itching at the application sites. Immediate open testing (without prick, scratch or chamber) to intact forearm skin revealed extensive wheal and flare to the following components of the formulation: allantoin (1% physiologic saline), whole egg (0.1% and 1%), lecithin, aloe gel, chamomile extract, melissa extract (all 1%) and the final formulation as is (skin mask). The saline control was negative, as were similar applications of the above to 10 controls. This would therefore appear to be immunologic contact urticaria. According to the authors, this multiplicity of positive immediate-type reactions suggests the possibility of an immediate-type hypersensitivity analogue of the excited skin syndrome seen in delayed-type testing, common chemical constituents in these natural products, or an individual with a unique immunologic system (3).

LITERATURE

1   Adams RM, Maibach HI, Clendenning WE, Fisher AA, Jordan WJ, Kanof N, et al. A five-year study of cosmetic reactions. J Am Acad Dermatol 1985;13:1062-1069

2   Kohl L, Blondeel A, Song M. Allergic contact dermatitis from cosmetics: retrospective analysis of 819 patch-tested patients. Dermatology 2002;204:334-337

3   West I, Maibach HI. Contact urticaria syndrome from multiple cosmetic components. Contact Dermatitis 1995;32:121

4   De Groot AC. Patch Testing, 3rd Edition. Wapserveen, The Netherlands: acdegroot publishing, 2008

5   Madrazo-Jiménez M, Rodríguez-Caballero Á, Serrera-Figallo MÁ, Garrido-Serrano R, Gutiérrez-Corrales A, Gutiérrez-Pérez JL, Torres-Lagares D. The effects of a topical gel containing chitosan, 0,2% chlorhexidine, allantoin and despanthenol on the wound healing process subsequent to impacted lower third molar extraction. Med Oral Patol Oral Cir Bucal 2016;21:e696-e702

2.8 ALPHA-GLUCAN OLIGOSACCHARIDE

IDENTIFICATION

Description/definition	: Alpha-glucan oligosaccharide is a glucose oligomer exhibiting a degree of polymerization ranging from 2 to 10; it is prepared by the action of glucosyl transferase on sucrose
Chemical class(es)	: Carbohydrates
CAS registry number (s)	: 27707-45-5; 9074-78-6 (mentioned in the article, but is the CAS number of α-D-glucan)
Function(s) in cosmetics	: EU: skin conditioning. USA: skin-conditioning agents - miscellaneous
Patch testing	: 5% water (1); the test concentration is probably not irritant

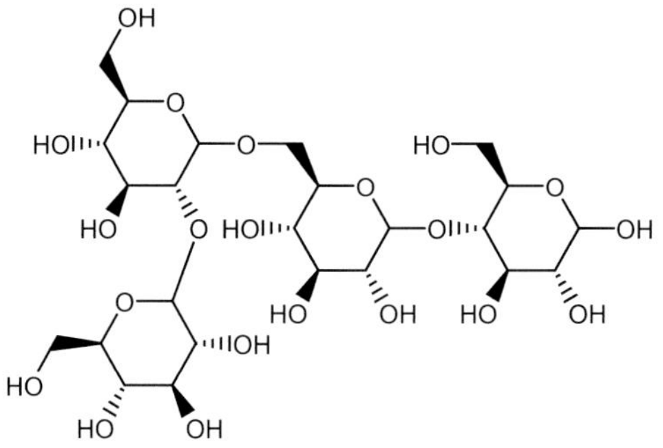

GENERAL

Glucan oligosaccharides are oligosaccharides obtained from maltose and sucrose that are used to regulate the balance of normal bacteria on the skin with the metabolites supposedly facilitating moisturization of the skin (1). In a report from Australia, glucan oligosaccharides were non-irritant, non-sensitizing and non- phototoxic in experimental animals (2).

CONTACT ALLERGY

Case reports and case series

A woman presented with a one day history of acute dermatitis on her face. Three days ago, she had started using a new skin lotion. The patient had previously also had an episode of dermatitis caused by a cosmetic. She was patch tested with her cosmetic products, which resulted in a positive reaction to the new skin lotion 'as is'. Further patch testing was performed with all ingredients of this skin lotion. There were positive reactions to glucan oligosaccharide 5% water and 1% water, which remained positive until D6. However, the reaction to glucan oligosaccharide 0.1% water was negative. Seven control patients were negative. The patient was also tested with skin lotions in which the glucan oligosaccharide content had been reduced to 10% and to 1% of the normal level, and to the same lotion without glucan oligosaccharide. There was a ?+ reaction to the lotion with 10% of the normal amount of glucan oligosaccharide, but the other two lotions were negative. After the patient ceased application of the cosmetic product, the dermatitis cleared. The cosmetic that had previously caused dermatitis proved to contain glucan oligosaccharide also (1).

Presence in cosmetic products and chemical analyses

In the USA, in April 2017, alpha-glucan oligosaccharide was present in 98 of 56,714 cosmetic products of which the composition is known in FDA's Voluntary Cosmetic Registration Program (VCRP) (data obtained from FDA, May 2017). In January 2017, alpha-glucan oligosaccharide was present in 35 of 64,475 cosmetic products of which the composition is known in EWG's Skin Deep Cosmetics Database, USA (http://www.ewg.org/skindeep/).

LITERATURE

1   Washizaki K, Kanto H, Ito M. A case of allergic contact dermatitis caused by glucan oligosaccharide. Contact Dermatitis 2009;60:345
2   National Occupational Health and Safety Commission. National Industrial Chemicals Notification And Assessment Scheme Full Public Report BioEcolia [NA/676]. Canberra, Australian Government Publishing Service, 1999

2.9 ALUMINA

IDENTIFICATION

Description/definition	: Alumina is an inorganic compound that conforms to the formula Al_2O_3
Chemical class(es)	: Inorganics
Chemical/IUPAC name	: Aluminium oxide
Other names	: Aluminii oxidum
CAS registry number (s)	: 1344-28-1; 1333-84-2 (hydrate)
EC number(s)	: 215-691-6
CIR review(s)	: Final report 2013 (access: www.cir-safety.org/ingredients)
SCCS opinion(s)	: SCCS 1525/14 (aluminium) (8)
Merck Index monograph	: 1620
Function(s) in cosmetics	: EU: abrasive; absorbent; anticaking; bulking; opacifying; viscosity controlling. USA: abrasives; absorbents; anticaking agents; bulking agents; opacifying agents
Patch testing	: Aluminum chloride 2% water; aluminum hydroxide 10% pet. (Chemotechnique, SmartPracticeCanada)
Molecular formula	: Al_2O_3

GENERAL

Alumina (aluminium oxide) is an extremely rare sensitizer in cosmetic products. The discussion of alumina in this chapter is limited to reactions from its presence in cosmetics. The far more frequent allergic reactions to aluminum in vaccines and hyposensitization injections (in the form of e.g., aluminum hydroxide, aluminum potassium, or aluminum phosphate) are also discussed briefly. Allergic contact dermatitis from aluminum compounds in antiperspirant cosmetics and OTC drugs, where the exact nature of the aluminum containing chemical was not specified, is discussed in Chapter 2.303 Miscellaneous under 'Aluminum compounds (unspecified)' in antiperspirants.

CONTACT ALLERGY

Case reports and case series

Three children had nodules at vaccination sites from aluminum contact allergy; these persisted from the use of toothpastes containing alumina (aluminium oxide). Stopping the use of the alumina-containing toothpastes resulted in clearing of the nodules. In two children, provocation tests with the toothpaste were positive. The children had probably previously been sensitized from vaccinations. Absorption of alumina from the oral mucosa while brushing their teeth was a likely explanation for the persistent nodules, termed systemically aggravated contact dermatitis (1).

Contact allergy to aluminum in non-cosmetic products: vaccination reactions

Aluminum is a malleable metal that is the most widely used adjuvant in human vaccines. Aluminum may be found in various forms in these products, including aluminum hydroxide, aluminum potassium, or aluminum phosphate, to potentiate the immune response to vaccination. Aluminum adjuvants can be found in many widely administered vaccines including tetanus, diphtheria, pertussis, hepatitis A, and hepatitis B (9). Hypersensitivity to aluminum is an infrequent but far from rare complication from repeated administration of vaccines and allergy injections (2-7,9-13,15). The clinical manifestations of these reactions are variable and multiple. Patients may develop localized dermatitis with erythema, edema and blistering (7,9) or extensive dermatitis (5,7). The most common presentation of vaccine hypersensitivity to aluminum are painful, pruritic nodules at the injection site(s) that develop weeks, months, or even years after the introduction of aluminum (2,10,11). Changes in pigmentation, hypertrichosis, and lichenification are not infrequently associated with such nodules (3,7,10,11). The pruritic, nodular reactions can persist for years (3) and may be exacerbated during upper respiratory infections and application of aluminum-containing substances onto the skin such as sunscreens (9,10,11). Patients generally demonstrate positive patch tests to aluminum (2,3,6,10), but not all reactions seem to be the result of delayed type allergy to the metal (11). Histopathologic examination of biopsy specimens reveals granulomatous and foreign body reactions and the nodules contain aluminum (5,11). The literature on this subject has been reviewed (9,14).

Cross-reactions, pseudo-cross-reactions and co-reactions

Patients have not been patch tested with alumina itself but with other aluminum compounds including aluminum chloride 2% water (1,2,3,4,5,6,12), aluminum sulfate 2% water (4), aluminum subacetate 1% water (4), aluminum powder pure (4) or 2% water (12), aluminum acetate 1.3-2% water (6,7,12), aluminum acetotartrate 1% pet. (6), aluminum chloride hexahydrate 0.5%-2% pet. (7,9,10), aluminum hydroxide 10% water (13) or a blank Finn chamber

(7,10). Many co-reactions of aluminum test substances were observed The allergen is the aluminum itself, so any preparation containing enough free aluminum may (pseudo)cross-react.

Presence in cosmetic products and chemical analyses
In the USA, in April 2017, alumina was present in 829 of 56,714 cosmetic products of which the composition is known in FDA's Voluntary Cosmetic Registration Program (VCRP) (data obtained from FDA, May 2017). In February 2017, alumina was present in 1246 of 64,482 cosmetic products of which the composition is known in EWG's Skin Deep Cosmetics Database, USA (http://www.ewg.org/skindeep/).

LITERATURE

1   Veien NK, Hattel T, Laurberg G. Systemically aggravated contact dermatitis caused by aluminium in toothpaste. Contact Dermatitis 1993;28:199-200
2   Veien NK, Hattel T, Justesen 0, Nerholm A. Aluminium allergy. Contact Dermatitis 1986;15:295-297
3   Kaaber K, Nielsen A0, Veien NK. Vaccination granulomas and aluminium allergy: course and prognostic factors. Contact Dermatitis 1992;26:304-306
4   Clemmensen 0, Knudsen HE. Contact sensitivity to aluminium in a patient hyposensitized with aluminium precipitated grass pollen. Contact Dermatitis 1980;6:305-308
5   Frost L, Johansen P, Pedersen S, Veien N, Aabel 0stergaard P, Nielsen M H. Persistent subcutaneous nodules in children hyposensitized with aluminium-containing allergen extracts. Allergy 1985;40:368-372
6   Cosnes A, Flechet M-L, Revuz J. Inflammatory nodular reactions after hepatitis B vaccination due to aluminium sensitization. Contact Dermatitis 1990;23:65-67
7   Cox NH, Moss C, Forsyth A. Allergy to non-toxoid constituents of vaccines and implications for patch testing. Contact Dermatitis 1988;18:143-146
8   SCCS (Scientific Committee on Consumer Safety). Opinion on the safety of aluminium in cosmetic products, 27 March 2014, SCCS 1525/14, revision of 18 June 2014. Available at: http://ec.europa.eu/health/scientific_committees/consumer_safety/docs/sccs_o_153.pdf
9   Leventhal JS, Berger EM, Brauer JA, Cohen DE. Hypersensitivity reactions to vaccine constituents: a case series and review of the literature. Dermatitis 2012;23:102-109
10   Bergfors E, Bjorkelund C, Trollfors B. Nineteen cases of persistent pruritic nodules and contact allergy to aluminum after injection of commonly used aluminum-adsorbed vaccines. Eur J Pediatr 2005;164:691-697
11   Garcia-Patos V, Pujol RM, Alomar A, Curell R, Fernández-Figueras MT, de Moragas JM. Persistent subcutaneous nodules in patients hyposensitized with aluminum-containing allergen extracts. Arch Dermatol 1995;131:1421-1424
12   Castelain P-Y, Castelain M, Vervloet D, Garbe L, Mallet B. Sensitization to aluminium by aluminium-precipitated dust and pollen extracts. Contact Dermatitis 1988;19:58-60
13   Böhler-Sommeregger K, Lindemayr H. Contact sensitivity to aluminium. Contact Dermatitis 1986;15:278-281
14   Rosenblatt AE, Stein SL. Cutaneous reactions to vaccinations. Clin Dermatol 2015;33:327-332
15   Bergfors E, Trollfors B. Sixty-four children with persistent itching nodules and contact allergy to aluminium after vaccination with aluminium-adsorbed vaccines-prognosis and outcome after booster vaccination. Eur J Pediatr 2013;172:171-177

2.10 ALUMINUM CHLORIDE

IDENTIFICATION

Description/definition   : Aluminum chloride is the inorganic compound that conforms to the formula shown
    below
Chemical class(es)   : Inorganic salts
Chemical/IUPAC name   : Trichloroalumane
Other names   : Aluminium chloride; alumin(i)um trichloride; trichloroaluminum
CAS registry number (s) : 7446-70-0; 7784-13-6
EC number(s)   : 231-208-1
SCCS opinion(s)   : SCCS 1525/14 (aluminium) (5)
Merck Index monograph : 1603
Function(s) in cosmetics : EU: antiperspirant; adstringent; deodorant. USA: antiperspirant agents; cosmetic
    adstringents; deodorant agents
Patch testing   : 2% water (1,2); aluminum hydroxide 10% pet. (Chemotechnique, SmartPracticeCanada)
Molecular formula   : $AlCl_3$

GENERAL

Aluminum chloride is a rare sensitizer in cosmetic products. The discussion of aluminum chloride in this chapter is limited to reactions from its presence in cosmetics. The far more frequent allergic reactions to aluminum in vaccines and hyposensitization injections (in the form of e.g., aluminum hydroxide, aluminum potassium, or aluminum phosphate) are discussed in Chapter 2.9 Alumina. Allergic contact dermatitis from aluminum compounds in antiperspirant cosmetics and OTC drugs, where the exact nature of the aluminum containing chemical was not specified, is discussed in Chapter 2.303 Miscellaneous under 'Aluminum compounds (unspecified)'.

CONTACT ALLERGY

Case reports and case series

A woman developed allergic contact dermatitis from aluminum chloride in an antiperspirant stick. Later, she had repeated attacks of symmetrical, eczematous lesions of the chest, axillary folds, proximal upper extremities and lower back probably caused by intradermal hyposensitization injections containing aluminum hydroxide (1). A man had axillary dermatitis from contact allergy to aluminum chloride in a roll-on antiperspirant (2). A similar case was described in ref. 3.

Cross-reactions, pseudo-cross-reactions and co-reactions

As the allergen in aluminum chloride is aluminum itself, other aluminum compounds containing enough free aluminum may (pseudo)cross-react.

Presence in cosmetic products and chemical analyses

In the USA, in April 2017, aluminum chloride was present in 5 of 56,714 cosmetic products of which the composition is known in FDA's Voluntary Cosmetic Registration Program (VCRP) (data obtained from FDA, May 2017). In February 2017, aluminum chloride was present in 1 of 64,482 cosmetic products of which the composition is known in EWG's Skin Deep Cosmetics Database, USA (http://www.ewg.org/skindeep/).

Miscellaneous side effects

Two patients developed axillary granulomas from a deodorant spray containing talc and aluminum chloride, which is hydrolysed into aluminum hydroxide under physiological conditions. The nature of the reaction was not investigated, but both talc and aluminum was demonstrated in the granulomas (4).

LITERATURE

1   Clemmensen O, Knudsen HE. Contact sensitivity to aluminium in a patient hyposensitized with aluminium
    precipitated grass pollen. Contact Dermatitis 1980;6:305-308
2   Fischer T, Rystedt I. A case of contact sensitivity to aluminium. Contact Dermatitis 1982;8:343
3   Fisher AA. Reactions to aluminum and its salts. Cutis 1984;33:154-159

4   Williams S, Freemont AJ. Aerosol antiperspirants and axillary granulomata. Br Med J 1984;288:1651-1652

5   SCCS (Scientific Committee on Consumer Safety). Opinion on the safety of aluminium in cosmetic products, 27 March 2014, SCCS 1525/14, revision of 18 June 2014. Available at:
     http://ec.europa.eu/health/scientific_committees/consumer_safety/docs/sccs_o_153.pdf

2.11 ALUMINUM CHLOROHYDRATE

IDENTIFICATION

Description/definition	: Aluminum chlorohydrate is an inorganic salt that conforms to the formula shown below
Chemical class(es)	: Inorganic salts
Chemical/IUPAC name	: Dialuminum;chloride;pentahydroxide
Other names	: Aluminum (III) chloride pentahydroxide; aluminum chlorohydrate (anhydrous); aluminum hydroxychloride
CAS registry number (s)	: 12042-91-0
EC number(s)	: 234-933-1
SCCS opinion(s)	: SCCS 1525/14 (aluminium) (2)
Merck Index monograph	: 1609
Function(s) in cosmetics	: EU: antiperspirant; astringent; deodorant. USA: antiperspirant agents; cosmetic astringents; deodorant agents
Patch testing	: Aluminum chloride 2% water or pet (1); aluminum hydroxide 10% pet. (Chemotechnique, SmartPracticeCanada)
Molecular formula	: $Al_2ClH_5O_5$

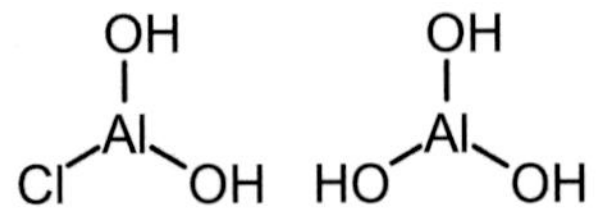

GENERAL

Aluminum chlorohydrate is a rare sensitizer in cosmetic products. The discussion of aluminum chlorohydrate in this chapter is limited to reactions from its presence in cosmetics. The far more frequent allergic reactions to aluminum in vaccines and hyposensitization injections (in the form of e.g., aluminum hydroxide, aluminum potassium, or aluminum phosphate) are discussed in Chapter 2.9 Alumina. Allergic contact dermatitis from aluminum compounds in antiperspirant cosmetics and OTC drugs, where the exact nature of the aluminum containing chemical was not specified, is discussed in Chapter 2.303 Miscellaneous under 'Aluminum compounds (unspecified)'.

CONTACT ALLERGY

Case reports and case series

A woman presented with eczema in both axillae which occurred after the use of deodorants, and settled when these were avoided. Patch testing was performed with the baseline series, fragrance series, and aluminum chloride. The patient reacted to aluminum chloride ($AlCl_3$ 2% pet.), quaternium-15, benzophenone-4, farnesol and citral. There was no reaction to the 8 mm aluminum Finn Chambers. Allergic contact dermatitis to aluminum salts was diagnosed. All the deodorants she had been using contained aluminum chlorohydrate, but did not contain the other allergens to which she reacted. After avoiding aluminum-containing deodorants, the patient has remained symptom free (1).

Cross-reactions, pseudo-cross-reactions and co-reactions

As the allergen in aluminum chlorohydrate is aluminum itself, other aluminum compounds containing enough free aluminum may (pseudo)cross-react.

Presence in cosmetic products and chemical analyses

In the USA, in April 2017, aluminum chlorohydrate was present in 89 of 56,714 cosmetic products of which the composition is known in FDA's Voluntary Cosmetic Registration Program (VCRP) (data obtained from FDA, May 2017). In March 2017, aluminum chlorohydrate was present in 33 of 64,983 cosmetic products of which the composition is known in EWG's Skin Deep Cosmetics Database, USA (http://www.ewg.org/skindeep/).

LITERATURE

1   Garg S, Loghdey S, Gawkrodger DJ. Allergic contact dermatitis from aluminium in deodorants. Contact Dermatitis. 2010;62:57-58

2   SCCS (Scientific Committee on Consumer Safety). Opinion on the safety of aluminium in cosmetic products, 27 March 2014, SCCS 1525/14, revision of 18 June 2014. Available at: http://ec.europa.eu/health/scientific_committees/consumer_safety/docs/sccs_o_153.pdf

2.12 4-AMINOAZOBENZENE

IDENTIFICATION

Description/definition   : 4-Aminoazobenzene is the aromatic compound that conforms to the structural formula
                             shown below
Chemical class(es)   : Aromatic compounds; azo compounds; aromatic amines
INCI name USA   : Not in the Personal Care Products Council Ingredient database
Chemical/IUPAC name   : 4-(2-Phenyldiazenyl)-benzenamine
Other names   : Solvent yellow 1; CI 11000; aniline yellow; *p*-aminoazobenzene
CAS registry number (s)   : 60-09-3
EC number(s)   : 200-453-6
Merck Index monograph   : 1684
Function(s) in cosmetics   : EU: formerly used for hair dyeing
EU cosmetic restrictions   : Regulated in Annex II/990 of the Regulation (EC) No. 1223/2009 (prohibited)
Patch testing   : 0.25% pet. (Chemotechnique); 1% pet. (SmartPracticeEurope, SmartPracticeCanada)
Molecular formula   : $C_{12}H_{11}N_3$

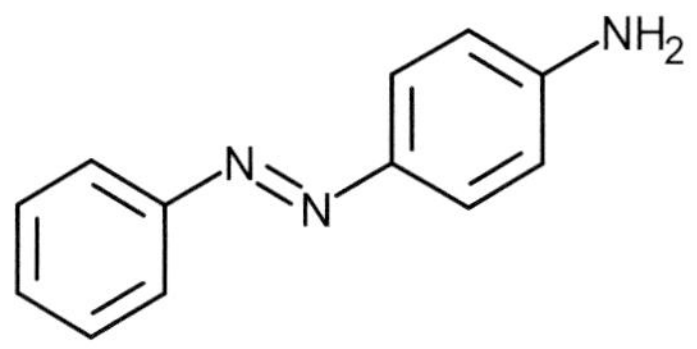

CONTACT ALLERGY

Patch testing in groups of patients
Results of routine patch testing with 4-aminoazobenzene (testing in consecutive patients suspected of contact dermatitis) and of testing in groups of *selected* patients (e.g., patients tested with a hairdresser's series, hairdressers suspected of occupational contact dermatitis, patients suspected of allergic contact dermatitis from footwear, patients with scalp dermatitis) are shown in table 2.12.1. In routine testing, frequencies of 2.5% and 2.7% positive reactions have been observed (8,11). Relevance was either not mentioned or only 12%. Most to all patients co-reacted to *p*-phenylenediamine (PPD). Hence, the relatively high percentages of sensitization may likely be explained by cross-reactivity to PPD (8,11). There were many late reactions (appearing on D7 or later), which were considered to be indicative of patch test sensitization. However, these may well have been late reactions caused by cross-sensitivity to PPD.

In groups of selected patients (table 2.12.1), high rates of sensitization of 31.9% and 41% were observed in hairdressers (4,5), but the relevance of these positive reactions was not specified. In patients with dermatitis of the scalp, a rate of 24% positive patch test reactions was observed. It is likely, that most of these reactions resulted from cross-sensitivity to PPD.

Case reports and case series
In the period 1996-2013, in a tertiary referral center in Valencia, Spain, 5419 patients were patch tested. Of these, 628 individuals had allergic contact dermatitis to cosmetics. 4-Aminoazobenzene was the responsible allergen in 7 cases (7).

Kum-Kum (also called 'sindhoor' or 'tilak') are colored cosmetics applied to the forehead by Indian women for socio-religious purposes. Kum-Kum is held in high esteem by the South Indians, especially the married women who apply it on their forehead as a sign of their marital status and these cosmetics are sold as powders or liquids (9). Contact dermatitis to Kum-Kum is a common cosmetic problem. It presents as erythema, papular and vesicular lesions at the site of Kum-Kum on the forehead, near the hair margin, and on the surrounding skin where it may trickle with sweat. One product and a refill pack were analyzed with thin layer chromatography and found to contain brilliant lake red R, Sudan I, *p*-aminoazobenzene and cananga oil. Twenty patients suspected of dermatitis from Kum-kum were patch tested with their own products and with these chemicals (test concentrations and vehicles not mentioned) and all 20 reacted to the product itself, brilliant lake red R, Sudan I, *p*-aminoazobenzene and cananga oil. There were no reactions to any of the chemicals in the standard series (9). These results appear to be too good to be true and the identification of cananga oil with thin layer chromatography is impossible as it contains over 150 chemicals which are also present in (many) other essential oils.

Contact allergy to 4-aminoazobenzene in non-cosmetic products

A woman presented with itching, erythema, and feeling of warmth in the area of a colored tattoo on her left leg. Patch tests were positive to 4-aminoazbenzene 0.25% pet., which was apparently present in the orange pigment used for the tattoo (13). A postal worker had ACD from 4-aminoazobenzene in stamp-ink (16).

Table 2.12.1 Patch testing in groups of patients

Years and Country	Test conc. & vehicle	Number of patients tested | positive (%)		Selection of patients (S); Relevance (R); Comments (C)	Ref.
Routine testing					
1992-1994 Netherlands		3461	(2.7%)	R: not stated; C: most patients co-reacted to *p*-phenylenediamine; there were many late reactions indicative of patch test sensitization	8
1992-1994 Netherlands		678	17 (2.5%)	R: 12%; C: 11 had positive reactions only >7 days; all co-reacted to *p*-phenylenediamine	11
Testing in groups of selected patients					
2007-2014 IVDK	1% pet.	586	30 (5.1%)	S: patients suspected of textile allergy and tested with a textile and leather dye series	12
1996-2013 Netherlands	0.25% pet.	146	4 (2.7%)	S: children aged 0-17 years; R: not stated	10
2000-2008 USA	0.25 pet.	149	(13%)	S: patients tested with a hairdresser's series; R: 90%	3
1994-2003 Spain		300	(41%)	S: hairdressers suspected of occupational contact dermatitis; R: not specified	4
1993-2003 IVDK	1% pet.	75	18 (24%)	S: patients with scalp dermatitis; R: not stated	2
1995-1999 IVDK	1% pet.	617	100 (16.2%)	S: patients tested with a 'para-amino' test series (criteria for inclusion not specified); R: not specified	1
1980-1993 Spain	0.25% pet.	379	121 (31.9%)	S: hairdressers; R: not specified	5
<1992 India	0.25% pet.	50	5 (10%)	S: patients suspected of ACD from footwear; R: not stated	15
1989 Italy	0.25% pet.	336	1 (0.3%)	S: male soldiers without skin disease; R: not stated	6

IVDK: Information Network of Departments of Dermatology, Germany, Austria, Switzerland

Cross-reactions, pseudo-cross-reactions and co-reactions

p-Aminoazobenzene may cross-react with structurally related chemicals, notably those with a para-structure. Cross-reactivity between para-compounds is discussed in Chapter 2.359 *p*-Phenylenediamine.

Patch test sensitization

Of 17 positive patch test reactions to 4-aminoazobenzene, 11 had developed at D7 or later, indicative of patch test sensitization (11). In a group of 3461 consecutive patients patch tested with 4-aminoazobenzene (test concentration not mentioned), there were 'many late reactions' indicative of patch test sensitization (8). Two patients were sensitized from a patch test with 4-aminoazobenzene 1% pet. (14).

Presence in cosmetic products and chemical analyses

In the USA, in April 2017, 4-aminoazobenzene was present in zero of 56,714 cosmetic products of which the composition is known in FDA's Voluntary Cosmetic Registration Program (VCRP) (data obtained from FDA, May 2017). In April 2017, 4-aminoazobenzene was present in zero of 66,647 cosmetic products of which the composition is known in EWG's Skin Deep Cosmetics Database, USA (http://www.ewg.org/skindeep/).

Other side effects

Patch testing 4-aminoazobenzene together with *p*-phenylenediamine (PPD) leads to a slight increase in positive reactions to PPD and to an increase in non-relevant reactions to PPD (11).

LITERATURE

1   Uter W, Lessmann H, Geier J, Becker D, Fuchs T, Richter G. The spectrum of allergic (cross-)sensitivity in clinical patch testing with '*para* amino' compounds. Allergy 2002;57:319-322

2   Hillen U, Grabbe S, Uter W. Patch test results in patients with scalp dermatitis: analysis of data of the Information Network of Departments of Dermatology. Contact Dermatitis 2007;56:87-93

3   Wang MZ, Farmer SA, Richardson DM, Davis MDP. Patch-testing with hairdressing chemicals. Dermatitis 2011;22:16-26

4   Valks R, Conde-Salazar L, Malfeito J, Ledo S. Contact dermatitis in hairdressers, 10 years later: patch-test results in 300 hairdressers (1994 to 2003) and comparison with previous study. Dermatitis 2005;16:28-31

5   Conde-Salazar L, Baz M, Guimaraens D, Cannavo A. Contact dermatitis in hairdressers: patch test results in 379 hairdressers (1980-1993). Am J Cont Dermat 1995;6:19-23

6   Seidenari S, Manzini BM, Danese P, Motolese A. Patch and prick test study of 593 healthy subjects. Contact Dermatitis 1990; 23:162-167

7   Zaragoza-Ninet V, Blasco Encinas R, Vilata-Corell JJ, Pérez-Ferriols A, Sierra-Talamantes C, Esteve-Martínez A, de la Cuadra-Oyanguren J. Allergic contact dermatitis due to cosmetics: A clinical and epidemiological study in a tertiary hospital. Actas Dermosifiliogr 2016;107:329-336

8   Arnold WP, van Joost T, van der Valk PGM. Adding *p*-aminoazobenzene may increase the sensitivity of the European standard series in detecting contact allergy to dyes, but carries the risk of active sensitization. Contact Dermatitis 1995;33:444

9   Kumar JV, Moideen R, Murugesh SB. Contactants in 'Kum-Kum' dermatitis. Indian J Dermatol Venereol Leprol 1996;62:220-221

10   Lubbes S, Rustemeyer T, Sillevis Smitt JH, Schuttelaar ML, Middelkamp-Hup MA. Contact sensitization in Dutch children and adolescents with and without atopic dermatitis - a retrospective analysis. Contact Dermatitis 2017;76:151-159

11   Devos SA, Van der Valk PGM. The risk of active sensitization to PPD. Contact Dermatitis 2001;44:273-275

12   Heratizadeh A, Geier J, Molin S, Werfel T. Contact sensitization in patients with suspected textile allergy. Data of the Information Network of Departments of Dermatology (IVDK) 2007-2014. Contact Dermatitis. 2017 Feb 24. doi: 10.1111/cod.12760. [Epub ahead of print]

13   Tammaro A, De Marco G, D'Arino A, Pigliacelli F, Daniele A, Borgert I, Parisella FR, Persechino S. Aminoazobenzene in tattoo: another case of allergic contact dermatitis. Int J Dermatol. 2017;56:e79-e81

14   Aalto-Korte K, Alanko K, Kuuliala O, Jolanki R. Late reactions in patch tests: a 4-year review from a clinic of occupational dermatology. Contact Dermatitis 2007;56:81-86

15   Saha M, Srinivas CR, Shenoy SD, Balachandran C, Acharya S. Footwear dermatitis. Contact Dermatitis 1993;28:260-264

16   Braun WP. Contact dermatitis from a stamp-ink of the German post office. Contact Dermatitis 1975;1:189-190

2.13 4-AMINO-M-CRESOL

IDENTIFICATION

Description/definition   : 4-Amino-*m*-cresol is the substituted aromatic compound that conforms to the formula shown below
Chemical class(es)   : Amines; color additives – hair; phenols
Chemical/IUPAC name : 4-Amino-3-methylphenol
Other names   : *p*-Amino-*m*-cresol; 4-hydroxy-*o*-toluidine
CAS registry number (s) : 2835-99-6
EC number(s)   : 220-621-2
CIR review(s)   : Int J Toxicol 2004;23(Suppl.2):1-22 (access: www.cir-safety.org/ingredients)
SCCS opinion(s)   : SCCP/0898/05 (3)
Function(s) in cosmetics : EU: hair dyeing. USA: hair colorants
EU cosmetic restrictions : Regulated in Annex III/244 of the Regulation (EC) No. 1197/2013
Patch testing   : 1% pet.
Molecular formula   : C_7H_9NO

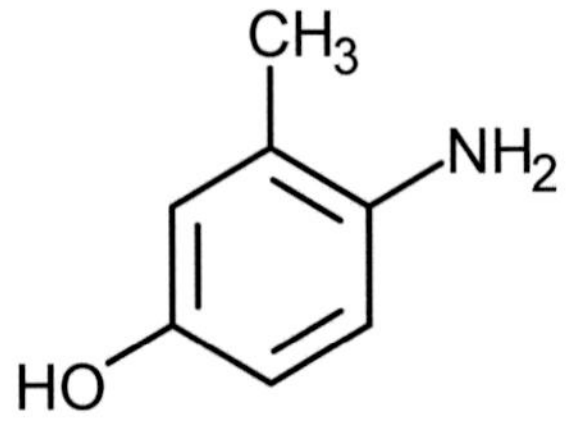

GENERAL

4-Amino-*m*-cresol is used as primary intermediate (synonyms: oxidation base, developer)in oxidative hair dying products. The chemistry of oxidative hair dying is discussed in Chapter 2.359 *p*-Phenylenediamine.

CONTACT ALLERGY

Patch testing in groups of patients

In 2007-2008, 847 consecutive patients suspected of contact dermatitis were patch tested with 4-amino-*m*-cresol 1% pet. (routine testing) in three European countries. There were four (0.5%) positive reactions, but their relevance was not specified (5).

Case reports and case series

4-Amino-*m*-cresol was stated to be the (or an) allergen in one patient in a group of 603 individuals suffering from cosmetic dermatitis, seen in the period 2010-2015 in Leuven, Belgium (2). A 12-year-old boy developed, one day after a home coloring with a permanent black hair dye, dermatitis and edema of the ears. The following days the face became very edematous and the child was admitted to hospital for two days, where he was treated with topical and systemic steroids. The symptoms lasted for one week. When patch tested, he reacted to *p*-phenylenediamine and many related (para- and other) compounds, including toluene-2,5-diamine, *p*-aminophenol, *m*-aminophenol, disperse orange 3, hydroquinone, black rubber mix, *N*-phenyl-*p*-phenylenediamine, benzocaine, pyrogallol, and *p*-aminoazobenzene. In addition, he had a positive patch test reaction to 4-amino-*m*-cresol, which was an ingredient of the hair dye. In the past, he had had a black henna tattoo with a subsequent skin reaction, which undoubtedly was the source of this strong sensitization (1).

Cross-reactions, pseudo-cross-reactions and co-reactions

4-Amino-*m*-cresol may cross-react with structurally related chemicals, notably those with a para-structure. Cross-reactivity between para-compounds is discussed in Chapter 2.359 *p*-Phenylenediamine.

Presence in cosmetic products and chemical analyses

In the USA, in April 2017, 4-amino-*m*-cresol was present in 152 of 56,714 cosmetic products of which the composition is known in FDA's Voluntary Cosmetic Registration Program (VCRP) (data obtained from FDA, May 2017). In March 2017, 4-amino-*m*-cresol was present in 1 of 64,983 cosmetic products of which the composition is known in EWG's Skin Deep Cosmetics Database, USA (http://www.ewg.org/skindeep/). In 2013-2014 labeled ingredient information from 252 home use and professional hair dye products (210 permanent and 42 non-permanent dyes) from 48 brands sold in Bangkok, Thailand, was collected to identify the type and frequency of potent contact sensitizers. 4-Amino-*m*-cresol was present in 17 (6.7%) products (4). In southern Germany, in 2013-2014, the labels of 924 permanent oxidative hair dyes were checked for the presence of hair dye components. There were 334 retail products (of seven different brands) and 590 professional products (of six different brands). The 924 products analyzed revealed a total of 58 different hair dye components, with retail products containing 32 and professional products 52. 4-Amino-*m*-cresol was present in 129 (14%) of the 924 products (7).

In 2011, labels and other information on 365 hair dye products (282 permanent dyes, 79 semi-permanent dyes, 4 direct dyes) available on the Danish market (159 hair dyes for private use, 206 for professional use by hairdressers) were collected to identify the presence of sensitizers. 4-Amino-*m*-cresol was present in 26 (7%) products (6). In April 2010, in Spain, 111 consumer-available oxidative hair dye products of 19 brands were purchased to check the labeling for sensitizers. A systematic selection of products to be purchased from each hair dye brand was applied, including the darkest blonde shade available, one 'regular' light brown shade, one 'regular' dark brown shade, one 'regular' black shade, and two further shades with different colours (red, blue, purple, etc.). In this group of 111 hair dyes, 4-amino-*m*-cresol was present in 10 (9%) products (9). In August - October 2008, the labels of 122 oxidative hair dye products on the Swedish market were examined for the presence of hair dye substances categorized as potent skin sensitizers. 4-Amino-*m*-cresol was present in 22 (18%) of these products (8).

LITERATURE

1   Søsted H, Johansen JD, Andersen KE, Menné T. Severe allergic hair dye reactions in 8 children. Contact Dermatitis 2006;54: 87-91
2   Goossens A. Cosmetic contact allergens. Cosmetics 2016, 3, 5; doi:10.3390/cosmetics3010005
3   SCCP (Scientific Committee on Consumer Products). Opinion on 4-Amino-*m*-cresol, 20 September 2005, SCCP/ 0898/05. Available at: http://ec.europa.eu/health/archive/ph_risk/committees/04_sccp/docs/sccp_o_003.pdf
4   Boonchai W, Bunyavaree M, Winayanuwattikun W, Kasemsarn P. Contact sensitizers in commercial hair dye products sold in Thailand. Contact Dermatitis 2016;74:222-229
5   Søsted H, Rustemeyer T, Gonçalo M, Bruze M, Goossens A, Giménez-Arnau AM, et al. Contact allergy to common ingredients in hair dyes. Contact Dermatitis 2013;69:32-39
6   The Danish Environmental Protection Agency. Survey and occurrence of PPD, PTD and other allergenic hair dye substances in hair dyes. Copenhagen, Denmark: The Danish Environmental Protection Agency, 2013 (ISBN 978-87-92903-92-1). Available at: http://www2.mst.dk/Udgiv/publications/2013/02/978-87-92903-92-1.pdf
7   Kirchlecher S, Hübner A, Uter W. Survey of sensitizing constituents of oxidative hair dyes (retail and professional products) in Germany. J Dtsch Dermatol Ges 2016;14:707-715
8   Yazar K, Boman A, Lidén C. Potent skin sensitizers in oxidative hair dye products on the Swedish market. Contact Dermatitis 2009;61:269-275
9   Yazar K, Boman A, Lidén C. *p*-Phenylenediamine and other hair dye sensitizers in Spain. Contact Dermatitis 2012;66:27-32

2.14 2-AMINO-4-HYDROXYETHYLAMINOANISOLE SULFATE

IDENTIFICATION

Description/definition   : 2-Amino-4-hydroxyethylaminoanisole sulfate is the substituted aromatic amine salt that
                           conforms to the formula shown below
Chemical class(es)   : Amines; color additives - hair
Chemical/IUPAC name   : 2-(3-Amino-4-methoxyanilino)ethanol;sulfuric acid
Other names   : (3-Ammonio-4-methoxyphenyl)(2-hydroxyethyl)ammonium sulfate; 2-amino-4-[(2-
                           hydroxyethyl)amino]anisole sulfate; 2-[(3-amino-4-methoxyphenyl)amino]ethanol
                           sulfate; ethanol, 2-[(3-amino-4-methoxyphenyl)amino]-, sulfate
CAS registry number (s)   : 83763-48-8
EC number(s)   : 280-734-8
CIR review(s)   : Int J Toxicol 2013;32(Suppl.1):25-35 (access: www.cir-safety.org/ingredients)
SCCS opinion(s)   : SCCP/1172/08 (1)
Function(s) in cosmetics : EU: hair dyeing. USA: hair colorants
EU cosmetic restrictions : Regulated in Annex III/245 of the Regulation (EC) No. 1223/2009
Patch testing   : 2% pet. (4)
Molecular formula   : $C_9H_{16}N_2O_6S$

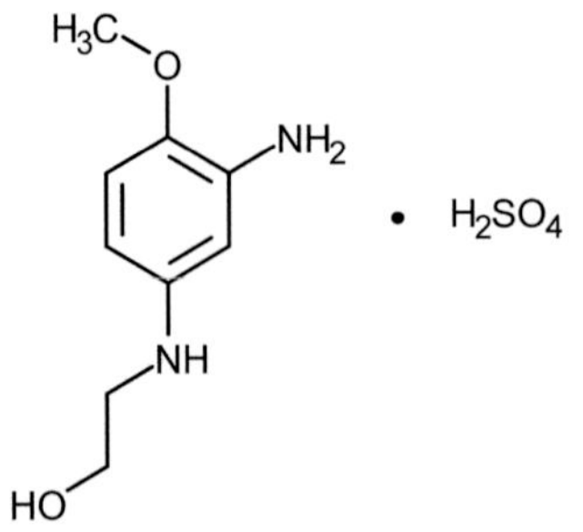

GENERAL

2-Amino-4-hydroxyethylaminoanisole sulfate is used as a coupler in oxidative hair dying products. For the chemistry of hair dying see Chapter 2.359 p-Phenylenediamine.

CONTACT ALLERGY

Patch testing in groups of patients

In Denmark, between 2005 and 2014, 902 patients suspected of contact dermatitis were tested in 66 practices with 2-amino-4-hydroxyethylaminoanisole sulfate 2% pet., presumably in a hairdressers series (4). There were 13 (1.4%) positive reactions. Two of these patients are discussed below (Case reports and case series). Clinical data of the remaining 11 are largely lacking, but all were women and two allergies were occupationally induced (2).

Case reports and case series

A woman had an acute severely itching scalp dermatitis spreading to the forehead, neck, ears, and cheeks, which developed a few days after she had dyed her hair. When patch tested, the patient developed a follicular reaction to p-phenylenediamine. Furthermore, she had a positive reaction to 2-amino-4-hydroxyethylaminoanisole sulfate, a constituent of the hair dye. The list of ingredients in the hair dye also included p-phenylenediamine (4). Another patient with scalp dermatitis caused by toluene-2,5-diamine in hair dye had a positive reaction to 2-amino-4-hydroxyethylaminoanisole sulfate. This was not an ingredient in the causative hair dye, but the patient had previously used several dyes containing it, from which she had probably been sensitized (4).

Cross-reactions, pseudo-cross-reactions and co-reactions

2-Amino-4-hydroxyethylaminoanisole sulfate may cross-react with structurally related chemicals, notably those with a para-structure. Cross-reactivity between para-compounds is discussed in Chapter 2.359 p-Phenylenediamine.

Presence in cosmetic products and chemical analyses

In the USA, in April 2017, 2-amino-4-hydroxyethylaminoanisole sulfate was present in 188 of 56,714 cosmetic products of which the composition is known in FDA's Voluntary Cosmetic Registration Program (VCRP) (data obtained from FDA, May 2017). In January 2017, 2-amino-4-hydroxyethylaminoanisole sulfate was present in 11 of

64,475 cosmetic products of which the composition is known in EWG's Skin Deep Cosmetics Database, USA (http://www.ewg.org/skindeep/). In southern Germany, in 2013-2014, the labels of 924 permanent oxidative hair dyes were checked for the presence of hair dye components. There were 334 retail products (of seven different brands) and 590 professional products (of six different brands). The 924 products analyzed revealed a total of 58 different hair dye components, with retail products containing 32 and professional products 52. 2-Amino-4-hydroxyethylaminoanisole (sulfate) was present in 120 (13%) of the 924 products (3). In 2011, labels and other information on 365 hair dye products (282 permanent dyes, 79 semi-permanent dyes, 4 direct dyes) available on the Danish market (159 hair dyes for private use, 206 for professional use by hairdressers) were collected to identify the presence of sensitizers. 2-Amino-4-hydroxyethylaminoanisole sulfate was present in 72 (20%) products (2).

LITERATURE

1   SCCP (Scientific Committee on Consumer Products). 2-amino-4-hydroxyethylaminoanisole sulfate, 24 June 2008, SCCP/1172/08. Available at:
     http://ec.europa.eu/health/archive/ph_risk/committees/04_sccp/docs/sccp_o_136.pdf
2   The Danish Environmental Protection Agency. Survey and occurrence of PPD, PTD and other allergenic hair dye substances in hair dyes. Copenhagen, Denmark: The Danish Environmental Protection Agency, 2013 (ISBN 978-87-92903-92-1). Available at: http://www2.mst.dk/Udgiv/publications/2013/02/978-87-92903-92-1.pdf
3   Kirchlecher S, Hübner A, Uter W. Survey of sensitizing constituents of oxidative hair dyes (retail and professional products) in Germany. J Dtsch Dermatol Ges 2016;14:707-715
4   Madsen JT, Andersen KE. 2-Amino-4-hydroxyethylaminoanisole sulfate – a coupler causing contact allergy from use in hair dyes. Contact Dermatitis 2016;74:102-104

2.15 4-AMINO-2-HYDROXYTOLUENE

IDENTIFICATION

Description/definition   : 4-Amino-2-hydroxytoluene is a substituted aromatic compound that conforms to the formula shown below
Chemical class(es)   : Amines; color additives - hair; phenols
Chemical/IUPAC name   : 5-Amino-2-methylphenol
Other names   : 5-Amino-*o*-cresol; 4-amino-2-hydroxy-1-methylbenzene
CAS registry number (s)   : 2835-95-2
EC number(s)   : 220-618-6
CIR review(s)   : J Am Coll Toxicol 1989;8:569-587 (access: www.cir-safety.org/ingredients)
SCCS opinion(s)   : SCCP/1001/06 (2)
Function(s) in cosmetics   : EU: hair dyeing. USA: hair colorants
EU cosmetic restrictions   : Regulated in Annex III/241of the Regulation (EC) No. 1197/2013
Patch testing   : 1.0% pet. (Chemotechnique)
Molecular formula   : C_7H_9NO

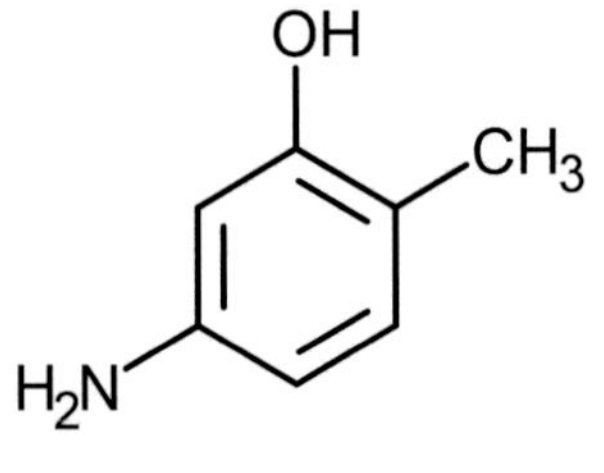

GENERAL

4-Amino-2-hydroxytoluene is used as a coupler in oxidative hair dying products. For the chemistry of hair dying see Chapter 2.359 *p*-Phenylenediamine.

CONTACT ALLERGY

Testing in groups of patients

In 2007-2008, 4-amino-2-hydroxytoluene 1% pet. was tested in 442 consecutive patients suspected of contact dermatitis (routine testing) in two European countries. There were 6 (1.4%) positive reactions, but their relevance was not specified (5).

Case reports and case series

A woman presented with a 3-week history of a scaly, erythematous dermatitis of the scalp, which began the day after the application of a brown semi-permanent hair dye. She had used a different hair dye previously without problems. Patch testing was performed with the standard series, several additional series and one component of the hair dye that fell outside of these series, supplied by the hair dye manufacturer. Positive reactions were seen to this component of the dye that caused the eruption (4-amino-2-hydroxytoluene 1% pet.) and also to *p*-phenylenediamine, toluene-2,5-diamine sulfate, 2-nitro-*p*-phenylenediamine, *m*-aminophenol and *p*-aminophenol (1).

Cross-reactions, pseudo-cross-reactions and co-reactions

p-Phenylenediamine, toluene-2,5-diamine sulfate, 2-nitro-*p*-phenylenediamine, *m*-aminophenol and *p*-aminophenol (1). 4-Amino-2-hydroxytoluene may cross-react with structurally related chemicals, notably those with a para-structure. Cross-reactivity between para-compounds is discussed in Chapter 2.359 *p*-Phenylenediamine.

Presence in cosmetic products and chemical analyses

In the USA, in April 2017, 4-amino-2-hydroxytoluene was present in 854 of 56,714 cosmetic products of which the composition is known in FDA's Voluntary Cosmetic Registration Program (VCRP) (data obtained from FDA, May 2017). In March 2017, 4-amino-2-hydroxytoluene was present in 50 of 64,983 cosmetic products of which the composition is known in EWG's Skin Deep Cosmetics Database, USA (http://www.ewg.org/skindeep/). In 2016, in Sweden, the labels of 26 oxidative hair dye products advertised with the signal words organic, natural or similar, or sold/used at a hair dressing salon advertised with the same terminology, were screened for the presence of known contact allergens. 4-Amino-2-hydroxytoluene was present in 11 (42%) products (4). In 2013-2014 labeled ingredient information from 252 home use and professional hair dye products (210 permanent and 42 non-permanent dyes) from 48 brands sold in Bangkok, Thailand, was collected to identify the type and frequency of potent contact sensitizers. 4-Amino-2-hydroxytoluene was present in 56 (22.2%) products (3). In southern Germany, in 2013-2014, the labels of 924 permanent oxidative hair dyes were checked for the presence of hair dye components. There were 334 retail products (of seven different brands) and 590 professional products (of six different brands). The 924 products analyzed revealed a total of 58 different hair dye components, with retail products containing 32 and professional products 52. 4-Amino-2-hydroxytoluene was present in 286 (31%) of the 924 products (7).

In 2013, in Korea, the labels of 99 oxidative hair dyes produced by Korean domestic manufacturers were examined for potent skin sensitizers. 4-Amino-2-hydroxytoluene was found to be present in 29 (29%) of the hair dyes (9). In the USA, in 2012, ingredient labels of 107 different consumer oxidative hair dyes from 10 different companies were assessed in stores across the city of Phoenix, Arizona. 4-Amino-2-hydroxytoluene (as free base, sulfate, or HCl) was present in 38 (36%) products (8). In 2011, labels and other information on 365 hair dye products (282 permanent dyes, 79 semi-permanent dyes, 4 direct dyes) available on the Danish market (159 hair dyes for private use, 206 for professional use by hairdressers) were collected to identify the presence of sensitizers. 4-Amino-2-hydroxytoluene was present in 111 (30%) products (6). In April 2010, in Spain, 111 consumer-available oxidative hair dye products of 19 brands were purchased to check the labeling for sensitizers. A systematic selection of products to be purchased from each hair dye brand was applied, including the darkest blonde shade available, one 'regular' light brown shade, one 'regular' dark brown shade, one 'regular' black shade, and two further shades with different colours (red, blue, purple, etc.). In this group of 111 hair dyes, 4-amino-2-hydroxytoluene was present in 39 (35%) products (11). In August - October 2008, the labels of 122 oxidative hair dye products on the Swedish market were examined for the presence of hair dye substances categorized as potent skin sensitizers. 4-Amino-2-hydroxytoluene was present in 43 (35%) products (10).

LITERATURE

1   Ellis RA, Wilkinson SM. Contact dermatitis to 4-amino-2-hydroxytoluene in hair dye. Contact Dermatitis 2009;60:118-119

2   SCCP (Scientific Committee on Consumer Products). Opinion on 4-Amino-2-hydroxytoluene, 10 October 2006, SCCP/1001/06. Available at:
     http://ec.europa.eu/health/archive/ph_risk/committees/04_sccp/docs/sccp_o_070.pdf

3   Boonchai W, Bunyavaree M, Winayanuwattikun W, Kasemsarn P. Contact sensitizers in commercial hair dye products sold in Thailand. Contact Dermatitis 2016;74:222-229

4   Thorén S, Yazar K. Contact allergens in 'natural' hair dyes. Contact Dermatitis 2016;74:302-304

5   Søsted H, Rustemeyer T, Gonçalo M, Bruze M, Goossens A, Giménez-Arnau AM, et al. Contact allergy to common ingredients in hair dyes. Contact Dermatitis 2013;69:32-39

6   The Danish Environmental Protection Agency. Survey and occurrence of PPD, PTD and other allergenic hair dye substances in hair dyes. Copenhagen, Denmark: The Danish Environmental Protection Agency, 2013 (ISBN 978-87-92903-92-1). Available at: http://www2.mst.dk/Udgiv/publications/2013/02/978-87-92903-92-1.pdf

7   Kirchlecher S, Hübner A, Uter W. Survey of sensitizing constituents of oxidative hair dyes (retail and professional products) in Germany. J Dtsch Dermatol Ges 2016;14:707-715

8   Hamann D, Yazar K, Hamann CR, Thyssen JP, Lidén C. p-Phenylenediamine and other allergens in hair dye products in the United States: a consumer exposure study. Contact Dermatitis 2014;70:213-218

9   Kim H, Kim K. Prevalence of potent skin sensitizers in oxidative hair dye products in Korea. Cutan Ocul Toxicol 2016;35:204-207

10   Yazar K, Boman A, Lidén C. Potent skin sensitizers in oxidative hair dye products on the Swedish market. Contact Dermatitis 2009;61:269-275

11   Yazar K, Boman A, Lidén C. p-Phenylenediamine and other hair dye sensitizers in Spain. Contact Dermatitis 2012;66:27-32

2.16 2-AMINOMETHYL-P-AMINOPHENOL HCL

IDENTIFICATION

Description/definition	: 2-Aminomethyl-*p*-aminophenol HCl is the substituted aromatic amine salt that conforms to the formula shown below
Chemical class(es)	: Amines; color additives - hair
Chemical/IUPAC name	: 4-Amino-2-(aminomethyl)phenol;dihydrochloride
Other names	: 2-Aminomethyl-4-aminophenol dihydrochloride; phenol, 2-aminomethyl-4-amino-, dihydrochloride; oxamitol
CAS registry number (s)	: 135043-64-0
Function(s) in cosmetics	: EU: formerly used for hair dying. USA: hair colorants
EU cosmetic restrictions	: Prohibited, delisted in 2006
Patch test allergens	: 1% water (1)
Molecular formula	: $C_7H_{12}Cl_2N_2O$

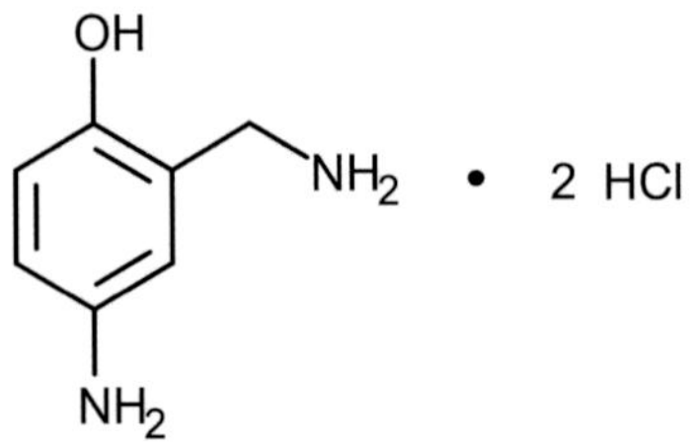

GENERAL

2-Aminomethyl-*p*-aminophenol HCl was formerly used in the EU and may still be used elsewhere as primary intermediate (synonyms: oxidation base, developer) in oxidative hair dying products. The chemistry of oxidative hair dying is discussed in Chapter 2.359 *p*-Phenylenediamine.

Case reports and case series

A woman presented with an acute itchy erythematous vesicular edematous eruption of the scalp, upper eyelids, and neck, 3 days after her hairdresser had applied hair dye. The same hair dye had been used by the patient for several years without any problems. The dermatitis cleared completely after 5 days on oral corticosteroids and local treatment. Six weeks later, patch testing with the standard series was negative. There were no reactions to *p*-phenylenediamine, *m*-aminophenol, *p*-aminophenol, or toluene-2,5-diamine. Patch testing was then performed with the ingredients of the hair dye, provided by the manufacturer. At D2 and D3, the investigators found a strongly positive reaction solely to the oxidation hair dye intermediate 2-aminomethyl-*p*-aminophenol HCl (oxamitol, 4-amino-2-aminomethyl-1-hydroxy-benzene-2HCl), whereas allergens of the para-group, which were also components of the hair dye (resorcinol, toluene-2,5-diamine sulfate, *p*-amino-*o*-cresol) were negative (1).

Cross-reactions, pseudo-cross-reactions and co-reactions

Not to *p*-phenylenediamine, *m*-aminophenol, *p*-aminophenol, toluene-2,5-diamine, toluene-2,5-diamine sulfate, resorcinol and *p*-amino-*o*-cresol (1). Cross-reactions between para-chemicals is discussed in Chapter 2.359 *p*-Phenylenediamine.

Presence in cosmetic products and chemical analyses

In the USA, in April 2017, 2-aminomethyl-p-aminophenol HCl was present in zero of 56,714 cosmetic products of which the composition is known in FDA's Voluntary Cosmetic Registration Program (VCRP) (data obtained from FDA, May 2017). In March 2017, 2-aminomethyl-*p*-aminophenol HCl was present in zero of 64,983 cosmetic products of which the composition is known in EWG's Skin Deep Cosmetics Database, USA (http://www.ewg.org/skindeep/).

LITERATURE

1   Wedi B, Hoting E, Koerner M, Kapp A. Allergic contact dermatitis due to monovalent sensitization to the oxidation hair dye intermediate oxamitol (2-aminomethyl-*p*-aminophenol-2HCl) without cross-sensitivity to haptens of the para-group. Contact Dermatitis 2000;42:104-105

2.17 4-AMINO-3-NITROPHENOL

IDENTIFICATION

Description/definition   : 4-Amino-3-nitrophenol is the substituted aromatic compound that conforms to the
                               formula shown below
Chemical class(es)   : Amine; color additives - hair; phenols
Chemical/IUPAC name   : 4-Amino-3-nitrophenol
Other names   : 1-Hydroxy-3-nitro-4-aminobenzene; 4-hydroxy-2-nitroaniline; 4-aminophenol-3-
                               nitrophenol
CAS registry number (s)   : 610-81-1
EC number(s)   : 210-236-8
CIR review(s)   : Int J Toxicol 2009;28(Suppl.3):217-251 (access: www.cir-safety.org/ingredients)
SCCS opinion(s)   : SCCP/1207/08 (3); SCCNFP, 17 February 2000 (4)
Function(s) in cosmetics   : EU: hair dyeing. USA: hair colorants
EU cosmetic restrictions   : Regulated in Annex III/215 of the Regulation (EC) No. 344/2013
Patch testing   : 1% pet.
Molecular formula   : $C_6H_6N_2O_3$

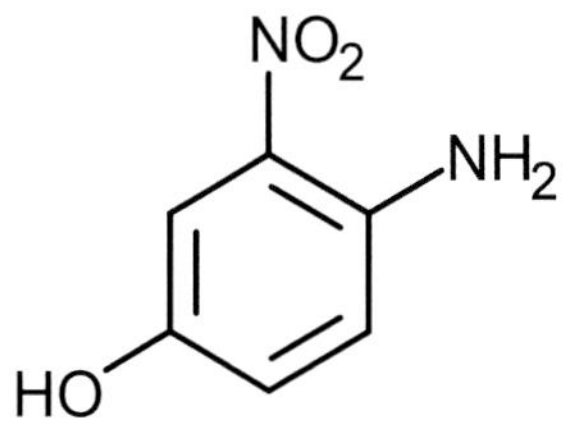

GENERAL

4-Amino-3-nitrophenol belongs to the amine family of coloring substances and is used in oxidative and non-oxidative hair dying products. The chemistry of oxidative hair dying is discussed in Chapter 2.359 *p*-Phenylene-diamine.

CONTACT ALLERGY

Patch testing in groups of patients

In 2007-2008, patch testing was performed in 2939 consecutive patients suspected of contact dermatitis (routine testing) with 4-amino-3-nitrophenol 1% pet. in three European countries. There were 133 (4.5%) positive reactions, but their relevance was not specified. Given this very high frequency of sensitization and the paucity of case reports of contact allergy to 4-amino-3-nitrophenol, it may be assumed that many cases were cross-sensitizations to *p*-phenylenediamine or other hair dyes with a para-structure.

Case reports and case series

A woman developed intensely itchy erythema and edema of the scalp, ears and neck several hours after application of a hair dye that she had previously tolerated well. Several months after resolution of the lesions, patch tests were carried out with the European standard series and the ingredients of the hair dye supplied by the manufacturer. The standard series was negative. 4-Amino-3-nitrophenol 2% pet. elicited a strongly positive reaction. Ten control persons were negative (1). A woman presented with a very itchy polymorphic dermatitis of 2 months duration. Large erythematous, edematous, slightly scaly patches were present on the upper trunk, sides of the neck and fronts of the wrists, with several excoriated or psoriasiform papules. The eruption had started 2 days after the use of a semi-permanent hair preparation containing 3 nitro dyes. Patch tests with the standard series were negative, while the patient's hair dye (as is) gave a strongly positive reaction. Further patch testing with the 3 nitro dyes showed positive patch tests to 4-amino-3-nitrophenol (termed 1-hydroxy-3-nitro-4-aminobenzene in the report) and the 2 other nitro dyes. Testing with the 3 dyes in 10 controls was negative (2).

   A woman dyed her hair with a non-permanent hair dye. After one day, she developed dermatitis of the scalp with severe itching, which spread to her face, neck and upper part of the thorax. As a further complication, the patient developed vesicular hand eczema for the first time in her life. When later patch tested, there were weak positive reactions to *p*-phenylenediamine and to her own hair, collected 3 days after the hair dying; there was a positive reaction to 4-amino-3-nitrophenol, an ingredient of the hair dye that had caused the eruption (10). Two days after applying a coral-red semi-permanent hair dye, a former hairdresser with known allergy to p-phenylenediamine and other para-colors developed itchy erythematous-crusted plaques on and behind the ears and in the neck. These lesions subsided in 4 weeks after frequent shampooing and treatment with topical corticosteroids. When patch tested with the components of the hair dye, she reacted to 4-amino-3-nitrophenol, which was incorrectly termed 4-amino-3-aminophenol twice, but correctly named in the discussion (11).

Cross-reactions, pseudo-cross-reactions and co-reactions
4-Amino-3-nitrophenol may cross-react with structurally related chemicals, notably those with a para-structure. Cross-reactivity between para-compounds is discussed in Chapter 2.359 *p*-Phenylenediamine.

Presence in cosmetic products and chemical analyses
In the USA, in April 2017, 4-amino-3-nitrophenol was present in 13 of 56,714 cosmetic products of which the composition is known in FDA's Voluntary Cosmetic Registration Program (VCRP) (data obtained from FDA, May 2017). In March 2017, 4-amino-3-nitrophenol was present in 10 of 64,983 cosmetic products of which the composition is known in EWG's Skin Deep Cosmetics Database, USA (http://www.ewg.org/skindeep/). In southern Germany, in 2013-2014, the labels of 924 permanent oxidative hair dyes were checked for the presence of hair dye components. There were 334 retail products (of seven different brands) and 590 professional products (of six different brands). The 924 products analyzed revealed a total of 58 different hair dye components, with retail products containing 32 and professional products 52. 4-Amino-3-nitrophenol was present in 19 (2%) of the 924 products (7). In 2011, labels and other information on 365 hair dye products (282 permanent dyes, 79 semi-permanent dyes, 4 direct dyes) available on the Danish market (159 hair dyes for private use, 206 for professional use by hairdressers) were collected to identify the presence of sensitizers. 4-Amino-3-nitrophenol was present in 2 (0.5%) products (6).

In April 2010, in Spain, 111 consumer-available oxidative hair dye products of 19 brands were purchased to check the labeling for sensitizers. A systematic selection of products to be purchased from each hair dye brand was applied, including the darkest blonde shade available, one 'regular' light brown shade, one 'regular' dark brown shade, one 'regular' black shade, and two further shades with different colours (red, blue, purple, etc.). In this group of 111 hair dyes, 4-amino-3-nitrophenol was present in 3 (3%) products (9). In August - October 2008, the labels of 122 oxidative hair dye products on the Swedish market were examined for the presence of hair dye substances categorized as potent skin sensitizers. 4-Amino-3-nitrophenol was present in 4 (3.3%) products (8).

LITERATURE

1   Blanco R, de la Hoz B, Sánchez-Fernández C, Sánchez-Cano M. Allergy to 4-amino-3-nitrophenol in a hair dye. Contact Dermatitis 1998;39:136
2   Perno P, Lisi P. Psoriasis-like contact dermatitis from a hair nitro dye. Contact Dermatitis 1990;23:123-124
3   Opinion of the SCCP on 4-amino-3-nitrophenol, 16 December 2008, SCCP/1207/08. Available at: http://ec.europa.eu/health/archive/ph_risk/committees/04_sccp/docs/sccp_o_157.pdf
4   SCCNFP (Scientific Committee on Cosmetics and Non Food Products). Opinion concerning 4-Amino-3-nitrophe-nol, 17 February 2000. Available at:http://ec.europa.eu/health/scientific_committees/consumer_safety/ opinions/ sccnfp_opinions_97_04/sccp_out105_en.htm
5   Søsted H, Rustemeyer T, Gonçalo M, Bruze M, Goossens A, Giménez-Arnau AM, et al. Contact allergy to common ingredients in hair dyes. Contact Dermatitis 2013;69:32-39
6   The Danish Environmental Protection Agency. Survey and occurrence of PPD, PTD and other allergenic hair dye substances in hair dyes. Copenhagen, Denmark: The Danish Environmental Protection Agency, 2013 (ISBN 978-87-92903-92-1). Available at: http://www2.mst.dk/Udgiv/publications/2013/02/978-87-92903-92-1.pdf
7   Kirchlecher S, Hübner A, Uter W. Survey of sensitizing constituents of oxidative hair dyes (retail and professional products) in Germany. J Dtsch Dermatol Ges 2016;14:707-715
8   Yazar K, Boman A, Lidén C. Potent skin sensitizers in oxidative hair dye products on the Swedish market. Contact Dermatitis 2009;61:269-275
9   Yazar K, Boman A, Lidén C. *p*-Phenylenediamine and other hair dye sensitizers in Spain. Contact Dermatitis 2012;66:27-32
10   Søsted H, Menné T. Allergy to 3-nitro-p-hydroxyethylaminophenol and 4-amino-3-nitrophenol in a hair dye. Contact Dermatitis 2005;52:317-319
11   Sánchez-Pérez J, Río IGD, Ruiz SA, Diez AG. Allergic contact dermatitis from direct dyes for hair colouration in hairdressers' clients. Contact Dermatitis 2004;50:261-262

2.18 M-AMINOPHENOL

IDENTIFICATION

Description/definition : *m*-Aminophenol is the substituted phenol that conforms to the formula shown below
Chemical class(es) : Amines; color additives - hair; phenols
Chemical/IUPAC name : 3-Aminophenol
Other names : CI 76545
CAS registry number (s) : 591-27-5
EC number(s) : 209-711-2
CIR review(s) : J Am Coll Toxicol 1988;7:279-333; Int J Toxicol 2008;27(Suppl.1):77-142 (access: www.cir-safety.org/ingredients)
SCCS opinion(s) : SCCP/0978/06 (11); SCCNFP 17 February 2000 (12)
Merck Index monograph : 1726
Function(s) in cosmetics : EU: hair dyeing. USA: hair colorants
EU cosmetic restrictions : Regulated in Annex III/217 of the Regulation (EC) No. 1197/2013
Patch testing : 1% pet. (Chemotechnique, SmartPracticeEurope, SmartPracticeCanada)
Molecular formula : C_6H_7NO

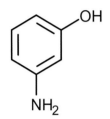

GENERAL
m-Aminophenol is used as a coupler in oxidative hair dying products. For the chemistry of hair dying see Chapter 2.359 *p*-Phenylenediamine.

CONTACT ALLERGY

Testing in groups of patients
Results of routine patch testing (testing in consecutive patients suspected of contact dermatitis) and of testing in groups of selected patients are shown in table 2.18.1. Routine testing has been performed in one study only, in 2007-2008 in nine European countries. One per cent of 2939 patients reacted to *m*-aminophenol; unfortunately, the relevance of these reactions was not mentioned (20). Selected patient groups were mostly hairdressers and patients suspected of allergy to hair dyes and/or other hair cosmetics. In hairdressers, the frequency of sensitization to *m*-aminophenol ranged from 1.7% to 4.0%. Relevance was mentioned in one study from Australia only: 80% (19). Quite curiously, the percentages of patients *non-hairdressers* reacting to *m*-aminophenol were (far) higher and ranged from 2.4% to 11.2%. In only 2 studies were relevance data provided: in one from the USA it was 80% (4 out of 5 reactions relevant [9]), in the other, a 1999-2004 study from the UK, only relevant reactions were mentioned (25 of 483 patients, 5.2% [27]).

Case reports and case series
m-Aminophenol was stated to be the (or an) allergen in 16 patients in a group of 603 individuals suffering from cosmetic dermatitis, seen in the period 2010-2015 in Leuven, Belgium (8). In the period 1996-2013, in a tertiary referral center in Valencia, Spain, 5419 patients were patch tested. Of these, 628 individuals had allergic contact dermatitis to cosmetics. *m*-Aminophenol was the responsible allergen in 19 cases (16). In the period 2000-2007, 202 patients with allergic contact dermatitis caused by cosmetics were seen in Valencia, Spain. In this group, 8 individuals reacted to *m*-aminophenol from its presence in hair dyes (13).

Two positive patch test reactions to *m*-aminophenol were ascribed to cosmetic allergy (3). Two patients with severe dermatitis of the scalp, face and neck from dyeing their hair were investigated. Both reacted to *p*-phenylenediamine, toluene-2,5-diamine and *m*-aminophenol. The causative products were analyzed and contained *m*-aminophenol in concentrations of resp. 0.38% and 2.1%, but also toluene-2,5-diamine. As the products did not contain *p*-phenylenediamine, *m*-aminophenol was one of the allergens (21). Two female patients had acute ACD of the scalp, neck and face from *m*-aminophenol in hair dyes. They both also reacted to the incriminated hair dye, and to *p*-phenylenediamine, toluene-2,5-diamine and *p*-aminophenol, which were also present in the hair dyes (30).

Cross-reactions, pseudo-cross-reactions and co-reactions

m-Aminophenol may cross-react with structurally related chemicals, notably those with a para-structure. Cross-reactivity between para-compounds is discussed in Chapter 2.359 *p*-Phenylenediamine.

Table 2.18.1 Patch testing in groups of patients

Years and Country	Test conc. & vehicle	Number of patients tested | positive (%)		Selection of patients (S); Relevance (R); Comments (C)	Ref.
Routine testing					
2007-2008, 9 European countries	1% pet.	2939	29 (1.0%)	R: not specified	20
Testing in groups of selected patients					
2012-2014 Japan	1% pet.	198	5 (2.5%)	S: patients suspected of allergic contact dermatitis from hair dyes or perming solutions, of who 13% were hairdressers; R: not stated; C: in hairdressers, the frequency of sensitization was 4%, in the non-occupational group 2.3%	33
2007-2012 IVDK	1% pet.	705	19 (2.6%)	S: female hairdressers with current or previous occupational contact dermatitis; R: not stated	25
		1692	135 (10.9%)	S: female patients, clients of hairdressers, in who hair cosmetics were regarded as a cause of dermatitis, and who had never worked as hairdressers; R: not stated	
2002-2011 Denmark		362	6 (1.7%)	S: hairdressers with contact dermatitis; R: not stated	24
2001-2010 Australia	1% pet.	571	26 (4.6%)	S: not stated; R: 58%	14
1993-2010 Australia		164	5 (3.0%)	S: hairdressers and apprentice hairdressers presenting at an occupational dermatology clinic; R: 80%	19
2000-2008 USA	1% pet.	210	(2.4%)	S: patients suspected of having ACD from hairdressing chemicals; R: 80%	9
1997-2007 UK	1% pet.	80	9 (11.2%)	S: patients suspected of hair dye allergy; R: not specified	2
2003-2006 IVDK	1% pet.	431	(4.0%)	S: female hairdressers with suspected occupational contact dermatitis; R: not stated	5
		612	(9.1%)	S: women with suspected reactions to hair cosmetics; R: not stated	
1991-1993 and 1997-2005 Germany		205	6 (2.9%)	S: patients suspected of having contact dermatitis caused by hair dyes and/or other hair cosmetics; R: not stated	4
1999-2004 UK		483	25 (5.2%)	S: patients tested with the hairdressing series; R: only reactions that were of current or past relevance were collected	27
1993-2003 IVDK	1% pet.	626	37 (5.9%)	S: patients with scalp dermatitis; R: not stated	7
1995-2002 IVDK		884	(3.6%)	S: female hairdressers with present or past occupational contact dermatitis; R: not specified	10
1995-2002 IVDK		1217	(4.2%)	S: clients of hairdressers suspected to react to hairdressing cosmetics or hair care products; R: not specified	

IVDK: Information Network of Departments of Dermatology, Germany, Austria, Switzerland

Presence in cosmetic products and chemical analyses

In the USA, in April 2017, *m*-aminophenol was present in 1466 of 56,714 cosmetic products of which the composition is known in FDA's Voluntary Cosmetic Registration Program (VCRP) (data obtained from FDA, May 2017). In March 2017, *m*-aminophenol was present in 154 of 64,983 cosmetic products of which the composition is known in EWG's Skin Deep Cosmetics Database, USA (http://www.ewg.org/skindeep/).In 2016, in Sweden, the labels of 26 oxidative hair dye products advertised with the signal words 'organic', 'natural' or similar, or sold/used at a hair dressing salon advertised with the same terminology, were screened for the presence of known contact allergens. *m*-Aminophenol was present in 21 (81%) products (17). Of 15 hair dyes advertised as 'hypoallergenic', 'para-phenylenediamine-free', or 'non-allergenic', purchased in South Korea in 2015, 10 (67%) proved to contain *m*-aminophenol (32). In 2013-2014, labeled ingredient information from 252 home use and professional hair dye products (210 permanent and 42 non-permanent dyes) from 48 brands sold in Bangkok, Thailand, was collected to identify the type and frequency of potent contact sensitizers. *m*-Aminophenol was present in 138 (55%) products (15). In southern Germany, in 2013-2014, the labels of 924 permanent oxidative hair dyes were checked for the presence of hair dye components. There were 334 retail products (of seven different brands) and 590 professional products (of six different brands). The 924 products analyzed revealed a total of 58 different hair dye components, with retail products containing 32 and professional products 52. *m*-Aminophenol was present in 71% of the 924 products (23).

In 2013, in Korea, the labels of 99 oxidative hair dyes produced by Korean domestic manufacturers were examined for potent skin sensitizers. *m*-Aminophenol was found to be present in 70 (70%) of the hair dyes (6). In the

USA, in 2012, ingredient labels of 107 different consumer oxidative hair dyes from 10 different companies were assessed in stores across the city of Phoenix, Arizona. *m*-Aminophenol (as free base, sulfate, or hydrochloride) was present in 75% of the products (26). In 2011, labels and other information on 365 hair dye products (282 permanent dyes, 79 semi-permanent dyes, 4 direct dyes) available on the Danish market (159 hair dyes for private use, 206 for professional use by hairdressers) were collected to identify the presence of sensitizers. *m*-Aminophenol was present in 193 (53%) products (22).

In April 2010, in Spain, 111 consumer-available oxidative hair dye products of 19 brands were purchased to check the labels for sensitizers. A systematic selection of products to be purchased from each hair dye brand was applied, including the darkest blonde shade available, one 'regular' light brown shade, one 'regular' dark brown shade, one 'regular' black shade, and two further shades with different colors (red, blue, purple, etc.). In this group of 111 hair dyes, *m*-aminophenol was present in 76% of the products (29). In August - October 2008, the labels of 122 oxidative hair dye products on the Swedish market were examined for the presence of hair dye substances categorized as potent skin sensitizers. *m*-Aminophenol was found in 83 (68%) of these products (28). In Denmark, in 2001-2002, nine hair coloring products that had caused classic ACD with face, scalp and neck dermatitis developing within 1-2 days (sometimes hours) after hair coloring in nine patients were subjected to chemical analysis. Three hair dye products contained *m*-aminophenol in a concentration range of 0.015 to 0.38% (21).

OTHER SIDE EFFECTS

Immediate-type reactions
One patient had immediate contact reactions to *m*-aminophenol in hair dyes; the patient also reacted in the same manner to a test with *o*-aminophenol (1). A review of contact urticaria caused by ingredients of cosmetics has been provided in ref. 18.

OTHER INFORMATION
Permeation of *m*-aminophenol through gloves has been investigated in ref. 31.

LITERATURE

1   Tsunoda T, Horiuchi N, Sato M. Two cases of contact urticaria syndrome by hair dye. Hifu 1993;35 (suppl. 16):178-183 (article in Japanese)
2   Basketter DA, English J. Cross-reactions among hair dye allergens. Cut Ocular Toxicol 2009;28:104-106
3   Kohl L, Blondeel A, Song M. Allergic contact dermatitis from cosmetics: retrospective analysis of 819 patch-tested patients. Dermatology 2002;204:334-337
4   Frosch PJ, Kügler K, Geier J. Patch testing with hydroxyethyl-*p*-phenylenediamine sulfate – cross-reactivity with *p*-phenylenediamine. Contact Dermatitis 2011;65:96-100
5   Uter W, Lessmann H, Geier J, Schnuch A. Contact allergy to hairdressing allergens in female hairdressers and clients – current data from the IVDK, 2003-2006. J Dtsch Dermatol Ges 2007;5:993-1001
6   Kim H, Kim K. Prevalence of potent skin sensitizers in oxidative hair dye products in Korea. Cutan Ocul Toxicol 2016;35:204-207
7   Hillen U, Grabbe S, Uter W. Patch test results in patients with scalp dermatitis: analysis of data of the Information Network of Departments of Dermatology. Contact Dermatitis 2007;56:87-93
8   Goossens A. Cosmetic contact allergens. Cosmetics 2016, 3, 5; doi:10.3390/cosmetics3010005
9   Wang MZ, Farmer SA, Richardson DM, Davis MDP. Patch-testing with hairdressing chemicals. Dermatitis 2011;22:16-26
10 Uter W, Lessmann H, Geier J, Schnuch A. Contact allergy to ingredients of hair cosmetics in female hairdressers and clients: an 8-year analysis of IVDK data. Contact Dermatitis 2003;49:236-240
11 Scientific Committee on Consumer Products (SCCP), 19 December 2006, Opinion on *m*-aminophenol COLIPA N° A15, SCCP/0978/06. Available at: http://ec.europa.eu/health/archive/ph_risk/committees/04_sccp/docs/sccp_o_088.pdf
12 SCCNFP (Scientific Committee on Cosmetics and Non Food Products). Opinion concerning *m*-Aminophenol, 17 February 2000. Available at: http://ec.europa.eu/health/scientific_committees/consumer_safety/opinions/ sccnfp _opinions_97_04/sccp_out107_en.htm
13 Laguna C, de la Cuadra J, Martín-González B, Zaragoza V, Martínez-Casimiro L, Alegre V. Allergic contact dermatitis to cosmetics. Actas Dermosifiliogr 2009;100:53-60
14 Toholka R, Wang Y-S, Tate B, Tam M, Cahill J, Palmer A, Nixon R. The first Australian Baseline Series: Recommendations for patch testing in suspected contact dermatitis. Australas J Dermatol 2015;56:107-115
15 Boonchai W, Bunyavaree M, Winayanuwattikun W, Kasemsarn P. Contact sensitizers in commercial hair dye products sold in Thailand. Contact Dermatitis 2016;74:222-229

16 Zaragoza-Ninet V, Blasco Encinas R, Vilata-Corell JJ, Pérez-Ferriols A, Sierra-Talamantes C, Esteve-Martínez A, de la Cuadra-Oyanguren J. Allergic contact dermatitis due to cosmetics: A clinical and epidemiological study in a tertiary hospital. Actas Dermosifiliogr 2016;107:329-336

17 Thorén S, Yazar K. Contact allergens in 'natural' hair dyes. Contact Dermatitis 2016;74:302-304

18 Verhulst L, Goossens A. Cosmetic components causing contact urticaria: a review and update. Contact Dermatitis 2016;75:333-344

19 Lyons G, Roberts H, Palmer A, Matheson M, Nixon R. Hairdressers presenting to an occupational dermatology clinic in Melbourne, Australia. Contact Dermatitis 2013;68:300-306

20 Søsted H, Rustemeyer T, Gonçalo M, Bruze M, Goossens A, Giménez-Arnau AM, et al. Contact allergy to common ingredients in hair dyes. Contact Dermatitis 2013;69:32-39

21 Søsted H, Rastogi SC, Andersen KE, Johansen JD, Menné T. Hair dye contact allergy: quantitative exposure assessment of selected products and clinical cases. Contact Dermatitis 2004;50:344-348

22 The Danish Environmental Protection Agency. Survey and occurrence of PPD, PTD and other allergenic hair dye substances in hair dyes. Copenhagen, Denmark: The Danish Environmental Protection Agency, 2013 (ISBN 978-87-92903-92-1). Available at: http://www2.mst.dk/Udgiv/publications/2013/02/978-87-92903-92-1.pdf

23 Kirchlecher S, Hübner A, Uter W. Survey of sensitizing constituents of oxidative hair dyes (retail and professional products) in Germany. J Dtsch Dermatol Ges 2016;14:707-715

24 Schwensen JF, Johansen JD, Veien NK, Funding AT, Avnstorp C, Østerballe M, et al. Occupational contact dermatitis in hairdressers: an analysis of patch test data from the Danish Contact Dermatitis Group, 2002–2011. Contact Dermatitis 2014;70:233-237

25 Uter W, Gefeller O, John SM, Schnuch A, Geier J. Contact allergy to ingredients of hair cosmetics – a comparison of female hairdressers and clients based on IVDK 2007–2012 data. Contact Dermatitis 2014;71:13-20

26 Hamann D, Yazar K, Hamann CR, Thyssen JP, Lidén C. p-Phenylenediamine and other allergens in hair dye products in the United States: a consumer exposure study. Contact Dermatitis 2014;70:213-218

27 Katugampola RP, Statham BN, English JSC, Wilkinson MM, Foulds IS, Green CM, Ormerod AD, et al. A multicentre review of the hairdressing allergens tested in the UK. Contact Dermatitis 2005;53:130-132

28 Yazar K, Boman A, Lidén C. Potent skin sensitizers in oxidative hair dye products on the Swedish market. Contact Dermatitis 2009;61:269-275

29 Yazar K, Boman A, Lidén C. p-Phenylenediamine and other hair dye sensitizers in Spain. Contact Dermatitis 2012;66:27-32

30 Gottlöber P, Gall H, Bezold G, Peter RU. Allergic contact dermatitis in beauty parlor clients. Hautarzt 2001;52:401-404 (Article in German)

31 Lee HS, Lin YW. Permeation of hair dye ingredients, p-phenylenediamine and aminophenol isomers, through protective gloves. Ann Occup Hyg 2009;53:289-296

32 Lee HJ, Kim WJ, Kim JY, Kim HS, Kim BS, Kim MB, Ko HC. Patch tests with commercial hair dye products in patients with allergic contact dermatitis to para-phenylenediamine. Indian J Dermatol Venereol Leprol 2016;82:645-650

33 Ito A, Nishioka K, Kanto H, Yagami A, Yamada S, Sugiura M, et al. A multi-institutional joint study of contact dermatitis related to hair colouring and perming agents in Japan. Contact Dermatitis 2017;77:42-48

2.19 P-AMINOPHENOL

IDENTIFICATION

Description/definition : *p*-Aminophenol is a substituted phenol that conforms to the formula shown below
Chemical class(es) : Amines; colour additives – hair; phenols
Chemical/IUPAC name : 4-Aminophenol
Other names : CI 76550
CAS registry number (s) : 123-30-8
EC number(s) : 204-616-2
CIR review(s) : J Am Coll Toxicol 1988;7:279-333 (access: www.cir-safety.org/ingredients)
SCCS opinion(s) : SCCS/1553/15 (14); SCCS/1409/11 (15); SCCP/0867 /05 (16)
Merck Index monograph : 1728
Function(s) in cosmetics : EU: hair dyeing. USA: hair colorants
EU cosmetic restrictions : Regulated in Annex III/272 of the Regulation (EC) No. 1197/2013
Patch testing : 1% pet. (Chemotechnique, SmartPracticeEurope, SmartPracticeCanada)
Molecular formula : C_6H_7NO

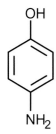

GENERAL

p-Aminophenol is used as a primary intermediate (synonyms: oxidation base, developer) in oxidative hair dying products. For the chemistry of hair dying see Chapter 2.359 *p*-Phenylenediamine.

CONTACT ALLERGY

Patch testing in groups of patients
Results of routine patch testing (testing in consecutive patients suspected of contact dermatitis) and of testing in groups of selected patients are shown in table 2.19.1. Routine testing has been performed in one study only, in 2007-2008 in nine European countries. Fifty-three of 2939 patients (1.8%) reacted to *p*-aminophenol; unfortunately, the relevance of these reactions was not mentioned (24). Selected patient groups were mostly hairdressers and patients suspected of allergy to hair dyes and/or other hair cosmetics. In hairdressers, the frequency of sensitization to *p*-aminophenol ranged from 1.4% to 35% (43). Relevance was mentioned in one study from Australia only: 83% (23). Quite curiously, the percentages of patients *non-hairdressers* reacting to *p*-aminophenol were often higher and ranged from 3.4% to 18%. In only 2 studies testing patients suspected of allergy to hair products were relevance data provided: in one from the USA it was 100% (all 8 reactions relevant [12]), in the other, a 1999-2004 study from the UK, only relevant reactions were mentioned (31 of 483 patients, 6.4% [31]).

Case reports and case series
p-Aminophenol was stated to be the (or an) allergen in 23 patients in a group of 603 individuals suffering from cosmetic dermatitis, seen in the period 2010-2015 in Leuven, Belgium (11). In the period 1996-2013, in a tertiary referral center in Valencia, Spain, 5419 patients were patch tested. Of these, 628 individuals had allergic contact dermatitis to cosmetics. *p*-Aminophenol was the responsible allergen in 19 cases (20). In the period 2000-2007, 202 patients with allergic contact dermatitis caused by cosmetics were seen in Valencia, Spain. In this group, four individuals reacted to *p*-aminophenol from its presence in hair dyes and one hairdresser had occupational allergic hand dermatitis from the hair color (17). Two positive patch test reactions to *p*-aminophenol were ascribed to cosmetic allergy (5). Two female patients had acute ACD of the scalp, neck and face from *p*-aminophenol in hair dyes. They both also reacted to the incriminated hair dye, and to *p*-phenylenediamine, toluene-2,5-diamine and *m*-aminophenol, which were also present in the hair dyes (8). In an older publication from Germany, an unknown number of patients had ACD from *p*-aminophenol in hair dye (39, data cited in ref. 40).

Contact allergy to p-aminophenol in non-cosmetic products

Two patients working in the production of paracetamol in a pharmaceutical company had occupational allergic contact dermatitis from p-aminophenol, one of the hands, arms and face and the other only of the face (airborne contact dermatitis). They also reacted to other para-compounds, but had never dyed their hair. Under humid conditions at room temperature, hydrolysis of paracetamol may take place to form p-aminophenol, which is then degraded through oxidation characterized by color change to pink, then brown and finally black. Despite working in different plants, both men reported that the factory floors where the paracetamol was processed had a black discoloration. This was, according to the authors, supportive of there being significant quantities of para-amino compounds present in the working environments of these individuals, enough to cause sensitization and allergic contact dermatitis (41).

Table 2.19.1 Patch testing in groups of patients

Years and Country	Test conc. & vehicle	Number of patients tested	positive (%)	Selection of patients (S); Relevance (R); Comments (C)	Ref.
Routine testing					
2007-2008, 9 European countries	1% pet.	2939	53 (1.8%)	R: not specified	24
Testing in groups of selected patients					
2012-2014 Japan	1% pet.	200	21 (10.5%)	S: patients suspected of allergic contact dermatitis from hair dyes or perming solutions, of who 13% were hairdressers; R: not stated; C: in hairdressers, the frequency of sensitization was 35%, in the non-occupational group 6.9%	43
2007-2012 IVDK	1% pet.	711	32 (4.4%)	S: female hairdressers with current or previous occupational contact dermatitis; R: not stated	29
		1701	204 (15.9%)	S: female patients, clients of hairdressers, in who hair cosmetics were regarded as a cause of dermatitis, and who had never worked as hairdressers; R: not stated	
2002-2011 Denmark		365	5 (1.4%)	S: hairdressers with contact dermatitis; R: not stated	28
2001-2010 Australia	1% pet.	572	42 (7.3%)	S: not stated; R: 55%	18
1993-2010 Australia		164	12 (7.3%)	S: hairdressers and apprentice hairdressers presenting at an occupational dermatology clinic; R: 83%	23
2000-2008 USA	1% pet.	210	(3.8%)	S: patients tested with a hairdresser's series; R: 100%	12
1997-2007 UK	1% pet.	80	14 (18%)	S: patients suspected of hair dye allergy; R: not stated	4
2003-2006 IVDK	1% pet.	431	(5.7%)	S: female hairdressers with suspected occupational contact dermatitis; R: not stated	7
		610	(11.9%)	S: women with suspected reactions to hair cosmetics; R: not stated	
1991-1993 and 1997-2005 Germany		205	7 (3.4%)	S: patients suspected of having contact dermatitis caused by hair dyes and/or hair cosmetics; R: not stated	6
1999-2004 UK		483	31 (6.4%)	S: patients tested with the hairdressing series; R: only reactions that were of current or past relevance were collected	31
1993-2003 IVDK	1% pet.	630	52 (8.3%)	S: patients with scalp dermatitis; R: not stated	10
2000-2002 Finland		500	(3.8%)	S: patients tested with a hairdressing series; R: not stated	9
1995-2002 IVDK		884	(6.1%)	S: female hairdressers with present or past occupational contact dermatitis; R: not specified	13
		1217	(6.5%)	S: clients of hairdressers suspected to react to hairdressing cosmetics or hair care products; R: not specified	
1995-1999 Germany	1% pet.	613	19 (3.1%)	S: patients tested with a 'para-amino series' (not further specified); R: not specified	3
1995-1996 Finland		374	(1.3%)	S: patients tested with a hairdressing series; R: not stated	9
1985-1994 Greece	1% pet.	106	2 (2.8%)	S: hairdressers with contact dermatitis; R: not specified	32

IVDK: Information Network of Departments of Dermatology, Germany, Austria, Switzerland

Cross-reactions, pseudo-cross-reactions and co-reactions

p-Aminophenol may cross-react with structurally related chemicals, notably those with a para-structure. Cross-reactivity between para-compounds is discussed in Chapter 2.359 p-Phenylenediamine.

Patch test sensitization

A patient was patch tested with 27 aromatic amines. After 48 and 72 hours, all tests were negative. A week later the patient reported with a focal flare of the test sites of o- and p-aminophenol, but there was no such reaction at the site of *m*-aminophenol. A repeat test with *m*-aminophenol was negative (33). This may have been a case of patch test sensitization to *o*- and *p*-aminophenol, but it was not proven, as the patient had no repeat test to show a positive reaction after 2 days.

Presence in cosmetic products and chemical analyses
In the USA, in April 2017, *p*-aminophenol was present in 1141 of 56,714 cosmetic products of which the composition is known in FDA's Voluntary Cosmetic Registration Program (VCRP) (data obtained from FDA, May 2017). In March 2017, *p*-aminophenol was present in 104 of 64,983 cosmetic products of which the composition is known in EWG's Skin Deep Cosmetics Database, USA (http://www.ewg.org/skindeep/). In 2016, in Sweden, the labels of 26 oxidative hair dye products advertised with the signal words organic, natural or similar, or sold/used at a hair dressing salon advertised with the same terminology, were screened for the presence of known contact allergens. *p*-Aminophenol was present in 9 (35%) products (21). Of 15 hair dyes advertised as 'hypoallergenic', 'para-phenylenediamine-free', or 'non-allergenic', purchased in South Korea in 2015, 5 (33%) proved to contain *p*-aminophenol (42). In 2013-2014, labeled ingredient information from 252 home use and professional hair dye products (210 permanent and 42 non-permanent dyes) from 48 brands sold in Bangkok, Thailand, was collected to identify the type and frequency of potent contact sensitizers. *p*-Aminophenol was present in 94 (37%) products (19). In southern Germany, in 2013-2014, the labels of 924 permanent oxidative hair dyes were checked for the presence of hair dye components. There were 334 retail products (of seven different brands) and 590 professional products (of six different brands). The 924 products analyzed revealed a total of 58 different hair dye components, with retail products containing 32 and professional products 52. *p*-Aminophenol was present in 31% of the 924 products (27).

In 2013, in Korea, the labels of 99 oxidative hair dyes produced by Korean domestic manufacturers were examined for potent skin sensitizers. *p*-Aminophenol was found to be present in 56 (56%) of the hair dyes (34). In the USA, in 2012, ingredient labels of 107 different consumer oxidative hair dyes from 10 different companies were assessed in stores across the city of Phoenix, Arizona. *p*-Aminophenol (as free base, sulfate, or hydrochloride) was present in 60% of the products (30). In 2011, labels and other information on 365 hair dye products (282 permanent dyes, 79 semi-permanent dyes, 4 direct dyes) available on the Danish market (159 hair dyes for private use, 206 for professional use by hairdressers) were collected to identify the presence of sensitizers. *p*-Aminophenol was present in 132 (36%) products (26). In April 2010, in Spain, 111 consumer-available oxidative hair dye products of 19 brands were purchased to check the labeling for sensitizers. A systematic selection of products to be purchased from each hair dye brand was applied, including the darkest blonde shade available, one 'regular' light brown shade, one 'regular' dark brown shade, one 'regular' black shade, and two further shades with different colours (red, blue, purple, etc.). In this group of 111 hair dyes, *p*-aminophenol was present in 32% of the products (35). In August - October 2008, the labels of 122 oxidative hair dye products on the Swedish market were examined for the presence of hair dye substances categorized as potent skin sensitizers. *p*-Aminophenol was present in 31(25%) of these products (36). In Denmark, in 2001-2002, nine hair coloring products that had caused classic ACD with face, scalp and neck dermatitis developing within 1-2 days (sometimes hours) after hair coloring in nine were subjected to chemical analysis. Three hair dye products contained *p*-aminophenol in a concentration range of 0.16 to 2.1% (25).

OTHER SIDE EFFECTS

Immediate-type reactions
A man with eczema of the hands had been using a commercial hair dye about one time a month for 20 years. After using the hair dye again, he began to develop upper airway stridor and generalized urticaria. The following month, while using the same hair dye, after about 30-40 minutes, the patient again had dyspnea and generalized urticaria. Open tests and prick tests with the hair dye and its ingredients (*p*-phenylenediamine, *p*-aminophenol, *o*-aminophenol, *p*-methylaminophenol and sodium methyl oleoyl taurate) were negative. Scratch tests with *p*-aminophenol (1%, 5% and 10% water) and *p*-methylaminophenol (1%, 5% and 10% water) were positive. Ten control subjects also scratch tested with *p*-aminophenol and *p*-methylaminophenol were all negative. The patient was diagnosed as having a type I allergy to *p*-aminophenol and *p*-methylaminophenol (1).

A woman complained that her head always felt itchy when her hair had been colored in the hair salon. One time, she developed pruritus of the scalp immediately after the oxidative hair dye was applied; this was followed by flushing over her entire body, with dyspnea, vomiting and hypotension. Skin prick tests were positive to the oxidative hair dye (10% water) and its ingredients *p*-aminophenol and sodium methyl oleoyl taurate. The subject was diagnosed with contact urticaria syndrome due to *p*-aminophenol and sodium methyl oleoyl taurate. Three controls were negative to the hair dye and the two causative ingredients (38). Another patient from Japan had an anaphylactic shock from *p*-aminophenol in a hair dye (2).

A review of contact urticaria to cosmetic ingredients has been provided in ref. 22.

OTHER INFORMATION

Permeation of *p*-aminophenol through gloves has been investigated in ref. 37.

LITERATURE

1   Oshima H, Tamaki T, Oh-I T, Koga M. Contact anaphylaxis due to para-aminophenol and para-methylamino-phenol in hair dye. Contact Dermatitis 2001;45:359

2   Nagano Y, Kanao K. A case of hair dye shock (about a RAST positive case). Hifubyou Sinryou 1991;13:57-60 (in Japanese) (data cited in ref. 1)

3   Uter W, Lessmann H, Geier J, Becker D, Fuchs T, Richter G. The spectrum of allergic (cross-)sensitivity in clinical patch testing with '*para* amino' compounds. Allergy (Eur J All Clin Immmunol) 2002;57:319-322

4   Basketter DA, English J. Cross-reactions among hair dye allergens. Cut Ocular Toxicol 2009;28:104-106

5   Kohl L, Blondeel A, Song M. Allergic contact dermatitis from cosmetics: retrospective analysis of 819 patch-tested patients. Dermatology 2002;204:334-337

6   Frosch PJ, Kügler K, Geier J. Patch testing with hydroxyethyl-*p*-phenylenediamine sulfate – cross-reactivity with *p*-phenylenediamine. Contact Dermatitis 2011;65:96-100

7   Uter W, Lessmann H, Geier J, Schnuch A. Contact allergy to hairdressing allergens in female hairdressers and clients – current data from the IVDK, 2003-2006. J Dtsch Dermatol Ges 2007;5:993-1001

8   Gottlöber P, Gall H, Bezold G, Peter RU. Allergic contact dermatitis in beauty parlor clients. Hautarzt 2001;52:401-404 (Article in German)

9   Hasan T, Rantanen T, Alanko K, Harvima RJ, Jolanki R, Kalimo K, et al. Patch test reactions to cosmetic allergens in 1995–1997 and 2000–2002 in Finland –a multicentre study. Contact Dermatitis 2005;53:40-45

10 Hillen U, Grabbe S, Uter W. Patch test results in patients with scalp dermatitis: analysis of data of the Information Network of Departments of Dermatology. Contact Dermatitis 2007;56:87-93

11 Goossens A. Cosmetic contact allergens. Cosmetics 2016, 3, 5; doi:10.3390/cosmetics3010005

12 Wang MZ, Farmer SA, Richardson DM, Davis MDP. Patch-testing with hairdressing chemicals. Dermatitis 2011;22:16-26

13 Uter W, Lessmann H, Geier J, Schnuch A. Contact allergy to ingredients of hair cosmetics in female hairdressers and clients: an 8-year analysis of IVDK data. Contact Dermatitis 2003;49:236-240

14 SCCS (Scientific Committee on Consumer Safety). Addendum to the scientific Opinion on the safety of oxidative hair dye substances and hydrogen peroxide in products to colour eyelashes, 25 March 2015, SCCS/1553/15. Available at: http://ec.europa.eu/health/scientific_committees/consumer_safety/docs/sccs_o_173.pdf

15 SCCS (Scientific Committee on Consumer Safety), Opinion on p-aminophenol, 13-14 December 2011, SCCS/1409/11. Available at: http://ec.europa.eu/health/scientific_committees/consumer_safety/docs/sccs_o_078.pdf

16 SCCP (Scientific Committee on Consumer Products). Opinion on para-Aminophenol, 15 March 2005, SCCP/0867 /05. Available at: http://ec.europa.eu/health/archive/ph_risk/committees/04_sccp/docs/sccp_o_00e.pdf

17 Laguna C, de la Cuadra J, Martín-González B, Zaragoza V, Martínez-Casimiro L, Alegre V. Allergic contact dermatitis to cosmetics. Actas Dermosifiliogr 2009;100:53-60

18 Toholka R, Wang Y-S, Tate B, Tam M, Cahill J, Palmer A, Nixon R. The first Australian Baseline Series: Recommendations for patch testing in suspected contact dermatitis. Australas J Dermatol 2015;56:107-115

19 Boonchai W, Bunyavaree M, Winayanuwattikun W, Kasemsarn P. Contact sensitizers in commercial hair dye products sold in Thailand. Contact Dermatitis 2016;74:222-229

20 Zaragoza-Ninet V, Blasco Encinas R, Vilata-Corell JJ, Pérez-Ferriols A, Sierra-Talamantes C, Esteve-Martínez A, de la Cuadra-Oyanguren J. Allergic contact dermatitis due to cosmetics: A clinical and epidemiological study in a tertiary hospital. Actas Dermosifiliogr 2016;107:329-336

21 Thorén S, Yazar K. Contact allergens in 'natural' hair dyes. Contact Dermatitis 2016;74:302-304

22 Verhulst L, Goossens A. Cosmetic components causing contact urticaria: a review and update. Contact Dermatitis 2016;75:333-344

23 Lyons G, Roberts H, Palmer A, Matheson M, Nixon R. Hairdressers presenting to an occupational dermatology clinic in Melbourne, Australia. Contact Dermatitis 2013;68:300-306

24 Søsted H, Rustemeyer T, Gonçalo M, Bruze M, Goossens A, Giménez-Arnau AM, et al. Contact allergy to common ingredients in hair dyes. Contact Dermatitis 2013;69:32-39

25 Søsted H, Rastogi SC, Andersen KE, Johansen JD, Menné T. Hair dye contact allergy: quantitative exposure assessment of selected products and clinical cases. Contact Dermatitis 2004;50:344-348

26 The Danish Environmental Protection Agency. Survey and occurrence of PPD, PTD and other allergenic hair dye substances in hair dyes. Copenhagen, Denmark: The Danish Environmental Protection Agency, 2013 (ISBN 978-87-92903-92-1). Available at: http://www2.mst.dk/Udgiv/publications/2013/02/978-87-92903-92-1.pdf

27 Kirchlecher S, Hübner A, Uter W. Survey of sensitizing constituents of oxidative hair dyes (retail and professional products) in Germany. J Dtsch Dermatol Ges 2016;14:707-715

28 Schwensen JF, Johansen JD, Veien NK, Funding AT, Avnstorp C, Østerballe M, et al. Occupational contact dermatitis in hairdressers: an analysis of patch test data from the Danish Contact Dermatitis Group, 2002–2011. Contact Dermatitis 2014;70:233-237

29 Uter W, Gefeller O, John SM, Schnuch A, Geier J. Contact allergy to ingredients of hair cosmetics – a comparison of female hairdressers and clients based on IVDK 2007–2012 data. Contact Dermatitis 2014;71:13-20

30 Hamann D, Yazar K, Hamann CR, Thyssen JP, Lidén C. p-Phenylenediamine and other allergens in hair dye products in the United States: a consumer exposure study. Contact Dermatitis 2014;70:213-218

31 Katugampola RP, Statham BN, English JSC, Wilkinson MM, Foulds IS, Green CM, Ormerod AD, et al. A multicentre review of the hairdressing allergens tested in the UK. Contact Dermatitis 2005;53:130-132

32 Katsarou A, Koufou B, Takou K, Kalogeromitros D, Papanayiotou G, Vareltzidis A. Patch test results in hairdressers with contact dermatitis in Greece (1985-1994). Contact Dermatitis 1995;33:347-348

33 Rudzki E, Napiórkowska T, Grzywa Z. Active sensitization to ortho and para-aminophenol with negative patch test to meta-aminophenol. Contact Dermatitis 1980;6:501

34 Kim H, Kim K. Prevalence of potent skin sensitizers in oxidative hair dye products in Korea. Cutan Ocul Toxicol 2016;35:204-207

35 Yazar K, Boman A, Lidén C. *p*-Phenylenediamine and other hair dye sensitizers in Spain. Contact Dermatitis 2012;66:27-32

36 Yazar K, Boman A, Lidén C. Potent skin sensitizers in oxidative hair dye products on the Swedish market. Contact Dermatitis 2009;61:269-275

37 Lee HS, Lin YW. Permeation of hair dye ingredients, p-phenylenediamine and aminophenol isomers, through protective gloves. Ann Occup Hyg 2009;53:289-296

38 Uehara S, Inomata N, Suzuki A et al. Severe contact urticarial syndrome due to oxidative hair dye containing para-aminophenol and sodium-methyl-oleoyl-taurate. J Dermatol 2014;41:560-561

39 Borelli S. Die Verträglichkeit gebräuchlicher Haarfärbungspraparate, Farbstoffsgrundsubstanzen und verwandter chemischer Verbindungen. Hautarzt 1958;9:19-25 (data cited in ref. 40)

40 Eskelinen A, Molitor C, Kanerva L. Allergic contact dermatitis from 2,7-dihydroxynaphthalene in hair dye. Contact Dermatitis 1997;36:312-313

41 Walker S, Ead R, Shackleton D, Beck M. Two cases of occupational allergic contact dermatitis to *p*-aminophenol in pharmaceutical workers manufacturing paracetamol. Contact Dermatitis 2005;52:290-291

42 Lee HJ, Kim WJ, Kim JY, Kim HS, Kim BS, Kim MB, Ko HC. Patch tests with commercial hair dye products in patients with allergic contact dermatitis to para-phenylenediamine. Indian J Dermatol Venereol Leprol 2016;82:645-650

43 Ito A, Nishioka K, Kanto H, Yagami A, Yamada S, Sugiura M, et al. A multi-institutional joint study of contact dermatitis related to hair colouring and perming agents in Japan. Contact Dermatitis 2017;77:42-48

2.20 AMMONIATED MERCURY*

Not an INCI name

IDENTIFICATION

Description/definition	: Ammoniated mercury is a metal amino salt (chloride)
Chemical class(es)	: Inorganic compounds
INCI name	: Neither in CosIng nor in the Personal Care Products Council Ingredient Database
Chemical/IUPAC name	: Amino(chloro)mercury
Other names	: Mercuric ammonium chloride; mercury, ammoniated; mercury(II) amide chloride
CAS registry number (s)	: 10124-48-8
EC number(s)	: 233-335-8
Merck Index monograph	: 817
Patch testing	: 1.0% pet. (Chemotechnique, SmartPracticeEurope, SmartPracticeCanada)
Molecular formula	: HCl_2HgN

GENERAL

Discussion of the side effects of ammoniated mercury is limited to allergic contact dermatitis from its presence in cosmetics and results of testing in groups of patients, excluding non-allergic reactions (e.g. mercury poisoning [12,20,22,23,24]) or contact allergy to ammoniated mercury in non-cosmetic products (3) such as pharmaceutical products (14). A useful review is presented in ref. 14. See also the chapters on other mercurials: Miscellaneous (mercury) (2.303.8) and Thimerosal (2.456).

CONTACT ALLERGY

Patch testing in groups of patients

General population and subgroups

In Germany, in 1997-1998, a group of 1141 adults aged 28-78 from the general population with >50% atopic individuals were patch tested with ammoniated mercury 1% pet. and 1% had a positive reaction (men 1%, women 1%) (9,11). In 1989, in Italy, 593 male soldiers without skin disease were tested and there were 7 (1.2%) reactions to ammoniated mercury (10). In neither study was information given on the relevance of these reactions (9,10,11).

Patch testing in groups of patients

Results of testing ammoniated mercury in consecutive patients selected of contact dermatitis (routine testing) and testing in groups of selected patients are shown in table 2.20.1. In routine testing, rates of sensitization ranged from 0.2% to a staggering 20.5% in China (4,5,6,7,8,18). In 5 of the 6 studies, frequencies were above 3%. The relevance of the reactions was not mentioned in all but one study. In this investigation from the USA, only 6% of the positive patch tests had current relevance (4).

In groups of selected patients (e.g., patients with periorbital contact dermatitis, patients with dermatitis of the face, patients with at least one positive patch test reaction to allergens associated with cosmetic ingredients) frequencies of sensitization ranged from 2.4% to 9.9%. The highest sensitization rate was in a study performed in the period 1999-2008 in Thailand among patients who had at least one positive patch test to allergens associated with cosmetic ingredients. Certain relevance was not found, but it was suggested that the reactions were caused by illegal skin-bleaching creams containing mercury or by sensitization to mercury from previous vaccinations (19). The next highest sensitization rate (9.1%) was found in an Australian study (16). Relevance was found in 44% of the 50 positive patch tests, but it was not stated what the causative products were and neither was the selection procedure explained (16). In an early study in Taiwan, 31 of 507 patients with dermatitis of the face (6.1%) reacted to ammoniated mercury 1% pet. Twenty-one of these (68%) had used skin-lightening creams containing mercury (13).

Case reports and case series

One patient had local and systemic contact dermatitis from a very old bleaching cream applied to the upper lip (1). She also developed the baboon syndrome from inhaling mercury from a broken thermometer (1). One patient had ACD from mercury in a skin bleaching cream; she reacted to ammoniated mercury and mercuric chloride. Mercury was demonstrated in the cream in a concentration of 7.2% (wt./wt.), but the exact chemical nature of the mercurial was unknown (2). Of 31 patients with positive patch tests to ammoniated mercury, 21 (20 women, one man) had used skin-lightening creams containing mercury; in 10, there was also a positive patch test to the creams (13).

Cross-reactions, pseudo-cross-reactions and co-reactions
Mercury and other mercurials, including merbromin and thimerosal (1,2,21).

Table 2.20.1 Patch testing in groups of patients

Years and Country	Test conc. & vehicle	Number of patients tested | positive (%)		Selection of patients (S); Relevance (R); Comments (C)	Ref.
Routine testing					
1990-2009 China	1% pet.	1858	380 (20.5%)	R: not stated; C: the high percentage was ascribed to the use of skin lightening creams containing (too much) mercury and to possible false-positive patch test reactions	18
2000-4 Switzerland		4094	(3.6%)	R: not stated; C: prevalence in women 4.2%, in men 2.6%	6
1998–2000 USA	1% pet.	611	(4.1%)	R: not stated	5
1992-1994 USA	1% pet.	3468	(3.2%)	R: present relevance: 6%	4
1985-1987 Singapore	5% pet.	3145	7 (0.2%)	R: not stated; C: prevalence in men 0.1%, in women 0.3%	7
1975-6 USA, Canada	1% pet.	?	(3.6%)	R: not stated	8
Testing in groups of selected patients					
2001-2010 Australia	1% pet.	549	50 (9.1%)	S: not stated; R: 44%	16
1999-2008 Thailand	1% pet.	1247	123 (9.9%)	S: patients with at least one positive patch test to an allergen associated with cosmetic ingredients; in the period of investigation, there was a significant increase in the frequency of sensitization which was ascribed to the use of illegal bleaching creams containing mercury	19
1995-1999 IVDK	1% pet.	971	(2.4%)	S: patients with allergic periorbital contact dermatitis; R: not stated	15
1990-1994 IVDK		587	15 (2.6%)	S: patients with periorbital eczema; R: not stated	17
<1987 Taiwan	1% pet.	507	31 (6.1%)	S: patients with facial dermatitis; R: 21 had used skin-lightening creams containing mercury; C: prevalence in men was 3.3%, in women 7.3%	13

IVDK: Information Network of Departments of Dermatology, Germany, Austria, Switzerland

Presence in cosmetic products and chemical analyses
In May 2017, ammoniated was present in zero of 66,975 cosmetic products of which the composition is known in EWG's Skin Deep Cosmetics Database, USA (http://www.ewg.org/skindeep/). In the USA, in April 2017, ammoniated mercury was present in zero of 56,714 cosmetic products of which the composition is known in FDA's Voluntary Cosmetic Registration Program (VCRP) (data obtained from FDA, May 2017).

LITERATURE
1 Özkaya E, Mirzoyeva L, Ötkür B. Mercury-induced systemic allergic dermatitis caused by 'white precipitate' in a skin lightening cream. Contact Dermatitis 2009; 60:61-63
2 Kawai K, Zhang X-M, Nakagawa M, Kawai J, Okada T, Kawai, K. Allergic contact dermatitis due to mercury in a wedding ring and a cosmetic. Contact Dermatitis 1994;31:330-331
3 Vena GA, Foti C, Grandolfo M, Angelini G. Mercury exanthem. Contact Dermatitis 1994;31:214-216
4 Marks JG, Belsito DV, DeLeo VA, Fowler JF, Fransway AF, Maibach HI,et al. North American Contact Dermatitis Group standard tray patch test results 1992 through 1994. Am J Contact Dermatitis 1995;6:160-165
5 Wetter DA, Davis MDP, Yiannias JA, Cheng JF, Connolly SM, el-Azhary RA, et al. Patch test results from the Mayo Contact Dermatitis Group, 1998–2000. J Am Acad Dermatol 2005;53:416-421
6 Janach M, Kühne A, Seifert B, French LE, Ballmer-Weber B, Hofbauer GFL. Changing delayed-type sensitizations to the baseline series allergens over a decade at the Zurich University Hospital. Contact Dermatitis 2010;63:42-48
7 Goh CL. Contact sensitivity to topical antimicrobials. Contact Dermatitis 1989;21:46-48
8 Rudner EJ. North American Group Results. Contact Dermatitis 1977;3:208-209
9 Schäfer T, Böhler E, Ruhdorfer S, Weigl L, Wessner D, Filipiak B, et al. Epidemiology of contact allergy in adults. Allergy 2001;56:1192-1196
10 Seidenari S, Manzini BM, Danese P, Motolese A. Patch and prick test study of 593 healthy subjects. Contact Dermatitis 1990; 23:162-167
11 Uter W, Ludwig A, Balda BR, Schnuch A, Pfahlberg A, Schäfer T, Wichmann HE, Ring J. The prevalence of contact allergy differed between population-based data and clinic–based data. J Clin Epidemiol 2004;57:627-632
12 Chan TY. Inorganic mercury poisoning associated with skin-lightening cosmetic products. Clin Toxicol (Phila) 2011;49:886-891

13 Sun C-C. Allergic contact dermatitis of the face from contact with nickel and ammoniated mercury in spectacle frames and skin-lightening creams. Contact Dermatitis 1987;17:306-309

14 Aberer W, Gerstner G, Pehamberger H. Ammoniated mercury ointment: outdated but still in use. Contact Dermatitis 1990;23:168-171

15 Herbst RA, Uter W, Pirker C, Geier J, Frosch PJ. Allergic and non-allergic periorbital dermatitis: patch test results of the Information Network of the Departments of Dermatology during a 5-year period. Contact Dermatitis 2004;51:13-19

16 Toholka R, Wang Y-S, Tate B, Tam M, Cahill J, Palmer A, Nixon R. The first Australian Baseline Series: Recommendations for patch testing in suspected contact dermatitis. Australas J Dermatol 2015;56:107-115

17 Ockenfels H, Seemann U, Goos M. Contact allergy in patients with periorbital eczema: an analysis of allergens. Dermatology 1997;195:119-124

18 Dou X, Zhao Y, Ni C, Zhu X, Liu L. Prevalence of contact allergy at a dermatology clinic in China from 1990-2009. Dermatitis 2011;22:324-331

19 Boonchai W, Desomchoke R, Iamtharachai P. Trend of contact allergy to cosmetic ingredients in Thais over a period of 10 years. Contact Dermatitis 2011;65:311-316

20 Pelclová D, Lukás E, Urban P, Preiss J, Rysavá R, Lebenhart P, Okrouhlík B, Fenclová Z, Lebedová J, Stejskalová A, Ridzon P. Mercury intoxication from skin ointment containing mercuric ammonium chloride. Int Arch Occup Environ Health 2002;75 (Suppl):S54-59

21 Audicana MT, Muñoz D, del Pozo MD, Fernández E, Gastaminza G, Fernández de Corres L. Allergic contact dermatitis from mercury antiseptics and derivatives: study protocol of tolerance to intramuscular injections of thimerosal. Am J Contact Dermat 2002;13:3-9

22 Deleu D, Hanssens Y, al-Salmy HS, Hastie I. Peripheral polyneuropathy due to chronic use of topical ammoniated mercury. J Toxicol Clin Toxicol 1998;36:233-237

23 Kern F, Roberts N, Ostlere L, Langtry J, Staughton RC. Ammoniated mercury ointment as a cause of peripheral neuropathy. Dermatologica 1991;183:280-282

24 Turk JL, Baker H. Nephrotic syndrome due to ammoniated mercury. Br J Dermatol 1968;80:623-624

2.21 AMMONIUM BISULFITE

IDENTIFICATION

Description/definition : Ammonium bisulfite is an inorganic salt that conforms to the formula shown below
Chemical class(es) : Inorganic salts
Chemical/IUPAC name : Ammonium hydrogen sulphite
CAS registry number (s) : 10192-30-0
EC number(s) : 233-469-7
CIR review(s) : Int J Toxicol 2003;22(Suppl.2):63-88 (access: www.cir-safety.org/ingredients)
Merck Index monograph : 1769
Function(s) in cosmetics : EU: hair waving or straightening; preservative; reducing. USA: hair-waving/straightening agents; reducing agents
EU cosmetic restrictions : Regulated in Annexes III/99 and V/9 of the Regulation (EC) No. 1223/2009
Patch testing : 2% pet. (1); 0.1 and 0.45% water (2)
Molecular formula : H_5NO_3S

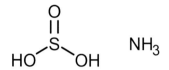

GENERAL

General information on (the adverse reactions to) sulfites is discussed in Chapter 2.422 Sodium metabisulfite. The literature on contact allergy to sodium bisulfite, sodium sulfite, sodium metabisulfite, and some other sulfites (ammonium bisulfite, potassium metabisulfite and sodium hyposulfite (sodium thiosulfate)) has been reviewed in 2012 (3).

CONTACT ALLERGY

Case reports and case series

An atopic woman used to dye her hair with henna for many years without any problem. After applying exactly the same henna dye as usual, her face started itching while she was still at the hairdresser's shop. One day later, she noticed itching and erythema over her forehead and temples and the next day over her cheeks. She had no scalp involvement and told that the hairdresser had applied two protective ointments over her face during the dying procedure. Patch tests with the European standard series, a preservative and diluent series and the two ointments that had been used gave a positive reaction to a 'colour bleaching ointment'. Later, the ingredients were tested and the allergenic culprit proved to be ammonium bisulfite, tested 2% in petrolatum (1).

A woman had used a bleaching cream containing 0.45% ammonium bisulfite for several months. Two days prior to presentation, she had repeated the procedure of bleaching her eyebrows and she developed a dermatitis at the sites of application spreading to the ears. Patch tests with the standard series, the bleaching cream, its individual ingredients and sodium bisulfite (not an ingredient of the cosmetic product) yielded positive reactions to ammonium bisulfite 0.1% and 0.45% in water and to sodium bisulfite 1%, 0.45% and 0.1% in water. It was not mentioned whether the cream itself gave a positive reaction. Six controls were negative to all test substances (2).

Cross-reactions, pseudo-cross-reactions and co-reactions

Sodium bisulfite (2).

Presence in cosmetic products and chemical analyses

In the USA, in April 2017, aluminum bisulfite was present in 1 of 56,714 cosmetic products of which the composition is known in FDA's Voluntary Cosmetic Registration Program (VCRP) (data obtained from FDA, May 2017). In April 2017, ammonium bisulfite was present in zero of 65,434 cosmetic products of which the composition is known in EWG's Skin Deep Cosmetics Database, USA (http://www.ewg.org/skindeep/).

LITERATURE

1   Nassif A. Ammonium bisulfite contact dermatitis: face eczema due to a bleaching ointment used during hair-dying. Contact Dermatitis 2006;55:124

2   Pambor M. Contact dermatitis due to ammonium bisulfite in a bleaching cream. Contact Dermatitis 1996;35:48-49

3   Garcia-Gavin J, Parente J, Goossens A. Allergic contact dermatitis caused by sodium metabisulfite: a challenging allergen. A case series and literature review. Contact Dermatitis 2012;67:260-269

2.22 AMMONIUM PERSULFATE

IDENTIFICATION

Description/definition : Ammonium persulfate is the inorganic salt that conforms to the formula shown below
Chemical class(es) : Inorganic salts
Chemical/IUPAC name : Diazanium sulfonatooxy sulfate
Other names : Ammonium peroxydisulfate; diammonium peroxodisulfate
CAS registry number (s) : 7727-54-0
EC number(s) : 231-786-5
CIR review(s) : Int J Toxicol 2001;20(Suppl.3):7-21; Re-evaluation - Re-opened, June 2016
(access: www.cir-safety.org/ingredients)
Merck Index monograph : 1809
Function(s) in cosmetics : EU: bleaching; oxidising. USA: oxidizing agents
Patch test allergens : 2.5% pet. (Chemotechnique, SmartPracticeEurope, SmartPracticeCanada)
Molecular formula : $H_8N_2O_8S_2$

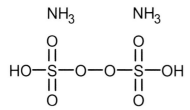

GENERAL

Persulfate salts (ammonium, potassium, sodium) are strongly oxidizing inorganic salts. Persulfates are widely used in various manufacturing processes in the textile, chemical, metallurgic, pharmaceutical, photographic, food and, particularly, cosmetic industries (2,7). They are present in hair-bleaching products and hair-coloring preparations to accelerate the bleaching process, thus reducing the amount of peroxide used. In addition to the bleaching products, consumers may have contact with persulfates in dental prosthesis cleansers (1).

The persulfates can cause irritant dermatitis in the production industry and in hairdressers (40) and allergic contact dermatitis (ACD). The first case reports of allergic contact dermatitis from the persulfates concerned European bakers who were exposed to the persulfate in 'flour correctors'. There were so many instances of allergic contact dermatitis of the hands in bakers, that its use was forbidden in 1957 in Germany (2) and in that period also in some other European countries (43). Most bakers retained their allergic sensitivity for over a decade, even after ceasing to work as baker (44). Currently, ACD from persulfates is seen especially in hairdressers (table 2.22.1) and, less fre- quently, in their clients (3) or individuals bleaching their own hair (57). Indeed, persulfates have been classified as moderate to strong sensitizers according to a murine LLNA study (64).

Immediate contact reactions (sometimes in combination with type IV allergy [7,50,51,58,59,63]) with localized and generalized urticaria and rarely anaphylactic shock (1,2,40,41,42) are not uncommon. This is seen both in individuals bleaching their hair (2) or having it done, and in hairdressers (2,45) (table 2.22.2). Other immediate reactions include rhinitis and asthma, which occurs mainly as occupational disease in hairdressers (5,10,11,13,45,51,52,53, 54,55,60,63) and in plants producing persulfates (56,60). Indeed, a life-time prevalence of 16.9% for allergic rhinitis and 4.5% for asthma among hairdressers has been established; 90% of the cases are caused by ammonium per- sulfate (62). The mechanism of the immediate reactions is as yet unclear. Positive prick tests, scratch and intra- dermal tests, skin application (sometimes with generalized urticaria [2] or severe bronchial obstruction [2,4] as result) and nasal and bronchial provocations (13) with negative responses in controls strongly suggest immuno- globulin E (IgE)-mediated allergy, but passive transfer tests have been negative. In only a few studies has specific IgE to persulfate been demonstrated (7,14).

For detailed procedures for performing skin prick tests with ammonium persulfate see references 1 and 10. Specific inhalation challenge (SIC) may be considered the 'gold standard' for the diagnosis of occupational asthma due to persulfate salts (70). The literature up to 2001 has been reviewed in ref. 38.

CONTACT ALLERGY

Patch testing in groups of patients

Ammonium persulfate has not been tested in consecutive patients suspected of contact dermatitis (routine testing). The results of studies in groups of selected patients back to 1990 are summarized in table 2.22.1. As ammonium persulfate is usually tested in a 'hairdressing' series, most studies have focused on hairdressers, and some on patients suspected of reactions to hairdressing chemicals (usually hair dyes). In the former group, high frequencies of sensitization to ammonium persulfate have been observed, ranging from 8 to 47%, depending on the selection criteria. In patients not being hairdressers and suspected to react to hair cosmetics or patients with dermatitis of the scalp, frequencies were usually in the 2-4% range, but was very high in a recent Japanese study (14.5% [74]). In most studies, no relevance data were provided, but in studies that addresses the issue, relevance percentages were high, ranging (in 3 of 4 studies) from 70 to 91%. These high percentages can easily be explained by selection of patients and the fact that contact allergy to ammonium persulfate is nearly always caused by hair bleach and thus easy to recognize.

Table 2.22.1 Patch testing in groups of patients: Selected patient groups

Years and Country	Test conc. & vehicle	Number of patients tested | positive (%)		Selection of patients (S); Relevance (R); Comments (C)	Ref.
2012-2014 Japan	1% pet.	192	28 (14.6%)	S: patients suspected of allergic contact dermatitis from hair dyes or perming solutions, of who 13% were hairdressers; R: not stated; C: in hairdressers, the frequency of sensitization was 15%, in the non-occupational group 14.5%	74
2007-2012 IVDK	2.5% pet.	696	148 (18.7%)	S: female hairdressers with current or previous occupational contact dermatitis; R: not stated	30
		1692	32 (2.1%)	S: female patients, clients of hairdressers, in who hair cosmetics were suspected as a cause of dermatitis, and who had never worked as hairdressers; R: not stated	
2002-2011 Denmark		397	43 (10.8%)	S: hairdressers with contact dermatitis; R: not stated	29
2009-2010 Poland		139	11 (8.3%)	S: apprentice hairdressers 17-19 years old; R: 10/11 (91%)	66
2001-2010 Australia	2.5% pet	1326	293 (22%)	S: not stated; R: 28%	25
1993-2010 Australia		164	78 (47%)	S: hairdressers and apprentice hairdressers presenting at an occupational dermatology clinic; R: 87%	28
2000-2008 USA	2.5% pet.	209	(14%)	S: patients tested with a hairdresser's series; R: 70%	19
1980-2007 UK	2.5% pet.	538	57 (10.6%)	S: hairdressers tested with a hairdressers series; R: not specified	31
2003-2006 IVDK	2.5% pet.	432	(21.7%)	S: female hairdressers with suspected occupational contact dermatitis; R: not stated	3
		616	(2.9%)	S: women with suspected reactions to hair cosmetics; R: not stated	
1999-2004 UK		567	68 (12.0%)	S: patients tested with the hairdressing series; R: only reactions that were of current or past relevance were collected	32
1994-2004 USA		35	1 (2.2%)	S: patients with allergic contact dermatitis of the eyelids; R: the reaction was relevant, the causative product was not mentioned	16
1994-2003 Spain		300	(14%)	S: hairdressers suspected of occupational contact dermatitis; R: not specified	20
1993-2003 IVDK	2.5% pet.	634	20 (3.2%)	S: patients with scalp dermatitis; R: not stated	6
2000-2002 Finland		723	(2.2%)	S: patients tested with a hairdressing series; R: not stated	15
1995-2002 IVDK		884	(26.1%)	S: female hairdressers with present or past occupational contact dermatitis; R: not specified	21
		1217	(4.2%)	S: clients of hairdressers suspected to react to hairdressing cosmetics or hair care products; R: not specified	
<2000 Italy		41	(12.1%)	S: hairdressers with contact dermatitis; R: not specified; C: in the group of 41, sixteen (39%) were diagnosed with occupational allergic contact dermatitis	34
1990-1999 Italy	2.5% water	209	25 (11.9%)	S: hairdressers with contact dermatitis; R: not specified	9
1996 Belgium, UK and Germany		475	6 (1.3%)	S: patients with contact allergy to cosmetic ingredients; R: not stated	17
1995-1996 Finland		395	(2.3%)	S: patients tested with a hairdressing series; R: not stated	15
1985-1994 Greece	2.5% pet.	106	19 (17.9%)	S: hairdressers with contact dermatitis; R: not specified	33
1980-1993 Spain	2.5% pet.	379	30 (7.9%)	S: hairdressers; R: not specified	23
1988-1991, 8 European countries		809	66 (8.2%)	S: hairdressers with hand dermatitis; R: not stated	22
1985-1990 Italy	2.5% pet.	302	34 (11.3%)	S: hairdressers with contact dermatitis; R: not specified	24

IVDK: Information Network of Departments of Dermatology, Germany, Austria, Switzerland

Case reports and case series

Case series
Ammonium persulfate was stated to be the (or an) allergen in 19 patients in a group of 603 individuals suffering from cosmetic dermatitis, seen in the period 2010-2015 in Leuven, Belgium (18). In the period 1996-2013, in a tertiary referral center in Valencia, Spain, 5419 patients were patch tested. Of these, 628 individuals had allergic contact dermatitis to cosmetics. Ammonium persulfate was the responsible allergen in 3 (0.5%) cases (26).

Case reports
A hairdresser developed acute eczematous dermatitis on both hands whenever she handled ammonium persulfate hair bleach; there was a strongly positive patch test reaction to ammonium persulfate 2% in water (42). A hairdresser had ACD of the hands from AP in hair bleach, combined with immediate-type reactions (acute rash, rhinitis, sneezing) (50). A hairdresser developed allergic contact dermatitis of the hands and forearms from ammonium persulfate. Previously, she had noticed nasal and ocular itching, sneezing, and rhinorrhea, whenever working with bleaching powder. Subsequently, she experienced episodes of dyspnea and dry cough, which usually started 1 to 2 hours after exposure to bleaching powder and aggravated especially during the night. Tests suggested that an immunologic mechanism with direct involvement of T cells not only played an important role in the pathogenesis of the cutaneous, but also in the respiratory and rhinoconjunctival reactions (58).

A hairdresser developed ACD of the hands from AP and dyes and thereafter started to work at the reception desk. Later, she would develop a running nose, coughing, and shortness of breath while leading customers from the reception desk to a seat in the hairdresser's shop. The patient had a combined type I and type IV allergy (59). A hairdresser had ACD of the hands from ammonium persulfate in combination with asthma; both a prick test and a patch test were positive. When she started using bleaches with potassium persulfate, both the dermatitis and the airway symptoms improved considerably (63). A hairdresser had a combined type IV allergy (allergic contact dermatitis of the hands) and type I allergy (asthma) to ammonium persulfate (10). A hairdresser first developed hand dermatitis from ammonium persulfate, followed by airborne contact dermatitis, rhinitis and asthma (71).

Contact allergy to ammonium persulfate in non-cosmetic products
Allergic contact dermatitis to ammonium persulfate has been observed from AP in flour in bakers (2,38,43,44) and in a pizza maker (68), and in industrial workers from AP dust (39).

Cross-reactions, pseudo-cross-reactions and co-reactions
Potassium persulfate (12,57). Reactions to other persulfates are to be expected in ammonium persulfate-sensitized patients, since the allergic reaction is due to the persulfate part (73).

Presence in cosmetic products and chemical analyses
In the USA, in April 2017, ammonium persulfate was present in 36 of 56,714 cosmetic products of which the composition is known in FDA's Voluntary Cosmetic Registration Program (VCRP) (data obtained from FDA, May 2017). In March 2017, ammonium persulfate was present in 1 of 64,983 cosmetic products of which the composition is known in EWG's Skin Deep Cosmetics Database, USA (http://www.ewg.org/skindeep/).

OTHER SIDE EFFECTS

Irritant contact dermatitis
Five hairdressers had occupational contact dermatitis of the hands, which was ascribed to the irritant effects of ammonium persulfate (40). A woman developed irritant contact dermatitis of the scalp and the forehead from a hair bleach containing 'more ammonium persulfate than usual'; there was also some temporary hair loss (42). In an early study, prolonged application of persulfate bleach produced irritant reactions of the scalp and forehead, also in some instances accompanied by a temporary loss of hair. Irritant reactions also occurred if the bleach contained a higher concentration of persulfate than was customarily used (46). In a plant producing ammonium and potassium persulfate, 34 of 75 workers (45%) developed irritant contact dermatitis from persulfate dust. The rashes consisted of itchy red papules and eczematous patches on the wrists and forearms, hands, neck and face. The eruptions most commonly developed within one month of the start of employment (47).

Immediate-type reactions
Immediate contact reactions include contact urticaria, asthma and anaphylactic shock. Most such reactions have been observed in hairdressers (see the section 'General' at the beginning of this chapter). Discussion of asthma and other airway symptoms (e.g., rhinitis) is considered to fall outside the scope of this book. Relevant references include

1,4,5,7,10,11,13,42,45,52,53,54,56,60,65 and 69. Late asthmatic reactions have also been observed (e.g., 8,58,61, 70,71,72). In these patients, prick tests are usually negative but patch tests positive (8,61,70).

In the period 1991-2011, 806 patients were prick tested with AP and potassium persulfate 2% water in an Occupational Health Institute in Finland (67). There were 17 (2.1%) positive reactions (not specified for ammonium and potassium persulfate); fifteen of these individuals were hairdressers. Eleven patients (65%) had occupational disease, all from persulfate hair bleach. Five suffered from contact urticaria plus rhinitis, 3 from contact urticaria alone, 2 from asthma alone and 1 from asthma, rhinitis and contact urticaria (67).

Case reports of immediate contact reactions with dermatological manifestations are shown in table 2.22.2.

Table 2.22.2 Case reports of immediate contact reactions from ammonium persulfate in hair bleach with dermatological manifestations

Year	Nr. Pat.	Symptoms	Other information	Ref.
Hairdressers				
2012	1	LU, GU, RS	Positive prick test and open test to AP and potassium persulfate	1
2010	1	LU, AE	Airborne contact urticaria and angioedema; also rhinitis and asthma	71
2003	6	Contact urticaria, AE, or contact dermatitis	Four also had rhinitis, one conjunctivitis; all 6 had positive prick tests, 2 positive patch tests, three of four had a positive open test on normal skin; in two, specific IgE to HSA-conjugated AP was demonstrated and in one, specific IgE in a RAST test was identified	7
1985	1	Contact urticaria	Also ACD of the hands from AP	51
1977	1	Acute rash on the hands and forearms	Also ACD of the hands from AP, rhinitis and sneezing	50
Non-hairdressers				
2012	1	GU, ANA	Positive prick test and patch test; negative direct open test to ammonium and potassium persulfate	1
2005	1	LU, GU, ANA	The patient had previously worked as hairdresser; a patch test resulted in generalized urticaria and dyspnea; positive open test (rub test) to ammonium persulfate	2
1993	1	LS	No open test performed, diagnosis uncertain	37
1985	2	LU	Open test positive	36
1977	2	LS (n=1), GU (n=1)	Open test with 2% AP strongly positive	35
1976	1	GU, ANA	Strongly positive open test to AP 5% water	42
1972	1	GU, RS, ANA	Open test positive, strongly in a rub test	41
1962	2	LU, ANA (n=1)	One patient had generalized itching with headache and drowsiness	40

AE Angioedema; ANA Anaphylactic reaction (shock); AP Ammonium persulfate; GU Generalized urticaria; LS Localized symptoms (erythema, tingling, burning); LU Localized urticaria; RS Respiratory symptoms (asthma, rhinoconjunctivitis, dyspnea)

Other patients with immediate reactions to ammonium persulfate or 'persulfate', of which the author does not have adequate clinical details, are presented in refs. 48 and 49. A review of contact urticaria caused by ingredients of cosmetics has been provided in ref 27.

LITERATURE

1 Hoekstra M, van der Heide S, Coenraads PJ, Schuttelaar M-LA. Anaphylaxis and severe systemic reactions caused by skin contact with persulfates in hair-bleaching products. Contact Dermatitis 2012;66:317-322

2 Babilas P, Landthaler M, Szeimies RM. Anaphylactic reaction following hair bleaching. Hautarzt 2005;56:1152-1155

3 Uter W, Lessmann H, Geier J, Schnuch A. Contact allergy to hairdressing allergens in female hairdressers and clients – current data from the IVDK, 2003-2006. J Dtsch Dermatol Ges 2007;5:993-1001

4 Perfetti L, Galdi E, Biale C, Garbelli N, Moscato G. Anaphylactoid reaction to patch testing with ammonium persulfate. Allergy 2000;55:94-95

5 Moscato G, Pignatti P, Yacoub MR, Romano C, Spezia S, Perfetti L. Occupational asthma and occupational rhinitis in hairdressers. Chest 2005;128:3590-3598

6 Hillen U, Grabbe S, Uter W. Patch test results in patients with scalp dermatitis: analysis of data of the Information Network of Departments of Dermatology. Contact Dermatitis 2007;56:87-93

7 Aalto-Korte K, Mäkinen-Kiljunen S. Specific immunoglobulin E in patients with immediate persulfate hypersensitivity. Contact Dermatitis 2003;49:22-25

8 Polychronakis I, Thanasias E, Raulf-Heimsoth M, Merget R. Occupational non-immediate type allergic asthma due to ammonium persulfate. Adv Exp Med Biol 2013;755:79-84

9   Iorizzo M, Parente G, Vincenzi C, Pazzaglia M, Tosti A. Allergic contact dermatitis in hairdressers; frequency and source of sensitization. Eur J Dermatol 2002;12:179-182

10   Hougaard MG, Menné T, Søsted H. Occupational eczema and asthma in a hairdresser caused by hair-bleaching products. Dermatitis 2012;23:284-287

11   Moscato G, Pala G, Perfetti L, Frascaroli M, Pignatti P. Clinical and inflammatory features of occupational asthma caused by persulphate salts in comparison with asthma associated with occupational rhinitis. Allergy 2010;65:784-790

12   Veien NK, Hattel T, Laurberg G. Contact dermatitis due to potassium persulfate. Contact Dermatitis 2001;45:176

13   Moscato G, Galdi E. Asthma and hairdressers. Curr Opin Allergy Clin Immunol 2006;6:91-95

14   Brauel R, Brauel P, Stresemann E. Kontakturticaria, Rhinopathie und allergisches Bronchialasthma durch Ammoniumpersulfat in Blondiermittel. Allergologie 1995;18:438-440

15   Hasan T, Rantanen T, Alanko K, Harvima RJ, Jolanki R, Kalimo K, et al. Patch test reactions to cosmetic allergens in 1995–1997 and 2000–2002 in Finland –a multicentre study. Contact Dermatitis 2005;53:40-45

16   Amin KA, Belsito DV. The aetiology of eyelid dermatitis: a 10-year retrospective analysis. Contact Dermatitis 2006;55:280-285

17   Goossens A, Beck MH, Haneke E, McFadden JP, Nolting S, Durupt G, Ries G. Adverse cutaneous reactions to cosmetic allergens. Contact Dermatitis 1999;40:112-113

18   Goossens A. Cosmetic contact allergens. Cosmetics 2016, 3, 5; doi:10.3390/cosmetics3010005

19   Wang MZ, Farmer SA, Richardson DM, Davis MDP. Patch-testing with hairdressing chemicals. Dermatitis 2011;22:16-26

20   Valks R, Conde-Salazar L, Malfeito J, Ledo S. Contact dermatitis in hairdressers, 10 years later: patch-test results in 300 hairdressers (1994 to 2003) and comparison with previous study. Dermatitis 2005;16:28-31

21   Uter W, Lessmann H, Geier J, Schnuch A. Contact allergy to ingredients of hair cosmetics in female hairdressers and clients: an 8-year analysis of IVDK data. Contact Dermatitis 2003;49:236-240

22   Frosch PJ, Burrows D, Camarasa JG, Dooms-Goossens A, Ducombs G, Lahti A, et al. Allergic reactions to a hairdressers' series: results from 9 European centres. Contact Dermatitis 1993;28:180-183

23   Conde-Salazar L, Baz M, Guimaraens D, Cannavo A. Contact dermatitis in hairdressers: patch test results in 379 hairdressers (1980-1993). Am J Cont Dermat 1995;6:19-23

24   Guerra L, Tosti A, Bardazzi F, Pigatto P, Lisi P, Santucci B, et al. Contact dermatitis in hairdressers: the Italian experience. Contact Dermatitis 1992;26:101-107

25   Toholka R, Wang Y-S, Tate B, Tam M, Cahill J, Palmer A, Nixon R. The first Australian Baseline Series: Recommendations for patch testing in suspected contact dermatitis. Australas J Dermatol 2015;56:107-115

26   Zaragoza-Ninet V, Blasco Encinas R, Vilata-Corell JJ, Pérez-Ferriols A, Sierra-Talamantes C, Esteve-Martínez A, de la Cuadra-Oyanguren J. Allergic contact dermatitis due to cosmetics: A clinical and epidemiological study in a tertiary hospital. Actas Dermosifiliogr 2016;107:329-336

27   Verhulst L, Goossens A. Cosmetic components causing contact urticaria: a review and update. Contact Dermatitis 2016;75:333-344

28   Lyons G, Roberts H, Palmer A, Matheson M, Nixon R. Hairdressers presenting to an occupational dermatology clinic in Melbourne, Australia. Contact Dermatitis 2013;68:300-306

29   Schwensen JF, Johansen JD, Veien NK, Funding AT, Avnstorp C, Østerballe M, et al. Occupational contact dermatitis in hairdressers: an analysis of patch test data from the Danish Contact Dermatitis Group, 2002–2011. Contact Dermatitis 2014;70:233-237

30   Uter W, Gefeller O, John SM, Schnuch A, Geier J. Contact allergy to ingredients of hair cosmetics – a comparison of female hairdressers and clients based on IVDK 2007–2012 data. Contact Dermatitis 2014;71:13-20

31   O'Connell RL, White IR, McFadden JP, White JML. Hairdressers with dermatitis should always be patch tested regardless of atopy status. Contact Dermatitis 2010;62:177-181

32   Katugampola RP, Statham BN, English JSC, Wilkinson MM, Foulds IS, Green CM, Ormerod AD, et al. A multicentre review of the hairdressing allergens tested in the UK. Contact Dermatitis 2005;53:130-132

33   Katsarou A, Koufou B, Takou K, Kalogeromitros D, Papanayiotou G, Vareltzidis A. Patch test results in hairdressers with contact dermatitis in Greece (1985-1994). Contact Dermatitis 1995;33:347-348

34   Lodi A, Mancini LL, Ambonati M, Coassini A, Ravanelli G, Crosti C. Epidemiology of occupational contact dermatitis in a North Italian population. Eur J Dermatol 2000;10:128-132

35   Fisher AA. Urticarial and systemic reactions to contactants varying from hair bleach to seminal fluids. Cutis 1977;19:715-717,736

36   Fisher AA. The persulfates: A triple threat. Cutis 1985;35:523-525

37   Fisher AA. Four flushers: Topical agents producing facial flushing simulating the systemic variety. Cutis 1993;51:225-227

38   Pang S, Fiume MA. Final report on the safety assessment of ammonium, potassium, and sodium persulfate. Int J Toxicol 2001;20 suppl.3:7-21 (access: www.cir-safety.org/ingredients).

39 Baur X, Fruhmann G, von Liebe V. Occupational asthma and dermatitis after exposure to dusts of persulfate salts in two industrial workers (article in German). Respiration 1979;38:144-150

40 Calnan CD, Shuster S. Reactions to ammonium persulfate. Arch Dermatol 1963;88:812-815

41 Brubaker MM. Urticarial reaction to ammonium persulfate. Arch Dermatol 1972;106:413-414

42 Fisher AA, Dooms-Goossens A. Persulfate hair bleach reactions. Cutaneous and respiratory manifestations. Arch Dermatol 1976;112:1407-1409

43 Schulz KH. Occupational disease. Z Haut Geschlechtskr 1967;42:499-509

44 Forck G. Occurrence and persistence of persulfate allergy. Berufsdermatosen 1968;16:84-92

45 Meindl K, Meyer R. Asthma and urticaria in hair dressers caused by bleaching agents containing persulfates. Zentralbl Arbeitsmed 1969;3:75-79

46 Gaultier R, Gervaise P, Mellario F. Two causes of occupational asthma and urticaria in hair dressers: Persulfate and silk. Arch Mal Prof 1966;27:809-813

47 White IR, Catchpole HE, Rycroft RJ. Rashes amongst persulphate workers. Contact Dermatitis 1982;8:168-172

48 Peiffer J, Hunziker N, Brun R, et al. Unusual contact dermatoses. Dermatologica 1974;148:289

49 Brun R, Jadassohn W, Paillard R. Epicutaneous test with immediate type reaction to ammonium persulfate. Dermatologica 1966;133:89-90

50 Widström L. Allergic reactions to ammonium persulphate in hair bleach. Contact Dermatitis 1977;3:343

51 Kellett JK, Beck MH. Ammonium persulphate sensitivity in hairdressers. Contact Dermatitis 1985;13:26-28

52 Blainey AD, Ollier S, Cundell D, Smith RE, Davies RJ. Occupational asthma in a hairdressing salon. Thorax 1986;41:42-50

53 Pankow W, Hein H, Bittner K, Wichert P. Persulfate asthma in hairdressers. Pneumologie 1989;43:173-175

54 Schwaiblmair M, Baur X, Fruhmann G. Bronchial asthma in a hairdresser caused by hair bleach. Dtsch Med Wochenschr 1990;115:695-697

55 Parra FM, Igea JM, Quirce S, Ferrando MC, Martín JA, Losada E. Occupational asthma in a hairdresser caused by persulphate salts. Allergy 1992;47:656-660

56 Wrbitzky R, Drexler H, Letzel S. Early reaction type allergies and diseases of the respiratory passages in employees from persulphate production. Int Arch Occup Environ Health 1995;67:413-417

57 van Joost T, Roesyanto ID. Sensitization to persulphates in occupational and non-occupational hand dermatitis. Contact Dermatitis 1991;24:376-378

58 Yawalkar N, Helbling A, Pichler CE, Zala L, Pichler WJ. T cell involvement in persulfate triggered occupational contact dermatitis and asthma. Ann Allergy Asthma Immunol 1999;82:401-404

59 Borelli S, Wüthrich B. Immediate and delayed hypersensitivity to ammonium persulfate. Allergy 1999;54:893-894

60 Munoz X, Cruz MJ, Orriols R, Bravo C, Espuga M, Morell F. Occupational asthma due to persulfate salts. Diagnosis and follow-up. Chest 2003;123:2124-2129

61 Harth V, Raulf-Heimsoth M, Brüning T, Merget R. Isolated late asthmatic reaction after exposure to ammonium persulfate in a hairdresser. Contact Dermatitis 2006;54:62-63

62 Leino T, Tammilehto L, Hytonen M, Sala E, Paakkulainen H, Kanerva L. Occupational skin and respiratory diseases among hairdressers. Scand J Work Environ Health 1998;24:398-406

63 Bregnhøj A, Søsted H. Type I ammonium persulfate allergy with no cross reactivity to potassium persulfate. Contact Dermatitis 2009;61:356-357

64 Cruz M-J, De Vooght V, Muñoz X, Hoet PHM, Morell F, Nemery B, Vanoirbeek JAJ. Assessment of the sensitization potential of persulfate salts used for bleaching hair. Contact Dermatitis 2009;60:85-90

65 Figueiredo JP, Pomiecinski F, Yang AC, Castro FF, Kalil J, Galvao CE. Diagnostic assessment of occupational asthma due to persulfate salts in a professional hairdresser: a case report. Clinics (Sao Paulo) 2008;63:149-150

66 Krecisz B, Kiec-Swierczynska M, Chomiczewska D. Dermatological screening and results of patch testing among Polish apprentice hairdressers. Contact Dermatitis 2011;64:90-95

67 Helaskoski E, Suolajehto H, Kuuliala O, Aalto-Korte K. Prick testing with chemicals in the diagnosis of occupational contact urticaria and respiratory diseases. Contact Dermatitis 2014;72:20-32

68 Lembo S, Lembo C, Patruno C, Balato A, Balato N, Ayala F. Pizza makers' contact dermatitis. Dermatitis 2014;25:191-194

69 Macchioni P, Kotopoulos C, Talini D, De Santis M, Masino E, Paggiaro PL. Asthma in hairdressers: a report of 5 cases. Med Lav 1999;90:776-785 (article in Italian)

70 Hagemeyer O, Marek E, van Kampen V, Sander I, Raulf M, Merget R, Brüning T. Specific inhalation challenge in persulfate asthma. Adv Exp Med Biol. 2015;861:85-91

71 Poltronieri A, Patrini L, Pigatto P, Riboldi L, Marsili C, Previdi M, Margonari M, Marraccini P. Occupational allergic "march". Rapid evolution of contact dermatitis to ammonium persulfate into airborne contact dermatitis with rhinitis and asthma in a hairdresser (article in Italian). Med Lav 2010;101:403-408

72 Gamboa PM, de la Cuesta CG, García BE, Castillo JG, Oehling A. Late asthmatic reaction in a hairdresser, due to the inhalation of ammonium persulphate salts. Allergol Immunopathol (Madr) 1989;17:109-111

73 Le Coz CJ, Bezard M. Allergic contact cheilitis due to effervescent dental cleanser: combined responsibilities of the allergen persulfate and prosthesis porosity. Contact Dermatitis 1999;41:268-271

74 Ito A, Nishioka K, Kanto H, Yagami A, Yamada S, Sugiura M, et al. A multi-institutional joint study of contact dermatitis related to hair colouring and perming agents in Japan. Contact Dermatitis 2017;77:42-48

2.23 AMMONIUM THIOGLYCOLATE

IDENTIFICATION

Description/definition	: Ammonium thioglycolate is the ammonium salt of thioglycolic acid that conforms to the formula shown below
Chemical class(es)	: Organic salts; thio compounds
Chemical/IUPAC name	: Azanium 2-sulfanylacetate
Other names	: Ammonium mercaptoacetate
CAS registry number (s)	: 5421-46-5
EC number(s)	: 226-540-9
CIR review(s)	: J Am Coll Toxicol 1991;10:135-192; Int J Toxicol 2009;28(Suppl.1):68-133 (access: www.cir-safety.org/ingredients)
SCCS opinion(s)	: SCCS/1520/13 (12)
Function(s) in cosmetics	: EU: depilatory; hair waving or straightening; reducing. USA: hair-waving/straightening agents; reducing agents
EU cosmetic restrictions	: Regulated in Annex III/2a of the Regulation (EC) No. 1223/2009
Patch testing	: 2.5% water (Chemotechnique); 1.0% water (SmartPracticeEurope, SmartPracticeCanada)
Molecular formula	: $C_2H_7NO_2S$

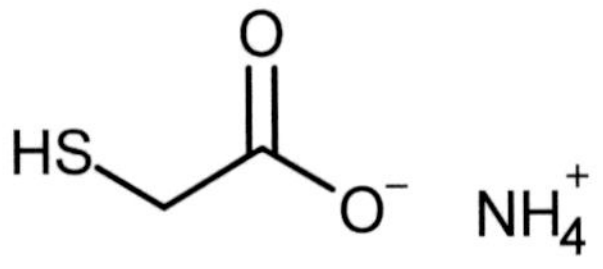

GENERAL

Ammonium thioglycolate is, or rather was, used in permanent waving. Permanent waves create a long-lasting curl in hair by a two-step process that involves reducing disulfide bonds in keratin and then reforming them once the hair has been wound into the desired shape. Ammonium thioglycolate was the reducing agent used in many 'cold permanent waving' products after its introduction in 1943. The chemical is a known irritant (26), but it rarely sensitized. It was largely replaced with glyceryl thioglycolate in the 1970s by the cosmetics industry in its search for a product that would be less damaging to hair during the waving process. From an allergological point of view, this replacement was an unlucky choice, as glyceryl thioglycolate has caused many cases of sensitization, especially in hairdressers, but also, albeit less frequently, in their clients and women perming their own hair (23,24) (see Chapter 2.203 Glyceryl thioglycolate).

CONTACT ALLERGY

Patch testing in groups of patients

Ammonium thioglycolate has not been tested in consecutive patients suspected of contact dermatitis (routine testing). Results of testing ammonium thioglycolate in groups of selected patients (e.g., hairdressers, patients tested with a hairdressing series, women with suspected reactions to hair cosmetics) back to 1990 are shown in table 2.23.1. Patch test concentrations/vehicles have included 1% water, 1% pet., 2.5% water, 2.5% pet. and 55 water as open test (29). Most studies have been performed in hairdressers. Frequencies of sensitization to ammonium thioglycolate in this occupational group have ranged from 0.3 to 15.4%. Relevance data were provided in one study only: 10 of 13 reactions (77%) were considered to be relevant in an Australian tertiary referral center, 1993-2010 (13). In non-hairdressers groups sensitization rates were – as can be expected – lower and ranged from 0.4-3.1%. Not a single study commented on the relevance of the observed positive patch tests.

Case reports and case series

Two positive patch test reactions to ammonium thioglycolate were ascribed to cosmetic allergy (1). Four hairdresser apprentices had eczematous dermatitis on both hands. The first symptoms were diffuse erythema and miliary sized vesicles with itching, which appeared a few months after they began work, followed by hyperkeratosis and swelling. Patch testing of all agents used at their beauty parlors was performed. Cold permanent wave lotions were tested by the open patch test method. In all 4 patients, a positive reaction was seen to the cold permanent wave lotion containing 5% ammonium thioglycolate. Subsequently, open patch tests were performed using 5% and 2% ammonium thioglycolate. Positive reactions were seen to both solutions in all 4 hairdressers, confirming occupational allergic contact dermatitis from ammonium thioglycolate in hair waving solutions. The results of open patch tests with 5%

ammonium thioglycolate in 18 healthy subjects and two hairdressers without dermatitis were negative (4). A similar patient with occupational ACD from ammonium thioglycolate in permanent wave solution had previously been reported from Germany (5).

Between 1982 and 1986, 17 beauticians (hairdressers) with contact dermatitis of the hands were investigated in a university hospital in Japan. Thirteen were tested with permanent wave primary solutions (tested undiluted, open test) and 7 (54%) had a positive reactions. An unknown number of these 7 women were tested with ammonium thioglycolate (5% water, open test) and 3 reacted positively. The authors suggested that contact allergy to ammonium thioglycolate is more frequent than previously thought (20).

Table 2.23.1 Patch testing in groups of patients: Selected patient groups

Years and Country	Test conc. & vehicle	Number of patients tested	positive (%)	Selection of patients (S); Relevance (R); Comments (C)	Ref.
2012-2014 Japan	5% water, open test	188	9 (4.8%)	S: patients suspected of allergic contact dermatitis from hair dyes or perming solutions, of who 13% were hairdressers; R: not stated; C: in hairdressers, the frequency of sensitization was 15.4%, in the non-occupational group 3.1%	29
2007-2012 IVDK	1% pet.	702	9 (1.9%)	S: female hairdressers with current or previous occupational contact dermatitis; R: not stated	15
		1676	6 (0.4%)	S: female patients, clients of hairdressers, in who hair cosmetics were regarded as a cause of dermatitis, and who had never worked as hairdressers; R: not stated	
2002-2011 Denmark		371	1 (0.3%)	S: hairdressers with contact dermatitis; R: not stated	14
1993-2010 Australia		164	13 (7.9%)	S: hairdressers and apprentice hairdressers presenting at an occupational dermatology clinic; R: 77%	13
1980-2007 UK	2.5% water	538	21 (3.9%)	S: hairdressers tested with a hairdressers series; R: not specified	16
2003-2006 IVDK	1% water	199	(1.6%)	S: female hairdressers with suspected occupational contact dermatitis; R: not stated	3
		341	(0.9%)	S: women with suspected reactions to hair cosmetics; R: not stated	
1999-2004 UK		504	4 (0.8%)	S: patients tested with the hairdressing series; R: only reactions that were of current or past relevance were collected	17
1994-2003 Italy		300	(12%)	S: hairdressers suspected of occupational contact dermatitis; R: not specified	8
2000-2002 Finland		474	(1.1%)	S: patients tested with a hairdressing series; R: not stated	6
<2000 Italy		41	(2.4%)	S: hairdressers with contact dermatitis; R: not specified; in the group of 41, sixteen (39%) were diagnosed with occupational allergic contact dermatitis	19
1990-1999 Italy	1% water	209	3 (1.4%)	S: hairdressers with contact dermatitis; R: not specified	2
1995-1996 Finland		369	(0.8%)	S: patients tested with a hairdressing series; R: not stated	6
1985-1994 Greece	2.5% pet.	106	12 (11.3%)	S: hairdressers with contact dermatitis; R: not specified	18
1980-1993 Spain	2.5% water	111	3 (2.7%)	S: hairdressers; R: not specified	10
1988-1991, 8 European countries		809	31 (3.8%)	S: hairdressers with hand dermatitis; R: not stated	9
1985-1990 Italy	2.5% pet.	261	3 (1.1%)	S: patients with eczema suspected to be caused by hair dyeing, bleaching or permanent wave solution; R: not stated	7
1985-1990 Italy	2.5% pet.	302	15 (5.0%)	S: hairdressers with contact dermatitis; R: not specified	11

IVDK: Information Network of Departments of Dermatology, Germany, Austria, Switzerland

Cross-reactions, pseudo-cross-reactions and co-reactions

In a group of 121 patients, 29% of those allergic to the glycolic ester of thioglycolic acid and 35% of those allergic to the hydrazide were also sensitive to ammonium thioglycolate, suggesting cross-reactivity (21). Cross-reactions to or from glyceryl thioglycolate have been observed infrequently (22,23,24).

Presence in cosmetic products and chemical analyses

In the USA, in April 2017, ammonium thioglycolate was present in 64 of 56,714 cosmetic products of which the composition is known in FDA's Voluntary Cosmetic Registration Program (VCRP) (data obtained from FDA, May 2017). In March 2017, ammonium thioglycolate was present in one of 64,451 cosmetic products of which the composition is known in EWG's Skin Deep Cosmetics Database, USA (http://www.ewg.org/skindeep/).

OTHER SIDE EFFECTS

Irritant contact dermatitis
Ammonium thioglycolate is a well-known irritant. Irritant contact dermatitis has been observed in users of ammonium thioglycolate permanent waves and clients of hairdressers about the scalp, neck, and ears (26,28). It may be assumed that some hairdressers had occupational irritant contact dermatitis of the hands from (ammonium thioglycolate in) permanent wave solutions.

Other non-eczematous contact reactions
Several cases of temporary alopecia from breakage of the hairs have been reported in the older literature (25,27).

LITERATURE

1   Kohl L, Blondeel A, Song M. Allergic contact dermatitis from cosmetics: retrospective analysis of 819 patch-tested patients. Dermatology 2002;204:334-337
2   Iorizzo M, Parente G, Vincenzi C, Pazzaglia M, Tosti A. Allergic contact dermatitis in hairdressers; frequency and source of sensitization. Eur J Dermatol 2002;12:179-182
3   Uter W, Lessmann H, Geier J, Schnuch A. Contact allergy to hairdressing allergens in female hairdressers and clients – current data from the IVDK, 2003-2006. J Dtsch Dermatol Ges 2007;5:993-1001
4   Yamasaki R, Dekio S, Jidoi J. Allergic contact dermatitis to ammonium thioglycolate. Contact Dermatitis, 1984;11:255
5   Borelli S, Moormann J, Dungemann H, Manok M. Ergebnisse einer vierjahrigen Untersuchungsreihe bei Berufsangern des Friseurgewerbes. Berufsdermatosen 1965;13:216- (last page unknown, data cited in ref. 4)
6   Hasan T, Rantanen T, Alanko K, Harvima RJ, Jolanki R, Kalimo K, et al. Patch test reactions to cosmetic allergens in 1995–1997 and 2000–2002 in Finland –a multicentre study. Contact Dermatitis 2005;53:40-45
7   Guerra L, Bardazzi F, Tosti A. Contact dermatitis in hairdressers' clients. Contact Dermatitis 1992;26:108-111
8   Valks R, Conde-Salazar L, Malfeito J, Ledo S. Contact dermatitis in hairdressers, 10 years later: patch-test results in 300 hairdressers (1994 to 2003) and comparison with previous study. Dermatitis 2005;16:28-31
9   Frosch PJ, Burrows D, Camarasa JG, Dooms-Goossens A, Ducombs G, Lahti A, et al. Allergic reactions to a hairdressers' series: results from 9 European centres. Contact Dermatitis 1993;28:180-183
10   Conde-Salazar L, Baz M, Guimaraens D, Cannavo A. Contact dermatitis in hairdressers: patch test results in 379 hairdressers (1980-1993). Am J Cont Dermat 1995;6:19-23
11   Guerra L, Tosti A, Bardazzi F, Pigatto P, Lisi P, Santucci B, et al. Contact dermatitis in hairdressers: the Italian experience. Contact Dermatitis 1992;26:101-107
12   SCCS (Scientific Committee on Consumer Safety). Opinion on thioglycolic acid and its salts (TGA), 11 November 2013, SCCS/1520/13. Available at: http://ec.europa.eu/health/scientific_committees/consumer_safety/docs/sccs_o_141.pdf
13   Lyons G, Roberts H, Palmer A, Matheson M, Nixon R. Hairdressers presenting to an occupational dermatology clinic in Melbourne, Australia. Contact Dermatitis 2013;68:300-306
14   Schwensen JF, Johansen JD, Veien NK, Funding AT, Avnstorp C, Østerballe M, et al. Occupational contact dermatitis in hairdressers: an analysis of patch test data from the Danish Contact Dermatitis Group, 2002–2011. Contact Dermatitis 2014;70:233-237
15   Uter W, Gefeller O, John SM, Schnuch A, Geier J. Contact allergy to ingredients of hair cosmetics – a comparison of female hairdressers and clients based on IVDK 2007–2012 data. Contact Dermatitis 2014;71:13-20
16   O'Connell RL, White IR, McFadden JP, White JML. Hairdressers with dermatitis should always be patch tested regardless of atopy status. Contact Dermatitis 2010;62:177-181
17   Katugampola RP, Statham BN, English JSC, Wilkinson MM, Foulds IS, Green CM, Ormerod AD, et al. A multicentre review of the hairdressing allergens tested in the UK. Contact Dermatitis 2005;53:130-132
18   Katsarou A, Koufou B, Takou K, Kalogeromitros D, Papanayiotou G, Vareltzidis A. Patch test results in hairdressers with contact dermatitis in Greece (1985-1994). Contact Dermatitis 1995;33:347-348
19   Lodi A, Mancini LL, Ambonati M, Coassini A, Ravanelli G, Crosti C. Epidemiology of occupational contact dermatitis in a North Italian population. Eur J Dermatol 2000;10:128-132
20   Matsunaga K, Hosokawa K, Suzuki M, Arima Y, Hayakawa R. Occupational allergic contact dermatitis in beauticians. Contact Dermatitis 1988;18:94-96
21   Schultz KH. Durch Thioglykolsäurederivate ausgelöste Kontaktekzeme im Friseurberuf. Berufsdermatosen 1961;9:244-257
22   Morrison LH, Storrs FJ. Persistence of an allergen in hair after glyceryl monothioglycolate-containing permanent wave solutions. J Am Acad Dermatol 1988;19:52-59

23 Storrs F. Permanent wave contact dermatitis: contact allergy to glyceryl monothioglycolate. J Am Acad Dermatol 1984;11:74-85

24 Tosti A, Melino M, Bardazzi F. Contact dermatitis due to glyceryl monothioglycolate. Contact Dermatitis 1988;19:71-72

25 Reiches AJ, Parker W. Alopecia-areata-like lesions due to cold-wave thioglycolate preparations. AMA Arch Derm Syphilol 1952;66:521-523

26 Goldman L, Mason L, McDaniel W. Permanent wave process : Clinical report with special reference to effect of ammonium thioglycolate on skin. JAMA 1948;137:354-357

27 Reiches AJ, Lane CW. Temporary baldness due to cold wave thioglycolate preparations. JAMA 1950;144:305-306

28 Schmidt HW. Dermatitis caused by ammonium thioglycolate; genesis and prevention of pathology in cold wave permanent waving. Z Gesamte Inn Med 1958;13:531-532

29 Ito A, Nishioka K, Kanto H, Yagami A, Yamada S, Sugiura M, et al. A multi-institutional joint study of contact dermatitis related to hair colouring and perming agents in Japan. Contact Dermatitis 2017;77:42-48

2.24 AMMONIUM THIOLACTATE

IDENTIFICATION

Description/definition   : Ammonium thiolactate is the organic salt that conforms to the formula shown below
Chemical class(es)   : Organic salts; thio compounds
Chemical/IUPAC name   : Azanium 2-sulfanylpropanoate
Other names   : Ammonium 2-mercaptopropionate; thiolactic acid, ammonium salt
CAS registry number (s) : 13419-67-5
EC number(s)   : 236-526-4
Function(s) in cosmetics : EU: depilatory; hair waving or straightening; reducing. USA: hair-waving/straightening
                           agents; reducing agents
Patch test allergens   : 1% and 2% water (1); as ammonium thiolactate composes rapidly, freshly prepared
                           solutions must always be used
Molecular formula   : $C_3H_9NO_2S$

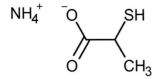

CONTACT ALLERGY

Patch testing in groups of patients
There have been no studies in which consecutive patients suspected of contact dermatitis have been patch tested with ammonium thiolactate (routine testing). Testing in *selected* patients was done by the members of the German Contact Dermatitis Research Group (1). In 2000-2001, patients selected for testing with the hairdressers series were also patch tested with ammonium thiolactate 1% and/or 2% in water. As this compound degrades quickly, the test materials were prepared fresh every week. One hundred and twenty patients were tested with ammonium thioglycolate 2% in water and 3 (2.5%) had a positive patch test reaction. One hundred and fifty individuals were tested with the chemical diluted 1% in water and 2 (1.3%) reacted positively. Relevance was not found with certainty (1). A ROAT was positive in one patient reacting to ammonium thiolactate. This individual was a hairdresser who had positive reactions to both 1% and 2% ammonium thiolactate, which makes relevance in this particular case likely (1).

Case reports and case series
Three hairdressers with occupational allergic contact dermatitis from ammonium thiolactate in perming products, and one non-occupational case were reported to IDOK up to 2001 (cited in ref. 1).

Cross-reactions, pseudo-cross-reactions and co-reactions
Probably not to thiolactic acid (1).

Presence in cosmetic products and chemical analyses
In the USA, in April 2017, ammonium thiolactate was present in 155 of 56,714 cosmetic products of which the composition is known in FDA's Voluntary Cosmetic Registration Program (VCRP) (data obtained from FDA, May 2017). In February 2017, ammonium thiolactate was present in 4 products of 64,631 cosmetic products of which the composition is known in EWG's Skin Deep Cosmetics Database, USA (http://www.ewg.org/skindeep/).

LITERATURE
1   Uter W, Geier J, Pirker C, Aberer W, Kränke B, Richter G, John SM, et al FOR THE GERMAN CONTACT DERMATITIS
    RESEARCH GROUP (DKG). Ammonium thiolactate and thiolactic acid: important hairdressers' allergens? Contact
    Dermatitis 2002;46:242-243

2.25 ANTHEMIS NOBILIS FLOWER EXTRACT

IDENTIFICATION

Description/definition : Anthemis nobilis flower extract is an extract of the flowers of the Roman chamomile, *Anthemis nobilis* L., Compositae.
Chemical class(es) : Botanical products and botanical derivatives
Other names : Chamomile (Anthemis nobilis) extract; chamomile flower, Roman, extract (*Anthemis nobilis* L.)
CAS registry number (s) : 84649-86-5
EC number(s) : 283-467-5
CIR review(s) : Final report, December 2013 (access: www.cir-safety.org/ingredients)
Function(s) in cosmetics : EU: masking; perfuming; skin conditioning. USA: fragrance ingredients; skin-conditioning agents - miscellaneous
Patch testing : 1.0% pet. (Chemotechnique); also present in the Compositae mix II (Chemotechnique); 1% physiologic saline for immediate open testing (7)

The accepted scientific name for *Anthemis nobilis* L. is *Chamaemelum nobile* (L.) All. It should be realized that the colloquial plant name 'Chamomile' (sometimes termed camomile) has been used interchangeably for at least three different species: Roman chamomile (*Chamaemelum nobile* (L.) All.; synonym *Anthemis nobilis* L.), German chamomile (*Chamomilla recutita* (L.) Rauschert), and dog fennel (*Anthemis cotula* L.). Roman and German chamomile are both important medicinal plants, but despite their allegedly similar properties, they differ considerably in their chemical composition (9). German chamomile is discussed in Chapter 2.89 Chamomilla recutita (matricaria) extract.

GENERAL

Roman chamomile (*Chamaemelum nobile* (L.) All.; *Anthemis nobilis* L.) has been a popular medicinal plant since the Middle Ages, especially in England, France and Belgium (9). Traditionally, chamomile is considered to be an antiseptic, disinfectant, bactericidal (13), fungicidal and vermifuge agent. It has been used for centuries as anti-inflammatory, antioxidant, mild astringent, mild sedative, antispasmodic, antibacterial and healing medicine. Oral dosage forms (decoctions and infusions) are used for the symptomatic treatment of gastrointestinal disorders and of the painful component of functional digestive symptoms. External applications of extracts and lotions are recommended as repellent, emollient, in the treatment of skin disorders, wound healing (13) and for eye irritation or discomfort of various etiologies. Furthermore, it is used as an analgesic agent in diseases of the oral cavity, oropharynx or both and as a mouthwash for oral hygiene . Many different preparations of chamomile have been developed, the most popular of which is in the form of herbal tea (2). The extract is also used in a host of 'natural' cosmetics.

Roman chamomile contains, among others, several sesquiterpene lactones (the most abundant of which is nobilin), flavonoids, α-pinene, limonene and bisabolol (9). Contact allergy to and chemical composition of Roman chamomile *essential oil* have been fully reviewed (2). The possible health effects of chamomile (not properly differentiated between the German and Roman varieties) have been reviewed (10). The European Medicines Agency in 2011 concluded that 'The provided clinical and non-clinical data do not fulfil the requirements of a well-established medicinal use with recognised efficacy and an acceptable level of safety of Roman chamomile products' (11). Discussion of contact allergy to Roman chamomile in this chapter is limited to its extracts.

CONTACT ALLERGY

Patch testing in groups of patients

In 2000-2007, in the USA, 545 patients were patch tested with '*Anthemis nobilis*' 1% pet. as part of a supplemental cosmetic screening series and there was only one (0.2%) positive patch test, which was considered to be relevant. However, relevance in this study included 'questionable' and 'past' relevance (16).

Case reports and case series

A patient had allergic contact dermatitis from a deodorant containing the extracts of *Anthemis nobilis* and *Laurus nobilis* (1). The patient reacted to the sesquiterpene lactone mix 0.1% pet. and to the deodorant. As he was not tested with *Anthemis nobilis* and *Laurus nobilis* separately, the allergen responsible for the dermatitis remained unknown. However, he also reacted to several other Compositae plants and extracts, indicating that sensitization to the chamomile component may have been more likely. The reaction was caused by his girlfriend's cosmetics, which is termed 'consort' or 'connubial' allergic contact dermatitis (1).

Contact allergy to Anthemis nobilis flower extract in non-cosmetic products
Two patients had ACD from chamomile tea (ex *Anthemis nobilis*) used in a compress (4,6). Extracts and oil of Roman chamomile in a botanical pharmaceutical ointment caused allergic contact dermatitis in two women (8). A man developed dermatitis of the face which was aggravated by an 'alternative' treatment with hot compresses saturated with various herbs including chamomile. When patch tested, he reacted to Anthemis nobilis homeopathic extract and to the sesquiterpene lactone mix (12).

Cross-reactions, pseudo-cross-reactions and co-reactions
German chamomile (*Chamomilla recutita, Matricaria recutica*) extract (3); parthenolide (3); sesquiterpene lactone mix (1,6,12); *Myroxylon pereirae* resin (8,12); other Compositae plants and extracts (1,6); fragrance mix (4,12); colophonium (4).

Provocation tests
Thirty-five patients previously reacting to the sesquiterpene lactone were patch tested with German chamomile tea and Roman chamomile tea. Thirty patients (86%) reacted to the German chamomile tea and 15 (43%) to Roman chamomile tea (15).

Presence in cosmetic products and chemical analyses
In the USA, in April 2017, Chamaemelum nobile (English/Roman chamomile) flower extract was present in 138 of 56,714 cosmetic products of which the composition is known in FDA's Voluntary Cosmetic Registration Program (VCRP) (data obtained from FDA, May 2017). In January 2017, Anthemis nobilis flower extract was present in 497 of 64,480 cosmetic products of which the composition is known in EWG's Skin Deep Cosmetics Database, USA (http://www.ewg.org/skindeep/).

OTHER SIDE EFFECTS

Immediate-type reactions
One patient had contact urticaria from chamomile extract in a cosmetic cream; it was not mentioned whether it concerned *Anthemis nobilis* (Roman chamomile) or *Chamomilla recutica* (German chamomile) (5). A woman applied a cosmetic skin mask formulation to her face and noted rapid onset of transient rash, burning, stinging and itching at the application sites. Immediate open testing (without prick, scratch or chamber) to intact forearm skin revealed extensive wheal and flare to the following components of the formulation: chamomile extract (1% physiologic saline) (unknown whether German or Roman chamomile), whole egg (0.1% and 1%), lecithin, allantoin, aloe gel, melissa extract (all 1%) and the final formulation as is (skin mask). The saline control was negative, as were similar applications of the above to 10 controls. This would therefore appear to be immunologic contact urticaria. According to the authors, this multiplicity of positive immediate-type reactions suggests the possibility of an immediate-type hypersensitivity analogue of the excited skin syndrome seen in delayed-type testing, common chemical constituents in these natural products, or an individual with a unique immunologic system (7).

LITERATURE
1   Bernedo N, Audicana MT, Uriel O, Velasco M, Gastaminza G, Fernández E, Muñoz D. Allergic contact dermatitis from cosmetics applied by the patient's girlfriend. Contact Dermatitis 2004;50:252-253
2   De Groot AC, Schmidt E. Essential oils: Contact allergy and chemical composition. Boca Raton, Fl, USA: CRC Press Taylor and Francis group, 2016:205-212
3   Lundh K, Gruvberger B, Möller H, Persson L, Hindsén M, Zimerson E, Svensson Å, Bruze, M. Patch testing with thin-layer chromatograms of chamomile tea in patients allergic to sesquiterpene lactones. Contact Dermatitis 2007;57:218-223
4   Giordano-Labadie F, Schwarze HP, Bazex J. Allergic contact dermatitis from camomile used in phytotherapy. Contact Dermatitis 2000;42:247
5   Rudzki E, Rapiejko EZP, Rebandel P, Jaworski E. Oral allergy syndrome with contact urticaria from cosmetic creams. Contact Dermatitis 1999;40:326
6   Pereira F, Santos R, Pereira A. Contact dermatitis from chamomile tea. Contact Dermatitis 1997;36:307
7   West I, Maibach HI. Contact urticaria syndrome from multiple cosmetic components. Contact Dermatitis 1995;32:121
8   McGeorge BCL, Steele MC. Allergic contact dermatitis of the nipple from Roman chamomile ointment. Contact Dermatitis 1991;24:139-140
9   Paulsen E. Contact sensitization from Compositae-containing herbal remedies and cosmetics. Contact Dermatitis 2002;47:189-198

10 Srivastava JK, Shankar E, Gupta S. Chamomile: a herbal medicine of the past with bright future. Mol Med Report 2010;3:895-901

11 European Medicines Agency. Assessment report on *Chamaemelum nobile* (L.) All., flos. EMA/HMPC/560906/2010, Committee on Herbal Medicinal Products (HMPC), 27 January 2011

12 Bossuyt L, Dooms-Goossens A. Contact sensitivity to nettles and camomile in 'alternative' remedies. Contact Dermatitis 1994;31:131-132

13 Kazemian H, Ghafourian S, Sadeghifard N, Badakhsh B, Heidari H1, Taji A, et al. *In vivo* antibacterial and wound healing activities of Roman chamomile (*Chamaemelum nobile*). Infect Disord Drug Targets 2016 Dec 30. (Epub ahead of print)

14 Paulsen E, Chistensen LP, Andersen KE. Cosmetics and herbal remedies with Compositae plant extracts – are they tolerated by Compositae-allergic patients? Contact Dermatitis 2008;58:15-23

15 Lundh K, Gruvberger B, Möller H, Persson L, Hindsén M, Zimerson E, Svensson Å, Bruze, M. Patch testing with thin-layer chromatograms of chamomile tea in patients allergic to sesquiterpene lactones. Contact Dermatitis 2007;57:218-223

16 Wetter DA, Yiannias JA, Prakash AV, Davis MD, Farmer SA, el-Azhary RA, et al. Results of patch testing to personal care product allergens in a standard series and a supplemental cosmetic series: an analysis of 945 patients from the Mayo Clinic Contact Dermatitis Group, 2000-2007. J Am Acad Dermatol 2010;63:789-798

2.26 ARACHIDYL GLUCOSIDE

IDENTIFICATION

Description/definition   : Arachidyl glucoside is the product obtained by the condensation of arachidyl alcohol
                            with glucose
Chemical class(es)   : Carbohydrates; ethers
Other names   : D-glucose, 1-eicosanol ether
CAS registry number (s)   : 144982-05-8
CIR review(s)   : Int J Toxcicol 2013;32(Suppl.3):22-48 (access: www.cir-safety.org/ingredients)
Function(s) in cosmetics : EU: emulsifying; surfactant. USA: surfactants - emulsifying agents
Patch testing   : Unknown: suggested: 3-5% in petrolatum or water (controls!)
Molecular formula   : $C_{26}H_{52}O_6$

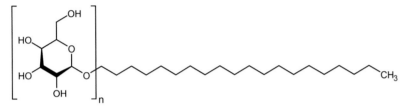

GENERAL

Arachidyl glucoside is one of the alkyl glucosides, a family of organic molecules of vegetal origin. They are produced by the condensation of a sugar, usually a cyclic form of glucose (D-glucopyranose), with a fatty alcohol composed of a linear side chain ranging from 2 to 22 carbons. Fatty alcohol is extracted from palm, coconut, or rapeseed oil, and glucose can be obtained from corn, wheat starch, and potato. The average number of carbon atoms composing the alcohol side chain determines the name of the alkyl glucoside. Members of the alkyl glucoside family include butyl, caprylyl, decyl, lauryl, coco-, cetearyl, undecyl, myristyl, hexadecyl, octadecyl, arachidyl, and caprylyl/capryl glucoside, C10-16, C12-18, C12-20, and C20-22 alkyl glucosides, branched isostearyl glucoside, and octyldodecyl glucoside.

Most of the alkyl glucosides are primarily used as mild non-ionic surfactants in cosmetics and cleansing products for human skin, mostly as a mixture of several alkyl glucosides, as it is difficult to obtain individual glucosides at high purity. They can also sometimes function as emulsion stabilizers in sunscreens, skin and hair cleansing agents, and humectants. They can be found in certain baby products such as wipes and cleansers and in antiseptic solutions (4). Other alkyl glucosides which have caused cosmetic allergy include cetearyl glucoside, coco-glucoside, decyl glucoside, lauryl glucoside and myristyl glucoside. These are discussed in their respective chapters. A comprehensive review of contact allergy to alkyl glucosides has been published in 2017 (3,5).

CONTACT ALLERGY

Case reports and case series

Arachidyl glucoside was stated to be the (or an) allergen in one patient in a group of 603 individuals suffering from cosmetic dermatitis, seen in the period 2010-2015 in Leuven, Belgium (2). Arachidyl glucoside was responsible for 1 out of 959 cases of non-fragrance cosmetic allergy where the causal allergen was identified, Belgium, 2000-2010 (1). A nurse had occupational allergic contact dermatitis of the hands from a cold cream. When tested with the ingredients, she reacted to a single compound called Glucolipide®, tested at a concentration of 3% (vehicle?). Glucolipide is a mixture of arachidyl alcohol 55%, arachidyl glucoside 15%, and behenyl alcohol 30%. Further tests at concentrations of 1% and 3% of a mixture of arachidyl alcohol and behenyl alcohol, as well as behenyl alcohol alone, were negative, suggesting that arachidyl glucoside was the actual sensitizer. The diagnosis of contact allergy to arachidyl glucoside was thus made per exclusionem. The patient did not react to lauryl glucoside 5% or to decyl glucoside 5% (3).

Cross-reactions, pseudo-cross-reactions and co-reactions

Often, a mixture of several alkyl glucosides is present in cosmetic products, as it is very difficult to obtain individual glucosides of high purity. Because of this and of their chemical similarity, concomitant reactivity or cross-reactions may occur with the various glucosides.

Presence in cosmetic products and chemical analyses
In the USA, in April 2017, arachidyl glucoside was present in 187 of 56,714 cosmetic products of which the composition is known in FDA's Voluntary Cosmetic Registration Program (VCRP) (data obtained from FDA, May 2017). In February 2017, arachidyl glucoside was present in 166 of 64,631 cosmetic products of which the composition is known in EWG's Skin Deep Cosmetics Database, USA (http://www.ewg.org/skindeep/).

LITERATURE
1   Travassos AR, Claes L, Boey L, Drieghe J, Goossens A. Non-fragrance allergens in specific cosmetic products. Contact Dermatitis 2011;65:276-285
2   Goossens A. Cosmetic contact allergens. Cosmetics 2016, 3, 5; doi:10.3390/cosmetics3010005
3   Loranger C, Alfalah M, Ferrier Le Bouedec M-C, Sasseville Denis. Alkyl glucosides in contact dermatitis: a systematic review. Dermatitis Dermatitis 2017;28:5-13
4   Fiume MM, Heldreth B, Bergfeld WF, Belsito DV, Hill RA, Klaassen CD, et al. Safety assessment of decyl glucoside and other alkyl glucosides as used in cosmetics. Int J Toxicol 2013;32(Suppl.5):22S-48S
5   Alfalah M, Loranger C, Sasseville D. Contact allergen of the year. Alkyl glucosides. Dermatitis 2017;28:3-4

2.27 ARBUTIN

IDENTIFICATION

Description/definition   : Arbutin is the organic compound that conforms to the formula shown below
Chemical class(es)   : Carbohydrates; phenols
Chemical/IUPAC name : 2-(Hydroxymethyl)-6-(4-hydroxyphenoxy)oxane-3,4,5-triol
Other names   : 4-Hydroxyphenyl-β-D-glucopyranoside
CAS registry number (s) : 497-76-7
EC number(s)   : 207-850-3
SCCS opinion(s)   : SCCS/1552/15 (α-arbutin) (5); SCCS/1550/15 (β-arbutin) (6); SCCP/1158/08 (β-arbutin)
                              (7)
Merck Index monograph : 2033
Function(s) in cosmetics : EU: antioxidant; bleaching; skin conditioning. USA: antioxidants; skin bleaching agents;
                              skin-conditioning agents - miscellaneous
Patch testing   : 5% pet. (1,4); 0.3-3% water (8); according to the group study of the Japanese Society for
                              Contact Dermatitis in 2003, the optimum concentration of arbutin for patch testing is
                              considered to be 5.0% pet. (4)
Molecular formula   : $C_{12}H_{16}O_7$

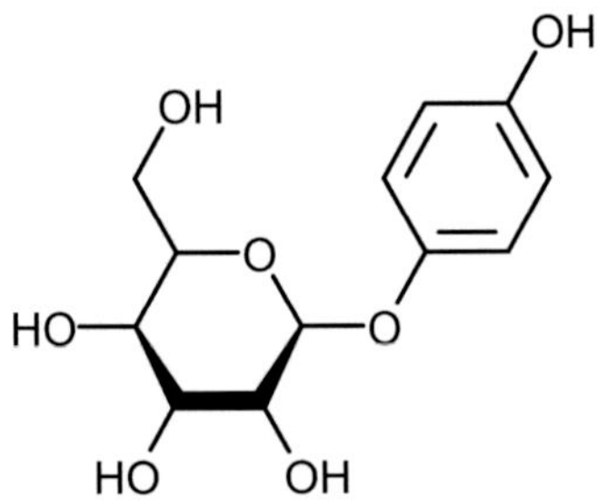

GENERAL

Arbutin is used in skin-lightening creams, which are used widely, especially by Asian women. It is a glycosylated hydroquinone produced by the bearberry that inhibits melanin production by decreasing tyrosinase activity (8). Contact dermatitis caused by arbutin has been reported in seven patients (see Case reports and case series). All patients were Japanese women and the average age was about 65 years. The allergic contact reactions were located on the face, mainly the cheeks, eyelids, and forehead. The dermatitis was mostly erythematous, sometimes also edematous (8).

CONTACT ALLERGY

Case reports and series

A Japanese woman presented with a 2-week history of redness and itching of the face. Clinical examination revealed erythema and edema on the face, mostly on the cheek and forehead. No leukoderma was observed. Contact dermatitis caused by an allergic response to a cosmetic cream was suspected. A ROAT with this cream resulted in erythema on the next day. Patch tests gave a positive reaction to the cosmetic cream. Testing with its ingredients showed a positive reaction to arbutin 3% water, but not to any of the other 31 components. Subsequent serial dilution patch tests were positive to arbutin 0.3% and 0.03%, doubtful to 0.003% and negative to 0.0003% water. Eight controls were negative (8). A woman had edematous pruritic erythema of the cheek and eyelid, caused by contact allergy to arbutin (2). Two older female individuals developed an allergic reaction to arbutin in whitening creams (3). Both had infiltrated erythema on the cheeks, eyelids and forehead, and one had a depigmented spot. Test concentrations used to demonstrate contact allergy to arbutin were 3% and 5% (3).

    A Japanese woman presented with a 9-month history of pruritic erythema on her cheeks and upper eyelids. She had used many cosmetics during this period. Allergic contact dermatitis caused by cosmetics was suspected. When patch tested, the patient reacted to a whitening lotion, which she had been using for more than a year. Additional patch testing was performed with all 18 ingredients of the whitening lotion, and only arbutin (5% pet.) elicited a positive reaction. After the patient had stopped using the whitening lotion, her facial erythema resolved (1). The Research Group of the Japanese Society for Contact Dermatitis in 2003 reported on two cases of contact allergy to arbutin used as whitening agent (4). Another Japanese woman had allergic facial contact dermatitis from arbutin in 2 skin-lightening products (9).

Cross-reactions, pseudo-cross-reactions and co-reactions

Part of the chemical structure of arbutin is similar to that of hydroquinone and *p*-phenylenediamine, and the possibility of cross-reactions with these chemicals has been suggested (3).

Presence in cosmetic products and chemical analyses

In the USA, in April 2017, arbutin was present in 171 of 56,714 cosmetic products of which the composition is known in FDA's Voluntary Cosmetic Registration Program (VCRP) (data obtained from FDA, May 2017). In January 2017, arbutin was present in 41 of 64,480 cosmetic products of which the composition is known in EWG's Skin Deep Cosmetics Database, USA (http://www.ewg.org/skindeep/).

LITERATURE

1 Matsuo Y, Ito A, Masui Y, Ito M. A case of allergic contact dermatitis caused by arbutin. Contact Dermatitis 2015;72:404-405

2 Sugawara K, Kobayashi H, Teramae K, et al. A case of contact dermatitis due to arbutin. Environ Dermatol 2002;9:146-148 (in Japanese)

3 Kanto H. Allergic contact dermatitis caused by new agents. J Environ Dermatol Cutan Allergol 2008;2:1-8 (in Japanese) (data cited in refs. 1 and 8)

4 Hizawa T, Research Group of Japanese Society for Contact Dermatitis (JSCD). Group study of the optimum patch testing concentrations of skin whitening agents and the results of patch testing with standard allergens of the Japanese Society for Contact Dermatitis in 2003. Environ Dermatol 2005;12:137-142 (in Japanese) (data cited in ref. 1)

5 SCCS (Scientific Committee on Consumer Safety). Opinion on α-arbutin, 27 May 2015, SCCS/1552/15. Available at: http://ec.europa.eu/health/scientific_committees/consumer_safety/docs/sccs_o_176.pdf

6 SCCS (Scientific Committee on Consumer Safety). Opinion on β-arbutin, SCCS/1550/15, 25 March 2015. Available at: http://ec.europa.eu/health/scientific_committees/consumer_safety/docs/sccs_o_169.pdf

7 SCCP (Scientific Committee on Consumer Products). Opinion on β-arbutin, 15 April 2008, SCCP/1158/08. Available at: http://ec.europa.eu/health/archive/ph_risk/committees/04_sccp/docs/sccp_o_134.pdf

8 Numata T, Tobita R, Tsuboi R, Okubo Y. Contact dermatitis caused by arbutin contained in skin-whitening cosmetics. Contact Dermatitis 2016;75:187-188

9 Oiso N, Tatebayashi M, Hoshiyama Y, Kawada A. Allergic contact dermatitis caused by arbutin and dipotassium glycyrrhizate in skin-lightening products. Contact Dermatitis 2017;77:51-53

2.28 ARGANIA SPINOSA (ARGAN) KERNEL OIL

IDENTIFICATION

Description/definition   : Argania spinosa kernel oil is the fixed oil expressed from the kernels of the African tree,
                            Argania spinosa, Sapotaceae
Chemical class(es)   : Fats and oils
Other names   : Argan oil
CAS registry number (s)   : 299184-75-1
CIR review(s)   : Final report, March 2011 (access: www.cir-safety.org/ingredients)
Function(s) in cosmetics : EU: emollient; skin conditioning. USA: skin-conditioning agents - emollient; skin-
                            conditioning agents – miscellaneous; skin-conditioning agents - occlusive
Patch testing   : 10% pet. and pure; these concentrations appear to be non-irritant

GENERAL

Argan oil is obtained following ancestral procedures by heating, roasting and pressing the nuts contained in fruits of *Argania spinosa* (Sapotaceae), an endemic tree growing in arid and semi-arid area in South-West Morocco. In that country, argan oil is traditionally used for its cosmetic, medicinal and nutritional properties (2,4). It is a complex mixture of acylglycerides (99%), primarily triglycerides of oleic acid, linoleic acid, palmitic acid and stearic acid, and unsaponifiable matter (1%). The latter contains triterpene alcohols, phenols (flavonoids), tocopherols, carotenes, sterols, and xanthophylls (4). The main natural phenols in argan oil are caffeic acid, oleuropein, vanillic acid, tyrosol, catechol, resorcinol, epicatechin, and catechin (3). The chemical composition of argan oils obtained by various methods and from various sources has been reviewed in 2014 (8).

Topical argan oil was historically used in Morocco as a photoprotector, anti-inflammatory agent, especially in eczemas, and an antiviral agent, especially in chicken pox. In some western European countries, such as Italy, topical argan oil has been recently launched in the market for the treatment of chronoaging and photoaging and as a moisturizer, particularly in postmenopausal women (3,7) and for nourishing the hair (3). The (potential) health benefits have been reviewed (4,8,9).

CONTACT ALLERGY

Case reports and case series

A patient had allergic contact dermatitis from argan oil in a moisturizing product used for scalp psoriasis. Patch tests and ROATs were positive to pure argan oil and argan oil 10% pet. (3). Another woman had an allergic reaction to argan perfume; she had positive patch tests to the perfume and to argan oil (5). Four women with allergic contact dermatitis caused by argan oil have been presented (6). All patients had applied a product containing argan oil for the treatment of dryness of the face or periocular wrinkles from 3 to 8 weeks before the occurrence of the rash. The products did not contain preservatives or fragrances. Dermatological examinations revealed dermatitis located especially at the periocular area and characterized by erythema and edema. All patients complained of pruritus and burning sensation. Patch tests were positive to argan oil as is and 10% pet. in these four women, whereas 10 healthy volunteers had negative results. All patients healed with mild desquamation and hyperpigmentation (6).

Contact allergy to argan oil from non-cosmetic sources

A child developed allergic contact dermatitis of the face from contact allergy to a colored pencil. When treated with argan oil, the eczema worsened. Patch tests were positive to pure argan oil and negative in controls (1). A woman had ACD of the neck from pure argan oil used to treat scalp psoriasis; she also reacted to argan perfume (5).

Cross-reactions, pseudo-cross-reactions and co-reactions

Not to olive oil (3,6).

Presence in cosmetic products and chemical analyses

In the USA, in April 2017, Argania spinosa (argan) kernel oil was present in 1118 of 56,714 cosmetic products of which the composition is known in FDA's Voluntary Cosmetic Registration Program (VCRP) (data obtained from FDA, May 2017). In February 2017, Argania spinose kernel oil was present in 681 of 64,631 cosmetic products of which the composition is known in EWG's Skin Deep Cosmetics Database, USA (http://www.ewg.org/skindeep/).

OTHER SIDE EFFECTS

Immediate-type reactions
A 34-year-old Moroccan man without allergy history reported rhinitis and conjunctivitis occurring when he smelled argan oil. The ingestion of argan oil induced epigastralgia and hypersalivation. Prick-tests to argan oil and argan paste (residue after oil extraction) were positive. Twenty minutes later, the patient developed a systemic reaction consisting of generalized erythema, beginning on the arms, with secondary urticarial lesions, dyspnoea and throat discomfort. The allergen was identified and proved to be a protein of 10 kDa (2).

LITERATURE

1   Barrientos N, Moreno de Vega M, Dominguez J. Allergic contact dermatitis caused by argan oil in an infant. Contact Dermatitis 2014;71:316-317
2   Astier C, Benchad Yel A, Moneret-Vautrin D A, Bihain BE, Kanny G. Anaphylaxis to argan oil. Allergy 2010;65:662-663
3   Foti C, Romita P, Ranieri LD, Bonamonte D. Allergic contact dermatitis caused by argan oil. Contact Dermatitis 2014;71:183-184
4   Monfalouti HE, Guillaume D, Denhez C, Charrouf Z. Therapeutic potential of argan oil: a review. J Pharm Pharmacol 2010;62:1669-1675
5   Lauriola MM, Corazza M. Allergic contact dermatitis caused by argan oil, neem oil, and *Mimosa tenuiflora*. Contact Dermatitis 2106;75:388-390
6   Veraldi S, Mascagni P, Tosi D, Brena M. Allergic contact dermatitis caused by argan oil. Dermatitis 2016;27:391
7   Boucetta KQ, Charrouf Z, Aguenaou H, Derouiche A, Bensouda Y. Does argan oil have a moisturizing effect on the skin of postmenopausal women? Skin Res Technol 2013;19:356-357
8   El Abbassi A, Khalid N, Zbakh H, Ahmad A. Physicochemical characteristics, nutritional properties, and health benefits of argan oil: a review. Crit Rev Food Sci Nutr 2014;54:1401-1414
9   Guillaume D, Charrouf Z. Argan oil. Monograph. Altern Med Rev 2011;16:275-279

2.29 ARNICA MONTANA EXTRACT

IDENTIFICATION

Description/definition   : Arnica montana extract is the extract of the whole plant, *Arnica montana*, Asteraceae
                            (Asteraceae are currently termed Compositae)
Chemical class(es)   : Botanical products and botanical derivatives
CAS registry number (s)   : 68990-11-4
EC number(s)   : 273-579-2
CIR review(s)   : Int J Toxicol 2001;20(Suppl.2):1-11 (access: www.cir-safety.org/ingredients)
Merck Index monograph   : 2050 (Arnica)
Function(s) in cosmetics : EU: skin conditioning. USA: skin-conditioning agents - miscellaneous
Patch testing   : 0.5% pet. (Chemotechnique); also present in the Compositae mix II (Chemotechnique)

GENERAL

Arnica montana is one of the most important European medicinal plants (7). It was first used as a folk remedy and from the 18th century on also officinally (17). In Germany, extracts of arnica flowers were constituents of more than 200 commercial phytomedicinal products in the 1980s (7,9). Arnica has anti-inflammatory effects and is perceived as wound-healing. Extracts from the flower heads, leaves, stalks, and roots are mainly used in topical remedies for bruises, muscle strains, crush injuries, hematomas, rheumatism, neuralgia, ischialgia, and venous circulatory disorders. It is also used in sanitary products, 'natural', 'herbal' or conventional cosmetics, herbal liquors, massage oils, first-aid ointments, and wound dressings. The most widely used form is arnica tincture, an ethanol-based extract, which is applied in compresses and bandages for sprains and minor sports-related injuries (7,10,17,21).

Both the weed, the commercially available drug and some of the sesquiterpene lactones in the plants and extracts have a strong sensitizing and irritant capacity. Important sesquiterpene lactone allergens include helenalin, its acetate and methacrylate, carabron, dihydrohelenalin acetate, arnecolid D, arnifolin and xanthalongin (5,7,10,17,19). It is therefore not surprising that, in a 1980 literature review of arnica allergy, more than 100 reported cases of allergic contact dermatitis from arnica between 1844 and 1977 (35 publications) were listed (7). The majority of these were ascribed to the use of the undiluted tincture of arnica (which contains the sesquiterpene lactones) (7). In Germany, in a large 1985-1990 study, about 25% of patients reacting to arnica extract were mono-sensitized (i.e. not to other Compositae plants), probably reflecting the widespread use of tincture of arnica in that country (4).

Discussion of *Arnica montana* in this chapter is limited to its extracts and products containing them.

CONTACT ALLERGY

Testing in groups of patients
There is one published study in which arnica extract has been patch tested in consecutive patients suspected of contact dermatitis (routine testing). In Austria, in 2000, 443 consecutive patients were patch tested with arnica extract 0.5% pet. and 5 (1.1%) had a positive reaction. Three of the 5 remembered having used arnica as a topical remedy (14).

Studies in which groups of *selected* patients have been tested with arnica are shown in table 2.29.1. In three of these investigations, patients were sensitive to Compositae and/or had previously reacted to the Compositae mix and were subsequently tested with its 5 ingredients, including arnica (4,20,23). Between 23% and 52% reacted to arnica; these rates are lower than of any other ingredient (*Achillea millefolium, Chamomilla recutita, Tanacetum parthenium, Tanacetum vulgare*, see the individual chapters). In a group of 122 patients suspected of contact dermatitis with self-declared adverse reactions to 'botanical products' (cosmetics, detergents, pharmaceutical ointments), only one (0.8%) reacted to arnica extract 0.5% pet. (24). Relevance in the groups of Compositae-sensitive individuals was either not provided or related to the Compositae mix, but was never provided for its ingredient Arnica extract. In a large group of patients with stasis dermatitis/chronic leg ulcers, there was a relatively high percentage of positive reactions to Arnica blossom extract, but their relevance was not provided (26).

Case reports and case series
In a group of 119 patients with allergic contact dermatitis from cosmetics, investigated in The Netherlands in 1986-1987, one case was caused by arnica extract in a herbal cosmetic (1,2). One patient had allergic contact dermatitis from arnica extract in a jogging cream used to prevent blisters during walking trips (3). A woman developed dermatitis of the auditory canal after washing her hair with a shampoo containing arnica, to which she was allergic (4). In a German study performed between 1985 and 1990, a group of 118 patients reacted to the Compositae mix consisting of five ingredients: arnica (*Arnica montana* L.), German chamomile (*Chamomilla recutita*), feverfew (*Tanacetum*

parthenium), tansy (*Tanacetum vulgare*) and yarrow (*Achillea millefolium*). In 4 patients, the sensitization was caused by 'natural cosmetics', in 3 by 'natural ointments', in one by a herbal massage oil and in one (probably) by a herbal shampoo, soap and ointment. However, it was not specified, which of the five plant extracts was/were the actual sensitizer(s) in these products (4). In a 4-month-period in 1996, 475 patients with contact allergy to 'cosmetic ingredients' were collected in 5 centres in Belgium, UK and Germany. There was one reaction to arnica; relevance was not stated (13).

Table 2.29.1 Patch testing in groups of patients: Selected patient groups

Years and Country	Test conc. & vehicle	Number of patients tested | positive (%)		Selection of patients (S); Relevance (R); Comments (C)	Ref.
2003-2014 IVDK	0.5% pet.	<4756	(5.1%)	S: patients with stasis dermatitis/ chronic leg ulcers; R: not stated	26
2011-2012 Italy	0.5% pet.	122 1	(0.8%)	S: patients tested with a botanical series, who declared having had adverse reactions to 'botanical' products (cosmetics, detergents, pharmaceutical ointments); R: the reaction was considered to be relevant	24
2000-2007 USA	0.5% pet.	544 2	(0.4%)	S: patients tested with a supplemental cosmetic screening series; R: 100%; C: weak study: a. high rate of macular erythema and weak reactions; b. relevance figures included 'questionable' and 'past' relevance	27
2000-2004 Denmark	1% pet.	76 20	(26%)	S: patients reacting to the Compositae mix 6% (Trolab); R: 80% of positive reactions to all components of the mix together were considered to be relevant (current or past)	23
1990-1998 Denmark	0.5% pet.	129 30	(23%)	S: patients sensitive to Compositae; R: not stated	20
1985-1990 Germany	0.5% pet.	85 44	(52%)	S: patients reacting to the Compositae mix; R: nearly all reactions to the Compositae mix were relevant and were most often caused by contact with plants, some by 'natural' cosmetics; thirty-three (28%) patients were occupationally sensitized (e.g., florists, gardeners) and 11 (9.3%) had air-borne allergic contact dermatitis. The relevance of the reactions to the individual ingredients of the Compositae mix including arnica was not specified	4

IVDK: Information Network of Departments of Dermatology, Germany, Austria, Switzerland

Contact allergy to Arnica montana extract in non-cosmetic products
In a review article on arnica allergy, more than 100 reported cases published between 1844 and 1977 were presented (7). Four more patients with allergic contact dermatitis from arnica tincture were reported by the author of the review. The majority of the cases have been ascribed to the use of the – often inexpediently undiluted – sesquiterpene lactones-containing tincture of arnica. Occupational contact dermatitis in drug sellers or pharmacists is rare (7). One patient had acute ACD from arnica tincture (9). Occupational ACD from arnica in massage oils has been observed (7). Two patients had positive patch tests to a herbal ointment containing 10% arnica extract. However, they both also reacted to lanolin, which was a constituent of the ointment, arnica itself was not tested and the relevance of the reactions was uncertain (15).

A woman developed ACD from an infusion of Flores arnicae (the officinal term for arnica flowers) applied to an abrasion. She had previously become sensitized by contact with *Arnica montana* plants in her garden and had a strongly positive patch test to fluid pressed from the stem of the plant. Controls tests were not performed for fear of active sensitization (16). Two patients were sensitized to arnica tincture applied to wounds (17). A man developed acute allergic contact dermatitis after applying a wet dressing with 10% arnica tincture to a minor swelling of the right hand after an accidental trauma. Previously, he had often applied arnica tincture to rosacea of the face, which was probably the source of sensitization (19).

Cross-reactions, pseudo-cross-reactions and co-reactions
Cross-reactivity may occur with chrysanthemums, sunflower and other Compositae species and their extracts (9,10,11,12,18,20,25). Fragrance mix I (14); *Myroxylon pereirae* resin (14,19); propolis (14).

Provocation tests
Six patients known to be allergic to arnica were patch tested with 6 pharmaceutical and cosmetic products containing arnica extract. One patient had negative reactions, 3 reacted to one product, one to two products and one individual reacted positively to three arnica-containing products. Three patient were patch tested with

ingredients of the products and they all reacted to arnica tincture or a combination tincture of arnica and sunflower. The authors concluded that Compositae-sensitive patients should be warned against the topical use of Compositae-containing cosmetics and herbal remedies, including herbal teas and other aqueous extracts and essential oils (5).

Eight patients previously diagnosed with arnica allergy were tested with three different arnica extracts, 4 commercial preparations containing arnica (tincture 25%, gel and ointment with 0.013% sesquiterpene lactones, oil 1%), the sesquiterpene-lactone mix and 3 sesquiterpene lactones known to be present in *Arnica montana* (22). All 8 reacted to one or more of the extracts, 4 to one or more of the commercial preparations, 2 to the sesquiterpene-lactone mix and two to a sesquiterpene lactone, dihydrohelenalin methacrylate (22).

Presence in cosmetic products and chemical analyses

In the USA, in April 2017, Arnica montana (arnica) flower extract was present in 327 of 56,714 cosmetic products of which the composition is known in FDA's Voluntary Cosmetic Registration Program (VCRP) (data obtained from FDA, May 2017). In February 2017, *Arnica montana* and its extract were present in 249 of 64,480 cosmetic products of which the composition is known in EWG's Skin Deep Cosmetics Database, USA (http://www.ewg.org/skindeep/).

OTHER SIDE EFFECTS

Irritant contact dermatitis

Undiluted arnica tincture may cause irritant dermatitis (7).

Photosensitivity

In a study performed in the USA in 1993-1996, 76 patients were photopatch tested with Arnica montana extract 0.5% pet. There was one (1%) positive photopatch test. However, it was not mentioned how the patient group had been selected nor what the relevance of the observed reactions was (28).

Other non-eczematous contact reactions

In one patient, a cream containing 1.5% arnica extract may have precipitated leukemia-related Sweet's syndrome (8).

LITERATURE

1   De Groot AC, Bruynzeel DP, Bos JD, van der Meeren HL, van Joost T, Jagtman BA, Weyland JW. The allergens in cosmetics. Arch Dermatol 1988;124:1525-1529
2   De Groot AC. Adverse reactions to cosmetics. PhD Thesis, University of Groningen, The Netherlands: 1988, chapter 3.4, pp.105-113
3   De Leeuw J, den Hollander P. A patient with a contact allergy to jogging cream. Contact Dermatitis 1987;17:260-261
4   Hausen BM. A 6-year experience with Compositae mix. Am J Cont Derm 1996;7:94-99
5   Paulsen E, Chistensen LP, Andersen KE. Cosmetics and herbal remedies with Compositae plant extracts – are they tolerated by Compositae-allergic patients? Contact Dermatitis 2008;58:15-23
6   Paulsen E. Contact sensitization from Compositae-containing herbal remedies and cosmetics. Contact Dermatitis 2002;47:189-198
7   Hausen BM. Arnika Allergie. Hautarzt 1980;31:10-17
8   Delmonte S, Brusati C, Parodi A, Rebora A. Leukemia-related Sweet's syndrome elicited by pathergy to arnica. Dermatology 1998;197:195-196
9   Hörmann H P, Korting H C. Akute allergische Kontaktdermatitis auf Arnika-Tinktur. Dermatosen 1994;42:246-249
10   Hausen BM. Allergiepflanzen/Pflanzenallergene: Handbuch und Atlas der allergie-induzierenden Wild-und Kulturpflanzen, 2nd Edition. Landsberg/München: Ecomed Verlagsgesellschaft, 1997
11   Machet L, Vaillant L, Callens A, Demasure M, Barruet K, Lorette G. Allergic contact dermatitis from sunflower (*Helianthus annuus*) with cross-sensitivity to arnica. Contact Dermatitis 1993;28:184-185
12   Hausen BM, Oestmann G. The incidence of occupationally-induced allergic skin diseases in a large flower market. Derm Beruf Umwelt 1988;36:117-124 (article in German)
13   Goossens A, Beck MH, Haneke E, McFadden JP, Nolting S, Durupt G, Ries G. Adverse cutaneous reactions to cosmetic allergens. Contact Dermatitis 1999;40:112-113
14   Reider N, Komericki P, Hausen BM, Fritsch P, Aberer W. The seamy side of natural medicines: contact sensitization to arnica (*Arnica montana* L.) and marigold (*Calendula officinalis* L.). Contact Dermatitis 2001;45:269-272
15   Bruynzeel DP, van Ketel WG, Young E, van Joost Th, Smeenk G. Contact sensitization by alternative topical medicaments containing plant extracts. Contact Dermatitis 1992;27:278-279
16   Rudzki R, Grzywa A. Dermatitis from *Arnica montana*. Contact Dermatitis 1977;3:281
17   Hausen BM. Identification of the allergens of *Arnica montana* L. Contact Dermatitis 1978;4:308

18 Pirker C, Möslinger T, Koller DY, Göutz M, Jarisch R. Cross-reactivity with *Tagetes* in *Arnica* contact eczema. Contact Dermatitis 1992;26:217-219

19 Hörmann HP, Korting HC. Allergic acute contact dermatitis due to *Arnica* tincture self-medication. Phytomedicine 1995;1:315-317

20 Paulsen E, Andersen KE, Hausen BM. Sensitization and cross-reaction patterns in Danish Compositae-allergic patients. Contact Dermatitis 2001;45:197-204

21 Aberer W. Contact allergy and medicinal herbs. J Dtsch Dermatol Ges 2008;6:15-24

22 Jocher A, Nist G, Weiss JM, Wetzel D, Merfort I, Jakob T, Schempp CM. Allergenic potential of Arnica-containing formulations in Arnica-allergic patients. Contact Dermatitis 2009;61:304-306

23 Paulsen E, Andersen KE. Patch testing with constituents of Compositae mixes. Contact Dermatitis 2012;66:241-246

24 Corazza M, Borghi A, Gallo R, Schena D, Pigatto P, Lauriola MM, et al. Topical botanically derived products: use, skin reactions, and usefulness of patch tests. A multicentre Italian study. Contact Dermatitis 2014;70:90-97

25 Hausen BM. The sensitizing capacity of Compositae plants. III. Test results and cross-reactions in Compositae-sensitive patients. Dermatologica 1979;159:1-11

26 Erfurt-Berge C, Geier J, Mahler V. The current spectrum of contact sensitization in patients with chronic leg ulcers or stasis dermatitis - new data from the Information Network of Departments of Dermatology (IVDK). Contact Dermatitis 2017 Feb 14. doi: 10.1111/cod.12763. [Epub ahead of print]

27 Wetter DA, Yiannias JA, Prakash AV, Davis MD, Farmer SA, el-Azhary RA, et al. Results of patch testing to personal care product allergens in a standard series and a supplemental cosmetic series: an analysis of 945 patients from the Mayo Clinic Contact Dermatitis Group, 2000-2007. J Am Acad Dermatol 2010;63:789-798

28 Victor FC, Cohen DE, Soter NA. A 20-year analysis of previous and emerging allergens that elicit photoallergic contact dermatitis. J Am Acad Dermatol 2010;62:605-610

2.30 ASCORBIC ACID

IDENTIFICATION

Description/definition   : Ascorbic acid is the organic compound that conforms to the formula shown below
Chemical class(es)   : Heterocyclic compounds; polyols
Chemical/IUPAC name   : (2R)-2-[(1S)-1,2-Dihydroxyethyl]-3,4-dihydroxy-2H-furan-5-one
Other names   : Vitamin C
CAS registry number (s)   : 50-81-7; 62624-30-0
EC number(s)   : 200-066-2; 263-644-3
CIR review(s)   : Int J Toxicol 2005;24(Suppl.2):51-111 (access: www.cir-safety.org/ingredients)
Merck Index monograph   : 2089
Function(s) in cosmetics   : EU: antioxidant; buffering; masking; skin conditioning. USA: antioxidants; fragrance
                               ingredients; skin-conditioning agents – miscellaneous; pH adjusters
Patch testing   : 5% water (3); pure (7): suggested test concentration and vehicle: 5% pet.
Molecular formula   : $C_6H_8O_6$

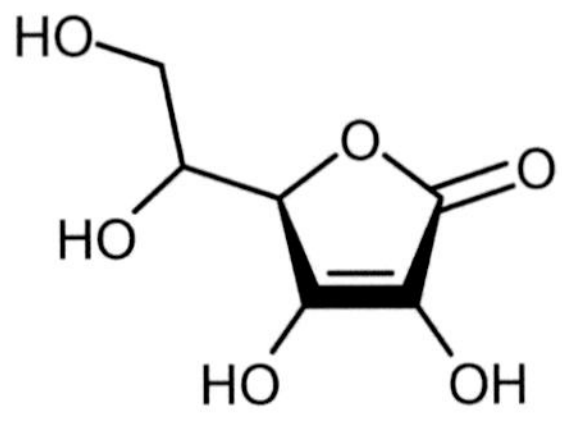

GENERAL

Ascorbic acid (vitamin C) is a six carbon compound related to glucose. It is found naturally in citrus fruits and many vegetables. It is an essential nutrient in human diets, and necessary to maintain connective tissue and bone. Its biologically active form, vitamin C, functions as a reducing agent and coenzyme in several metabolic pathways and is considered an antioxidant. Antioxidants are photoprotective, and are nowadays frequently used in anti-aging products (2). Ascorbic acid is extremely unstable and is therefore often chemically modified by esterification of the hydroxyl group, leading to derivatives such as ascorbyl tetraisopalmitate or ascorbyl palmitate (2).

CONTACT ALLERGY

Patch testing in groups of patients

Ascorbic acid has been patch tested in one study in a group of selected patients, who were patch tested with an supplemental cosmetic screening series. In this 2000-2007 USA study, 869 patients were patch tested with ascorbic acid 5% pet.; 14 individuals (1.6%) had a positive reaction. Thirteen reactions (86%) were considered to be relevant, but the causative or suspected products were nog mentioned. Also, in this study, there was a high rate of macular erythema (counted as positive patch test) and weak reactions, and relevance figures included 'questionable' and 'past' relevance (1).

Case reports and case series

A woman presented with a 3-month history of dermatitis of the face, which had consisted initially of edematous erythematous lesions on the eyelids, and then spread to the remainder of the face and the folds of the neck. Patch tests were performed with the European standard series and cosmetic, fragrance and plant series, as well as with five of the cosmetic products used by the patient. There was a positive reaction to a cosmetic cream. Subsequent patch tests with the ingredients of this cream showed positivity only to ascorbic acid 5% water. Twenty controls were negative to the same preparation of vitamin C. Oral provocation tests were then performed with 50, 100, 500, 1000 and 2000 mg of ascorbic acid, also with negative results. Discontinuation of the use of the cosmetic product resulted in complete healing of the eczema without relapse during 6 months (3).

Contact allergy to ascorbic acid in non-cosmetic products

A patient developed widespread dermatitis due to allergy to oral vitamin C. A patch test with pure vitamin C was positive and 30 controls negative. Oral provocation with 2 gram of vitamin C elicited an eczematous eruption after twenty hours. A vitamin C-free diet led to complete resolution of the skin problems (7).

Cross-reactions, pseudo-cross-reactions and co-reactions

Not to ascorbyl tetraisopalmitate (2).

Presence in cosmetic products and chemical analyses
In the USA, in April 2017, ascorbic acid was present in 3022 of 56,714 cosmetic products of which the composition is known in FDA's Voluntary Cosmetic Registration Program (VCRP) (data obtained from FDA, May 2017). In January 2017, ascorbic acid was present in 1067 of 64,480 cosmetic products of which the composition is known in EWG's Skin Deep Cosmetics Database, USA (http://www.ewg.org/skindeep/).

Other information
In patients sensitized to *p*-phenylenediamine, pre-treatment with a cream or emulsion containing ascorbic acid can lead to a reduction in the intensity, or ablation, of the cutaneous allergic reaction to *p*-phenylenediamine and hair dye patch tests in 50-75% of cases as compared to untreated skin or the emulsion without ascorbic acid (8,10).

OTHER SIDE EFFECTS

Miscellaneous side effects
A 51-year-old man developed scurvy from vitamin C-deficiency caused by deliberate elimination of vitamin C-rich foods from his diet. The reason for doing this was presumed allergy to vitamin C, characterized by hives within an hour of ingesting oral ascorbic acid supplements, after consuming oranges during childhood, drinking orange soda as a teenager, and after exposure to orange peel zest. Skin prick testing by his childhood allergist had revealed reactivity to oranges. Instead of testing the patient for allergy to ascorbic acid (patch tests, prick tests, scratch tests, oral provocation), the investigators desensitized him and gave the patient oral ascorbic acid, which made the scurvy heal. Allergy to ascorbic acid has, according to the authors, never been proven, but neither did they (9).

The occurrence of ascorbic acid-induced allergic asthma has been described in an early report from France. The sensitivity to vitamin C was verified by positive skin tests and a positive Prausnitz-Küstner reaction (6). An urticarial hemorrhagic exanthema developed in an 11-year-old girl after oral intake of vitamin C tablets (4). In a further observation from this early German investigator, a generalized itching papular exanthema appeared in a patient after the third intravenous injection of a vitamin C-containing medicament; epicutaneous and intracutaneous skin tests with vitamin C were positive (4). Fatal anaphylactic shock from injection of vitamin C apparently caused by allergy to ascorbic acid has been described in a report from Russia (5).

LITERATURE

1 Wetter DA, Yiannias JA, Prakash AV, Davis MD, Farmer SA, el-Azhary RA, et al. Results of patch testing to personal care product allergens in a standard series and a supplemental cosmetic series: an analysis of 945 patients from the Mayo Clinic Contact Dermatitis Group, 2000-2007. J Am Acad Dermatol 2010;63:789-798

2 Swinnen I, Goossens A. Allergic contact dermatitis caused by ascorbyl tetraisopalmitate. Contact Dermatitis 2011;64:241-242

3 Belhadjali H, Giordano-Labadie F, Bazex J. Contact dermatitis from vitamin C in a cosmetic anti-aging cream. Contact Dermatitis 2001;45:317

4 Rust S. Über allergische Reaktionen bei Vitamintherapie. Zeitschr Haut Geschl Kr 1954;17:317-319 (cited in refs. 3 and 7)

5 Severova E. Anaphylactic shock due to sensitisation to ascorbic acid. Klin Med (Mosk) 1972;50:130-131 (cited in refs. 3 and 7)

6 Panzani N. Un cas d'asthme par sensibilisation à l'acide ascorbique. Presse Médicale 1961;69:1928 (cited in refs. 3 and 7)

7 Metz J, Hundertmark U, Pevny I. Vitamin C allergy of the delayed type. Contact Dermatitis 1980;6:172-174

8 Basketter DA, White IR, Kullavanijaya P, Tresukosol P, Wichaidit M, McFadden JP. Influence of vitamin C on the elicitation of allergic contact dermatitis to *p*-phenylenediamine. Contact Dermatitis 2016;74:368-372

9 Shaath T, Fischer R, Goeser M, Rajpara A, Aires D. Scurvy in the present times: vitamin C allergy leading to strict fast food diet. Dermatol Online J 2016;22(1). pii: 13030/qt50b8w28b.

10 Coenraads PJ, Vogel TA, Blömeke B, Goebel C, Roggeband R, Schuttelaar ML. The role of the antioxidant ascorbic acid in the elicitation of contact allergic reactions to *p*-phenylenediamine. Contact Dermatitis 2016;74:267-272

2.31 ASCORBYL TETRAISOPALMITATE

IDENTIFICATION

Description/definition	: Ascorbyl tetraisopalmitate is the tetraester of ascorbic acid and isopalmitic acid. It conforms generally to the formula shown below, where RCO- represents the isopalmitic acid moiety
Chemical class(es)	: Esters
Other names	: L-Ascorbic acid, tetraisohexadecanoate
CAS registry number (s)	: 161436-56-2
Function(s) in cosmetics	: EU: antioxidant; emollient; skin conditioning. USA: antioxidants; skin-conditioning agents - emollient
Patch testing	: 20% paraffinum liquidum (twenty controls were negative) (2); 0.05% (vehicle?: liquid paraffin or water) (3)
Molecular formula	: $C_{70}H_{128}O_{10}$

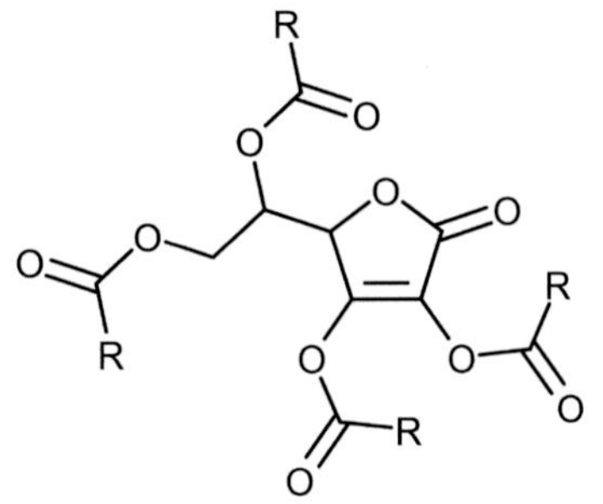

GENERAL

Ascorbyl tetraisopalmitate is a lipid-soluble synthetic derivative of ascorbic acid, used as an antioxidant, emollient, and skin conditioning agent. Antioxidants are photoprotective, and are nowadays frequently used in anti-aging products. One of the most frequently used antioxidants is ascorbic acid, which is extremely unstable. Therefore, it is often chemically modified by esterification of the hydroxyl group, leading to derivatives such as ascorbyl tetraisopalmitate and ascorbyl palmitate. Ascorbyl tetraisopalmitate can also be found in other cosmetic products such as sunscreens, depigmenting creams (2) and moisturizers (3).

CONTACT ALLERGY

Case reports and case series

Ascorbyl tetraisopalmitate was stated to be the (or an) allergen in one patient in a group of 603 individuals suffering from cosmetic dermatitis, seen in the period 2010-2015 in Leuven, Belgium (4). Ascorbyl tetraisopalmitate was responsible for 1 out of 959 cases of non-fragrance cosmetic allergy where the causal allergen was identified, Belgium, 2000-2010 (1). A woman presented with a history of a skin reaction 2 days after the first application of an anti-aging skin care product. The reaction had started on the face, and spread to the arms and chest. Patch testing with the European baseline series, a cosmetic series, a pharmaceutical series and her own products was performed. There was a positive reaction to the cream, tested as is. A repeated open application test (ROAT) with this product became positive after 3 days. Four months later, additional patch testing with the ingredients of the anti-aging skin care product revealed a strong positive reaction to ascorbyl tetraisopalmitate, diluted 20% in liquid paraffin. Twenty control subjects gave negative results on patch testing to this substance. In order to look for possible cross-reactions, additional testing was performed with ascorbyl palmitate (5% in alcohol), isopropyl palmitate (as is), and ascorbic acid (5% in water), but all remained negative. During this second test session, the patient presented with a flare-up on the cheeks and upper arm, the latter being at the ROAT site of application with the cream (2).

Another patient had allergic contact dermatitis manifesting as exacerbation of atopic dermatitis from ascorbyl tetraisopalmitate present in a non-steroidal moisturizer used in the management of atopic dermatitis. The concentration of ascorbyl tetraisopalmitate in the product, which is actually a cosmetic product, though it is marketed as a non-steroidal topical pharmaceutical product, was 0.05%, which was also the concentration used for patch testing (liquid paraffin or water, unspecified). The patient tolerated ascorbic acid in foods well (3).

Cross-reactions, pseudo-cross-reactions and co-reactions

No cross-reactions were observed in one patient to ascorbyl palmitate (5% in alcohol), isopropyl palmitate (as is), or ascorbic acid (5% in water) (2).

Presence in cosmetic products and chemical analyses

In the USA, in April 2017, ascorbyl tetraisopalmitate was present in 152 of 56,714 cosmetic products of which the composition is known in FDA's Voluntary Cosmetic Registration Program (VCRP) (data obtained from FDA, May 2017). In February 2016, ascorbyl tetraisopalmitate was present in 42 of 64,631 cosmetic products of which the composition is known in EWG's Skin Deep Cosmetics Database, USA (http://www.ewg.org/skindeep/).

LITERATURE

1   Travassos AR, Claes L, Boey L, Drieghe J, Goossens A. Non-fragrance allergens in specific cosmetic products. Contact Dermatitis 2011;65:276-285
2   Swinnen I, Goossens A. Allergic contact dermatitis caused by ascorbyl tetraisopalmitate. Contact Dermatitis 2011;64:241-242
3   Assier H, Wolkenstein P, Grille C, Chosidow O. Contact dermatitis caused by ascorbyl tetraisopalmitate in a cream used for the management of atopic dermatitis. Contact Dermatitis 2014;71:60-61
4   Goossens A. Cosmetic contact allergens. Cosmetics 2016, 3, 5; doi:10.3390/cosmetics3010005

2.32 AVENA SATIVA (OAT) BRAN EXTRACT

IDENTIFICATION

Description/definition	: Avena sativa bran extract is an extract of the bran of the oat, *Avena sativa* L., Poaceae
Chemical class(es)	: Botanical products and botanical derivatives
INCI name USA	: Avena sativa (oat) bran extract
Other names	: Oat bran extract
CAS registry number (s)	: 84012-26-0
EC number(s)	: 281-672-4
Function(s) in cosmetics	: EU: abrasive. USA: skin-conditioning agents - miscellaneous
Patch testing	: Oat extract 5% pet. (1) or water (10); extract, undiluted (5)

GENERAL

Oat (*Avena sativa*) is a cereal grain belonging to the Poaceae (Graminaceae) family that is grown to harvest for its seeds. Various over-the-counter moisturizers contain oat proteins, often referred to as colloidal oatmeal, which is produced by finely grinding the oat and boiling it to extract. Colloidal oatmeal consists of polysaccharides, protein, lipids, saponins, vitamins, polyphenols, and flavonoids. The high concentration of starch and β-glucan is responsible for the water-holding function, whereas phenols are supposed to have antioxidant and anti-inflammatory activity and also should act as ultraviolet absorbers. The cleansing activity of oat is from saponins (8,9). Other forms of oat used as an ingredient in personal care products include oat bran, oat kernel, oat peptide or protein, and oat starch. Oat-containing moisturizers have been widely used as topical treatment of certain skin conditions, especially atopic dermatitis (8).

Discussion of side effects of Avena sativa bran extract is limited to reactions caused by its presence in cosmetic products. A review of contact urticaria caused by ingredients of cosmetics has been provided in ref. 11.

CONTACT ALLERGY

Testing in groups of patients

Positive patch tests to oat extract present in their emollient was seen in 2.6% of atopic patients, but they probably did not have clinical symptoms (no details known, article not read, ref. 2).

Case reports and case series

Avena sativa (oatmeal) extract was stated to be the (or an) allergen in one patient in a group of 603 individuals suffering from cosmetic dermatitis, seen in the period 2010-2015 in Leuven, Belgium (7). In a group of 641 children with atopic dermatitis patch tested with their emollients, 17 (3%) had positive reactions. Nine were subsequently patch tested with the ingredients of these cosmetic products and in five, Avena extract, tested 5% pet. was the responsible allergen. It was not mentioned whether the patients had previously reacted to these products (probably not, they were using them at the time of patch testing) and whether ceasing their use improved the atopic dermatitis (1).

A child developed worsening of atopic dermatitis from contact allergy to oat extract in an emollient; the prick test was also positive but she had no contact urticaria. The patient had complete regression of her dermatitis after avoiding further contact with the cosmetic cream (5). Three children had exacerbations of atopic dermatitis after bathing with an 'oatmeal product'. A patch test with 'oatmeal' (not further specified) was positive as were RAST tests showing the presence of IgE antibodies; after stopping the use of the bath oatmeal product the dermatitis improved in all patients (6). A woman who had suffered from allergic contact dermatitis caused by hair dye reacted upon patch testing to a cosmetic cream. When tested with its ingredients, there were multiple positive reactions including to Avena sativa oat extract 5% water (10).

Provocation tests

In twenty-five children with atopic dermatitis, who reacted to either an atopy patch test (n=17) and/or a skin prick test (n=10) with oat extract, a ROAT was performed with a moisturizing cream containing 3.25% oat extract and omega-6 polyunsaturated fatty acids. Seven (28%) had a positive repeated open application test, which was more often positive in children with a positive atopy patch test than in those only reacting to the skin prick test. Probably about ¾ or more had previously used moisturizing creams containing oat extract, but it was not specified for this subgroup of the study population of 67 children, how many had previously experienced clinical reactions. This study does show, however, that children sensitized to oat may be at risk of developing allergic contact dermatitis or worsening of atopic dermatitis from moisturizers containing oat extract (12).

Presence in cosmetic products and chemical analyses
In the USA, in April 2017, Avena sativa (oat) bran extract was present in 9 of 56,714 cosmetic products of which the composition is known in FDA's Voluntary Cosmetic Registration Program (VCRP) (data obtained from FDA, May 2017). In April 2017, Avena sativa (oat) bran extract was present in 10 of 66,647 cosmetic products of which the composition is known in EWG's Skin Deep Cosmetics Database, USA (http://www.ewg.org/skindeep/).

OTHER SIDE EFFECTS

Immediate-type reactions
A woman suffering from atopic dermatitis and allergic rhinoconjunctivitis developed an itchy and erythematous eruption with papules and patchy lesions on the face immediately after the application of a moisturizer emollient cream. She had been using this cream for approximately one year, but the symptoms had been present for about six months. The skin lesions were localized at the application site and faded a few hours after the application. Later on, the patient noticed that immediately after eating certain biscuits or bread containing oatmeal, she experienced itching and swelling of her lips, as well as pruritic, erythematous papules and patchy lesions on the trunk. Patch tests with the European baseline series and the patient's own cosmetic products were negative. A prick tests with the cream 'as is' was positive and a blood sample showed slightly elevated specific IgE-antibodies to oat. Further prick tests with the different components of the cream showed a positive reaction to Avena sativa alcoholic extract (3).

A woman applied 'oat cream' after bathing and developed contact urticaria after 15 minutes. The patient reacted to an open application test and to a skin (prick?) test with the cream; the colloidal suspension of oats that was present in the cream itself was not tested. The authors nevertheless considered it to be an IgE-mediated reaction to this ingredient, as oat-specific IgE was demonstrated (4).

LITERATURE

1   Mailhol C, Lauwers-Cances V, Rancé F, Paul C, Giordano-Labadie F. Prevalence and risk factors for allergic contact dermatitis to topical treatment in atopic dermatitis: a study in 641 children. Allergy 2009:64:801-806
2   Rancé F, Dargassies J, Dupuy P, et al. Faut-il contre-indiquer l'utilisation des émollients à base d'avoine chez l'enfant atopique. Rev Fr Allergol Immunol Clin 2001;41:477-483
3   Vansina S, Debilde D, Morren M-A, Goossens A. Sensitizing oat extracts in cosmetic creams: is there an alternative? Contact Dermatitis 2010;63:169-171
4   De Paz Arranz S, Pérez Montero A, Zapatero Remón L, Martínez Molero MI. Allergic contact urticaria to oatmeal. Allergy 2002;57:1215
5   Pazzaglia M, Jorizzo M, Parente G, Tosti A. Allergic contact dermatitis due to avena extract. Contact Dermatitis 2000;42:364
6   Riboldi A, Pigato P, Altomare G, Gibelli E. Contact allergic dermatitis from oatmeal. Contact Dermatitis 1988;18:316
7   Goossens A. Cosmetic contact allergens. Cosmetics 2016, 3, 5; doi:10.3390/cosmetics3010005
8   Pootongkam S, Nedorost S. Oat and wheat as contact allergens in personal care products. Dermatitis 2013;24:291-295
9   Kurtz ES, Wallo W. Colloidal oatmeal: history, chemistry, and clinical properties. J Drugs Dermatol 2007;6:167-170
10 Madsen JT, Andersen KE. 2-Amino-4-hydroxyethylaminoanisole sulfate – a coupler causing contact allergy from use in hair dyes. Contact Dermatitis 2016;74:102-104
11 Verhulst L, Goossens A. Cosmetic components causing contact urticaria: a review and update. Contact Dermatitis 2016;75:333-344
12 Boussault P, Léauté-Labrèze C, Saubusse E, Maurice-Tison S, Perromat M, Roul S, et al. Oat sensitization in children with atopic dermatitis: prevalence, risks and associated factors. Allergy 2007;62:1251-1256

2.33 AZULENE

IDENTIFICATION

Description/definition   : Azulene is an organic compound that conforms to the formula shown below
Chemical class(es)   : Hydrocarbons
Chemical/IUPAC name   : Azulene
Other names   : Cyclopentacycloheptene; bicyclo[5.3.0]decapentaene
CAS registry number (s)   : 275-51-4
EC number(s)   : 205-993-6
CIR review(s)   : Int J Toxicol 1999;18(Suppl.3):27-32 (access: www.cir-safety.org/ingredients)
Merck Index monograph   : 2189
Function(s) in cosmetics   : EU: skin conditioning; soothing. USA: skin-conditioning agents - miscellaneous
Patch testing   : 1% pet. (1)
Molecular formula   : $C_{10}H_8$

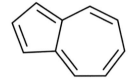

CONTACT ALLERGY

Case reports and case series
A woman developed redness, scaling, cracking and dryness of the vermillion and skin surrounding the lips. She had used the same toothpaste for some years. The clinical manifestations cleared rapidly with avoidance of the toothpaste and topical steroid therapy. Patch tests were positive to the toothpaste as is and later to its ingredient azulene 1% pet. (1). Another woman had allergic contact cheilitis from azulene in her lipstick (2).

Presence in cosmetic products and chemical analyses
In the USA, in April 2017, azulene was present in 7 of 56,714 cosmetic products of which the composition is known in FDA's Voluntary Cosmetic Registration Program (VCRP) (data obtained from FDA, May 2017). In February 2017, azulene was present in 13 of 64,631 cosmetic products of which the composition is known in EWG's Skin Deep Cosmetics Database, USA (http://www.ewg.org/skindeep/).

LITERATURE
1   Balato N, Lembo G, Nappa P, Ayala R. Allergic cheilitis to azulene. Contact Dermatitis 1985;13:39-40
2   Cronin E. Contact dermatitis from cosmetics. J Soc Cosm Chem 1967;18:681-691

2.34 BASIC BLUE 99

IDENTIFICATION

Description/definition	: Basic blue 99 is the naphthoquinoneimine color that conforms to the formula shown below
Chemical class(es)	: Color additives - hair
Chemical/IUPAC name	: [3-[(4,8-Diamino-6-bromo-1,5-dioxonaphthalen-2-yl)amino]phenyl]-trimethylazanium chloride
Other names	: CI 56059; CI basic blue 99; 3-[(4-amino-6-bromo-5,8-dihydro-1-hydroxy-8-imino-5-oxo-2-naphtyl)amino]-N,N,N-trimethylanilinium chloride
CAS registry number (s)	: 68123-13-7
EC number(s)	: 268-544-3
CIR review(s)	: Int J Toxicol 2007;26(Suppl.2):51-63 (access: www.cir-safety.org/ingredients)
SCCS opinion(s)	: SCCS/1537/14 (5); SCCS/1437/11 (6)
Function(s) in cosmetics	: EU: hair dyeing. USA: hair colorants
Patch testing	: 1% pet. or water (3)
Molecular formula	: $C_{19}H_{20}BrClN_4O_2$

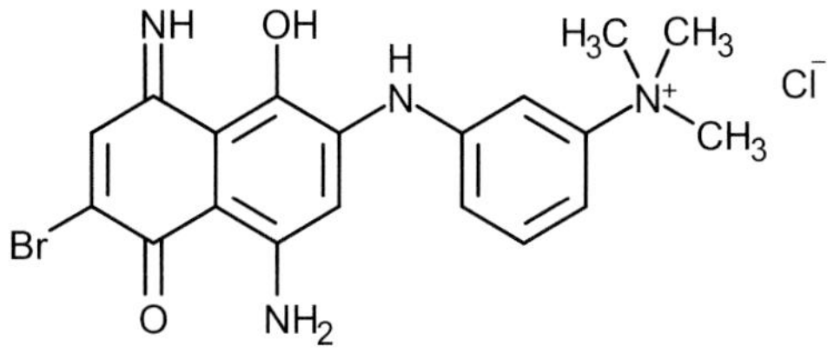

GENERAL

Basic blue 99 is used in semi-permanent non-oxidative hair dying products. It is a mixture of 23-32 substances of varying concentrations, as demonstrated by the HPLC analysis of two batches of the commercial dye (6).

CONTACT ALLERGY

Case reports and case series

A woman had treated a frontal grey lock of hair with a colored foam product weekly for 6 months without ill-effects. Eight hours after she had applied the liquid variety of this cosmetic to the hair (and unintentionally to the scalp), she noticed burning and itching of the scalp and forehead, with redness and swelling of the forehead and upper eyelids. An exudative eruption developed on the scalp. After 4 days, the patient experienced significant hair loss. When seen by a dermatologist 7 weeks later, the hair frontally was obviously thinner, with localized seborrheic-like dermatitis. Five months later, most of the hair had regrown, though the frontoparietal recessions were apparently deeper than before. The patient was patch tested with the European standard series, a cosmetic series, and a hairdressers' series, with negative results. An open test with the implicated product in the elbow flexure resulted in papular dermatitis after 2 days. Later, its ingredients were patch tested, and a positive reaction was noted to the color basic blue 99 1% pet. Seven months later, the patient was tested again and reacted to the color in water and in pet. at 0.1% and 1%; 25 controls were negative (3).

Presence in cosmetic products and chemical analyses

In the USA, in April 2017, basic blue 99 was present in 61 of 56,714 cosmetic products of which the composition is known in FDA's Voluntary Cosmetic Registration Program (VCRP) (data obtained from FDA, May 2017). In February 2017, basic blue 99 was present in 2 of 64,631 cosmetic products of which the composition is known in EWG's Skin Deep Cosmetics Database, USA (http://www.ewg.org/skindeep/). In 2011, labels and other information on 365 hair dye products (282 permanent dyes, 79 semi-permanent dyes, 4 direct dyes) available on the Danish market (159 hair dyes for private use, 206 for professional use by hairdressers) were collected to identify the presence of sensitizers. Basic blue 99 was present in 3 (0.8%) products (8). In southern Germany, in 2013-2014, the labels of 924 permanent oxidative hair dyes were checked for the presence of hair dye components. There were 334 retail products (of seven different brands) and 590 professional products (of six different brands). The 924 products analyzed revealed a total of 58 different hair dye components, with retail products containing 32 and professional products 52. Basic blue 99 was present in 9 (0.1%) of the 924 products (9).

OTHER SIDE EFFECTS

Immediate-type reactions

A woman experienced severe itching of the scalp 3 days after her hairdresser applied hair setting lotion containing a hair dye. Wheals also developed over her trunk and limbs, disappearing after 1 week. A second exposure reproduced the symptoms. After resolution of the urticaria, she was patch tested with the European standard series, a hairdressers series and the ingredients of the setting lotion-hair dye combination including basic blue 99. All tests were negative after 2 and 3 days. Patch testing again with the constituents of the setting lotion and the hair dye, but this time read after one day, revealed several wheals around the tests with the setting lotion-hair dye (as is) and basic blue 99 (1% water). Subsequently, scratch tests showed strongly positive reactions to the lotion and the dye. The author concluded that the widespread urticaria in this case indicated systemic absorption (1).

A hairdresser, with no personal history of atopy, had experienced repeated rhinoconjunctivitis, mild coughing, and swelling of eyelids related to his work. He mostly observed these symptoms during the procedure of hair dyeing, especially after brushing the dried hair. Skin prick tests were positive to a hair dye (30% water). Later, the individual ingredients of this product were tested and there was a very strong reaction to the color ingredient basic blue 99 prick tested undiluted; 3 controls were negative. Patch tests were negative (2).

A woman, formerly employed as a hairdresser but still practicing in her spare time, had allergic contact dermatitis of the hands and feet from hair dyes and shoes. In her history, she mentioned severe itching on the hands and in the ears, accompanied by a 'bad taste' in the mouth, immediately following the application of a particular dye to a client's scalp. Prick testing with the dye was performed, which resulted in a strong positive reaction within 15 minutes following the test. Additional prick tests with all ingredients of the product showed strong reactions to both basic blue 99 1% water and basic brown 17 1% water on two occasions. Patch testing with the same components remained negative. Additionally, the color solution was separated by thin-layer chromatography (TLC). Prick tests were performed with each spot (moistened with physiological saline) of the TLC strips. The patient showed positive immediate reactions to the main spots and some other spots. This indicated, according to the authors, that the patient was probably also sensitized to some impurities present in the dye (12).

A hairdresser suffered from occupational allergic rhinitis and urticaria caused by basic blue 99 and azo dyes (10). One patient allergic to a cosmetic had a positive prick test to basic blue 99; clinical details were not provided (4, likely the same patient as presented above [12]). A woman had recently replaced her brown semi-permanent, non-oxidative hair dye product with a deeper-colored shade. She applied it on her head for the first time, and then showered; 10 min later, she had generalized wheals, nausea, dyspnoea, and impaired consciousness. Later, prick tests with the hair dye containing basic blue 99 and later with basic blue itself (0.1% water) were positive (13).

A review of contact urticaria caused by ingredients of cosmetics has been provided in ref. 7, a review of such reactions to cosmetic and industrial dyes in ref. 11.

LITERATURE

1   Jagtman BA. Urticaria and contact urticaria due to basic blue 99 in a hair dye. Contact Dermatitis1996;35:52
2   Wigger-Alberti W, Eisner R, Wüthrich B. Immediate-type allergy to the hair dye basic blue 99 in a hairdresser. Allergy 1996;51:64-65
3   De Groot AC, Weyland JW. Cosmetic allergy from the aminoketone colour Basic Blue 99 (CI 56059). Contact Dermatitis 1990;23:56-57
4   Goossens A. Cosmetic contact allergens. Cosmetics 2016, 3, 5; doi:10.3390/cosmetics3010005
5   SCCS (Scientific Committee on Consumer Safety), Opinion on Basic Blue 99, 23 September 2014, SCCS/1537/14. Available at: http://ec.europa.eu/health/scientific_committees/consumer_safety/docs/sccs_o_161.pdf
6   SCCS (Scientific Committee on Consumer Safety). Opinion on Basic Blue 99, 20 September 2011, SCCS/1437/11. Available at: http://ec.europa.eu/health/scientific_committees/consumer_safety/docs/sccs_o_068.pdf
7   Verhulst L, Goossens A. Cosmetic components causing contact urticaria: a review and update. Contact Dermatitis 2016;75:333-344
8   The Danish Environmental Protection Agency. Survey and occurrence of PPD, PTD and other allergenic hair dye substances in hair dyes. Copenhagen, Denmark: The Danish Environmental Protection Agency, 2013 (ISBN 978-87-92903-92-1). Available at: http://www2.mst.dk/Udgiv/publications/2013/02/978-87-92903-92-1.pdf
9   Kirchlecher S, Hübner A, Uter W. Survey of sensitizing constituents of oxidative hair dyes (retail and professional products) in Germany. J Dtsch Dermatol Ges 2016;14:707-715
10   Peters KP, Drexler H, Heese A, Koch HU. Typ I-Allergie auf Friseursubstanzen. Fallbeispiel einer Soforttypallergie auf den Farbstoff Basic Blue 99 und auf Azofarben [Abstract]. Allergologie 1992;9:321
11   Davari P, Maibach HI. Contact urticaria to cosmetic and industrial dyes. Clin Exp Dermatol 2011;36:1-5

12 Vanden Broecke K, Bruze M, Persson L, Deroo H, Goossens A. Contact urticaria syndrome caused by direct hair dyes in a hairdresser. Contact Dermatitis 2014;71:124-126

13 Washio K, Ijuin K, Fukunaga A, Nagai H, Nishigori C. Contact anaphylaxis caused by Basic Blue 99 in hair dye. Contact Dermatitis 2017;77:122-123

2.35 BASIC RED 2

IDENTIFICATION

Description/definition	: Basic red 2 is a phenazine color, which conforms to the formula shown below
Chemical class(es)	: Color additives - hair
Chemical/IUPAC name	: 3,7-Diamino-2,8-dimethyl-5-phenylphenazinium chloride
Other names	: CI 50240; safranine; CI basic red 2; tolusafranine
CAS registry number (s)	: 477-73-6
EC number(s)	: 207-518-8
Function(s) in cosmetics	: EU: formerly used for hair dyeing. USA: hair colorants
EU cosmetic restrictions	: Regulated in Annex II/1322 of the Regulation (EC) No. 1223/2009 (prohibited)
Patch testing	: Unknown; suggested: 1% pet.
Molecular formula	: $C_{20}H_{19}ClN_4$

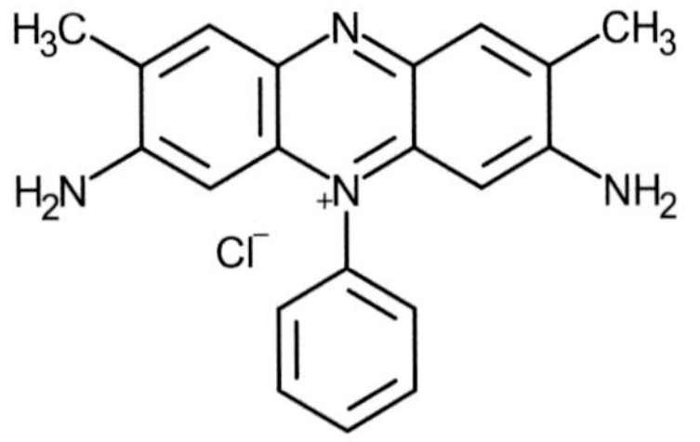

GENERAL

Basic red 2 was formerly used in the EU and may still be used elsewhere in semi-permanent non-oxidative hair dying products.

Case reports and case series

One patient had allergic contact dermatitis (cheilitis?) from tolusafranine (basic red 2) in a facial makeup product (1).

Presence in cosmetic products and chemical analyses

In the USA, in April 2017, basic red 2 was present in 8 of 56,714 cosmetic products of which the composition is known in FDA's Voluntary Cosmetic Registration Program (VCRP) (data obtained from FDA, May 2017). In February 2017, basic red 2 was present in zero of 64,631 cosmetic products of which the composition is known in EWG's Skin Deep Cosmetics Database, USA (http://www.ewg.org/skindeep/). In 2011, labels and other information on 365 hair dye products (282 permanent dyes, 79 semi-permanent dyes, 4 direct dyes) available on the Danish market (159 hair dyes for private use, 206 for professional use by hairdressers) were collected to identify the presence of sensitizers. Basic red 2 was present in 2 (0.5%) products, which is surprising, as the dye is prohibited in the EU (3).

LITERATURE

1   Sézary A, Horowitz A, Genet H. Cheilite du rouge (tolusafranine). Bull Soc Franç Derm Syph 1936;43:402-404. (data cited in ref. 2)
2   De Groot AC. Adverse reactions to cosmetics. PhD Thesis, Groningen, The Netherlands, 1988
3   The Danish Environmental Protection Agency. Survey and occurrence of PPD, PTD and other allergenic hair dye substances in hair dyes. Copenhagen, Denmark: The Danish Environmental Protection Agency, 2013 (ISBN 978-87-92903-92-1). Available at: http://www2.mst.dk/Udgiv/publications/2013/02/978-87-92903-92-1.pdf

2.36 BASIC RED 22

IDENTIFICATION

Description/definition : Basic red 22 is the monoazo color that conforms to the formula shown below
Chemical class(es) : Color additives - hair
Chemical/IUPAC name : 5-(4'-Dimethylaminophenylazo)-1,4-dimethyltriazolium chloride
Other names : CI 11055
CAS registry number (s) : 12221-52-2
Function(s) in cosmetics : EU: formerly used for hair dyeing. USA: hair colorants
EU cosmetic restrictions : Regulated in Annex II/1292 of the Regulation (EC) No. 1223/2009 (prohibited)
Patch testing : 1% water (1); 1% pet. (2)
Molecular formula : $C_{12}H_{17}ClN_6$

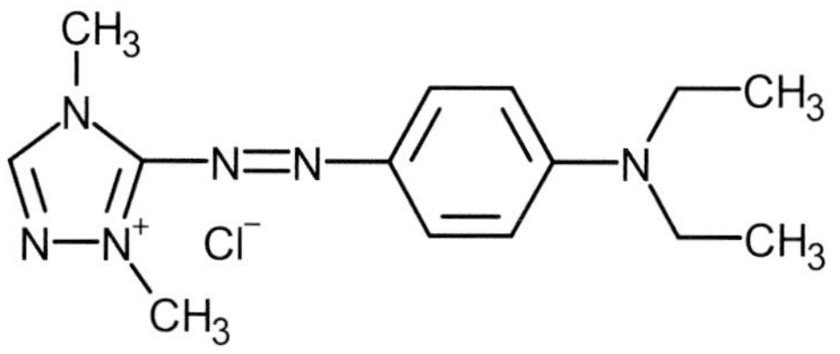

GENERAL

Basic red 22 was formerly used in the EU and may still be used elsewhere in semi-permanent non-oxidative hair dying products. In Cosing, basic red 22 is described as 5-(4'-dimethylaminophenylazo)-1,4-dimethyltriazolium or it salts. In the Personal Care Products Council Ingredient Database, basic red 22 is indicated as 5-(4'-dimethylaminophenylazo)-1,4-dimethyltriazolium *per se*. In chemical databases, the same discrepancy exists.

CONTACT ALLERGY

Case reports and case series

A woman developed a pruritic erythematous, edematous eruption of her scalp, forehead, eyelids and upper face several hours after applying a leave-on *p*-phenylenediamine-free hair-coloring mousse. She had experienced a less-severe reaction after having her hair dyed. Patch testing was positive to *p*-phenylenediamine but not to the mousse. A use test on the upper arm, however, provoked a reaction to the product. Patch testing was then performed with the individual constituents of the hair mousse, which gave a positive reaction to basic red 22 (1).

Contact allergy to basic red 22 in non-cosmetic products

One patient working in a carpet factory had occupational allergic hand contact dermatitis from basic red 22 (2).

Cross-reactions, pseudo-cross-reactions and co-reactions

p-Phenylenediamine, disperse orange 3, disperse red 1 (1).

Presence in cosmetic products and chemical analyses

In the USA, in April 2017, basic red 22 was present in zero of 56,714 cosmetic products of which the composition is known in FDA's Voluntary Cosmetic Registration Program (VCRP) (data obtained from FDA, May 2017). In February 2017, basic red 22 was present in zero of 64,631 cosmetic products of which the composition is known in EWG's Skin Deep Cosmetics Database, USA (http://www.ewg.org/skindeep/). In 2011, labels and other information on 365 hair dye products available on the Danish market were collected to identify the presence of sensitizers. Basic red 22 was present in 1 (0.3%) product (3).

LITERATURE

1   Salim A, Orton D, Shaw S. Allergic contact dermatitis from Basic Red 22 in a hair-colouring mousse. Contact Dermatitis 2001;45:123
2   Sadhra S, Duhra P, Foulds IS. Occupational dermatitis from Synacril Red 3B liquid (CI Basic Red 22). Contact Dermatitis 1989;21:316-320
3   The Danish Environmental Protection Agency. Survey and occurrence of PPD, PTD and other allergenic hair dye substances in hair dyes. Copenhagen, Denmark: The Danish Environmental Protection Agency, 2013 (ISBN 978-87-92903-92-1). Available at: http://www2.mst.dk/Udgiv/publications/2013/02/978-87-92903-92-1.pdf

2.37 BASIC VIOLET 10

IDENTIFICATION

Description/definition : Basic violet 10 is the xanthene color which conforms to the formula shown below
Chemical class(es) : Color additives - miscellaneous
Chemical/IUPAC name : [9-(2-Carboxyphenyl)-6-(diethylamino)xanthen-3-ylidene]-diethylazanium chloride
Other names : CI 45170; rhodamine B; D&C red no. 19
CAS registry number (s) : 81-88-9
EC number(s) : 201-383-9
Merck Index monograph : 9577
Function(s) in cosmetics : EU: formerly used as cosmetic colorant. USA: hair colorants
EU cosmetic restrictions : Regulated in Annex II/398 of the Regulation (EC) No. 1223/2009 (prohibited)
Patch testing : No data available; suggested: 1% pet.
Molecular formula : $C_{28}H_{31}ClN_2O_3$

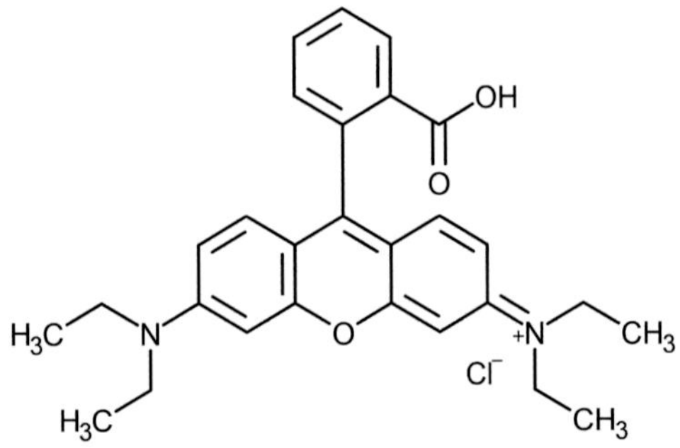

GENERAL

Basic violet 10 was formerly used in the EU and may still be used elsewhere in semi-permanent non-oxidative hair dying products.

CONTACT ALLERGY

Case reports and case series

One patient had allergic contact cheilitis from basic violet 10 in a lipstick (1).

Presence in cosmetic products and chemical analyses

In the USA, in April 2017, basic violet 10 was present in zero of 56,714 cosmetic products of which the composition is known in FDA's Voluntary Cosmetic Registration Program (VCRP) (data obtained from FDA, May 2017). In February 2017, basic violet 10 was present in 4 older and 6 new products of 64,631 cosmetic products of which the composition is known in EWG's Skin Deep Cosmetics Database, USA (http://www.ewg.org/skindeep/).

LITERATURE

1   Cronin E. Contact dermatitis from cosmetics. J Soc Cosm Chem 1967;18:681-691

2.38 BENZALKONIUM CHLORIDE

IDENTIFICATION

Description/definition	: Benzalkonium chloride is a mixture of alkylbenzyldimethylammonium chlorides that conforms generally to the formula shown below, where R represents a mixture of alkyls, including all or some of the group beginning with capryl and extending through higher homologs with lauryl, myristyl and cetyl predominating
Chemical class(es)	: Quaternary ammonium compounds
Chemical/IUPAC name	: Benzyl(dimethyl)azanium chloride
Other names	: Alkyldimethylbenzylammonium chloride
CAS Registry number(s)	: 8001-54-5; 61789-71-7; 68391-01-5; 68424-85-1; 85409-22-9
EC number(s)	: 263-080-8; 269-919-4; 270-325-2; 287-089-1
CIR review(s)	: J Am Coll Toxicol 1989;8:589-625; Int J Toxicol 2008;27(Suppl.1):77-142 (access: www.cir-safety.org/ingredients)
Merck Index monograph	: 2331
Function(s) in cosmetics	: EU: antimicrobial; antistatic; deodorant; preservative; surfactant. USA: antimicrobial agents; antistatic agents; cosmetic biocides; deodorant agents; pesticides; surfactants-dispersing agents
EU cosmetic restrictions	: Regulated in Annexes V/54 and III/65 of the Regulation (EC) No. 1223/2009
Patch testing	: 0.1% water (Chemotechnique); 0.1% pet. (SmartPracticeEurope, SmartPracticeCanada); this test concentration may cause irritant reactions and most weak (+) reactions are probably false positive (9,63). A test concentration of 0.01% may be preferable (25)
Molecular formula	: $C_9H_{14}ClN$

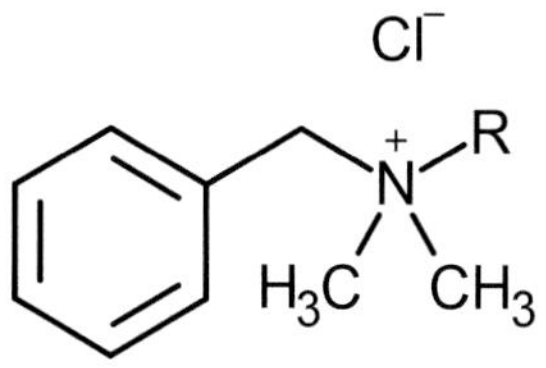

GENERAL

Benzalkonium chloride is a cationic quaternary ammonium compound, which is widely used as preservative and antimicrobial in cosmetics, skin disinfectants, ophthalmic preparations and various other products. It is generally considered to be a significant skin irritant and as such is widely used as a model irritant in the investigation of skin irritation, typically at a concentration of 0.5% in water or above (23). Very high prevalences of sensitization to benzalkonium chloride in routine testing up to 10.7% (2) and in groups of selected patients up to 12.1% (63) have been reported. It should be appreciated, however, that most weak positive (+) reactions (and most *are* weak positive or even ?+) are probably irritant (9). Therefore, contact allergy to benzalkonium chloride is probably overestimated and it is very likely that, in a considerable number of reported cases, patch test reactions have been wrongfully interpreted as allergic (9,23,25,27,47). Nevertheless, allergic reactions do occur occasionally.

CONTACT ALLERGY

Patch testing in groups of patients
Results of routine patch testing (testing in consecutive patients suspected of contact dermatitis) with benzalkonium chloride are shown in table 2.38.1. Results of testing in groups of selected patients (e.g., patients suspected of cosmetic dermatitis, individuals with eyelid/periorbital dermatitis, patients with leg ulcers) are shown in table 2.38.2.

Patch testing in consecutive patients suspected of contact dermatitis: routine testing
Most recent data are from the USA, especially from the Mayo Clinic. Frequencies of sensitization have ranged from 0.8% to 8.8%. However, in one clinic (54), erythema only was considered to be a 'positive' 'patch test, which is not in agreement with international standards. The percentage of relevant reactions ranged from about 30% to 40%. In a study from the NACDG, a lower rate of sensitization of 4.3% was observed (55). 'Definite + probable' relevance was scored in 6% of the reactions only, and this may have been the reason that in subsequent NACDG studies benzalkonium chloride was not tested anymore in the screening series.

Table 2.38.1 Patch testing in groups of patients: Routine testing

Years and Country	Test conc. & vehicle	Number of patients tested | positive (%)		Selection of patients (S); Relevance (R); Comments (C)	Ref.
2006-2010 USA	0.1% water	2979	(8.8%)	R: 34%	67
2000-2010 USA	0.1% water	<8448	(8.8%)	R: about 1/3 was considered to be relevant; C: nearly 60% of the reactions were macular erythema only; only 6% ++ or +++ reactions; increase of rate of positive reactions in time	54
2000-2005 USA	0.1% water	3838	(8.3%)	R: 39%	4
2001-2 USA, Canada	0.1% water	4892	(4.3%)	R: definite + probable relevance: 6%	55
1998-2000 USA	0.1% water	686	(5.5%)	R: not stated	56
1989-90 Switzerland	0.1% water	2295	(5.5%)	R: not stated	59
1972-1973 Denmark	0.1% water	371	3 (0.8%)	R: one patient developed dermatitis after contact with benzalkonium chloride (product not mentioned)	24

Patch testing in groups of selected patients

Data on patch testing with benzalkonium chloride in groups of selected patients back to 1979 are summarized in table 2.38.2. Generally, low frequencies of sensitization were observed. High percentages, however, were seen in patients suspected of allergic cosmetic dermatitis (12.1% [63]), patients tested with a cosmetic series (10.7% [2]), patients with leg ulcers (10.4% [60], but not in a recent IVDK study [83]), in an older study from Germany with unknown selection criteria (10.5% [47]) and in a group of patients treated by the ophthalmologist for chronic conjunctivitis (6% [24]). In the latter series, all patients had used eye drops containing benzalkonium chloride. In most other studies, no relevance data have been provided. In a study from the USA, 92% of 99 positive patch tests to thimerosal were scored as relevance, but this included 'questionable' and 'past' relevance (2).

Table 2.38.2 Patch testing in groups of patients: Selected patient groups

Years and Country	Test conc. & vehicle	Number of patients tested | positive (%)		Selection of patients (S); Relevance (R); Comments (C)	Ref.
2003-2014 IVDK	0.1% pet.	1944	(1.7%)	S: patients with stasis dermatitis/ chronic leg ulcers; R: not stated	83
2010-2011 Korea	0.1% pet.	584	71 (12.1%)	S: patients suspected of allergic cosmetic dermatitis; R: not stated	63
2001-2010 Australia	0.1% pet.	4063	80 (2.0%)	S: not stated; R: 11%	72
2000-2010 IVDK		2282	34 (1.5%)	S: patients with periorbital dermatitis; R: not stated	10
2004-2008 France	0.1% pet.	423	44 (10.4%)	S: patients with leg ulcers; R: not stated	60
2000-2007 USA	0.1% water	928	99 (10.7%)	S: patients tested with a supplemental cosmetic screening series; R: 92%; C: weak study: a. high rate of macular erythema and weak reactions; b. relevance figures included 'questionable' and 'past' relevance	2
1996-2006 IVDK	0.1% pet.	42,898	361 (0.84%)	S: patients tested with a topical drug and/or ophthalmics and/or disinfectant series; R: not specified; C: most + reactions are probably false positive	9
2000-2002 Finland		6538	(0.7%)	S: patients tested with a cosmetic series; R: not stated	57
1995-1999 IVDK	0.1% pet.	893	(1.9%)	S: patients with allergic periorbital contact dermatitis; R: not stated	70
1994-1998 UK	0.01% water	232	3 (1.3%)	S: patients with eyelid dermatitis; R: 2 reactions were currently relevant	64
1991-1998 Finland	0.1 or 0.01% water or pet.	948	3 (0.3%)	S: not stated; R: not specified; C: many irritant reactions were observed	27
1995-1996 Finland		5238	(1.3%)	S: patients tested with a cosmetic series; R: not stated	57
1990-1994 IVDK	0.1% pet.	11,308	207 (1.8%)	S: patients tested with a preservative series; R: not stated	58
1990-1994 IVDK		462	15 (3.2%)	S: patients with periorbital eczema; R: not stated	74
1990-1991 Germany	0.1% pet.	2146	225 (10.5%)	S: unknown; R: 12 cases were relevant; C: 258 irritant reactions; unrealistically high percentage of 'proven' allergic reactions; probably many of these were irritant, for which the authors warned themselves	47
1989 Italy	0.1% water	336	1 (0.3%)	S: male soldiers without skin disease; R: not stated	68
<1979 Denmark	0.07% water	100	6 (6%)	S: patients treated by ophthalmologists for chronic conjunctivitis; R: they all used eye drops preserved with benzalkonium chloride; C: all six reacted positively to a dilution series	24

IVDK: Information Network of Departments of Dermatology, Germany, Austria, Switzerland

Case reports and case series

Case series
Benzalkonium chloride was stated to be the (or an) allergen in one patient in a group of 603 individuals suffering from cosmetic dermatitis, seen in the period 2010-2015 in Leuven, Belgium (65). Benzalkonium chloride was responsible for 1 out of 959 cases of non-fragrance cosmetic allergy where the causal allergen was identified, Belgium, 2000-2010 (1). Benzalkonium chloride was responsible for 2 out of 399 cases of cosmetic allergy where the causal allergen was identified in a study of the NACDG, USA, 1977-1983 (3). Twenty-four positive patch test reactions ascribed to cosmetic allergy (5); this can hardly be accurate, most patch test reactions have probably been irritant.

Case reports
Six patients had allergic contact dermatitis from benzalkonium chloride, present in a high concentration (6%) in an antiseptic bath oil (11). One patient had exacerbation of hand dermatitis from the application of the same bath oil containing benzalkonium chloride, to which he was allergic (50); this product also caused irritant contact dermatitis (see below). Two patients allergic to benzalkonium chloride had used hair dressings with 1% benzalkonium chloride as an ingredient (66).

Contact allergy to benzalkonium chloride in non-cosmetic products
Contact allergy to benzalkonium chloride in non-cosmetic products has resulted most often from its presence in surface cleansing products, eye drops and contact lens solutions, plaster of Paris and topical pharmaceutical products. In the former category, this lead to occupational hand dermatitis in cleaners. Allergy to eye drops resulted in both allergic conjunctivitis and periorbital dermatitis.

Cleansers and disinfectants
A cleaning lady had occupational airborne allergic contact dermatitis from benzalkonium chloride (16). Six hospital cleaners had occupational allergic contact dermatitis from benzalkonium chloride in a surface-cleaning agent (17). Two cases of occupational allergic contact dermatitis from disinfectants (27). A dental nurse had occupational ACD from an equipment sterilizing agent (31). Occupational ACD to benzalkonium chloride was diagnosed in 4 nurses from surface disinfectants; two had positive serial dilution tests. A ROAT was positive in only one patient and the authors therefore concluded that the others did *not* have contact allergy; however, the material had been applied for 4 days only, which is far too short (34). A child had dermatitis of her earlobes from contact allergy to benzalkonium chloride in a disinfectant used for cleaning her golden earrings (35). One patient with occupational ACD from disinfectants containing benzalkonium chloride and benzethonium chloride (48). A farmer had occupational ACD from benzalkonium chloride in disinfectants (51). A workers in a pig farm developed airborne occupational ACD from benzalkonium chloride in a disinfectant (52). Nine children had ACD from benzalkonium chloride in antiseptic solutions (73). One individual had ACD from benzalkonium chloride present in disinfectants in the hospital workplace (36).

Plaster of Paris
Two patients had ACD from benzalkonium chloride in Plaster of Paris bandage (19,40). Another one reacted to the bandage, but had previously been sensitized to the related quaternary ammonium compound cetrimonium bromide in a pharmaceutical cream (20). Five children were sensitized to benzalkonium chloride in Plaster of Paris (Gypsona plaster) (21).

Eye drops and other ophthalmological drugs
Six patients reacted to benzalkonium chloride in eye drops (24). Three patients had allergic contact reactions to benzalkonium chloride in eye drops (26,29,34). Dermatitis from benzalkonium chloride in eye drops masquerading as dermatomyositis has been reported in one patient (33). Three patients had conjunctivitis from contact allergy to benzalkonium chloride in contact lens solutions (42). One individual developed allergic contact conjunctivitis from benzalkonium chloride in an ophthalmic solution (43). One patient reacted to an ophthalmological drug (44). Another patient had eyelid dermatitis from benzalkonium chloride in eye drops (53). Two patients were seen with ACD from benzalkonium chloride in ophthalmological preparations (78).

Topical pharmaceutical preparations
One patient reacted to benzalkonium chloride in an antimycotic preparation (28), another to the preservative in a corticosteroid-antimycotic preparation (32). Two patients with varicose ulcers reacted to benzalkonium chloride in cleansing solutions as well as in compresses and ointments (49). A woman had ACD from benzalkonium chloride by assisting her son to use a nebulizer containing the preservative (36). Twelve patients had chronic otitis externa from benzalkonium chloride in topical medications (79).

Miscellaneous products containing benzalkonium chloride
One patient had occupational ACD from benzalkonium chloride used as a denaturant of alcohol (41). In a group of 46 patients with allergic contact dermatitis of the eyelids seen in Kansas City, USA, between 1994 and 2004, four cases (8.7%) were caused by contact allergy to benzalkonium chloride (source not mentioned) (61).

Cross-reactions, pseudo-cross-reactions and co-reactions
Benzethonium chloride (6,8,36,48); cetalkonium chloride (7,17); cetrimonium bromide (20,21); hexamethonium bromide (22).

Presence in cosmetic products and chemical analyses
In the USA, in April 2017, benzalkonium chloride was present in 136 of 56,714 cosmetic products of which the composition is known in FDA's Voluntary Cosmetic Registration Program (VCRP) (data obtained from FDA, May 2017). In March 2017, benzalkonium chloride was present in 116 of 64,983 cosmetic products of which the composition is known in EWG's Skin Deep Cosmetics Database, USA (http://www.ewg.org/skindeep/). Benzalkonium chloride was present in 102 of 4737 (2.2%) commonly used cosmetic products of which the full composition was known in 2016 in The Contact Allergen Management Program (CAMP) database of the American Contact Dermatitis Society (84). In Germany, in 2006-2009, the labels of 4680 cosmetic products were screened for the presence of preservatives. Benzalkonium chloride was present in 0% of the products (n=2 or 3), according to labelling information (82). Benzalkonium chloride was present in 8 of 1774 (0.5%) cosmetics and toiletries (2002) resp. in zero of 1170 such products (2005) filed in the Danish Product Register Database (PROBAS) (69). In 2009, in the USA, the ingredient lists of 796 hair products from one company were screened for the presence of benzalkonium chloride. The preservative was present in 0% of 279 shampoos, in 0% of 231 conditioners, and in 1 of 286 styling products (71).

Other information
Sensitization assays have been discussed in ref. 23. Of 2642 cases of occupational allergic contact dermatitis seen in Finland in the period 1990-1996, nine (0.3%) were caused by benzalkonium chloride, according to the Finnish Register of Occupational Diseases (data cited in ref. 27).

OTHER SIDE EFFECTS

Irritant contact dermatitis
Irritant contact dermatitis, notably in a flexural and anogenital distribution, has been reported repeatedly from contact with an antiseptic bath oil containing 6% benzalkonium chloride: 2 patients (12,13), 2 siblings (14), 7 individuals (15). One patient had irritant contact dermatitis of the face, which was (unconvincingly) ascribed to benzalkonium chloride (18). One patient had occupational irritant contact dermatitis from benzalkonium chloride solution (30). Irritancy tests with benzalkonium chloride have been summarized in ref. 23.

Immediate-type reactions
A woman had an immediate hypersensitivity reaction to benzalkonium chloride in an ophthalmological preparation with chemosis and angioneurotic edema; she had previously suffered from an anaphylactic shock to a related quaternary ammonium-type anesthetic (78). A woman went into anaphylactic shock following insertion of a central venous catheter that was coated with benzalkonium chloride. One month later, an intradermal test with benzalkonium chloride was positive (62). A woman, while being examined by an ENT specialist, developed increasing massive bilateral obstruction of the nose and a strong sense of heat in the head 20-30 minutes after the application of a mucosal detumescence spray preserved with benzalkonium chloride. Other symptoms and signs included itching in the throat, hoarseness, edematous swelling of the uvula and soft palate, and vesicles on the posterior pharyngeal wall. Six weeks later, prick tests were positive to benzalkonium chloride 0.1% and 0.5% water, while being negative in 15 controls, thereby confirming an immediate-type reaction to benzalkonium chloride (38).

Immediate contact reactions of the airways
One patient developed asthma from benzalkonium chloride (46). A woman working in a plant manufacturing household cleaning products experienced recurrent wheezing and shortness of breath, but no skin symptoms. When investigated, within 5 minutes after exposure to a liquid toilet bowl cleaner containing benzalkonium chloride, the patient developed a diffuse erythematous, pruritic, urticarial rash on her face, neck, and chest; she also had chest tightness and dyspnea. Epicutaneous challenge tests were performed with the individual components of the liquid cleaner. Within 15 minutes after exposure to benzalkonium chloride, the patient had a 15 centimeter erythematous pruritic urticarial reaction, which persisted for several days. Pulmonary function testing revealed a 38-50% decrease in her forced expiratory volume in 1 second (FEV1) after 10 minutes. Subsequent removal from the work environment resulted in complete resolution of her symptoms. The patient was diagnosed with occupational asthma

from benzalkonium chloride (75). A woman with asthma complained of exacerbation of cough and dyspnea after inhalation therapy with a nebulizer solution containing benzalkonium chloride. She underwent skin prick tests with serial dilutions of the nebulizer, which were negative. Subsequently, an intradermal skin test was performed. A positive reaction was observed with the 1:10 solution. About 10 minutes later, she presented with dizziness, palpitations, and dyspnea. Later, a bronchial provocation test resulted in a drop in FEV1 of 23% after inhalation of 1,800 µg benzalkonium chloride (76). A female patient presented to the emergency department with difficulty in breathing, eye redness and pain. The symptoms had begun 20 minutes after using ophthalmic anti-allergy prescription drops preserved with benzalkonium chloride. Later, prick tests were positive to benzalkonium chloride in saline, resulting in the patient having itchy eyes, cough and throat tightness (77).

Other non-eczematous contact reactions
A woman had onycholysis of the toenails from contact allergy to benzalkonium chloride in a nail lacquer (37). Sustained use of benzalkonium chloride in the nose induces nasal mucosal swelling and, in combination with oxymetazoline, it appears to have a long-term adverse effect on the nasal mucosa. Its presence may also contribute to the rhinitis medicamentosa resulting from overuse of decongestant sprays (39).

Systemic side effects
Benzalkonium chloride was apparently responsible for the death of an asthmatic patients (no clinical details known [45]).

Miscellaneous side effects
Occupational asthma from benzalkonium chloride in disinfectants has been observed in nurses. The etiology is unknown (80,81).

LITERATURE
1   Travassos AR, Claes L, Boey L, Drieghe J, Goossens A. Non-fragrance allergens in specific cosmetic products. Contact Dermatitis 2011;65:276-285
2   Wetter DA, Yiannias JA, Prakash AV, Davis MD, Farmer SA, el-Azhary RA, et al. Results of patch testing to personal care product allergens in a standard series and a supplemental cosmetic series: an analysis of 945 patients from the Mayo Clinic Contact Dermatitis Group, 2000-2007. J Am Acad Dermatol 2010;63:789-798
3   Adams RM, Maibach HI, Clendenning WE, Fisher AA, Jordan WJ, Kanof N, et al. A five-year study of cosmetic reactions. J Am Acad Dermatol 1985;13:1062-1069
4   Davis MD, Scalf LA, Yiannias JA, Cheng JF, El-Azhary RA, Rohlinger AL, et al. Changing trends and allergens in the patch test standard series. Arch Dermatol 2008;144:67-72
5   Kohl L, Blondeel A, Song M. Allergic contact dermatitis from cosmetics: retrospective analysis of 819 patch-tested patients. Dermatology 2002;204:334-337
6   Fisher AA. Allergic reactions to feminine hygiene sprays. Arch Dermatol 1973;108:801-802
7   Shmunes E, Levy EJ. Quaternary ammonium compound contact dermatitis from a deodorant. Arch Dermatol 1972;105:91-93
8   Dao H, Fricker C, Nedorost ST. Sensitization prevalence for benzalkonium chloride and benzethonium chloride. Dermatitis 2012;23:162-166
9   Uter W, Lessmann H, Geier J, Schnuch A. Is the irritant benzalkonium chloride a contact allergen? A contribution to the ongoing debate from a clinical perspective. Contact Dermatitis 2008;58:359-363
10   Landeck L, John SM, Geier J. Periorbital dermatitis in 4779 patients – patch test results during a 10-year period. Contact Dermatitis 2014;70:205-212
11   Hann S, Hughes TM, Stone NM. Flexural allergic contact dermatitis to benzalkonium chloride in antiseptic bath oil. Br J Dermatol 2007;157:795-798
12   Loo WJ, Alexandroff A, Burrows NP. Irritant dermatitis due to prolonged contact with Oilatum Plus. Br J Dermatol 2003;148:171-92
13   Saw NK, Hindmarsh JR. Acute irritant reaction to an antiseptic bath emollient. Postgrad Med J 2005;81:131-132
14   Storer E, Koh KJ, Warren L. Severe contact dermatitis as a result of an antiseptic bath oil. Australas J Dermatol 2004;45:73-75
15   Ling TC, Highet AS. Irritant reactions to an antiseptic bath emollient. J Dermatol Treat 2000;11:263-267
16   Mauleón C, Mauleón P, Chavarría E, De La Cueva P, Suárez R, Pablo L. Airborne contact dermatitis from n-alkyl dimethylbenzylammonium chloride and n-alkyl dimethylethyl-benzylammonium chloride in a detergent. Contact Dermatitis 2006;55:311-312
17   Haj-Younes L, Sanchez-Politta S, Pasche-Koo F, Denereaz N, Bessire N, Saurat J-H, Piletta P. Occupational contact dermatitis to Mikrobac Extra™ in 8 hospital cleaners. Contact Dermatitis 2006;54:69-70

18   Oiso N, Fukai K, Ishii M. Irritant contact dermatitis from benzalkonium chloride in shampoo. Contact Dermatitis 2005;52:54

19   Wong DA, Watson AB. Allergic contact dermatitis due to benzalkonium chloride in plaster of Paris. Australas J Dermatol 2001;42:33-35

20   Staniforth P. Allergy to benzalkonium chloride in plaster of Paris after sensitisation to cetrimide. A case report. J Bone Joint Surg Br 1980;62:500-501

21   Lovell CR, Staniforth P. Contact allergy to benzalkonium chloride in plaster of Paris. Contact Dermatitis 1983;7:343-344

22   Huriez C, Agache P, Martin P, Vandamme G, Mennecier J. Fréquences des sensibilisation aux ammoniums quaternaires. La Semaine des Hopitaux 1965;41:2301-2304

23   Basketter DA, Marriott M, Gilmour NJ, White IR. Strong irritants masquerading as skin allergens: the case of benzalkonium chloride. Contact Dermatitis 2004;50:213-217

24   Afzelius H, Thulin H. Allergic reactions to benzalkonium chloride. Contact Dermatitis 1979;5:60

25   Brasch J, Henseler T, Frosch P J. Patch test reactions to a preliminary preservative series. Dermatosen 1993;41:71-75

26   Fisher AA, Stillman MA. Allergic contact sensitivity to benzalkonium chloride (B.A.K.). Cutaneous, ophthalmic and general medical implications. Arch Dermatol 1972;106:169-171

27   Kanerva L, Jolanki R, Estlander T. Occupational contact dermatitis from benzalkonium chloride. Contact Dermatitis 2000;42:357-358

28   Park HJ, Kang HA, Lee JY, Kim HO. Allergic contact dermatitis from benzalkonium chloride in an antifungal solution. Contact Dermatitis 2000;42:306-307

29   Tosti A, Tosti G. Thimerosal: a hidden allergen in ophthalmology. Contact Dermatitis 1988;18:268-273

30   Krogsrud NE, Larsen AI. Airborne irritant contact dermatitis from benzalkonium chloride. Contact Dermatitis 1997;36:112

31   Cusano F, Luciano S. Contact allergy to benzalkonium chloride and glutaraldehyde in a dental nurse. Contact Dermatitis 1993;28:127

32   Chowdhury MMU, Statham B. Allergic contact dermatitis from dibutyl phthalate and benzalkonium chloride in Timodine® cream. Contact Dermatitis 2002;46:57

33   Cox NH. Allergy to benzalkonium chloride simulating dermatomyositis. Contact Dermatitis 1994;31:50

34   Klein GF, Sepp N, Fritsch P. Allergic reactions to benzalkonium chloride? Do the use test! Contact Dermatitis 1991;25:269-270

35   Trevisan GG. Ital Dermatol Venereol 1988;123:513 (title unknown, case cited by ref. 34)

36   Benjamin B, Chris F, Salvador G, et al. Visual and confocal microscopic interpretation of patch tests to benzethonium chloride and benzalkonium chloride. Skin Res Technol 2012;18:272-277

37   Guin JD, Wilson P. Onycholysis from nail lacquer: a complication of nail enhancement? Am J Cont Derm 1999;10:34-36

38   Mezger E, Wendler O, Mayr S, Bozzato A. Anaphylactic reaction following administration of nose drops containing benzalkonium chloride. Head Face Med 2012;8:29. doi: 10.1186/1746-160X-8-29.

39   Graf P. Adverse effects of benzalkonium chloride on the nasal mucosa: allergic rhinitis and rhinitis medicamentosa Clin Ther 1999;21:1749-1755

40   Stanford D, Georgouras K. Allergic contact dermatitis from benzalkonium chloride in plaster of Paris. Contact Dermatitis 1996;35:371-372

41   Ortiz-Frutos FJ, Argila D, Rivera R, Zammarro O, Miguelez S. Allergic contact dermatitis from benzalkonium chloride used as a denaturant of ethanol. Contact Dermatitis 1996;35:302

42   Fisher AA. Allergic reactions to contact lens solutions. Cutis 1985;36:209-211

43   Haetinen A, Teraesvirta M, Fraeki IE. Contact allergy to components in topical ophthalmologic preparations. Acta Dermato-venerologica 1985:63:424-426

44   Frosch PI, Weickel R, Schmitt T, Krastel H. Nebenwirkungen von ophthalmologischen Externa. Z Hautkr 1988;63:126-136

45   Anonymous. Benzalkonium chloride: death of an asthmatic patient. Prescrire Int 2008;17:160

46   Ponder RD, Wray BB. A case report: sensitivity to benzalkonium chloride. J Asthma 1993;30:229-231

47   Fuchs T, Meinert A, Aberer W, Bahmer FA, Peters KP, Lischka GG, et al. Benzalkonium chloride – a relevant contact allergen or irritant? Results of a multicenter study of the German contact allergy group. Hautarzt 1993;44:699-702

48   Norrlind R. Two cases of hypersensitivity to quaternary ammonium compounds. Acta Dermato-Venereol 1962;42:230-234

49   Wahlberg JE. Two cases of hypersensitivity to quaternary ammonium compounds. Acta Derm Venereol (Stockh.) 1962;42:230-234

50 Walker SL, Yel JA, Beck MH. Occupational allergic contact dermatitis caused by 1,2-benzisothiazolin-3-one in a varnish maker, followed by sensitization to benzalkonium chloride in Oilatum® Plus bath additive. Contact Dermatitis 2004;50:104-105

51 Kieć-Świerczyńska M, Krecisz B, Pałczyński C, Walusiak J, Wittczak T, Ruta U. Allergic contact dermatitis from disinfectants in farmers. Contact Dermatitis 2001;45:168-169

52 Corazza M, Virgili A. Airborne allergic contact dermatitis from benzalkonium chloride. Contact Dermatitis 1993;28:195-196

53 Svensson Å, Möller H. Eyelid dermatitis: the rôle of atopy and contact allergy. Contact Dermatitis 1986;15:178-182

54 Wentworth AB, Yiannias JA, Davis MDP, Killian JM. Benzalkonium chloride: a known irritant and novel allergen. Dermatitis 2016;27:14-20

55 Pratt MD, Belsito DV, DeLeo VA, Fowler JF Jr, Fransway AF, Maibach HI, et al. North American Contact Dermatitis Group patch-test results, 2001–2002 study period. Dermatitis 2004;15:176-183

56 Wetter DA, Davis MDP, Yiannias JA, Cheng JF, Connolly SM, el-Azhary RA, et al. Patch test results from the Mayo Contact Dermatitis Group, 1998–2000. J Am Acad Dermatol 2005;53:416-421

57 Hasan T, Rantanen T, Alanko K, Harvima RJ, Jolanki R, Kalimo K, et al. Patch test reactions to cosmetic allergens in 1995–1997 and 2000–2002 in Finland –a multicentre study. Contact Dermatitis 2005;53:40-45

58 Schnuch A, Geier J, Uter W, Frosch PJ. Patch testing with preservatives, antimicrobials and industrial biocides. Results from a multicentre study. Br J Dermatol 1998;138:467-476

59 Perrenoud D, Bircher A, Hunziker T, Suter H, Bruckner-Tuderman L, Stäger J, et al. Frequency of sensitization to 13 common preservatives in Switzerland. Contact Dermatitis 1994;30:276-279

60 Barbaud A, Collet E, Le Coz CJ, Meaume S, Gillois P. Contact allergy in chronic leg ulcers: results of a multicentre study carried out in 423 patients and proposal for an updated series of patch tests. Contact Dermatitis 2009;60:279-287

61 Amin KA, Belsito DV. The aetiology of eyelid dermatitis: a 10-year retrospective analysis. Contact Dermatitis 2006;55:280-285

62 Shih CK, Huang SH, Tsai CJ, Chu KS, Wu SH. Anaphylaxis to benzalkonium chloride-coated central venous catheter. J Clin Anesth 2010;22:632-634

63 Lee SS, Hong DK, Jeong NJ, Lee JH, Choi YS, Lee AY, et al. Multicenter study of preservative sensitivity in patients with suspected cosmetic contact dermatitis in Korea. J Dermatol 2012;39:677-681

64 Cooper SM, Shaw S. Eyelid dermatitis: an evaluation of 232 patch test patients over 5 years. Contact Dermatitis 2000: 42;291-293

65 Goossens A. Cosmetic contact allergens. Cosmetics 2016, 3, 5; doi:10.3390/cosmetics3010005

66 Hannuksela M, Kousa M, Pirilä V. Allergy to ingredients of vehicles. Contact Dermatitis 1976;2:105-110

67 Wentworth AB, Yiannias JA, Keeling JH, Hall MR, Camilleri MJ, Drage LA, et al. Trends in patch-test results and allergen changes in the standard series: a Mayo Clinic 5-year retrospective review (January 1, 2006, to December 31, 2010). J Am Acad Dermatol 2014;70:269-275

68 Seidenari S, Manzini BM, Danese P, Motolese A. Patch and prick test study of 593 healthy subjects. Contact Dermatitis 1990; 23:162-167

69 Flyvholm, MA. Preservatives in registered chemical products. Contact Dermatitis 2005;53:27-32

70 Herbst RA, Uter W, Pirker C, Geier J, Frosch PJ. Allergic and non-allergic periorbital dermatitis: patch test results of the Information Network of the Departments of Dermatology during a 5-year period. Contact Dermatitis 2004;51:13-19

71 Scheman A, Jacob S, Katta R, Nedorost S, Warshaw E, Zirwas M, et al. Part 2 of a 4 part series. Hair cosmetics: trends and alternatives. Data from the American Contact Alternative Group. J Clin Aesthet Dermatol 2011;4:42-46

72 Toholka R, Wang Y-S, Tate B, Tam M, Cahill J, Palmer A, Nixon R. The first Australian Baseline Series: Recommendations for patch testing in suspected contact dermatitis. Australas J Dermatol 2015;56:107-115

73 Milpied B, Darrigade A-S, Labreze C, Boralevi F. Antiseptic contact dermatitis in children: not just chlorhexidine. Contact Dermatitis 2016;75(Suppl.1):37

74 Ockenfels H, Seemann U, Goos M. Contact allergy in patients with periorbital eczema: an analysis of allergens. Dermatology 1997;195:119-124

75 Bernstein JA, Stauder T, Bernstein DI, Bernstein IL. A combined respiratory and cutaneous hypersensitivity syndrome induced by work exposure to quaternary amines. J Allergy Clin Immunol 1994;94(2 Pt 1):257–259

76 Kim SH, Ahn Y. Anaphylaxis caused by benzalkonium in a nebulizer solution. J Korean Med Sci 2004;19:289-290

77 Anderson D, Faltay B, Haller NA. Anaphylaxis with use of eye-drops containing benzalkonium chloride preservative. Clin Exp Optom 2009;92:444-446

78 Chiambaretta F, Pouliquen P, Rigal D. Allergy and preservatives. A propos of 3 cases of allergy to benzalkonium chloride. J Fr Ophtalmol 1997;20:8-16

79   Fräki JE, Kalimo K, Tuohimaa P, Aantaa E. Contact allergy to various components of topical preparations for treatment of external otitis. Acta Otolaryngol 1985;100:414-418

80   Purohit A, Kopferschmitt-Kubler MC, Moreau C, Popin E, Blaumeiser M, Pauli G. Quaternary ammonium compounds and occupational asthma. Int Arch Occup Environ Health 2000;73:423-427

81   Innocenti A. Occupational asthma due to benzalkonium chloride. Med Lav 1978;69:713-715 (Article in Italian)

82   Uter W, Yazar K, Kratz EM, Mildau G, Lidén C. Coupled exposure to ingredients of cosmetic products: II. Preservatives. Contact Dermatitis 2014;70:219-226

83   Erfurt-Berge C, Geier J, Mahler V. The current spectrum of contact sensitization in patients with chronic leg ulcers or stasis dermatitis - new data from the Information Network of Departments of Dermatology (IVDK). Contact Dermatitis 2017 Feb 14. doi: 10.1111/cod.12763. [Epub ahead of print]

84   Beene KM, Scheman A, Severson D, Reeder MJ. Prevalence of preservatives across all product types in the Contact Allergen Management Program. Dermatitis 2017;28:81-87

2.39 BENZETHONIUM CHLORIDE

IDENTIFICATION

Description/definition : Benzethonium chloride is the quaternary ammonium salt that conforms to the formula shown below

Chemical class(es) : Quaternary ammonium compounds

Chemical/IUPAC name : Benzenemethanaminium, *N*,*N*-dimethyl-*N*-[2-[2-[4-(1,1,3,3,-tetramethylbutyl) phenoxy]ethoxy]ethyl]-, chloride

CAS registry number (s) : 121-54-0

EC number(s) : 204-479-9

CIR review(s) : J Am Coll Toxicol 1985;4:65-106 (access: www.cir-safety.org/ingredients)

SCCS opinion(s) : SCCNFP/0762/03 (6); SCCNFP/0539/01 (7)

Merck Index monograph : 2346

Function(s) in cosmetics : EU: antimicrobial; deodorant; preservative; surfactant. USA: antimicrobial agents; cosmetic biocides; deodorant agents; pesticides; preservatives; surfactants – dispersing agents

EU cosmetic restrictions : Regulated in Annex V/53 of the Regulation (EC) No. 1223/2009

Patch testing : 0.1% water (9); irritant reactions may be expected

Molecular formula : $C_{27}H_{42}ClNO_2$

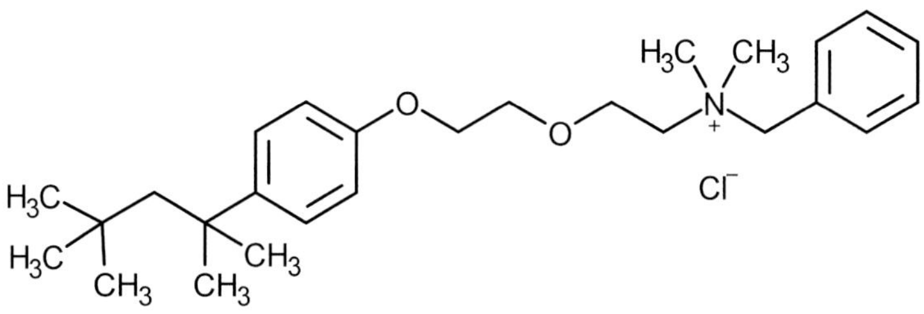

GENERAL

Benzethonium chloride is a quaternary ammonium compound which is mainly used in disinfectants. In cosmetics, it is an extremely rare sensitizer. A few cases of allergic contact dermatitis to benzethonium chloride in disinfectant preparations have been described. In many, ulcers and/or erosion were part of the clinical picture (11-15), which suggests that irritant effects also played a role (11). However, all patients were patch tested with benzethonium chloride 0.1%, which may well result in irritant patch test reactions and controls tests may not always have been performed.

CONTACT ALLERGY

Patch testing in groups of patients: Routine testing

In 2011 (?), in the USA, 142 consecutive patients suspected of contact dermatitis were patch tested with benzethonium chloride (BEC) 0.15% and 0.5% water and benzalkonium chloride (BAK) 0.15% in water and in petrolatum. The results were presented in a rather confusing and unclear manner, as they were not specified for the chemical nor for the concentration. There was one 'definite' case of allergic contact dermatitis from BAK and/or BEC and 13 (9%) 'possible' cases, whereas in 15 patients, who had apparently some kind of patch test reactions, ACD was considered to be 'unlikely'. In the 14 patients with definite and possible ACD to BAK/BEC, the most frequent causative agents were cleansing wipes (5 patients) and eye drops (4 patients). Other sources included saline nasal sprays (1 patient), shampoos (1 patient), and disinfectant spray (1 patient). Four patients had unknown sources of their dermatitis (2). It should be realized that concentrations of >0.1% probably may induce irritant patch test reactions.

Patch testing in groups of patients: Selected patient groups

In the USA, in the beginning of the 1980s, 41 patients, most of who wore contact lenses and had unexplained conjunctivitis or keratitis, were patch tested with benzethonium chloride 1% in water. There were 3 reactions considered to be truly allergic. However, there were also 3 irritant reactions, it was not mentioned whether the patients had used eye products containing benzethonium chloride and the test concentration of 1% may be considered too high for quaternary ammonium compounds of this type (5). In a group of 20 patients with contact lens intolerance, two reacted to benzethonium chloride 0.1% water. The relevance of these reactions was considered dubious as they did not react to benzalkonium chloride (0.1% water), which they were using (10).

Case reports and case series

Two patients had allergic contact dermatitis from benzethonium chloride in a feminine hygiene spray. One was a woman with vulvar dermatitis, the other a male patient who developed penile and scrotal dermatitis each time he had had intercourse with his wife, who used the spray containing benzethonium chloride ('consort' or 'connubial' allergic contact dermatitis) (1).

Contact allergy to benzethonium chloride in non-cosmetic products

One patient had occupational ACD from disinfectants containing benzethonium chloride and benzalkonium chloride (4). A woman had ulcerative allergic contact dermatitis of the big toe from treatment with a disinfectant containing 0.1% benzethonium chloride (11). It was thought that irritant reactions also played a role, as benzethonium as quaternary ammonium compound is a well-known skin irritant. Other publications from Japan (in Japanese, cited in ref. 11) have also presented patients with (ulcerative) allergic contact dermatitis (12-15).

Cross-reactions, pseudo-cross-reactions and co-reactions

Benzalkonium chloride (1,2,4).

Presence in cosmetic products and chemical analyses

In the USA, in April 2017, benzethonium chloride was present in 40 of 56,714 cosmetic products of which the composition is known in FDA's Voluntary Cosmetic Registration Program (VCRP) (data obtained from FDA, May 2017). In April 2017, benzethonium chloride was present in 12 of 65,434 cosmetic products of which the composition is known in EWG's Skin Deep Cosmetics Database, USA (http://www.ewg.org/skindeep/). In Germany, in 2006-2009, the labels of 4680 cosmetic products were screened for the presence of preservatives. Benzethonium chloride was present in zero of the products, according to labelling information (8).

OTHER SIDE EFFECTS

Irritant contact dermatitis

A bland ointment containing an unknown concentration of *methyl* benzethonium chloride may have caused irritant dermatitis of the vulva (3).

LITERATURE

1   Fisher AA. Allergic reactions to feminine hygiene sprays. Arch Dermatol 1973;108:801-802
2   Dao H, Fricker C, Nedorost ST. Sensitization prevalence for benzalkonium chloride and benzethonium chloride. Dermatitis 2012;23:162-166
3   Maibach HI, Mathias CT. Vulvar dermatitis and fissures/irritant dermatitis from methyl benzethonium chloride. Contact Dermatitis 1985;13:340
4   Norrlind R. Two cases of hypersensitivity to quaternary ammonium compounds. Acta Dermato-Venereol 1962;42:230-234
5   Rietschel RL, Wilson LA. Ocular inflammation in patients using soft contact lenses. Arch Dermatol 1982;118:147-149
6   SCCNFP (Scientific Committee on Cosmetics and Non Food Products). Opinion concerning benzethonium chloride, 9 December 2003, SCCNFP/0762/03. Available at: http://ec.europa.eu/health/archive/ph_risk/committees/sccp/documents/out250_en.pdf
7   SCCNFP (Scientific Committee on Cosmetics and Non Food Products). Opinion concerning benzethonium chloride, 27 February 2002, SCCNFP/0539/01. Available at: http://ec.europa.eu/health/archive/ph_risk/committees/sccp/documents/out158_en.pdf
8   Uter W, Yazar K, Kratz EM, Mildau G, Lidén C. Coupled exposure to ingredients of cosmetic products: II. Preservatives. Contact Dermatitis 2014;70:219-226
9   De Groot AC. Patch Testing, 3rd Edition. Wapserveen, The Netherlands: acdegroot publishing, 2008 (ISBN 978-90-813233-1-4)
10   Podmore P, Storrs F I. Contact lens intolerance; allergic conjunctivitis? Contact Dermatitis 1989;20:98-103
11   Hirata Y, Yanagi T, Yamaguchi Y, Sato K, Shinkuma S, Hata H, Shimizu H. Ulcerative contact dermatitis caused by benzethonium chloride. Contact Dermatitis 2017;76:188-190

12 Katoh J, Orifuji T, Tanii T, et al. Contact dermatitis due to benzethonium chloride. Skin Res 1991;33:350-353 (in Japanese) (cited in ref. 11)

13 Jinnohara Y, Kondo S, Hirosaki K, et al. A case of contact dermatitis caused by Makiron. Rinsho derma (Tokyo) 2000;42:151-153 (in Japanese) (cited in ref. 11)

14 Sato A, Yokomi A, Ogido Y, Higashiyama M. Contact dermatitis due to Makiron. Jpn J Dermatoallergol 2006;14:125-130 (in Japanese) (data cited in ref. 11)

15 Kamei R, Mizoguchi N, Nakai D, et al. Leg ulcers caused by benzethonium chloride. Pract Dermatol 2015;37:47-50 (in Japanese) (data cited in ref. 11)

2.40 BENZISOTHIAZOLINONE

IDENTIFICATION

Description/definition	: Benzisothiazolinone is the heterocyclic compound that conforms to the formula shown below
Chemical class(es)	: Amides; heterocyclic compounds; thio compounds
Chemical/IUPAC name	: 1,2-Benzisothiazol-3(2H)-one; BIT
CAS registry number (s)	: 2634-33-5
EC number(s)	: 220-120-9
SCCS opinion(s)	: SCCS/1482/12 (1); SCCNFP/0811/04 (2)
Function(s) in cosmetics	: EU: antimicrobial. USA: preservatives
Patch testing	: 0.05% pet. (Chemotechnique); 0.1% pet., sodium salt (SmartPracticeEurope); 0.1% pet. (SmartPracticeCanada)
Molecular formula	: C_7H_5NOS

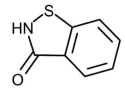

GENERAL

Benzisothiazolinone (BIT) is an antimicrobial agent used as a preservative in multiple water-based solutions, such as glues, cleaning agents, polishes, paints, varnishes, and hardeners (5). It may occasionally be present in PVC gloves (6) and (imitation) leather shoes (7). BIT has been recognized as an allergen since 1976 from its use in many different occupations, for example carpet, water-softener, air-freshener and paint manufacturing, in painters, pottery workers, paper makers, woodwork teachers, plumbers, metal workers, and laboratory technicians (3). In addition to reports of multiple cases caused by direct skin contact, systemic skin reactions following airborne exposure to BIT have been described (4).

The use of this preservative is allowed in household and industrial products. It has been stated that its use in cosmetics is not allowed (3), but no evidence for this can be found in CosIng. However, in 2012, the Scientific Committee on Consumer Safety expressed its concerns about the sensitizing properties of benzisothiazolinone, which are similar to those of methylisothiazolinone; hence, use of BIT in cosmetics has not been considered to be safe (1).

Discussion of this preservative is limited to cases of contact allergy in cosmetics. In fact, only one case of allergic contact dermatitis from benzisothiazolinone in a liquid soap appears to have been reported. Probably, this chemical is hardly used in cosmetic products. In the USA, for example, benzisothiazolinone in July 2017 was present in only 4 of 69,577 cosmetic products of which the composition is known in EWG's Skin Deep Cosmetics Database (http://www.ewg.org/skindeep/).

A full review of contact allergy to and other side effects from benzisothiazolinone is planned for a future volume in this series on Monographs in Contact Allergy.

CONTACT ALLERGY

Case reports and case series

A man, known to have non-relevant contact allergy to nickel and cobalt, had had dermatitis of his hands and feet for many years. His occupation consisted of printing foil, which was used to coat furniture, and parquet and laminate floor panels. During work, he would also wash his hands many times a day with a 'mild liquid soap'. Patch tests with the European baseline series, a shoe series, fragrance mix I ingredients, and the patient's own materials gave positive reactions to fragrance mix I and to cinnamal, which were considered not to be relevant. However, he also reacted to benzisothiazolinone, which was found in the biocide added to the water-based printing ink, and also in the liquid soap used at work. After avoiding exposure to this preservative and changing his job, the patient became completely symptom-free, including on his feet (3).

Presence in cosmetic products and chemical analyses

In July 2017, benzisothiazolinone was present in 4 of 69,577 cosmetic products of which the composition is known in EWG's Skin Deep Cosmetics Database, USA (http://www.ewg.org/skindeep/).

LITERATURE

1 SCCS (Scientific Committee on Consumer Safety). Opinion on Benzisothiazolinone, SCCS/1482/12, 26-27 June, 2012. Available at:
   http://ec.europa.eu/health/scientific_committees/consumer_safety/docs/sccs_o_099.pdf
2 SCCFNP (Scientific Committee on Cosmetic Products and Non-Food Products Intended for Consumers). Opinion on Benzisothiazolinone, 1 July 2004, SCCNFP/0811/04. Available at:
   http://ec.europa.eu/health/ph_risk/committees/sccp/documents/out289_en.pdf
3 Meysman T, Goossens A. Occupational allergic contact dermatitis caused by benzisothiazolinone in printing ink and soap. Contact Dermatitis 2017;76:51-53
4 Schwensen J, Menné T, Andersen KE. Occupations at risk of developing contact allergy to isothiazolinones in Danish contact dermatitis patients: results from a Danish multicentre study (2009–2012). Contact Dermatitis 2014;71:295-302
5 Kaur-Knudsen D, Menné T, Carlsen BC. Systemic allergic dermatitis following airborne exposure to 1,2-benzisothiazolin-3-one. Contact Dermatitis 2012;67:306-320
6 Aalto-Korte K, Alanko K, Henriks-Eckerman ML. Antimicrobial allergy from polyvinyl chloride gloves. Arch Dermatol 2006;142:1326-1330
7 Ayadi M, Martin P. Pulpitis of the fingers from a shoe glue containing 1,2-benzisothiazolin-3-one (BIT). Contact Dermatitis 1999;40:115-116

2.41 BENZOIC ACID

IDENTIFICATION

Description/definition   : Benzoic acid is an aromatic acid that conforms to the formula shown below
Chemical class(es)   : Carboxylic acids
Chemical/IUPAC name   : Benzoic acid
Other names   : Benzenecarboxylic acid
CAS registry number (s)   : 65-85-0
EC number(s)   : 200-618-2
CIR review(s)   : Int J Toxicol 2001;20(Suppl.3):23-50; Final Report, October 2011 (access:
                              www.cir-safety.org/ingredients)
SCCS opinion(s)   : SCCP/0891/05 (24); SCCNFP/0532/01 (25)
Merck Index monograph   : 2363
EU cosmetic restrictions   : Regulated in Annex V/1 of the Regulation (EC) No. 1223/2009
Function(s) in cosmetics   : EU: bulking; masking; preservative. USA: fragrance ingredients; preservatives;
                              pH adjusters
Patch testing   : 5.0% pet. (Chemotechnique, SmartPracticeEurope); benzoic acid 5% causes irritant
                              reactions (17); 1% alc. (SmartPracticeCanada)
Molecular formula   : $C_7H_6O_2$

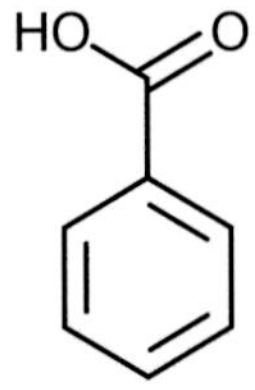

CONTACT ALLERGY

General
Benzoic acid 5% pet. has in 2017 been added to The American Contact Dermatitis Society Core Allergen Series (31). It is important to realize that benzoic acid 5% in petrolatum may cause irritant reactions (17).

Patch testing in groups of patients
Results of patch testing benzoic acid in consecutive patients suspected of contact dermatitis (routine testing) and of testing in groups of selected patients are shown in table 2.41.1. In routine testing, rates of sensitization were 4.9% (3) and 5.7% (18). Relevance scores were 43% and 45%. In none of the studies was mentioned which products were the allergenic culprits. It is to be expected that many reactions in these studies were false-positive.

In groups of selected patients, frequencies of sensitization ranged from 2.1% to 20% (2,5,27,28). The highest score (20%) was in patients previously shown to be allergic to *Myroxylon pereirae* resin (balsam of Peru), of which benzoic acid is a constituent (5). Relevance was high in two studies (94% and 100%) (2,28), but in one, this included 'questionable' and 'past' relevance (2).

Table 2.41.1 Patch testing in groups of patients

Years and Country	Test conc. & vehicle	Number of patients tested	positive (%)	Selection of patients (S); Relevance (R); Comments (C)	Ref.
Routine testing					
2006-2010 USA	5% pet.	3077	(5.7%)	R: 43%	18
2000-2005 USA	5% pet.	1963	(4.9%)	R: 45%	3
Testing in groups of selected patients					
2001-2011 USA	1% pet.	40	5 (13%)	S: patients with allergic contact cheilitis; R: 5/5 relevant	28
2000-2007 USA	5% pet.	864	53 (6.1%)	S: patients tested with a supplemental cosmetic screening series; R: 94%; C: weak study: a. high rate of macular erythema and weak reactions; b. relevance figures included 'questionable' and 'past' relevance	2
1995-1998 Germany	5% pet.	102	20 (20%)	S: patients allergic to *Myroxylon pereirae*; R: not specified	5
1981 France	5% pet.	465	10 (2.1%)	S: patients suspected of allergy to cosmetics, drugs, industrial products, or clothes; R: not stated	27

Case reports and case series

Benzoic acid was stated to be the (or an) allergen in 6 patients in a group of 603 individuals suffering from cosmetic dermatitis, seen in the period 2010-2015 in Leuven, Belgium (16). Benzoic acid was responsible for 7 out of 959 cases of non-fragrance cosmetic allergy where the causal allergen was identified, Belgium, 2000-2010 (1). In 3 clinics in Belgium, in the period 1978-1985, 279 patients with allergic contact dermatitis exclusively caused by cosmetics were seen. In this group, there were 3 reactions to benzoic acid. It was implied that this was the cause of the allergic reaction (26). Eleven positive patch test reactions to benzoic acid were ascribed to cosmetic allergy (4).

A woman had allergic contact dermatitis of the eyelids from methylisothiazolinone in cosmetics. The patient also had a positive reaction to benzoic acid, which was present in a purifying lotion and cleansing tissues she had previously used as well (30). A man had allergic contact dermatitis to benzoic acid in various skin care products (38). Another male patient man had ACD of the back of his arms from benzoic acid in a sunscreen (39).

Presence in cosmetic products and chemical analyses

In the USA, in April 2017, benzoic acid was present in 1184 of 56,714 cosmetic products of which the composition is known in FDA's Voluntary Cosmetic Registration Program (VCRP) (data obtained from FDA, May 2017). In April 2017, benzoic acid was present in 689 of 66,647 cosmetic products of which the composition is known in EWG's Skin Deep Cosmetics Database, USA (http://www.ewg.org/skindeep/). Benzoic acid was present in 545 of 4737 (11.5%) commonly used cosmetic products of which the full composition was known in 2016 in The Contact Allergen Management Program (CAMP) database of the American Contact Dermatitis Society (36). Benzoic acid was present in 31 (17%) of 178 facial wipes for which ingredient information was obtained online and from retail stores, USA, 2016 (35). In the USA, in 2015-2016, 63 diaper wipes and 41 topical diaper preparations from a large retailer were screened for the presence of potential sensitizers. Benzoic acid was found in 3/63 (5%) disposable diaper wipes and in 2/41 (5%) topical diaper preparations (37). In 2009, in the USA, the ingredient lists of 796 hair products from one company were screened for the presence of preservatives. Benzoic acid was present in 3% of 279 shampoos, in 2% of 231 conditioners, and in 21% of 286 styling products (21).

In 2009, in the USA, the ingredient lists of 730 lip cosmetics and dental care products from one company were screened for the presence of preservatives. Benzoic acid was present in 0% of 31 lip liners, in 16% of 429 lipsticks, in 3% of 92 lip moisturizers, in 9% of 153 toothpastes, and in 60% of 25 mouth washes (22). In 2009, in the USA, the ingredient lists of 657 miscellaneous cosmetics from one company were screened for the presence of preservatives. Benzoic acid was present in 16% of 195 antiperspirants/deodorants, in 0% of 41 powders, in 0% of 167 shaving products, in 13% of 201 sunblocks, and in 0% of 53 wipes (23).

In Germany, in 2006-2009, the labels of 4680 cosmetic products were screened for the presence of preservatives. Benzoic acid was present in 3.1% of the products, according to labelling information (29). Benzoates (benzoic acid or sodium benzoate) were present in 250/3541 (6.7%) randomly sampled leave-on cosmetic products in Germany, 2006-2009 (6). Benzoic acid was present in 11% of 204 cosmetic products (92 shampoos, 61 hair conditioners, 34 liquid soaps, 17 wet tissues) in Sweden, 2008 (7). Benzoic acid was present in 13 of 1774 (0.7%) cosmetics and toiletries (2002) resp. in 13 of 1170 (1.1%) such products (2005) filed in the Danish Product Register Database (PROBAS) (19). In a group of 67 samples of skin creams, randomly selected from retail outlets in Denmark in 1999, 2 (3%) contained benzoic acid in a concentration range of 0.003-0.037%. In one product it was present but not declared (20).

OTHER SIDE EFFECTS

Immediate-type reactions

Benzoic acid is widely used in studies of immediate contact reactions. It causes a dose-dependent non-immunologic reaction in many, sometimes most, test subjects (8-13,15,32). In a kindergarten, 18 of 20 children developed perioral contact urticaria from benzoic acid in a mayonnaise-containing salad dressing (14). Two patients suffering from burning mouth syndrome and reacting with contact urticaria to patch tests became asymptomatic after dietary avoidance of benzoic acid (34).

LITERATURE

1   Travassos AR, Claes L, Boey L, Drieghe J, Goossens A. Non-fragrance allergens in specific cosmetic products. Contact Dermatitis 2011;65:276-285
2   Wetter DA, Yiannias JA, Prakash AV, Davis MD, Farmer SA, el-Azhary RA, et al. Results of patch testing to personal care product allergens in a standard series and a supplemental cosmetic series: an analysis of 945 patients from the Mayo Clinic Contact Dermatitis Group, 2000-2007. J Am Acad Dermatol 2010;63:789-798
3   Davis MD, Scalf LA, Yiannias JA, Cheng JF, El-Azhary RA, Rohlinger AL, et al. Changing trends and allergens in the patch test standard series. Arch Dermatol 2008;144:67-72

4   Kohl L, Blondeel A, Song M. Allergic contact dermatitis from cosmetics: retrospective analysis of 819 patch-tested patients. Dermatology 2002;204:334-337

5   Hausen BM. Contact allergy to Balsam of Peru. II. Patch test results in 102 patients with selected Balsam of Peru constituents. Am J Contact Derm 2001;12:93-102

6   Schnuch A, Mildau G, Kratz E-M, Uter W. Risk of sensitization to preservatives estimated on the basis of patch test data and exposure, according to a sample of 3541 leave-on products. Contact Dermatitis 2011;65:167-174

7   Yazar K, Johnsson S, Lind M-L, Boman A, Lidén C. Preservatives and fragrances in selected consumer-available cosmetics and detergents. Contact Dermatitis 2011;64:265-272

8   Lahti A. Non-immunologic contact urticaria. Acta Dermato-venereologica 1980;60 (suppl. 91):1-49

9   Lahti A. Terfenadine does not inhibit non-immunologic contact urticarcia. Contact Dermatitis 1987;16:220-223

10   Lammintausta K, Maibach HI, Wilson D. Mechanisms of subjective (sensory) irritation. Dermatosen 1988;36:45-49

11   Larmi E, Lahti A, Hannuksela M. Ultraviolet light inhibits nonimmunologic immediate contact reactions to benzoic acid. Arch Dermatol Res 1989;280:420-423

12   Lahti A, Pylvänen V, Hannuksela, M. Immediate irritant reactions to benzoic acid are enhanced in washed skin areas. Contact Dermatitis 1995;33:177-182

13   Larmi E, Lahti A, Hannuksela M. Immediate contact reactions to benzoic acid and the sodium salt of pyrrolidone carboxylic acid Comparison of various skin sites. Contact Dermatitis 1989;20:38-40

14   Clemmensen O, Hjorth N. Perioral contact urticaria from sorbic acid and benzoic acid in a salad dressing. Contact Dermatitis 1982;8:1-6

15   Lahti A. Skin reactions to some antimicrobial agents. Contact Dermatitis 1978;4:302-303

16   Goossens A. Cosmetic contact allergens. Cosmetics 2016, 3, 5; doi:10.3390/cosmetics3010005

17   De Groot AC, Weyland JW, Bos JD, Jagtman BA. Contact allergy to preservatives (I). Contact Dermatitis 1986;14:120-122

18   Wentworth AB, Yiannias JA, Keeling JH, Hall MR, Camilleri MJ, Drage LA, et al. Trends in patch-test results and allergen changes in the standard series: a Mayo Clinic 5-year retrospective review (January 1, 2006, to December 31, 2010). J Am Acad Dermatol 2014;70:269-275

19   Flyvholm MA. Preservatives in registered chemical products. Contact Dermatitis 2005;53:27-32

20   Rastogi SC. Analytical control of preservative labelling on skin creams. Contact Dermatitis 2000;43:339-343

21   Scheman A, Jacob S, Katta R, Nedorost S, Warshaw E, Zirwas M, et al. Part 2 of a 4 part series. Hair cosmetics: trends and alternatives. Data from the American Contact Alternative Group. J Clin Aesthet Dermatol 2011;4:42-46

22   Scheman A, Jacob S, Katta R, Nedorost S, Warshaw E, Zirwas M, et al. Part 3 of a 4 part series. Lips and common Dental Care products: trends and alternatives. Data from the American Contact Alternative Group. J Clin Aesthet Dermatol 2011;4:50-53

23   Scheman A, Jacob S, Katta R, Nedorost S, Warshaw E, Zirwas M, et al. Part 4 of a 4 part series. Miscellaneous products: trends and alternatives in deodorants, antiperspirants, sunblocks, shaving products, powder, and wipes. Data from the American Contact Alternative Group. J Clin Aesthet Dermatol 2011;4:35-39

24   SCCP (Scientific Committee on Consumer Products). Opinion on Benzoic Acid and Sodium Benzoate, 21 June 2005, SCCP/0891/05. Available at:
http://ec.europa.eu/health/archive/ph_risk/committees/04_sccp/docs/sccp_o_015.pdf

25   SCCNFP (Scientific Committee on Cosmetics and Non Food Products). Opinion concerning benzoic acid and sodium benzoate, 4 June 2002, SCCNFP/0532/01. Available at:
http://ec.europa.eu/health/archive/ph_risk/committees/sccp/documents/out166_en.pdf

26   Dooms-Goossens A, de Boulle K, Dooms M, Degreef H. Imidazolidinyl urea dermatitis. Contact Dermatitis 1986;14:322-324

27   Meynadier JM, Meynadier J, Colmas A, Castelain PY, Ducombs G, Chabeau G, et al. Allergy to preservatives. Ann Dermatol Venereol 1982;109:1017-1023

28   O'Gorman SM, Torgerson RR. Contact allergy in cheilitis. Int J Dermatol 2016;55:e386-e391

29   Uter W, Yazar K, Kratz EM, Mildau G, Lidén C. Coupled exposure to ingredients of cosmetic products: II. Preservatives. Contact Dermatitis 2014;70:219-226

30   García-Gavín J, Vansina S, Kerre S, Naert A, Goossens A. Methylisothiazolinone, an emerging allergen in cosmetics? Contact Dermatitis 2010;63:96-101

31   Schalock PC, Dunnick CA, Nedorost S, Brod B, Warshaw E, Mowad C. American Contact Dermatitis Society Core Allergen Series: 2017 Update. Dermatitis. 2017;28:141-143

32   Zhai H, Zheng Y, Fautz R, Fuchs A, Maibach HI. Reactions of non-immunologic contact urticaria on scalp, face, and back. Skin Res Technol 2012;18:436-441

33   Hausen BM. Contact allergy to balsam of Peru. II. Patch test results in 102 patients with selected balsam of Peru constituents. Am J Contact Dermat 2001;12:93-102

34 Lamey PJ, Lamb AB, Hughes A, Milligan KA, Forsyth A. Type III burning mouth syndrome: psychological and allergic aspects. J Oral Pathol Med 1994;23:216-219

35 Aschenbeck KA, Warshaw EM. Allergenic ingredients in facial wet wipes. Dermatitis 2017 Mar 23. doi: 10.1097/DER.0000000000000268. [Epub ahead of print]

36 Beene KM, Scheman A, Severson D, Reeder MJ. Prevalence of preservatives across all product types in the Contact Allergen Management Program. Dermatitis 2017;28:81-87

37 Yu J, Treat J, Chaney K, Brod B. Potential allergens in disposable diaper wipes, topical diaper preparations, and disposable diapers: under-recognized etiology of pediatric perineal dermatitis. Dermatitis 2016;27:110-118

38 Wuyts L, van Hoof T, Lambert J, Aerts O. Allergic contact dermatitis caused by aftershave creams containing *Glycyrrhiza inflata*. Contact Dermatitis 2017;77:49-51

39 Martínez-González MI, González-Pérez R, García-Rio I, Heras-González S. Allergic contact dermatitis caused by benzoic acid and lauryl glucoside in a sunscreen. Contact Dermatitis 2017;77:186-187

2.42 BENZOPHENONE-2

IDENTIFICATION

Description/definition	: Benzophenone-2 is a benzophenone derivative that conforms to the formula shown below
Chemical class(es)	: Benzophenones
Chemical/IUPAC name	: bis(2,4-Dihydroxyphenyl)methanone
Other names	: 2,2',4,4'-Tetrahydroxybenzophenone
CAS registry number (s)	: 131-55-5
EC number(s)	: 205-028-9
CIR review(s)	: J Am Coll Toxicol 1983;2:79-84 (access: www.cir-safety.org/ingredients)
Function(s) in cosmetics	: EU: masking; UV-absorber. USA: fragrance ingredients; light stabilizers
Patch testing	: 2% pet. (1); most benzophenones are tested 10% pet.
Molecular formula	: $C_{13}H_{10}O_5$

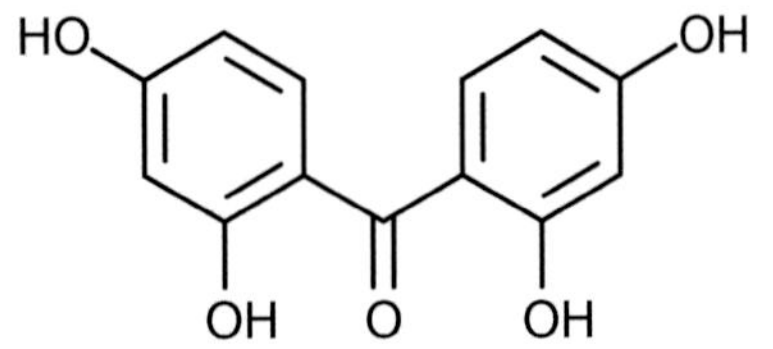

GENERAL

Benzophenone-2 is a UVA/B filter with UV absorbance maxima ($\lambda_{max,1}$, $\lambda_{max,2}$) at 287 and 349 nm (10). The literature on adverse reactions to sunscreens has been reviewed in several recent and older publications (4-9,14). A review of photocontact allergy to sunscreens was published in 2010 (11).

Case reports and case series

A man presented with subacute dermatitis of the chest and arm. He used to spray toilet water on his chest, hence an allergic reaction to perfume was suspected. A repeated open application test with his product was already positive after two applications. Patch tests with the European standard series, a cosmetics series and the constituents of the fragrance mix were all negative. Later, patch tests with the additives of the toilet water and a sunscreen series showed a positive reaction to benzophenone-2, tested 2% in petrolatum. Fifteen controls were negative. The patient refused to be photopatch tested. Whether the product itself was tested was not mentioned, and neither whether benzophenone-2 was present in the toilet water. However, the author did state that 'it is necessary to look out for benzophenone-2, which also seems to be common, at least in toilet water or perfume (1). One or possibly two patients had allergic contact dermatitis from benzophenone-2- in nail varnish remover (2).

Cross-reactions, pseudo-cross-reactions and co-reactions

Because of the shared chemical structure, cross-reactions within the benzophenone family are plausible, but have not been documented with certainty (4).

Presence in cosmetic products and chemical analyses

In the USA, in April 2017, benzophenone-2 was present in 164 of 56,714 cosmetic products of which the composition is known in FDA's Voluntary Cosmetic Registration Program (VCRP) (data obtained from FDA, May 2017). In April 2017, benzophenone-2 was present in 42 of 65,521 cosmetic products of which the composition is known in EWG's Skin Deep Cosmetics Database, USA (http://www.ewg.org/skindeep/). It should be realized that sunscreen products containing UV-filters are classified as drugs in the USA, not as cosmetics; the number mentioned here, therefore, is that of cosmetics containing the UV-filter, but it does *not* include their presence in sunscreens.

OTHER SIDE EFFECTS

Photosensitivity

In a group of 11 patients who identified themselves as 'allergic' or 'having a reaction' to sunscreens and who were photopatch tested extensively, one had a positive photopatch test to benzophenone-2; the relevance was unknown (3).

Other non-eczematous contact reactions
Benzophenone-2 in nail lacquers has caused discoloration of the nails in two women (12). A woman had yellow-green discoloration from benzophenone-2 in nail lacquer (13).

LITERATURE
1   Jacobs M-C. Contact allergy to benzophenone-2 in toilet water. Contact Dermatitis 1998;39:42
2   Boehncke WH, Schmitt M, Zollner T M, Hensel O. Nail polish allergy; an important differential diagnosis in contact dermatitis. Dtsch Med Wochenschr 1997;122:849-852 (article in German)
3   Shaw T, Simpson B, Wilson B, Oostman H, Rainey D, Storrs F. True photoallergy to sunscreens is rare despite popular belief. Dermatitis 2010;21:185-198
4   Heurung AR, Raju SI, Warshaw EM. Contact allergen of the year. Benzophenones. Dermatitis 2014;25:3-10 (contains many mistakes; Erratum in Dermatitis 2014;25:92-95)
5   Heurung AR, Raju SI, Warshaw EM. Adverse reactions to sunscreen agents: epidemiology, responsible irritants and allergens, clinical characteristics, and management. Dermatitis 2014;25:289-326
6   Avenel-Audran M. Sunscreen products: finding the allergen. Eur J Dermatol 2010;20:161-166
7   Scheuer E, Warshaw E. Sunscreen allergy: a review of epidemiology, clinical characteristics, and responsible allergens. Dermatitis 2006;17:3-11
8   Funk JO, Dromgoole SH, Maibach HI. Sunscreen intolerance: contact sensitization, photocontact sensitization, and irritancy of sunscreen agents. Dermatol Clin 1995;13:473-481
9   Dromgoole SH, Maibach HI. Sunscreening agent intolerance: Contact and photocontact sensitization and contact urticaria. J Am Acad Dermatol 1990;22:1068-1078
10 Shaath NA. Ultraviolet filters. Photochem Photobiol Sci 2010;9:464-469
11 Shaw T, Simpson B, Wilson B, Oostman H, Rainey D, Storrs F. True photoallergy to sunscreens is rare despite popular belief. Dermatitis 2010;21:185-198
12 Schauder S. Adverse reactions to sunscreening agents in 58 patients (part 3). Z Hautkr 1991;66:294-318 (article in German)
13 Winckler H. Dyschromie der Nägel durch Nagellack. Akt Dermatol 1989;15:127-128 (article in German)
14 Schauder S. Survey of the literature on adverse reactions to preparations containing UV filters (1947-1989) (Literaturübersicht über Unverträglichkeitsreaktionen auf lichtfilterhaltige Produkte von 1947 bis 1989). Z Hautkr 1990;65:982-998 (article in German)

2.43 BENZOPHENONE-3

IDENTIFICATION

Description/definition	: Benzophenone-3 is a benzophenone derivative that conforms to the formula shown below
Chemical class(es)	: Benzophenones
Chemical/IUPAC name	: (2-Hydroxy-4-methoxyphenyl)-phenylmethanone
Other names	: Oxybenzone; 2-hydroxy-4-methoxybenzophenone; Eusolex® 4360
CAS registry number (s)	: 131-57-7
EC number(s)	: 205-031-5
CIR review(s)	: J Am Coll Toxicol 1983;2:35-77 (access: www.cir-safety.org/ingredients)
SCCS opinion(s)	: SCCP/1201/08 (124); SCCP/1069/06 (125)
Merck Index monograph	: 8323
Function(s) in cosmetics	: EU: UV-absorber; UV-filter. USA: light stabilizers; sunscreens
EU cosmetic restrictions	: Regulated in Annex VI/4 of the Regulation (EC) No. 1223/2009
Patch testing	: 10.0% pet. (Chemotechnique, SmartPracticeEurope, SmartPracticeCanada)
Molecular formula	: $C_{14}H_{12}O_3$

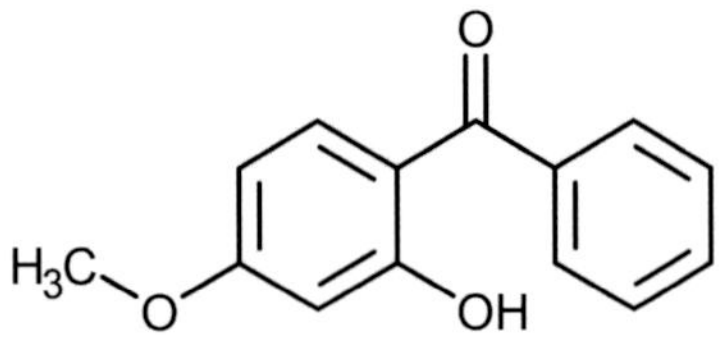

GENERAL

Benzophenone-3 is a UVA/B filter with UV absorbance maxima ($\lambda_{max,1}$, $\lambda_{max,2}$) at 286 and 324 nm (131), which has been used in Europe since 1980 (96). Although, of all sunscreens, benzophenone-3 has caused most cases of (photo)contact allergy, it has been suggested that sunscreen products formulated with 1-6% benzophenone-3 do not possess a significant sensitization or irritation potential for the general public (27). The literature on adverse reactions to sunscreens has been reviewed in several recent and older publications (21,104-108,134). A review of photocontact allergy to sunscreens was published in 2010 (90).

CONTACT ALLERGY

Patch testing in groups of patients

Results of routine patch testing (testing in consecutive patients suspected of contact dermatitis) with benzopheno-ne-3 back to 1998 are shown in table 2.43.1. Results of testing benzophenone-3 in groups of *selected* patients (e.g., patients suspected of photosensitivity, patients with dermatitis affecting mainly light-exposed skin or with a history of a sunscreen skin reactions) back to 1990 are shown in table 2.43.2.

Patch testing in consecutive patients suspected of contact dermatitis: routine testing

As benzophenone-3 has been included in the screening tray of the North American Contact Dermatitis Group (NACDG) since 1996, but is not present in the European baseline series or other routine screening series, virtually all data on routine testing with benzophenone-3 are from the USA + Canada, where the NACDG publishes their patch test results biannually. It should be appreciated that the test concentration up to 2008 was 3% pet., and in 2009 it was raised to 10% pet. Although in one study, testing with 10% pet. yielded more positive reactions than testing with 3% pet. (1.4% versus 0.5% [118]), the frequencies of sensitization in the NACDG studies in the period 2009-2014 were not higher that in the period 1996-2008, when the lower test concentration was used (table 2.43.1).

In routine testing, frequencies of sensitization have always been fairly low, ranging from 0.3% to 3.3%, with 11/17 studies having had a rate of sensitization lower than 1%. In the NACDG studies, 'definite' or 'probably' relevance was found for 28-59% of the positive patch test reactions, in recent years around 50% (51,52,129). Causative products were never mentioned.

Patch testing in groups of selected patients

Results of testing benzophenone-3 in groups of selected patients (e.g., patients suspected of photosensitivity, patients with dermatitis affecting mainly light-exposed skin or with a history of a sunscreen skin reactions) are shown in table 2.43.2. Test concentrations used have been 2% pet., 3% pet. and/or 10% pet., but the higher test concen-trations have not clearly resulted in more positive reactions, the mode of selection being the more important determinant. In selected groups, frequencies of sensitization have ranged from 0.1% to 10.6%, with 14/20 of the studies having had a rate of <2%. However, the study presenting 10.6% positive patch test reactions had certain weaknesses in design (130).

Table 2.43.1 Patch testing in groups of patients: Routine testing

Years and Country	Test conc. & vehicle	Number of patients tested	positive (%)	Selection of patients (S); Relevance (R); Comments (C)	Ref.
2013-14 USA, Canada	10% pet.	4859	31 (0.6%)	R: definite + probable relevance: 52%	129
2011-12 USA, Canada	10% pet.	4231	35 (0.8%)	R: definite + probable relevance: 57%	51
2009-10 USA, Canada	10% pet.	4302	39 (0.9%)	R: definite + probable relevance: 47%	52
2006-2010 USA	10% pet.	208	(1.4%)	R: 33%	118
	3% pet.	2859	(0.5%)	R: 39%	
2001-10 USA, Canada	3% pet, later 10% pet.	23908	82 (0.3%)	R: definite relevance 22%, probable relevance 46%; C: the lower prevalence of this study than in the other studies from the NACDG, from which this is composed, must be explained by the data retrieval method	89
2007-8 USA, Canada	3% pet.	5083	(0.9%)	R: definite + probable relevance: 59%	44
2005-6 USA, Canada	3% pet.	4436	(0.7%)	R: definite + probable relevance: 28%	43
2003-2005 China		599	7 (1.2%)	R: not stated	116
2000-2005 USA	3% pet.	3845	(0.7%)	R: 48%	37
2003-4 USA, Canada	3% pet.	5144	35 (0.7%)	R: not stated	45
2001-2002 USA	3% pet.	4899	(0.6%)	R: definite + probable relevance: 41%	112
1998-2000 USA	3% pet.	5800	(0.6%)	R: definite + probable relevance: 32%	111
1998–2000 USA	2% pet.	1321	(3.3%)	R: not stated	114
1996-1998 USA	3% pet.	4094	(0.5%)	R: definite + probable + possible relevance: 74%	113

In most studies, no data on relevance of the positive patch test reactions have been presented or specified for benzophenone-3 (often, a percentage was given for all tested sunscreens together). In studies that did, often some 2/3 up to 100% (also a study with certain weaknesses [36]) of the reactions were classified as relevant, but causative ingredients were mentioned in one study only (5 sunscreen products, 2 cosmetics [77]).

Table 2.43.2 Patch testing in groups of patients: Selected patient groups

Years and Country	Test conc. & vehicle	Number of patients tested	positive (%)	Selection of patients (S); Relevance (R); Comments (C)	Ref.
2011-2013 Colombia	10% pet.	112	4 (3.4%)	S: dermatitis affecting mainly light-exposed skin, or a history of a sunscreen or topical NSAID skin reaction; R: 75%	23
2008-2011 12 European countries	10% pet.	1031	6 (0.6%)	S: patients with exposed site dermatitis or history of a reaction to a sunscreen or topical NSAID; R: not specified	47
2001-2010 Australia	10% pet.	3573	60 (1.7%)	S: not stated; R: 37%	128
2001-2010 Canada		160	17 (10.6%)	S: patients with a photodistributed rash, photosensitivity or rash after sunscreen application; R: not stated; C: weak study: inadequate reading of test results, erythema only was considered to represent a positive patch test reaction	130
2000-2007 USA	3% pet.	994	11 (1.2%)	S: patients tested with a supplemental cosmetic screening series; R: 100% (both test concentrations); C: weak study: a. high rate of macular erythema and weak reactions; b. relevance figures included 'questionable' and 'past' relevance	36
	10% pet.	867	15 (1.7%)		
2000-2005 USA	3% pet.	178	3 (1.7%)	S: patients photopatch tested for suspected photodermatitis; R: 2 reactions were relevant	91
2001-4 USA, Canada	3% pet.	60	3 (5%)	S: patients with allergic contact cheilitis; R: only relevant reactions were mentioned	119
2001-2003 Colombia	10% pet.	82	1 (1.2%)	S: patients with a clinical diagnosis of photoallergic contact dermatitis; R: 65% of all reactions in the study were relevant	25
2000-2002 Finland		3296	(0.2%)	S: patients tested with a cosmetic series; R: not stated	115
2000-2002 UK, I, NL	10% pet.	1155	9 (0.8%)	S: patients suspected of photosensitivity or reaction to a sunscreen; R: current 8, unknown 1	1
1993-2000 Australia	2% pet.	149	1 (0.7%)	S: patients suspected of photosensitivity; R: of 17 patient who had contact or photocontact reactions to a panel of 10 sunscreens, 10 were considered to have relevant reactions	82
1994-1999 NL	10% pet.	55	2 (3.6%)	S: patients suspected of photosensitivity disorders; R: not stated	24

Table 2.43.2 Patch testing in groups of patients: Selected patient groups (*continued*)

Years and Country	Test conc. & vehicle	Number of patients tested	positive (%)		Selection of patients (S); Relevance (R); Comments (C)	Ref.
1983-1998 UK	2% or 10% pet.	2715	8	(0.3%)	S: patients suspected of photosensitivity or with (a history of) dermatitis at exposed sites; R: not stated	2
1995-1996 Finland		702		(0.1%)	S: patients tested with a cosmetic series; R: not stated	115
1990-1996 Sweden	2% pet.	355	1	(0.3%)	S: patients suspected of photosensitivity; R: not stated	87
1981-1996 Germany	2% or 10% pet.	355	3	(0.8%)	S: patients suspected of clinical photosensitivity; R: not stated	8
1990-1994 France	2% or 10% pet.	370	6	(1.6%)	S: patients with suspected photodermatitis; R: not specified, 72% of all reactions in the study were considered relevant	14
1989-1991 UK	2% pet.	99	2	(2%)	S: 45 patients with photosensitivity dermatitis/actinic reticuloid syndrome and 54 with polymorphic light eruption; R: not stated; R: not specified	9
1989-1990 France	2% pet.	54	4	(3.7%)	S: patients suspected of photosensitivity; R: in the group of 7 patients who had contact allergy, photo-aggravated contact allergy or photocontact allergy, the causative products were sunscreens in 5 patients and other cosmetics in 2; C: 2 of the 4 had photoaggravated contact dermatitis	77
1985-1990 USA	2% pet.	187	5	(2.7%)	S: patients with a history of photosensitivity; R: four with a combined contact/photocontact allergy were relevant	12

I: Ireland; NL: Netherlands; UK: United Kingdom

Case reports and case series

Case series

Benzophenone-3 was stated to be the (or an) allergen in 5 patients in a group of 603 individuals suffering from cosmetic dermatitis, seen in the period 2010-2015 in Leuven, Belgium (117). In the period 1996-2013, in a tertiary referral center in Valencia, Spain, 5419 patients were patch tested. Of these, 628 individuals had allergic contact dermatitis to cosmetics. Benzophenone-3 was the responsible allergen in 9 cases (98, overlap with ref. 126). Benzophenone-3 was responsible for 5 out of 959 cases of non-fragrance cosmetic allergy where the causal allergen was identified, Belgium, 2000-2010 (35). In the period 2000-2007, 202 patients with allergic contact dermatitis caused by cosmetics were seen in Valencia, Spain. In this group, two individuals reacted to benzophenone-3 from its presence in sunscreens (126, overlap with ref. 98).

In a retrospective study of 196 patients with cheilitis, investigated by the members of the NACDG, there were five clinically relevant positive patch test reactions to benzophenone-3 (80). Twenty-four relevant cases of contact allergy or photocontact allergy to benzophenone were seen in one clinic in Melbourne, Australia in an 18-year period up to 2012 (46). Four positive patch test reactions to benzophenone-3 were ascribed to cosmetic allergy (38). In the period 1981-1989, 56 patients (43 women, 13 men) were diagnosed with contact allergy or photocontact allergy to UV-filters in one center in Germany. There were 2 contact allergic, 1 photoaggravated contact allergic and 4 photoallergic reactions to benzophenone-3. All reactions were relevant and all 46 patients who could be (photo)patch tested with their own sunscreens (and a few of them with other cosmetics) had one or more positive (photo)patch tests to these products (132, overlap with ref. 8). In the period 1978-1991, there were 5 relevant patch test reactions to benzophenone-3 in one hospital in Leuven, Belgium (81).

Case reports

Sunscreen products
Several single case reports of allergic contact dermatitis from benzophenone-3 in sunscreen products have been described (4,39,71,73,78). One patient had contact allergy and photocontact allergy to benzophenone-3 in a sunscreen (68). Another individual had photoaggravated allergic contact dermatitis combined with immediate-type allergy from benzophenone-3 in a sunscreen (76).

Other cosmetics
Several single case reports of cheilitis from contact allergy to benzophenone-3 in lip balms and UV-lipsticks have been reported (20,30,73,79,92,133). Three patients had allergic contact cheilitis from benzophenone-3 in lipsticks (120). A woman had allergic contact dermatitis from her own cosmetics (products not specified) (88). Three other women had allergic contact dermatitis from benzophenone-3 in respectively a moisturizing cream (59), artificial nail material (62) and a facial cosmetic (78).

Contact allergy to benzophenone-3 in non-cosmetic products

A child had combined immediate and delayed reactions to benzophenone-3 in plastic products (94). In a group of 46 New Zealand farmers with dermatitis, investigated in one center in 1994-1997, one had occupational contact allergy to benzophenone-3. It was not mentioned how many had been tested with benzophenone-3, nor what the culprit product was (101).

Cross-reactions, pseudo-cross-reactions and co-reactions

Because of the shared chemical structure, cross-reactions within the benzophenone family are plausible, but have not been documented with certainty (102). Benzophenone-4 (39,74); benzophenone-8 (39, 73,74); benzophenone-10 (68,74). Photocross-reactions are discussed below (Photocross-reactions and pseudo-photocross-reactions).

Presence in cosmetic products and chemical analyses

In May 2017, benzophenone-3 was present in 1032 of 68,703 cosmetic products of which the composition is known in EWG's Skin Deep Cosmetics Database, USA (http://www.ewg.org/skindeep/). It should be realized that sunscreen products containing UV-filters are classified as drugs in the USA, not as cosmetics; the number mentioned here, therefore, is that of cosmetics containing the UV-filter, but it does *not* include their presence in sunscreens. In the USA, in April 2017, benzophenone-3 was present in 1023 of 56,714 cosmetic products of which the composition is known in FDA's Voluntary Cosmetic Registration Program (VCRP) (data obtained from FDA, May 2017). In 2012, in Switzerland, 116 cosmetics from seven widely used leave-on product categories (19 lip care products, 8 lipsticks, 29 face creams, 11 liquid makeup foundations, 3 aftershaves, 7 hand creams and 39 sunscreens) were investigated to determine the frequency of occurrence and concentrations of 22 organic UV filters in these products. Benzophenone -3 was found in 3% of the products in a concentration range of 1.03-5.06%, mean 3.27% (127). In a sample of 337 sunscreens marketed in the UK in 2010, benzophenone-3 was present in 15% (103).

In 2009, in the USA, the ingredient lists of 796 hair products from one company were screened for the presence of benzophenone-3. Benzophenone-3 was present in 3% of 279 shampoos, in 3% of 231 conditioners, and in 9% of 286 styling products (121). In 2009, in the USA, the ingredient lists of 730 lip cosmetics and dental care products from one company were screened for the presence of benzophenone-3. Benzophenone-3 was present in 0% of 31 lip liners, in 0% of 429 lipsticks, in 30% of 92 lip moisturizers, in 0% of 153 toothpastes, and in 0% of 25 mouth washes (122). In 2009, in the USA, the ingredient lists of 657 miscellaneous cosmetics from one company were screened for the presence of benzophenone-3. Benzophenone-3 was present only in 68% of 201 sunblocks (123).

Benzophenone-3 was present in 8.8% of 4447 cosmetic products collected in Germany, 2006-2009 (49). Benzophe-none-3 was present in 17% of 329 sunscreen products (incl. 21 lipstick sunscreens) marketed in the UK in 2005 (97). In the Netherlands, in 2002-2003, benzophenone-3 was found in 49 of 162 (30%) tested samples of commercial sunscreens (54). Benzophenone-3 was present in 14 of 75 (19%) sunscreen creams and lotions from 30 European and US producers purchased in Denmark in 2001 in a concentration range of 0.01-5.3% (84).

OTHER SIDE EFFECTS

Photosensitivity

Photocontact allergy is the most frequent adverse reaction to benzophenone-3. It should be appreciated that, in countries where ketoprofen (an NSAID) is frequently used in topical analgesic and anti-inflammatory preparations such as Belgium, France, Italy and Spain, many positive photopatch tests to benzophenone-3 are the result of photocross-reactivity to primary ketoprofen photocontact sensitization (110).

Photopatch testing in groups of patients

Results of photopatch testing benzophenone-3 in groups of selected patients back to 1985 are shown in table 2.43.3. Selection criteria usually were exposed site dermatitis, skin reactions to sunscreens or a topical NSAID preparation, or suspicion of photoallergic contact dermatitis or other photosensitivity disorders.

Table 2.43.3 Photopatch testing in groups of patients

Years and Country	Test conc. & vehicle	Number of patients tested	positive (%)	Selection of patients (S); Relevance (R); Comments (C)	Ref.
2011-2013 Colombia	10% pet.	112	11 (9.8%)	S: dermatitis affecting mainly light-exposed skin, a history of a sunscreen or topical NSAID skin reaction; R: 27%	23
2008-2011 12 European countries	10% pet.	1031	37 (3.6%)	S: patients with exposed site dermatitis or history of a reaction to a sunscreen or topical NSAID; R: 44% current and 11% past relevance for all photoallergens together; over half may have photo-cross-reacted to ketoprofen photosensitivity; frequent co-sensitivity to octocrylene	47

Table 2.43.3 Photopatch testing in groups of patients (*continued*)

Years and Country	Test conc. & vehicle	Number of patients tested | positive (%)		Selection of patients (S); Relevance (R); Comments (C)	Ref.
2007-2011 Singapore	10% pet.	22	6 (27%)	S: not stated; R: all reactions were relevant	11
2000-2011 UK	10% pet.	157	3 (1.9%)	S: children <18 years suspected of photosensitivity; R: 2/3 were caused by sunscreen products	86
2001-2010 Canada		160	12 (7.5%)	S: patients with a photodistributed rash, photosensitivity or rash after sunscreen application; R: not stated	130
1993-2009 USA	3% pet.	30	5 (17%)	S: patients with chronic actinic dermatitis; R: not stated	48
2003-2007 Portugal	10% pet.	83	3 (3.6%)	S: patients with suspected photoaggravated facial dermatitis or systemic photosensitivity; R: all sunscreen photopatch tests were of current or past relevance	83
2004-2006 Italy	10% pet.	1082	15 (1.4%)	S: patients with histories and clinical features suggestive of photoallergic contact dermatitis; 6 were cases of photoaggravated contact allergy; R: 88%	40
1993-2006 USA	3% pet.	76	3 (3.9%)	S: not stated; R: 56% of all reactions to sunscreens were considered to be 'probably relevant'	28
1992-2006 Greece		207	26 (12.5%)	S: unknown; R: unknown; C: no details known, article not read	26
2000-2005 USA	3% pet.	178	5 (2.8%)	S: patients photopatch tested for suspected photodermatitis; R: 4 reactions were relevant	91
2001-2003 Colombia	10% pet.	82	22 (27%)	S: patients with a clinical diagnosis of photoallergic contact dermatitis; R: 65% of all reactions in the study were relevant	25
2000-2002 UK, I, NL	10% pet.	1155	27 (2.3%)	S: patients suspected of photosensitivity or reaction to a sunscreen; R: current 20, unknown 4, past relevance 3	1
1991-2001 France		2076	54 (2.6%)	S: patients suspected of photoallergy; R: ? (article not read)	75
1993-2000 Australia	2% pet.	149	3 (2.0%)	S: patients suspected of photosensitivity; R: of 17 patient who had contact or photocontact reactions to a panel of 10 sunscreens, 10 were considered to have relevant reactions	82
1994-1999 NL	10% pet.	55	3 (5.5%)	S: patients suspected of photosensitivity disorders; R: not stated	24
1996-1998 UK		167	5 (3.0%)	S: patients with suspected photosensitivity; R: 'most cases' in the entire group were relevant	13
1983-1998 UK	2% or 10% pet.	2715	14 (0.5%)	S: patients suspected of photosensitivity or with (a history of) dermatitis at exposed sites; R: 37% for all photoallergens together	2
1991-97 Ger, Au, Swi	10% pet.	1261	8 (0.6%)	S: patients suspected of photosensitivity; R: not stated	5
1990-1996 Sweden	2% pet.	355	15 (4.2%)	S: patients suspected of photosensitivity; R: not stated	87
1981-1996 Germany	2% or 10% pet.	355	9 (2.5%)	S: patients suspected of clinical photosensitivity; R: not stated	8
1990-1994 France	2% or 10% pet.	370	25 (6.8%)	S: patients with suspected photodermatitis; R: not specified, 72% of all reactions in the study were considered relevant	14
1985-1994 Italy		1050	10 (1.0%)	S: patients with histories or clinical pictures suggestive of allergic contact photodermatitis; R: 97% for all sunscreens together	6
1982-1992 France		283	35 (12.4%)	S: patients suspected of photodermatitis; R: unknown (article not read)	16
1989-1990 France	2% pet.	54	3 (6%)	S: patients suspected of photosensitivity; R: in the group of 7 patients who had contact allergy, photo-aggravated contact allergy or photocontact allergy, the causative products were sunscreens in 5 patients and other cosmetics in 2; C: 2 other patients had photoaggravated contact dermatitis	77
1985-1990 USA	2% pet.	94	9 (9.6%)	S: patients with a history of photosensitivity; R: all relevant	12
1980-85 Ger, Au, Swi	2% pet.	1129	8 (0.7%)	S: patients suspected of photoallergy, polymorphic light eruption, phototoxicity and skin problems with photodistribution; R: not stated	7

Au: Austria; Ger: Germany; I: Ireland; NL: Netherlands; UK: United Kingdom; Swi: Switzerland

Test concentrations used have been 2% pet., 3% pet. and/or 10% pet., but the higher test concentrations have not clearly resulted in more positive reactions, the mode of selection probably being the more important determinant. In 27 studies, frequencies of sensitization have ranged from 0.5% to 27% (11,25). In studies where relevance was mentioned, 27 to 100% of all positive photopatch tests were considered to be relevant; in most, more than half were relevant, but causative products were rarely (86) mentioned.

Case reports and series

Case series
Twenty-four relevant cases of contact allergy or photocontact allergy to benzophenone-3 were seen in one center in Australia in an 18-year period (46). In the period 1981-1989, 56 patients (43 women, 13 men) were diagnosed with contact allergy or photocontact allergy to UV-filters in one center in Germany. There were 2 contact allergic, 1 photo-aggravated contact allergic and 4 photoallergic reactions to benzophenone-3. All reactions were relevant and all 46 patients who could be (photo)patch tested with their own sunscreens (and a few of them with other cosmetics) had one or more positive (photo)patch tests to these products (132, overlap with ref. 8). Five patients had photo-allergic contact dermatitis from benzophenone-3 in sunscreens (78). There have also been publications presenting 3 patients (3,18) and 4 patients (19,93) with photocontact allergy to benzophenone-3 in sunscreen products. Of 35 patients who had photocontact allergy to benzophenone-3, over 1/3 reacted to a moisturizer that contained this sunscreen (16).

Case reports

Sunscreen products
Several single case reports of photoallergic contact dermatitis from benzophenone-3 in sunscreen products have been described (10,15,29,69,70,92,95,99,135). One patient had both immediate (urticarial) and delayed reactions upon photopatch testing benzophenone-3 (17). Another patient had erythema multiforme-like photoallergic contact dermatitis from benzophenone-3 in a sunscreen (65). One individual was diagnosed with photoaggravated allergic contact dermatitis from benzophenone-3 in a sunscreen (76). In a group of 11 patients who identified themselves as 'allergic' or 'having a reaction' to sunscreens and who were photopatch tested extensively, one had a positive photopatch test to benzophenone-3; the patient had previously used sunscreens containing benzophenone-3 (90).

Other cosmetics
Single case reports have been published of photocontact dermatitis caused by benzophenone-3 present in lip salve (57), photoprotective lipstick (67), and moisturizing cream (69). A woman had facial erythema from photocontact allergy to benzophenone-3 in a moisturizing cream, combined with photocontact urticaria (30). Another patient had both contact and photocontact allergy from a moisturizing cream (59). Two patients had photoallergic contact dermatitis from their own cosmetics (88). Three patients were diagnosed with photoallergic contact dermatitis from benzophenone-3 in cosmetic creams (15). Three other women had photocontact allergy to benzophenone-3 in anti-ageing day creams (66). Three individuals had photoallergic contact dermatitis from benzophenone-3 in facial cosmetics (85). One patient was reported to have photocontact allergy to benzophenone-3, but curiously the authors did not report whether the patient had used products containing the UV-filter (58).

Photocontact allergy to benzophenone-3 in non-cosmetic products
One patient had photoallergic contact dermatitis from benzophenone-3 present in the ink of a magazine (50).

Photocross-reactions and pseudo-photocross-reactions
Photoallergy to ketoprofen leads in 27-80% of the patients to photocontact allergy to benzophenone-3 (34, 41,42,61,63,109,110). This is probably due to photocross-reactivity: when irradiated with sunlight, ketoprofen is broken down into various benzophenones structurally related to benzophenone-3 (64). As octocrylene also photo-cross-reacts to ketoprofen, many patients reacting to benzophenone-3 are also photoallergic to octocrylene. Of 37 patients with a positive photopatch test to benzophenone-3, 22 (59%) co-reacted to ketoprofen and 18 (49%) to octocrylene (47). Benzophenone-10 (59,68,72).

Immediate-type reactions
One patient had an immediate contact reaction to benzophenone 3, and a similar reaction with benzophenone-4 (22). A woman had anaphylaxis 15 minutes after application of a sunscreen containing benzophenone-3. She fainted and had generalized wheals, an inspiratory stridor, low blood pressure, and increased heart rate. A patch test with benzophenone-3 gave an urticarial wheal at the test site within 20 minutes (53). A similar reaction with contact urticaria from benzophenone-3 in various cosmetics and an anaphylactic reaction with syncope from a 'false tan' lotion was seen in another individual (55). A very similar case from benzophenone-3 in a sunscreen product and urticarial reaction from kissing someone who had used the same product has also been reported (56). One patient had (photoaggravated) allergic contact dermatitis plus immediate-type allergy from benzophenone-3 in a sunscreen (76). Another had an immediate reaction upon patch testing with benzophenone-3, which was a chance finding (87). A child had combined immediate and delayed reactions to benzophenone-3 in plastic products (94). A review of contact urticaria caused by ingredients of cosmetics has been provided in 2016 (100).

Immediate photocontact reactions

An immediate urticarial reaction (and delayed reaction) upon photopatch testing benzophenone-3 was observed in one patient (17). One individual had combined photocontact allergy and photocontact urticaria from benzophenone-3- in a moisturizing cream (30). Another patient had photocontact urticaria to benzophenone-3, the sunscreen product in which it was present, and benzophenone-10 (60).

Systemic side effects

Some 0.5% of the applied dose of benzophenone-3 may be absorbed through the skin; the relevance of this finding is unknown (32). Benzophenone-3 and other benzophenones potentially have estrogen-like effects (33).

Miscellaneous side effects

Milia developed in one patient after an episode of bullous photoallergic contact dermatitis from sunscreens containing benzophenone-3, butyl methoxydibenzoylmethane and ethylhexyl methoxycinnamate (31).

LITERATURE

1   Bryden A, Moseley H, Ibbotson S, Chowdhury MM, Beck MH, Bourke J, et al. Photopatch testing of 1155 patients: results of the U.K. multicentre photopatch test study group. Brit J Dermatol 2006;155:737-747

2   Darvay A, White I, Rycroft R, Jones AB, Hawk JL, McFadden JP. Photoallergic contact dermatitis is uncommon. Br J Dermatol 2001;145:597-601

3   Thune P. Contact and photocontact allergy to sunscreens. Photodermatol 1984;1:5-9

4   Thompson G, Maibach H, Epstein J. Allergic contact dermatitis from sunscreen preparations complicating photodermatitis. Arch Dermatol 1977;113:1252-1253

5   Neumann NJ, Hölzle E, Plewig G, Schwarz T, Panizzon RG, Breit R, et al. Photopatch testing: The 12-year experience of the German, Austrian and Swiss Photopatch Test Group. J Am Acad Dermatol 2000;42:183-192

6   Pigatto PD, Legori A, Bigardi AS, Guarrera M, Tosti A, Santucci B, et al. Gruppo Italiano recerca dermatiti da contatto ed ambientali Italian multicenter study of allergic contact photodermatitis: epidemiological aspects. Am J Contact Dermatitis 1996;17:158-163

7   Hölzle E, Neumann N, Hausen B, Przybilla B, Schauder S, Hönigsmann H, et al. Photopatch testing: the 5-year experience of the German, Austrian and Swiss Photopatch Test Group. J Am Acad Dermatol 1991;25:59-68

8   Schauder S, Ippen H. Contact and photocontact sensitivity. Review of a 15-year experience and of the literature to suncreens. Contact Dermatitis 1997;37:221-232

9   Bilsland D, Ferguson J. Contact allergy to sunscreen chemicals in photosensitivity dermatitis/actinic reticuloid syndrome (PD/AR) and polymorphic light eruption. Contact Dermatitis 1993;29:70-73

10 Hölzle E, Plewig G. Photoallergic contact dermatitis by benzophenone containing sunscreen preparations. Hautarzt 1982;33:391-393

11 Chuah SY, Leow YH, Goon AT, Theng CT, Chong WS. Photopatch testing in Asians: a 5-year experience in Singapore. Photodermatol Photoimmunol Photomed 2013;29:116-120

12 DeLeo VA, Suarez SM, Maso MJ. Photoallergic contact dermatitis. Results of photopatch testing in New York, 1985 to 1990. Arch Dermatol 1992;128:1513-1518

13 Bell HK, Rhodes LE. Photopatch testing in photosensitive patients. Br J Dermatol 2000;142:589-590

14 Journe F, Marguery M-C, Rakotondrazafy J, El Sayed F, Bazex J. Sunscreen sensitization: a 5-year study. Acta Derm Venereol (Stockh) 1999;79:211-213

15 Marguery MC, Bazex J. Photoallergic contact dermatitis due to 2-hydroxy, 4-methoxybenzophenone (oxybenzone), report of four cases. Br J Dermatol 1989;121 (suppl. 34):59-60

16 Szczurko C, Dompmartin A, Michel M, Moreau A, Leroy D. Photocontact allergy to oxybenzone: ten years of experience. Photodermatol Photoimmunol Photomed 1994;10:144-147

17 Collins P, Ferguson J. Photoallergic contact dermatitis to oxybenzone. Br J Dermatol 1994;131:124-129

18 Boulitrop-Morvan A, Dalac S, Collet E, et al. Photoallergie à l'oxybenzone. À propos de trois nouveaux cas. Nouv Dermatol 1990;9:844

19 Knobler E, Almeida L, Ruzkowski AM, Held J, Harber L, DeLeo V. Photoallergy to benzophenone. Arch Dermatol 1989;125:801-804

20 Fowler JF. Allergic cheilitis due to benzophenone-3. Presented at the Patch Test Clinic Symposium at the Fortysixth Annual Meeting of the American Academy of Dermatology, San Antonio, Texas., Dec. 5-10, 1987

21 Dromgoole SH, Maibach HI. Sunscreening agent intolerance: Contact and photocontact sensitization and contact urticaria. J Am Acad Dermatol 1990;22:1068-1078

22 Ramsay DL, Cohen HJ, Baer RL. Allergic reaction to benzophenones. Simultaneous occurrence of urticaria and contact sensitivities. Arch Dermatol 1972;105:906-908

23 Valbuena Mesa MC, Hoyos Jiménez EV. Photopatch testing in Bogota (Colombia): 2011–2013. Contact Dermatitis 2016;74:11-17

24 Bakkum RS, Heule F. Results of photopatch testing in Rotterdam during a 10-year period. Br J Dermatol 2002;146:275-279

25 Rodriguez E, Valbuena M, Rey M, Porras de Quintana L. Causal agents of photoallergic contact dermatitis diagnosed in the national institute of dermatology of Columbia. Photoderm Photoimmunol Photomed 2006;22:189-192

26 Katsarou A, Makris M, Zarafonitis G, Lagogianni E, Gregoriou S, Kalogeromitros D. Photoallergic contact dermatitis: the 15-year experience of a tertiary referral center in a sunny Mediterranean city. Int J Immunopathol Pharmacol 2008;21:725-727

27 Agin PP, Ruble K, Hermansky SJ, McCarthy TJ. Rates of allergic sensitization and irritation to oxybenzone-containing sunscreen products: a quantitative meta-analysis of 64 exaggerated use studies. Photodermatol Photoimmunol Photomed 2008;24:211-217

28 Victor FC, Cohen DE, Soter NA. A 20-year analysis of previous and emerging allergens that elicit photoallergic contact dermatitis. J Am Acad Dermatol 2010;62:605-610

29 Cook N, Freeman S. Photosensitive dermatitis due to sunscreen allergy in a child. Australas J Dermatol 2002;43:133-135

30 Nedorost ST. Facial erythema as a result of benzophenone allergy. J Am Acad Dermatol 2003;49:S259-S261

31 Bryden AM, Ferguson J, Ibbotson SH. Milia complicating photocontact allergy to absorbent sunscreen chemicals. Clin Exp Dermatol 2003;28:668-669

32 Gonzalez HG, Farbrot A, Larkö O. Percutaneous absorption of benzophenone-3, a common component of topical sunscreens. Clin Exp Dermatol 2002;27:691-694

33 Kunz P, Fent K. Estrogenic activity of UV filter mixtures. Toxicol Appl Pharmacol 2006;15:86-99

34 Avenel-Audran M, Dutartre H, Goossens A, Jeanmougin M, Comte C, Bernier C, et al. Octocrylene, an emerging photoallergen. Arch Dermatol 2010;146:753-757

35 Travassos AR, Claes L, Boey L, Drieghe J, Goossens A. Non-fragrance allergens in specific cosmetic products. Contact Dermatitis 2011;65:276-285

36 Wetter DA, Yiannias JA, Prakash AV, Davis MD, Farmer SA, el-Azhary RA, et al. Results of patch testing to personal care product allergens in a standard series and a supplemental cosmetic series: an analysis of 945 patients from the Mayo Clinic Contact Dermatitis Group, 2000-2007. J Am Acad Dermatol 2010;63:789-798

37 Davis MD, Scalf LA, Yiannias JA, Cheng JF, El-Azhary RA, Rohlinger AL, et al. Changing trends and allergens in the patch test standard series. Arch Dermatol 2008;144:67-72

38 Kohl L, Blondeel A, Song M. Allergic contact dermatitis from cosmetics: retrospective analysis of 819 patch-tested patients. Dermatology 2002;204:334-337

39 Sasseville D, Nantel-Battista M, Molinari R. Multiple contact allergies to benzophenones. Contact Dermatitis 2011;65:179-181

40 Pigatto PD, Guzzi G, Schena D, Guarrera M, Foti C, Francalanci S, et al. Photopatch tests: an Italian multicentre study from 2004 to 2006. Contact Dermatitis 2008;59:103-108

41 Karlsson I, VandenBroecke K, Martensson J, Goossens A, Börje A. Clinical and experimental studies of octocrylene's allergenic potency. Contact Dermatitis 2011;64:343-352

42 Devleeschouwer V, Roelandts R, Garmyn M, Goossens A. Allergic and photoallergic contact dermatitis from ketoprofen: results of (photo) patch testing and follow-up of 42 patients. Contact Dermatitis 2008;58:159-166

43 Zug KA, Warshaw EM, Fowler JF Jr, Maibach HI, Belsito DL, Pratt MD, et al. Patch-test results of the North American Contact Dermatitis Group 2005-2006. Dermatitis 2009;20:149-160

44 Fransway AF, Zug KA, Belsito DV, Deleo VA, Fowler JF Jr, Maibach HI, et al. North American Contact Dermatitis Group patch test results for 2007-2008. Dermatitis 2013;24:10-21

45 Warshaw EM, Belsito DV, DeLeo VA, Fowler JF Jr, Maibach HI, Marks JG, et al. North American Contact Dermatitis Group patch-test results, 2003-2004 study period. Dermatitis 2008;19:129-136

46 Nixon RL. Contact dermatitis to sunscreens. Dermatitis 2012;23:140-141

47 The European Multicentre Photopatch Test Study (EMCPPTS) Taskforce. A European multicentre photopatch test study. Br J Dermatol 2012;166:1002-1009

48 Que SK, Brauer JA, Soter NA, Cohen DE. Chronic actinic dermatitis: an analysis at a single institution over 25 years. Dermatitis 2011;22:147-154

49 Uter W, Gonçalo M, Yazar K, Kratz E-M, Mildau G, Lidén C. Coupled exposure to ingredients of cosmetic products: III. Ultraviolet filters. Contact Dermatitis 2014;71:162-169

50 Infante Hernando L., Serra-Baldrich E, Dordal T, Puig Sanz L. Photoallergic contact dermatitis caused by benzophenones in magazine inks. Contact Dermatitis 2013;69:124-126

51 Warshaw EM, Maibach HI, Taylor JS, Sasseville D, DeKoven JG, Zirwas MJ, et al. North American Contact Dermatitis Group patch test results: 2011-2012. Dermatitis 2015;26:49-59

52 Warshaw EM, Belsito DV, Taylor JS, Sasseville D, DeKoven JG, Zirwas MJ, et al. North American Contact Dermatitis Group patch test results: 2009 to 2010. Dermatitis 2013;24:50-59

53 Spijker GT, Schuttelaar M-LA, Barkema L, Velders A, Coenraads P-J. Anaphylaxis caused by topical application of a sunscreen containing benzophenone-3. Contact Dermatitis 2008;59:248-249

54 Dutch Food and Consumer Product Safety Authority. Survey UV Filters in Sun Screens. Report: ND04o030 (Dutch). Food and Consumer Product Safety Authority (VWA), Den Haag, the Netherlands, 2004

55 Yesudian PD, King CM. Severe contact urticaria and anaphylaxis from benzophenone-3(2-hydroxy-4-methoxy benzophenone). Contact Dermatitis 2002;46:55-56

56 Emonet S, Pasche-Koo F, Perin-Minisini M-J, Hauser C. Anaphylaxis to oxybenzone, a frequent constituent of sunscreens. J Allergy Clin Immunol 2001;46:556-557

57 Veysey EC, Orton DI. Photoallergic contact cheilitis due to oxybenzone found in a lip cosmetic. Contact Dermatitis 2006;55:54

58 Langan SM, Collins P. Photocontact allergy to oxybenzone and contact allergy to lignocaine and prilocaine. Contact Dermatitis 2006;54:173-174

59 Kiec-Swierczynska M, Krecisz B, Swierczynska-Machura D. Photoallergic and allergic reaction to 2-hydroxy-4-methoxybenzophenone (sunscreen) and allergy to cetyl alcohol in cosmetic cream. Contact Dermatitis 2005;53:170-171

60 Bourrain JL, Amblard P, Béani JC. Contact urticaria photoinduced by benzophenones. Contact Dermatitis 2003;48:45-46

61 Kawada A, Aragane Y, Asai M, Tezuka T. Simultaneous photocontact sensitivity to ketoprofen and oxybenzone. Contact Dermatitis 2001;44:370

62 Guin JD. Eyelid dermatitis from benzophenone used in nail enhancement. Contact Dermatitis 2000; 43:308-309

63 Horn HM, Humphreys F, Aldridge RD. Contact dermatitis and prolonged photosensititivity induced by ketoprofen and associated with sensitivity to benzophenone-3. Contact Dermatitis 1998;38:353-354

64 Bosca F, Miranda MA, Carganico G, Mauleon D. Photochemical and photobiological properties of ketoprofen associated with the benzophenone chromophore. Photochem Photobiol 1994;60:96-101

65 Zhang X-M, Nakagawa M, Kawai K, Kawai K. Erythema-multiforme-like eruption following photoallergic contact dermatitis from oxybenzone. Contact Dermatitis 1998;38:43-44

66 Silva R, Almeida LMS, Brandão FM. Photoallergy to oxybenzone in cosmetic creams. Contact Dermatitis 1995;32:176

67 Aguirre A, Izu R, Gardeazahal J, Gil N, Diaz Pérez JL. Allergic contact cheilitis from a lipstick containing oxybenzone. Contact Dermatitis 1992;27:267

68 Torres V, Correia T. Contact and photocontact allergy to oxybenzone and mexenone. Contact Dermatitis 1991;25:126

69 Peluso AM, Bardazzi F, Tosti A. Photocontact dermatitis due to Eusolex 4360. Contact Dermatitis 1991;25:65-66

70 Green C, Norris PG, Hawk JLM. Photoallergic contact dermatitis from oxybenzone aggravating polymorphic light eruption. Contact Dermatitis 1991;24:62-63

71 Camarasa JG, Serra-Baldrich E. Allergic contact dermatitis to sunscreens. Contact Dermatitis 1986;15:253-254

72 Burry JN. Photo allergies from benzophenones and beta carotene in sunscreens. Contact Dermatitis 1980;6:211-212

73 Pariser RJ. Contact dermatitis to dioxybenzone. Contact Dermatitis 1977;3:172

74 Hanson JL, Warshaw EM. Sensitivity to multiple benzophenone sunscreen agents. Dermatitis 2015;26:192-194

75 Leonard F, Adamski H, Bonnevalle A, Bottlaender A, Bourrain JL, Goujon-Henry C, et al. The prospective multicenter study on standard photopatch tests by the French Society of Photodermatology from 1991-2001. Ann Dermatol Venereol 2005;132:313-320 (article in French)

76 Landers M, Law S, Storrs FJ. Contact urticaria, allergic contact dermatitis, and photoallergic contact dermatitis from oxybenzone. Am J Cont Derm 2003;14:33-34

77 Lenique P, Machet L, Vaillant L, Bensaid P, Muller C, Khallouf R, Lorette G. Contact and photocontact allergy to oxybenzone. Contact Dermatitis 1992;26:177-181

78 Gonçalo M, Ruas E, Figueiredo A, Gonçalo S. Contact and photocontact sensitivity to sunscreens. Contact Dermatitis 1995;33:278-280

79 Schram SE, Glesne LA, Warshaw EM. Allergic contact cheilitis from benzophenone-3 in lip balm and fragrance/flavorings. Dermatitis 2007;18:221-224

80 Zug KA, Kornik RI, Belsito DV, et al. Patients with cheilitis referred for patch testing: a retrospective analysis of cross-sectional data from the North American Contact Dermatitis Group [abstract]. Proceedings of the joint meeting of the American Contact Dermatitis Society and the Experimental Contact Dermatitis Research Group; 2006 Sep 28–30; Baltimore, MD, USA. (data cited in ref. 79)

81 Theeuwes M, Degreef H, Dooms-Goossens A. Para-aminobenzoic acid (PABA) and sunscreen allergy. Am J Cont Derm 1992;3:206-207

82 Crouch RB, Foley PA, Baker CS. The results of photopatch testing 172 patients to sunscreening agents at the photobiology clinic, St Vincent's Hospital, Melbourne. Australas J Dermatol 2002;43:74

83 Cardoso J, Canelas MM, Gonçalo M, Figueiredo A. Photopatch testing with an extended series of photoallergens: a 5-year study. Contact Dermatitis 2009;60:325-329

84 Rastogi SC. UV filters in sunscreen products – a survey. Contact Dermatitis 2002;46:348-351

85 Ricci C, Pazzaglia M, Tosti A. Photocontact dermatitis from UV filters. Contact Dermatitis 1998;38:343-344

86 Haylett AK, Chiang YZ, Nie Z, Ling TC, Rhodes LE. Sunscreen photopatch testing: a series of 157 children. Br J Dermatol 2014;171:370-375

87 Berne B, Ross AM. 7 years experience of photopatch testing with sunscreen allergens in Sweden. Contact Dermatitis 1998;38:61-64

88 Fischer T, Bergström K. Evaluation of customers' complaints about sunscreen cosmetics sold by the Swedish pharmaceutical company. Contact Dermatitis 1991;25:319-322

89 Warshaw EM, Wang MZ, Maibach HI, Belsito DV, Zug KA, Taylor JS, et al. Patch test reactions associated with sunscreen products and the importance of testing to an expanded series: retrospective analysis of North American Contact Dermatitis Group data, 2001 to 2010. Dermatitis 2013;24:176-182

90 Shaw T, Simpson B, Wilson B, Oostman H, Rainey D, Storrs F. True photoallergy to sunscreens is rare despite popular belief. Dermatitis 2010;21:185-198

91 Scalf LA, Davis MDP, Rohlinger AL, Connolly SM. Photopatch testing of 182 patients: A 6-year experience at the Mayo Clinic. Dermatitis 2009;20:44-52

92 Ang P, Ng SK, Goh CL. Sunscreen allergy in Singapore. Am J Cont Derm 1998;9:42-44

93 Freeman S, Frederiksen P. Sunscreen allergy. Am J Cont Derm 1990;1:240-243

94 Nedorost S, Averitte R, Ahmad N, Arnold J, Cooper K. Urticarial and eczematous reaction to benzophenone in finished plastic [abstract]. Am J Contact Dermat 2000;11:136

95 Green C, Catterall M, Hawk JLM. Chronic actinic dermatitis and sunscreen allergy. Clin Exp Dermatol 1991;16:70-71

96 Kerr A, Ferguson J. Photoallergic contact dermatitis. Photodermatol Photoimmunol Photomed 2010;26:56-65

97 Wahie S, Lloyd JJ, Farr PM. Sunscreen ingredients and labelling: a survey of products available in the U.K. Clin Exp Dermatol 2007;32:359-364

98 Zaragoza-Ninet V, Blasco Encinas R, Vilata-Corell JJ, Pérez-Ferriols A, Sierra-Talamantes C, Esteve-Martínez A, de la Cuadra-Oyanguren J. Allergic contact dermatitis due to cosmetics: A clinical and epidemiological study in a tertiary hospital. Actas Dermosifiliogr 2016;107:329-336

99 Schmidt T, Ring J, Abeck D. Photoallergic contact dermatitis due to combined UVB (4-methylbenzylidene camphor/octyl methoxycinnamate) and UVA (benzophenone-3/butyl methoxydibenzoylmethane) absorber sensitization. Dermatology 1998;196:354-357

100 Verhulst L, Goossens A. Cosmetic components causing contact urticaria: a review and update. Contact Dermatitis 2016;75:333-344

101 Rademaker M. Occupational contact dermatitis among New Zealand farmers. Australas J Dermatol 1998;39:164-167

102 Heurung AR, Raju SI, Warshaw EM. Contact allergen of the year. Benzophenones. Dermatitis 2014;25:3-10 (contains many mistakes; Erratum in Dermatitis 2014;25:92-95)

103 Kerr AC. A survey of the availability of sunscreen filters in the U.K. Clin Exp Dermatol 2011;36:541-543

104 Heurung AR, Raju SI, Warshaw EM. Adverse reactions to sunscreen agents: epidemiology, responsible irritants and allergens, clinical characteristics, and management. Dermatitis 2014;25:289-326

105 Heurung AR, Raju SI, Warshaw EM. Contact allergen of the year. Benzophenones. Dermatitis 2014;25:3-10 (contains many mistakes; Erratum in Dermatitis 2014;25:92-95)

106 Avenel-Audran M. Sunscreen products: finding the allergen. Eur J Dermatol 2010;20:161-166

107 Scheuer E, Warshaw E. Sunscreen allergy: a review of epidemiology, clinical characteristics, and responsible allergens. Dermatitis 2006;17:3-11

108 Funk JO, Dromgoole SH, Maibach HI. Sunscreen intolerance: contact sensitization, photocontact sensitization, and irritancy of sunscreen agents. Dermatol Clin 1995;13:473-481

109 Avenel-Audran M, Dutartre H, Goossens A, Jeanmougin M, Comte C, Bernier C, et al. Octocrylene, an emerging photoallergen. Arch Dermatol 2010;146:753-757

110 De Groot AC, Roberts DW. Contact and photocontact allergy to octocrylene: a review. Contact Dermatitis 2014;70:193-204

111 Marks JG Jr, Belsito DV, DeLeo VA, Fowler JF Jr, Fransway AF, Maibach HI, et al. North American Contact Dermatitis Group patch-test results, 1998–2000. Am J Contact Dermat 2003;14:59-62

112 Pratt MD, Belsito DV, DeLeo VA, Fowler JF Jr, Fransway AF, Maibach HI, et al. North American Contact Dermatitis Group patch-test results, 2001–2002 study period. Dermatitis 2004;15:176-183

113 Marks JG Jr, Belsito DV, DeLeo VA, Fowler JF Jr, Fransway AF, Maibach HI, et al. North American Contact Dermatitis Group patch test results, 1996–1998. Arch Dermatol 2000;136:272-273

114 Wetter DA, Davis MDP, Yiannias JA, Cheng JF, Connolly SM, el-Azhary RA, et al. Patch test results from the Mayo Contact Dermatitis Group, 1998–2000. J Am Acad Dermatol 2005;53:416-421

115 Hasan T, Rantanen T, Alanko K, Harvima RJ, Jolanki R, Kalimo K, et al. Patch test reactions to cosmetic allergens in 1995–1997 and 2000–2002 in Finland –a multicentre study. Contact Dermatitis 2005;53:40-45

116 Li L-F, Liu G, Wang J. Patch test in Chinese patients with cosmetic allergic contact dermatitis to common cosmetic allergens from a European cosmetic series. Contact Dermatitis 2007;57:50-54

117 Goossens A. Cosmetic contact allergens. Cosmetics 2016, 3, 5; doi:10.3390/cosmetics3010005

118 Wentworth AB, Yiannias JA, Keeling JH, Hall MR, Camilleri MJ, Drage LA, et al. Trends in patch-test results and allergen changes in the standard series: a Mayo Clinic 5-year retrospective review (January 1, 2006, to December 31, 2010). J Am Acad Dermatol 2014;70:269-275

119 Zug KA, Kornik R, Belsito DV, DeLeo VA, Fowler JF Jr, Maibach HI, et al. Patch-testing North American lip dermatitis patients: Data from the North American Contact Dermatitis Group, 2001 to 2004. Dermatitis 2008;19:202-208

120 Freeman S, Stephens R. Cheilitis: Analysis of 75 cases referred to a contact dermatitis clinic. Am J Cont Dermat 1999;10:198-200

121 Scheman A, Jacob S, Katta R, Nedorost S, Warshaw E, Zirwas M, et al. Part 2 of a 4 part series. Hair cosmetics: trends and alternatives. Data from the American Contact Alternative Group. J Clin Aesthet Dermatol 2011;4:42-46

122 Scheman A, Jacob S, Katta R, Nedorost S, Warshaw E, Zirwas M, et al. Part 3 of a 4 part series. Lips and common Dental Care products: trends and alternatives. Data from the American Contact Alternative Group. J Clin Aesthet Dermatol 2011;4:50-53

123 Scheman A, Jacob S, Katta R, Nedorost S, Warshaw E, Zirwas M, et al. Part 4 of a 4 part series. Miscellaneous products: trends and alternatives in deodorants, antiperspirants, sunblocks, shaving products, powder, and wipes. Data from the American Contact Alternative Group. J Clin Aesthet Dermatol 2011;4:35-39

124 SCCP (Scientific Committee on Consumer Products). Opinion on Benzophenone-3, 16 December 2008, SCCP/ 1201/08. Available at: http://ec.europa.eu/health/archive/ph_risk/committees/04_sccp/docs/sccp_o_159.pdf

125 SCCP (Scientific Committee on Consumer Products). Opinion on Benzophenone-3, 19 December 2006, SCCP/ 1069/06. Available at: http://ec.europa.eu/health/archive/ph_risk/committees/04_sccp/docs/sccp_o_078.pdf

126 Laguna C, de la Cuadra J, Martín-González B, Zaragoza V, Martínez-Casimiro L, Alegre V. Allergic contact dermatitis to cosmetics. Actas Dermosifiliogr 2009;100:53-60

127 Manová E, von Goetz N, Hauri U, Bogdal C, Hungerbühler K. Organic UV filters in personal care products in Switzerland: A survey of occurrence and concentrations. Int J Hyg Environ Health 2013;216:508-514

128 Toholka R, Wang Y-S, Tate B, Tam M, Cahill J, Palmer A, Nixon R. The first Australian Baseline Series: Recommendations for patch testing in suspected contact dermatitis. Australas J Dermatol 2015;56:107-115

129 DeKoven JG, Warshaw EM, Belsito DV, Sasseville D, Maibach HI, Taylor JS, et al. North American Contact Dermatitis Group Patch Test Results: 2013-2014. Dermatitis 2017;28:33-46

130 Greenspoon J, Ahluwalia R, Juma N, Rosen CF. Allergic and photoallergic contact dermatitis: a 10-year experience. Dermatitis 2013;24:29-32

131 Shaath NA. Ultraviolet filters. Photochem Photobiol Sci 2010;9:464-469

132 Schauder S. Adverse reactions to sunscreening agents in 58 patients (part 3). Z Hautkr 1991;66:294-318 (article in German)

133 Kleinhans D. Kontaktallergie gegen UV-Filtersubstanzen in Lichtschutzpräparaten. Derm und Kosm 1988;29:28-34 (article in German)

134 Schauder S. Survey of the literature on adverse reactions to preparations containing UV filters (1947-1989) (Literaturübersicht über Unverträglichkeitsreaktionen auf lichtfilterhaltige Produkte von 1947 bis 1989). Z Hautkr 1990;65:982-998 (article in German)

135 Martina E, Rosa L, Postacchini V, Simonetti O, Cataldi I, Offidani A. Photoprotection and photodermatitis: a case. Contact Dermatitis 2017;76:54-55

2.44 BENZOPHENONE-4

IDENTIFICATION

Description/definition	: Benzophenone-4 is a benzophenone derivative that conforms to the formula shown below
Chemical class(es)	: Benzophenones
Chemical/IUPAC name	: 5-Benzoyl-4-hydroxy-2-methoxybenzenesulfonic acid
Other names	: Sulisobenzone; 2-hydroxy-4-methoxybenzophenone-5-sulfonic acid
CAS registry number (s)	: 4065-45-6
EC number(s)	: 223-772-2
CIR review(s)	: J Am Coll Toxicol 1983;2:35-77 (access: www.cir-safety.org/ingredients)
SCCS opinion(s)	: SCCNFP, 17 February 1999 (43)
Merck Index monograph	: 10383
Function(s) in cosmetics	: EU: UV-absorber; UV-filter. USA: light stabilizers; sunscreen agents
EU cosmetic restrictions	: Regulated in Annex VI/22 of the Regulation (EC) No. 1223/2009
Patch testing	: 2.0% pet. (Chemotechnique, SmartPracticeCanada); 10.0% pet. (Chemotechnique, SmartPracticeEurope, SmartPracticeCanada); 10% pet. may cause irritant reactions (18)
Molecular formula	: $C_{14}H_{12}O_6S$

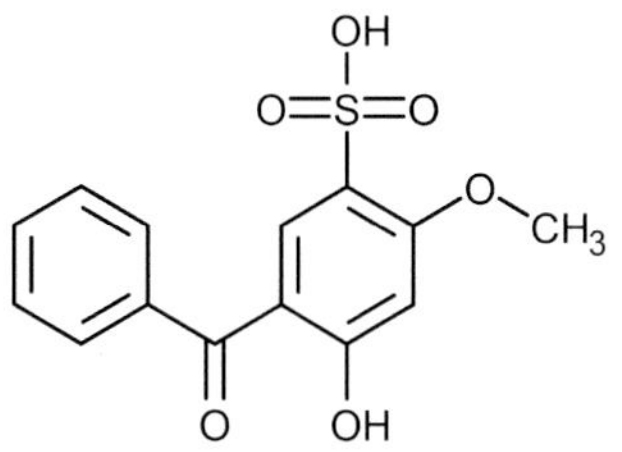

GENERAL

Benzophenone-4 is a UVA/B filter with UV absorbance maxima ($\lambda_{max,1}, \lambda_{max,2}$) at 286 and 324 nm (49), which has been used in Europe since the 1980s (33). The literature on adverse reactions to sunscreens has been reviewed in several recent and older publications (8,35-39,50). A review of photocontact allergy to sunscreens has been provided in 2010 (26).

CONTACT ALLERGY

Patch testing in groups of patients

Results of patch testing benzophenone-4 in consecutive patients suspected of contact dermatitis (routine testing) and of testing groups of *selected* patients (e.g., patients suspected of cosmetic intolerance, patients with suspected photosensitivity or reactions to a sunscreen) back to 2002 are shown in table 2.44.1. In one study performing routines testing by the members of the NACDG, the frequency of sensitization was 2.1%, but relevance was only 20% (46) (benzophenone-4 was added to the NACDG screening series in 2013).

In groups of selected patients, rates of sensitization ranged from 0.6% to 6.6%. The highest percentage (6.6%) was in a study from the USA (13), which can be explained by the fact that there were many macular erythema and weak reactions counted as positive, and the fact that the 10% pet. test substance can cause irritant, false-positive, reactions (18). 98% Per cent of the 57 positive reactions in this study were considered to be relevant, but this included 'questionable' and 'past' relevance (13). Most other studies did not mention relevance or specify it, but in those that did, relevance scores were only 17-27%. Causative products were not mentioned.

Case reports and case series

Benzophenone-4 was stated to be the (or an) allergen in one patient in a group of 603 individuals suffering from cosmetic dermatitis, seen in the period 2010-2015 in Leuven, Belgium (40). Benzophenone-4 was responsible for 7 out of 959 cases of non-fragrance cosmetic allergy where the causal allergen was identified, Belgium, 2000-2010 (12). Nineteen cases of relevant contact allergy or photocontact allergy were seen in one center in Australia in an 18-year period up to 2011 (15). Benzophenone-4 was responsible for 2 out of 399 cases of cosmetic allergy where the causal allergen was identified in a study of the NACDG, USA, 1977-1983 (7).

One patient had allergic contact dermatitis from benzophenone-4 in a sunscreen (1). A man reacted to benzophenone-4 in a sunscreen used for light sensitivity (5). A child had contact allergy to benzophenone-4 and octocrylene in sunscreens (11). A hairdresser had occupational allergic contact dermatitis from benzophenone-4 in shampoos, hairsprays and conditioners (24). A woman had allergic contact dermatitis from benzophenone-4 present in artificial nail material (25). Four patients had allergic contact dermatitis from benzophenone-4 in sunscreens (27). A female patient developed allergic contact dermatitis of the face from benzophenone-4 present in facial cosmetics (30).

Table 2.44.1 Patch testing in groups of patients

Years and Country	Test conc. & vehicle	Number of patients tested | positive (%)		Selection of patients (S); Relevance (R); Comments (C)	Ref.
Routine testing					
2013-14 USA, Canada	10% pet.	4857	100 (2.1%)	R: definite + probable relevance: 20%	46
Testing in groups of selected patients					
1996-2013 Netherlands	10% pet.	231	6 (2.6%)	S: children aged 0-17 years; R: not stated	28
2006-2011 IVDK	10% pet.	5600	(1.1%)	S: patients suspected of cosmetic intolerance and tested with an ointment base series (selection procedure not stated); R: not stated	48
2000-2011 UK	5% or 10% pet.	157	1 (0.6%)	S: children <18 years suspected of photosensitivity; R: not stated; C: the reaction was photo-augmented contact allergy	31
2001-2010 Australia	10% pet.	1924	84 (4.4%)	S: not stated; R: 23%	45
2000-2007 USA	10% pet.	864	57 (6.6%)	S: patients tested with a supplemental cosmetic screening series; R: 98%; C: weak study: a. high rate of macular erythema and weak reactions; b. relevance figures included 'questionable' and 'past' relevance	13
2003-2005 UK	10% pet.	553	13 (2.4%)	S: patients tested with a facial series; R: not stated	23
2000-2005 USA	10% pet.	178	6 (3.4%)	S: patients photopatch tested for suspected photodermatitis; R: 1 reaction was relevant	32
2001-2003 Colombia	10% pet.	82	1 (1.2%)	S: patients with a clinical diagnosis of photoallergic contact dermatitis; R: 65% of all reactions in the study were relevant	9
2000-2002 UK, I, NL	5% or 10%	1155	11 (1.0%)	S: patients suspected of photosensitivity or reaction to a sunscreen; R: current 3, unknown relevance 8	2

I: Ireland; NL: Netherlands; UK: United Kingdom; WSP White soft paraffin
IVDK: Information Network of Departments of Dermatology, Germany, Austria, Switzerland

Contact allergy to benzophenone-4 in non-cosmetic products
One patient had occupational airborne allergic contact dermatitis from benzophenone-4 present in printing ink (22).

Cross-reactions, pseudo-cross-reactions and co-reactions
Because of the shared chemical structure, cross-reactions within the benzophenone family are plausible, but have not been documented with certainty (35). Benzophenone-4 does not cross-react with benzophenone-3 (23,24). Occasional co-reactivities (8,21) probably are the result of co-sensitizations rather than cross-sensitivity.

Presence in cosmetic products and chemical analyses
In June 2017, benzophenone-4 was present in 614 of 68,746 cosmetic products of which the composition is known in EWG's Skin Deep Cosmetics Database, USA (http://www.ewg.org/skindeep/). It should be realized that sunscreen products containing UV-filters are classified as drugs in the USA, not as cosmetics; the number mentioned here, therefore, is that of cosmetics containing the UV-filter, but it does *not* include their presence in sunscreens. In the USA, in April 2017, benzophenone-4 was present in 1826 of 56,714 cosmetic products of which the composition is known in FDA's Voluntary Cosmetic Registration Program (VCRP) (data obtained from FDA, May 2017). In 2012, in Switzerland, 116 cosmetics from seven widely used leave-on product categories (19 lip care products, 8 lipsticks, 29 face creams, 11 liquid makeup foundations, 3 aftershaves, 7 hand creams and 39 sunscreens) were investigated to determine the frequency of occurrence and concentrations of 22 organic UV filters in these products. Benzophenone-4 was found in one product only in a concentration of 3.88% (44).

In 2009, in the USA, the ingredient lists of 796 hair products from one company were screened for the presence of benzophenone-4. Benzophenone-4 was present in 6% of 279 shampoos, in 5% of 231 conditioners, and in 17% of 286 styling products (41). In 2009, in the USA, the ingredient lists of 657 miscellaneous cosmetics from one company were screened for the presence of benzophenone-4. Benzophenone-4 was present in 7% of 167 shaving products only (42). Benzophenone-4 was present in 5.5% of 4447 cosmetic products collected in Germany, 2006-2009 (20). Benzophenone-4 was present in 3% of 329 sunscreen products (incl. 21 lipstick sunscreens) marketed in the UK in 2005 (34).

OTHER SIDE EFFECTS

Photosensitivity

Photopatch testing in groups of patients

Results of photopatch testing benzophenone-4 in groups of selected patients back to 1985 are shown in table 2.44.2. Selection criteria usually were exposed site dermatitis, skin reactions to sunscreens or a topical NSAID preparation, or suspicion of photoallergic contact dermatitis or other photosensitivity disorders. In 14 studies, the frequency of photosensitization ranged from 0.2% to 7% (the latter in a very small study of 30 patients suffering from chronic actinic dermatitis [19]), but in 7 of the studies, the rates were below 1% positive photopatch tests. In 9 studies, data on relevance were either not provided or not specified for benzophenone-4. In studies that did, relevance ranged from 0% to 100%. It should be realized that the number of positive reactions were always very small, ranging from 1 to 8.

Table 2.44.2 Photopatch testing in groups of patients

Years and Country	Test conc. & vehicle	Number of patients tested	positive (%)		Selection of patients (S); Relevance (R); Comments (C)	Ref.
2011-2013 Colombia	2% pet.	112	1	(0.9%)	S: dermatitis affecting mainly light-exposed skin, a history of a sunscreen or topical NSAID skin reaction; R: not relevant	47
2008-2011 12 European countries	2% pet.	1031	3	(0.3%)	S: patients with exposed site dermatitis or history of a reaction to a sunscreen or topical NSAID; R: 44% current and 11% past relevance for all photoallergens together	17
2000-2011 UK	5% or 10% pet.	157	1	(0.6%)	S: children <18 years suspected of photosensitivity; R: not stated; C: the reaction was photo-augmented contact allergy	31
2001-2010 Canada		160	3	(1.9%)	S: patients with suspected photosensitivity and patients who developed pruritus or a rash after sunscreen application; R: not stated; C: very weak study: inadequate reading of test results, erythema only was considered to represent a positive patch test reaction	16
1993-2009 USA	10% pet.	30	2	(7%)	S: patients with chronic actinic dermatitis; R: not stated	19
2003-2007 Portugal	10% pet.	83	3	(3.6%)	S: patients with suspected photoaggravated facial dermatitis or systemic photosensitivity; R: all sunscreen photopatch tests were of current or past relevance	29
2004-2006 Italy	10% pet.	1082	3	(0.3%)	S: patients with histories and clinical features suggestive of photoallergic contact dermatitis; 1/3 were cases of photoaugmented contact allergy; R: 100%	14
1993-2006 USA	10% pet.	76	3	(3.9%)	S: not stated; R: 56% of all reactions to sunscreens were considered 'probably relevant'	10
2000-2005 USA	10% pet.	178	8	(4.5%)	S: patients photopatch tested for suspected photodermatitis; R: 5 reactions were relevant	32
2001-2003 Colombia	10% pet.	82	2	(2.4%)	S: patients with a clinical diagnosis of photoallergic contact dermatitis; R: 65% of all reactions in the study were relevant	9
2000-2002 UK, I, NL	5% and 10% pet.	1155	7	(0.6%)	S: patients suspected of photosensitivity or reaction to a sunscreen; R: current 3, unknown 2, past 2	2
1990-1994 France	2% or 10% pet.	370	2	(0.5%)	S: patients with suspected photodermatitis; R: not specified, 72% of all reactions in the study were considered relevant	6
1985-1994 Italy		1050	2	(0.2%)	S: patients with histories or clinical pictures suggestive of allergic contact photodermatitis; R: 97% for all sunscreens together	4
1980-1985 USA	10% pet.	70	2	(2.9%)	S: not stated; R: not stated	3

I: Ireland; NL: Netherlands; UK: United Kingdom

Case reports and series

Nineteen cases of relevant contact allergy or photocontact allergy to benzophenone-4 were seen in one center in Australia in an 18-year period up to 2011 (15).

Immediate-type reactions

One individual had contact urticaria from benzophenone-4 in a sunscreen; the patient also had a contact allergic reaction to benzophenone-4 and an immediate contact reaction to benzophenone-3 (1).

LITERATURE

1   Ramsay DL, Cohen HJ, Baer RL. Allergic reaction to benzophenone. Simultaneous occurrence of urticarial and contact sensitivities. Arch Dermatol 1972;105:906-908

2   Bryden A, Moseley H, Ibbotson S, Chowdhury MM, Beck MH, Bourke J, et al. Photopatch testing of 1155 patients: results of the U.K. multicentre photopatch test study group. Brit J Dermatol 2006;155:737-747

3   Menz J, Muller SA, Connnolly SM. Photopatch testing: A six year experience. J Am Acad Dermatol 1988;18:1044-1047

4   Pigatto PD, Legori A, Bigardi AS, Guarrera M, Tosti A, Santucci B, et al. Gruppo Italiano recerca dermatiti da contatto ed ambientali Italian multicenter study of allergic contact photodermatitis: epidemiological aspects. Am J Contact Dermatitis 1996;17:158-163

5   Baer RL, Ramsay DL. Polyvalent light sensitivity (persistent light reactivity?); allergic contact dermatitis to sulisobenzone. Arch Dermatol 1971;104:446-448

6   Journe F, Marguery M-C, Rakotondrazafy J, El Sayed F, Bazex J. Sunscreen sensitization: a 5-year study. Acta Derm Venereol (Stockh) 1999;79:211-213

7   Adams RM, Maibach HI, Clendenning WE, Fisher AA, Jordan WJ, Kanof N, et al. A five-year study of cosmetic reactions. J Am Acad Dermatol 1985;13:1062-1069

8   Dromgoole SH, Maibach HI. Sunscreening agent intolerance: Contact and photocontact sensitization and contact urticaria. J Am Acad Dermatol 1990;22:1068-1078

9   Rodriguez E, Valbuena M, Rey M, Porras de Quintana L. Causal agents of photoallergic contact dermatitis diagnosed in the national institute of dermatology of Columbia. Photoderm Photoimmunol Photomed 2006;22:189-192

10 Victor FC, Cohen DE, Soter NA. A 20-year analysis of previous and emerging allergens that elicit photoallergic contact dermatitis. J Am Acad Dermatol 2010;62:605-610

11 Avenel-Audran M. Dutartre H, Goossens A, Jeanmougin M, Comte C, Bernier C, et al. Octocrylene, an emerging photoallergen. Arch Dermatol 2010;146:753-757

12 Travassos AR, Claes L, Boey L, Drieghe J, Goossens A. Non-fragrance allergens in specific cosmetic products. Contact Dermatitis 2011;65:276-285

13 Wetter DA, Yiannias JA, Prakash AV, Davis MD, Farmer SA, el-Azhary RA, et al. Results of patch testing to personal care product allergens in a standard series and a supplemental cosmetic series: an analysis of 945 patients from the Mayo Clinic Contact Dermatitis Group, 2000-2007. J Am Acad Dermatol 2010;63:789-798

14 Pigatto PD, Guzzi G, Schena D, Guarrera M, Foti C, Francalanci S, et al. Photopatch tests: an Italian multicentre study from 2004 to 2006. Contact Dermatitis 2008;59:103-108

15 Nixon RL. Contact dermatitis to sunscreens. Dermatitis 2012;23:140-141

16 Greenspoon J, Ahluwalia R, Juma N, Rosen CF. Allergic and photoallergic contact dermatitis: A 10-year experience. Dermatitis 2013;24:29-32

17 The European Multicentre Photopatch Test Study (EMCPPTS) Taskforce. A European multicentre photopatch test study. Br J Dermatol 2012;166:1002-1009

18 Kerr AC, Niklasson B, Dawe RS, Escoffier AM, Krasteva M, Sanderson B, et al. A double-blind, randomized assessment of the irritant potential of sunscreen chemical dilutions used in photopatch testing. Contact Dermatitis 2009;60:203-209

19 Que SK, Brauer JA, Soter NA, Cohen DE. Chronic actinic dermatitis: an analysis at a single institution over 25 years. Dermatitis 2011;22:147-154

20 Uter W, Gonçalo M, Yazar K, Kratz E-M, Mildau G, Lidén C. Coupled exposure to ingredients of cosmetic products: III. Ultraviolet filters. Contact Dermatitis 2014;71:162-169

21 Sasseville D, Nantel-Battista M, Molinari R. Multiple contact allergies to benzophenones. Contact Dermatitis 2011;65:179-180

22 Caruana DM, McPherson T, Cooper S. Allergic contact dermatitis caused by benzophenone-4 in a printer. Contact Dermatitis 2011;64:183-184

23 Hughes TM, Stone NM. Benzophenone 4: an emerging allergen in cosmetics and toiletries?. Contact Dermatitis 2007;56:153-156

24 Alanko K, Jolanki R, Estlander T, Kanerva L. Occupational allergic contact dermatitis from benzophenone-4 in hair-care products. Contact Dermatitis 2001;44:188

25 Guin JD. Eyelid dermatitis from benzophenone used in nail enhancement. Contact Dermatitis 2000; 43:308-309

26 Shaw T, Simpson B, Wilson B, Oostman H, Rainey D, Storrs F. True photoallergy to sunscreens is rare despite popular belief. Dermatitis 2010;21:185-198

27 Gonçalo M, Ruas E, Figueiredo A, Gonçalo S. Contact and photocontact sensitivity to sunscreens. Contact Dermatitis 1995;33:278-280

28 Lubbes S, Rustemeyer T, Sillevis Smitt JH, Schuttelaar ML, Middelkamp-Hup MA. Contact sensitization in Dutch children and adolescents with and without atopic dermatitis - a retrospective analysis. Contact Dermatitis 2017;76:151-159

29 Cardoso J, Canelas MM, Gonçalo M, Figueiredo A. Photopatch testing with an extended series of photoallergens: a 5-year study. Contact Dermatitis 2009;60:325-329

30 Ricci C, Pazzaglia M, Tosti A. Photocontact dermatitis from UV filters. Contact Dermatitis 1998;38:343-344

31 Haylett AK, Chiang YZ, Nie Z, Ling TC, Rhodes LE. Sunscreen photopatch testing: a series of 157 children. Br J Dermatol 2014;171:370-375

32 Scalf LA, Davis MDP, Rohlinger AL, Connolly SM. Photopatch testing of 182 patients: A 6-year experience at the Mayo Clinic. Dermatitis 2009;20:44-52

33 Kerr A, Ferguson J. Photoallergic contact dermatitis. Photodermatol Photoimmunol Photomed 2010;26:56-65

34 Wahie S, Lloyd JJ, Farr PM. Sunscreen ingredients and labelling: a survey of products available in the U.K. Clin Exp Dermatol 2007;32:359-364

35 Heurung AR, Raju SI, Warshaw EM. Contact allergen of the year. Benzophenones. Dermatitis 2014;25:3-10 (contains many mistakes; Erratum in Dermatitis 2014;25:92-95)

36 Heurung AR, Raju SI, Warshaw EM. Adverse reactions to sunscreen agents: epidemiology, responsible irritants and allergens, clinical characteristics, and management. Dermatitis 2014;25:289-326

37 Avenel-Audran M. Sunscreen products: finding the allergen. Eur J Dermatol 2010;20:161-166

38 Scheuer E, Warshaw E. Sunscreen allergy: a review of epidemiology, clinical characteristics, and responsible allergens. Dermatitis 2006;17:3-11

39 Funk JO, Dromgoole SH, Maibach HI. Sunscreen intolerance: contact sensitization, photocontact sensitization, and irritancy of sunscreen agents. Dermatol Clin 1995;13:473-481

40 Goossens A. Cosmetic contact allergens. Cosmetics 2016, 3, 5; doi:10.3390/cosmetics3010005

41 Scheman A, Jacob S, Katta R, Nedorost S, Warshaw E, Zirwas M, et al. Part 2 of a 4 part series. Hair cosmetics: trends and alternatives. Data from the American Contact Alternative Group. J Clin Aesthet Dermatol 2011;4:42-46

42 Scheman A, Jacob S, Katta R, Nedorost S, Warshaw E, Zirwas M, et al. Part 4 of a 4 part series. Miscellaneous products: trends and alternatives in deodorants, antiperspirants, sunblocks, shaving products, powder, and wipes. Data from the American Contact Alternative Group. J Clin Aesthet Dermatol 2011;4:35-39

43 SCCNFP (Scientific Committee on Cosmetics and Non Food Products). Opinion concerning 2-Hydroxy-4-methoxybenzophenone-5-sulphonic acid, 17 February 1999. Available at: http://ec.europa.eu/health/scientific_committees/consumer_safety/opinions/sccnfp_opinions_97_04/sccp_out57_en.htm

44 Manová E, von Goetz N, Hauri U, Bogdal C, Hungerbühler K. Organic UV filters in personal care products in Switzerland: A survey of occurrence and concentrations. Int J Hyg Environ Health 2013;216:508-514

45 Toholka R, Wang Y-S, Tate B, Tam M, Cahill J, Palmer A, Nixon R. The first Australian Baseline Series: Recommendations for patch testing in suspected contact dermatitis. Australas J Dermatol 2015;56:107-115

46 DeKoven JG, Warshaw EM, Belsito DV, Sasseville D, Maibach HI, Taylor JS, et al. North American Contact Dermatitis Group Patch Test Results: 2013-2014. Dermatitis 2017;28:33-46

47 Valbuena Mesa MC, Hoyos Jiménez EV. Photopatch testing in Bogota (Colombia): 2011–2013. Contact Dermatitis 2016;74:11-17

48 Dinkloh A, Worm M, Geier J, Schnuch A, Wollenberg A. Contact sensitization in patients with suspected cosmetic intolerance: results of the IVDK 2006-2011. J Eur Acad Dermatol Venereol 2015;29:1071-1081

49 Shaath NA. Ultraviolet filters. Photochem Photobiol Sci 2010;9:464-469

50 Schauder S. Survey of the literature on adverse reactions to preparations containing UV filters (1947-1989) (Literaturübersicht über Unverträglichkeitsreaktionen auf lichtfilterhaltige Produkte von 1947 bis 1989). Z Hautkr 1990;65:982-998 (article in German)

2.45 BENZOPHENONE-8

IDENTIFICATION

Description/definition	: Benzophenone-8 is a benzophenone derivative that conforms to the formula shown below
Chemical class(es)	: Benzophenones
Chemical/IUPAC name	: (2-Hydroxy-4-methoxyphenyl)-(2-hydroxyphenyl)methanone
Other names	: 2,2'-Dihydroxy-4-methoxybenzophenone; dioxybenzone
CAS registry number (s)	: 131-53-3
EC number(s)	: 205-026-8
CIR review(s)	: J Am Coll Toxicol 1983;2:79-84 (access: www.cir-safety.org/ingredients)
Merck Index monograph	: 4602
Function(s) in cosmetics	: EU: UV-absorber. USA: light stabilizers; sunscreen agents
Patch testing	: 2% pet. (2); most benzophenones are tested 10% pet.
Molecular formula	: $C_{14}H_{12}O_4$

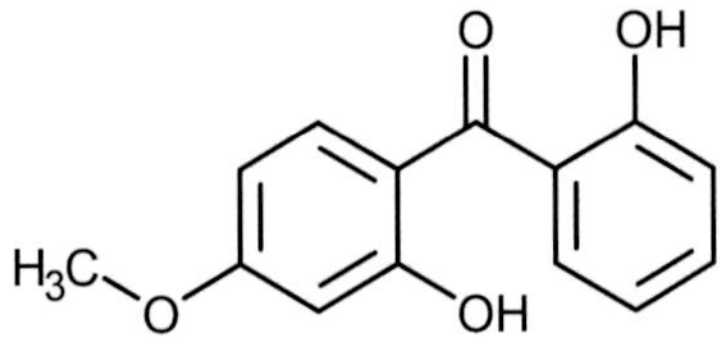

GENERAL

Benzophenone-8 is a UVA/B filter with UV absorbance maxima ($\lambda_{max,1}$, $\lambda_{max,2}$) at 284 and 327 nm (12). The literature on adverse reactions to sunscreens has been reviewed in several recent and older publications (5-11,14). A review of photocontact allergy to sunscreens was published in 2010 (13).

CONTACT ALLERGY

Case reports and case series

Benzophenone-8 was responsible for 1 out of 399 cases of cosmetic allergy where the causal allergen was identified in a study of the NACDG, USA, 1977-1983 (3). A male patient presented with a scaling, hyperpigmented, impetiginized dermatitis of the face, neck and upper chest and back. He had been using several topical preparations, including a sunscreen. He was treated with compresses and oral antibiotics, and his eruption quickly cleared. Patch tests were positive to the sunscreen preparation and to its ingredients dioxybenzone (benzophenone-8) and oxybenzone (benzophenone-3), both tested 2% pet. Photopatch tests did not intensify any of the reactions. Ten controls were negative (2).

A man with psoriasis and polymorphic light eruption developed an erythematous dermatitis involving the dorsa of his hands, face, and neck. He felt that sunlight was responsible for the eruption. Patch tests and photopatch tests with the routine series of the International Contact Dermatitis Research Group (ICDRG) and several sunscreens were applied. When seen at D2, a severe exacerbation of the dermatitis over the face and dorsa of the hands was noted. Positive reactions were observed to a benzophenone sunscreen formulation with and without light exposure. The active compounds oxybenzone and dioxybenzone (benzophenone-8), at product use concentration (not specified), also gave positive patch test reactions; 10 controls were negative. It was learned subsequently that the patient had applied the benzophenone-containing sunscreen to his face and hands on the same day that the initial patch tests were applied (1).

Cross-reactions, pseudo-cross-reactions and co-reactions

Because of the shared chemical structure, cross-reactions within the benzophenone family are plausible, but have not been documented with certainty (6). Benzophenone-3 (2,4).

Presence in cosmetic products and chemical analyses

In the USA, in April 2017, benzophenone-8 was present in 2 of 56,714 cosmetic products of which the composition is known in FDA's Voluntary Cosmetic Registration Program (VCRP) (data obtained from FDA, May 2017). In April 2017, benzophenone-8 was present in zero of 65,521 cosmetic products of which the composition is known in EWG's Skin Deep Cosmetics Database, USA (http://www.ewg.org/skindeep/). It should be realized that sunscreen products containing UV-filters are classified as drugs in the USA, not as cosmetics; the number mentioned here, therefore, is that of cosmetics containing the UV-filter, but it does *not* include their presence in sunscreens.

LITERATURE

1 Thompson G, Maibach H, Epstein J. Allergic contact dermatitis from sunscreen preparations complicating photodermatitis. Arch Dermatol 1977;113:1252-1253

2 Pariser RJ. Contact dermatitis to dioxybenzone. Contact Dermatitis 1977;3:172

3 Adams RM, Maibach HI, Clendenning WE, Fisher AA, Jordan WJ, Kanof N, et al. A five-year study of cosmetic reactions. J Am Acad Dermatol 1985;13:1062-1069

4 Sasseville D, Nantel-Battista M, Molinari R. Multiple contact allergies to benzophenones. Contact Dermatitis 2011;65:179-180

5 Shaw T, Simpson B, Wilson B, Oostman H, Rainey D, Storrs F. True photoallergy to sunscreens is rare despite popular belief. Dermatitis 2010;21:185-198

6 Heurung AR, Raju SI, Warshaw EM. Contact allergen of the year. Benzophenones. Dermatitis 2014;25:3-10 (contains many mistakes; Erratum in Dermatitis 2014;25:92-95)

7 Heurung AR, Raju SI, Warshaw EM. Adverse reactions to sunscreen agents: epidemiology, responsible irritants and allergens, clinical characteristics, and management. Dermatitis 2014;25:289-326

8 Avenel-Audran M. Sunscreen products: finding the allergen. Eur J Dermatol 2010;20:161-166

9 Scheuer E, Warshaw E. Sunscreen allergy: a review of epidemiology, clinical characteristics, and responsible allergens. Dermatitis 2006;17:3-11

10 Funk JO, Dromgoole SH, Maibach HI. Sunscreen intolerance: contact sensitization, photocontact sensitization, and irritancy of sunscreen agents. Dermatol Clin 1995;13:473-481

11 Dromgoole SH, Maibach HI. Sunscreening agent intolerance: Contact and photocontact sensitization and contact urticaria. J Am Acad Dermatol 1990;22:1068-1078

12 Shaath NA. Ultraviolet filters. Photochem Photobiol Sci 2010;9:464-469

13 Shaw T, Simpson B, Wilson B, Oostman H, Rainey D, Storrs F. True photoallergy to sunscreens is rare despite popular belief. Dermatitis 2010;21:185-198

14 Schauder S. Survey of the literature on adverse reactions to preparations containing UV filters (1947-1989) (Literaturübersicht über Unverträglichkeitsreaktionen auf lichtfilterhaltige Produkte von 1947 bis 1989). Z Hautkr 1990;65:982-998 (article in German)

2.46 BENZOPHENONE-10

IDENTIFICATION

Description/definition   : Benzophenone-10 is a benzophenone derivative that conforms to the formula shown
                                  below
Chemical class(es)   : Benzophenones
Chemical/IUPAC name   : (2-Hydroxy-4-methoxyphenyl)-(4-methylphenyl)methanone
Other names   : 2-Hydroxy-4-methoxy-4'-methylbenzophenone; mexenone
CAS registry number (s)   : 1641-17-4
EC number(s)   : 216-688-2
Merck Index monograph : 7516
Function(s) in cosmetics : EU: UV-absorbers. USA: light stabilizers
Patch testing   : 10.0% pet. (Chemotechnique)
Molecular formula   : $C_{15}H_{14}O_3$

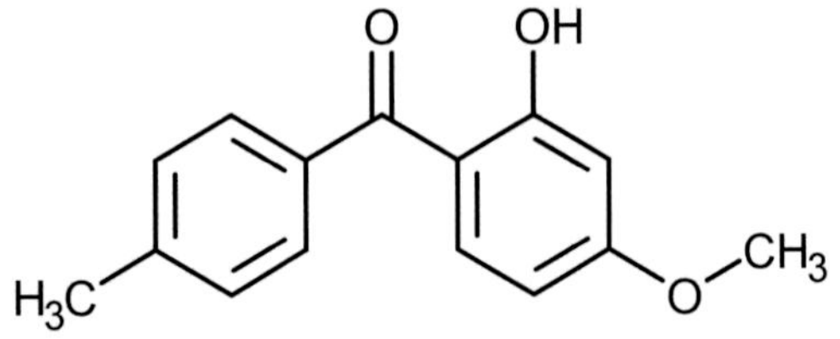

GENERAL

The literature on adverse reactions to sunscreens has been reviewed in several recent and older publications (18-23,31). A review of photocontact allergy to sunscreens was published in 2010 (28).

CONTACT ALLERGY

Patch testing in groups of patients

There are no studies in which benzophenone-10 has been patch tested in consecutive patients suspected of contact dermatitis (routine testing). Results of testing benzophenone-10 in groups of *selected* patients (e.g., patients suspected of photosensitivity, patients with dermatitis affecting mainly light-exposed skin or with a history of a sunscreen skin reactions) back to 1991 are shown in table 2.46.1. Test concentrations used have been 2% pet. and/or 10% pet., but the higher test concentrations has not resulted in more positive reactions, the mode of selection probably being the more important determinant. In 4 studies (1,2,10,26), frequencies of sensitization ranged from 0.5% to 5%. The latter percentage was seen in a group of 99 patients with photosensitivity dermatitis/actinic reticuloid syndrome and with polymorphic light eruption, who are probably heavy users of sunscreen products (2). In 3 studies, relevance of the reactions was either not stated or specified for benzophenone-10, in the fourth, two positive patch test reactions to benzophenone-10 were not relevant (26).

Table 2.46.1 Patch testing in groups of patients: Selected patient groups

Years and Country	Test conc. & vehicle	Number of patients tested	positive (%)	Selection of patients (S); Relevance (R); Comments (C)	Ref.
2011-2013 Colombia	10% pet.	112	2 (1.8%)	S: dermatitis affecting mainly light-exposed skin, or a history of a sunscreen or topical NSAID skin reaction; R: not relevant	26
1993-2000 Australia	2% pet.	149	3 (2.0%)	S: patients suspected of photosensitivity; R: of 17 patient who had contact or photocontact reactions to a panel of 10 sunscreens, 10 were considered to have relevant reactions	10
1983-1998 UK	2% pet.	2715	13 (0.5%)	S: patients suspected of photosensitivity or with (a history of) dermatitis at exposed sites; R: not stated	1
1989-1991 UK	2% pet.	99	5 (5%)	S: 45 patients with photosensitivity dermatitis/actinic reticuloid syndrome and 54 with polymorphic light eruption; R: not specified	2

Case reports and case series

Benzophenone-10 was stated to be the (or an) allergen in 3 patients in a group of 603 individuals suffering from cosmetic dermatitis, seen in the period 2010-2015 in Leuven, Belgium (24). Two patients had apparent worsening of atopic dermatitis and actinic reticuloid syndrome from contact allergy to benzophenone-10 in sunscreens (9). Of 280 patients tested with sunscreens in London, 1985-1987, four had allergic contact dermatitis from benzophenone-10 in sunscreens and 2 from its presence in other cosmetics (13). A young girl with polymorphic light eruption had acute edema of the face from contact allergy to benzophenone-10 in het sunscreen (25).

Contact allergy to benzophenone-10 in non-cosmetic products
In a group of 46 New Zealand farmers with dermatitis, investigated in one center in 1994-1997, one had occupational contact allergy to benzophenone-10. It was not mentioned how many had been tested with benzophenone-10, nor what the culprit product was (17).

Cross-reactions, pseudo-cross-reactions and co-reactions
Because of the shared chemical structure, cross-reactions within the benzophenone family are plausible, but have not been documented with certainty (18).

Presence in cosmetic products and chemical analyses
In June 2017, benzophenone-10 was present in zero of 68,864 cosmetic products of which the composition is known in EWG's Skin Deep Cosmetics Database, USA (http://www.ewg.org/skindeep/). I should be realized that sunscreen products containing UV-filters are classified as drugs in the USA, not as cosmetics; the number mentioned here, therefore, is that of cosmetics containing the UV-filter, but it does *not* include their presence in sunscreens. In the USA, in April 2017, benzophenone-10 was present in zero of 56,714 cosmetic products of which the composition is known in FDA's Voluntary Cosmetic Registration Program (VCRP) (data obtained from FDA, May 2017).

OTHER SIDE EFFECTS

Photosensitivity

Photopatch testing in groups of patients
Results of photopatch testing benzophenone-10 in groups of selected patients (e.g., patients suspected of photosensitivity, patients with dermatitis affecting mainly light-exposed skin or with a history of a sunscreen skin reactions) back to 1993 are shown in table 2.46.2. In seven studies, frequencies of photosensitization have ranged from 0.3% to 14%, but with one exception all scored lower than 2.5%. The high percentage of 14 was seen in a very small group of 22 patients investigated in Singapore (selection procedure not explained), of who 3 had a positive photopatch test to benzophenone-10. All reactions were considered to be relevant, but the culprit products were not mentioned (27). In the other studies, where relevance was mentioned, most reactions (e.g., 14 of 16 [88%] in an Italian study [6]) were relevant. Causative products were not mentioned.

Table 2.46.2 Photopatch testing in groups of patients

Years and Country	Test conc. & vehicle	Number of patients tested | positive (%)		Selection of patients (S); Relevance (R); Comments (C)	Ref.
2011-2013 Colombia	10% pet.	112	1 (0.9%)	S: dermatitis affecting mainly light-exposed skin, or a history of a sunscreen or a topical NSAID skin reaction; R: the photo-patch test reaction was not relevant	26
2007-2011 Singapore	10% pet.	22	3 (14%)	S: not stated; R: all reactions were relevant	27
2003-2007 Portugal	10% pet.	83	1 (1.2%)	S: patients with suspected photoaggravated facial dermati-tis or systemic photosensitivity; R: all sunscreen photopatch tests were of current or past relevance	11
2004-2006 Italy	10% pet.	1082	16 (1.5%)	S: patients with histories and clinical features suggestive of photoallergic contact dermatitis; 7/16 were cases of photoaugmented contact allergy; R: 88%	6
2001-2003 Colombia	10% pet.	82	2 (2.4%)	S: patients with a clinical diagnosis of photoallergic contact dermatitis; R: 65% of all reactions in the study were relevant	3
1983-1998 UK	2% pet.	2715	9 (0.3%)	S: patients suspected of photosensitivity or with (a history of) dermatitis at exposed sites; R: 37% for all photoallergens together	1
1991-1993 Singapore	2% pet.	62	1 (2%)	S: patients with clinical features suggestive of photosensitivity; R: not stated	12

Case reports and series
One patient had photocontact allergy to benzophenone-10 in a sunscreen (8). Another patient had exacerbations of chronic actinic dermatitis from photoallergy to benzophenone-10 in sunscreens (15). A patient with polymorphic

light eruption became photosensitized to benzophenone-10 in a sunscreen (16). Another individual also had photoallergic contact dermatitis from benzophenone-10 in a sunscreen (14).

Photocross-reactions, pseudo-photocross-reactions and photo-co-reactions
Benzophenone-3 (8). Up to 20% of patients photoallergic to ketoprofen may show positive photopatch tests to benzophenone-10 (4,5,30). This may be due to photocross-reactivity: when irradiated with sunlight, ketoprofen is broken down into various benzophenones (29).

Immediate-type reactions
One patient had photocontact urticaria to a sunscreen and its ingredient benzophenone-3; there was also an immediate photocontact reaction to benzophenone-10 (7).

LITERATURE

1   Darvay A, White I, Rycroft R, Jones AB, Hawk JL, McFadden JP. Photoallergic contact dermatitis is uncommon. Br J Dermatol 2001;145:597-601
2   Bilsland D, Ferguson J. Contact allergy to sunscreen chemicals in photosensitivity dermatitis/actinic reticuloid syndrome (PD/AR) and polymorphic light eruption. Contact Dermatitis 1993;29:70-73
3   Rodriguez E, Valbuena M, Rey M, Porras de Quintana L. Causal agents of photoallergic contact dermatitis diagnosed in the national institute of dermatology of Columbia. Photoderm Photoimmunol Photomed 2006;22:189-192
4   Avenel-Audran M. Dutartre H, Goossens A, Jeanmougin M, Comte C, Bernier C, et al. Octocrylene, an emerging photoallergen. Arch Dermatol 2010;146:753-757
5   Foti C, Bonamonte D, Conserva A, Stingeni L, Lisi P, Lionetti N, et al. Allergic and photoallergic contact dermatitis from ketoprofen: evaluation of cross-reactivities by a combination of photopatch testing and computerized conformational analysis. Curr Pharm Des 2008;14:2833-2839
6   Pigatto PD, Guzzi G, Schena D, Guarrera M, Foti C, Francalanci S, et al. Photopatch tests: an Italian multicentre study from 2004 to 2006. Contact Dermatitis 2008;59:103-108
7   Bourrain JL, Amblard P, Béani JC. Contact urticaria photoinduced by benzophenones. Contact Dermatitis 2003;48:45-46
8   Burry JN. Photo allergies from benzophenones and beta carotene in sunscreens. Contact Dermatitis 1980;6:211-212
9   Millard LG, Barrett PL. Contact allergy from Mexenone masquerading as an exacerbation of light sensitivity. Contact Dermatitis 1980;6:222-223
10 Crouch RB, Foley PA, Baker CS. The results of photopatch testing 172 patients to sunscreening agents at the photobiology clinic, St Vincent's Hospital, Melbourne. Australas J Dermatol 2002;43:74
11 Cardoso J, Canelas MM, Gonçalo M, Figueiredo A. Photopatch testing with an extended series of photoallergens: a 5-year study. Contact Dermatitis 2009;60:325-329
12 Leow YH, Wong WK, Ng SK, Goh CL. 2 years experience of photopatch testing in Singapore. Contact Dermatitis 1994;31:181-182
13 English JSC, White IR, Cronin K. Sensitivity to sunscreens. Contact Dermatitis 1987;17:159-162
14 Ang P, Ng SK, Goh CL. Sunscreen allergy in Singapore. Am J Cont Derm 1998;9:42-44
15 Green C, Catterall M, Hawk JLM. Chronic actinic dermatitis and sunscreen allergy. Clin Exp Dermatol 1991;16:70-71
16 Gudmunsen KJ, Murphy M, O'Sullivan D, Powell FC, O'Loughlin S. Polymorphic light eruption with contact and photocontact allergy. Br J Dermatol 1991;124:379-382
17 Rademaker M. Occupational contact dermatitis among New Zealand farmers. Australas J Dermatol 1998;39:164-167
18 Heurung AR, Raju SI, Warshaw EM. Contact allergen of the year. Benzophenones. Dermatitis 2014;25:3-10 (contains many mistakes; Erratum in Dermatitis 2014;25:92-95)
19 Heurung AR, Raju SI, Warshaw EM. Adverse reactions to sunscreen agents: epidemiology, responsible irritants and allergens, clinical characteristics, and management. Dermatitis 2014;25:289-326
20 Avenel-Audran M. Sunscreen products: finding the allergen. Eur J Dermatol 2010;20:161-166
21 Scheuer E, Warshaw E. Sunscreen allergy: a review of epidemiology, clinical characteristics, and responsible allergens. Dermatitis 2006;17:3-11
22 Funk JO, Dromgoole SH, Maibach HI. Sunscreen intolerance: contact sensitization, photocontact sensitization, and irritancy of sunscreen agents. Dermatol Clin 1995;13:473-481
23 Dromgoole SH, Maibach HI. Sunscreening agent intolerance: Contact and photocontact sensitization and contact urticaria. J Am Acad Dermatol 1990;22:1068-1078
24 Goossens A. Cosmetic contact allergens. Cosmetics 2016, 3, 5; doi:10.3390/cosmetics3010005

25 Cronin E. Contact Dermatitis. Edinburgh: Churchill Livingstone, 1980: 453

26 Valbuena Mesa MC, Hoyos Jiménez EV. Photopatch testing in Bogota (Colombia): 2011–2013. Contact Dermatitis 2016;74:11-17

27 Chuah SY, Leow YH, Goon AT, Theng CT, Chong WS. Photopatch testing in Asians: a 5-year experience in Singapore. Photodermatol Photoimmunol Photomed 2013;29:116-120

28 Shaw T, Simpson B, Wilson B, Oostman H, Rainey D, Storrs F. True photoallergy to sunscreens is rare despite popular belief. Dermatitis 2010;21:185-198

29 Bosca F, Miranda MA, Carganico G, Mauleon D. Photochemical and photobiological properties of ketoprofen associated with the benzophenone chromophore. Photochem Photobiol 1994;60:96-101

30 Leroy D, Dompmartin A, Szczurko C, Michel M, Louvet S. Photodermatitis from ketoprofen with cross-reactivity to fenofibrate and benzophenones. Photodermatol Photoimmunol Photomed 1997;13:93-97

31 Schauder S. Survey of the literature on adverse reactions to preparations containing UV filters (1947-1989) (Literaturübersicht über Unverträglichkeitsreaktionen auf lichtfilterhaltige Produkte von 1947 bis 1989). Z Hautkr 1990;65:982-998 (article in German)

2.47 BENZOXONIUM CHLORIDE

IDENTIFICATION

Description/definition	: Benzoxonium chloride is the quaternary ammonium compound that conforms to the formula shown below
Chemical class(es)	: Quaternary ammonium compounds
Chemical/IUPAC name	: Benzyl-dodecyl-bis(2-hydroxyethyl)azanium chloride
Other name(s)	: Bradophen®
CAS registry number (s)	: 19379-90-9
EC number(s)	: 243-008-1
Merck Index monograph	: 2384
Function(s) in cosmetics	: EU: antimicrobial. USA: cosmetic biocides
Patch testing	: 0.1% water and preferably also 0.01% water; 0.1% water may be slightly irritant (1,3); 0.02% water (2)
Molecular formula	: $C_{23}H_{42}ClNO_2$

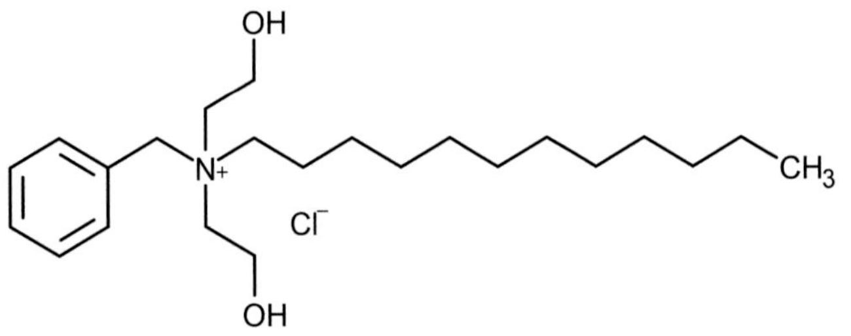

GENERAL

Benzoxonium chloride is a quaternary ammonium compound used, because of its antibacterial, antiviral and antimycotic activity, in the topical therapy of burns, for disinfection of surgical instruments, for inhibition of dental plaque formation, and also in veterinary products (1). The cases of 'cosmetic allergy' presented here were actually caused by topical veterinary products ('udder ointments'), but were used as cosmetic products to treat dry skin and are also marketed as such.

CONTACT ALLERGY

Case reports and case series

In a group of 119 patients with allergic contact dermatitis from cosmetics, investigated in The Netherlands in 1986-1987, one case was caused by benzoxonium chloride in a veterinary cream used as a cosmetic (4,5, same patient as in ref. 2). In a group of 75 patients allergic to cosmetic products, seen in a private practice in The Netherlands in the period 1981-1986, two cases were caused by benzoxonium chloride in skin care products (6, overlap with ref. 3). A male patient had dermatitis of the face, arms, hands, left shoulder and axilla. He had used an emollient to treat his dry skin of the hands and arms. Patch tests with the European standard series and the patient's own products gave positive reactions to the emollient and lanolin alcohol. In a second patch test session, the ingredients of this product and a series of quaternary ammonium compounds were tested, which resulted in an excited skin syndrome. Retesting with the quaternary ammonium compounds gave a reaction only to benzoxonium chloride tested at 0.02% in water, to which 20 controls were negative. The ointment did not contain lanolin or lanolin alcohol. After discontinuing the use of the preparation, the dermatitis healed and has not recurred (2).

A woman had an itchy eruption on her face, which had started 3 days earlier. On examination, an erythematous rash was noted on the face and neck with a free perioral zone; the eyelids were mildly edematous and scaly. Patch tests with the ICDRG standard series, a cosmetic series of 16 fragrances and 9 preservatives, and the patient's seven personal cosmetics gave a positive reaction to a (veterinary) ointment used intermittently by the patient for rhagades of the fingers. Later, the ingredients of this ointment were tested separately, which yielded an allergic reaction to the quaternary ammonium compound benzoxonium chloride 0.1% water and 0.01% in water. The patient was later tested with an additional series of quaternary ammonium compounds (all 0.1% and 0.01% in water) and positive reactions were seen to domiphen bromide and benzalkonium chloride. Thirty controls were tested with benzoxonium chloride 0.1% in water, and 2 showed a ?+ reaction at D2, which subsided one day later; no reactions were seen to the chemical 0.01% in water. Since the patient has stopped using the implicated ointment, she has had no recurrences of her facial dermatitis for at least one year (3).

Contact allergy to benzoxonium chloride in non-cosmetic products
One patient had allergic contact dermatitis from benzoxonium chloride in a topical pharmaceutical product (1).

Cross-reactions, pseudo-cross-reactions and co-reactions
Not to other quaternary ammonium compounds: domiphen bromide, benzoxonium chloride, benzalkonium chloride, cetylpyridinium chloride, cetrimonium bromide, cetalkonium chloride, toloconium methyl sulfate (2). Domiphen bromide, benzalkonium chloride (3).

Presence in cosmetic products and chemical analyses
In the USA, in April 2017, benzoxonium chloride was present in zero of 56,714 cosmetic products of which the composition is known in FDA's Voluntary Cosmetic Registration Program (VCRP) (data obtained from FDA, May 2017). In April 2017, benzoxonium chloride was present in zero of 65,521 cosmetic products of which the composition is known in EWG's Skin Deep Cosmetics Database, USA (http://www.ewg.org/skindeep/).

LITERATURE

1   Díaz-Ramón L, Aguirre A, Ratón-Nieto JA, de Miguel M. Contact dermatitis from benzoxonium chloride. Contact Dermatitis 1999;41:53-54
2   Bruynzeel DP, de Groot AC, Weyland JW. Contact dermatitis to lauryl pyridinium chloride and benzoxonium chloride. Contact Dermatitis 1987;17:41-42
3   De Groot AC, Conemans J, Liem DH. Contact allergy to benzoxonium chloride (Bradophen®). Contact Dermatitis 1984;11:324-325
4   De Groot AC, Bruynzeel DP, Bos JD, van der Meeren HL, van Joost T, Jagtman BA, Weyland JW. The allergens in cosmetics. Arch Dermatol 1988;124:1525-1529
5   De Groot AC. Adverse reactions to cosmetics. PhD Thesis, University of Groningen, The Netherlands: 1988, chapter 3.4, pp.105-113
6   De Groot AC. Contact allergy to cosmetics: Causative ingredients. Contact Dermatitis 1987;17:26-34

2.48 BENZOYL PEROXIDE

IDENTIFICATION

Description/definition   : Benzoyl peroxide is the inorganic compound that conforms to the formula shown
                             below
Chemical class(es)   : Inorganics
Chemical/IUPAC name   : Benzoyl benzenecarboperoxoate
Other names   : Dibenzoyl peroxide
CAS registry number (s)   : 94-36-0
EC number(s)   : 202-327-6
SCCS opinion(s)   : SCCNFP/0486/01 (25)
Merck Index monograph   : 2389
Function(s) in cosmetics   : EU: oxidising. USA: antiacne agents; artificial nail builders
EU cosmetic restrictions   : Regulated in Annex III/94 of the Regulation (EC) No. 1223/2009
Patch testing   : 1.0% pet. (Chemotechnique, SmartPracticeEurope, SmartPracticeCanada); great risk of
                             irritant reactions (28)
Molecular formula   : $C_{14}H_{10}O_4$

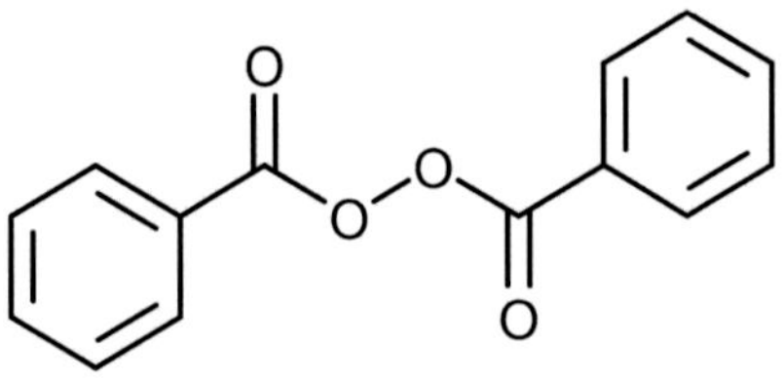

GENERAL

Benzoyl peroxide is widely used in the treatment of acne, but is infrequently employed in cosmetics. In the EU and the USA, it may be present in artificial nail material as an initiator for polymerization of (meth)acrylates; in such products, benzoyl peroxide has rarely caused allergic contact dermatitis (1).

Contact allergy to benzoyl peroxide was common in the 1980s, when 20% benzoyl peroxide was used to treat leg ulcers in chronic venous insufficiency. In these patients, (very) high sensitization rates have been described (3,4,19, 20,21). Still earlier, many bakers had developed occupational allergic contact dermatitis from benzoyl peroxide used for flour improvement (26). However, this compound has been banned as a flour bleaching agent more than 60 years ago, and nowadays, benzoyl peroxide is no longer an occupational allergen in bakers (5). Currently, allergic reactions may occur in dental technicians, as benzoyl peroxide is used as an initiator in the production of dentures (2,11). In other industries too, cases of occupationally acquired sensitization to benzoyl peroxide have been observed, because the chemical is also used in the manufacturing of plastic materials, resins, and elastomers and as a bleaching agent in the production of candles (6-10). Benzoyl peroxide has also been reported to cause allergic reactions in orthopedic patients from its use in bone cement (24).

There are several case reports of allergic contact dermatitis due to benzoyl peroxide following topical treatmentin acne patients (e.g. 12,13,23). Larger studies on the frequency of contact sensitization to benzoyl peroxide in acne patients having undergone treatment with it revealed less than 1% positive reactions to benzoyl peroxide 1% pet. (14-18). Thus, it appears that the widely used acne treatments with benzoyl peroxide rarely sensitize (2,22). It should be appreciated that patch testing with benzoyl peroxide 1% pet. frequently leads to weak positive reactions, especially in patients with atopic dermatitis. Mostly, their clinical relevance remains uncertain and the majority may be irritant patch test responses (2). Benzoyl peroxide as a drug will be discussed in more detail in a future publication (Monographs in Contact Allergy. III. Topical and systemic drugs).

CONTACT ALLERGY

Case reports and case series
A manicurist had occupational allergic contact dermatitis from benzoyl peroxide present in several artificial nail materials she used (1). She also reacted to HEMA, which was not declared on the Material Data safety Sheets. However, chemical analysis showed HEMA to be present in several of the products used by the patient, with a maximum concentration of 9.1% in one artificial nail material (1).

Presence in cosmetic products and chemical analyses
In the USA, in April 2017, benzoyl peroxide was present in 62 of 56,714 cosmetic products of which the composition is known in FDA's Voluntary Cosmetic Registration Program (VCRP) (data obtained from FDA, May 2017). In April

2017, benzoyl peroxide was present in 43 of 65,521 cosmetic products of which the composition is known in EWG's Skin Deep Cosmetics Database, USA (http://www.ewg.org/skindeep/).

LITERATURE

1 Andersen SL, Rastogi SC, Andersen KE. Occupational allergic contact dermatitis to hydroxyethyl methacrylate (2-HEMA) in a manicurist. Contact Dermatitis 2009;61:48-50

2 Ockenfels H-M, Uter W, Lessmann H, Schnuch A, Geier J. Patch testing with benzoyl peroxide: reaction profile and interpretation of positive patch test reactions. Contact Dermatitis 2009;61:209-216

3 Bandmann HJ, Agathos M. Die posttherapeutische Benzoylperoxidkontaktallergie bei Ulcus-cruris-Patienten. Hautarzt 1985;36:670-674

4 Jensen O, Petersen SH, Vesterager L. Contact sensitization to benzoyl peroxide following topical treatment of chronic leg ulcers. Contact Dermatitis 1980;6:179-182

5 Bauer A, Geier J, Elsner P. Type IV allergy in the food processing industry: sensitization profiles in bakers, cooks, and butchers. Contact Dermatitis 2002;46:228-235

6 Bonnekoh B, Merk HF. Airborne allergic contact dermatitis from benzoyl peroxide as a bleaching agent of candle wax. Contact Dermatitis 1991;24:367-368

7 Dejobert Y, Martin P, Piette F, Thomas P, Bergoend H. Contact dermatitis caused by benzoyl peroxide in podiatrists. Contact Dermatitis 1999;40:163

8 Quirce S, Olaguibel JM, Garcia BE, Tabar AI. Occupational airborne contact dermatitis due to benzoyl peroxide. Contact Dermatitis 1993;29:165-166

9 Tsovilis E, Crepy MN, Jonathan AM, Ameille J. Occupational contact dermatitis due to a marbler's exposure to benzoyl peroxide. Contact Dermatitis 2005;52:117-118

10 Forschner K, Zuberbier T, Worm M. Benzoyl peroxide as a cause of airborne contact dermatitis in an orthopaedic technician. Contact Dermatitis 2002;47:241

11 Rustemeyer T, Frosch PJ. Occupational skin disease in dental laboratory technicians. (I). Clinical picture and causative factors. Contact Dermatitis 1996;34:125-134

12 Mora Morillas I, Aguilar Martinez A, Sanchez Lozano JL, Garcia Perez A. Is benzoyl peroxide an irritant or sensitizer? Contact Dermatitis 1987;16:232-233

13 Romaguera C, Grimalt F. Sensitization to benzoyl peroxide, retinoic acid and carbon tetrachloride. Contact Dermatitis 1980;6:442

14 Cunliffe WJ, Burke B. Benzoyl peroxide: lack of sensitization. Acta Derm Venereol 1982;62:458-459

15 Balato N, Lembo G, Nappa P, Ayala F. Benzoyl peroxide reactions in acne patients. Contact Dermatitis 1984;10:255

16 Balato N, Lembo G, Cuccurullo FM, Patruno C, Nappa P, Ayala F. Acne and allergic contact dermatitis. Contact Dermatitis 1996;34:68-69

17 Haustein UF, Tegetmeyer L, Ziegler V. Allergic and irritant potential of benzoyl peroxide. Contact Dermatitis 1985;13:252-257

18 Lindemayr H, Dobril M. Contact sensitization to benzoyl peroxide. Contact Dermatitis 1981;7:137-140

19 Bahmer FA, Schulze-Dirks A, Zaun H. Sensibilisierende Wirkung einer fur die Behandlung des Ulcus cruris verwendeten 20%igen Benzoylperoxid-Zubereitung. Derm Beruf Umwelt 1984;32:21-24

20 Vena GA, Angelini G, Meneghini CL. Contact dermatitis to benzoyl peroxide. Contact Dermatitis 1982;8:338

21 Agathos M, Bandmann H-J. Benzoyl peroxide contact allergy in leg ulcer patients. Contact Dermatitis 1984;11:316-317

22 Veraldi S, Brena M, Barbareschi M. Allergic contact dermatitis caused by topical antiacne drugs. Expert Rev Clin Pharmacol. 2015;8:377-381

23 Felton SJ, Orton D, Williams JD. Benzoyl peroxide in topical acne preparations: an underreported contact allergen? Dermatitis 2013;24:146-147

24 Bircher A, Friederich NF, Seelig W, Scherer K. Allergic complications from orthopaedic joint implants: the role of delayed hypersensitivity to benzoyl peroxide in bone cement. Contact Dermatitis 2012;66:20-26

25 SCCNFP (Scientific Committee on Cosmetics and Non Food Products). Opinion concerning SCCNFP (Scientific Committee on Cosmetics and Non Food Products). Opinion concerning the use of Benzoyl Peroxide (BPO) Hydroquinone (HQ), Hydroquinone Methylether (MEHQ) in artificial nail systems, 4 June 2002, SCCNFP/0486/01. Available at: http://ec.europa.eu/health/archive/ph_risk/committees/sccp/documents/out167_en.pdf

26 Fisher AA. Hand dermatitis- A 'baker' dozen'. Cutis 1982;29:214-221; data cited in ref. 27

27 Scheman A, Cha C, Jacob SE, Nedorost S. Food avoidance diets for systemic, lip, and oral contact allergy: an American Contact Alternatives Group article. Dermatitis 2012;23:248-257

28 Kanerva L, Jolanki R, Alanko K, Estlander T. Patch-test reactions to plastic and glue allergens. Acta Derm Venereol 1999;79:296-300

2.49 BENZYLHEMIFORMAL

IDENTIFICATION

Description/definition	: Benzylhemiformal is the organic compound that conforms to the formula shown below
Chemical class(es)	: Ethers
Chemical/IUPAC name	: Phenylmethoxymethanol
Other names(s)	: (Benzyloxy)methanol; Preventol® D2
CAS registry number (s)	: 14548-60-8
EC number(s)	: 238-588-8
SCCS opinion(s)	: SCCNFP, 17 February 1999 (10)
Function(s) in cosmetics	: EU: preservative. USA: preservatives
EU cosmetic restrictions	: Regulated in Annex V/55 of the Regulation (EC) No. 1223/2009
Patch testing	: 1% pet. (SmartPracticeEurope, SmartPracticeCanada)
Molecular formula	: $C_8H_{10}O_2$

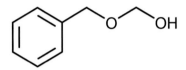

GENERAL

Benzylhemiformal is a formaldehyde-releaser permitted, but rarely used, in cosmetics. Non-cosmetic applications include biocide in metalworking fluids, slurries, filler suspensions, adhesives, various emulsions and dispersions, paints and lacquers, paper industry, spinning baths in the textile industry, polishes, waxes, and cleaning products (4).

CONTACT ALLERGY

Testing in groups of patients

There is one published report on the frequency of sensitization to benzylhemiformal in a population of consecutive patients patch tested for suspected contact dermatitis. In Denmark, in 1983, 671 patients were tested with benzyl-hemiformal (in the form of the commercial product Preventol D2) 2% and 981 consecutive patients with benzylhemiformal 1% (14). In the first group, there were 15 (2.2%) positive reactions, of who 11 co-reacted to formaldehyde. In the group of 981 individuals tested with the 1% pet. test substance, 14 (1.4%) had a positive reaction, of who 11 co-reacted to formaldehyde. In not a single patient could relevance be ascertained (14).

The experience with testing benzylhemiformal in groups of *selected* patients is limited in number and geographic area: all studies have been performed by the IVDK (Germany, Austria, Switzerland) (table 2.49.1). In three small series of patients with suspected metalworking fluid dermatitis, 1%-2.9% reacted to benzylhemiformal 1% pet. (5,6,7). In two larger series of 947 and 1759 patients, 2.3% and 2.4% had positive patch tests (8,9). It was not quite clear how these patients had been selected and there may have been an overlap in the two latter populations. The relevance of the observed positive patch test reactions was not stated and it is unknown whether these patients also reacted to formaldehyde.

Table 2.49.1 Patch testing in groups of patients: Selected patient groups

Years and Country	Test conc. & vehicle	Number of patients tested | positive (%)		Selection of patients (S); Relevance (R); Comments (C)	Ref.
2004-2005 IVDK	1% pet.	102	1 (1.0%)	S: patients with suspected metalworking fluid dermatitis; R: not stated	5
2002-2003 IVDK	1% pet.	199	3 (1.5%)	S: Patients with suspected metalworking fluid dermatitis; R: not stated	6
1999-2001 IVDK	1% pet.	105	3 (2.9%)	S: Metalworkers exposed to water-based metalworking fluids; R: not stated	7
1992-1995 IVDK [a]	1% pet.	1759	42 (2.4%)	S: not stated, selected from 35,062 patients; R: not stated	8
1990-1993 IVDK [a]	1% pet.	947	22 (2.3%)	S: not specified, approximately 30% were patients working with metals and metal objects; R: not stated	9

[a] it may be assumed that there is an overlap in the patient populations in these IVDK studies
IVDK: Informationsverbund Dermatologischer Kliniken, Germany, Austria, Switzerland (Information Network of Departments of Dermatology), www.ivdk.org

Case reports
A cook and a dental nurse both had occupational allergic contact dermatitis from benzylhemiformal in a moisturizing cream, independent of formaldehyde allergy (3).

Contact allergy to benzylhemiformal in non-cosmetic products
A nurse had occupational ACD from formaldehyde released by benzylhemiformal in a liquid detergent and a sweet worker from a dishwashing liquid containing benzylhemiformal (3).

Cross-reactions, pseudo-cross-reactions and co-reactions
Benzylhemiformal is a formaldehyde-releaser. In a number of patients, contact allergy to the preservative is the result of sensitivity to formaldehyde. In these cases, pseudo-cross-reactions may be observed to formaldehyde (14) and -theoretically, there are no data available - to other formaldehyde-releasers including diazolidinyl urea, DMDM hydantoin, imidazolidinyl urea, and – to a lesser degree – 2-bromo-2-nitropropane-1,3-diol.

Presence of benzylhemiformal in cosmetic products
In the USA, in April 2017, benzylhemiformal was present in zero of 56,714 cosmetic products of which the composition is known in FDA's Voluntary Cosmetic Registration Program (VCRP) (data obtained from FDA, May 2017). In April 2017, benzylhemiformal was present in zero of 65,521 cosmetic products of which the composition is known in EWG's Skin Deep Cosmetics Database, USA (http://www.ewg.org/skindeep/). In 2010, the preservative had been listed in the same database as ingredient in none of 41,113 products on file (4). In 2008, benzylhemiformal was present in not a single product of 33,212 cosmetics and toiletries registered in the USA Food and Drug Administration (FDA) Voluntary Cosmetic Registration Database (2). In the same period, of 496 stay-on cosmetic products present in a local drugstore in The Netherlands and investigated by checking the ingredient labelling, zero products proved to contain this preservative (2).

Amounts of free formaldehyde released by benzylhemiformal and chemical analyses
Benzylhemiformal is the reaction product of benzyl alcohol and formaldehyde, and is rarely used in cosmetic products. It degrades rapidly in an aqueous solution, and at pH 5 the maximum possible amount of 300 ppm formaldehyde of an 0.1% benzylhemiformal solution can be demonstrated (12). German investigators found that benzylhemiformal at 2% w/w aqueous solution mixes spontaneously, with decomposition of 97% of the benzyl-hemiformal. Higher dilution leads to instantaneous, complete decomposition of the releaser into formaldehyde and benzyl alcohol. At the maximum permissible concentration of 0.15% benzylhemiformal in cosmetic rinse-off products, the concentration of free formaldehyde should according to these authors be just under 0.05 wt% (500 ppm) (11).

In the commercial benzylhemiformal 1% petrolatum patch test material no free formaldehyde is found, but contact with water will release formaldehyde (1). A 1% aqueous solution prepared by a supplier of patch test materials at pH 8.5 contained 0.37% (3700 ppm) free formaldehyde (1). Benzylhemiformal 0.1% preservative solution was found to contain 300 ppm free formaldehyde and a shampoo preserved with 0.2% benzylhemiformal contained 100 ppm (13).

LITERATURE
1   Emeis D, De Groot AC, Brinkmann J. Determination of formaldehyde in formaldehyde-releaser patch test preparations. Contact Dermatitis 2010;63:57-62
2   De Groot AC, Veenstra M. Formaldehyde-releasers in cosmetics in the USA and in Europe. Contact Dermatitis 2010;62:221-224
3   Aalto-Korte K, Kuuliala O, Suuronen K, Alanko K. Occupational contact allergy to formaldehyde and formaldehyde releasers. Contact Dermatitis 2008;59:280-289
4   De Groot AC, White IR, Flyvholm M-A, Lensen G, Coenraads P-J. Formaldehyde-releasers in cosmetics: relationship to formaldehyde contact allergy. Part 1. Characterization, frequency and relevance of sensitization, and frequency of use in cosmetics. Contact Dermatitis 2010;62:2-17
5   Geier J, Lessmann H, Becker D, Bruze M, Frosch PJ, Fuchs T, et al. Patch testing with components of water-based metalworking fluids: results of a multicentre study with a second series. Contact Dermatitis 2006;55:322-329
6   Geier J, Lessmann H, Dickel H, Frosch PJ, Koch P, Becker D, et al. Patch test results with the metalworking fluid series of the German Contact Dermatitis Research Group (DKG). Contact Dermatitis 2004;51:118-130
7   Geier J, Lessmann H, Schnuch A, Uter W. Contact sensitizations in metalworkers with occupational dermatitis exposed to water-based metalworking fluids: results of the research project "FaSt". Int Arch Occup Environ Health 2004;77:543-551
8   Geier J, Lessmann H, Schuch A, Fuchs Th. Kontaktallergien durch formaldehydabspaltende Biozide. Allergologie 1997;20:215-224 (article in German)

9   Geier J, Kleinhans D, Peters K-P. Kontaktallergien durch industriel verwendete Biozide. Ergebnisse des Informationsverbunds Dermatologischer Kliniken (IVDK) und der Deutschen Kontaktallergiegruppe. Dermatosen 1996;44:154-159

10 SCCNFP (Scientific Committee on Cosmetics and Non Food Products). Opinion concerning benzylhemiformal, 17 February 1999. Available at: http://ec.europa.eu/health/scientific_committees/consumer_safety/ opinions/sccnfp_opinions_97_04/sccp_out62_en.htm

11 Emeis D, Anker W, Wittern K-P. Quantitative ^{13}C NMR spectroscopic studies on the equilibrium of formaldehyde with its releasing preservatives. Anal Chem 2007;79:2096-2100

12 Rastogi SC. Analytical control of preservative labelling on skin creams. Contact Dermatitis 2000;43:339-343

13 Engelhardt H, Klinkner R. Determination of free formaldehyde in the presence of donators in cosmetics by HPLC and post-column derivation. Chromatographia 1985;20:559-565

14 Andersen KE, Veien NK. Biocide patch tests. Contact Dermatitis 1985;12:99-103

2.50 BETULA ALBA (BIRCH) BARK EXTRACT

IDENTIFICATION

Description/definition   : Betula alba bark extract is the extract of the bark of the birch, *Betula alba* L., Betulaceae
Chemical class(es)   : Botanical products and botanical derivatives
Other names   : Birch bark extract; white birch bark extract
CAS registry number (s)   : 84012-15-7
EC number(s)   : 281-660-9
Function(s) in cosmetics   : EU: flavouring; masking; perfuming. USA: fragrance Ingredients; skin-conditioning
                                agents - miscellaneous
Patch testing   : extract 10% in jojoba oil (1)

CONTACT ALLERGY

Case reports and case series
Four months after starting to use a skin care cream, a male patient developed itchy erythema and papules on his hands and face. Topical application of glucocorticosteroids resulted in only transient relief followed by relapses after discontinuation. Two years previously, this patient had been diagnosed with occupational allergic contact dermatitis of the hands. Since then, he had strictly avoided any contact with the allergens that he was found to react to. Because the patient's working conditions had remained unchanged, his newly introduced skin care product was suspected to be the cause of his recent dermatitis. Patch tests were performed and there was a positive reaction to the skin care cream. The patient then started using another skin care product, and his skin permanently cleared. According to the manufacturer, the product contained the following ingredients: 5% birch (*Betula alba*) bark extract, 50% jojoba (*Simmondsia chinensis*) oil, and 45% water. Four months after healing of the dermatitis, further patch tests were performed with birch bark extract (tested 10% in jojoba oil) and jojoba oil pure. This resulted in a positive reaction to the birch bark extract material, but jojoba oil was negative (1).

According to the manufacturer, the tested birch bark extract consisted of betulin (80%) plus some other triterpenes, such as betulinic acid (3%) and lupeol (2%). As betulin was the major triterpene in the cream used by the patient, the authors supposed that this chemical was the relevant allergen in this case, while admitting, however, that they could not exclude the possibility that an admixed different triterpene could have been the culprit (1). Chemically, betulin is a triterpenoid with a lupane structure. It has a pentacyclic ring structure and hydroxyl groups in positions C3 and C28 (figure 1). Triterpenes are attractive pharmacological substances, with antiphlogistic and antiproliferative effects (1).

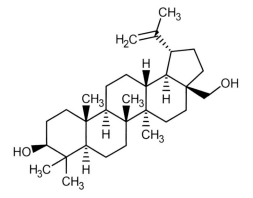

Figure 1 Structural formula of betulin

Presence in cosmetic products and chemical analyses
In the USA, in April 2017, birch extract was present in 12 of 56,714 cosmetic products of which the composition is known in FDA's Voluntary Cosmetic Registration Program (VCRP) (data obtained from FDA, May 2017). In March 2017, Betula alba (birch) bark extract was present in 26 of 64,983 cosmetic products of which the composition is known in EWG's Skin Deep Cosmetics Database, USA (http://www.ewg.org/skindeep/).

LITERATURE
1   Meyer-Hoffert U, Brasch J. Allergic contact dermatitis caused by betulin-containing triterpene extract from the outer bark of birch (*Betula alba*). Contact Dermatitis 2013;68:382-383

2.51 BHA

IDENTIFICATION

Description/definition	: BHA is a mixture of isomers of tertiary butyl-substituted 4-methoxyphenols. It consists chiefly of 3-*t*-butyl-4-hydroxyanisole with lesser amounts of 2-*t*-butyl-4-hydroxyanisole and conforms generally to the formula shown below
Chemical class(es)	: Phenols
Chemical/IUPAC name	: 2-*tert*-Butyl-4-methoxyphenol
Other names	: Butylated hydroxyanisole
CAS registry number (s)	: 25013-16-5
EC number(s)	: 246-563-8
CIR review(s)	: J Am Coll Toxicol 1984;3:83-146 (access: www.cir-safety.org/ingredients)
Merck Index monograph	: 2819
Function(s) in cosmetics	: EU: antioxidant; masking. USA: antioxidants; fragrance ingredients
Patch testing	: 2.0% pet. (Chemotechnique, SmartPracticeEurope, SmartPracticeCanada); 2.0% alc. (SmartPracticeCanada)
Molecular formula	: $C_{11}H_{16}O_2$

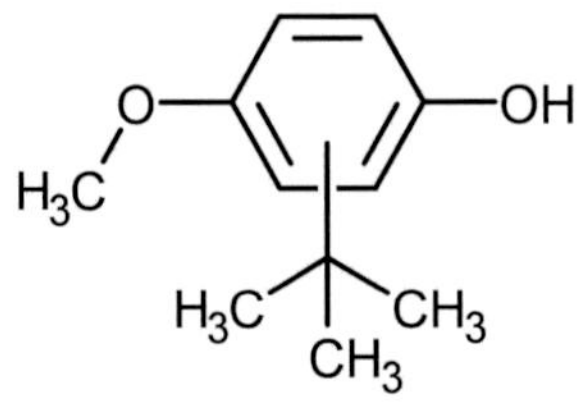

GENERAL

BHA is a mixture of isomers of tertiary butyl-substituted 4-methoxyphenols. It consists chiefly of 3-*t*-butyl-4-hydroxy-anisole with lesser amounts of 2-*t*-butyl-4-hydroxyanisole. BHA It is used widely as an antioxidant by food, pharmaceutical and cosmetics manufacturers. The literature on adverse reactions to BHA from before 1990 has been reviewed (40).

CONTACT ALLERGY

Patch testing in groups of patients
Results of studies patch testing BHA in consecutive patients suspected of contact dermatitis (routine testing) are shown in table 2.51.1 and results of testing in groups of *selected* patients (e.g., patients with stasis dermatitis / chronic leg ulcers, patients suspected of cosmetic intolerance, patients with facial allergic contact dermatitis)are shown in table 2.51.2. In routine testing, generally low frequencies of sensitization to BHA have been observed, ranging from 0.2% to 2.7% (the latter being a small study of 112 patients from Denmark [6]). Relevance rates varied considerably and ranged from 7% to 57%. In not one single study were causative products mentioned.

Table 2.51.1 Patch testing in groups of patients: Routine testing

Years and Country	Test conc. & vehicle	Number of patients tested | positive (%)		Selection of patients (S); Relevance (R); Comments (C)	Ref.
2003-2005 China		599	9 (1.5%)	R: not stated	23
2000-2005 USA	2% pet.	2702	(0.3%)	R: 33%	3
1998-2000 USA	2% pet.	1322	(0.3%)	R: not stated	21
1994-1996 USA	2% pet.	3076	(0.5%)	R: definite + probable relevance: 7%	19
1992-1994 USA	2% pet.	3472	(0.2%)	R: present relevance: 57%	20
<1976 Denmark	2% pet.	112	3 (2.7%)	R: one or two had positive oral provocation tests with BHA, but a contact product containing BHA was not found	6
<1971 Italy	5% pet.	360	1 (0.3%)	R: not stated	5

In groups of selected patients (e.g., patients with stasis dermatitis / chronic leg ulcers, patients suspected of cosmetic intolerance, patients with facial allergic contact dermatitis), rates of sensitization were not elevated and ranged from 0.4% to 2% (table 2.51.2). Relevance was usually not mentioned, but in one UK study, all 7 reactions in patients with facial dermatitis were relevant and were caused by various cosmetic products (7). In a study from the USA, 6 of 7 positive patch test reactions were scored as relevant, but this included 'questionable' and 'past' relevance (1).

Table 2.51.2 Patch testing in groups of patients: Selected patient groups

Years and Country	Test conc. & vehicle	Number of patients tested | positive (%)		Selection of patients (S); Relevance (R); Comments (C)	Ref.
2003-2014 IVDK	2% pet.	4756	(1.4%)	S: patients with stasis dermatitis / chronic leg ulcers; R: not stated	33
2006-2011 IVDK	2% pet.	7771	(0.5%)	S: patients suspected of cosmetic intolerance and tested with an ointment base series (selection procedure not stated); R: not stated	31
2000-2007 USA	2% pet.	944	7 (0.6%)	S: patients tested with a supplemental cosmetic screening series; R: 83%; C: weak study: a. high rate of macular erythema and weak reactions; b. relevance figures included 'questionable' and 'past' relevance	1
1995-1997 USA		57	1 (2%)	S: patients with facial allergic contact dermatitis; R: only relevant reactions were mentioned	26
1990-1994 Germany	2% pet.	11,454	41 (0.4%)	S: patients tested with a preservative series; R: not stated	22
1982-1983 UK	1% pet.	1096	7 (0.7%)	S: patients with facial dermatitis; all reactions were relevant and were caused by various cosmetics; C: 5 co-reactions to TBHQ	7
1975-6 USA, Canada	2% pet.	409	(0.9%)	S: not stated; R: not stated	25

IVDK: Information Network of Departments of Dermatology, Germany, Austria, Switzerland

Case reports and case series

BHA was responsible for 3 out of 399 cases of cosmetic allergy where the causal allergen was identified in a study of the NACDG, USA, 1977-1983 (2). In a group of 146 patients patch tested for cheilitis in Amersham, UK, between 1982 and 2001, there were two positive patch test reactions to BHA considered to be relevant for the lip dermatitis. Over half of the reactions in the entire group were ascribed to lipsticks and lip salves (18). In a 4-month-period in 1996, 475 patients with contact allergy to 'cosmetic ingredients' were collected in 5 centers in Belgium, UK and Germany. There were 3 reactions to BHA; relevance was not mentioned (24). Two positive patch test reactions to BHA were ascribed to cosmetic allergy (4).

Seven patients seen in London in 1982-1983 had allergic contact dermatitis from BHA in various cosmetics: lipsticks (n=3), cream blusher, sunscreen, eyeshadow and hair cream (one each) (7). A woman had allergic contact cheilitis from BHA in a sunscreen lipstick (12). Another patient had allergic contact dermatitis from BHA in a hand cream (17). A female patient developed allergic contact dermatitis from BHA in a tinted foundation cream and a liquid cosmetic (16).

Contact allergy to BHA in non-cosmetic products

Occupational hand dermatitis and cheilitis from contact allergy to BHA in mayonnaise developed in a cook (9). One patient had allergic contact dermatitis from BHA in miconazole antifungal cream (10). A woman had recurrent swelling of the lip; she was allergic to BHA and the symptoms completely disappeared on an appropriate diet; there was a rapid recurrence of lip swelling on rechallenge (11). BHA in food stuffs may have been responsible for airborne allergic contact dermatitis of the face in a pastry cook; the source of BHA, however, was not identified (13). One patient with occupation-related allergic reaction to BHA in food has been reported (14, cited in ref. 13). Two patients became sensitized to BHA in their topical medications (15). Two other individuals had allergic contact dermatitis from BHA in a topical corticosteroid-antifungal pharmaceutical product. They both had positive patch tests to pharmaceutical grade BHA (2% pet.) as supplied by the manufacturer, but did not react to analytical grade BHA (2% pet.) from a patch test material supplier. The cause of the discrepancy was unknown (8). A woman had allergic contact dermatitis on several occasions after a dental appointment from BHA present in the latex gloves worn by her dentist (38).

Cross-reactions, pseudo-cross-reactions and co-reactions

BHT; TBHQ (6,7). Cutaneous demethylation of BHA could form TBHQ (34).

Presence in cosmetic products and chemical analyses

In the USA, in April 2017, BHA was present in 803 of 56,714 cosmetic products of which the composition is known in FDA's Voluntary Cosmetic Registration Program (VCRP) (data obtained from FDA, May 2017). In April 2017, BHA was present in 95 of 66,647 cosmetic products of which the composition is known in EWG's Skin Deep Cosmetics Database, USA (http://www.ewg.org/skindeep/). Of 38 cosmetic products marketed for babies in the UK in 2007, 4 (11%) contained BHA (27).

Provocation tests
Oral administration of BHA resulted in vesicular eczema on the fingers in two patients sensitized to BHA and BHT (6).

OTHER SIDE EFFECTS

Photosensitivity
Photocontact allergy to BHA has been mentioned in ref. 28 (details unknown)

Immediate-type reactions
A 5% alcoholic solution swabbed on one finger of a patient allergic to BHA and BHT caused contact urticaria (6). BHA has caused 'non-immunologic contact urticaria' from its presence in artificial nails (29).

OTHER INFORMATION
BHA and other additives in foods and drugs have been held responsible for exacerbations of recurrent urticaria by some authors (35). This was doubted by some (36), but it does seem to exist (37), although it is probably quite rare (32,39).

LITERATURE

1   Wetter DA, Yiannias JA, Prakash AV, Davis MD, Farmer SA, el-Azhary RA, et al. Results of patch testing to personal care product allergens in a standard series and a supplemental cosmetic series: an analysis of 945 patients from the Mayo Clinic Contact Dermatitis Group, 2000-2007. J Am Acad Dermatol 2010;63:789-798
2   Adams RM, Maibach HI, Clendenning WE, Fisher AA, Jordan WJ, Kanof N, et al. A five-year study of cosmetic reactions. J Am Acad Dermatol 1985;13:1062-1069
3   Davis MD, Scalf LA, Yiannias JA, Cheng JF, El-Azhary RA, Rohlinger AL, et al. Changing trends and allergens in the patch test standard series. Arch Dermatol 2008;144:67-72
4   Kohl L, Blondeel A, Song M. Allergic contact dermatitis from cosmetics: retrospective analysis of 819 patch-tested patients. Dermatology 2002;204:334-337
5   Meneghini CL, Rantuccio F, Lomuto M. Additives, vehicles and active drugs of topical medicaments as causes of delayed-type allergic dermatitis. Dermatologica 1971;143:137-147
6   Roed-Petersen J, Hjorth N. Contact dermatitis from antioxidants. Br J Dermatol 1976;94:233-241
7   White IR, Lovell CR, Cronin E. Antioxidants in cosmetics. Contact Dermatitis 1984;11:265-267
8   Orton DI, Shaw S. Allergic contact dermatitis from pharmaceutical grade BHA in Timodine, with no patch test reaction to analytical grade BHA. Contact Dermatitis 2001;44:191-192
9   Fisher AA. Contact dermatitis due to food additives. Cutis 1975;16:961-966
10   Degreef H, Verhoeve L. Contact dermatitis to miconazole nitrate. Contact Dermatitis 1975;1:269-270
11   Lewis FM, Shah M, Gawkrodger DJ. Contact sensitivity to food additives can cause oral and perioral symptoms. Contact Dermatitis 1995;33:429-430
12   Baes H, van Hecke E. Contact dermatitis from Zovirax cream. Contact Dermatitis 1990;23:200-201
13   Gola M, Acciai MC, Brusi C, Giorgini S, Sertoli A. Allergic contact dermatitis in a pastry cook. Contact Dermatitis 1989;21:57
14   Zanca A, Schena D, Luciani P, Chieregato GC. Butilato di idrossianisolo: un caso di DAC professionale. Atti del 9th Congresso GIRDCA, Cosenza, Italy, 18-19 November 1988, p. 99.
15   Tosti A, Bardazzi F, Valeri F, Russo R. Contact dermatitis from butylated hydroxyanisole. Contact Dermatitis 1987;17:257-258
16   Turner TW. Dermatitis from butylated hydroxy anisole. Contact Dermatitis 1977;3:282
17   Fisher AA. Reactions to antioxidants in cosmetics and foods. Cutis 1976;17:21-28 (cited in ref. 16)
18   Strauss RM, Orton DI. Allergic contact cheilitis in the United Kingdom: a retrospective study. Am J Contact Dermat 2003;14:75-77
19   Marks JG Jr, Belsito DV, DeLeo VA, Fowler JF Jr, Fransway AF, Maibach HI,et al. North American Contact Dermatitis Group patch test results for the detection of delayed-type hypersensitivity to topical allergens. J Am Acad Dermatol 1998;38:911-918
20   Marks JG, Belsito DV, DeLeo VA, Fowler JF, Fransway AF, Maibach HI,et al. North American Contact Dermatitis Group standard tray patch test results 1992 through 1994. Am J Contact Dermatitis 1995;6:160-165
21   Wetter DA, Davis MDP, Yiannias JA, Cheng JF, Connolly SM, el-Azhary RA, et al. Patch test results from the Mayo Contact Dermatitis Group, 1998–2000. J Am Acad Dermatol 2005;53:416-421
22   Schnuch A, Geier J, Uter W, Frosch PJ. Patch testing with preservatives, antimicrobials and industrial biocides. Results from a multicentre study. Br J Dermatol 1998;138:467-476

23 Li L-F, Liu G, Wang J. Patch test in Chinese patients with cosmetic allergic contact dermatitis to common cosmetic allergens from a European cosmetic series. Contact Dermatitis 2007;57:50-54

24 Goossens A, Beck MH, Haneke E, McFadden JP, Nolting S, Durupt G, Ries G. Adverse cutaneous reactions to cosmetic allergens. Contact Dermatitis 1999;40:112-113

25 Rudner EJ. North American Group Results. Contact Dermatitis 1977;3:208-209

26 Katz AS, Sherertz EF. Facial dermatitis: Patch test results and final diagnoses. Am J Cont Dermat 1999;10:153-156

27 White JML, McFadden JP. Exposure to haptens/contact allergens in baby cosmetic products. Contact Dermatitis 2008;59:176-177

28 Pevny I, Lurz Ch. Photoallergische dermatitis. Allergologie 1985;8:128-138

29 Schubert HJ, Lindner K, Prater E. Kontaktallergie in Nagelstudio. Z Hautkr 1992;67:1067-1069 (in German, data cited in ref. 30)

30 Baran R. Nail cosmetics: allergies and irritations. Am J Clin Dermatol 2002;3:547-555

31 Dinkloh A, Worm M, Geier J, Schnuch A, Wollenberg A. Contact sensitization in patients with suspected cosmetic intolerance: results of the IVDK 2006-2011. J Eur Acad Dermatol Venereol 2015;29:1071-1081

32 Rajan JP, Simon RA, Bosso JV. Prevalence of sensitivity to food and drug additives in patients with chronic idiopathic urticaria. J Allergy Clin Immunol Pract 2014;2:168-171

33 Erfurt-Berge C, Geier J, Mahler V. The current spectrum of contact sensitization in patients with chronic leg ulcers or stasis dermatitis - new data from the Information Network of Departments of Dermatology (IVDK). Contact Dermatitis 2017 Feb 14. doi: 10.1111/cod.12763. [Epub ahead of print]

34 Le Coz CJ, Schneider GA. Contact dermatitis from tertiary-butylhydroquinone in a hair dye, with cross-sensitivity to BHA and BHT. Contact Dermatitis 1998;39:39-40

35 Juhlin L. Recurrent urticaria: clinical investigation of 330 patients. Br J Dermatol 1981;104:369-381

36 Simon RA. Adverse reactions to food additives. N Engl Reg Allergy Proc 1986;7:533-542

37 Goodman DL, McDonnell JT, Nelson HS, Vaughan TR, Weber RW. Chronic urticaria exacerbated by the antioxidant food preservatives, butylated hydroxyanisole (BHA) and butylated hydroxytoluene (BHT). J Allergy Clin Immunol 1990;86(4 Pt 1):570-575

38 Rich P, Belozer ML, Norris P, Storrs FJ. Allergic contact dermatitis to two antioxidants in latex gloves: 4,4'-thiobis(6-tert-butyl-meta-cresol) (Lowinox 44S36) and butylhydroxyanisole. Allergen alternatives for glove-allergic patients. J Am Acad Dermatol 1991;24:37-43

39 Hannuksela M, Lahti A. Peroral challenge tests with food additives in urticaria and atopic dermatitis. Int J Dermatol 1986;25:178-180

40 Fransway AF. The problem of preservation in the 1990s. III. Agents with preservative function independent of formaldehyde release. Am J Contact Derm 1991;2:145-174

2.52 BHT

IDENTIFICATION

Description/definition	: BHT is a substituted toluene that conforms to the formula shown below
Chemical class(es)	: Phenols
Chemical/IUPAC name	: 2,6-*ditert*-Butyl-4-methylphenol
Other names	: Butylated hydroxytoluene
CAS registry number (s)	: 128-37-0
EC number(s)	: 204-881-4
CIR review(s)	: Int J Toxicol 2002;21(Suppl.2):19-94 (access: www.cir-safety.org/ingredients)
Merck Index monograph	: 2820
Function(s) in cosmetics	: EU: antioxidant; masking. USA: antioxidants; fragrance ingredients
Patch testing	: 2.0% pet. (Chemotechnique, SmartPracticeEurope, SmartPracticeCanada); 1% alc. (SmartPracticeCanada)
Molecular formula	: $C_{15}H_{24}O$

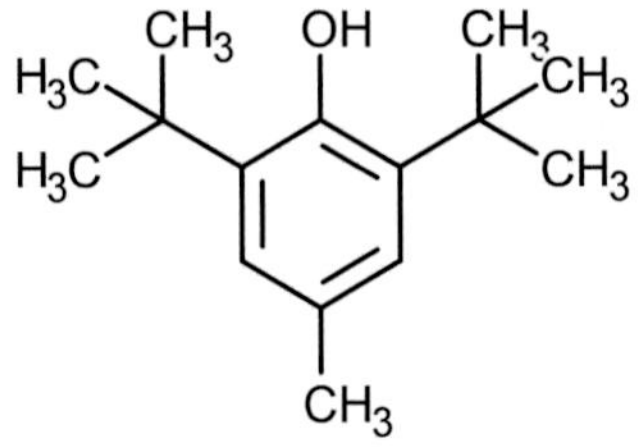

GENERAL

BHT is an antioxidant used especially in food, cosmetics and products such as paints and lacquers, hardeners for 2-component paints, glues, fillers, etc., binders, adhesives/glues, industrial oil and grease (including cutting fluids), fillings and mouldings, cleaning agents, printing/offset products, thinners and solvents, flooring materials, rubber and plastic materials (7,8). The literature on side effects of BHT up to 1990 has been reviewed (34).

CONTACT ALLERGY

Patch testing in groups of patients
Results of studies testing BHT in consecutive patients suspected of contact dermatitis (routine testing) are shown in table 2.52.1. Results of testing in groups of *selected* patients (usually patients suspected of cosmetic allergy) are shown in table 2.52.2.

Patch testing in consecutive patients suspected of contact dermatitis: routine testing
In routine testing (table 2.52.1), frequencies of sensitization have ranged from 0% to 2.7%, but they were > 0.5% in 2 studies only (3,15). In one of these studies, no causative products were found (3), in the other relevance was not mentioned (15).

Table 2.52.1 Patch testing in groups of patients: Routine testing

Years and Country	Test conc. & vehicle	Number of patients tested	positive (%)	Selection of patients (S); Relevance (R); Comments (C)	Ref.
2006-2010 USA	2% pet.	3084	(0.2%)	R: 14%	17
2003-2005 China		599	10 (1.7%)	R: not stated	15
2000-2005 USA	2% pet.	3743	(0.3%)	R: 33%	2
1998-2000 USA	2% pet.	1323	(0.5%)	R: not stated	13
1994-1996 USA	2% pet.	3076	(0.2%)	R: definite + probable relevance: 14%	11
1992-1994 USA	2% pet.	3470	(0.1%)	R: present relevance: 0%	12
1987-1989 Denmark	2% pet.	1336	0 -		7
<1976 Denmark	2% pet.	112	3 (2.7%)	R: no causative products found	3

Patch testing in groups of selected patients

In groups of selected patients (usually patients suspected of cosmetic allergy, table 2.52.2), rates of sensitization were not significantly higher than in routine testing with the exception of a 9.5% frequency of sensitization in a small group of 147 patients suspected of cosmetic allergy from Brazil. The authors admitted they could not find relevance of the reactions, but indicated that all patients had used topical products for prolonged periods of time (35).

Table 2.52.2 Patch testing in groups of patients: Selected patient groups

Years and Country	Test conc. & vehicle	Number of patients tested | positive (%)		Selection of patients (S); Relevance (R); Comments (C)	Ref.
2006-2011 IVDK	2% pet.	7772	(0.2%)	S: patients suspected of cosmetic intolerance and tested with an ointment base series (selection procedure not stated); R: not stated	25
2008-2010 Brazil	2% pet.	147	14 (9.5%)	S: patients suspected of cosmetic allergy; R: none found	35
2000-2007 USA	2% pet.	934	4 (0.4%)	S: patients tested with a supplemental cosmetic screening series; R: 100%; C: weak study: a. high rate of macular erythema and weak reactions; b. relevance figures included 'questionable' and 'past' relevance	1
1997-2000 Israel		244	5 (2.0%)	S: patients suspected of cosmetic dermatitis; R: 64% of all patch test reactions in the cosmetic series was relevant	20
1990-1994 Germany	2% pet.	11,454	11 (0.1%)	S: patients tested with a preservative series; R: not stated	14
1975-6 USA, Canada	2% pet.	224	(0.9%)	S: not stated; R: not stated	16

IVDK: Information Network of Departments of Dermatology, Germany, Austria, Switzerland

Case reports and case series

A man had suffered from recalcitrant hand dermatitis for 1,5 year. Within one week of daily use of an antifungal liquid spray he developed dermatitis on both his dorsal feet and hands, spreading to affect the whole body. The patient immediately stopped using the spray, but his hand dermatitis persisted and worsened, despite the use of high-potency topical steroids. Patch tests gave positive reactions to the antifungal spray, a deodorant stick, and BHT. Both the antifungal spray and the deodorant contained BHT, as did a shave gel the patient used. Avoidance of products containing BHT led to resolving of the patient's hand dermatitis. On re-exposure to BHT in his personal hygiene products and the antifungal spray, he developed foot and recalcitrant hand dermatitis again. The authors hypothesize that the patient formerly may have become sensitized to BHT from contact with aviation fuel containing BHT, while working as military engineer during his enlistment (5). One patient had allergic contact cheilitis from BHT (and BHA and TBHQ) in lipsticks (4).

Contact allergy to BHT in non-cosmetic products

A man had allergic contact dermatitis of the feet spreading to the rest of the body from BHT in an antifungal cream (5). Two patients, one with leg ulcer, the other with venous stasis, reacted to BHT present in support bandage (one also had a positive patch test to the bandage containing BHT) (8). BHT, present in a concentration of 0.02% in a topical antifungal pharmaceutical product, caused allergic contact dermatitis in one individual (9).

Cross-reactions, pseudo-cross-reactions and co-reactions

BHA (3,4,34); TBHQ (3,4).

Presence in cosmetic products and chemical analyses

In May 2017, BHT was present in 2034 of 66,647 cosmetic products of which the composition is known in EWG's Skin Deep Cosmetics Database, USA (http://www.ewg.org/skindeep/). In the USA, in April 2017, BHT was present in 8765 of 56,714 cosmetic products of which the composition is known in FDA's Voluntary Cosmetic Registration Program (VCRP) (data obtained from FDA, May 2017). In 2009, in the USA, the ingredient lists of 1591 facial cosmetics from one company were screened for the presence of BHT. BHT was present in 35% of 132 blushers and 38 bronzers, in 17% of 90 concealers, in 26% of 174 eyeliners, in 41% of 304 eyeshadows, in 12% of 457 foundations, in 33% of 140 loose and pressed powders, and in 14% of 256 mascaras (21). In 2009, in the USA, the ingredient lists of 796 hair products from one company were screened for the presence of BHT. BHT was present in 1% of 279 shampoos, in 1% of 231 conditioners, and in 2% of 286 styling products (22). In 2009, in the USA, the ingredient lists of 730 lip cosmetics and dental care products from one company were screened for the presence of BHT. BHT was present in 9% of 31 lip liners, in 38% of 429 lipsticks, in 15% of 92 lip moisturizers, in 1 of 153 toothpastes, and in 0% of 25 mouth washes (23).

In 2009, in the USA, the ingredient lists of 657 miscellaneous cosmetics from one company were screened for the presence of BHT. BHT was present in 18% of 195 antiperspirants/deodorants, in 5% of 41 powders, in 17% of 167 shaving products, in 16% of 201 sunblocks, and in 0% of 53 wipes (24). BHT was present in 189 of 1774 (10.7%) cosmetics and toiletries (2002) resp. in 189 of 1170 (16.2%) such products (2005) filed in the Danish Product Register Database (PROBAS) (19).

Other information
Oral administration of BHT resulted in vesicular eczema of the fingertips in a patient allergic to BHT (3). In an investigation of the depigmenting properties of BHT, after a usage test, 50 volunteers were patch tested with BHT 0.5% and 3% in a cream vehicle. Nine had a positive reaction to BHT 3% on day 9. The authors assumed these reactions to be non-specific and not indicative of allergic sensitization (27).

OTHER SIDE EFFECTS

Photosensitivity
Photocontact allergy to BHT was probably presented in ref. 18, but details are unknown (article not read).

Immediate-type reactions
A young woman for 8 months had recurrent eruptions on the hands, wrists, forearms, ears and the neck. She claimed that the eruption could be provoked by jewellery and plastic. Patch tests with the ICDRG standard series and a plastic and glues series were negative. A patch test with nickel was negative after 20 minutes, but a prick test strongly positive. A 20-min patch test was performed with a piece from two plastic bags, which happened to be in the clinic, which produced very strong urticarial reactions corresponding to both pieces of plastic. Urticarial reactions were also elicited by many other plastic folders, foils and bags. With the co-operation of the manufacturers, it was determined that reactions were provoked by articles containing either butylhydroxytoluene (BHT) and/or oleylamide (amide of oleic acid). When a 20-min patch test was performed with BHT and BHA in ethanol, a positive reaction was elicited by both substances 1%, while 0.1% and 0.01% did not evoke a reaction. Oleylamide also gave strong immediate contact reactions (6). BHT in plastic also caused contact urticaria in another individual (10). In a patient allergic to BHT and BHA, contact urticaria developed 15 minutes after swabbing a 5% alcoholic solutions of BHT to a finger at the application site (3).

Other non-eczematous contact reactions
In two children with pigmented skin, depigmentation of their skin developed at the site of contact with a PVC tape which contained BHT as an antioxidant. It was suggested that the depigmentation was due to the BHT (26). However, one child had severe atopic eczema and the other psoriasis, and it is possible that post-inflammatory depigmentation had occurred (4). An evaluation of the depigmenting abilities of BHT was thereafter performed in volunteers with pigmented skin with negative results (27,28). In one investigation (28), up to 3.3% dilutions of BHT were applied under occlusion on the skin of 16 men for two months. A slight irritant erythema was sometimes produced, but there was no evidence of hypo- or depigmentation (28). A more recent review concludes that BHT does not induce leukoderma / vitiligo (37).

Miscellaneous side effects
A woman presented with a cutaneous urticarial disseminated eruption. Immunohistological analysis of a cutaneous lesion revealed signs of vasculitis. The patients recently regular used chewing-gums containing BHT. Within one week after stopping chewing gum, the eruption resolved. Oral provocation tests provoked the cutaneous signs within a few hours (36).

OTHER INFORMATION
BHT and other additives in foods and drugs have been held responsible for exacerbations of chronic idiopathic urticaria by some authors (e.g., 30). It was doubted by some (31), but it does seem to exist (32), although it is probably quite rare (29,33).

LITERATURE
1   Wetter DA, Yiannias JA, Prakash AV, Davis MD, Farmer SA, el-Azhary RA, et al. Results of patch testing to personal care product allergens in a standard series and a supplemental cosmetic series: an analysis of 945 patients from the Mayo Clinic Contact Dermatitis Group, 2000-2007. J Am Acad Dermatol 2010;63:789-798
2   Davis MD, Scalf LA, Yiannias JA, Cheng JF, El-Azhary RA, Rohlinger AL, et al. Changing trends and allergens in the patch test standard series. Arch Dermatol 2008;144:67-72
3   Roed-Petersen J, Hjorth N. Contact dermatitis from antioxidants. Br J Dermatol 1976;94:233-241
4   White IR, Lovell CR, Cronin E. Antioxidants in cosmetics. Contact Dermatitis 1984;11:265-267

5   Dever TT, Herro EM, Jacob SE. Butylhydroxytoluene – from jet fuels to cosmetics? Dermatitis 2012;23:90-91

6   Osmundsen PE. Contact urticaria from nickel and plastic additives (butylhydroxytoluene, oleylamide). Contact Dermatitis 1980;6:452-454

7   Flyvholm M-A, Menné T. Sensitizing risk of butylated hydroxytoluene based on exposure and effect data. Contact Dermatitis 1990;23:341-345

8   Dissanayake M, Powell SM. Allergic contact dermatitis from BHT in leg ulcer patients. Contact Dermatitis 1989;21:195-196

9   Bardazzi F, Misciali C, Borrello P, Capoblanco, C. Contact dermatitis due to antioxidants. Contact Dermatitis 1988;19:385-386

10 Osmundsen PE. Contact urticaria from nickel and plastic additives (Butylhydroxytoluene, oleylamide). Contact Dermatitis 1980;6:452-454

11 Marks JG Jr, Belsito DV, DeLeo VA, Fowler JF Jr, Fransway AF, Maibach HI,et al. North American Contact Dermatitis Group patch test results for the detection of delayed-type hypersensitivity to topical allergens. J Am Acad Dermatol 1998;38:911-918

12 Marks JG, Belsito DV, DeLeo VA, Fowler JF, Fransway AF, Maibach HI,et al. North American Contact Dermatitis Group standard tray patch test results 1992 through 1994. Am J Contact Dermatitis 1995;6:160-165

13 Wetter DA, Davis MDP, Yiannias JA, Cheng JF, Connolly SM, el-Azhary RA, et al. Patch test results from the Mayo Contact Dermatitis Group, 1998–2000. J Am Acad Dermatol 2005;53:416-421

14 Schnuch A, Geier J, Uter W, Frosch PJ. Patch testing with preservatives, antimicrobials and industrial biocides. Results from a multicentre study. Br J Dermatol 1998;138:467-476

15 Li L-F, Liu G, Wang J. Patch test in Chinese patients with cosmetic allergic contact dermatitis to common cosmetic allergens from a European cosmetic series. Contact Dermatitis 2007;57:50-54

16 Rudner EJ. North American Group Results. Contact Dermatitis 1977;3:208-209

17 Wentworth AB, Yiannias JA, Keeling JH, Hall MR, Camilleri MJ, Drage LA, et al. Trends in patch-test results and allergen changes in the standard series: a Mayo Clinic 5-year retrospective review (January 1, 2006, to December 31, 2010). J Am Acad Dermatol 2014;70:269-275

18 Pevny I, Lurz Ch. Photoallergische dermatitis. Allergologie 1985;8:128-138

19 Flyvholm, MA. Preservatives in registered chemical products. Contact Dermatitis 2005;53:27-32

20 Trattner A, Farchi Y, David M. Cosmetics patch tests: first report from Israel. Contact Dermatitis 2002;47:180-181

21 Scheman A, Jacob S, Katta R, Nedorost S, Warshaw E, Zirwas M, et al. Part 1 of a 4 part series. Facial cosmetics: trends and alternatives. Data from the American Contact Alternative Group. J Clin Aesthet Dermatol 2011;4:25-30

22 Scheman A, Jacob S, Katta R, Nedorost S, Warshaw E, Zirwas M, et al. Part 2 of a 4 part series. Hair cosmetics: trends and alternatives. Data from the American Contact Alternative Group. J Clin Aesthet Dermatol 2011;4:42-46

23 Scheman A, Jacob S, Katta R, Nedorost S, Warshaw E, Zirwas M, et al. Part 3 of a 4 part series. Lips and common Dental Care products: trends and alternatives. Data from the American Contact Alternative Group. J Clin Aesthet Dermatol 2011;4:50-53

24 Scheman A, Jacob S, Katta R, Nedorost S, Warshaw E, Zirwas M, et al. Part 4 of a 4 part series. Miscellaneous products: trends and alternatives in deodorants, antiperspirants, sunblocks, shaving products, powder, and wipes. Data from the American Contact Alternative Group. J Clin Aesthet Dermatol 2011;4:35-39

25 Dinkloh A, Worm M, Geier J, Schnuch A, Wollenberg A. Contact sensitization in patients with suspected cosmetic intolerance: results of the IVDK 2006-2011. J Eur Acad Dermatol Venereol 2015;29:1071-1081

26 Vollum D. Hypomelanosis from an antioxidant in polyethylene film. Arch Dermatol 1971;104:70-72

27 Bentley-Phillips B, Bayles AH. Butylated hydroxytoluene as a skin lightener. Arch Dermatol 1974;109:216-217

28 Maibach HI, Gellin G, Ring M. Is the antioxidant butylated hydroxytoluene a depigmenting agent in man? Contact Dermatitis 1975;1:295-296

29 Rajan JP, Simon RA, Bosso JV. Prevalence of sensitivity to food and drug additives in patients with chronic idiopathic urticaria. J Allergy Clin Immunol Pract 2014;2:168-171

30 Juhlin L. Recurrent urticaria: clinical investigation of 330 patients. Br J Dermatol 1981;104:369-381

31 Simon RA. Adverse reactions to food additives. N Engl Reg Allergy Proc 1986;7:533-542

32 Goodman DL, McDonnell JT, Nelson HS, Vaughan TR, Weber RW. Chronic urticaria exacerbated by the antioxidant food preservatives, butylated hydroxyanisole (BHA) and butylated hydroxytoluene (BHT). J Allergy Clin Immunol 1990;86(4 Pt 1):570-575

33 Hannuksela M, Lahti A. Peroral challenge tests with food additives in urticaria and atopic dermatitis. Int J Dermatol 1986;25:178-180

34 Fransway AF. The problem of preservation in the 1990s. III. Agents with preservative function independent of formaldehyde release. Am J Contact Derm 1991;2:145-174

35 Silva EA, Bosco MR, Mozer E. Study of the frequency of allergens in cosmetics components in patients with suspected allergic contact dermatitis. An Bras Dermatol 2012;87:263-268

36 Moneret-Vautrin DA, Faure G, Bene MC. Chewing-gum preservative induced toxidermic vasculitis. Allergy 1986;41:546-548

37 Broding HC, Monsé C, Brüning T, Fartasch M. Induction of occupational leucoderma and vitiligo. Can butylated hydroxytoluene induce vitiligo similarly to *p*-tert-butylphenol? Hautarzt 2011;62:209-214 (Article in German)

2.53 BIOSACCHARIDE GUM-4

IDENTIFICATION

Description/definition	: Biosaccharide gum-4 is a fermentation gum derived from sorbitol. It is a deacetylated branched polymer consisting of L-fucose, 2-D-glucose and glucuronic acid repetitive units
Chemical class(es)	: Biologic polymers and their derivatives
CAS registry number (s)	: 283602-75-5; 905593-86-4 (Glycofilm 1.5P)
CIR review(s)	: Final Report, September 2012 (access: www.cir-safety.org/ingredients)
Function(s) in cosmetics	: EU: skin conditioning. USA: skin conditioning agents - miscellaneous
Patch testing	: Glycofilm 1.5P pure (mixture of biosaccharide gum-4, phenoxyethanol and water)
Molecular formula	: $(C_{24}H_{38}O_{20})_nH.HO$

GENERAL

Biosaccharide gum-4 is an anionic polysaccharide obtained through biotechnological means from plant material. It is a fermentation gum derived from sorbitol. Chemically, biosaccharide gum-4 is a deacetylated branched polymer consisting of L-fucose, 2-D-glucose and glucuronic acid repetitive units. The material is added to cosmetics as an aqueous solution for its hydrating and protective properties (1).

CONTACT ALLERGY

Case reports and case series
A woman presented with eczematous lesions involving the face, neck, and trunk. The eruption had developed two months after she started the daily application of an anti-wrinkle cream. She was treated with a topical corticosteroid and at the same time she stopped applying the cosmetic product. One month after complete resolution of the dermatitis, she was patch tested with the Italian Society of Allergological, Occupational and Environmental Dermatology (SIDAPA) baseline series, a cosmetics series, and with the anti-wrinkle cream 'as is'. Readings showed positive reactions to colophonium and to the anti-wrinkle cream. Later, patch tests were performed with the ingredients of the cream, provided by the manufacturer. A positive reaction was observed to Glycofilm® 1.5P, an aqueous solution containing biosaccharide gum-4 and phenoxyethanol. The reaction to phenoxyethanol, which was tested separately, was negative. Ten healthy volunteers were patch tested with Glycofilm® 1.5P and with the anti-wrinkle cream 'as is', and the results were negative. It was concluded that the patient was allergic to biosaccharide gum-4 in Glycofilm® 1.5P (1).

Presence in cosmetic products and chemical analyses
In the USA, in April 2017, biosaccharide gum-4 was present in 68 of 56,714 cosmetic products of which the composition is known in FDA's Voluntary Cosmetic Registration Program (VCRP) (data obtained from FDA, May 2017). In March 2017, biosaccharide gum-4 was present in zero resp. 10 ('biosaccharide gum') of 64,467 cosmetic products of which the composition is known in EWG's Skin Deep Cosmetics Database, USA (http://www.ewg.org/skindeep/).

LITERATURE
1   Foti C, Romita P, Guida S, Antelmi A, Bonamonte D. Allergic contact dermatitis caused by Glycofilm® 1.5P contained in an anti-wrinkle cream. Contact Dermatitis 2013;69:186-187

2.54 BISABOLOL

IDENTIFICATION

Description/definition	: Bisabolol is the terpene that conforms to the formula shown below
Chemical class(es)	: Alcohols
Chemical/IUPAC name	: (2S)-6-Methyl-2-(4-methylcyclohex-3-en-1-yl)hept-5-en-2-ol
Other names	: Levomenol
CAS registry number (s)	: 23089-26-1; 515-69-5
EC number(s)	: 245-423-3; 208-205-9
Merck Index monograph	: 2515
CIR review(s)	: Int J Toxicol 1999;18(Suppl.3):33-40 (access: www.cir-safety.org/ingredients)
Function(s) in cosmetics	: EU: masking; skin conditioning; soothing. USA: Fragrance ingredients; skin-conditioning agents - miscellaneous
Patch testing	: 5% pet. (2); 1% pet. may result in a false-negative reaction (4)
Molecular formula	: $C_{15}H_{26}O$

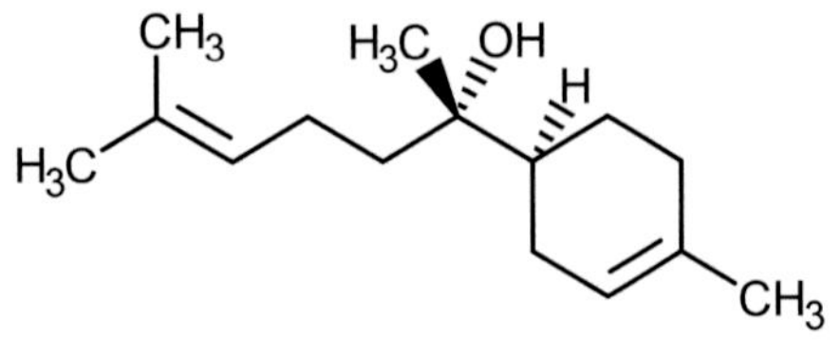

GENERAL

Bisabolol, a monocyclic sesquiterpene alcohol, is one of the primary active ingredients in *Chamomilla recutita* (synonym: *Matricaria chamomilla*, German chamomile), a member of the Asteraceae (Compositae) family. Bisabolol ranges from colorless to pale yellow and is a slightly viscous liquid with a floral scent. It is thought to have skin-soothing, anti-inflammatory, and antimicrobial properties although there is little evidence and few studies to support these claims. Bisabolol is used for flavoring liquids and coloring foods and as an additive in cosmetics. In addition to being extracted from plants, bisabolol can be made synthetically and has been shown to enhance the absorption of other chemicals topically. Because of its claimed anti-inflammatory properties, manufacturers include bisabolol in several cosmetics, especially 'natural' ones targeted at children with sensitive skin and emollients intended to soothe the skin of people with (atopic) dermatitis (4,5). Bisabolol is also perceived to have wound-healing, anxiolytic, and smooth muscle relaxant properties, and because of this, it is used in many herbal remedies (9).

Case reports and case series

Bisabolol was stated to be the (or an) allergen in 2 patients in a group of 603 individuals suffering from cosmetic dermatitis, seen in the period 2010-2015 in Leuven, Belgium (7). In a 4-month-period in 1996, 475 patients with contact allergy to 'cosmetic ingredients' were collected in 5 centers in Belgium, UK and Germany. There was one reaction to bisabolol; its relevance was not stated (6).

One patient had allergic contact cheilitis from bisabolol (and polysilicone-15) in a lipcare stick (1). A woman had dermatitis of the lips from contact allergy to bisabolol in a lipstick (2). Another female patient had a 2-week history of 3 episodes of periorbital swelling, spreading to the cheeks and forehead. Patch tests with a standard and facial series, together with her own cosmetics, gave a positive reaction to a cosmetic containing 12.5% plant extracts, but the sesquiterpene lactone mix was negative. Testing the individual ingredients produced a positive patch test at D2 and D4 to bisabolol 1% pet. The test material contained bisabolene, bisabolol oxide, farnesol, nerolidol and chamazulene as impurities. Patch tests in 30 controls were negative (3).

Three children had exacerbation of their atopic dermatitis while using an emollient. Stopping its use improved the dermatitis. When patch tested, they all reacted to sesquiterpene lactone mix, the Compositae mix, the two who were tested with it reacted to the emollient preparation itself and one also reacted to lanolin alcohol, which is also an ingredient of the emollient. Bisabolol itself, which is also contained in the preparation, was not tested, but because of the reactions to the sesquiterpene lactone mix and the especially the Compositae mix the authors suggested it to be the allergenic culprit (9). Four children had ACD from bisabolol in a moisturizing ointment, the same as in ref. 9. All four also reacted to the Compositae mix, two to the sesquiterpene lactone mix and one to lanolin alcohol, which is also an ingredient of the emollient (4).

Cross-reactions, pseudo-cross-reactions and co-reactions

Sesquiterpene lactone mix (4,9); compositae-mix (4,9).

Presence in cosmetic products and chemical analyses
In the USA, in April 2017, bisabolol was present in 1193 of 56,714 cosmetic products of which the composition is known in FDA's Voluntary Cosmetic Registration Program (VCRP) (data obtained from FDA, May 2017). In April 2017, bisabolol was present in 674 of 65,521 cosmetic products of which the composition is known in EWG's Skin Deep Cosmetics Database, USA (http://www.ewg.org/skindeep/). In the USA, in 2015-2016, 63 diaper wipes and 41 topical diaper preparations from a large retailer were screened for the presence of potential sensitizers. Bisabolol was found in 2/63 (3%) disposable diaper wipes and in 2/41 (5%) topical diaper preparations (10).

Other non-eczematous contact reactions
A cream containing 0.5% α-bisabolol may have a skin whitening effect on pigmented skin (8).

LITERATURE

1   Sarre, ME, Guérin-Moreau M, Lepoittevin JP, Martin L, Avenel-Audran M. Allergic contact cheilitis caused by polysilicone-15 (Parsol® SLX) in a lipcare balm. Contact Dermatitis 2014;70:119-121
2   Pastor N, Silvestre JF, Mataix J, Lucas A, Pérez M. Contact cheilitis from bisabolol and polyvinylpyrrolidone/hexadecene copolymer in lipstick. Contact Dermatitis 2008;58:178-179
3   Wilkinson SM, Hausen BM, Beck MH. Allergic contact dermatitis from plant extracts in a cosmetic. Contact Dermatitis 1995;33:58-59
4   Jacob SE, Matiz C, Herro EM. Compositae-associated allergic contact dermatitis from bisabolol. Dermatitis 2011;22:102-105
5   Russell K, Jacon SE. Bisabolol. Dermatitis 2010;21:57-58
6   Goossens A, Beck MH, Haneke E, McFadden JP, Nolting S, Durupt G, Ries G. Adverse cutaneous reactions to cosmetic allergens. Contact Dermatitis 1999;40:112-113
7   Goossens A. Cosmetic contact allergens. Cosmetics 2016, 3, 5; doi:10.3390/cosmetics3010005
8   Lee J, Jun H, Jung E, Ha J, Park D. Whitening effect of alpha-bisabolol in Asian women subjects. Int J Cosmet Sci 2010;32:299-303
9   Jacob SE, Hsu JW. Reactions to Aquaphor: is bisabolol the culprit? Pediatr Dermatol 2010;27:103-104
10 Yu J, Treat J, Chaney K, Brod B. Potential allergens in disposable diaper wipes, topical diaper preparations, and disposable diapers: under-recognized etiology of pediatric perineal dermatitis. Dermatitis 2016;27:110-118

2.55 BITHIONOL

IDENTIFICATION

Description/definition   : Bithionol is the aromatic organic compound that conforms to the structural formula
                            shown below
Chemical class(es)   : Chlorinated aromatic compounds; organic sulfur compounds
INCI name USA   : Not in the Personal Care Products Council Ingredient Database
Chemical/IUPAC name   : bis(3,5-Dichloro-2-hydroxyphenyl) sulfide
Other names   : 2,2'-Thiobis(4,6-dichlorophenol)
CAS registry number (s)   : 97-18-7
EC number(s)   : 202-565-0
Merck Index monograph   : 2577
Function(s) in cosmetics : EU: formerly used as antimicrobial (fungicide; bactericide)
EU cosmetic restrictions : Regulated in Annex II/352 of the Regulation (EC) No. 1223/2009 (prohibited)
USA cosmetic restrictions : Prohibited (FDA)
Patch testing   : 1.0% pet. (Chemotechnique, SmartPracticeEurope, SmartPracticeCanada)
Molecular formula   : $C_{12}H_6Cl_4O_2S$

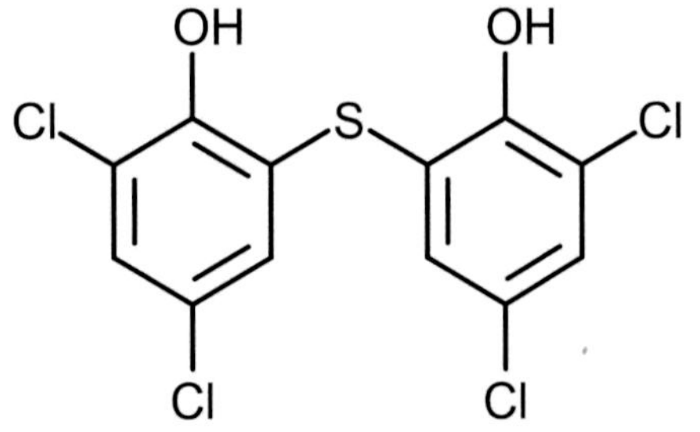

GENERAL

Bithionol is a halogenated phenolic compound, which was used in the 1960s as an antimicrobial in antiseptic creams
and to a lesser extent in cosmetics in certain countries, notably the USA. This chemical at that time caused many
cases of photosensitization and was banned from use in topical drugs in 1967. The United States Food and Drug
Administration (FDA) prohibited the use of bithionol in cosmetics in 1968 (32). It cross-reacted to hexachlorophene
and to and from halogenated salicylanilides, notably tetrachlorosalicylanilide. Currently, it is not used in cosmetics
either in the USA (banned by the FDA) or in the EU (prohibited). It may currently, however, be used as an
anthelmintic to treat *Anoplocephala perfoliata* (tapeworms) in horses (31) and *Fasciola hepatica* (liver flukes) (30)
(Wikipedia).

A general introduction to the halogenated salicylanilides and halogenated phenols can be found in Chapter 2.450
Tetrachlorosalicylanilide. In assessing the data from early studies, and notably in the distinction between contact
allergy and photocontact allergy, it should be realized that, in those days, experience with photopatch tests was
limited and such tests may not always have been reliable.

CONTACT ALLERGY

Patch testing in groups of patients
There are no studies in which bithionol has been tested in consecutive patients suspected of contact dermatitis
(routine testing). Results of patch testing bithionol in groups of *selected* patients (patients suspected of photosensitivity or with reactions after sunscreen application) are shown in table 2.55.1. In two studies, rates of positive
reactions were 0.7% (6) and 2.5% (1), but the study with the highest rate had certain weaknesses and the relevance
of the 4 positive patch tests was not mentioned (1).

Case reports and case series
A man developed a weeping dermatitis of the forehead and scalp with edema of the eyelids from contact allergy to a
hair dressing containing bithionol; bithionol itself was apparently not tested (18). In a period of 2.5 years in the late
1960s, 59 patients suspected of contact photosensitivity were examined in one center in New Orleans, USA. Eighteen
had contact allergy to bithionol and 2 photocontact allergy. Causative products were not mentioned, but the authors
suggested the patients had allergic or photoallergic contact dermatitis from bithionol and they should use only
soaps, shampoos and cosmetics known not to contain bithionol or related substances. At least 3 of the patients
became persistent light reactors (20).

Contact allergy to bithionol in non-cosmetic products

A girl and a woman had ACD from bithionol in antiseptic creams (18,19). A young woman had dermatitis of the hands spreading to the forearms, eyelids and face from contact allergy to bithionol in an antiseptic cream (18).

Table 2.55.1 Patch testing in groups of patients: Selected patient groups

Years and Country	Test conc. & vehicle	Number of patients tested	positive (%)		Selection of patients (S); Relevance (R); Comments (C)	Ref.
2001-2010 Canada		160	4	(2.5%)	S: patients with suspected photosensitivity and patients who developed pruritus or a rash after sunscreen application; R: not stated; C: weak study: inadequate reading of test results, erythema only was considered to represent a positive patch test reaction	1
2000-2005 USA	1% pet.	149	1	(0.7%)	S: patients photopatch tested for suspected photodermatitis; R: not relevant	6

Cross-reactions, pseudo-cross-reactions and co-reactions (including photoreactions)

(Photo)cross-reactions from bithionol

About 2/3 of patient contact allergic to bithionol cross-reacted to hexachlorophene (20). Three patients photosensitive to bithionol gave a plain contact allergic cross-reaction to hexachlorophene (21). In another study, there was also no photocross-reactivity from primary bithionol photosensitization to hexachlorophene or triclocarban, but limited contact allergic cross-sensitivity to these chemicals (29). Many patients with photocontact allergy to bithionol have photocross-sensitivity (and some plain contact allergic cross-sensitivity) to tetrachlorosalicylanilide (21). Also, there may be occasional photocross-reactivity from bithionol to tribromosalicylanilide (21).

(Photo)cross-reactions to bithionol

Patients photosensitized to fenticlor (Chapter 2.457 2,2'-Thiobis(4-chlorophenol)) may photocross-react to bithionol. The structures of these chemicals are very similar and it has been suggested that, when irradiated, bithionol loses two chlorine atoms to become fenticlor (17). Frequent photocross-reactivity from tetrachlorosalicylanilide to bithionol (25).

In a group of 18 patients photosensitized to ketoprofen, 2 (11%) had positive photopatch tests to bithionol. As there were also many photoreactions to fenticlor (n=12, 67%), tetrachlorosalicylanilide (n=5, 28%), triclosan (n=3, 17%), and tribromosalicylanilide (n=2, 11%) with no clinical relevance, the authors raised the question of hyper-photosusceptibility to non-relevant allergens induced by photosensitivity to ketoprofen (27). In another group of 35 patients photoallergic to ketoprofen from Sweden, simultaneous photoallergy to bithionol was seen in 6%, to fenticlor in 74%, to tetrachlorosalicylanilide in 40%, to triclosan in 9% and to tribromosalicylanilide and hexachlorophene in 6% of the patients. No explanation for these co-reactivities was offered (28).

Presence in cosmetic products and chemical analyses

In May 2017, bithionol was present in zero of 66,975 cosmetic products of which the composition is known in EWG's Skin Deep Cosmetics Database, USA (http://www.ewg.org/skindeep/). In the USA, in April 2017, bithionol was present in zero of 56,714 cosmetic products of which the composition is known in FDA's Voluntary Cosmetic Registration Program (VCRP) (data obtained from FDA, May 2017).

OTHER SIDE EFFECTS

Photosensitivity

Photopatch testing in groups of patients

Results of photopatch testing with bithionol in groups of selected patients (e.g., patients suspected of photosensitivity, dermatitis affecting mainly light-exposed skin, patients with histories or clinical pictures suggestive of allergic contact photodermatitis) are shown in table 2.55.2. In 15 studies, rates of photosensitization have ranged from 0.1% to 20%, but were 2.2% or less in 10 of the fifteen investigations (table 2.55.2). The highest frequencies of positive photopatch tests (20% and 10%) were found in two very small study of 18 patients with persistent light reactions (12) and in 30 patients with chronic actinic dermatitis (5), highly selected patient groups. In an older study from the USA (1967-1975), when bithionol was still widely used, 21 of 354 patients (5.9%) of patients with a history suggestive of a photosensitivity problem or an eruption involving sun-exposed areas had positive photopatch tests to bithionol, but relevance was not mentioned (26). In fact, in 11 of the studies, relevance was either not mentioned or not specified for bithionol. In the four that did address the issue, none of the 12 positive photopatch tests were scored as relevant (6,7,8,10).

Table 2.55.2 Photopatch testing in groups of patients

Years and Country	Test conc. & vehicle	Number of patients tested	positive (%)	Selection of patients (S); Relevance (R); Comments (C)	Ref.
2001-2010 Canada		160	1 (0.6%)	S: patients with suspected photosensitivity and patients who developed pruritus or a rash after sunscreen application; R: not stated; C: weak study: inadequate reading of test results, erythema only was considered to represent a positive photopatch test reaction	1
1993-2009 USA	1% pet.	30	3 (10%)	S: patients with chronic actinic dermatitis; R: not stated	5
2004-2006 Italy	1% pet.	1082	3 (0.3%)	S: patients with histories and clinical features suggestive of photoallergic contact dermatitis; C: 1 reaction was photo-augmented contact allergy; R: 0 reactions were relevant	7
1993-2006 USA	1% pet.	76	3 (4.3%)	S: not stated; R: only 7% of all reactions to antimicrobials were relevant	3
2000-2005 USA	1% pet.	149	3 (2.0%)	S: patients photopatch tested for suspected photodermatitis; R: 0 reactions were relevant	6
2004-2005 Spain	1% pet.	224	3 (1.3%)	S: not stated; R: not relevant	8
1991-97 Ger, Au, Swi	1% pet.	1261	(0.3%)	S: patients suspected of photosensitivity; R: not stated	14
1985-1994 Italy		1050	3 (0.3%)	S: patients with histories or clinical pictures suggestive of allergic contact photodermatitis; R: 78% for all photoallergens together	2
1986-1993 USA	1% pet.	138	3 (2.2%)	S: patients suspected of photosensitivity; R: not stated	9
1985-1990 USA	1% pet.	187	3 (1.6%)	S: patients with a history of photosensitivity; R: not relevant	10
1980-85 Ger, Au, Swi	2% pet.	1129	3 (0.3%)	S: patients suspected of photoallergy, polymorphic light eruption, phototoxicity and skin problems with photo-distribution; R: not stated	4
1980-1985 USA	1% pet.	70	3 (4%)	S: not stated; R: not stated	11
<1984 Norway	1% pet.	18	5 (20%)	S: patients with persistent light reactions; R: not stated	12
1980-1981 4 Scandinavian countries	1% pet.	745	6 (0.8%)	S: patients suspected of sun-related skin disease; R: not stated	13
1967-1975 USA		354	21 (5.9%)	S: patients with a history suggestive of a photosensitivity problem or an eruption involving sun-exposed areas; R: not stated	26

Au: Austria; Ger: Germany; NL: Netherlands; Swi: Switzerland

Case reports and case series

Twelve patients in a US study had photocontact allergy to bithionol and one had contact allergy. Most reactions were caused by an antiseptic cream (21). Two individuals had photoallergic contact dermatitis from bithionol in antiseptic creams (22,23). An unspecified number of patients suffered from photoallergic contact dermatitis to bithionol in pharmaceutical creams (24). Of 19 patients with the clinical picture of soap photocontact dermatitis (mostly sharply demarcated erythematous and lichenoid eruption limited to sun-exposed areas of the body, such as the face, neck, hands, and forearms), 16 photo-reacted to tetrachlorosalicylanilide, 4 to bithionol, 3 to hexachlorophene and each one to tribromosalicylanilide and triclocarban. Most patients had a definite history of exposure to a soap containing the offending sensitizing agent (15).

In a period of 1.5 year (1966-1967), in a university center in San Francisco, USA, 26 patients suspected of photosensitivity were investigated with photopatch tests with halogenated salicylanilides and related compounds. Tetrachlorosalicylanilide was the most frequent photosensitizer (21/22 tested), followed by bithionol (10/26), tribromosalicylanilide (9/22), hexachlorophene (n=4), triclocarban (n=3) and dichlorophene (n=3). Six patients became persistent light reactors. The relevance of the reactions was not specified. In fact, the authors stated that it was generally impossible to determine which was the original photosensitizer and which positive photopatch tests were the result of photocross-sensitivity (16). In a period of 2.5 years, 59 patients suspected of contact photosensitivity were examined in one center in New Orleans, USA. Eighteen had contact allergy to bithionol and 2 photocontact allergy. Causative products were not mentioned, but the authors suggested the patients had allergic contact dermatitis or photocontact dermatitis from bithionol and they should use only soaps, shampoos and cosmetics known not to contain bithionol or related substances. At least 3 of the patients became persistent light reactors (20).

LITERATURE

1   Greenspoon J, Ahluwalia R, Juma N, Rosen CF. Allergic and photoallergic contact dermatitis: A 10-year experience. Dermatitis 2013;24:29-32

2   Pigatto PD, Legori A, Bigardi AS, Guarrera M, Tosti A, Santucci B, et al. Gruppo Italiano recerca dermatiti da contatto ed ambientali Italian multicenter study of allergic contact photodermatitis: epidemiological aspects. Am J Contact Dermatitis 1996;17:158-163

3   Victor FC, Cohen DE, Soter NA. A 20-year analysis of previous and emerging allergens that elicit photoallergic contact dermatitis. J Am Acad Dermatol 2010;62:605-610

4   Hölzle E, Neumann N, Hausen B, Przybilla B, Schauder S, Hönigsmann H, et al. Photopatch testing: the 5-year experience of the German, Austrian and Swiss Photopatch Test Group. J Am Acad Dermatol 1991;25:59-68

5   Que SK, Brauer JA, Soter NA, Cohen DE. Chronic actinic dermatitis: an analysis at a single institution over 25 years. Dermatitis 2011;22:147-154

6   Scalf LA, Davis MDP, Rohlinger AL, Connolly SM. Photopatch testing of 182 patients: A 6-year experience at the Mayo Clinic. Dermatitis 2009;20:44-52

7   Pigatto PD, Guzzi G, Schena D, Guarrera M, Foti C, Francalanci S, et al. Photopatch tests: an Italian multicentre study from 2004 to 2006. Contact Dermatitis 2008;59:103-108

8   De La Cuadra-Oyanguren J, Perez-Ferriols A, Lecha-Carrelero M, et al. Results and assessment of photopatch testing in Spain: towards a new standard set of photoallergens. Actas DermoSifiliograficas 2007;98:96-101

9   Fotiades J, Soter NA, Lim HW. Results of evaluation of 203 patients for photosensivity in a 7.3 year period. J Am Acad Dermatol 1995;33:597-602

10 DeLeo VA, Suarez SM, Maso MJ. Photoallergic contact dermatitis. Results of photopatch testing in New York, 1985 to 1990. Arch Dermatol 1992;128:1513-1518

11 Menz J, Muller SA, Connolly SM. Photopatch testing: a 6-year experience. J Am Acad Dermatol 1988;18:1044-1047

12 Thune P, Eeg-Larsen T. Contact and photocontact allergy in persistent light reactivity. Contact Dermatitis 1984;11:98-107

13 Wennersten G, Thune P, Brodthagen H, Jansen C, Rystedt I, Crames M, et al. The Scandinavian multicenter photopatch study. Contact Dermatitis 1984;10:305-309

14 Neumann NJ, Hölzle E, Plewig G, Schwarz T, Panizzon RG, Breit R, et al. Photopatch testing: The 12-year experience of the German, Austrian and Swiss Photopatch Test Group. J Am Acad Dermatol 2000;42:183-192

15 Freeman RG, Knox JM. The action spectrum of photocontact dermatitis caused by halogenated salicylanilide and related compounds. Arch Dermatol 1968;97:130-136

16 Epstein JH, Wuepper KD, Maibach HI. Photocontact dermatitis to halogenated salicylanilides and related compounds: A clinical and histologic review of 26 patients. Arch Dermatol 1968;97:236-244

17 Burry J. Cross sensitivity between fenticlor and bithionol. Arch Dermatol 1968;97:497-502

18 Gaul LE. Sensitivity to bithionol. Arch Dermatol 1960;81:600

19 Gaul LE. Sensitivity to bithionol. Arch Dermatol 1963;87:383

20 O'Quinn S, Kennedy D, Isbell K. Contact photodermatitis due to bithionol and related compounds. JAMA 1967;199:89-92

21 Baughman RD. Contact photodermatitis from bithionol. II. Cross-sensitivities to hexachlorophene and salicylanilides. Arch Dermatol 1964;90:153-157

22 Harber LC, Harris H, Baer RL. Photoallergic contact dermatitis due to halogenated salicylanilides and related compounds. Arch Dermatol 1966;94:255-262

23 Epstein S. Photocontact dermatitis from bithionol. Arch Dermatol 1965;92:591

24 Harber LC, Targovnik SE, Baer RL. Contact photosensitivity patterns to halogenated salicylanilides in man and guinea pigs. Arch Dermatol 1967;96:646-656

25 Crow KD, Wilkinson DS, Osmundsen PE. A review of photoreactions to halogenated salicylanilides. Br J Dermatol 1969;81:180-185

26 Smith SZ, Epstein JH. Photocontact dermatitis to halogenated salicylanilides and related compounds. Our experience between 1967 and 1975. Arch Dermatol 1977;113:1372-1374

27 Durbize E, Vigan M, Puzenat E, Girardin P, Adessi B, Desprez PH, Humbert PH, Laurent R, Aubin F. Spectrum of cross-photosensitization in 18 consecutive patients with contact photoallergy to ketoprofen: associated photoallergies to non-benzophenone-containing molecules. Contact Dermatitis 2003;48:144-149

28 Hindsén M, Zimerson E, Bruze M. Photoallergic contact dermatitis from ketoprofen in southern Sweden. Contact Dermatitis 2006;54:150-157

29   Harber LC, Targovnik SE, Baer RL. Studies on contact photosensitivity to hexachlorophene and trichlorocarbanilide in guinea pigs and man. J Invest Dermatol 1968; 51:373-377

30   Aksoy DY, Kerimoglu U, Oto A, Erguven S, Arslan S, Unal S, Batman F, Bayraktar Y. Infection with *Fasciola hepatica*. Clin Microbiol Infect 2005;11:859-861

31   Sanada Y, Senba H, Mochizuki R, Arakaki H, Gotoh T, Fukumoto S, Nagahata H. Evaluation of marked rise in fecal egg output after bithionol administration to horse and its application as a diagnostic marker for equine *Anoplocephala perfoliata* infection. J Vet Med Sci 2009;71:617-620

32   Wolverton JE, Soter NA, Cohen DE. Fentichlor photocontact dermatitis: A persistent enigma. Dermatitis 2013;24:77-81

2.56 BORNELONE

IDENTIFICATION

Description/definition : Bornelone is the organic compound that conforms to the formula shown below
Chemical class(es) : Ketones
Chemical/IUPAC name : (E,5Z)-5-(3,3-Dimethyl-2-bicyclo[2.2.1]heptanylidene)pent-3-en-2-one
Other names : 5-(3,3-Dimethyl-2-norbornyliden)-3-penten-2-one ; 3-penten-2-one, 5-(3,3-dimethylbicyclo[2.2.1]hept-2-ylidene)-
CAS registry number (s) : 2226-11-1
EC number(s) : 218-757-2
Function(s) in cosmetics : EU: UV-absorber. USA: light stabilizers
Patch testing : 5% pet. (1)
Molecular formula : $C_{14}H_{20}O$

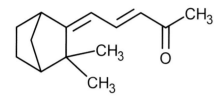

GENERAL

The literature on adverse reactions to sunscreens has been reviewed in several recent and older publications (3-8,10).

CONTACT ALLERGY

Case reports and case series

Two patients had allergic contact dermatitis from bornelone in a cosmetic face cream and a third from its presence in a sunscreen cream (1,2). In a group of 75 patients allergic to cosmetic products, seen in a private practice in The Netherlands in the period 1981-1986, one case was caused by bornelone in a skin care product (9, same patient as in ref. 1).

Presence in cosmetic products and chemical analyses

In the USA, in April 2017, bornelone was present in zero of 56,714 cosmetic products of which the composition is known in FDA's Voluntary Cosmetic Registration Program (VCRP) (data obtained from FDA, May 2017). In March 2017, bornelone was present in zero of 64,983 cosmetic products of which the composition is known in EWG's Skin Deep Cosmetics Database, USA (http://www.ewg.org/skindeep/).

LITERATURE

1 De Groot AC, Bos JD, Liem DH. Contact allergy to bornelone. Contact Dermatitis 1984;10:45
2 De Groot AC, Weyland JW. Cosmetic allergy to the UV absorber bornelone. Dermatosen 1989;37:13-15
3 Heurung AR, Raju SI, Warshaw EM. Adverse reactions to sunscreen agents: epidemiology, responsible irritants and allergens, clinical characteristics, and management. Dermatitis 2014;25:289-326
4 Heurung AR, Raju SI, Warshaw EM. Contact allergen of the year. Benzophenones. Dermatitis 2014;25:3-10 (contains many mistakes; Erratum in Dermatitis 2014;25:92-95)
5 Avenel-Audran M. Sunscreen products: finding the allergen. Eur J Dermatol 2010;20:161-166
6 Scheuer E, Warshaw E. Sunscreen allergy: a review of epidemiology, clinical characteristics, and responsible allergens. Dermatitis 2006;17:3-11
7 Funk JO, Dromgoole SH, Maibach HI. Sunscreen intolerance: contact sensitization, photocontact sensitization, and irritancy of sunscreen agents. Dermatol Clin 1995;13:473-481
8 Dromgoole SH, Maibach HI. Sunscreening agent intolerance: Contact and photocontact sensitization and contact urticaria. J Am Acad Dermatol 1990;22:1068-1078
9 De Groot AC. Contact allergy to cosmetics: Causative ingredients. Contact Dermatitis 1987;17:26-34
10 Schauder S. Survey of the literature on adverse reactions to preparations containing UV filters (1947-1989) (Literaturübersicht über Unverträglichkeitsreaktionen auf lichtfilterhaltige Produkte von 1947 bis 1989). Z Hautkr 1990;65:982-998 (article in German)

2.57 5-BROMO-5-NITRO-1,3-DIOXANE

IDENTIFICATION

Description/definition	: 5-Bromo-5-nitro-1,3-dioxane is the substituted cyclic ether that conforms to the formula shown below
Chemical class(es)	: Ethers; halogen compounds; heterocyclic compounds
Chemical/IUPAC name	: 5-Bromo-5-nitro-1,3-dioxane
Other names	: 1,3-Dioxane, 5-bromo-5-nitro-; Bronidox®
CAS registry number (s)	: 30007-47-7
EC number(s)	: 250-001-7
CIR review(s)	: J Am Coll Toxicol 1990;9:279-288 (access: www.cir-safety.org/ingredients)
Function(s) in cosmetics	: EU: preservative. USA: preservatives
EU cosmetic restrictions	: Regulated in Annex V/20 of the Regulation (EC) No. 1223/2009
Patch testing	: 0.5% pet. (6)
Molecular formula	: $C_4H_6BrNO_4$

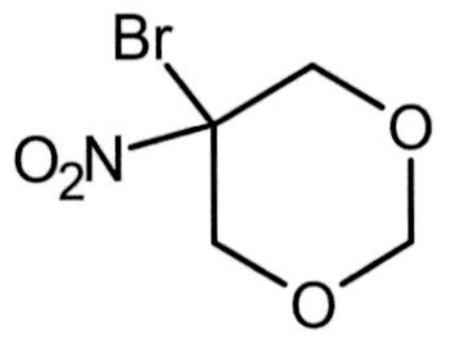

GENERAL

5-Bromo-5-nitro-1,3-dioxane is a bromine containing preservative used in cosmetics, but also has non-cosmetic applications as a biocide in cleaning/washing agents, rinsing agents, water systems, glossing agents, laboratory chemicals, metalworking fluids, protein preparations, antibodies and antisera preparations, and in column matrices. The chemical is also used in leather processing and as a stabilizer and surfactant (3).

CONTACT ALLERGY

Testing in groups of patients

Contact allergy to 5-bromo-5-nitro-1,3-dioxane appears to be rare or at least rarely reported. In the period 1985-1997, in Belgium, 8521 patients were patch tested, and only one positive reaction was observed. It was not stated, however, how many patients had been tested with the preservative, whether the reaction was relevant and in which product it had been present (4).

Case reports and case series

5-Bromo-5-nitro-1,3-dioxane was stated to be the (or an) allergen in one patient in a group of 603 individuals suffering from cosmetic dermatitis, seen in the period 2010-2015 in Leuven, Belgium (5). The preservative was responsible for 1 out of 959 cases of non-fragrance cosmetic allergy where the causal allergen was identified, Belgium, 2000-2010 (1).

Presence in cosmetic products and chemical analyses

In the USA, in April 2017, 5-bromo-5-nitro-1,3-dioxane was present in 24 of 56,714 cosmetic products of which the composition is known in FDA's Voluntary Cosmetic Registration Program (VCRP) (data obtained from FDA, May 2017). In March 2017, 5-bromo-5-nitro-1,3-dioxane was present in one of 64,983 cosmetic products of which the composition is known in EWG's Skin Deep Cosmetics Database, USA (http://www.ewg.org/skindeep/). In 2010, the preservative had been listed in the same database as ingredient in 12 (0.03%) of 41,113 products on file (3). In Germany, in 2006-2009, the labels of 4680 cosmetic products were screened for the presence of preservatives.

5-Bromo-5-nitro-1,3-dioxane was present in 0.1% of the products, according to labelling information (9). In 2008, 19.5% of 33,212 cosmetics and toiletries registered in the USA Food and Drug Administration (FDA) Voluntary Cosmetic Registration Database contained a formaldehyde-releaser. They were more frequently used in rinse-off products (27.3%) than in stay-on cosmetics (16.9%). 5-Bromo-5-nitro-1,3-dioxane was present in 0.1% of all products; in stay-on cosmetics, the percentage was 0.02 and in rinse-off products 0.2 (2). In the same period, of 496 stay-on cosmetic products present in a local drugstore in The Netherlands and investigated by checking the ingredient labelling, zero products proved to contain this preservative (2).

In 1992, 161 rinse-off products and 124 leave-on products produced in various European countries and the USA were investigated in Denmark for the presence of formaldehyde. According to the labelling, 7 products contained 5-

bromo-5-nitro-1,3-dioxane. These were analysed for the presence of free formaldehyde, but this was not found in any product (detection limit 0.001%, 10 ppm) (7). Four cosmetics labelled as containing 5-bromo-5-nitro-1,3-dioxane were analysed. A dermatologic shampoo contained 0.0077 ± 0.0004% (w/w) of the preservative, a pediatric shampoo 0.0130 ± 0.0002%, an anti-fall shampoo 0.0136 ± 0.0001% and Aloe vera gel 0.0028 ± 0.0003% (8).

LITERATURE

1 Travassos AR, Claes L, Boey L, Drieghe J, Goossens A. Non-fragrance allergens in specific cosmetic products. Contact Dermatitis 2011;65:276-285
2 De Groot AC, Veenstra M. Formaldehyde-releasers in cosmetics in the USA and in Europe. Contact Dermatitis 2010;62:221-224
3 De Groot AC, White IR, Flyvholm M-A, Lensen G, Coenraads P-J. Formaldehyde-releasers in cosmetics: relationship to formaldehyde contact allergy. Part 1. Characterization, frequency and relevance of sensitization, and frequency of use in cosmetics. Contact Dermatitis 2010;62:2-17
4 Goossens A, Claes L, Drieghe J, Put E. Antimicrobials, preservatives, antiseptics and disinfectants. Contact Dermatitis 1998;39:133-134
5 Goossens A. Cosmetic contact allergens. Cosmetics 2016, 3, 5; doi:10.3390/cosmetics3010005
6 De Groot AC. Patch Testing, 3rd Edition. Wapserveen, The Netherlands: acdegroot publishing, 2008 (ISBN 978-90-813233-1-4)
7 Rastogi SC. A survey of formaldehyde in shampoos and skin creams on the Danish market. Contact Dermatitis 1992;27:235-240
8 Fernandez-Alvarez M, Lamas JP, Sanchez-Prado L, Llompart M, Garcia-Jares C, Lores M. Development of a solid-phase microextraction gas chromatography with microelectron-capture detection method for the determination of 5-bromo-5-nitro-1,3-dioxane in rinse-off cosmetics. J Chromatogr A 2010;1217(43):6634-6639
9 Uter W, Yazar K, Kratz EM, Mildau G, Lidén C. Coupled exposure to ingredients of cosmetic products: II. Preservatives. Contact Dermatitis 2014;70:219-226

2.58 2-BROMO-2-NITROPROPANE-1,3-DIOL

IDENTIFICATION

Description/definition	: 2-Bromo-2-nitropropane-1,3-diol is a substituted aliphatic diol that conforms to the formula shown below
Chemical class(es)	: Alcohols; halogen compounds
Chemical / IUPAC name	: 2-Bromo-2-nitropropane-1,3-diol
Other names	: Bronopol®
CAS registry number (s)	: 52-51-7
EC number(s)	: 200-143-0
CIR review(s)	: J Environ Pathol Toxicol 1980;4:47-61; J Amer Coll Toxicol 1984;3:139-155 (access: www.cir-safety.org/ingredients)
Merck Index monograph	: 2727
Function(s) in cosmetics	: EU: preservative. USA: preservatives
EU cosmetic restrictions	: Regulated in Annex V/21 of the Regulation (EC) No. 1223/2009
Patch testing	: 0.25% pet. (Chemotechnique); 0.5% pet. (Chemotechnique, SmartPracticeEurope, SmartPracticeCanada)
Molecular formula	: $C_3H_6BrNO_4$

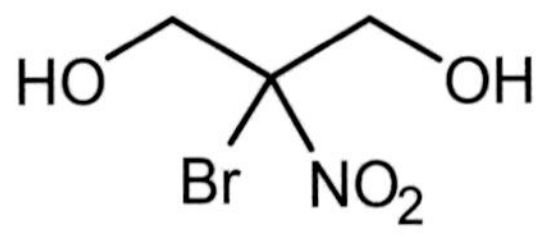

GENERAL

The preservative 2-bromo-2-nitropropane-1,3-diol (often termed bronopol, abbreviation: BP) is used as a preservative since the 1960s in a wide variety of cosmetics and other applications. It is water-soluble and is active against fungi, yeasts, and gram-positive and gram-negative bacteria, especially against *Pseudomonas aeruginosa*. Typical use levels are 0.01%-0.1%. BP is also used in non-cosmetic applications such as adhesives and glues, cleaning agents, binding agents, coloring agents, construction materials, filling agents, flooring agents, humidifiers, impregnating agents, metalworking fluids, milk processing plants, paints/lacquers, paper mills water circulating systems, pharmaceutical products, polishes, printing inks, slurries, surface treatment for paper, cardboard and other non-metals, viscosity adjustors, and washing detergents (49,75).

2-Bromo-2-nitropropane-1,3-diol is a formaldehyde-releaser. Depending on chemical and physical factors, BP may degrade into formaldehyde and other chemicals such as 2-(hydroxymethyl)-2-nitropropane-1,3-diol (tris nitro), methanol, formic acid and brominated compounds including bromonitroethanol, bromonitromethane, bromo-ethanol and hydrogen bromide (9,84,86). Alkaline pH (9) and higher temperature (9,86) hasten the degradation process. The half-life is more than 5 years at pH 4 but drops to 2 months at pH 8 (79,80). Since the early 1980s, the use of 2-bromo-2-nitropropane-1,3-diol has declined (10). This is because the brominated compounds develop a yellow or brown color on exposure to light (9). Additionally, BP can react with amines or amides to produce potentially carcinogenic nitrosamines or nitrosamides (10,89).

Review articles on contact allergy to 2-bromo-2-nitropropane-1,3-diol and other preservatives were published in 2004 and 2014 (105,106). The literature on contact allergy to formaldehyde and formaldehyde-releasers up to 1990 has been reviewed in 1991 (38,39). The literature on formaldehyde-releasers in cosmetics up to 2009 has been reviewed in 2010 (75,76).

CONTACT ALLERGY

Patch testing in groups of patients
Results of routine patch testing (testing in consecutive patients suspected of contact dermatitis) with 2-bromo-2-nitropropane-1,3-diol back to 1990 are shown in table 2.58.1. Results of testing in groups of *selected* patients (e.g., patients with eyelid dermatitis, individuals suspected of cosmetic allergy, patients with suspected metalworking fluid dermatitis) back to 1994 are shown in table 2.58.2.

Patch testing in consecutive patients suspected of contact dermatitis: Routine testing
2-Bromo-2-nitropropane-1,3-diol is not routinely tested in Europe, but has been part of the screening series of the North American Contact Dermatitis Group (NACDG) since over 25 years. Their results have been published biannually (table 2.58.1). In these NADG studies, frequencies of sensitization have ranged from 1.0% to 3.4%, with a decline from >3% in the period 1996-2008 (with the exception of 2.3% in 2003-2004) to 1.0% and 1.6% in the period 2009-

2012 (14,15,16,20,21,30,32,33,35,36), but an increase to 2.1% in 2013-2014 (90). In other US centers, rates of 2.5% (53), and 2.1% (5) have been observed, although the population in the latter study was tested with a lower concentration of 0.25% BP in pet. (5). In European countries, prevalences have been consistently lower, ranging from 0.4% to 1.4% (1,7,29,31,34,37,40,41,96). In only a single European investigation was a relevance figure provided (80% [31]). In the NACDG studies, 'definite + probable relevance' has ranged from 6 to 37% (mean 20%). The causative products were never mentioned, but contact allergy to BP is in the majority of cases the result of its presence in cosmetic products.

Table 2.58.1 Patch testing in groups of patients: Routine testing

Years and Country	Test conc. & vehicle	Number of patients tested	positive (%)	Selection of patients (S); Relevance (R); Comments (C)	Ref.
2013-14 USA, Canada	0.5% pet.	4859	101 (2.1%)	R: definite + probable relevance: 28%	90
2011-12 USA, Canada	0.5% pet.	4231	67 (1.6%)	R: definite + probable relevance: 40%	20
2009-2012, 12 European countries [b]	0.25% pet.	11,000	(0.9%) [a]	R: not stated; C: range per country 0.4-1.0%	96
	0.5% pet.	22,086	(0.7%) [a]	R: not stated; C: range per country 0.3-1.1%	
2009-10 USA, Canada	0.5% pet.	4304	43 (1.0%)	R: definite + probable relevance: 20%	21
2006-2010 USA	0.5% pet.	2142	(2.5%)	R: 30%	53
	0.25% pet.	944	(0.7%)	R: 43%	
2004-2009 IVDK	0.5% pet.	42,882	613 (1.4%)	R: not stated	7
2007-2008, 7 European countries [b]	0.5% pet.	12,443	140 (1.1%)	R: not stated; prevalences ranged from 0% (Lithuania) to 1.7% (Austria)	1
2007-8 USA, Canada	0.5% pet.	5081	(3.1%)	R: definite + probable relevance: 13%	15
2005-6 USA, Canada	0.5% pet.	4435	(3.4%)	R: definite + probable relevance: 19%	14
2004-2005 UK	0.25% pet.	6958	(1.2%)	R: not stated; C: prevalence was 1.3% in women, 1.0% in men	29
2000-2005 USA	0.25% pet.	3841	(2.1%)	R: 51%	5
2003-4 USA, Canada	0.5% pet.	5140	118 (2.3%)	R: not stated	16
2001-2002 USA	0.5% pet.	4897	(3.3%)	R: definite + probable relevance: 7%	30
2000 United Kingdom	0.5% pet.	3063	(0.8%)	R: 80% (in one of the centers current + past relevance)	31
1998-2000 USA	0.5% pet.	5800	(3.1%)	R: definite + probable relevance: 6%	32
1996-1998 USA	0.5% pet.	4094	(3.2%)	R: definite + probable + possible relevance: 69%	33
1992-1998 IVDK	0.5% pet.	33,368	(1.1%)	R: not stated	34
1994-1996 USA	0.5% pet.	3074	(2.3%)	R: definite + probable relevance: 37%	35
1992-1994 USA	0.5% pet.	3477	(2.2%)	R: definite + probable + possible relevance: 42%	36
1992-1993 Austria	0.5% pet.	11,516	(0.4%)	R: not stated; C: prevalence in women 0.4%, in men 0.2%	37
1989-90 Switzerland	0.5% pet.	2295	(1.2%)	R: not stated	40
<1990 Europe	0.5% pet.	8149	(0.5%)	R: 45%; C: EECDRG study. 80% of the patients came from the London area	41

[a] age-standardized and sex-standardized proportions
[b] study of the ESSCA (European Surveillance System on Contact Allergies)
EECDRG: European Environmental and Contact Dermatitis Research Group
IVDK: Information Network of Departments of Dermatology, Germany, Austria, Switzerland

Patch testing in groups of selected patients
Data on patch testing with 2-bromo-2-nitropropane-1,3-diol in groups of selected patients back to 1994 are summarized in table 2.58.2. Patch test concentrations have included 0.25% pet. and 0.5% pet. Despite selection, high prevalence rates have been observed in a few studies only: 4% (patients with eyelid dermatitis [17]), 5.5% (children with [atopic] dermatitis [85]), 6.5% (patients with allergic contact dermatitis of the eyelids [50]) and 9% (patients with leg ulcers [98]). Relevance figures were given in 5 studies only, ranging from 16% to 100% (50,66,71,85,98), but the incriminated products containing BP were never mentioned. Nurses and other health care workers had a significantly increased rate of sensitization to 2-bromo-2-nitropropane-diol (81,82), as did patients with leg ulcers / stasis dermatitis (101).

Case reports and case series
2-Bromo-2-nitropropane-1,3-diol (BP) was stated to be the (or an) allergen in 11 patients in a group of 603 individuals suffering from cosmetic dermatitis, seen in the period 2010-2015 in Leuven, Belgium (52). In the period 1996-2013, in a tertiary referral center in Valencia, Spain, 5419 patients were patch tested. Of these, 628 individuals had allergic contact dermatitis to cosmetics. 2-Bromo-2-nitropropane-1,3-diol was the responsible allergen in 2 cases (91). BP was responsible for 40 out of 959 cases of non-fragrance cosmetic allergy where the causal allergen was identified, Belgium, 2000-2010 (3). In the period 2011-2014, 79 patients with a positive patch test reaction to an allergen identified with a wet wipe source were identified by the members of the NACDG. Bronopol was the (or an)

allergen in 27% of the cases. Patients with wipe allergy were 15 times more likely to have anal/genital dermatitis compared with those without wipe allergy (107).

Table 2.58.2 Patch testing in groups of patients: Selected patient groups

Years and Country	Test conc. & vehicle	Number of patients tested	positive (%)	Selection of patients (S); Relevance (R); Comments (C)	Ref.
2003-2014 IVDK	0.5% pet.	5202	(2.4%)	S: patients with stasis dermatitis/ chronic leg ulcers; R: not stated; C: percentage of reactions significantly higher than in a control group of routine testing	101
1996-2013 Netherlands	0.25% pet.	438	2 (0.5%)	S: children aged 0-17 years; R: not stated	100
2007-2012 IVDK	0.5% pet.	702	4 (0.4%)	S: female hairdressers with current or previous occupational contact dermatitis; R: not stated	93
		1904	15 (0.8%)	S: female patients, clients of hairdressers, in who hair cosmetics were regarded as a cause of dermatitis, and who had never worked as hairdressers; R: not stated	
2003-2012 IVDK		1984	39 (2.0%)	S: nurses with occupational contact dermatitis; R: not stated	19
2010-2011 Korea	0.25% pet.	584	19 (3.3%)	S: patients suspected of allergic cosmetic dermatitis; R: not stated	51
2006-2011 Singapore	0.25% pet.	506	4 (0.8%)	S: not specified; R: not stated; C: prevalence in men was 0.7%, in women 0.8%	54
2006-2011 IVDK	0.5% pet.	10,124	120 (1.3%)	S: patients suspected of cosmetic intolerance; R: not stated	92
2006-2010 USA	0.5% pet.	100	4 (4%)	S: patients with eyelid dermatitis; R: not stated	17
2001-2010 Australia	0.25% pet.	4354	49 (1.1%)	S: not stated; R: 16%	66
1994-2010 USA, Canada	0.5% pet.	432	? (?)	S: hairdressers/cosmetologists; R: in the group of 187 patients who had at least one relevant occupationally related reaction, 8 (4.3%) reacted to BP	94
2005-2009 Spain	0.25 or 0.5% pet.	1192	2 (0.2%)	S: patients allergic to formaldehyde or quaternium-15, or suspicion of cosmetic or industrial contact dermatitis; R: not specified	2
2002-2008 UK	0.5% pet.	110	6 (5.5%)	S: children 2-18 year referred for patch testing, of who half had atopic dermatitis; R: 4/6 were relevant, all had facial dermatitis; C: the source products were not mentioned and finding these allergens was not associated with a better clinical outcome	85
1993-2006 Australia	0.25% pet.	4756	(0.9%)	S: not stated; R: 27%	71
2004–2005 IVDK	0.5% pet.	90	(0%)	S: patients with suspected metalworking fluid dermatitis; R: not stated	42
1994-2004 USA		46	3 (6.5%)	S: patients with ACD of the eyelids; R: the reactions were relevant, but the causative products were not mentioned	50
<2004 USA, Canada	0.5% pet	54	5 (9%)	S: patients with leg ulcers; R: 80% probable relevance	98
2002-2003 IVDK	0.5% pet.	199	(1.1%)	S: patients with suspected metalworking fluid dermatitis; R: not stated	43
2001-2002 Sweden	0.25% pet.	1075	(1.0%)	S: patients referred for routine testing willing to participate in a study on cosmetic use and adverse reactions; R: not stated	8
2000-2002 Finland	0.5% pet.	6562	(0.2%)	S: not stated, selected from approximately 11,800 patients; R: not stated	44
1999-2001 IVDK	0.5% pet.	148	(1.4%)	S: metalworkers exposed to water-based metalworking fluids; R: not stated	45
1998-2000 USA	0.25% pet.	991	(2.0%)	S: not stated; R: not stated	46
1995-1996 Finland	0.5% pet.	5150	(0.5%)	S: not stated, selected from approximately 9400 patients; R: not stated	44
1992-1995 IVDK [a]	0.5% pet.	16,934	(1.1%)	S: not stated, selected from 35,062 patients; R: not stated	47
1990-1994 IVDK [a]	0.5% pet.	1781	(1.8%)	S: not stated, selected from 28,349 patients; R: not stated	48
		11,443	(1.2%)	S: not stated, selected from 28, 349 patients; R: not stated	

[a] it may be assumed that there is an overlap in the patient populations in these IVDK studies

IVDK: Information Network of Departments of Dermatology, Germany, Austria, Switzerland

In the period 2000-2007, 202 patients with allergic contact dermatitis caused by cosmetics were seen in Valencia, Spain. In this group, one individual reacted to BP from its presence in a moisturizing cream (63). In a cohort of 2193 patients (1582 women, 611 men) with (presumed) cosmetic allergy, 75 reactions (3.4%) were caused by 2-bromo-2-nitropropane-1,3-diol in a study of the NACDG, 2001-2004 (6).

In a Finnish occupational contact dermatitis clinic, in a period of 6.5 year, the following cases of occupational allergic contact dermatitis from formaldehyde released by 2-bromo-2-nitropropaner-1,3-diol in cosmetics were observed (occupation and causative products mentioned): two nurses and liquid soaps; a plastic worker and liquid soap; a home aid and liquid soap; a production worker and liquid soap. In addition, a masseuse had occupational ACD from BP and a physiotherapist from massage liniment independent of formaldehyde contact allergy (64). In a group of 119 patients with allergic contact dermatitis from cosmetics, investigated in The Netherlands in 1986-1987, one case was caused by BP in a skin care product (57,58). In 3 clinics in Belgium, in the period 1978-1985, 279 patients with allergic contact dermatitis exclusively caused by cosmetics were seen. In this group, there were 4 reactions to BP. It was implied that this was the cause of the allergic cosmetic reactions (65).

BP was responsible for 16 out of 399 cases of cosmetic allergy where the causal allergen was identified in a study of the NACDG, USA, 1977-1983 (4). At the Mayo Clinic, USA, 72 patients were patch tested from January to July 1980 with BP 0.5% and 0.25% pet. Twelve (17%) had positive reactions to one or both concentrations, of which 9 were considered to be relevant. In most cases, exposure to BP occurred through a moisturizer containing BP that was widely prescribed by the hospital. When routine use of this cream was stopped, a marked decrease in the number of positive patch tests to BP was noted (73). In another report, 7 patients were described in detail with contact allergy to BP in the same cream (9).

A woman had dermatitis of the face and neck from contact allergy to BP in a baby wipe (13). A man had hand eczema from BP in a hand cleanser (18). Two individuals working in a cosmetic manufacturing plant became occupationally sensitized to 2-bromo-2-nitropropane-1,3-diol they had to weigh for producing cosmetic creams (25). A woman had dermatitis of the face and reacted to 2-bromo-2-nitropropane-1,3-diol and to diazolidinyl urea. It was implied that this was the cause of her dermatitis, but apparently she did not use any cosmetics and no products were tested or even mentioned (28). Three patients reacted to formaldehyde in BP in cosmetics (88). A woman had ACD from 2-bromo-2-nitropropane-1,3-diol in a sunscreen (97).

Contact allergy to 2-bromo-2-nitropropane-1,3-diol in non-cosmetic products
One patient reacted to 2-bromo-2-nitropropane-1,3-diol in a topical pharmaceutical product (23). Another had occupational ACD from BP in a spin finish (24). A veterinary surgeon had contact allergy to the preservative in a lubricant jelly for rectally examining horses (26). In a series of 6 patients from Germany reacting to BP, heparin ointments were found to be the main source of sensitization (69). Three milk recorders developed occupational ACD of the hands from BP contained in milk preservative solutions (72). A motor mechanic developed occupational dermatitis of the hands and forearms from contact allergy to BP in a heavy duty cleaner (74).

Cross-reactions, pseudo-cross-reactions and co-reactions
2-Bromo-2-nitropropane-1,3-diol is a formaldehyde-releaser (9,87). In a number of patients, contact allergy to the preservative is the result of sensitivity to formaldehyde (7,108). In these cases, pseudo-cross-reactions may be observed to formaldehyde and other formaldehyde-releasers including diazolidinyl urea, DMDM hydantoin, imidazolidinyl urea and quaternium-15, but they are infrequent, as BP releases very little formaldehyde. The subject of formaldehyde-releasers and pseudo-cross-reactivity is summarized in chapter 2.188 Formaldehyde and discussed in detail in ref. 76.

Cross-reactivity from tris nitro has been observed (83); actually, this may rather be pseudo-cross-reactivity, as tris nitro has been found to be a degradation product of 2-bromo-2-nitropropane-1,3-diol (9,86). Contact allergies to BP and to the preservatives methyldibromoglutaronitrile and methylchloroisothiazolinone/methylisothiazolinone have been observed to be significantly associated. This probably results from concomitant or successive sensitization to these chemicals in the same or different products rather than from cross-reactivity (70).

Presence of 2-bromo-2-nitropropane-1,3-diol in cosmetic products
In June 2017, BP was present in 46 of over 69,510 cosmetic products (0.07%) of which the composition is known in EWG's Skin Deep Cosmetics Database, USA (http://www.ewg.org/skindeep/), versus 0.3% in 2009 (75). In the USA, in April 2017, 2- bromo-2-nitropropane-1,3-diol was present in 229 of 56,714 cosmetic products of which the composition is known in FDA's Voluntary Cosmetic Registration Program (VCRP) (data obtained from FDA, May 2017). 2-Bromo-2-nitropropane-1,3-diol was present in 12 (22%) of 54 personal hygiene wet wipes for which ingredient information was obtained online and from retail stores, USA, 2016 (103). 2-Bromo-2-nitropropane-1,3-diol was present in 26 (15%) of 178 facial wipes for which ingredient information was obtained online and from retail stores, USA, 2016 (102). In the USA, in 2015-2016, 63 diaper wipes and 41 topical diaper preparations from a large retailer were screened for the presence of potential sensitizers. 2-Bromo-2-nitropropane-1,3-diol was found in 3/63 (5%) disposable diaper wipes and in none of 41 topical diaper preparations (104). In 2014, in Thailand, the labels of 1000 cosmetic products (593 leave-on, 407 rinse-off products) were examined for the presence of preservatives. These were partly purchased in shops and on markets and partly brought in by patients. 2-Bromo-2-nitropropane-

1,3-diol was present in 1 product (0.01%); in the leave-on products, the percentage was 0.2 and in the rinse-off products zero (99).

In 2013, 60 cosmetic products manufactured and purchased in Israel (40 stay-on and 20 rinse-off products) were investigated for preservatives. According to the labelling, 3 (5%) cosmetics contained BP. In the stay-on products (hand and body creams), the percentage was 8, whereas none of the 20 shampoos and soaps was preserved with BP (67). In 2009, in the USA, the ingredient lists of 796 hair products from one company were screened for the presence of BP. 2-Bromo-2-nitropropane-1,3-diol was present in 0% of 279 shampoos, in 1% of 231 conditioners, and in 0% of 286 styling products (61). In 2009, in the USA, the ingredient lists of 657 miscellaneous cosmetics from one company were screened for the presence of BP. This preservative was present in 26% of 53 wipes, but in no other cosmetic product type (62). 2-Bromo-2-nitropropane-1,3-diol was present in 46/3541 (1.2%) randomly sampled leave-on cosmetic products, Germany, 2006-2009 (11). In Germany, in 2006-2009, the labels of 4680 cosmetic products were screened for the presence of preservatives. 2-Bromo-2-nitropropane-1,3-diol was present in % of the products, according to labelling information (95). Of 204 cosmetic products (92 shampoos, 61 hair conditioners, 34 liquid soaps, 17 wet tissues) investigated in Sweden, 2008, six per cent proved to contain BP (12).

In 2008, 19.5% of 33,212 cosmetics and toiletries registered in the USA Food and Drug Administration (FDA) Voluntary Cosmetic Registration Database contained a formaldehyde-releaser. They were more frequently used in rinse-off products (27.3%) than in stay-on cosmetics (16.9%). 2-Bromo-2-nitropropane-1,3-diol was present in 0.5% of all products; in stay-on cosmetics, the percentage was 0.6 and in rinse-off products 0.4 (27). In the same period, of 496 stay-on cosmetic products present in a local drugstore in The Netherlands and investigated by checking the ingredient labelling, 26 products (5.2%) proved to contain this preservative. *Any* formaldehyde-releaser was found in 122 of this group of stay-on products (24.6%) (27). Of 38 cosmetic products marketed for babies in the UK in 2007, 11 (29%) contained BP (56). 2-Bromo-2-nitropropane-1,3-diol was present in 60 of 1774 (3.4%) cosmetics and toiletries in 2002 and in 36 of 1170 (3.1%) such products in 2005, filed in the Danish Product Register Database (PROBAS) (49). In 1998, 100 moisturizers sold in Sweden were analyzed for the presence and amount of preservatives. Thirty-five products contained a formaldehyde-releaser, of which two contained BP (55).

Amounts of free formaldehyde released by 2-bromo-2-nitropropane-1,3-diol and chemical analyses
In a group of 67 samples of skin creams, randomly selected from retail outlets in Denmark in 1999, 5 (7%) contained 2-bromo-2-nitropropane-1,3-diol in a concentration range of 0.012% to 0.109% (60). A shampoo preserved with 0.02% BP was analyzed and contained 10 ppm free formaldehyde; an emulsion with 0.02% BP was found to have 15 ppm free formaldehyde (9). A lotion preserved with 0.02% BP was found to contain 20 ppm free formaldehyde; at higher concentrations of 0.08%, 0.16% and 0.24%, the amounts were 30, 50 resp. 70 ppm (78).

In 4 commercial shampoos, BP was demonstrated by HPLC in concentrations (w/w) ranging from 0.01% to 0.067% (84). Four homemade cosmetics (2 lotions, 2 gels), of which 2 contained 0.1% w/v BP and the other two 0.05%, all had released 15 ppm formaldehyde after 50 days storage at 25^0 (87). In a group of 67 samples of skin creams, randomly selected from retail outlets in Denmark in 1999, 5 (7%) contained BP in a concentration range of 0.012% to 0.109% (77). In experiments, BP in cosmetics released the lowest amount of formaldehyde of all formaldehyde-releasers investigated (paraformaldehyde, diazolidinyl urea, DMDM hydantoin, quaternium-15 , imi-dazolidinyl urea, methenamine and 2-bromo-2-nitropropane-1,3-diol) (68). Analyses of free formaldehyde in 2-bromo-2-nitropropane-1,3-diol patch test preparations are presented in Chapter 2.188 Formaldehyde (22). A 0.5% aqueous solution of BP prepared by a supplier of patch test materials at pH 5 contained no free formaldehyde (detection limit: 100 ppm) (22).

OTHER SIDE EFFECTS

Immediate-type reactions
Of 50 individuals who had open tests with 2-bromo-2-nitropropane-1,3-diol 0.25% in water on the forearm, 8 (16%) showed local macular erythema after 45 minutes, termed 'contact urticaria' by the authors (59).

LITERATURE

1   Uter W, Aberer W, Armario-Hita JC, Fernandez-Vozmediano JM, Ayala F, Balato A, et al. Current patch test results with the European baseline series and extensions to it from the 'European Surveillance System on Contact Allergy' network, 2007-2008. Contact Dermatitis 2012;67:9-19
2   Latorre N, Borrego L, Fernández-Redondo V, García-Bravo B, Giménez-Arnau AM, Sánchez J, et al. Patch testing with formaldehyde and formaldehyde-releasers: multicenter study in Spain (2005-2009). Contact Dermatitis 2011;65:286-292
3   Travassos AR, Claes L, Boey L, Drieghe J, Goossens A. Non-fragrance allergens in specific cosmetic products. Contact Dermatitis 2011;65:276-285

4   Adams RM, Maibach HI, Clendenning WE, Fisher AA, Jordan WJ, Kanof N, et al. A five-year study of cosmetic reactions. J Am Acad Dermatol 1985;13:1062-1069

5   Davis MD, Scalf LA, Yiannias JA, Cheng JF, El-Azhary RA, Rohlinger AL, et al. Changing trends and allergens in the patch test standard series. Arch Dermatol 2008;144:67-72

6   Warshaw EM, Buchholz HJ, Belsito DV Maibach HI, Fowler JF Jr, Rietschel RL, et al. Allergic patch test reactions associated with cosmetics: Retrospective analysis of cross-sectional data from the North American Contact Dermatitis Group, 2001-2004. J Am Acad Dermatol 2009;60:23-38

7   Schnuch A, Lessmann H, Geier J, Uter W. Contact allergy to preservatives. Analysis of IVDK data 1996-2009. Br J Dermatol 2011;164:1316-1325

8   Lindberg M, Tammela M, Bostrom A, Fischer T, Inerot A, Sundberg K, et al. Are adverse skin reactions to cosmetics underestimated in the clinical assessment of contact dermatitis? A prospective study among 1075 patients attending Swedish patch test clinics. Acta Derm Venereol 2004;84:291-295

9   Storrs FJ, Bell DE. Allergic contact dermatitis to 2-bromo-2-nitropropane-1,3-diol in a hydrophilic ointment. J Am Acad Dermatol 1983;8:157-170

10 Larsen WG, Jackson EM, Barker MD, Bednarz RM, Engasser PG, O'Donoghue MN, et al. A primer on cosmetics. J Am Acad Dermatol 1992;27:469-484

11 Schnuch A, Mildau G, Kratz E-M, Uter W. Risk of sensitization to preservatives estimated on the basis of patch test data and exposure, according to a sample of 3541 leave-on products. Contact Dermatitis 2011;65:167-174

12 Yazar K, Johnsson S, Lind M-L, Boman A, Lidén C. Preservatives and fragrances in selected consumer-available cosmetics and detergents. Contact Dermatitis 2011;64:265-272

13 Fields KS, Nelson T, Powell D. Contact dermatitis caused by baby wipes. J Am Acad Dermatol 2006;54:S230-S232

14 Zug KA, Warshaw EM, Fowler JF Jr, Maibach HI, Belsito DL, Pratt MD, et al. Patch-test results of the North American Contact Dermatitis Group 2005-2006. Dermatitis 2009;20:149-160

15 Fransway AF, Zug KA, Belsito DV, Deleo VA, Fowler JF Jr, Maibach HI, et al. North American Contact Dermatitis Group patch test results for 2007-2008. Dermatitis 2013;24:10-21

16 Warshaw EM, Belsito DV, DeLeo VA, Fowler JF Jr, Maibach HI, Marks JG, et al. North American Contact Dermatitis Group patch-test results, 2003-2004 study period. Dermatitis 2008;19:129-136

17 Wenk KS, Ehrlich AE. Fragrance series testing in eyelid dermatitis. Dermatitis 2012;23:22-26

18 Andersen KE, Goossens A. Decyl glucoside contact allergy from a sunscreen product. Contact Dermatitis 2006;54:349-350

19 Molin S, Bauer A, Schnuch A, Geier J. Occupational contact allergy in nurses: results from the Information Network of Departments of Dermatology 2003–2012. Contact Dermatitis 2015;72:164-171

20 Warshaw EM, Maibach HI, Taylor JS, Sasseville D, DeKoven JG, Zirwas MJ, et al. North American Contact Dermatitis Group patch test results: 2011-2012. Dermatitis 2015;26:49-59

21 Warshaw EM, Belsito DV, Taylor JS, Sasseville D, DeKoven JG, Zirwas MJ, et al. North American Contact Dermatitis Group patch test results: 2009 to 2010. Dermatitis 2013;24:50-59

22 Emeis D, De Groot AC, Brinkmann J. Determination of formaldehyde in formaldehyde-releaser patch test preparations. Contact Dermatitis 2010;63:57-62

23 Choudry K, Beck MH, Muston HL. Allergic contact dermatitis from 2-bromo-2-nitropropane-1,3-diol in Metrogel®. Contact Dermatitis 2002;46:60-61

24 Podmore P. Occupational allergic contact dermatitis from both 2-bromo-2-nitropropane-1,3-diol and methylchloroisothiazolinone plus methylisothiazolinone in spin finish. Contact Dermatitis 2000;43:45

25 Rudzki E, Rebandel P, Grzywa Z. Occupational dermatitis from cosmetic creams. Contact Dermatitis 1993;29:210

26 Wilson CL, Powell SM. An unusual case of allergic contact dermatitis in a veterinary surgeon. Contact Dermatitis 1990;23:42

27 De Groot AC, Veenstra M. Formaldehyde-releasers in cosmetics in the USA and in Europe. Contact Dermatitis 2010;62:221-224

28 Fowler JF Jr, Skinner SL. Contact dermatitis due to cosmetic preservatives. Am J Contact Dermatitis 1991;2:143-144

29 Jong CT, Statham BN, Green CM, King CM, Gawkrodger DJ, Sansom JE, et al. Contact sensitivity to preservatives in the UK 2004–2005: results of a multicenter study. Contact Dermatitis 2007;57:165-168

30 Pratt MD, Belsito DV, DeLeo VA, Fowler JF Jr, Fransway AF, Maibach HI, et al. North American Contact Dermatitis Group patch-test results, 2001–2002 study period. Dermatitis 2004;15:176-183

31 Britton JE, Wilkinson SM, English JSC, Gawkrodger DJ, Ormerod AD, Sansom JE, et al. The British standard series of contact dermatitis allergens: validation in clinical practice and value for clinical governance. Br J Dermatol 2003;148:259-264

32 Marks JG Jr, Belsito DV, DeLeo VA, Fowler JF Jr, Fransway AF, Maibach HI, et al. North American Contact Dermatitis Group patch-test results, 1998–2000. Am J Contact Dermat 2003;14:59-68

33　Marks JG Jr, Belsito DV, DeLeo VA, Fowler JF Jr, Fransway AF, Maibach HI, et al. North American Contact Dermatitis Group patch test results, 1996–1998. Arch Dermatol 2000;136:272-273

34　Brinkmeier T, Geier J, Lepoittevin J-P, Frosch PJ. Patch test reactions to Biobans in metalworkers are often weak and not reproducible. Contact Dermatitis 2002; 47:27-31

35　Marks JG Jr, Belsito DV, DeLeo VA, Fowler JF Jr, Fransway AF, Maibach HI,et al. North American Contact Dermatitis Group patch test results for the detection of delayed-type hypersensitivity to topical allergens. J Am Acad Dermatol 1998;38:911-918

36　Marks JG, Belsito DV, DeLeo VA, Fowler JF, Fransway AF, Maibach HI,et al. North American Contact Dermatitis Group standard tray patch test results 1992 through 1994. Am J Contact Dermatitis 1995;6:160-165

37　Kränke B, Szolar-Platzer C, Aberer W. Reactions to formaldehyde and formaldehyde releasers in a standard series. Contact Dermatitis 1996;35:192-193

38　Fransway AF. The problem of preservation in the 1990s: I. Statement of the problem. Solution(s) of the industry, and the current use of formaldehyde and formaldehyde-releasing biocides. Am J Contact Dermatitis 1991;2:6-23

39　Fransway AF, Schmitz NA. The problem of preservation in the 1990s: II. Formaldehyde and formaldehyde-releasing biocides: incidences of cross-reactivity and the significance of the positive response to formaldehyde. Am J Contact Dermatitis 1991;2:78-88

40　Perrenoud D, Bircher A, Hunziker T, Suter H, Bruckner-Tuderman L, Stäger J, et al. Frequency of sensitization to 13 common preservatives in Switzerland. Contact Dermatitis 1994;30:276-279

41　Frosch PJ, White IR, Rycroft RJG, e Lahti A, Burrows D, Camarasa JG, et al. Contact allergy to bronopol. Contact Dermatitis 1990;22:24-26

42　Geier J, Lessmann H, Becker D, Bruze M, Frosch PJ, Fuchs T, et al. Patch testing with components of water-based metalworking fluids: results of a multicentre study with a second series. Contact Dermatitis 2006;55:322-329

43　Geier J, Lessmann H, Dickel H, Frosch PJ, Koch P, Becker D, et al. Patch test results with the metalworking fluid series of the German Contact Dermatitis Research Group (DKG). Contact Dermatitis 2004;51:118-130

44　Hasan T, Rantanen T, Alanko K, Harvima RJ, Jolanki R, Kalimo K, et al. Patch test reactions to cosmetic allergens in 1995–1997 and 2000–2002 in Finland –a multicentre study. Contact Dermatitis 2005;53:40-45

45　Geier J, Lessmann H, Schnuch A, Uter W. Contact sensitizations in metalworkers with occupational dermatitis exposed to water-based metalworking fluids: results of the research project "FaSt". Int Arch Occup Environ Health 2004;77:543-551

46　Wetter DA, Davis MDP, Yiannias JA, Cheng JF, Connolly SM, el-Azhary RA, et al. Patch test results from the Mayo Contact Dermatitis Group, 1998–2000. J Am Acad Dermatol 2005;53:416-421

47　Geier J, Lessmann H, Schuch A, Fuchs Th. Kontaktallergien durch formaldehydabspaltende Biozide. Allergologie 1997;20:215-224 (article in German)

48　Schnuch A, Geier J, Uter W, Frosch PJ. Patch testing with preservatives, antimicrobials and industrial biocides. Results from a multicentre study. Br J Dermatol 1998;138:467-476

49　Flyvholm M-A. Preservatives in registered chemical products. Contact Dermatitis 2005;53:27-32

50　Amin KA, Belsito DV. The aetiology of eyelid dermatitis: a 10-year retrospective analysis. Contact Dermatitis 2006;55:280-285

51　Lee SS, Hong DK, Jeong NJ, Lee JH, Choi YS, Lee AY, et al. Multicenter study of preservative sensitivity in patients with suspected cosmetic contact dermatitis in Korea. J Dermatol 2012;39:677-681

52　Goossens A. Cosmetic contact allergens. Cosmetics 2016, 3, 5; doi:10.3390/cosmetics3010005

53　Wentworth AB, Yiannias JA, Keeling JH, Hall MR, Camilleri MJ, Drage LA, et al. Trends in patch-test results and allergen changes in the standard series: a Mayo Clinic 5-year retrospective review (January 1, 2006, to December 31, 2010). J Am Acad Dermatol 2014;70:269-275

54　Cheng S, Leow YH, Goh CL, Goon A. contact sensitivity to preservatives in Singapore: frequency of sensitization to 11 common preservatives 2006–2011. Dermatitis 2014;25:77-82

55　Gruvberger B, Bruze M, Tammela M. Preservatives in moisturizers on the Swedish market. Acta Derm Venereol 1998;78:52-56

56　White JML, McFadden JP. Exposure to haptens/contact allergens in baby cosmetic products. Contact Dermatitis 2008;59:176-177

57　De Groot AC, Bruynzeel DP, Bos JD, van der Meeren HL, van Joost T, Jagtman BA, Weyland JW. The allergens in cosmetics. Arch Dermatol 1988;124:1525-1529

58　De Groot AC. Adverse reactions to cosmetics. PhD Thesis, University of Groningen, The Netherlands: 1988, chapter 3.4, pp.105-113

59　Emmons WW, Marks JG. Immediate and delayed reactions to cosmetic ingredients. Contact Dermatitis 1985;13:258-265

60　Rastogi SC. Analytical control of preservative labelling on skin creams. Contact Dermatitis 2000;43:339-343

61 Scheman A, Jacob S, Katta R, Nedorost S, Warshaw E, Zirwas M, et al. Part 2 of a 4 part series. Hair cosmetics: trends and alternatives. Data from the American Contact Alternative Group. J Clin Aesthet Dermatol 2011;4:42-46

62 Scheman A, Jacob S, Katta R, Nedorost S, Warshaw E, Zirwas M, et al. Part 4 of a 4 part series. Miscellaneous products: trends and alternatives in deodorants, antiperspirants, sunblocks, shaving products, powder, and wipes. Data from the American Contact Alternative Group. J Clin Aesthet Dermatol 2011;4:35-39

63 Laguna C, de la Cuadra J, Martín-González B, Zaragoza V, Martínez-Casimiro L, Alegre V. Allergic contact dermatitis to cosmetics. Actas Dermosifiliogr 2009;100:53-60

64 Aalto-Korte K, Kuuliala O, Suuronen K, Alanko K. Occupational contact allergy to formaldehyde and formaldehyde releasers. Contact Dermatitis 2008;59:280-289

65 Dooms-Goossens A, de Boulle K, Dooms M, Degreef H. Imidazolidinyl urea dermatitis. Contact Dermatitis 1986;14:322-324

66 Toholka R, Wang Y-S, Tate B, Tam M, Cahill J, Palmer A, Nixon R. The first Australian Baseline Series: Recommendations for patch testing in suspected contact dermatitis. Australas J Dermatol 2015;56:107-115

67 Horev L, Isaksson M, Engfeldt M, Persson L, Ingber A, Bruze M. Preservatives in cosmetics in the Israeli market conform well to the EU legislation. J Eur Acad Dermatol Venereol 2015;29:761-766

68 Lv C, Hou J, Xie W, Cheng H. Investigation on formaldehyde release from preservatives in cosmetics. Int J Cosm Sci 2015;37:474-478

69 Frosch PJ, Weickel R. Kontaktallergie auf das Konservierungsmittel Bronopol. Hautarzt 1987;38:267-270 (article in German)

70 Statham BN, Smith EV, Bodger OG, Green CM, King CM, Ormerod AD, et al. Concomitant contact allergy to methylchloroisothiazolinone/ methylisothiazolinone and formaldehyde-releasing preservatives. Contact Dermatitis 2010;62:56-57

71 Chow ET, Avolio AM, Lee A, Nixon R. Frequency of positive patch test reactions to preservatives: The Australian experience. Australas J Dermatol 2013;54:31-35

72 Grattan CEH, Harman RRM, Tan RSH. Milk recorder dermatitis. Contact Dermatitis 1986;14:217-220

73 Peters MS, Connolly SM, Schröder AL. Bronopol allergic contact dermatitis. Contact Dermatitis 1983;9:397-401

74 Wong CSM, Beck MH. Occupational contact allergy to methyldibromo glutaronitrile in abrasive cleansers and work creams. Contact Dermatitis 2001;44:311-312

75 De Groot AC, White IR, Flyvholm M-A, Lensen G, Coenraads P-J. Formaldehyde-releasers: relationship to formaldehyde contact allergy. II. Formaldehyde-releasers used in cosmetics. Part 1. Characterization, frequency and relevance of sensitization, and frequency of use in cosmetics. Contact Dermatitis 2010;62:2-17

76 De Groot AC, White IR, Flyvholm M-A, Lensen G, Coenraads P-J. Formaldehyde-releasers in cosmetics: relationship to formaldehyde contact allergy. Part 2. Patch test relationship to formaldehyde contact allergy, experimental provocation tests, amount of formaldehyde released and assessment of risk to consumers allergic to formaldehyde. Contact Dermatitis 2010;62:18-31

77 Rastogi SC. Analytical control of preservative labelling on skin creams. Contact Dermatitis 2000;43:339-343

78 Karlberg A-T, Skare L, Lindberg I, Nyhammer E. A method for quantification of formaldehyde in the presence of formaldehyde donors in skin-care products. Contact Dermatitis 1998;38:20-28

79 Croshaw B. Preservatives for cosmetics and toiletries. J Soc Cosmet Chem 1977;28:3-17

80 Bryce DM, Croshaw B, Hall JE, Holland VR, Lessel B. The activity and safety of the antimicrobial agent bronopol (2-bromo-2-nitropropane-1,3-diol). J Soc Cosmet Chem 1978;29:3-24

81 Molin S, Bauer A, Schnuch A, Geier J. Occupational contact allergy in nurses: results from the Information Network of Departments of Dermatology 2003-2012. Contact Dermatitis 2015;72:164-171

82 Kadivar S, Belsito DV. Occupational dermatitis in health care workers evaluated for suspected allergic contact dermatitis. Dermatitis 2015;26:177-183

83 Robertson MH, Storrs FJ. Allergic contact dermatitis in two machinists. Arch Dermatol 1982;118:997-1002

84 Wang H, Provan GJ, Helliwell K. Determination of bronopol and its degradation products by HPLC. J Pharm Biomed Anal 2002;29:387-392

85 Moustafa M, Holden CR, Athavale P, Cork MJ, Messenger AG, Gawkrodger DJ. Patch testing is a useful investigation in children with eczema. Contact Dermatitis 2011;65:208-212

86 Matczuk M, Obarski N, Mojski M. The impact of the various chemical and physical factors on the degradation rate of bronopol. Int J Cosmet Sci 2012;34:451-457

87 Kajimura K, Tagami T, Yamamoto T, Iwagami S. The release of formaldehyde upon decomposition of 2-bromo-2-nitropropane-1,3-diol (Bronopol). J Health Sci 2008;54:488-492

88 Fisher AA. Cosmetic dermatitis. Part II. Reactions to some commonly used preservatives. Cutis 1980;26:136-7, 141-2, 147-8

89 Cosmetic Ingredient Review Expert Panel. Addendum to the Final report on the safety assessment of 2-bromo-2-nitropropane-1,3-diol. J Amer Coll Toxicol 1984;3:139-155

90 DeKoven JG, Warshaw EM, Belsito DV, Sasseville D, Maibach HI, Taylor JS, et al. North American Contact Dermatitis Group Patch Test Results: 2013-2014. Dermatitis 2017;28:33-46

91 Zaragoza-Ninet V, Blasco Encinas R, Vilata-Corell JJ, Pérez-Ferriols A, Sierra-Talamantes C, Esteve-Martínez A, de la Cuadra-Oyanguren J. Allergic contact dermatitis due to cosmetics: A clinical and epidemiological study in a tertiary hospital. Actas Dermosifiliogr 2016;107:329-336

92 Dinkloh A, Worm M, Geier J, Schnuch A, Wollenberg A. Contact sensitization in patients with suspected cosmetic intolerance: results of the IVDK 2006-2011. J Eur Acad Dermatol Venereol 2015;29:1071-1081

93 Uter W, Gefeller O, John SM, Schnuch A, Geier J. Contact allergy to ingredients of hair cosmetics – a comparison of female hairdressers and clients based on IVDK 2007–2012 data. Contact Dermatitis 2014;71:13-20

94 Warshaw EM, Wang MZ, Mathias CGT, Maibach HI, Belsito DV, Zug KA, et al. Occupational contact dermatitis in hairdressers/cosmetologists; retrospective analysis of North American Contact Dermatitis Group data, 1994 to 2010. Dermatitis 2012;23:258-268

95 Uter W, Yazar K, Kratz EM, Mildau G, Lidén C. Coupled exposure to ingredients of cosmetic products: II. Preservatives. Contact Dermatitis 2014;70:219-226

96 Giménez-Arnau AM, Deza G, Bauer A, Johnston GA, Mahler V, Schuttelaar ML, et al. Contact allergy to preservatives: ESSCA* results with the baseline series, 2009-2012. J Eur Acad Dermatol Venereol 2017;31:664-671

97 Lübben U. Kontaktallergie auf Lichtschutzmittel. Z Hautkr 1987;62:1233 (article in German)

98 Saap L, Fahim S, Arsenault E, Pratt M, Pierscianowski T, Falanga V, Pedvis-Leftick A. Contact sensitivity in patients with leg ulcerations: a North American study. Arch Dermatol 2004;140:1241-1246

99 Bunyavaree M, Kasemsarn P, Boonchai W. Cosmetic preservative labelling on the Thai market. Contact Dermatitis 2016;74:217-221

100 Lubbes S, Rustemeyer T, Sillevis Smitt JH, Schuttelaar ML, Middelkamp-Hup MA. Contact sensitization in Dutch children and adolescents with and without atopic dermatitis - a retrospective analysis. Contact Dermatitis 2017;76:151-159

101 Erfurt-Berge C, Geier J, Mahler V. The current spectrum of contact sensitization in patients with chronic leg ulcers or stasis dermatitis - new data from the Information Network of Departments of Dermatology (IVDK). Contact Dermatitis 2017 Feb 14. doi: 10.1111/cod.12763. [Epub ahead of print]

102 Aschenbeck KA, Warshaw EM. Allergenic ingredients in facial wet wipes. Dermatitis 2017 Mar 23. doi: 10.1097/DER.0000000000000268. [Epub ahead of print]

103 Aschenbeck KA, Warshaw EM. Allergenic ingredients in personal hygiene wet wipes. Dermatitis 2017 Mar 23. doi: 10.1097/DER.0000000000000275. [Epub ahead of print]

104 Yu J, Treat J, Chaney K, Brod B. Potential allergens in disposable diaper wipes, topical diaper preparations, and disposable diapers: under-recognized etiology of pediatric perineal dermatitis. Dermatitis 2016;27:110-118

105 Sasseville D. Hypersensitivity to preservatives. Dermatol Ther 2004;17:251-263

106 Yim E, Baquerizo Nole KL, Tosti A. Contact dermatitis caused by preservatives. Dermatitis 2014;25:215-231

107 Warshaw EM, Aschenbeck KA, Zug KA, Belsito DV, Zirwas MJ, Fowler JF Jr, Taylor JS, et al. Wet wipe allergens: Retrospective analysis from the North American Contact Dermatitis Group 2011-2014. Dermatitis 2017;28:64-69

108 Lynch MD, White JM, McFadden JP, Wang Y, White IR, Banerjee P. A dynamic landscape of allergen associations in delayed-type cutaneous hypersensitivity. Br J Dermatol 2017;176:184-196

2.59 1,4-BUTANEDIOL DIMETHACRYLATE

IDENTIFICATION

Description/definition   : 1,4-Butanediol dimethacrylate is the organic compound that conforms to the formula
                             shown below
Chemical class(es)   : Esters
Chemical/IUPAC name   : 4-(2-Methylprop-2-enoyloxy)butyl 2-methylprop-2-enoate
Other names   : Tetramethylene dimethacrylate; tetramethylene glycol dimethacrylate
CAS registry number (s)   : 2082-81-7
EC number(s)   : 218-218-1
Function(s) in cosmetics   : EU: film forming. USA: artificial nail builders
Patch testing   : 2.0% pet. (Chemotechnique, SmartPracticeEurope, SmartPracticeCanada)
Molecular formula   : $C_{12}H_{18}O_4$

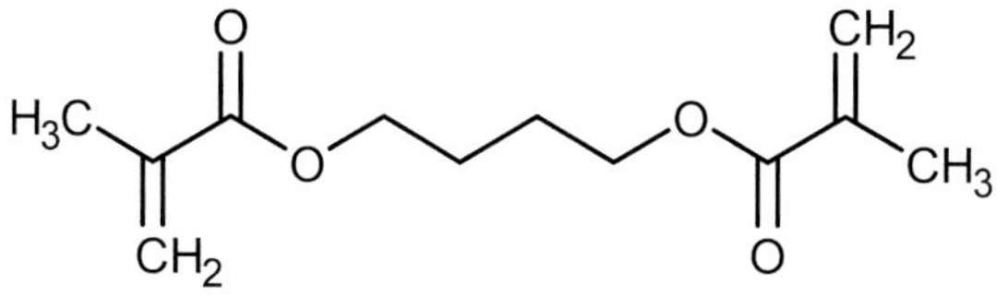

GENERAL

Discussion of contact allergy to (meth)acrylates *from non-cosmetic sources* is considered to fall outside the scope of this book. Therefore, only contact allergy from their presence in cosmetics is presented, which virtually always is from artificial nails. There are many reports of contact allergy to artificial nails, but the specific sensitizers have rarely been identified and – consequently - such publications are not presented in this and other acrylate and methacrylate monographs. Discussion is limited to publications in which the culprit (meth)acrylates have been identified, e.g., from information found in Material Data Safety Sheets, data obtained from the manufacturer or from chemical analyses.

Patients often react to many (meth)acrylates on patch testing. Primary sensitization to methacrylates may result in both methacrylate and acrylate cross-sensitization. Conversely, patients sensitized to acrylates are unlikely to show cross-sensitization to methacrylates (2).

General aspects of acrylates and methacrylates are presented in Chapter 2.219 HEMA (hydroxyethyl methacrylate). A discussion of general aspects of artificial nails, contact allergy to these products, the clinical picture of allergic contact dermatitis and other side effects of sculptured nails can also be found there.

CONTACT ALLERGY

Patch testing in groups of patients
Studies in which consecutive patients suspected of contact dermatitis have been tested with 1,4-butanediol dimethacrylate (routine testing) and studies testing groups of selected patients are planned to be discussed in a future publication.

Case reports and case series
In the period 1996-2013, in a tertiary referral center in Valencia, Spain, 5419 patients were patch tested. Of these, 628 individuals had allergic contact dermatitis to cosmetics. 1,4-Butanediol dimethacrylate was the responsible allergen in three cases (3). In the period 2000-2007, 202 patients with allergic contact dermatitis caused by cosmetics were seen in the same clinic in Valencia, Spain (overlap with ref. 3). In this group, there were 10 beauticians with occupational allergic contact dermatitis of the hands, who reacted to multiple (meth)acrylates from their presence in artificial nail materials. Of these ten individuals, one reacted to 1,4-butanediol dimethacrylate, which reaction was apparently relevant (although it can be doubted that the presence of these specific chemicals in the products could always be verified) (1).

Presence in cosmetic products and chemical analyses
In the USA, in April 2017, 1,4-butanediol dimethacrylate was present in zero of 56,714 cosmetic products of which the composition is known in FDA's Voluntary Cosmetic Registration Program (VCRP) (data obtained from FDA, May 2017). In February 2017, 1,4-butanediol dimethacrylate was present in zero of 64,467 cosmetic products of which the composition is known in EWG's Skin Deep Cosmetics Database, USA (http://www.ewg.org/skindeep/).

LITERATURE

1   Laguna C, de la Cuadra J, Martín-González B, Zaragoza V, Martínez-Casimiro L, Alegre V. Allergic contact dermatitis to cosmetics. Actas Dermosifiliogr 2009;100:53-60

2   Aalto-Korte K, Henriks-Eckerman M-L, Kuuliala O, Jolanki R. Occupational methacrylate and acrylate allergy – cross-reactions and possible screening allergens. Contact Dermatitis 2010;63:301-312

3   Zaragoza-Ninet V, Blasco Encinas R, Vilata-Corell JJ, Pérez-Ferriols A, Sierra-Talamantes C, Esteve-Martínez A, de la Cuadra-Oyanguren J. Allergic contact dermatitis due to cosmetics: A clinical and epidemiological study in a tertiary hospital. Actas Dermosifiliogr 2016;107:329-336

2.60 BUTYL ACRYLATE*
Not an INCI name

IDENTIFICATION

Description/definition : Butyl acrylate is the organic compound that conforms to the formula shown below
Chemical class(es) : Esters
INCI name USA : Neither in Cosing nor in the Personal Care Products Council Ingredient Database
Chemical/IUPAC name : Butyl prop-2-enoate
CAS registry number (s) : 141-32-2
EC number(s) : 205-480-7
Merck Index monograph : 2811
Patch testing : 0.1% pet. (Chemotechnique, SmartPracticeEurope, SmartPracticeCanada)
Molecular formula : $C_7H_{12}O_2$

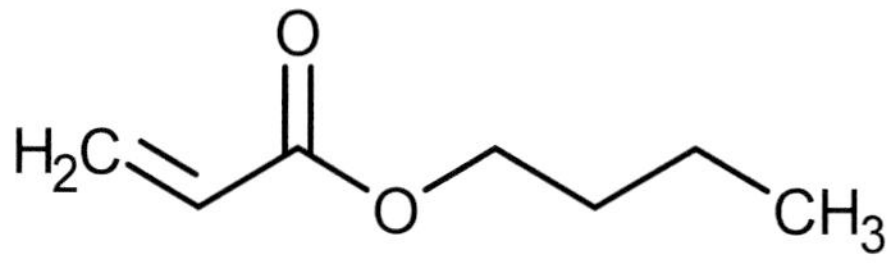

GENERAL

Discussion of contact allergy to (meth)acrylates *from non-cosmetic sources* is considered to fall outside the scope of this book. Therefore, only contact allergy from their presence in cosmetics is presented, which virtually always is from artificial nails. There are many reports of contact allergy to artificial nails, but the specific sensitizers have rarely been identified and – consequently - such publications are not presented in this and other acrylate and methacrylate monographs. Discussion is limited to publications in which the culprit (meth)acrylates have been identified, e.g., from information found in Material Data Safety Sheets, data obtained from the manufacturer or from chemical analyses.

Patients often react to many (meth)acrylates on patch testing. Primary sensitization to methacrylates may result in both methacrylate and acrylate cross-sensitization. Conversely, patients sensitized to acrylates are unlikely to show cross-sensitization to methacrylates (2).

General aspects of acrylates and methacrylates are presented in Chapter 2.219 HEMA (hydroxyethyl methacrylate). A discussion of general aspects of artificial nails, contact allergy to these products, the clinical picture of allergic contact dermatitis and other side effects of sculptured nails can also be found there. A very useful review of contact sensitization to allergens in nail cosmetics, with emphasis on acrylic manicures, was published in 2017 (6).

CONTACT ALLERGY

Case reports and case series

In the period 1996-2013, in a tertiary referral center in Valencia, Spain, 5419 patients were patch tested. Of these, 628 individuals had allergic contact dermatitis to cosmetics. Butyl acrylate was the responsible allergen in four cases (4). In the period 2000-2007, 202 patients with allergic contact dermatitis caused by cosmetics were seen in Valencia, Spain. In this group, there were 10 beauticians with occupational allergic contact dermatitis of the hands, who reacted to multiple (meth)acrylates from their presence in artificial nail materials. Of these ten individuals, two reacted to butyl acrylate, which reactions were apparently relevant (although it can be doubted that the presence of these specific chemicals in the products could always be verified) (3).

A group of 55 female patients presenting with hand eczema, who had contact with artificial nails, were patch tested with a series of acrylates in one center in Israel, 2001-2004. Twenty-one had one or more positive reactions, of who 14 were professional beauticians specializing in nail sculpturing. All reactions, including one to butyl acrylate, were stated to be of current relevance (1). Because of the general lack of information on the composition of artificial nail materials, the fact that the author did no analyses of these products and the frequent occurrence of cross-reactivity among acrylates, one may wonder whether this statement can be accepted as entirely correct.

Patch test sensitization

One patient became sensitized from a patch test with butyl acrylate 1% pet. (5).

Presence in cosmetic products and chemical analyses

In the USA, in April 2017, butyl acrylate was present in zero of 56,714 cosmetic products of which the composition is known in FDA's Voluntary Cosmetic Registration Program (VCRP) (data obtained from FDA, May 2017). In February

2017, butyl acrylate was present in zero of 64,467 cosmetic products of which the composition is known in EWG's Skin Deep Cosmetics Database, USA (http://www.ewg.org/skindeep/).

LITERATURE

1   Lazarov A. Sensitization to acrylates is a common adverse reaction to artificial fingernails. J Eur Acad Derm Venereol 2007;21:169-174
2   Aalto-Korte K, Henriks-Eckerman M-L, Kuuliala O, Jolanki R. Occupational methacrylate and acrylate allergy – cross-reactions and possible screening allergens. Contact Dermatitis 2010;63:301-312
3   Laguna C, de la Cuadra J, Martín-González B, Zaragoza V, Martínez-Casimiro L, Alegre V. Allergic contact dermatitis to cosmetics. Actas Dermosifiliogr 2009;100:53-60
4   Zaragoza-Ninet V, Blasco Encinas R, Vilata-Corell JJ, Pérez-Ferriols A, Sierra-Talamantes C, Esteve-Martínez A, de la Cuadra-Oyanguren J. Allergic contact dermatitis due to cosmetics: A clinical and epidemiological study in a tertiary hospital. Actas Dermosifiliogr 2016;107:329-336
5   Kanerva L, Estlander T, Jolanki R. Sensitization to patch test acrylates. Contact Dermatitis 1988;18:10-15
6   Chou M, Dhingra N, Strugar TL. Contact sensitization to allergens in nail cosmetics. Dermatitis 2017;28:231-240

2.61 T-BUTYL ALCOHOL

IDENTIFICATION

Description/definition	: t-Butyl alcohol is the aliphatic alcohol that conforms to the formula shown below
Chemical class(es)	: Alcohols
Chemical/IUPAC name	: 2-Methylpropan-2-ol
CAS registry number (s)	: 75-65-0
EC number(s)	: 200-889-7
CIR review(s)	: J Am Coll Toxicol 1989;8:627-641; Int J Toxicol 2005;24(Suppl.2):1-20 (access: www.cir-safety.org/ingredients)
Merck Index monograph	: 2814
Function(s) in cosmetics	: EU: denaturant; perfuming; solvent. USA: denaturants; fragrance ingredients; solvents
Patch testing	: 10%, 30% and 70% in water
Molecular formula	: $C_4H_{10}O$

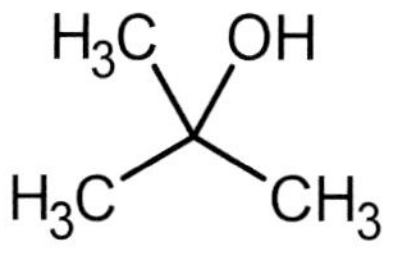

GENERAL

t-Butyl alcohol is used in the manufacture of perfumes. Its primary use in cosmetics is as an alcohol denaturant, but it is also used as a solvent in hair sprays and aftershave lotions and as a perfume carrier in cosmetics. t-Butyl alcohol is ubiquitous in the environment, and human exposure is likely. It may be present in alcoholic beverages up to 0.25%, and it is permitted as an indirect food additive. Other applications include its use in formulating defoaming agents used in the preparation and application of coatings for paper and paperboard, in surface lubricants employed in the manufacture of metallic articles that contact food and in surface lubricants used in the rolling of metallic foil or sheet stock. The chemical has also been used as flotation agent, dehydration agent, solvent, octane booster in gasoline, in paint removers, as a chemical intermediate, and in chemical analyses (3).

CONTACT ALLERGY

Case reports and case series
A man presented with a widespread, pruritic, red, vesicular eruption of his face, neck, arms, and chest. He had used a variety of sunscreens. He was tested with sunscreens and with the individual components of the product to which he reacted. A 70% concentration of t-butyl alcohol was applied to the forearms. At D3, erythema was observed and at D4, there was vesiculation at the test site. No reactions were observed in two controls who also had applied the test material to their forearms (1).

Contact allergy to t-butyl alcohol in non-cosmetic products
Unknown number of patients allergic to t-butyl alcohol in unknown products (article not read, in Polish) (2).

Cross-reactions, pseudo-cross-reactions and co-reactions
In various studies, patients allergic to (ethyl) alcohol have cross-reacted to butanol / butyl alcohol (data summarized in ref. 4).

Presence in cosmetic products and chemical analyses
In the USA, in April 2017, butyl alcohol was present in 278 of 56,714 cosmetic products of which the composition is known in FDA's Voluntary Cosmetic Registration Program (VCRP) (data obtained from FDA, May 2017). In April 2017, t-butyl alcohol was present in 28 of 65,521 cosmetic products of which the composition is known in EWG's Skin Deep Cosmetics Database, USA (http://www.ewg.org/skindeep/).

OTHER SIDE EFFECTS

Irritant contact dermatitis
Dermatitis has been observed when t-butyl alcohol is applied to the skin; it caused irritation, moderate hyperaemia and erythema, dryness, and vesiculation (3).

Immediate-type reactions

In a patient with the (ethyl) alcohol contact urticaria syndrome, 'butanol' also induced an immediate reaction when applied to the skin (5).

LITERATURE

1   Edwards EK Jr, Edwards EK. Allergic reaction to tertiary butyl alcohol in a sunscreen. Cutis 1982;29:476-478
2   Rudzki E. Two not yet described contact allergens: sodium hyposulfite and tertiary butyl alcohol. Przegl Dermatol 1979;66:375-377 (article in Polish)
3   Chen M. Amended final report of the safety assessment of *t*-butyl alcohol as used in cosmetics. Int J Toxicol 2005;24(Suppl.2):1-20
4   Ophaswongse S, Maibach HI. Alcohol dermatitis: allergic contact dermatitis and contact urticaria syndrome. Contact Dermatitis 1994;30:1-6
5   Rilliet A, Hunziker N, Brun R. Alcohol contact urticaria syndrome (immediate-type hypersensitivity). Case report. Dermatologica 1980;161:361-364

2.62 BUTYLENE GLYCOL

IDENTIFICATION

Description/definition : Butylene glycol is the aliphatic diol that conforms to the formula shown below
Chemical class(es) : Alcohols
Chemical/IUPAC name : Butane-1,3-diol
CAS registry number (s) : 107-88-0
EC number(s) : 203-529-7
CIR review(s) : J Am Coll Toxicol 1985;4:223-248 (access: www.cir-safety.org/ingredients)
Merck Index monograph : 2840
Function(s) in cosmetics : EU: humectant; masking; skin conditioning; solvent; viscosity controlling. USA: fragrance ingredients; skin-conditioning agents – miscellaneous; solvents; viscosity decreasing agents
Patch testing : 5-10% water; a test concentration of 20% in water causes irritant reactions (19)
Molecular formula : $C_4H_{10}O_2$

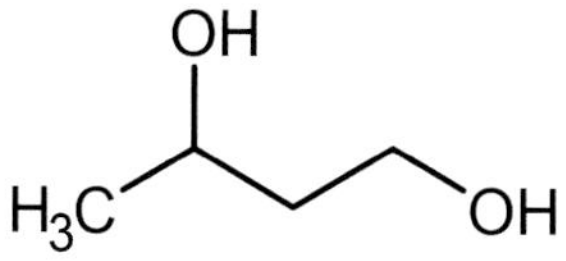

GENERAL

Butylene glycol is a dihydric alcohol frequently used in cosmetics and medicaments because of its marked moist-urizing properties, capacity to retard loss of aromas and ability to protect against spoilage by microorganisms. Butylene glycol is considered to be a milder skin irritant than propylene glycol (15). It is also used as a humectant in polyurethane, polyester, cellophane, and cigarettes (18). Nearly all cases of allergic contact dermatitis from butylene glycol have been reported from Japan.

CONTACT ALLERGY

Patch testing in groups of patients

Results of patch testing with butylene glycol in groups of unselected patients (routine testing) and in selected patient groups are shown in table 2.62.1. In Finland, only 0.2-0.3% of consecutive patients had allergic reactions to butylene glycol. However, there were many irritant reactions, indicating that the 20% water test solution was too high for adequate patch testing (19). In Japan, 4 of 364 (1.1%) routinely tested patients reacted positively, of which 2 (50%) had used cosmetic products containing butylene glycol (7).

In Japan, in 1994-1999, 758 patients suspected of cosmetic dermatitis were tested with butylene glycol 5% water and 13 (1.7%) had a positive patch test reaction. In nine of them (69%) the reaction was relevant, as they had used 'hypo-irritant' cosmetics containing butylene glycol (14).

Table 2.62.1 Patch testing in groups of patients

Years and Country	Test conc. & vehicle	Number of patients tested	positive (%)	Selection of patients (S); Relevance (R); Comments (C)	Ref.
Routine testing					
<1997 Japan	5% water	364	4 (1.1%)	R: 2 patients had used cosmetics containing butylene glycol	7
1989-1990 Finland	20% water	1701	4 (0.2%)	R: not stated; C: there were 7.5% irritant reactions; the test preparation was 1,3-butylene glycol	19
1989-1990 Finland	20% water	1701	5 (0.3%)	R: not stated; C: there were 6.8% irritant reactions; the test preparation was 2,3-butylene glycol	19
Testing in groups of selected patients					
1994-1999 Japan	5% water	758	13 (1.7%)	S: patients suspected of cosmetic dermatitis; R: 9/13 (69%) were relevant and reacted to 'hypo-irritant' cosmetics	14
<1997 Japan	?	272	1 (0.4%)	S; patients with (roseacea-like) contact dermatitis; no details known	17

Case reports and case series

Butylene glycol was stated to be the (or an) allergen in 2 patients in a group of 603 individuals suffering from cos-metic dermatitis, seen in the period 2010-2015 in Leuven, Belgium (18). A woman had allergic contact dermatitis from butylene glycol in a cream (1). A young girl developed allergic contact dermatitis of the eyelids from butylene glycol in an eyeliner (2). A female patient had facial allergic contact dermatitis caused by butylene glycol in a cosmetic lotion and cleansing foam (3). Another woman had dermatitis of the face from butylene glycol in a beauty essence, foundation and eyeliner (15). Two young women had ACD from butylene glycol in a 'supertanning' cream (9).

A female individual suffered from dermatitis of the face caused by contact allergy to butylene glycol in a foundation cream and 18 'hypo-irritant' cosmetics (7). One Japanese patient had occupational allergic contact dermatitis from butylene glycol in soap (12,13). Probably one individual had allergic contact dermatitis from a cosmetic lotion that contained 33% butylene glycol (16). An unknown number of patients had allergic reactions to butylene glycol by their presence in cosmetic products (4,6). Two patients had dermatitis from contact allergy to butylene glycol in unknown cosmetic products (5,8,20; 8 and 20 may have presented the same patient).

Contact allergy to butylene glycol in non-cosmetic products
One patient reacted to butylene glycol in an antifungal topical preparation (11). An unknown number of patients was allergic to butylene glycol in unknown products (10,21, articles in Japanese).

Cross-reactions, pseudo-cross-reactions and co-reactions
Not to or from propylene glycol (7); not to hexylene glycol or propylene glycol (9); possibly to and/or from propylene glycol and hexylene glycol; very frequent co-reactions between 1,3- and 2,3-butylene glycol (19).

Presence in cosmetic products and chemical analyses
In the USA, in April 2017, butylene glycol was present in 8690 of 56,714 cosmetic products of which the composition is known in FDA's Voluntary Cosmetic Registration Program (VCRP) (data obtained from FDA, May 2017). In April 2017, butylene glycol was present in 2491 of 65,521 cosmetic products of which the composition is known in EWG's Skin Deep Cosmetics Database, USA (http://www.ewg.org/skindeep/). Butylene glycol was present in 37 (21%) of 178 facial wipes for which ingredient information was obtained online and from retail stores, USA, 2016 (22). In 2000, in Japan, 70-99% of lotions, emulsions and creams contained butylene glycol (14).

LITERATURE
1   Sugiura M, Hayakawa R, Sugiura K. Contact dermatitis due to lipsticks and a cream containing isopalmityl diglyceryl sebacate. Contact Dermatitis 2006;54:213-214
2   Magerl A, Pirker C, Frosch PJ. Allergic contact eczema from shellac and 1,3-butylene glycol in an eyeliner. J Dtsch Dermatol Ges 2003;1:300-302
3   Tamagawa-Mineoka R, Katoh N, Kishimoto S. Allergic contact dermatitis due to 1,3-butylene glycol and glycerol. Contact Dermatitis 2007;56:297-298
4   Okada Y, Noda H, Matsunaga K, Hamamatsu T, Kawashima R. Cosmetic dermatitis in 1991. Skin Res 1993;35:75-80 (in Japanese)
5   Fujimoto Y, Hayakawa R, Suzuki M, Ogino Y, Kato Y, Hanamura A, Sato A, Hirose O. A case with contact dermatitis due to 1,3-butylene glycol. Environ Dermatol 1994;1:;106-110 (in Japanese)
6   Matsunaga K, Katoh C, Takeuchi M, Kato Y. Allergic contact dermatitis from 1,3-butylene glycol. Allergy in Practice 1994;14:492-495
7   Sugiura M, Hayakawa R. Contact dermatitis due to 1,3-butylene glycol. Contact Dermatitis 1997;37: 90
8   Yashiro K, Mishimoto M. A case of contact dermatitis due to 1,3-butylene glycol and trisodiumhydroxyethyl ethylenediamine triacetate. Environ Dermatol 1999;6(Suppl. 1):59 (in Japanese)
9   Diegenant C, Constandt L, Goossens A. Allergic contact dermatitis due to 1,3-butylene glycol. Contact Dermatitis 2000; 43:234-235
10   Hashimoto R, Hayakawa R, Kato Y, Sugiura M. A case of contact dermatitis due to 1,3-butylene glycol. Environ Dermatol 2001;8:11-14 (in Japanese)
11   Oiso N, Fukai K, Ishii M. Allergic contact dermatitis due 1,3-butylene glycol in medicaments. Contact Dermatitis 2004;51:40-41
12   Xie Z, Hayakawa R, Sugiura M, Kato Y, Takeuchi Y. Causes of 15 cases with occupational contact dermatitis in the secondary industries. Environ Dermatol 1999;6:22-25 (in Japanese)
13   Xie Z, Hayakawa R, Sugiura M, Kato Y, Takeuchi Y. Causative agents and prognosis of 66 patients with occupational contact dermatitis. Environ Dermatol 1999;6:133-141 (in Japanese)
14   Sugiura M, Hayakawa R, Kato Y, Sugiura K, Hashimoto R, Shamoto M. Results of patch testing with 1,3-butylene glycol from 1994 to 1999. Environ Dermatol 2001;8:1-5 (in Japanese)
15   Aizawa A, Ito A, Masui Y, Ito M. Case of allergic contact dermatitis due to 1,3-butylene glycol. J Dermatol 2014;41:815-816

16 Takahashi S. A case of contact dermatitis due to 1,3-butylene glycol. Nishinihon J Dermatol 2001;63:141-144 (in Japanese).

17 Matsunaga K, Sugai T, Katoh J, et al. Group study on contact sensitivity of 1,3-butylene glycol. Environ Dermatol 1997;4:195-201 (in Japanese)

18 Goossens A. Cosmetic contact allergens. Cosmetics 2016, 3, 5; doi:10.3390/cosmetics3010005

19 Fan W, Kinnunen T, Niinimäki A, Hannuksela M. Skin reactions to glycols used in dermatological and cosmetic vehicles. Am J Cont Dermatit 1991;2:181-183

20 Yashiro K, Nishimoto M. A case of contact dermatitis due to 1,3-butylene glycol and trisodium hydroxyethyl ethylenediamine triacetate. Environ Dermatol 2003;10:14–20 (in Japanese)

21 Ikezawa Y, Aihara M, Kondo M, Takahashi S, Takahashi K, Ikezawa Z. Two cases of contact dermatitis due to 1,3-butylene glycol. Environ Dermatol 2004;11:59-64 (in Japanese)

22 Aschenbeck KA, Warshaw EM. Allergenic ingredients in facial wet wipes. Dermatitis 2017 Mar 23. doi: 10.1097/DER.0000000000000268. [Epub ahead of print]

2.63 DI-T-BUTYLHYDROQUINONE

IDENTIFICATION

Description/definition   : Di-*t*-butylhydroquinone is the compound that conforms to the formula shown below
Chemical class(es)   : Phenols
Chemical/IUPAC name   : 2,5-Ditert-butylbenzene-1,4-diol
Other names   : 2,5-Di-*tert*-butylhydroquinone; DTBHQ; 2,5-bis(1,1-dimethylethyl)-1,4-benzenediol
CAS registry number (s)   : 88-58-4
EC number(s)   : 201-841-8
CIR review(s)   : J Am Coll Toxicol 1996;15:301-310 (access: www.cir-safety.org/ingredients)
Function(s) in cosmetics   : EU: antioxidant. USA: antioxidants
Patch testing   : 1% pet.
Molecular formula   : $C_{14}H_{22}O_2$

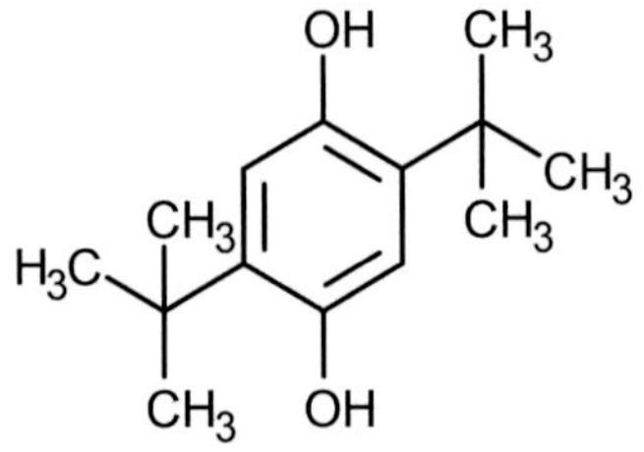

CONTACT ALLERGY

Case reports and case series

Three patients had allergic contact dermatitis from di-*t*-butylhydroquinone in eyeshadow (1,2). A woman complained of recurrent dermatitis of her eyelids for one year; on the last occasion her neck was also affected. Patch testing, which included an array of her cosmetics, evoked a weak reaction to one night cream. This she applied to one of her antecubital fossae without producing a reaction, but when she used it on her face the original dermatitis relapsed. When tested with the constituents of this cream, she reacted only to di-*t*-butylhydroquinone 1% (3).

Presence in cosmetic products and chemical analyses

In the USA, in April 2017, 2,5-di-*tert*-butylhydroquinone was present in zero of 56,714 cosmetic products of which the composition is known in FDA's Voluntary Cosmetic Registration Program (VCRP) (data obtained from FDA, May 2017). In March 2017, di-*t*-butylhydroquinone was present in zero of 64,983 cosmetic products of which the composition is known in EWG's Skin Deep Cosmetics Database, USA (http://www.ewg.org/skindeep/).

LITERATURE

1   Calnan CD. Ditertiarybutylhydroquinone in eyeshadow. Contact Dermatitis Newsletter 1973;13:368
2   Calnan CD. Ditertiarybutylhydroquinone. Contact Dermatitis Newsletter 1973;14:402
3   Cronin E. Contact Dermatitis. Edinburgh: Churchill Livingstone, 1980:98

2.64 BUTYL METHACRYLATE

IDENTIFICATION

Description/definition   : Butyl methacrylate is the ester of *n*-butyl alcohol and methacrylic acid, which conforms
                            to the formula shown below
Chemical class(es)   : Esters
Chemical/IUPAC name   : 2-Propenoic acid, 2-methyl-, butyl ester
Other names   : Butyl 2-methyl-2-propenoate
CAS registry number (s)   : 97-88-1; 44914-03-6
EC number(s)   : 202-615-1; 256-170-3
CIR review(s)   : Int J Toxicol 2005;24(Suppl.5):53-100 (access: www.cir-safety.org/ingredients)
Function(s) in cosmetics : EU: film forming; masking; viscosity controlling. USA: artificial nail builders; fragrance
                            ingredients
Patch testing   : 2.0% pet. (Chemotechnique)
Molecular formula   : $C_8H_{14}O_2$

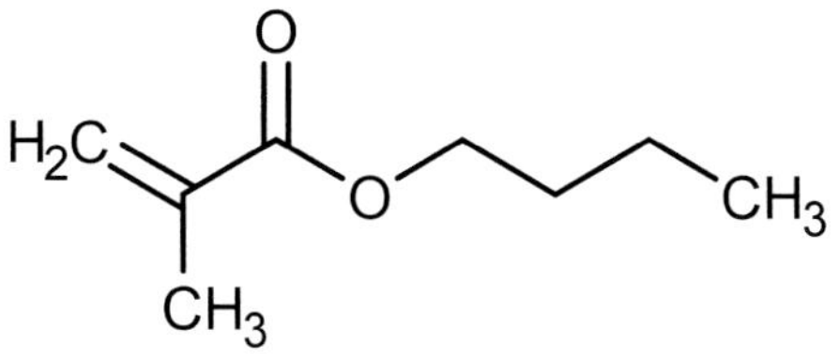

GENERAL

Discussion of contact allergy to (meth)acrylates *from non-cosmetic sources* is considered to fall outside the scope of this book. Therefore, only contact allergy from their presence in cosmetics is presented, which virtually always is from artificial nails. There are many reports of contact allergy to artificial nails, but the specific sensitizers have rarely been identified and – consequently - such publications are not presented in this and other acrylate and methacrylate monographs. Discussion is limited to publications in which the culprit (meth)acrylates have been identified, e.g., from information found in Material Data Safety Sheets, data obtained from the manufacturer or from chemical analyses.

Patients often react to many (meth)acrylates on patch testing. Primary sensitization to methacrylates may result in both methacrylate and acrylate cross-sensitization. Conversely, patients sensitized to acrylates are unlikely to show cross-sensitization to methacrylates (1).

General aspects of acrylates and methacrylates are presented in Chapter 2.219 HEMA (hydroxyethyl methacrylate). A discussion of general aspects of artificial nails, contact allergy to these products, the clinical picture of allergic contact dermatitis and other side effects of sculptured nails can also be found there.

CONTACT ALLERGY

Patch testing in groups of patients
Studies in which consecutive patients suspected of contact dermatitis have been tested with butyl methacrylate (routine testing) and studies testing groups of selected patients are planned to be discussed in a future publication.

Case reports and case series
A group of 55 female patients presenting with hand eczema and who had contact with artificial nails, were patch tested with a series of acrylates in one center in Israel, 2001-2004. Twenty-one had one or more positive reactions, of who 14 were professional beauticians specializing in nail sculpturing. All reactions, including three to butyl methacrylate, were stated to be of current relevance (2). Because of the general lack of information on the composition of artificial nail materials, the fact that the author did no analyses of these products and the frequent occurrence of cross-reactivity among acrylates, one may wonder whether this statement can be accepted as entirely correct.

Presence in cosmetic products and chemical analyses
In the USA, in April 2017, butyl methacrylate was present in zero of 56,714 cosmetic products of which the composition is known in FDA's Voluntary Cosmetic Registration Program (VCRP) (data obtained from FDA, May 2017). In February 2017, butyl methacrylate was present in zero of 64,480 cosmetic products of which the composition is known in EWG's Skin Deep Cosmetics Database, USA (http://www.ewg.org/skindeep/).

LITERATURE

1   Aalto-Korte K, Henriks-Eckerman M-L, Kuuliala O, Jolanki R. Occupational methacrylate and acrylate allergy –
    cross-reactions and possible screening allergens. Contact Dermatitis 2010;63:301-312
2   Lazarov A. Sensitization to acrylates is a common adverse reaction to artificial fingernails. J Eur Acad Derm
    Venereol 2007;21:169-174

2.65 BUTYL METHOXYDIBENZOYLMETHANE

IDENTIFICATION

Description/definition	: Butyl methoxydibenzoylmethane is the substituted aromatic compound that conforms to the formula shown below
Chemical class(es)	: Ethers; ketones
Chemical/IUPAC name	: 1-(4-*tert*-Butylphenyl)-3-(4-methoxyphenyl)propane-1,3-dione
Other names	: Avobenzone; Parsol® 1789
CAS registry number (s)	: 70356-09-1
EC number(s)	: 274-581-6
Merck Index monograph	: 2151
Function(s) in cosmetics	: EU: UV-absorber; UV-filter. USA: light stabilizers; sunscreen agents
EU cosmetic restrictions	: Regulated in Annex VI/8 of the Regulation (EC) No. 1223/2009
Patch testing	: 5.0% pet. (Chemotechnique); 10.0% pet. (Chemotechnique, SmartPracticeCanada)
Molecular formula	: $C_{20}H_{22}O_3$

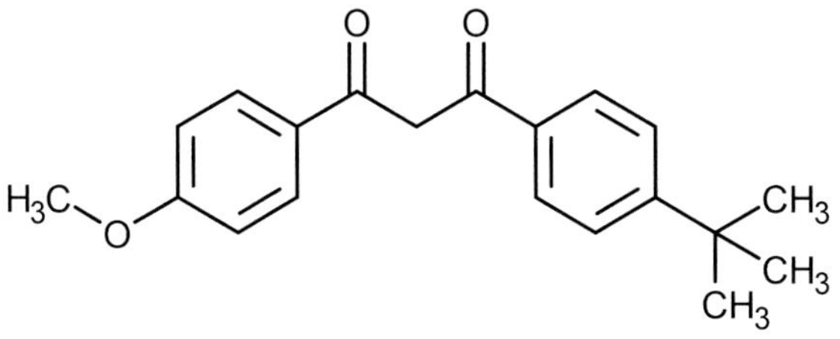

GENERAL

Butyl methoxydibenzoylmethane is a UVA filter with UV absorbance maximum (λ_{max}) at 357 nm (72), which has been used in Europe since 1981 (44). It is often combined with octocrylene in sunscreens because butyl methoxydibenzoylmethane is easily photodegraded by UV light, losing its UV protection capacity, and octocrylene is able to stabilize this filter, which therefore keeps its effectiveness (21,71). Butyl methoxydibenzoylmethane can also be photostabilized by bis-ethylhexyloxyphenol methoxyphenyl triazine (73,74). Combinations with ethylhexyl methoxycinnamate are also frequent (71).

Many patients allergic or photoallergic to butyl methoxydibenzoylmethane have been reported in literature. However, it is likely that in a number of such cases, (photo)contact allergy to butyl methoxydibenzoylmethane was a cross-reaction from primary sensitization to isopropyl dibenzoylmethane. Indeed, since the removal of isopropyl dibenzoylmethane from the market (see Chapter 2.255 Isopropyl dibenzoylmethane), (photo)contact allergy to butyl methoxydibenzoylmethane has become infrequent (2,4), despite its widespread use in sunscreen and other cosmetic products (see 'Presence in cosmetic products and chemical analyses' below.

The literature on adverse reactions to sunscreens has been reviewed in several recent and older publications (50-55,76). A review of photocontact allergy to sunscreens was published in 2010 (67). General information, use and mechanism of action, method of preparation, physical characteristics, methods of analysis, stability, and toxicity of butyl methoxydibenzoylmethane have been reviewed in 2013 (70).

CONTACT ALLERGY

There have been no studies in which butyl methoxydibenzoylmethane was tested in consecutive patients suspected of contact dermatitis (routine testing). The results of testing in groups of *selected* patients (e.g., patients suspected of photosensitivity, patients with dermatitis affecting mainly light-exposed skin or with a history of a sunscreen skin reaction, patients tested with a cosmetic screening series) back to 1991 are shown in table 2.65.1. Test concentrations used have been 2% pet., 5% pet. and/or 10% pet., but the higher test concentrations have not clearly resulted in more positive reactions, the mode of selection probably being the more important determinant. Frequencies of sensitization have ranged from 0.1% to 7.5%. In 8 of 10 studies, rates were 1% or lower. The high frequency of 7.5% was seen in a study from Canada, which had certain weaknesses (19). In most investigations, the relevance of positive patch test reactions to butyl methoxydibenzoylmethane was either not stated or specified for the UV-filter. In studies that did, most reactions were considered to be relevant (1,15).

Table 2.65.1 Patch testing in groups of patients: Selected patient groups

Years and Country	Test conc. & vehicle	Number of patients tested	positive (%)		Selection of patients (S); Relevance (R); Comments (C)	Ref.
2011-2013 Colombia	10% pet.	112	1	(0.9%)	S: dermatitis affecting mainly light-exposed skin, a history of a sunscreen or a topical NSAID skin reaction; R: relevant	65
2008-2011 12 European countries	10% pet.	1031	3	(0.3%)	S: patients with exposed site dermatitis or history of a reaction to a sunscreen or topical NSAID; R: not specified	20
2001-2010 Canada		160	12	(7.5%)	S: patients with suspected photosensitivity and patients who developed pruritus or a rash after sunscreen application; R: not stated; C: very weak study: inadequate reading of test results, erythema only was considered to represent a positive patch test reaction	19
2000-2007 USA	10% pet.	869	3	(0.3%)	S: patients tested with a supplemental cosmetic screening series; R: 100%; C: weak study: a. high rate of macular erythema and weak reactions; b. relevance figures included 'questionable' and 'past' relevance	15
2000-2002 UK, I, NL	10% pet.	1155	10	(0.9%)	S: patients suspected of photosensitivity or reaction to a sunscreen; R: 9 current, 1 unknown	1
1993-2000 Australia	2% pet.	172	1	(0.6%)	S: patients suspected of photosensitivity; R: of 17 patient who had contact or photocontact reactions to a panel of 10 sunscreens, 10 were considered to have relevant reactions	34
1996-1998 UK		167	1	(0.6%)	S: patients with suspected photosensitivity; R: 'most cases' in the total group were relevant	6
1983-1998 UK	2% or 10% pet.	2715	3	(0.1%)	S: patients suspected of photosensitivity or with (a history of) dermatitis at exposed sites; R: not stated	3
1981-1996 Germany	5% pet.	378	15	(4.0%)	S: patients suspected of clinical photosensitivity; R: not stated	2
1989-1991 UK	2% pet.	99	1	(1%)	S: 45 patients with photosensitivity dermatitis/actinic reticuloid syndrome and 54 with polymorphic light eruption; R: not specified	5

I: Ireland; NL: Netherlands; UK: United Kingdom

Butyl methoxydibenzoylmethane was responsible for 2 out of 959 cases of non-fragrance cosmetic allergy where the causal allergen was identified, Belgium, 2000-2010 (14). In the period 2000-2007, 202 patients with allergic contact dermatitis caused by cosmetics were seen in Valencia, Spain. In this group, two individuals reacted to butyl methoxydibenzoylmethane from its presence in sunscreens (63, overlap with ref. 66). In the period 1981-1989, 56 patients (43 women, 13 men) were diagnosed with contact allergy or photocontact allergy to UV-filters in one center in Germany. There were 6 contact allergic, 5 photoaggravated contact allergic and 10 photoallergic reactions to butyl methoxydibenzoylmethane. All reactions were relevant and all 46 patients who could be (photo)patch tested with their own sunscreens (and a few of them with other cosmetics) had one or more positive (photo)patch tests to these products (75, overlap with refs 2,8 and 9).

In the period 1978-1991, there was one relevant patch test reaction to butyl methoxydibenzoylmethane in one center in Leuven, Belgium (33). In a group of 119 patients with allergic contact dermatitis from cosmetics, investigated in The Netherlands in 1986-1987, one case was caused by butyl methoxydibenzoylmethane in a lipstick with UV-filter (57,58). Of 280 patients tested with sunscreens in London, 1985-1987, one had ACD from butyl methoxydibenzoylmethane in a sunscreen (40). In a group of 75 patients allergic to cosmetic products, seen in a private practice in The Netherlands in the period 1981-1986, one case was caused by butyl methoxydibenzoylmethane in a lipstick with UV-absorber (59, same patient as in ref. 27).

Case reports
There are two single case reports of patients with allergic contact dermatitis from butyl methoxydibenzoylmethane in sunscreens (9,26) and two from sunscreen lipsticks (27,32), one of who also had photocontact allergy to the UV-absorber (32). In one publication, two patients with ACD from butyl methoxydibenzoylmethane in sunscreens were presented (4). A young girl suffering from atopic dermatitis and photosensitivity became sensitized to butyl methoxydibenzoylmethane in sunscreens (68). Two children had ACD from butyl methoxydibenzoylmethane present in sunscreen products (69). Several centers have reported positive patch tests to butyl methoxydibenzoylmethane, but did not comment on their relevance (8,10,16,43).

Cross-reactions, pseudo-cross-reactions and co-reactions (including photo-reactions)
Cross-reactivity from isopropyl dibenzoylmethane (2,11,24,31,75). Cross-reactivity to isopropyl dibenzoylmethane (32).

Presence in cosmetic products and chemical analyses

In June 2017, butyl methoxydibenzoylmethane was present in 1241 of 68,864 cosmetic products of which the composition is known in EWG's Skin Deep Cosmetics Database, USA (http://www.ewg.org/skindeep/). It should be realized that sunscreen products containing UV-filters are classified as drugs in the USA, not as cosmetics; the number mentioned here, therefore, is that of cosmetics containing the UV-filter, but it does *not* include their presence in sunscreens. In the USA, in April 2017, butyl methoxydibenzoylmethane was present in 4042 of 56,714 cosmetic products of which the composition is known in FDA's Voluntary Cosmetic Registration Program (VCRP) (data obtained from FDA, May 2017). In 2012, in Switzerland, 116 cosmetics from seven widely used leave-on product categories (19 lip care products, 8 lipsticks, 29 face creams, 11 liquid makeup foundations, 3 aftershaves, 7 hand creams and 39 sunscreens) were investigated to determine the frequency of occurrence and concentrations of 22 organic UV filters in these products. Butyl methoxydibenzoylmethane was found in 71% of the products in a concentration range of 0.06-5.11%, mean 2.61% (64). In a sample of 337 sunscreens marketed in the UK in 2010, butyl methoxydibenzoylmethane was present in 96% (49).

In the USA, sunscreen products were purchased and evaluated in 1997 (n=59), 2003 (n=188) and again in 2009 (n=330) (71). In 1997, 3% of the products contained butyl methoxydibenzoylmethane, in 2003 29% and in 2009 54%. The combination with octocrylene was found in 0% in 1997, in 12% in 2003 and in 36% of the products in 2009. A combination of butyl methoxydibenzoylmethane and ethylhexyl methoxycinnamate was present in 2% of the products in 1997, in 20% in 2003 and in 19% in 2009 (71). In 2009, in the USA, the ingredient lists of 796 hair products from one company were screened for the presence of butyl methoxydibenzoylmethane. Butyl methoxydibenzoylmethane was present in 1% of 279 shampoos, in 5% of 231 conditioners, and in 3% of 286 styling products (60).

In 2009, in the USA, the ingredient lists of 657 miscellaneous cosmetics from one company were screened for the presence of butyl methoxydibenzoylmethane. This sunscreen was present in 53% of 201 sunblocks only (61). Butyl methoxydibenzoylmethane was present in 48.7% of 4447 cosmetic products collected in Germany, 2006-2009 (21). Butyl methoxydibenzoylmethane was present in 73% of 329 sunscreen products (incl. 21 lipstick sunscreens) marketed in the UK in 2005 (45). Butyl methoxydibenzoylmethane was present in 33 of 75 (44%) sunscreen creams and lotions from 30 European and US producers purchased in Denmark in 2001 in a concentration range of 0.42-4.8% (36).

OTHER SIDE EFFECTS

Photosensitivity

Photopatch testing in groups of patients

Results of photopatch testing butyl methoxydibenzoylmethane in groups of selected patients (e.g., patients suspected of photosensitivity, patients with dermatitis affecting mainly light-exposed skin or with a history of a sunscreen skin reaction) back to 1990 are shown in table 2.65.2. Test concentrations used have been 2% pet., 5% pet. and/or 10% pet., but the higher test concentrations have not clearly resulted in more positive reactions, the mode of selection probably being the more important determinant. In 19 studies, frequencies of photosensitization have ranged from 0.1% to 27% (table 2.65.2). In 12 studies, positive reactions scored 2% or lower. The very high sensitization rate of 27% was seen in a small group of 30 patients from the USA suffering from chronic actinic dermatitis, in which 8 had a positive photopatch test to butyl methoxydibenzoylmethane. Heavy use of sunscreens for their affliction may explain the high sensitization rate (29). Another high rate (9.1%) was seen in a Dutch study among a group of 55 patients suspected of photosensitivity disorders. Most allergic patients also reacted to isopropyl dibenzoylmethane, which possibly was the primary sensitizer in many cases (11). In most studies, relevance was either not mentioned or specified for butyl methoxydibenzoylmethane, but in the studies that provided relevance data, most reactions were considered to be relevant (1,17).

Case reports and case series

In the period 1981-1989, 56 patients (43 women, 13 men) were diagnosed with contact allergy or photocontact allergy to UV-filters in one center in Germany. There were 6 contact allergic, 5 photoaggravated contact allergic and 10 photoallergic reactions to butyl methoxydibenzoylmethane. All reactions were relevant and all 46 patients who could be (photo)patch tested with their own sunscreens (and a few of them with other cosmetics) had one or more positive (photo)patch tests to these products (75, overlap with refs 2,8 and 9).

There are several single case reports of photoallergic contact dermatitis from butyl methoxydibenzoylmethane in sunscreen preparations (22,23,24,25,46,47,48). One patient had both contact allergy and photocontact allergy to butyl methoxydibenzoylmethane in sunscreens (32). Seven relevant cases of contact allergy or photocontact allergy to butyl methoxydibenzoylmethane were seen in one center in Australia in an 18-year period up to 2012 (18). Three patients had allergic photocontact dermatitis from butyl methoxydibenzoylmethane in sunscreens (42). Positive photopatch tests to butyl methoxydibenzoylmethane in two patients were of past relevance from its presence in sunscreens (37).

Table 2.65.2 Photopatch testing in groups of patients

Years and Country	Test conc. & vehicle	Number of patients tested | positive (%)		Selection of patients (S); Relevance (R); Comments (C)	Ref.
2011-2013 Colombia	10% pet.	112	1 (0.9%)	S: dermatitis affecting mainly light-exposed skin, a history of a sunscreen or a topical NSAID skin reaction; R: relevant	65
2008-2011 12 European countries	10% pet.	1031	18 (1.7%)	S: patients with exposed site dermatitis or history of a reaction to a sunscreen or topical NSAID; R: 44% current and 11% past relevance for all photoallergens together	20
2000-2011 UK	10% pet.	157	1 (0.6%)	S: children <18 years suspected of photosensitivity; R: the reaction was caused by a sunscreen product	38
2001-2010 Canada		160	5 (3.1%)	S: patients with suspected photosensitivity and patients who developed pruritus or a rash after sunscreen application; R: not stated; C: very weak study: inadequate reading of test results, erythema only was considered to represent a positive patch test reaction	19
1993-2009 USA		30	8 (27%)	S: patients with chronic actinic dermatitis; R: not stated	29
2003-2007 Portugal	10% pet.	83	1 (1.2%)	S: patients with suspected photoaggravated facial dermatitis or systemic photosensitivity; R: all sunscreen photopatch tests were of current or past relevance	35
2004-2006 Italy	10% pet.	1082	9 (0.8%)	S: patients with histories and clinical features suggestive of photoallergic contact dermatitis; R: 89%; C: 4/9 were cases of photoaugmented contact allergy	17
1993-2006 USA	10% pet.	76	3 (3.9%)	S: not stated; R: 56% of all reactions to sunscreens were considered 'probably relevant'	12
2000-2005 USA	5% pet.	156	2 (1.3%)	S: patients photopatch tested for suspected photodermatitis; R: 1 reaction was relevant	41
2000-2002 UK, I, NL	10% pet.	1155	22 (1.9%)	S: patients suspected of photosensitivity or reaction to a sunscreen; R: 16 current relevance, 4 unknown, 1 exposed, but not resulting in dermatitis	1
1993-2000 Australia	2% pet.	172	5 (2.9%)	S: patients suspected of photosensitivity; R: of 17 patient who had contact or photocontact reactions to a panel of 10 sunscreens, 10 were considered to have relevant reactions	34
1994-1999 NL	10% pet.	55	5 (9.1%)	S: patients suspected of photosensitivity disorders; R: not stated; C: most patients also reacted to isopropyl dibenzoylmethane, which was probably the primary sensitizer	11
1996-1998 UK		167	8 (4.8%)	S: patients with suspected photosensitivity; R: 'most cases' in the total group were relevant	6
1983-1998 UK	2% or 10% pet.	2715	4 (0.1%)	S: patients suspected of photosensitivity or with (a history of) dermatitis at exposed sites; R: 37% for all photoallergens together	3
1990-1996 Sweden	2% pet.	355	6 (1.7%)	S: patients suspected of photosensitivity; R: not stated	39
1981-1996 Germany	5% pet.	378	13 (3.4%)	S: patients suspected of clinical photosensitivity; R: not stated	2
1990-1994 France	2% or 10% pet.	370	4 (1.1%)	S: patients with suspected photodermatitis; R: not specified, 72% of all reactions in the study were considered relevant	7
1985-1994 Italy		1050	4 (0.4%)	S: patients with histories or clinical pictures suggestive of allergic contact photodermatitis; R: 97% for all sunscreens together	28
1989-1990 France	2% pet.	54	1 (2%)	S: patients suspected of photosensitivity; R: the reaction was relevant	30

I: Ireland; NL: Netherlands; UK: United Kingdom

Four cases of photocontact allergy to butyl methoxydibenzoylmethane were seen in Germany; it was not specified how many photopatch test reactions were relevant (8); the authors mentioned three more cases (8, note added in proof). Eight patients had positive photopatch tests to butyl methoxydibenzoylmethane in one center in Australia, 1992-1999; it was not mentioned how many reactions were relevant and what the culprit products were (10).

Miscellaneous side effects

Milia developed in one patient after an episode of bullous photoallergic contact dermatitis from sunscreens containing butyl methoxydibenzoylmethane, benzophenone-3 and ethylhexyl methoxycinnamate (13).

OTHER INFORMATION

When butyl methoxydibenzoylmethane photodegrades, various arylglyoxals and benzils are formed. The benzils are cytotoxic rather than allergenic, but the arylglyoxals are strong skin sensitizers based on the LLNA (murine local lymph node assay). Thus, it is very likely that photocontact allergy to butyl methoxydibenzoylmethane is caused by arylglyoxals (62).

LITERATURE

1   Bryden A, Moseley H, Ibbotson S, Chowdhury MM, Beck MH, Bourke J, et al. Photopatch testing of 1155 patients: results of the U.K. multicentre photopatch test study group. Brit J Dermatol 2006;155:737-747

2   Schauder S, Ippen H. Contact and photocontact sensitivity. Review of a 15-year experience and of the literature to suncreens. Contact Dermatitis 1997;37:221-232

3   Darvay A, White I, Rycroft R, Jones AB, Hawk JL, McFadden JP. Photoallergic contact dermatitis is uncommon. Br J Dermatol 2001;145:597-601

4   Gonçalo M, Ruas E, Figueiredo A, Gonçalo S. Contact and photocontact sensitivity to sunscreens. Contact Dermatitis 1995;33:278-280

5   Bilsland D, Ferguson J. Contact allergy to sunscreen chemicals in photosensitivity dermatitis/actinic reticuloid syndrome (PD/AR) and polymorphic light eruption. Contact Dermatitis 1993;29:70-73

6   Bell HK, Rhodes LE. Photopatch testing in photosensitive patients. Br J Dermatol 2000;142:589-590

7   Journe F, Marguery M-C, Rakotondrazafy J, El Sayed F, Bazex J. Sunscreen sensitization: a 5-year study. Acta Derm Venereol (Stockh) 1999;79:211-213

8   Schauder S, Ippen H. Photoallergic and allergic contact eczema caused by dibenzoylmethane compounds and other sunscreening agents. Hautarzt 1988;39:435-440

9   Schauder S, Ippen H. Photoallergic and allergic contact dermatitis from dibenzoylmethanes. Photodermatol 1986;3:140-147

10 Cook N, Freeman S. Report of 19 cases of photoallergic contact dermatitis to sunscreens seen at the Skin and Cancer Foundation. Austral J Dermatol 2001;42:257-259

11 Bakkum RS, Heule F. Results of photopatch testing in Rotterdam during a 10-year period. Br J Dermatol 2002;146:275-279

12 Victor FC, Cohen DE, Soter NA. A 20-year analysis of previous and emerging allergens that elicit photoallergic contact dermatitis. J Am Acad Dermatol 2010;62:605-610

13 Bryden AM, Ferguson J, Ibbotson SH. Milia complicating photocontact allergy to absorbent sunscreen chemicals. Clin Exp Dermatol 2003;28:668-669

14 Travassos AR, Claes L, Boey L, Drieghe J, Goossens A. Non-fragrance allergens in specific cosmetic products. Contact Dermatitis 2011;65:276-285

15 Wetter DA, Yiannias JA, Prakash AV, Davis MD, Farmer SA, el-Azhary RA, et al. Results of patch testing to personal care product allergens in a standard series and a supplemental cosmetic series: an analysis of 945 patients from the Mayo Clinic Contact Dermatitis Group, 2000-2007. J Am Acad Dermatol 2010;63:789-798

16 Kohl L, Blondeel A, Song M. Allergic contact dermatitis from cosmetics: retrospective analysis of 819 patch-tested patients. Dermatology 2002;204:334-337

17 Pigatto PD, Guzzi G, Schena D, Guarrera M, Foti C, Francalanci S, et al. Photopatch tests: an Italian multicentre study from 2004 to 2006. Contact Dermatitis 2008;59:103-108

18 Nixon RL. Contact dermatitis to sunscreens. Dermatitis 2012;23:140-141

19 Greenspoon J, Ahluwalia R, Juma N, Rosen CF. Allergic and photoallergic contact dermatitis: A 10-year experience. Dermatitis 2013;24:29-32

20 The European Multicentre Photopatch Test Study (EMCPPTS) Taskforce. A European multicentre photopatch test study. Br J Dermatol 2012;166:1002-1009

21 Uter W, Gonçalo M, Yazar K, Kratz E-M, Mildau G, Lidén C. Coupled exposure to ingredients of cosmetic products: III. Ultraviolet filters. Contact Dermatitis 2014;71:162-169

22 Sommer S, Wilkinson SM, English JSC, Ferguson J. Photoallergic contact dermatitis from the sunscreen octyl triazone. Contact Dermatitis 2002;46:304-305

23 Perez Ferriols A, Aliaga Boniche A. Photoallergic eczema caused by sunscreens in a 12-year-old girl. Contact Dermatitis 2000;43:229-230

24 Parry EJ, Bilsland D, Morley WN. Photocontact allergy to 4-tert,buty-4'-methoxy-dibenzoylmethane (Parsol 1789). Contact Dermatitis 1995;32:251-252

25 Buckley DA, O'Sullivan D, Murphy GM. Contact and photocontact allergy to dibenzoylmethanes and contact allergy to methylbenzylidene camphor. Contact Dermatitis 1993;29:47

26 Goldermann R, Vardarman E, Neumann N, Scharffetter-Kochanek K, Goerz G. Contact dermatitis from UV-A and UV-B filters in a patient with erythropoietic protoporphyria. Contact Dermatitis 1993;28:300-301

27 De Groot AC, Weyland JW. Contact allergy to butyl methoxydibenzoylmethane. Contact Dermatitis 1987;16:278

28 Pigatto PD, Legori A, Bigardi AS, Guarrera M, Tosti A, Santucci B, et al. Gruppo Italiano recerca dermatiti da contatto ed ambientali Italian multicenter study of allergic contact photodermatitis: epidemiological aspects. Am J Contact Dermatitis 1996;17:158-163

29 Que SK, Brauer JA, Soter NA, Cohen DE. Chronic actinic dermatitis: an analysis at a single institution over 25 years. Dermatitis 2011;22:147-154

30 Lenique P, Machet L, Vaillant L, Bensaid P, Muller C, Khallouf R, Lorette G. Contact and photocontact allergy to oxybenzone. Contact Dermatitis 1992;26:177-181

31 Motley RJ, Reynolds AJ. Photocontact dermatitis due to isopropyl and butyl methoxy dibenzoylmethanes (Eusolex 8020 and Parsol 1789). Contact Dermatitis 1989;21:109-110

32 Crowe MJ, Banks SL, Guin JD. Photoallergic and allergic contact dermatitis to butyl-methoxydibenzoylmethane. Am J Cont Derm 1992;3:33-34

33 Theeuwes M, Degreef H, Dooms-Goossens A. Para-aminobenzoic acid (PABA) and sunscreen allergy. Am J Cont Derm 1992;3:206-207

34 Crouch RB, Foley PA, Baker CS. The results of photopatch testing 172 patients to sunscreening agents at the photobiology clinic, St Vincent's Hospital, Melbourne. Australas J Dermatol 2002;43:74

35 Cardoso J, Canelas MM, Gonçalo M, Figueiredo A. Photopatch testing with an extended series of photoallergens: a 5-year study. Contact Dermatitis 2009;60:325-329

36 Rastogi SC. UV filters in sunscreen products – a survey. Contact Dermatitis 2002;46:348-351

37 Ricci C, Pazzaglia M, Tosti A. Photocontact dermatitis from UV filters. Contact Dermatitis 1998;38:343-344

38 Haylett AK, Chiang YZ, Nie Z, Ling TC, Rhodes LE. Sunscreen photopatch testing: a series of 157 children. Br J Dermatol 2014;171:370-375

39 Berne B, Ross AM. 7 years experience of photopatch testing with sunscreen allergens in Sweden. Contact Dermatitis 1998;38:61-64

40 English JSC, White IR, Cronin K. Sensitivity to sunscreens. Contact Dermatitis 1987;17:159-162

41 Scalf LA, Davis MDP, Rohlinger AL, Connolly SM. Photopatch testing of 182 patients: A 6-year experience at the Mayo Clinic. Dermatitis 2009;20:44-52

42 Freeman S, Frederiksen P. Sunscreen allergy. Am J Cont Derm 1990;1:240-243

43 Nixon RL, Frowen KE, Lewis AE. Skin reactions to sunscreens. Australas J Dermatol 1997;38:S83-S85.

44 Kerr A, Ferguson J. Photoallergic contact dermatitis. Photodermatol Photoimmunol Photomed 2010;26:56-65

45 Wahie S, Lloyd JJ, Farr PM. Sunscreen ingredients and labelling: a survey of products available in the U.K. Clin Exp Dermatol 2007;32:359-364

46 Collaris E, Frank J. Photoallergic contact dermatitis caused by ultraviolet filters in different sunscreens. Int J Dermatol 2008;47:35-37

47 Schmidt T, Ring J, Abeck D. Photoallergic contact dermatitis due to combined UVB (4-methylbenzylidene camphor/octyl methoxycinnamate) and UVA (benzophenone-3/butyl methoxydibenzoylmethane) absorber sensitization. Dermatology 1998;196:354-357

48 Stitt WZ, Scott GA, Martin RE, Gaspari AA. Multiple chemical sensitivities, including iatrogenic allergic contact dermatitis, in a patient with chronic actinic dermatitis: implications for management. Am J Contact Dermat 1996;7:166-170

49 Kerr AC. A survey of the availability of sunscreen filters in the U.K. Clin Exp Dermatol 2011;36:541-543

50 Heurung AR, Raju SI, Warshaw EM. Adverse reactions to sunscreen agents: epidemiology, responsible irritants and allergens, clinical characteristics, and management. Dermatitis 2014;25:289-326

51 Heurung AR, Raju SI, Warshaw EM. Contact allergen of the year. Benzophenones. Dermatitis 2014;25:3-10 (contains many mistakes; Erratum in Dermatitis 2014;25:92-95)

52 Avenel-Audran M. Sunscreen products: finding the allergen. Eur J Dermatol 2010;20:161-166

53 Scheuer E, Warshaw E. Sunscreen allergy: a review of epidemiology, clinical characteristics, and responsible allergens. Dermatitis 2006;17:3-11

54 Funk JO, Dromgoole SH, Maibach HI. Sunscreen intolerance: contact sensitization, photocontact sensitization, and irritancy of sunscreen agents. Dermatol Clin 1995;13:473-481

55 Dromgoole SH, Maibach HI. Sunscreening agent intolerance: Contact and photocontact sensitization and contact urticaria. J Am Acad Dermatol 1990;22:1068-1078

56 Freeman S, Stephens R. Cheilitis: Analysis of 75 cases referred to a contact dermatitis clinic. Am J Cont Dermat 1999;10:198-200

57 De Groot AC, Bruynzeel DP, Bos JD, van der Meeren HL, van Joost T, Jagtman BA, Weyland JW. The allergens in cosmetics. Arch Dermatol 1988;124:1525-1529

58 De Groot AC. Adverse reactions to cosmetics. PhD Thesis, University of Groningen, The Netherlands: 1988, chapter 3.4, pp.105-113

59 De Groot AC. Contact allergy to cosmetics: Causative ingredients. Contact Dermatitis 1987;17:26-34

60 Scheman A, Jacob S, Katta R, Nedorost S, Warshaw E, Zirwas M, et al. Part 2 of a 4 part series. Hair cosmetics: trends and alternatives. Data from the American Contact Alternative Group. J Clin Aesthet Dermatol 2011;4:42-46

61 Scheman A, Jacob S, Katta R, Nedorost S, Warshaw E, Zirwas M, et al. Part 4 of a 4 part series. Miscellaneous products: trends and alternatives in deodorants, antiperspirants, sunblocks, shaving products, powder, and wipes. Data from the American Contact Alternative Group. J Clin Aesthet Dermatol 2011;4:35-39

62 Karlsson I, Hillerstrom L, Stenfeldt AL, Mårtensson J, Börje A. Photodegradation of dibenzoylmethanes; potential cause of photocontact allergy to sunscreens. Chem Res Toxicol 2009;22:1881-1892

63 Laguna C, de la Cuadra J, Martín-González B, Zaragoza V, Martínez-Casimiro L, Alegre V. Allergic contact dermatitis to cosmetics. Actas Dermosifiliogr 2009;100:53-60

64 Manová E, von Goetz N, Hauri U, Bogdal C, Hungerbühler K. Organic UV filters in personal care products in Switzerland: A survey of occurrence and concentrations. Int J Hyg Environ Health 2013;216:508-514

65 Valbuena Mesa MC, Hoyos Jiménez EV. Photopatch testing in Bogota (Colombia): 2011–2013. Contact Dermatitis 2016;74:11-17

66 Zaragoza-Ninet V, Blasco Encinas R, Vilata-Corell JJ, Pérez-Ferriols A, Sierra-Talamantes C, Esteve-Martínez A, de la Cuadra-Oyanguren J. Allergic contact dermatitis due to cosmetics: A clinical and epidemiological study in a tertiary hospital. Actas Dermosifiliogr 2016;107:329-336

67 Shaw T, Simpson B, Wilson B, Oostman H, Rainey D, Storrs F. True photoallergy to sunscreens is rare despite popular belief. Dermatitis 2010;21:185-198

68 Simonsen AB, Koppelhus, U, Sommerlund M, Deleuran M. Photosensitivity in atopic dermatitis complicated by contact allergy to common sunscreen ingredients. Contact Dermatitis 2016;74:56-58

69 Macías E, González AM, De Lamas C, Ponce V, Muñoz-Bellido F, Moreno E. Allergic contact dermatitis due to sensitisation to sunscreen in two infants. Allergol Immunopathol (Madr) 2013;41:419-420

70 Kockler J, Robertson S, Oelgemöller M, Davies M, Bowden B, Brittain HG, Glass BD. Butyl methoxy dibenzoylmethane. Profiles Drug Subst Excip Relat Methodol 2013;38:87-111

71 Wang SQ, Tanner PR, Lim HW, Nash JF. The evolution of sunscreen products in the United States- a 12-year cross sectional study. Photochem Photobiol Sci 2013;12:197-202.

72 Shaath NA. Ultraviolet filters. Photochem Photobiol Sci 2010;9:464-469

73 Antoniou C, Kosmadaki MG, Stratigos AJ, Katsambas AD. Sunscreens - what's important to know. J Eur Acad Dermatol Venereol 2008;22:1110-1118

74 Chatelain E, Gabard B. Photostabilization of butyl methoxydibenzoylmethane (avobenzone) and ethylhexyl methoxycinnamate by bis-ethylhexyloxyphenol methoxyphenyl triazine (Tinosorb S), a new UV broadband filter. Photochem Photobiol 2001;74:401-406

75 Schauder S. Adverse reactions to sunscreening agents in 58 patients (part 3). Z Hautkr 1991;66:294-318 (article in German)

76 Schauder S. Survey of the literature on adverse reactions to preparations containing UV filters (1947-1989) (Literaturübersicht über Unverträglichkeitsreaktionen auf lichtfilterhaltige Produkte von 1947 bis 1989). Z Hautkr 1990;65:982-998 (article in German)

2.66 BUTYLPARABEN

IDENTIFICATION

Description/definition	: Butylparaben is the ester of butyl alcohol and *p*-hydroxybenzoic acid, which conforms to the formula shown below
Chemical class(es)	: Esters; phenols
Chemical/IUPAC name	: Butyl 4-hydroxybenzoate
CAS registry number (s)	: 94-26-8
EC number(s)	: 202-318-7
CIR review(s)	: J Am Coll Toxicol 1984;3:147-209; Int J Toxicol 2008;27(Suppl.4):1-82 (access: www.cir-safety.org/ingredients)
SCCS opinion(s)	: SCCS/1514/13 (5); SCCS/1348/10 (6); SCCS/1348/10 (7); SCCP/1183/08 (8); SCCP/1017/06 (9); SCCP/0874/05 (10)
Merck Index monograph	: 2857
Function(s) in cosmetics	: EU: masking; preservative. USA: fragrance ingredients; preservatives
EU cosmetic restrictions	: Regulated in Annex VI/12 bis of the Regulation (EC) No. 1004/2014
Patch testing	: 3.0% pet. (Chemotechnique, SmartPracticeEurope, SmartPracticeCanada); also present in the paraben mix (see there)
Molecular formula	: $C_{11}H_{14}O_3$

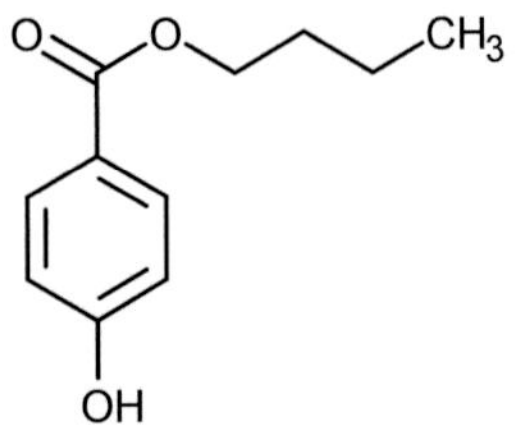

GENERAL

For general information on paraben esters see Chapter 2.333 Paraben mix. The literature on contact allergy to and other information on parabens, in which the ester is not specified ('paraben mix', 'paraben', 'parabens'), is also discussed in that chapter. The literature on contact allergy to butylparaben and other paraben esters from before 1991 has been reviewed in ref. 12. Other, more recent, useful reviews were published in 2005 (parabens) (16), 2004 (17) and 2014 (24) (parabens and other preservatives).

CONTACT ALLERGY

Testing in groups of patients

Routine testing
In 1985, in The Netherlands, 627 consecutive patients suspected of contact dermatitis were patch tested with butylparaben 5% pet. There was one (0.2%) positive reaction, the relevance of which was not mentioned (2).

Testing in groups of selected patients
Between 1971 and 1986, in Denmark, 60 patients previously reacting to the paraben mix (benzyl-, butyl-, ethyl-, methyl- and propylparaben) were tested with all five components at 5% pet. Forty (67%) reacted to one or more of the paraben-esters, most of who reacted to 2 or more. There were 30 reactions (50%) to butylparaben. The relevance of these positive patch test reactions was not mentioned (14).

Case reports and case series
In the period 1996-2013, in a tertiary referral center in Valencia, Spain, 5419 patients were patch tested. Of these, 628 individuals had allergic contact dermatitis to cosmetics. Butylparaben was the responsible allergen in one case (11). A woman reported severe itching and erythema of the face and scalp, with eyelid edema, after using a tar shampoo for the treatment of dandruff. This happened on several occasions, she having initially tolerated the preparation. Patch testing with the European standard series, a facial series, and coal and wood tars gave positive reactions to the paraben mix and balsam of Peru. Further testing with individual components of paraben mix showed positive results to butylparaben, ethylparaben and propylparaben. The ingredient listing of the shampoo included 'parabens'; no specific data on the esters were provided (23).

Contact allergy to butylparaben in non-cosmetic products
One patient probably had ACD from butylparaben (and presumably also other parabens) in topical pharmaceuticals (15). Three patients developed ACD from the application of a corticosteroid cream. They all reacted to the paraben mix. The cream contained butylparaben and methylparaben, but it was not explicitly stated that these paraben-esters were tested separately whether or not they reacted positively (20).

Cross-reactions, pseudo-cross-reactions and co-reactions
Co-reactions with other paraben-esters are seen frequently (12,13,14). As most patients are exposed to more than one paraben, it is difficult to determine whether these co-reactions result from cross-sensitivity or from concomitant sensitization (19). See also this section in Chapter 2.333 Paraben mix.

Presence in cosmetic products and chemical analyses
In the USA, in April 2017, butylparaben was present in 4653 of 56,714 cosmetic products of which the composition is known in FDA's Voluntary Cosmetic Registration Program (VCRP) (data obtained from FDA, May 2017). In February 2017, butylparaben was present in 899 of 64,482 cosmetic products of which the composition is known in EWG's Skin Deep Cosmetics Database, USA (http://www.ewg.org/skindeep/). Butylparaben was present in 3 (6%) of 54 personal hygiene wet wipes for which ingredient information was obtained online and from retail stores, USA, 2016 (26). Butylparaben was present in 6 (3%) of 178 facial wipes for which ingredient information was obtained online and from retail stores, USA, 2016 (25). Of 179 emollients available in Poland in 2014, 15 (8%) contained butylparaben (21). In Germany, in 2006-2009, the labels of 4680 cosmetic products were screened for the presence of preservatives. Butylparaben was present in 18% of the products, according to labeling information (22). Butylparaben was present in 14% of 204 cosmetic products (92 shampoos, 61 hair conditioners, 34 liquid soaps, 17 wet tissues) in Sweden, 2008 (1). Butylparaben was present in 82 of 1774 (4.6%) cosmetics and toiletries in 2002 resp. in 81 of 1170 (6.9%) such products in 2005, filed in the Danish Product Register Database (PROBAS) (3).

In a group of 67 samples of skin creams, randomly selected from retail outlets in Denmark in 1999, 24 (35%) contained butylparaben in a concentration range of 0.003% to 0.100% (4). In the beginning of the 1990s, 215 cosmetic products, 158 leave-on cosmetics and 57 rinse-off cosmetics, from 79 cosmetic-producing companies, collected in Denmark, were analysed for paraben content with high performance liquid chromatography (HPLC) (18).Of all the products investigated, 93% were found to contain paraben(s). Paraben was detected in 77% of the rinse-off products and in 99% of the leave-on products. Total paraben content in the paraben-positive cosmetics was 0.01%-0.59%, except in one sun-lotion that contained 0.87% parabens. Rinse-off cosmetics contained 0.01-0.50% parabens and the paraben content in leave-on products was 0.01-0.59%. Butylparaben was present in 16% of the paraben-positive products in a concentration range of 0.01% to 0.06% (w/w) (18).

LITERATURE

1   Yazar K, Johnsson S, Lind M-L, Boman A, Lidén C. Preservatives and fragrances in selected consumer-available cosmetics and detergents. Contact Dermatitis 2011;64:265-272
2   de Groot AC, Weyland JW, Bos JD, Jagtman BA. Contact allergy to preservatives (I). Contact Dermatitis 1986;14:120-122
3   Flyvholm, MA. Preservatives in registered chemical products. Contact Dermatitis 2005;53:27-32
4   Rastogi SC. Analytical control of preservative labelling on skin creams. Contact Dermatitis 2000;43:339-343
5   SCCS (Scientific Committee on Consumer Safety). Opinion on parabens, SCCS/1514/13, 3 May 2013. Available at: http://ec.europa.eu/health/scientific_committees/consumer_safety/docs/sccs_o_132.pdf
6   SCCS (Scientific Committee on Consumer Safety). Clarification on Opinion SCCS/1348/10 in the light of the Danish clause of safeguard banning the use of parabens in cosmetic products intended for children under three years of age, 10 October 2011. Available at: http://ec.europa.eu/health/scientific_committees/consumer_safety/docs/sccs_o_069.pdf
7   SCCS (Scientific Committee on Consumer Safety). Opinion on parabens, 14 December 2010, SCCS/1348/10. Available at: http://ec.europa.eu/health/scientific_committees/consumer_safety/docs/sccs_o_041.pdf
8   SCCP (Scientific Committee on Consumer Products). Opinion on parabens, 24 June 2008, SCCP/1183/08. Available at: http://ec.europa.eu/health/archive/ph_risk/committees/04_sccp/docs/sccp_o_138.pdf
9   SCCP (Scientific Committee on Consumer Products). Opinion on Parabens, 10 October 2006, SCCP/1017/06. Available at: http://ec.europa.eu/health/archive/ph_risk/committees/04_sccp/docs/sccp_o_074.pdf
10   SCCP (Scientific Committee on Consumer Products). Extended Opinion on Parabens, underarm cosmetics and breast cancer, 28 January 2005, SCCP/0874/05. Available at: http://ec.europa.eu/health/archive/ph_risk/committees/04_sccp/docs/sccp_o_00d.pdf
11   Zaragoza-Ninet V, Blasco Encinas R, Vilata-Corell JJ, Pérez-Ferriols A, Sierra-Talamantes C, Esteve-Martínez A, de la Cuadra-Oyanguren J. Allergic contact dermatitis due to cosmetics: A clinical and epidemiological study in a tertiary hospital. Actas Dermosifiliogr 2016;107:329-336

12 Fransway AF. The problem of preservation in the 1990s: III. Agents with preservative function independent of formaldehyde release. Am J Cont Derm 1991;2:145-174

13 Hjorth N, Trolle-Lassen C. Skin reactions to ointment bases. Trans St John Hosp Derm Soc 1963;49:127-140

14 Menné T, Hjorth N. Routine patch testing with paraben esters. Contact Dermatitis 1988;19:189-191

15 Schorr WF. Paraben allergy. A cause of intractable dermatitis. JAMA 1968;204:859-862

16 Cashman AL, Warshaw EM. Parabens: A review of epidemiology, structure, allergenicity, and hormonal properties. Dermatitis 2005;16:57-66

17 Sasseville D. Hypersensitivity to preservatives. Dermatol Ther 2004;17:251-263

18 Rastogi SC, Schouten A, de Kruijf N, Weijland JW. Contents of methyl-, ethyl-, propyl-, butyl- and benzylparaben in cosmetic products. Contact Dermatitis 1995;32:28-30

19 Hansen J, Møllgaard B, Avnstorp C, Menné T. Paraben contact allergy: Patch testing and in vitro absorption/metabolism. Am J Cont Derm 1993;4:78-86

20 Fisher AA. Cortaid cream dermatitis and the 'paraben paradox'. J Am Acad Dermatol 1982;6:116-117

21 Osinka K, Karczmarz A, Krauze A, Feleszko W. Contact allergens in cosmetics used in atopic dermatitis: analysis of product composition. Contact Dermatitis 2016;75:241-243

22 Uter W, Yazar K, Kratz EM, Mildau G, Lidén C. Coupled exposure to ingredients of cosmetic products: II. Preservatives. Contact Dermatitis 2014;70:219-226

23 Cooper SM, Shaw S. Allergic contact dermatitis from parabens in a tar shampoo. Contact Dermatitis 1998;39:140

24 Yim E, Baquerizo Nole KL, Tosti A. Contact dermatitis caused by preservatives. Dermatitis 2014;25:215-231

25 Aschenbeck KA, Warshaw EM. Allergenic ingredients in facial wet wipes. Dermatitis 2017 Mar 23. doi: 10.1097/DER.0000000000000268. [Epub ahead of print]

26 Aschenbeck KA, Warshaw EM. Allergenic ingredients in personal hygiene wet wipes. Dermatitis 2017 Mar 23. doi: 10.1097/DER.0000000000000275. [Epub ahead of print]

2.67 4-TERT-BUTYLPHENOL

IDENTIFICATION

Description/definition   : 4-*tert*-Butylphenol is the phenol that conform to the formula shown below
Chemical class(es)   : Phenols
INCI name USA   : Not in the Personal Care Products Council Database
Chemical/IUPAC name   : 4-(1,1-Dimethylethyl)phenol
Other names   : *p-tert*-Butylphenol; phenol, 4-(1,1-dimethylethyl); butylphen
CAS registry number (s)   : 98-54-4
EC number(s)   : 202-679-0
Merck Index monograph   : 2825
Function(s) in cosmetics   : EU: prohibited
EU cosmetic restrictions   : Regulated in Annex II/340 of the Regulation (EC) No. 1223/2009 (prohibited)
Patch testing   : 1.0% pet. (Chemotechnique, SmartPracticeEurope)
Molecular formula   : $C_{10}H_{14}O$

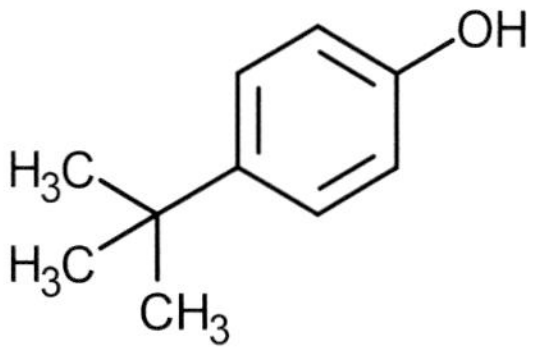

GENERAL

The major use of 4-*tert*-butylphenol is as a monomer in chemical synthesis, e.g. for the production of polycarbonate, phenolic resins, and epoxy resins. In the synthesis of polycarbonate polymers, the chemical is used as a chain termi-nator. 4-*tert*-Butylphenol is probably hardly, if at all (prohibited in the EU) used in cosmetics, and literature on contact allergy to the chemical in other products and on other side effects is not reviewed.

CONTACT ALLERGY

Case reports and case series

A woman presented with a pruriginous dermatitis which had appeared suddenly in the perilabial zone or the mouth. For the few days prior to presentation, she had been using a new lip liner pencil. The dermatitis, which was confined to the lip margins, without involvement of the lips themselves, consisted of vesicles on a slightly erythematous base. Patch testing showed a positive reaction to 4-*tert*-butylphenolformaldehyde resin. Next, 4-*tert*-butylphenol was patch tested at 2% pet., which was positive. Gas chromatography together with mass spectrometry (GC-MS) was used to confirm the presence of this specific hapten in the lip liner. GC-MS analyses of the lip liner pencil and the 4-*tert*-butylphenolformaldehyde resin standard both showed peaks corresponding to 4-*tert*-butylphenol. It was concluded that this established the causative role of this substance in the patient's allergic contact dermatitis (1). Later, both the site of the dermatitis and of the positive patch test to 4-*tert*-butylphenol became depigmented, which is a well-known effect of this chemical (2).

Presence in cosmetic products and chemical analyses

In May 2017, 4-*tert*-butylphenol present in zero of 66,975 cosmetic products of which the composition is known in EWG's Skin Deep Cosmetics Database, USA (http://www.ewg.org/skindeep/). In the USA, in April 2017, 4-*tert*-butylphenol was present in zero of 56,714 cosmetic products of which the composition is known in FDA's Voluntary Cosmetic Registration Program (VCRP) (data obtained from FDA, May 2017).

Other non-eczematous contact reactions

Both the sites of the allergic contact dermatitis and of a positive patch test later became depigmented in one patient allergic to 4-*tert*-butylphenol (1).

LITERATURE

1   Angelini E, Marinaro C, Carrozzo AM, Bianchi L, Delogu A, Giannelo G, Nini G. Allergic contact dermatitis of the lip margins from para-tertiary-butylphenol in a lip liner. Contact Dermatitis 1993;28:146-148
2   Bajaj AK, Gupta SC, Chatterjee AK. Contact depigmentation from free para-tertiary-butylphenol in bindi adhesive. Contact Dermatitis 1990;22:99-102

2.68 BUTYROSPERMUM PARKII (SHEA) BUTTER

IDENTIFICATION

Description/definition   : Butyrospermum parkii butter is the fat obtained from the fruit of the shea tree,
                                Butyrospermum parkii, Sapotaceae
Chemical class(es)   : Fats and oils
INCI name USA   : Butyrospermum parkii (shea) butter
Other names   : Shea butter; karite butter
CAS registry number (s)   : 194043-92-0; 68920-03-6
CIR review(s)   : Final report, March 2011 (access: www.cir-safety.org/ingredients)
Function(s) in cosmetics   : EU: skin conditioning; viscosity controlling. USA: skin-conditioning agents –
                                miscellaneous; skin-conditioning agents – occlusive; viscosity increasing
                                agents - nonaqueous
Patch testing   : No data available; suggested: pure and 30% pet.

CONTACT ALLERGY

Case reports and case series
Butyrospermum parkii (shea) butter was stated to be the (or an) allergen in one patient in a group of 603 individuals suffering from cosmetic dermatitis, seen in the period 2010-2015 in Leuven, Belgium (2). The product was responsible for 4 out of 959 cases of non-fragrance cosmetic allergy where the causal allergen was identified, Belgium, 2000-2010 (1).

Presence in cosmetic products and chemical analyses
In March 2017, Butyrospermum parkii butter was present in 4039 of 64,983 cosmetic products of which the composition is known in EWG's Skin Deep Cosmetics Database, USA (http://www.ewg.org/skindeep/).

LITERATURE
1   Travassos AR, Claes L, Boey L, Drieghe J, Goossens A. Non-fragrance allergens in specific cosmetic products. Contact Dermatitis 2011;65:276-285
2   Goossens A. Cosmetic contact allergens. Cosmetics 2016, 3, 5; doi:10.3390/cosmetics3010005

2.69 CALCIUM LITHOL RED*
* Not an INCI name

IDENTIFICATION

Description/definition : Calcium lithol red is a monoazo color which conforms to the formula shown below
Chemical class(es) : Color additives
INCI name EU : Not in CosIng
INCI name USA : Aka206
Chemical/IUPAC name : 1-Naphthalenesulfonic acid, 2-((2-hydroxy-1-naphthalenyl)azo)-, calcium salt (2:1)
Other names : CI Pigment red 49 Ca salt; CI 15630:2; D&C red no. 11; pigment red 49:2
CAS registry number (s) : 1103-39-5; 1248-18-6
EC number(s) : 214-998-2
Function(s) in cosmetics : USA: not approved in the USA
Patch testing : 5% polyethylene glycol (1)
Molecular formula : $C_{40}H_{26}CaN_4O_8S_2$

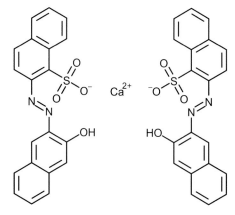

GENERAL

In the Personal Care Products Council Ingredient Database it is stated: 'To identify the colorant allowed for use in the European Union (EU), the INCI Name CI 15630 must be used'. However, this is sodium 2-[(2-hydroxy-naphthyl)-azo]naphthalenesulphonate, not the calcium salt. This color, which is used in the EU as colorant, is not allowed in cosmetics in the USA.

CONTACT ALLERGY

Patch testing in groups of patients
Of 38 Japanese patients with pigmented cosmetic dermatitis, patch tested and photopatch tested with coal tar dyes in 1975-1976, 8 had positive patch tests to calcium lithol red. It was not mentioned (and probably unknown) whether this color was present in the cosmetics used by the patients (1).

Cross-reactions, pseudo-cross-reactions and co-reactions
Other coal tar dyes (1).

Presence in cosmetic products and chemical analyses
In March 2017, calcium lithol red was present in zero of 64,983 cosmetic products of which the composition is known in EWG's Skin Deep Cosmetics Database, USA (http://www.ewg.org/skindeep/).

Photosensitivity
Of 38 Japanese patients with pigmented cosmetic dermatitis, patch tested and photopatch tested with coal tar dyes in 1975-1976, one had a positive photopatch test to calcium lithol red. It was not mentioned (and probably un-known) whether this color was present in the cosmetics used by the patients (1).

LITERATURE
1   Sugai T, Takahashi Y, Tagaki T. Pigmented cosmetic dermatitis and coal tar dyes. Contact Dermatitis 1977;3:249-256

2.70 CALENDULA OFFICINALIS EXTRACT

IDENTIFICATION

Description/definition	: Calendula officinalis extract is the extract of the whole plant of the calendula, *Calendula officinalis* L., Compositae
	: Calendula officinalis flower extract is the extract of the flowers of the calendula, *Calendula officinalis* L., Compositae
Chemical class(es)	: Botanical products and botanical derivatives
Other names	: Marigold extract
CAS registry number (s)	: 84776-23-8
EC number(s)	: 283-949-5
CIR review(s)	: Int J Toxicol 2001;20(Suppl.2):13-20; Int J Toxicol 2010;29(Suppl.4):221-243 (access: www.cir-safety.org/ingredients)
Merck Index monograph	: 2985 (Calendula)
Function(s) in cosmetics	: EU: skin conditioning. USA: skin conditioning agents – miscellaneous (extract)
	: EU: masking; perfuming; skin conditioning. USA: fragrance Ingredients; skin-conditioning agents - miscellaneous (flower extract)
Patch testing	: plant ether extract, 10% pet. (3); commercial extract, 10% alc. (6)

GENERAL

The flowers of the herb *Calendula officinalis* provide the crude drug Calendula Flowers (Calendulae Flos). The EU Community herbal monograph recognizes a longstanding traditional use of extracts prepared in various ways for the symptomatic treatment of minor inflammations of the skin, including sunburn, and as an aid in the healing of minor wounds. The flowers are also used to prepare a mouthwash or gargle for treating inflammatory conditions in the mouth and throat (9). Various parts of Calendula officinalis are also used to prepare extracts for use in cosmetic products.

Reactions to *Calendula officinalis* and its products appear to be rare. The literature has been reviewed (7,9). The allergens in this plant of the Compositae family are unknown. However, the flowers have been reported to contain a variety of phenolic acids and phenylpropanoids that have previously been identified from other plants/plant-derived products as sensitizers or elicitors of contact dermatitis. These include vanillic acid, cinnamic acid, ferulic acid, caffeic acid, and a variety of mono-caffeyl and di-caffeyl esters of quinic acid (10).

CONTACT ALLERGY

Patch testing in groups of patients
In Austria, in 2000, 443 consecutive patients suspected of contact allergy were patch tested with a short ether extract of the marigold plant 10% pet. and 9 (2.0%) had a positive patch test reaction. Six of them had previously used ointments containing marigold; one patient had possibly photoallergic contact dermatitis (3).

Case reports and case series
Calendula officinalis extract was responsible for 3 out of 959 cases of non-fragrance cosmetic allergy where the causal allergen was identified, Belgium, 2000-2010 (1). In a group of 119 patients with allergic contact dermatitis from cosmetics, investigated in The Netherlands in 1986-1987, one case was caused by 'calendula extract' in a herbal cosmetic (4,5). An atopic child had contact allergy to 'Calendula officinalis' present in an emollient he used (2).

Contact allergy to Calendula officinalis extract in non-cosmetic products
Of 1032 consecutive patients patch tested with Calendula ointment (containing 10% Calendula extract) in The Netherlands, 2 had a positive reaction. One also reacted to lanolin, which was a major constituent of the ointment. In the other patient, no patch testing with the separate ingredients of the ointment (including the Calendula extract) were performed (8).

Presence in cosmetic products and chemical analyses
In the USA, in April 2017, Calendula officinalis extract was present in 105 of 56,714 cosmetic products of which the composition is known in FDA's Voluntary Cosmetic Registration Program (VCRP) (data obtained from FDA, May 2017). In March 2017, Calendula officinalis extract was present in 127 and Calendula officinalis flower extract in 962 of 64,983 cosmetic products of which the composition is known in EWG's Skin Deep Cosmetics Database, USA (http://www.ewg.org/skindeep/). In the USA, in 2015-2016, 63 diaper wipes and 41 topical diaper preparations from

a large retailer were screened for the presence of potential sensitizers. Calendula officinalis (extract) was found in 4/63 (6%) disposable diaper wipes and in 15/41 (37%) topical diaper preparations (12).

OTHER SIDE EFFECTS

Immediate-type reactions
In older literature from Russia, one patient was described who developed an anaphylactic shock which was ascribed to an infusion (which is an extract) of *Calendula* (11).

LITERATURE

1 Travassos AR, Claes L, Boey L, Drieghe J, Goossens A. Non-fragrance allergens in specific cosmetic products. Contact Dermatitis 2011;65:276-285
2 Mailhol C, Lauwers-Cances V, Rancé F, Paul C, Giordano-Labadie F. Prevalence and risk factors for allergic contact dermatitis to topical treatment in atopic dermatitis: a study in 641 children. Allergy 2009:64:801-806
3 Reider N, Komericki P, Hausen BM, Fritsch P, Aberer W. The seamy side of natural medicines: contact sensitization to arnica (*Arnica montana* L.) and marigold (*Calendula officinalis* L.). Contact Dermatitis 2001;45:269-272
4 De Groot AC, Bruynzeel DP, Bos JD, van der Meeren HL, van Joost T, Jagtman BA, Weyland JW. The allergens in cosmetics. Arch Dermatol 1988;124:1525-1529
5 De Groot AC. Adverse reactions to cosmetics. PhD Thesis, University of Groningen, The Netherlands: 1988, chapter 3.4, pp.105-113
6 De Groot AC. Patch Testing, 3rd Edition. Wapserveen, The Netherlands: acdegroot publishing, 2008 (ISBN 978-90-813233-1-4)
7 Paulsen E. Contact sensitization from Compositae-containing herbal remedies and cosmetics. Contact Dermatitis 2002;47:189-198
8 Bruynzeel DP, van Ketel WG, Young E, van Joost Th, Smeenk G. Contact sensitization by alternative topical medicaments containing plant extracts. Contact Dermatitis 1992;27:278-279
9 Calapai G, Miroddi M, Minciullo PL, Caputi AP, Gangemi S, Schmidt RJ. Contact dermatitis as an adverse reaction to some topically used European herbal medicinal products - part 1: Achillea millefolium-Curcuma longa. Contact Dermatitis 2014;71:1-12
10 Olennikov DN, Kashchenko NI. New isorhamnetin glycosides and other phenolic compounds from *Calendula officinalis*. Chem Nat Compd 2013;49:833-840
11 Goldman II. Anaphylactic shock after gargling with an infusion of Calendula. Klin Med (Mosk) 1974;52:142-143 (article in Russian)
12 Yu J, Treat J, Chaney K, Brod B. Potential allergens in disposable diaper wipes, topical diaper preparations, and disposable diapers: under-recognized etiology of pediatric perineal dermatitis. Dermatitis 2016;27:110-118

2.71 CANDELILLA CERA

IDENTIFICATION

Description/definition   : Candelilla cera is the extract of the wax obtained from the candelilla, *Euphorbia cerifera*, Euphorbiaceae
Chemical class(es)   : Waxes
INCI name USA   : Euphorbia cerifera (candelilla) wax
Other names   : Candelilla wax; Euphorbia antisyphilitica wax
CAS registry number (s)   : 8006-44-8
EC number(s)   : 232-347-0
CIR review(s)   : J Am Coll Toxicol 1984;3:1-41 (access: www.cir-safety.org/ingredients)
Merck Index monograph   : 3011
Function(s) in cosmetics   : EU: emollient; film forming. USA: cosmetic astringents; emulsion stabilizers; film formers; fragrance ingredients; skin-conditioning agents - miscellaneous; skin-conditioning agents - occlusive; viscosity increasing agents - nonaqueous
Patch testing   : 10% paraffin (1); 10% pet. (2); pure (3)

GENERAL

Candelilla wax is a natural vegetable wax obtained by boiling the leaves of the candelilla shrub and stems with diluted sulfuric acid, and the resulting 'cerote' is skimmed from the surface and further processed. The product may be obtained from several species of Euphorbiacea; the primary sources are *Euphorbia cerifera* and *Euphorbia antisyphilitica*, which are native to northern Mexico and the southwest of the United States. Candelilla cera is mostly used mixed with other waxes to harden them. As a food additive, it has the E number E-902, and is used as a glazing agent. Because of its emollient properties, as well as its shine, candelilla wax appears as an ingredient in many cosmetic formulas, where it is used to thicken lipstick, lip balm, eyeliner, and mascara, but it may also be present in protective creams, pomades, glosses, and lotions. Other products in which candelilla wax could be included are polishes for wood, leather, lubricants, adhesives, paper coating and sizing, chewing gum base, and candles. Candelilla wax consists of a mixture of mainly hydrocarbons, esters of higher molecular weight, free acids, and resins (1).

CONTACT ALLERGY

Case reports and case series

In a group of 146 patients patch tested for cheilitis in Amersham, UK, between 1982 and 2001, there were two positive patch test reactions to candelilla wax considered to be relevant for the lip dermatitis. Over half of the reactions in the entire group were ascribed to lipsticks and lip salves (4). Three patients had contact cheilitis from contact allergy to candelilla cera in lipsticks / lip balms (1,2,3).

Presence in cosmetic products and chemical analyses

In the USA, in April 2017, Euphorbia cerifera (candelilla) wax was present in 1841 of 56,714 cosmetic products of which the composition is known in FDA's Voluntary Cosmetic Registration Program (VCRP) (data obtained from FDA, May 2017). In March 2017, candelilla cera (Euphorbia cerifera [candelilla] wax) was present in 1715 of 64,983 cosmetic products of which the composition is known in EWG's Skin Deep Cosmetics Database, USA (http://www.ewg.org/skindeep/).

LITERATURE

1   Barrientos N, Abajo P, Moreno de Vega M, Domínguez J. Contact cheilitis caused by candelilla wax contained in lipstick. Contact Dermatitis 2013; 69:126-127
2   Tan BB, Noble AL, Roberts ME, Lear JT, English JSC. Allergic contact dermatitis from oleyl alcohol in lipstick cross-reacting with ricinoleic acid in castor oil and lanolin. Contact Dermatitis 1997;37:41-42
3   De Darko E, Osmundsen PE. Allergic contact dermatitis to Lipcare® lipstick. Contact Dermatitis 1984;11:46
4   Strauss RM, Orton DI. Allergic contact cheilitis in the United Kingdom: a retrospective study. Am J Contact Dermat 2003;14:75-77

2.72 CAPRYLHYDROXAMIC ACID

IDENTIFICATION

Description/definition	: Caprylhydroxamic acid is the organic compound that conforms to the formula shown below
Chemical class(es)	: Amides
Chemical/IUPAC name	: *N*-Hydroxyoctanamide
Other names	: Octanohydroxamic acid; octanamide, *N*-hydroxy-
CAS registry number (s)	: 7377-03-9
EC number(s)	: 230-936-7
Merck Index monograph	: 8109 (octanohydroxamic acid)
Function(s) in cosmetics	: EU: chelating. USA: chelating agents
Patch testing	: 1% pet. (either as caprylhydroxamic acid or its potassium salt)
Molecular formula	: $C_8H_{17}NO_2$

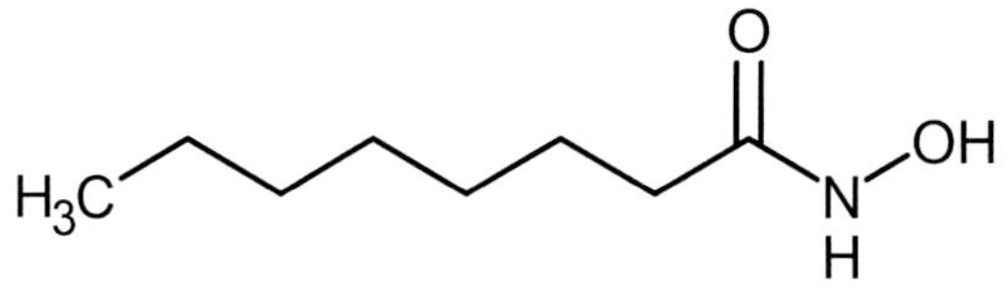

Case reports and case series

At the beginning of 2014, the parabens in three moisturizers of one brand used widely in Finland for the management of atopic dermatitis and other dry skin conditions were replaced with a new preservative: a mixture of phenoxyethanol, caprylhydroxamic acid and methylpropanediol. At the beginning of 2016, several Finnish dermatologists reported suspected cases of allergic contact dermatitis after the use of these moisturizers. Consequently, in February 2016 the products were recalled from the Finnish market. The new preservative mixture was suspected early on to be the cause of the skin reactions, as it was the only new component in the new formulas of the moisturizers (1).

The symptoms of patients with suspected allergic contact dermatitis appeared as acute, itchy, often sharply demarcated erythematous eczema of the exposed areas. Some patients were hospitalized because of widespread severe eczema or severe localized eczema of the face, hands, or legs. The symptoms improved after discontinuation of the use of the suspected products.

Thirty-nine patients were investigated in 4 university hospitals in Finland. Patch tests were performed with the new formula products (containing the suspected preservative mixture), old formula products containing parabens, 2 products containing only phenoxyethanol as preservative, and an oily cream without any preservatives, all tested 'as is'. In addition, the patients were tested with the preservative mixture 1.5%, 0.5%, 0.15% and 0.05% pet., caprylhydroxamic acid or its potassium salt in a dilution series or 3.2% to 0.001%, phenoxyethanol 1%, methylpropanediol, the baseline series, a preservatives series and a skin treatment series. There were positive reactions to the new formula products, the preservative mixture, its ingredient caprylhydroxamic acid (tested as caprylhydroxamic acid or its potassium salt), but not to the products preserved with parabens, phenoxyethanol or without preservatives; also, methylpropanediol and phenoxyethanol showed negative reactions. Patch tests in control subjects were negative. The patch test reactivities to caprylhydroxamic acid and to its potassium salt were similar in intensity with all concentrations. The optimum test concentration appeared to be 1% (1).

Presence in cosmetic products and chemical analyses

In August 2017, caprylhydroxamic acid (termed octanohydroxamic acid) was present in 242 of 70,678 cosmetic products of which the composition is known in EWG's Skin Deep Cosmetics Database, USA (http://www.ewg.org/skindeep/).

LITERATURE

1 Ackermann L, Virtanen H, Korhonen L, Laukkanen A, Huilaja L, Riekki R, Hasan T. An epidemic of allergic contact dermatitis caused by a new allergen, caprylhydroxamic acid, in moisturizers. Contact Dermatitis 2017;77:159-162

2.73 CAPRYLIC/CAPRIC TRIGLYCERIDE

IDENTIFICATION

Description/definition : Caprylic/capric triglyceride is the mixed triester of glycerin and caprylic and capric acids
Chemical class(es) : Fats and oils
Chemical/IUPAC name : 11-(2,3-Dihydroxypropoxycarbonyl)heptadecanoate
Other names : Decanoic acid, ester with 1,2,3-propanetriol octanoate; glycerides, mixed decanoyl and octanoyl; glyceryl caprylate-caprate
CAS registry number (s) : 73398-61-5; 65381-09-1
EC number(s) : 277-452-2; 265-724-3
CIR review(s) : J Environ Pathol Toxicol 1980;4:105-120 (access: www.cir-safety.org/ingredients)
Function(s) in cosmetics : EU: masking; perfuming; skin conditioning. USA: fragrance ingredients; skin-conditioning agents - occlusive; solvents
Patch test allergens : 1% pet. (1)

CONTACT ALLERGY

Case reports and case series

A woman had eczema of her face and arms, possibly exacerbated by sunlight. Previous patch testing had shown contact allergy to colophonium and a doubtful reaction to fragrance. The patient was now patch tested with the British Contact Dermatitis Society standard series (excluding colophonium), preservatives, a cosmetics series, a photopatch test series and the patient's own cosmetics. Day (D)2 and D4 readings showed a definite positive reaction to her cucumber moisturizing lotion. Subsequently, she was patch tested to the individual ingredients of the lotion. She reacted to 1% caprylic/capric triglyceride at both D2 and D4 and also to the related dicaprylyl maleate. Twenty patients were tested as controls and one was also positive to the lotion. He has not been available for further tests (1).

Cross-reactions, pseudo-cross-reactions and co-reactions

Co-reactivity with or (pseudo)cross-reactivity to or from dicaprylyl maleate (1).

Presence in cosmetic products and chemical analyses

In the USA, in April 2017, caprylic/capric triglyceride was present in 6045 of 56,714 cosmetic products of which the composition is known in FDA's Voluntary Cosmetic Registration Program (VCRP) (data obtained from FDA, May 2017). In March 2017, caprylic/capric triglyceride was present in 3080 of 64,983 cosmetic products of which the composition is known in EWG's Skin Deep Cosmetics Database, USA (http://www.ewg.org/skindeep/).

OTHER SIDE EFFECTS

Other non-eczematous contact reactions

In (somewhat) older literature, caprylic/capric triglyceride has been suspected of being comedogenic, based on the rabbit ear assay (2).

LITERATURE

1   Laube S, Davies MG, Prais L, Foulds IS. Allergic contact dermatitis from medium-chain triglycerides in a moisturizing lotion. Contact Dermatitis 2002;47:171
2   Lanzet M. Comedogenic effects of cosmetic raw materials. Cosmetics & Toiletries 1986;101:63-72

2.74 CAPRYLOYL SALICYLIC ACID

IDENTIFICATION

Description/definition : Caprloyl salicylic acid is the ester of salicylic acid and caprylic acid; its structural formula is shown below
Chemical class(es) : Carboxylic acids; esters
Chemical/IUPAC name : 2-Hydroxy-5-octanoylbenzoic acid
Other names : 5-Octanoylsalicylic acid; 2-Hydroxy-5-(1-oxooctyl)benzoic acid
CAS registry number (s) : 78418-01-6
CIR review(s) : Int J Toxicol 2003;22(Suppl.3):1-108 (access: www.cir-safety.org/ingredients)
Function(s) in cosmetics : EU: skin conditioning. USA: skin-conditioning agents - miscellaneous
Patch testing : 1% alcohol (2)
Molecular formula : $C_{15}H_{20}O_4$

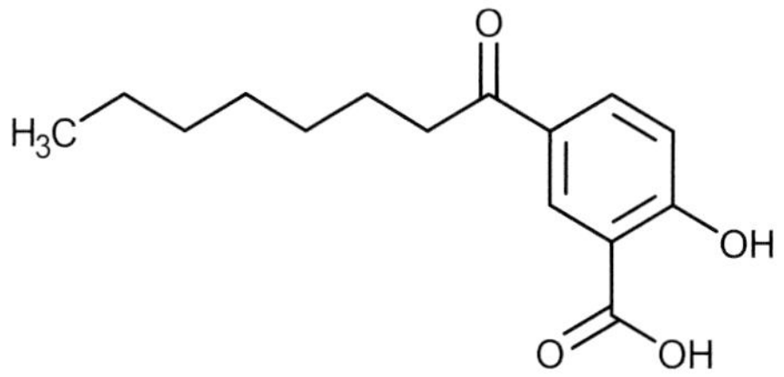

GENERAL

Caprloyl salicylic acid was developed in the late 1980s, and has appeared in the literature under various names. Studies have indicated that this lipophilic derivative of salicylic acid may have the potential to increase cell renewal in the epidermis, stimulate dermal collagen formation, counteract the effects of chronic cutaneous photodamage, increase the skin's resistance to ultraviolet-induced damage, and have comedolytic, anti-acne, antibacterial, antidandruff, and anti-inflammatory activity (2).

In the database of the Personal Care Products Council (the former Cosmetic, Toiletry and Fragrance Association) (4), caprloyl salicylic acid is described as the ester of salicylic acid and caprylic acid (synonym: octanoic acid). A structural formula is not provided, but $C_{19}H_{20}O_4$ is indicated as the empirical formula, which is incorrect, as caprylic acid and salicylic acid combined have 15 C atoms (4). In CosIng, the European Commission database with information on cosmetic substances, caprloyl salicylic acid is defined with the CAS no. 70424-62-3 and benzoic acid, 2-octanoyloxy- (= 2-octanoyloxybenzoic acid, o-octanoyloxybenzoic acid) as a synonym (5). In the CAS Scifinder database (3), this number indeed indicates caprloyl salicylic acid with the following synonyms: benzoic acid, 2-[(1-oxooctyl)oxy]-; octanoic acid, ester with salicylic acid; o-octanoyloxybenzoic acid (3). The CosIng, CAS and Personal Care Products Council descriptions of caprloyl salicylic acid appear all to be incorrect.

CONTACT ALLERGY

Case reports and case series

A woman presented with dermatitis of the face that had started 3 months earlier. She was advised to stop the use of her cosmetic products, and was treated with a corticosteroid cream, after which the facial eruption quickly subsided. Patch tests were performed with the European baseline series, a cosmetic series, and her personal cosmetic products. There were positive reactions to both a day and a night cream of the same brand and type, tested undiluted. Later, the patient was again patch tested with these cosmetic products and with their ingredients, obtained from the manufacturer. The night cream again gave positive reactions, as did the day cream. In addition, there were positive patch test reactions to caprloyl salicylic acid 1% in alcohol, which was tested twice, as it was present in both creams. There was no reaction to caprloyl glycol 1% pet. or to any other ingredient. The patient has remained free of dermatitis since stopping the use of these products (2).

Another woman, seen by the same authors, reacted to a night cream of the same brand and proved to be allergic to its ingredient caprloyl salicylic acid. The manufacturer of these products was informed of these results, but the request for some more caprloyl salicylic acid material for the performance of control tests was declined (2). However, Spanish investigators, who reported a case of allergic contact dermatitis from caprloyl salicylic acid in an anti-wrinkle cream, performed controls tests with caprloyl salicylic acid 1% in alcohol (obtained from the manufacturer also producing the cosmetics of the 2 patients described above) in 15 individuals, with negative results (6).

Cross-reactions, pseudo-cross-reactions and co-reactions
Not to capryloyl glycol 1% pet. (2)

Presence in cosmetic products and chemical analyses
In the USA, in April 2017, capryloyl salicylic acid was present in 98 of 56,714 cosmetic products of which the composition is known in FDA's Voluntary Cosmetic Registration Program (VCRP) (data obtained from FDA, May 2017). In March 2017, capryloyl salicylic acid was present in 69 of 64,983 cosmetic products of which the composition is known in EWG's Skin Deep Cosmetics Database, USA (http://www.ewg.org/skindeep/). In 2014, EWG's Skin Deep Cosmetics Database had indicated its presence in 52 products whose formulas were on file, mostly facial moisturizers, anti-ageing preparations, acne treatment products, sunscreens, and facial cleansers. All these cosmetics at that time were from French manufacturers (2).

Other information
According to some authors, capryloyl salicylic acid (5-capryloyl salicylic acid) may not itself be a sensitizer, but can contain an allergenic impurity, 3-capryloyl salicylic acid, at levels that can vary from sample to sample, that is responsible for the sensitization observed (1).

LITERATURE
1   Roberts DW, Aptula AO. Contact allergy to capryloyl salicylic acid: a mechanistic chemistry and structure–activity perspective. Contact Dermatitis 2015;72:347-351
2   De Groot AC, Rustemeyer T, Hissink D, Bakker M. Contact allergy to capryloyl salicylic acid. Contact Dermatitis 2014;71:185-187
3   CAS Scifinder. Available (for subscribers) at: http://www.cas.org/products/scifinder
4   Personal Care Products Council on-line Infobase. Available (for subscribers) at: http://www.personalcarecouncil.org/science-safety/line-infobase
5   European Commission, Health and Consumers. Cosing database with information on cosmetic substances. Available at: http://ec.europa.eu/consumers/cosmetics/cosing/index.cfm?fuseaction=search.simple
6   González-Pérez R, Carnero-González L, Martínez-González MI. Allergic contact dermatitis due to capryloyl salicylic acid. Actas Dermosifiliogr 2016;107:694-695

2.75 CAPRYLYL GALLATE

IDENTIFICATION

Description/definition   : Caprylyl gallate is the organic compound that conforms to the formula shown below
Chemical class(es)   : Esters; phenols
Chemical/IUPAC name   : Benzoic acid, 3,4,5-trihydroxy-, octyl ester
Other names   : Octyl 3,4,5-trihydroxybenzoate; octyl gallate
CAS registry number (s)   : 1034-01-1
EC number(s)   : 213-853-0
Function(s) in cosmetics : EU: antioxidant. USA: antioxidants
Patch testing   : 0.25% pet. (Chemotechnique); 0.3% pet. (SmartPracticeEurope, SmartPracticeCanada);
                            1% pet. may cause irritant reactions (10)
Molecular formula   : $C_{15}H_{22}O_5$

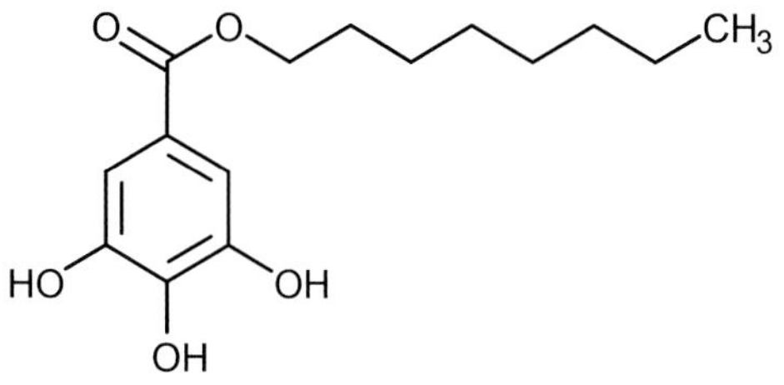

GENERAL

Gallates are antioxidants which, when added in small quantities, retard or prevent oxidation; they have been in use since 1947. The most commonly used gallic acid esters are propyl, octyl (= caprylyl) and dodecyl (= lauryl) gallate, which differ from each other in terms of the length of their side chain. Propyl gallate and other gallates are widely used as antioxidants in the cosmetic industry (creams, lotions, and lipsticks; only propyl gallate), food industry (bakery goods, frying oils, soups, sauces, chewing gum, and potato chips), and in pharmaceutical and industrial products (eardrops, suppositories, and transformer oils) (29,30). Gallates are potential allergens (moderate to strong sensitizers in animal experiments [29]), but relatively few cases of contact dermatitis due to gallates have been reported to date (19). The low rates of sensitization has been explained by oral tolerance (30).

In this chapter the more commonly used and better known name octyl gallate is used instead of caprylyl gallate. An extensive review of the literature on contact allergy to gallates has been published in 2017 (31).

CONTACT ALLERGY

Patch testing in groups of patients
Results of studies patch testing octyl gallate in consecutive patients suspected of contact dermatitis (routine testing) and in groups of selected patients are shown in table 2.75.1. In one study performing routine testing with octyl gallate, there were 8/599 (1.3%) positive reactions, but their relevance was not mentioned (14). In groups of *selected* patients (patients with stasis dermatitis / leg ulcers, patients suspected of cosmetic allergy, patients with periorbital dermatitis, patients with contact cheilitis), frequencies of sensitization to octyl gallate have ranged from 1.1% to 16%, most being 2-3% (table 2.75.1). The high frequency of 15% was seen in a group of 41 patients with allergic contact cheilitis, of who 6 reacted to octyl gallate (gallates are frequently present in lipsticks and lip balms, though most often propyl gallate) (27). The highest sensitization rate (16%) was observed in a US study among 75 patients tested with 'skin care product allergens', but the selection procedure was not explained. Relevance was high (11/12, 92%), but this included 'questionable' and 'past' relevance and causative products were not mentioned (32).

A high prevalence (12.1%) was also observed in patients with burning mouth syndrome. A number of these patients improved significantly after avoiding gallates in foods and lipsticks (20). In most other studies, no relevance rates were provided or specified for individual allergens tested, in those that did, they ranged from 7% (24) to 100% (27).

Case reports and case series
In the period 1996-2013, in a tertiary referral center in Valencia, Spain, 5419 patients were patch tested. Of these, 628 individuals had allergic contact dermatitis to cosmetics. Octyl gallate was the responsible allergen in six cases (25, overlap with ref. 23). In the period 2000-2007, 202 patients with allergic contact dermatitis caused by cosmetics

were seen in Valencia, Spain. In this group, 9 individuals reacted to octyl gallate from its presence in lipsticks (23, overlap with ref. 25; it is odd that there were more reactions in the period 2000-2007 than in the period 1996-2013).

Table 2.75.1 Patch testing in groups of patients

Years and Country	Test conc. & vehicle	Number of patients tested | positive (%)		Selection of patients (S); Relevance (R); Comments (C)	Ref.
Routine testing					
2003-2005 China		599	8 (1.3%)	R: not stated	14
Testing in groups of selected patients					
2003-2014 IVDK	0.3% pet.	4756	(2.3%)	S: patients with stasis dermatitis / chronic leg ulcers; R: not stated	28
2008-2012 Canada	0.3% pet.	132	16 (12.1%)	S: patients with burning mouth syndrome; R: 74% relevance for all allergens together	20
2003-2012 IVDK		1718	30 (1.7%)	S: nurses with occupational contact dermatitis; R: not stated	1
2010-2011 Korea	0.25% pet.	584	13 (2.2%)	S: patients suspected of allergic cosmetic dermatitis; R: not stated	16
2006-2011 IVDK	0.3% pet.	7772	(2.5%)	S: patients suspected of cosmetic intolerance and tested with an ointment base series (selection procedure not stated); R: not stated	26
2001-2011 USA	0.25% pet.	41	6 (15%)	S: patients with allergic contact cheilitis; R: 6/6 relevant	27
2001-2010 Australia	0.25% pet.	2541	168 (6.6%)	S: not stated; R: 7%	24
2000-2010 IVDK		3407	95 (2.8%)	S: patients with periorbital dermatitis; R: not stated	2
2004-2008 France	0.3% pet.	423	10 (2.4%)	S: patients with leg ulcers; R: not stated	13
2000-2007 USA	0.25% pet.	75	12 (16%)	S: patients tested with 'skin care product allergens', select-ion procedure unknown; R: 92%; C: weak study: a. high rate of macular erythema and weak reactions; b. relevance figures included 'questionable' and 'past' relevance	32
1985-2006 Spain	1% pet. & 0.25% pet.	1173	27 (2.3%)	S: patients tested with a preservative and cosmetic series or with a bakery series (n=69); R: of 46 patients reacting to one or more gallates (propyl, octyl, dodecyl), 35 had relevant reactions; 29 were caused by cosmetics, of which 24 were lip products causing allergic contact cheilitis; there were 7 relevant reactions to octyl gallate in bakery products	19
1993-2003 IVDK	0.3% pet.	735	16 (2.2%)	S: patients with scalp dermatitis; R: not stated	15
1997-2000 Israel		244	6 (2.5%)	S: patients suspected of cosmetic dermatitis; R: 64% of all patch test reactions in the cosmetic series was relevant	22
1995-1999 IVDK	0.3% pet.	705	(4.2%)	S: patients with allergic periorbital contact dermatitis; R: not stated	21
1990-1994 Germany	0.3% pet.	3460	38 (1.1%)	S: patients tested with a preservative series; R: not stated	12

IVDK: Information Network of Departments of Dermatology, Germany, Austria, Switzerland

In a group of 119 patients with allergic contact dermatitis from cosmetics, investigated in The Netherlands in 1986-1987, one case was caused by octyl gallate in a lip cream (17,18). A woman had cheilitis and perioral dermatitis from contact allergy to octyl gallate in a lipstick (3).

Out of 7 patients with cheilitis and tested with various gallates, there were 4 reactions to octyl gallate. The authors did not specify the causative products (except that one had also a positive reaction to a sunblock lipstick), but did describe the 7 cases as 'allergic contact dermatitis from lip preparations used for cosmetic and sunscreening purposes' (8).

Contact allergy to octyl gallate from non-cosmetic products
One worker in the food industry had occupational ACD from octyl gallate in margarine (5). Contact allergy to octyl gallate in products such as margarine, fats, soups, sauces, cakes and pastries was the cause of itching and tingling of the palate and swelling of the lip in one individual (6, also mentioned in ref. 7). A production worker in the food industry had extensive airborne ACD from mixing propyl gallate powder with heated chicken fat (9). Another individual working in the food industry developed occupational ACD from octyl gallate, which he mixed with peanut butter (11).

Cross-reactions, pseudo-cross-reactions and co-reactions

Dodecyl gallate (4); not to propyl- and dodecyl gallate (3,8). Of 46 patients allergic to gallates, 16 (35%) reacted to more than one gallate (propyl, octyl, dodecyl) (19). In animal experiments, cross-reactions occurred when the difference between the sensitizing compound and the related gallate was 4 or less carbon atoms (29).

Presence in cosmetic products and chemical analyses

In the USA, in April 2017, caprylyl gallate was present in zero of 56,714 cosmetic products of which the composition is known in FDA's Voluntary Cosmetic Registration Program (VCRP) (data obtained from FDA, May 2017). In May 2017, caprylyl gallate was present in zero of 66,669 cosmetic products of which the composition is known in EWG's Skin Deep Cosmetics Database, USA (http://www.ewg.org/skindeep/).

OTHER SIDE EFFECTS

Miscellaneous side effects

Contact allergy to octyl gallate, present in foods, has been linked with Melkersson–Rosenthal syndrome (4).

LITERATURE

1 Molin S, Bauer A, Schnuch A, Geier J. Occupational contact allergy in nurses: results from the Information Network of Departments of Dermatology 2003–2012. Contact Dermatitis 2015;72:164-171

2 Landeck L, John SM, Geier J. Periorbital dermatitis in 4779 patients – patch test results during a 10-year period. Contact Dermatitis 2014;70:205-212

3 Giordano-Labadie F, Schwarze HP, Bazex J. Allergic contact dermatitis from octyl gallate in lipstick. Contact Dermatitis 2000;42:51

4 Wong GAE, Shear NH. Melkersson–Rosenthal syndrome associated with allergic contact dermatitis from octyl and dodecyl gallates. Contact Dermatitis 2003;,49:266-267

5 Burckhardt W, Fierz U. Antioxidantien in der Margarine als Ursache von Gewerbeekzemen. Dermatologica 1964;129:431-432

6 Pemberton M, Yeoman CM, Clark A, Craig GT, Franklin CD, Gawkrodger DJ. Allergy to octyl gallate causing stomatitis. Br Dent J 1993;175:106-108

7 Lewis FM, Shah M, Gawkrodger DJ. Contact sensitivity to food additives can cause oral and perioral symptoms. Contact Dermatitis 1995;33:429-430

8 Serra-Baldrich E, Puig LL, Arnau AG, Camarasa JG. Lipstick allergic contact dermatitis from gallates. Contact Dermatitis 1995;32:359-360

9 De Groot A C, Gerkens F. Occupational airborne contact dermatitis from octyl gallate. Contact Dermatitis 1990;23:184-186

10 Bojs G, Nicklasson B, Svensson A. Allergic contact dermatitis to propyl gallate. Contact Dermatitis 1987;17:294-298

11 Van Ketel WG. Dermatitis from octyl gallate in peanut butter. Contact Dermatitis 1978;4:60-61

12 Schnuch A, Geier J, Uter W, Frosch PJ. Patch testing with preservatives, antimicrobials and industrial biocides. Results from a multicentre study. Br J Dermatol 1998;138:467-476

13 Barbaud A, Collet E, Le Coz CJ, Meaume S, Gillois P. Contact allergy in chronic leg ulcers: results of a multicentre study carried out in 423 patients and proposal for an updated series of patch tests. Contact Dermatitis 2009;60:279-287

14 Li L-F, Liu G, Wang J. Patch test in Chinese patients with cosmetic allergic contact dermatitis to common cosmetic allergens from a European cosmetic series. Contact Dermatitis 2007;57:50-54

15 Hillen U, Grabbe S, Uter W. Patch test results in patients with scalp dermatitis: analysis of data of the Information Network of Departments of Dermatology. Contact Dermatitis 2007;56:87-93

16 Lee SS, Hong DK, Jeong NJ, Lee JH, Choi YS, Lee AY, et al. Multicenter study of preservative sensitivity in patients with suspected cosmetic contact dermatitis in Korea. J Dermatol 2012;39:677-681

17 De Groot AC, Bruynzeel DP, Bos JD, van der Meeren HL, van Joost T, Jagtman BA, Weyland JW. The allergens in cosmetics. Arch Dermatol 1988;124:1525-1529

18 De Groot AC. Adverse reactions to cosmetics. PhD Thesis, University of Groningen, The Netherlands: 1988, chapter 3.4, pp.105-113

19 García-Melgares ML, de la Cuadra J, Martín B, Laguna C, Martínez L, Alegre V. Sensitization to gallates: review of 46 cases. Actas Dermosifiliogr 2007;98:688-693

20 Lynde CB, Grushka M, Walsh SR. Burning mouth syndrome: patch test results from a large case series. J Cutan Med Surg 2014;18:174-179

21   Herbst RA, Uter W, Pirker C, Geier J, Frosch PJ. Allergic and non-allergic periorbital dermatitis: patch test results of the Information Network of the Departments of Dermatology during a 5-year period. Contact Dermatitis 2004;51:13-19

22   Trattner A, Farchi Y, David M. Cosmetics patch tests: first report from Israel. Contact Dermatitis 2002;47:180-181

23   Laguna C, de la Cuadra J, Martín-González B, Zaragoza V, Martínez-Casimiro L, Alegre V. Allergic contact dermatitis to cosmetics. Actas Dermosifiliogr 2009;100:53-60

24   Toholka R, Wang Y-S, Tate B, Tam M, Cahill J, Palmer A, Nixon R. The first Australian Baseline Series: Recommendations for patch testing in suspected contact dermatitis. Australas J Dermatol 2015;56:107-115

25   Zaragoza-Ninet V, Blasco Encinas R, Vilata-Corell JJ, Pérez-Ferriols A, Sierra-Talamantes C, Esteve-Martínez A, de la Cuadra-Oyanguren J. Allergic contact dermatitis due to cosmetics: A clinical and epidemiological study in a tertiary hospital. Actas Dermosifiliogr 2016;107:329-336

26   Dinkloh A, Worm M, Geier J, Schnuch A, Wollenberg A. Contact sensitization in patients with suspected cosmetic intolerance: results of the IVDK 2006-2011. J Eur Acad Dermatol Venereol 2015;29:1071-1081

27   O'Gorman SM, Torgerson RR. Contact allergy in cheilitis. Int J Dermatol 2016;55:e386-e391

28   Erfurt-Berge C, Geier J, Mahler V. The current spectrum of contact sensitization in patients with chronic leg ulcers or stasis dermatitis - new data from the Information Network of Departments of Dermatology (IVDK). Contact Dermatitis 2017 Feb 14. doi: 10.1111/cod.12763. [Epub ahead of print]

29   Hausen BM, Beyer W. The sensitizing capacity of the antioxidants propyl, octyl and dodecyl gallate and some related gallic acid esters. Contact Dermatitis 1992;26:253-258

30   Perez A, Basketter DA, White IR, McFadden J. Positive rates to propyl gallate on patch testing: a change in trend. Contact Dermatitis 2008;58:47-48

31   Holcomb ZE, Van Noord MG, Atwater AR. Gallate contact dermatitis: product update and systematic review. Dermatitis 2017;28:115-127

32   Wetter DA, Yiannias JA, Prakash AV, Davis MD, Farmer SA, el-Azhary RA, et al. Results of patch testing to personal care product allergens in a standard series and a supplemental cosmetic series: an analysis of 945 patients from the Mayo Clinic Contact Dermatitis Group, 2000-2007. J Am Acad Dermatol 2010;63:789-798

2.76 CAPTAN

IDENTIFICATION

Description/definition	: Captan is the organic compound that conforms to the formula shown below
Chemical class(es)	: Halogen compounds; heterocyclic compounds
Chemical/IUPAC name	: 2-(Trichloromethylsulfanyl)-3a,4,7,7a-tetrahydroisoindole-1,3-dione
CAS registry number (s)	: 133-06-2
EC number(s)	: 205-087-0
CIR review(s)	: J Am Coll Toxicol 1989;8:643-680 (access: www.cir-safety.org/ingredients)
Merck Index monograph	: 3044
Function(s) in cosmetics	: EU: formerly used as antimicrobial; delisted in 1990. USA: cosmetic biocides; preservatives
EU cosmetic restrictions	: Regulated in Annex II/370 of the Regulation (EC) No. 1223/2009 (prohibited)
Patch testing	: 0.5% pet. (Chemotechnique)
Molecular formula	: $C_9H_8Cl_3NO_2S$

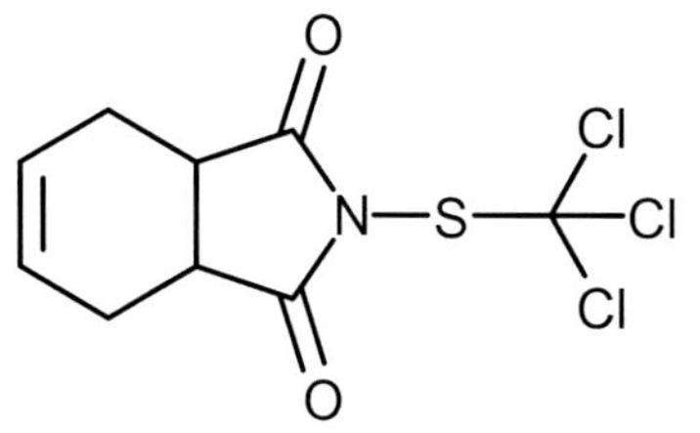

GENERAL

Captan was formerly used in cosmetics as an antimicrobial agent / preservative, but has been prohibited in the EU for nearly 30 years and is apparently hardly, if at all, used anymore in cosmetics in the USA. However, it was and is still used as a pesticide in agriculture, and has caused and may occasionally cause allergic contact dermatitis (sometimes airborne [16]) in farmers and agricultural workers (3,10,14) or gardeners and greenhouse workers (15); photocontact dermatitis has rarely been observed (4,13). The literature from before 1991 on allergy to captan has been reviewed (11). Discussion of contact allergy to and other side effects of captan in this chapter is limited to those caused by its presence in cosmetic products.

CONTACT ALLERGY

Patch testing in groups of patients
Results of patch testing captan in successive patients suspected of contact dermatitis (routine testing) and in groups of selected patients are shown in table 2.76.1. In early USA and international (ICDRG) studies, prevalences of sensitization of 3-5% have been observed (6,11,12). However, relevance rates were either zero or below 20% and the ICDRG thought that all reactions to captan, which was tested at 1% in petrolatum, were due to irritation (12). In three studies testing captan in groups of selected patients (hairdressers with hand eczema and patients tested with a hairdressing series), high prevalences of sensitization were observed in the USA (7) and in Taiwan (8). In the latter series, no relevance was found, in the USA study, apparently 6 of the 15 reactions (40%) were relevant (7). In a study from the UK, performed between 1999 and 2004, the frequency of relevant reactions was only 0.8% (9). It is surprising to find any such reactions, though, as captan had already been banned from cosmetics in the EU 10 years earlier.

Case reports and case series
Captan was responsible for 2 out of 399 cases of cosmetic allergy where the causal allergen was identified in a study of the NACDG, USA, 1977-1983 (1). A hairdresser was presented with occupational ACD from captan and many hair dyes. The authors could not identify a precise source of captan, but 'we think that the patient was probably sensitized by its presence as a bacteriostat in shampoos used in hairdressing' (2). A similar patient had previously been observed, but here, also, a definite source for the positive patch test to captan could not be identified; a second positive test to captan ruled out a false-positive reaction due to the excited skin syndrome (5).

Table 2.76.1 Patch testing in groups of patients

Years and Country	Test conc. & vehicle	Number of patients tested | positive (%)		Selection of patients (S); Relevance (R); Comments (C)	Ref.
Routine testing					
<1980 ICDRG	1% pet.	509	16 (3.1%)	R: 0%; C: all positive reactions were thought to have been caused by irritation	12
<1991 USA	1% pet.	2329	112 (4.8%)	R: <20%	11
1975-6 USA, Canada	1% pet.	?	(4.9%)	R: not stated; C: the number of patients tested was not specified, but was in the 900-2000 range	6
Testing in groups of selected patients					
2000-2008 USA	0.5% pet.	208	15 (7.2%)	S: patients tested with a hairdresser's series; R: 40%	7
1999-2004 UK		483	4 (0.8%)	S: patients tested with the hairdressing series; R: only reactions that were of current or past relevance were collected	9
1994 Taiwan	1% pet.	98	6 (6%)	S: hairdressers with hand eczema; R: not stated, but the authors mentioned that 'captan was used *in the past* in shampoos'	8

Presence in cosmetic products and chemical analyses

In the USA, in April 2017, captan was present in 1 of 56,714 cosmetic products of which the composition is known in FDA's Voluntary Cosmetic Registration Program (VCRP) (data obtained from FDA, May 2017). In April 2017, captan was present in zero of 65,521 cosmetic products of which the composition is known in EWG's Skin Deep Cosmetics Database, USA (http://www.ewg.org/skindeep/).

LITERATURE

1   Adams RM, Maibach HI, Clendenning WE, Fisher AA, Jordan WJ, Kanof N, et al. A five-year study of cosmetic reactions. J Am Acad Dermatol 1985;13:1062-1069
2   Aguirre A, Manzano D, Zabala R, Ratón JA, Pérez JLD. Contact allergy to captan in a hairdresser. Contact Dermatitis 1994;31:46
3   Fregert S. Allergic contact dermatitis from the pesticides captan and phaltan. Contact Dermatitis Newsletter 1967;2:28
4   Epstein S. Photoallergic contact dermatitis: report of case due to Dangard. Cutis 1968;4:856
5   Vilaplana J, Romaguera C. Captan, a rare contact sensitizer in hairdressing. Contact Dermatitis 1993;29:107
6   Rudner EJ. North American Group Results. Contact Dermatitis 1977;3:208-209
7   Wang MZ, Farmer SA, Richardson DM, Davis MDP. Patch-testing with hairdressing chemicals. Dermatitis 2011;22:16-26
8   Guo YL, Wang BJ, Lee JY, Chou SY. Occupational hand dermatoses of hairdressers in Tainan City. Occup Environ Med 1994;51:689-692
9   Katugampola RP, Statham BN, English JSC, Wilkinson MM, Foulds IS, Green CM, Ormerod AD, et al. A multicentre review of the hairdressing allergens tested in the UK. Contact Dermatitis 2005;53:130-132
10 Verma G, Sharma NL, Shanker V, Mahajan VK, Tegta GR. Pesticide contact dermatitis in fruit and vegetable farmers of Himachal Pradesh (India). Contact Dermatitis 2007;57:316-320
11 Fransway AF. The problem of preservation in the 1990s. III. Agents with preservative function independent of formaldehyde release. Am J Contact Derm 1991;2:145-174
12 Cronin E. Pesticides. In: Contact Dermatitis. Churchill Livingstone: Edinburgh, London, New York, 1980: 391-413
13 Mark KA, Brancaccio RR, Soter NA, Cohen DE. Allergic contact and photoallergic contact dermatitis to plant and pesticide allergens. Arch Dermatol 1999;135:67-70
14 Lisi P, Caraffini S, Assalve D. Irritation and sensitization potential of pesticides. Contact Dermatitis 1987;17:212-218
15 Paulsen E. Occupational dermatitis in Danish gardeners and greenhouse workers (II). Etiological factors. Contact Dermatitis 1998;38:14-19
16 Dooms-Goossens AE, Debusschere KM, Gevers DM, Dupré KM, Degreef HJ, Loncke JP, Snauwaert JE. Contact dermatitis caused by airborne agents. A review and case reports. J Am Acad Dermatol 1986;15:1-10

2.77 CERA ALBA

IDENTIFICATION

Description/definition	: Cera alba is the wax obtained from the honeycomb of the bee, *Apis mellifera* L.
Chemical class(es)	: Waxes
INCI name USA	: Beeswax
Other names	: Beeswax; cera alba/cera flava; yellow/white beeswax
CAS registry number (s)	: 8012-89-3
EC number(s)	: 232-383-7
CIR review(s)	: J Am Coll Toxicol 1984;3:1-41 (access: www.cir-safety.org/ingredients)
Merck Index monograph	: 2289
Function(s) in cosmetics	: EU: emollient; emulsifying; film forming; perfuming. USA: emulsion stabilizers; film formers; fragrance ingredients; skin-conditioning agents - emollient
Patch testing	: 30% pet. (4); 20% pet. (7); 20 controls were negative to yellow beeswax pure, but being a natural product, the composition of such substance can differ considerably depending on the source (9)

The EU INCI system also has an entry termed '**Beeswax**', which largely seems to overlap with cera alba:

IDENTIFICATION (CosIng)

Description/definition	: Beeswax is the purified wax from the honeycomb of the bee, *Apis mellifera*, free from all other waxes
Other names	: Beeswax absolute; beeswax concrete; beeswax, white (*Apis mellifera* L.); bleached beeswax; cera alba (EU); white beeswax; white wax; yellow wax
CAS registry number (s)	: 8006-40-4; 8012-89-3
EC number(s)	: 232-383-7
Function(s) in cosmetics	: Binding; emulsion stabilising; masking; skin conditioning; viscosity controlling

GENERAL

Beeswax is secreted by bees from their abdominal wax glands; it is then masticated and a salivary solvent is added so as to form hexagonal scales once dry. Beeswax is a complex material containing more than 300 constituents. It consists for two-thirds of myricyl palmitate, cerotic acid and esters, 14% hydrocarbons of the alkane family, of 12% free fatty acids, of free alcohols and various other substances including 50 aroma compounds. Residues of pollen, propolis and brood alter the initial white color of beeswax into yellow (5,16). Wax production depends not only on the age of the bees but also on how much honey is produced and on the temperature inside the hive (16).

Yellow beeswax is the purified wax obtained from the honeycomb of the bee. White beeswax is derived from yellow beeswax by a bleaching process. Contact sensitization to beeswax appears to be rare (8), most reported cases being a consequence of (presumed) contamination with propolis (3,4,8,17). Beeswax may sometimes be mistaken for bee *glue* (propolis, propolis cera) (7). Beeswax is used in cosmetics, as a food additive (E901), as a coating and glazing agent (mostly for fresh fruits and candy), to make wax and varnish for wood and leather, in topical pharmaceuticals (18) and to make candles (9,16).

CONTACT ALLERGY

Patch testing in groups of patients

Results of studies patch testing cera alba / beeswax in consecutive patients suspected of contact dermatitis (routine testing) and in groups of selected patients are shown in table 2.77.1. In routine testing (one study found), 13 of 2828 (0.5%) patients reacted to beeswax 10% pet. There were 10 reactions to yellow and 3 to white beeswax. Two reactions were of current and 3 of past relevance, but the causative products were not mentioned (3). Two studies have patch tested beeswax in patients with cheilitis (13,14). In one of these investigations (13), an incredible 16% had positive reactions, but these were both reactions to beeswax and to propolis, the latter of which will undoubtedly have caused the majority. In an Italian study, the reactions to beeswax in 2 patients were considered relevant, but causative products were not mentioned (14).

Table 2.77.1 Patch testing in groups of patients

Years and Country	Test conc. & vehicle	Number of patients tested | positive (%)		Selection of patients (S); Relevance (R); Comments (C)	Ref.
Routine testing					
2007-2008 (?) UK	10% pet.	2828	13 (0.5%)	C: 10 reactions to yellow beeswax, 3 to white beeswax; R: 2 current relevance, 3 past, 7 uncertain, 1 due to cross-sensitivity to other allergens; C: 4 co-reactions (31%) to propolis; responsible products not mentioned	3
Testing in groups of selected patients					
2009-2016 Sweden	pure	94	15 (16%)	S: patients suspected of having contact allergic cheilitis, eczema around the lips or contact allergy to products containing beeswax; R: not stated; C: the 15 patients reacted to propolis and/or to beeswax (not specified); caffeic acid and its esters were not important sensitizers in beeswax	13
2001-2006 Italy	30% pet.	129	2 (2%)	S: patients with chronic cheilitis; R: 2 reactions were relevant	14

Case reports and case series

Beeswax was responsible for 1 out of 399 cases of cosmetic allergy where the causal allergen was identified in a study of the NACDG, USA, 1977-1983 (1). Three positive patch test reactions to cera alba were ascribed to cosmetic allergy (2). A young girl suffering from atopic dermatitis was seen because of an intensely itchy acute cheilitis that had developed one week after using an emollient lip formulation. Clinical examination revealed erythema and vesicles on and around her lips. Patch tests with the GIRDCA standard series and the lip formulation showed a positive reaction to the lip cream at D4; propolis was negative. Later, patch tests were performed with the individual ingredients of the lip cream and the patient now reacted to beeswax 30% pet. at D2 and D4 (4).

An atopic woman had a serious flare-up of dermatitis of the face and neck with pronounced cheilitis. Patch tests with the European standard series and her own products gave a positive reaction to her lip balm. When tested with its ingredients, the patient now reacted to cera alba, and during this, she experienced a flare-up of eczema on the face and hands. Ceasing the use of the lip balm resulted in clearing of her skin condition, except that she still had dry and chapped lips regularly. It was later found that the patient frequently ate wine gum and that these were coated with cera alba. When this type of candy was avoided, the cheilitis cleared completely. Later, the patient was tested again, and now she had positive patch tests to propolis 10% pet., to cera alba 20% and cera flava 30% in pet. Patch testing again resulted in a flare-up of dermatitis of the hands (7).

A woman had dermatitis of the eyelids. She had a positive patch test to propolis. The patient used a lip gloss containing beeswax and the authors concluded that daily application of this lip gloss using her fingers implicated 'propolis in beeswax' as the relevant allergen (ectopic contact dermatitis) (15). It is uncertain whether the authors suggested that the beeswax was contaminated with propolis (for which they offered no evidence nor did they explicitly mention this possibility) or that they were unaware of the difference between propolis (bee *glue*) and beeswax. Another female patient had perioral eczema from cera alba present in lip balms (19).

Contact allergy to cera alba in non-cosmetic products

Two patients were allergic to beeswax in adhesive plaster (11, cited in ref. 10). A woman moulding figures from beeswax had occupational allergic contact dermatitis and reacted strongly to the product. It is very likely that the material was contaminated with propolis (bee glue), but propolis itself was not tested (12). A woman with non-Hodgkin B-cell lymphoma had a 3-year history of a recurrent itchy widespread rash presenting as confluent erythematous and scaly plaques of the scalp, ears, chest, axillae, back, abdomen, upper arms, and thighs. Lesional skin suggested mycosis fungoides. Treatment with triamcinolone cream and narrowband UVB phototherapy over 2 years relieved itching but not the rash. Patch tests were positive to *Myroxylon pereirae* and propolis. *Myroxylon pereirae* was judged relevant, given her known sensitivity to fragrance-containing skin care products. Propolis was also relevant because her hobby was glass beading, in which she manually lubricated the wire with beeswax. Avoidance of fragrance-containing products and of glass beading resolved her dermatitis (15). It is uncertain whether the authors suggested that the beeswax was contaminated with propolis (for which they offered no evidence nor did they explicitly mention this possibility) or that they were unaware of the difference between propolis (bee *glue*) and beeswax.

A woman had allergic contact dermatitis from a nipple protective made of beeswax. A commercial beeswax gave a positive reaction, but the patient had extreme contact allergy to propolis and many of its constituents, so the beeswax was highly likely contaminated with propolis, which would then be the actual allergen (17).

Cross-reactions, pseudo-cross-reactions and co-reactions
Propolis cera (approx. 30%, ref. 3); of 5 patients allergic to propolis, four co-reacted to beeswax (6); cera flava (9); propolis (9).

Presence in cosmetic products and chemical analyses
In the USA, in April 2017, beeswax was present in 3083 of 56,714 cosmetic products of which the composition is known in FDA's Voluntary Cosmetic Registration Program (VCRP) (data obtained from FDA, May 2017). In April 2017, beeswax (USA INCI name of cera alba) was present in 3562 of 66,647 cosmetic products of which the composition is known in EWG's Skin Deep Cosmetics Database, USA (http://www.ewg.org/skindeep/).

LITERATURE
1   Adams RM, Maibach HI, Clendenning WE, Fisher AA, Jordan WJ, Kanof N, et al. A five-year study of cosmetic reactions. J Am Acad Dermatol 1985;13:1062-1069
2   Kohl L, Blondeel A, Song M. Allergic contact dermatitis from cosmetics: retrospective analysis of 819 patch-tested patients. Dermatology 2002;204:334-337
3   Rajpara S, Wilkinson MS, King CM, Gawkrodger DJ, English JS, Statham BN, et al. The importance of propolis in patch testing: a multicentre survey. Contact Dermatitis 2009;61:287-290
4   Lucente P, Cavalli M, Vezzani C, Orlandi C, Vincenzi C. Contact cheilitis due to beeswax. Contact Dermatitis 1996;35:258
5   Bogdanov S. Quality and standards of pollens and beeswax. Apiacta 2004;38:334-341
6   Rudzki E, Grzywa Z. Dermatitis from propolis. Contact Dermatitis 1983;9:40-45
7   Jensen CD, Andersen KE. Allergic contact dermatitis from cera alba (purified propolis) in a lip balm and candy. Contact Dermatitis 2006;55:312-313
8   Junghans V, Geier J, Fuchs Th. Allergy to propolis caused by beeswax-containing ointment. Am J Cont Derm 2002;13:87
9   Nyman G, Hagvall L. A case of allergic contact cheilitis caused by propolis and honey. Contact Dermatitis 2016;74:186-187
10 García M, del Pozo MD, Díaz J, Muñoz D, Fernández de Corrés L. Allergic contact dermatitis from a beeswax nipple-protective. Contact Dermatitis 1995;33:440-441
11 Schwartz L, Peck SM. The irritants in adhesive plaster. Public Health Reports 1935;50:811
12 Camarasa G. Occupational dermatitis from beeswax. Contact Dermatitis 1975;1:124
13 Nyman G, Tang M, Inerot A, Hagvall L. Contact allergy to beeswax in patients with cheilitis. Contact Dermatitis 2016;75(Suppl.1):63-64
14 Schena D, Fantuzzi F, Girolomoni G. Contact allergy in chronic eczematous lip dermatitis. Eur J Dermatol 2008;18:688-692
15 Baker L, Litzner B, Le EN, Cruz PD Jr. Ectopic periorbital dermatitis and mycosis fungoides-like dermatitis due to propolis. Dermatitis 2013;24:328-329
16 Pecquet C. Allergic reactions to insect secretions. Eur J Dermatol 2013;23:767-773
17 Garcia M, Del Pozo D, Diez J, Muñoz D, de Corrès LF. Allergic contact dermatitis from a beeswax nipple-protective. Contact Dermatitis 1995;33:440-441
18 Lübbe J, Sanchez-Politta S. Propolis, beeswax, and the sensitization potential of topical calcineurin inhibitors. Clin Exp Dermatol 2006;31:147-148
19 Verheyden M, Rombouts S, Lambert J, Aerts O. Contact allergy to castor oil, but not to castor wax. Cosmetics 2017, 4, 5; doi:10.3390/cosmetics4010005

2.78 CERA MICROCRISTALLINA

IDENTIFICATION

Description/definition	: Cera microcristallina is a complex combination of long, branched chain hydrocarbons obtained from residual oils by solvent crystallization. It consists predominantly of saturated straight and branched chain hydrocarbons mostly greater than C35. It is a wax derived from petroleum and characterized by the fineness of its crystals in contrast to the larger crystals of paraffin wax
Chemical class(es)	: Hydrocarbons; waxes
INCI name USA	: Microcrystalline wax
Other names	: Paraffin waxes and hydrocarbon waxes, microcrystalline
CAS registry number (s)	: 63231-60-7; 64742-42-3
EC number(s)	: 264-038-1; 265-144-0
CIR review(s)	: J Am Coll Toxicol 1984;3:43-99 (access: www.cir-safety.org/ingredients)
Function(s) in cosmetics	: EU: binding; emulsion stabilizing; opacifying; viscosity controlling. USA: binders; bulking agents; emulsion stabilizers; viscosity increasing agents – non-aqueous
Patch testing	: pure and 10% pet. (2)

CONTACT ALLERGY

Case reports and case series

Microcrystalline wax was responsible for 1 out of 399 cases of cosmetic allergy where the causal allergen was identified in a study of the NACDG, USA, 1977-1983 (1).

A man suddenly developed periorbital and facial edema, with simultaneous lesions of the lips and in the nose. He was twice admitted to hospital suspected of having angioedema. On re-admission with less pronounced but identical symptoms, he mentioned that he had a particular lipstick. Patch testing showed positive reactions to the lipstick and to cera microcristallina 10% pet. (2). Another male patient developed a severe dermatitis on the lips and around the mouth. For the previous few days, he had used the same lipstick as the patient described above. Previously, he had used this lipstick at intervals for several months without complaints. Patch testing showed positive reactions to the lipstick and to cera microcristallina 100% (2).

A woman had suffered from dry lips for many years, so she had been using many different lipsticks, including the same lipstick as in the previous two patients without complications until a severe, vesicular dermatitis appeared on the lips and around the mouth. The dermatitis disappeared when she stopped using the lipstick. Since then she had tried using the product twice; in both cases a severe dermatitis developed. Patch testing showed positive reactions to the lipstick and to cera microcristallina 100% (2). All 3 patients had a positive usage test with the product in the elbow flexure. The supplier of the microcrystalline wax was not willing to give information about the composition of this substance, but did change the composition of the lipstick (2).

Presence in cosmetic products and chemical analyses

In the USA, in April 2017, microcrystalline wax was present in 2324 of 56,714 cosmetic products of which the composition is known in FDA's Voluntary Cosmetic Registration Program (VCRP) (data obtained from FDA, May 2017). In March 2017, microcrystalline wax (USA INCI name of cera microcristallina) was present in 992 of 64,983 cosmetic products of which the composition is known in EWG's Skin Deep Cosmetics Database, USA (http://www.ewg.org/skindeep/).

Other non-eczematous contact reactions

In (somewhat) older literature, microcrystalline waxes (cera microcristallina) has been suspected of being comedogenic and causing 'pomade acne' (3).

LITERATURE

1. Adams RM, Maibach HI, Clendenning WE, Fisher AA, Jordan WJ, Kanof N, et al. A five-year study of cosmetic reactions. J Am Acad Dermatol 1985;13:1062-1069
2. De Darko E, Osmundsen PE. Allergic contact dermatitis to Lipcare® lipstick. Contact Dermatitis 1984;11:46
3. Plewig G, Fulton JE, Kligman AM. Pomade acne. Arch Dermatol 1970;101:580-584

2.79 CERESIN

IDENTIFICATION

Description/definition : Ceresin is a complex combination of hydrocarbons produced by the purification of ozokerite with sulfuric acid and filtration through bone black to form waxy cakes
Chemical class(es) : Waxes
Other names : Ceresin wax; ozokerite wax
CAS registry number (s) : 8001-75-0
EC number(s) : 232-290-1
CIR review(s) : J Am Coll Toxicol 1984;3:43-99 (access: www.cir-safety.org/ingredients)
Merck Index monograph : 3256
Function(s) in cosmetics : EU: antistatic; binding; emulsion stabilizing; hair conditioning; opacifying; viscosity controlling. USA: binders; epilating agents; viscosity increasing agents - nonaqueous
Patch testing : 30% pet. (1)

GENERAL

Ceresin is a mineral wax obtained from ozokerite. Its structure is similar to that of paraffin, providing a good level of flexibility, adhesiveness, and water resistance. When chlorinated, ceresin is a useful varnish product, and it is thus commonly used in floor waxes, textiles, and rubber compounds. In its natural form, ceresin is suitable for use in personal care products such as creams, mascara, and lipsticks (1).

CONTACT ALLERGY

Case reports and case series

A woman presented with a 1-year history of recurrent cheilitis of the upper and lower lip. Its onset seemed to coincide with the use of a new lipstick. Patch testing was performed in two separate sessions. First, the patient was tested with the North American Contact Dermatitis Group screening series, additional series (antimicrobials, vehicles, cosmetics, bakers' ingredients), and four of the patient's own products. The patient reacted only to the suspected lipstick, while the other 125 tested allergens remained negative. Later, patch tests were performed with the (unnamed) individual ingredients of the lipstick formulation, provided by the manufacturer. On D2 and D4, there was a positive reaction to the divulged ingredient, called ceresin (tested in 30% pet.). Testing in four control patients was negative (1).

Contact allergy to ceresin in non-cosmetic products

Although rare, there are reports of occupational dermatoses from ceresin, particularly among workers using ceresin-containing varnishes (2, data cited in ref. 1).

Presence in cosmetic products and chemical analyses

In the USA, in April 2017, ceresin was present in 840 of 56,714 cosmetic products of which the composition is known in FDA's Voluntary Cosmetic Registration Program (VCRP) (data obtained from FDA, May 2017). In March 2017, ceresin was present in 347 of 64,983 cosmetic products of which the composition is known in EWG's Skin Deep Cosmetics Database, USA (http://www.ewg.org/skindeep/).

LITERATURE

1   Powell M, Moreau L. Case report: allergic contact cheilitis caused by ceresin wax. Contact Dermatitis 2012;66:46-47
2   Schwartz L, Tulipan L, Birmingham D. Dermatoses caused by resins and waxes. In: Occupational diseases of the skin, 3rd edition. Philadelphia, PA, USA: Lea & Febiger, 1957: 546-549 (data cited in ref. 1)

2.80 CETALKONIUM CHLORIDE

Description/definition   : Cetalkonium chloride is the quaternary ammonium salt that conforms generally to the
                            formula shown below
Chemical class(es)   : Quaternary ammonium compounds
Chemical/IUPAC name   : Benzyl-hexadecyl-dimethylazanium chloride
Other names   : Benzenemethanaminium, *N*-hexadecyl-*N,N*-dimethyl, chloride; cetyl dimethyl benzyl
                            ammonium chloride
CAS registry number (s)   : 122-18-9
EC number(s)   : 204-526-3
Merck Index monograph   : 3286
Function(s) in cosmetics : EU: antimicrobial; antistatic; preservative. USA: antistatic agents; cosmetic biocides
EU cosmetic restrictions : Regulated in Annexes III/65 and V/54 of the Regulation (EC) No. 1223/2009
Patch testing   : 0.1% pet. (SmartPracticeEurope, SmartPracticeCanada)
Molecular formula   : $C_{25}H_{46}ClN$

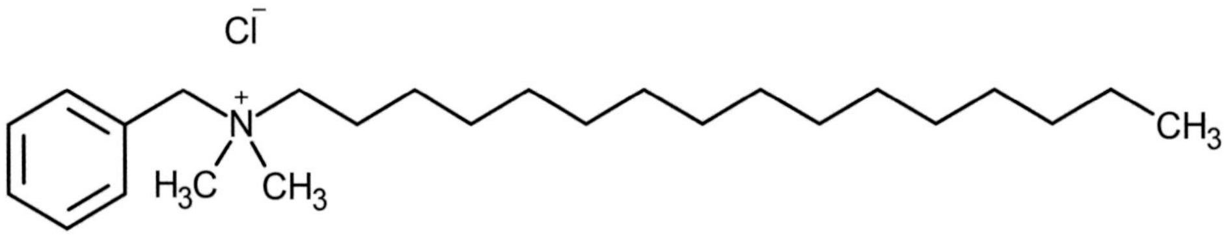

CONTACT ALLERGY

Patch testing in groups of patients

Between 1990 and 1994, in Germany, Austria and Switzerland, 11,237 selected patients suspected of contact dermatitis were tested with a preservative series containing cetalkonium chloride 0.1% pet. There were 26 positive reactions, but their relevance was not mentioned (3).

Case reports and case series

A man had axillary dermatitis. When patch tested, he reacted to a roll-on deodorant he had used for years. Upon cessation of the use of the deodorant, the dermatitis cleared rapidly. Because of lack of cooperation by the manufacturer, the patient could not be tested with all ingredients. The deodorant contained cetalkonium chloride. As this component was not available for testing, a patch test was performed with the related quaternary ammonium compound benzalkonium chloride 0.1%, which was positive. Therefore, contact allergy to cetalkonium chloride in the deodorant was likely, but not proven (1).

Contact allergy to cetalkonium chloride in non-cosmetic products

Three patients had periocular allergic contact dermatitis from cetalkonium chloride in ophthalmic preparations (2).

Cross-reactions, pseudo-cross-reactions and co-reactions

Benzalkonium chloride (4).

Presence in cosmetic products and chemical analyses

In the USA, in April 2017, cetalkonium chloride was present in zero of 56,714 cosmetic products of which the composition is known in FDA's Voluntary Cosmetic Registration Program (VCRP) (data obtained from FDA, May 2017). In March 2017, cetalkonium chloride was present in zero of 64,983 cosmetic products of which the composition is known in EWG's Skin Deep Cosmetics Database, USA (http://www.ewg.org/skindeep/).

LITERATURE

1   Shmunes E, Levy EJ. Quaternary ammonium compound contact dermatitis from a deodorant. Arch Dermatol 1972;105:91-93
2   Maucher OM. Periorbitalekzem als iatrogene Erkrankung. Klin Monatsbl Augenheilkd 1974;164:350—356
3   Schnuch A, Geier J, Uter W, Frosch PJ. Patch testing with preservatives, antimicrobials and industrial biocides. Results from a multicentre study. Br J Dermatol 1998;138:467-476
4   Haj-Younes L, Sanchez-Politta S, Pasche-Koo F, Denereaz N, Bessire N, Saurat JH, Piletta P. Occupational contact dermatitis to Mikrobac Extra in 8 hospital cleaners. Contact Dermatitis 2006;54:69-70

2.81 CETEARETH-2

IDENTIFICATION

Description/definition	: Ceteareth-2 is the polyethylene glycol ether of cetearyl alcohol that conforms to the formula shown below, where R represents a blend of alkyl groups derived from cetyl and stearyl alcohol and n has an average value of 2
Chemical class(es)	: Alkoxylated alcohols
Other names	: PEG-2 cetyl/stearyl ether; polyethylene glycol 100 cetyl/stearyl ether; polyoxyethylene (2) cetyl/stearyl ether
CAS registry number (s)	: 68439-49-6 (generic for ceteareth's)
EC number(s)	: 500-212-8
CIR review(s)	: Int J Toxicol 1999;18(Suppl.3):41-49; Int J Toxicol 2012;31(Suppl.2):169-244 (access: www.cir-safety.org/ingredients)
Function(s) in cosmetics	: EU: emulsifying; surfactant. USA: surfactants - emulsifying agents
Patch testing	: 20% pet. (1)
Molecular formula	: $R(OCH_2CH_2)_nOH$

CONTACT ALLERGY

Case reports and case series

A woman complained of a relapsing itching dermatitis of the armpits after the use of a 'hypoallergenic' roll-on deodorant. Patch tests with the Italian Baseline Societa Italiana di Dermatologia Allergologica Professionale e Ambientale series, the preservatives and the perfumes series were performed. All tests were negative. A repeated open application test (ROAT) with the patient's deodorant in the antecubital fossa induced an eczematous reaction after 6 days. Further patch tests with all of the ingredients of this product showed positive reactions to myristyl alcohol 5% pet., to ceteareth-2 20% pet. and to ceteareth-3 20% pet. No reactions were observed to ceteareth-20, -25 and -30, which were also ingredients of the deodorant. Allergic contact dermatitis caused by fatty alcohols contained in the deodorant was diagnosed. As ceteareth molecules are composed of cetyl-stearyl alcohol and a variable number of molecules of ethoxylene, for research purposes further patch tests with cetyl alcohol, stearyl alcohol and cetearyl alcohol 30% pet. were performed and they all gave a positive response (1).

Cross-reactions, pseudo-cross-reactions and co-reactions

Ceteareth-3, cetyl alcohol, stearyl alcohol, cetearyl alcohol, myristyl alcohol (1). Not to ceteareth-20, ceteareth-25, and ceteareth-30 (1).

Presence in cosmetic products and chemical analyses

In the USA, in April 2017, ceteareth-2 was present in 5 of 56,714 cosmetic products of which the composition is known in FDA's Voluntary Cosmetic Registration Program (VCRP) (data obtained from FDA, May 2017). In March 2017, ceteareth-2 was present in 5 of 64,983 cosmetic products of which the composition is known in EWG's Skin Deep Cosmetics Database, USA (http://www.ewg.org/skindeep/).

LITERATURE

1   Corazza M, Zauli S, Bianchi A, Benetti S, Borghi A, Virgili A. Contact dermatitis caused by fatty alcohols: may polyethoxylation of the fatty alcohols influence their sensitizing potential? Contact Dermatitis 2013;68:189-190

2.82 CETEARETH-3

IDENTIFICATION

Description/definition	: Ceteareth-3 is the polyethylene glycol ether of cetearyl alcohol that conforms to the formula shown below, where R represents a blend of alkyl groups derived from cetyl and stearyl alcohol and n has an average value of 3
Chemical class(es)	: Alkoxylated alcohols
Other names	: PEG-3 cetyl/stearyl ether; polyethylene glycol (3) cetyl/stearyl ether; polyoxyethylene (3) cetyl/stearyl ether
CAS registry number (s)	: 68439-49-6 (generic for ceteareth's)
CIR review(s)	: Int J Toxicol 1999;18(Suppl.3):41-49; Int J Toxicol 2012;31(Suppl.2):169-244 (access: www.cir-safety.org/ingredients)
Function(s) in cosmetics	: EU: emulsifying; surfactant. USA: surfactants - emulsifying agents
Patch testing	: 20% pet. (1)
Molecular formula	: $R(OCH_2CH_2)_nOH$

CONTACT ALLERGY

Case reports and case series

A woman complained of a relapsing itching dermatitis of the armpits after the use of a 'hypoallergenic' roll-on deodorant. Patch tests with the Italian Baseline Societa Italiana di Dermatologia Allergologica Professionale e Ambientale series, the preservatives and the perfumes series were performed. All tests were negative. A repeated open application test (ROAT) with the patient's deodorant in the antecubital fossa induced an eczematous reaction after 6 days. Further patch tests with all of the ingredients of this product showed positive reactions to myristyl alcohol 5% pet., to ceteareth-3 20% pet. and to ceteareth-2 20% pet. No reactions were observed to ceteareth-20, -25 and -30, which were also ingredients of the deodorant. Allergic contact dermatitis caused by fatty alcohols contained in the deodorant was diagnosed. As ceteareth molecules are composed of cetyl-stearyl alcohol and a variable number of molecules of ethoxylene, for research purposes further patch tests with cetyl alcohol, stearyl alcohol and cetearyl alcohol 30% pet. were performed and they all gave a positive response (1).

Cross-reactions, pseudo-cross-reactions and co-reactions

Ceteareth-2, cetyl alcohol, stearyl alcohol, cetearyl alcohol, myristyl alcohol (1). Not to ceteareth-20, ceteareth-25, and ceteareth-30 (1).

Presence in cosmetic products and chemical analyses

In the USA, in April 2017, ceteareth-3 was present in 9 of 56,714 cosmetic products of which the composition is known in FDA's Voluntary Cosmetic Registration Program (VCRP) (data obtained from FDA, May 2017). In March 2017, ceteareth-3 was present in 3 older products of 64,983 cosmetic products of which the composition is known in EWG's Skin Deep Cosmetics Database, USA (http://www.ewg.org/skindeep/).

LITERATURE

1   Corazza M, Zauli S, Bianchi A, Benetti S, Borghi A, Virgili A. Contact dermatitis caused by fatty alcohols: may polyethoxylation of the fatty alcohols influence their sensitizing potential? Contact Dermatitis 2013;68:189-190

2.83 CETEARYL ALCOHOL

IDENTIFICATION

Description/definition	: Cetearyl alcohol is a mixture of fatty alcohols consisting predominantly of cetyl and stearyl alcohols (C16-C18)
Chemical class(es)	: Fatty alcohols
Chemical/IUPAC name	: Hexadecan-1-ol; octadecan-1-ol
Other names	: Cetostearyl alcohol; cetyl/stearyl alcohol; Lanette® O
CAS registry number (s)	: 8005-44-5; 67762-27-0
EC number(s)	: 267-008-6
CIR review(s)	: J Am Coll Toxicol 1988;7:359-413 (access: www.cir-safety.org/ingredients)
Function(s) in cosmetics	: EU: emollient; emulsifying; emulsion stabilizing; foam boosting; opacifying; surfactant; viscosity controlling. USA: emulsion stabilizers; opacifying agents; surfactants – foam boosters; viscosity increasing agents – aqueous / non-aqueous
Patch testing	: 20% pet. (Chemotechnique, SmartPracticeEurope, SmartPracticeCanada); many positive patch tests are not reproducible (12)
Molecular formula	: $C_{18}H_{38}O.C_{16}H_{34}O$; $CH_3(CH_2)_{15}OH$ (cetyl alcohol); $CH_3(CH_2)_{17}OH$ (stearyl alcohol)

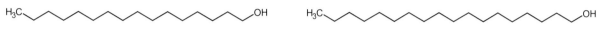

cetyl alcohol   stearyl alcohol

GENERAL

Cetearyl alcohol (or cetostearyl alcohol) is a combination of cetyl and stearyl alcohol which is present in many topical medicaments and cosmetics in which it acts as an emulsifier and stabilizer. Contact allergy from its presence in cosmetics is rare. Allergic contact dermatitis from cetearyl alcohol is almost always associated with a previous alteration of the skin barrier that facilitates its absorption. Therefore, most cases of sensitization result from the use of pharmaceutical preparations containing cetearyl alcohol, notably those used on leg ulcers and stasis dermatitis (13,20,21). It should be realized that many positive patch tests to cetearyl alcohol are not reproducible (12), probably indicating that false-positive reactions may occur with the 20% pet. test material.

CONTACT ALLERGY

General population and subgroups

In 1997-1998 a group of 1141 individuals aged 28-78 year, largely selected on the basis of a positive RAST test or clinical signs of an atopic constitution, was patch tested in Germany with cetearyl alcohol 20% pet. The prevalence of positive patch test reaction in the entire group was 0.8%, in women 1.0% and in men 0.7% (26,27). Estimates of the 10-year prevalence of contact allergy to cetearyl alcohol in the general population of Germany based on the CE-DUR method ranged from 0.2-0.4% (25).

Patch testing in groups of patients

Results of routine patch testing (testing in consecutive patients suspected of contact dermatitis) cetearyl alcohol are shown in table 2.83.1. Results of testing in groups of *selected* patients (e.g., patients with leg ulcers or stasis dermatitis, patients suspected of cosmetic intolerance) are shown in table 2.83.2.

Patch testing groups of patients: routine testing

Data on routine patch testing with cetearyl alcohol back to 1979 are summarized in table 2.83.2. In studies performing routine testing, frequencies of sensitization were usually below 1.5%, most even below 1% (table 2.83.1). In an early study from Germany, 27 of 1101 patients (2.7%) had positive reactions, but cetearyl alcohol was tested pure (which may probably induce some irritant reactions) and the relevance of the positive patch tests was not mentioned (16). Nevertheless, 89% of these patients had leg ulcers and/or stasis dermatitis, a patient group prone to develop contact allergy to materials such as cetyl alcohol, stearyl alcohol, cetearyl alcohol (8,21,37,41) and lanolin alcohol from their presence in topical pharmaceutical products. In the other studies, the relevance of positive reactions was usually not mentioned. In a 2000 study from the UK, 90% of 25 reactions were scored as relevant, but the causative products were not mentioned (17).

Table 2.83.1 Patch testing in groups of patients: Routine testing

Years and Country	Test conc. & vehicle	Number of patients tested | positive (%)		Selection of patients (S); Relevance (R); Comments (C)	Ref.
2009-2012 12 European countries, ESSCA	20% pet.	29,248	(0.9%)	R: not stated	35
2001-2010 Australia	20% pet.	5093	68 (1.3%)	R: 25%	32
2007-2008 Austria	20% pet.	678	(0.9%) [a]	R: not stated	1
2007-2008 Germany	20% pet.	2694	(0.8%) [a]	R: not stated	1
2007-2008 Lithuania	20% pet.	229	(0.9%) [a]	R: not stated	1
2007-08 Switzerland	20% pet.	2402	(1.0%) [a]	R: not stated	1
2007-2008 UK	20% pet.	8909	(0.4%) [a]	R: not stated	1
2004, 11 European countries, ESSCA	20% pet.	5896	(0.5%) [a]	R: not stated	4
2002-2003, 9 European countries, ESSCA	20% pet.	4207	(1.5%)	R: not stated; C: prevalence range per cener: 0.6%-2.1%	19
2000 United Kingdom	20% pet.	3063	25 (0.8%)	R: 90% (current and past relevance in one centre)	17
1986-1987 Finland	20% pet.	1374	11 (0.8%)	R: not stated	2
1979-1983 Finland	20% pet.	3095	22 (0.7%)	R: not stated	2
1977-1979 Germany	pure	1101	27 (2.7%)	R: not stated; C: 24/27 had stasis dermatitis and/or leg ulcers	16

[a] age-standardized and sex-standardized proportions
ESSCA: European Surveillance System on Contact Allergies

Patch testing in groups of selected patients

Data on patch testing with cetearyl alcohol in groups of selected patients back to 1981 are summarized in table 2.83.2. Frequencies of sensitization have ranged from 0.5% to 16%. The three highest rates (16%, 14% and 5.7%) were all seen in groups with leg ulcers or chronic venous insufficiency. Unfortunately, the relevance of the positive patch tests to cetearyl alcohol was mentioned in none of the studies. In a recent German study, it was shown that reactions to cetearyl alcohol are significantly more frequent than in a control group of patients routinely tested (37). Relevance was mentioned in one study only: 3 of 6 reactions in an Italian study were relevant and caused by the same popular antibiotic cream (23).

Table 2.83.2 Patch testing in groups of patients: Selected patient groups

Years and Country	Test conc. & vehicle	Number of patients tested | positive (%)		Selection of patients (S); Relevance (R); Comments (C)	Ref.
2003-2014 IVDK	20% pet.	5202	(4.4%)	S: patients with stasis dermatitis / chronic leg ulcers; R: not stated; C: the percentage of reactions was significantly higher than in a control group of routinely tested patients	37
2006-2011 IVDK	20% pet.	7554	(1.0%)	S: patients suspected of cosmetic intolerance and tested with an ointment base series (selection procedure not stated); R: not stated	34
2004-2008 France	20% pet.	423	24 (5.7%)	S: patients with leg ulcers; R: not stated	20
2000-2002 Finland		8418	(0.5%)	S: patients tested with a cosmetic series; R: not stated	18
2000-2002 Serbia	20% pet.	75	3 (4%)	S: patients with venous leg ulcers and dermatitis of the surrounding skin; R: not stated	36
1995-2002 IVDK		884	(0.5%)	S: female hairdressers with present or past occupational contact dermatitis; R: not specified	24
1996-1997 Germany	30% pet.	36	5 (14%)	S: patients with chronic venous insufficiency; R: not stated	41
1995-1996 Finland		9399	(0.6%)	S: patients tested with a cosmetic series; R: not stated	18
1988-1989 UK		81	13 (16%)	S: patients with leg ulcers; R: not specified	21
1986-1989 Italy	20% pet.	737	6 (0.8%)	S: patients with contact dermatitis apparently related to the use of topical preparations; R: 3 reactions were relevant and caused by the same popular antibiotic cream	23
1977-1981 Germany		2064	80 (3.9%)	S: unknown; R: unknown; C: 85% of the patients allergic to cetearyl alcohol had stasis dermatitis and/or leg ulcer; of this group of patients, 15% reacted to cetearyl alcohol	8

IVDK: Information Network of Departments of Dermatology, Germany, Austria, Switzerland

Case reports and case series

Cetearyl alcohol was responsible for 1 out of 399 cases of cosmetic allergy where the causal allergen was identified in a study of the NACDG, USA, 1977-1983 (3). One patient had allergic contact dermatitis from cetearyl alcohol in a hand cream (10). A woman had allergic contact dermatitis of the face from cetearyl alcohol present in multiple cosmetics she used (33,42). One patient reacted to cetearyl alcohol in 3 moisturizing products from one brand (43).

Contact allergy to cetearyl alcohol in non-cosmetic products

In a group of 31 patients allergic to topical pharmaceutical products, cetearyl alcohol was the allergen or one of the allergens in 6 patients (7). Of 9 patients (of who 7 had leg ulcers) allergic to Lanette cream, a non-proprietary base for topical pharmaceutical preparations, all reacted to cetearyl alcohol 20% pet. (14). Six leg ulcer patients had contact allergy to a pharmaceutical cream containing cetearyl alcohol; (at least) 2 reacted to cetearyl alcohol 20% pet., (at least) one to cetyl alcohol 5% pet. and (at least) 2 to stearyl alcohol 30% pet. (13). Five patients (9) and one more (10) had contact allergy to cetearyl alcohol and many other chemicals, probably from topical corticosteroid preparations.

One patient reacted to cetearyl alcohol in Lanette SX® present in a pharmaceutical cream (6). Cetearyl alcohol in a topical pharmaceutical product caused allergic contact dermatitis in one more individual (11). Two women had allergic contact dermatitis from a pharmaceutical ointment for treating varicose veins and hematomas (39). An unknown number of patients (article not read) had allergic contact dermatitis from cetearyl alcohol in topical anti-mycotic preparations; the authors claim this compound to be one of the most frequent sensitizers in these pharmaceuticals (40). An unknown number of patients (probably 1-3) reacted to cetearyl alcohol in a topical medication (22). A woman had worsening of stasis dermatitis caused by contact allergy to cetearyl alcohol in a corticosteroid cream (42).

Cross-reactions, pseudo-cross-reactions and co-reactions

Lanolin alcohol (10,15,44); Amerchol® L 101 (10); hydrogenated lanolin (10); 'eucerin' (10); lanolin (15); cetyl alcohol (15,16); stearyl alcohol (16). Possibly cross-reactivity from or to ceteareth-2 and/or ceteareth-3; ceteareth molecules are composed of cetearyl alcohol and a variable number of oxyethylene molecules (5).

Presence in cosmetic products and chemical analyses

In June 2017, cetearyl alcohol was present in 3760 of 69,510 cosmetic products of which the composition is known in EWG's Skin Deep Cosmetics Database, USA (http://www.ewg.org/skindeep/). In the USA, in April 2017, cetearyl alcohol was present in 7317 of 56,714 cosmetic products of which the composition is known in FDA's Voluntary Cosmetic Registration Program (VCRP) (data obtained from FDA, May 2017). Cetearyl alcohol was present in 46 (26%) of 178 facial wipes for which ingredient information was obtained online and from retail stores, USA, 2016 (38). In 2009, in the USA, the ingredient lists of 1591 facial cosmetics from one company were screened for the presence of cetearyl alcohol. Cetearyl alcohol was present in 26% of 132 blushers and 38 bronzers, in 28% of 90 concealers, in 18% of 174 eyeliners, in 32% of 304 eyeshadows, in 32% of 457 foundations, in 28% of 140 loose and pressed powders, and in 77% of 256 mascaras (28).

In 2009, in the USA, the ingredient lists of 796 hair products from one company were screened for the presence of cetearyl alcohol. Cetearyl alcohol was present in 36% of 279 shampoos, in 85% of 231 conditioners, and in 22% of 286 styling products (29). In 2009, in the USA, the ingredient lists of 730 lip cosmetics and dental care products from one company were screened for the presence of cetearyl alcohol (derivatives). Cetearyl alcohol (derivatives) were present in 0% of 31 lip liners, in 16% of 429 lipsticks, in 40% of 92 lip moisturizers, in 0% of 153 toothpastes, and in 0% of 25 mouth washes (30). In 2009, in the USA, the ingredient lists of 657 miscellaneous cosmetics from one company were screened for the presence of cetearyl alcohol (derivatives). These were present in 49% of 195 antiperspirants/deodorants, in 5% of 41 powders, in 48% of 167 shaving products, in 27% of 201 sunblocks, and in 4% of 53 wipes (31).

LITERATURE

1   Uter W, Aberer W, Armario-Hita JC, Fernandez-Vozmediano JM, Ayala F, Balato A, et al. Current patch test results with the European baseline series and extensions to it from the 'European Surveillance System on Contact Allergy' network, 2007-2008. Contact Dermatitis 2012;67:9-19
2   Hannuksela M. Skin contact allergy to emulsifiers. Int J Cosmet Sci 1988;10:9-14
3   Adams RM, Maibach HI, Clendenning WE, Fisher AA, Jordan WJ, Kanof N, et al. A five-year study of cosmetic reactions. J Am Acad Dermatol 1985;13:1062-1069
4   ESSCA Writing Group. The European Surveillance System of Contact Allergies (ESSCA): results of patch testing the standard series, 2004. J Eur Acad Dermatol Venereol 2008;22:174-181
5   Corazza M, Zauli S, Bianchi A, Benetti S, Borghi A, Virgili A. Contact dermatitis caused by fatty alcohols: may polyethoxylation of the fatty alcohols influence their sensitizing potential? Contact Dermatitis 2013;68:189-190
6   Milpied B, Collet E, Genillier N, Vigan M. Allergic contact dermatitis caused by sodium dehydroacetate, not hyaluronic acid, in Ialuset® cream. Contact Dermatitis 2011;65:359-361

7   Pecegueiro M, Brandao M, Pinto J, Concalo S. Contact dermatitis to Hirudoid® cream. Contact Dermatitis 1987;17:290-293

8   Keilig W. Kontaktallergie auf Cetylstearylalkohol (Lanette O) als therapeutisches Problem bei Stauungsdermatitis und Ulcus cruris. [English title: Contact allergy to cetylstearyl alcoho! (Lanette O) as a therapeutic problem in stasis dermatitis and leg ulcer]. Derm Beruf Umwelt 1983;51:50-54 (in German).

9   Rademaker M, Wood B, Greig D. Contact dermatitis from cetostearyl alcohol. Australas J Dermatol 1997;38:220-221

10   Marston S. Contact dermatitis from cetostearyl alcohol in hydrocortisone butyrate lipocream and from lanolin. Contact Dermatitis 1991: 24: 372

11   Leow Y-H, Tan CS-C. Allergic contact dermatitis from cetrimide and cetearyl alcohol in Burnol-plus ® cream. Contact Dermatitis 2000;43:174-175

12   Von der Werth JM English JSC, Dalziel KL. Loss of patch test positivity to cetylstearyl alcohol. Contact Dermatitis 1998;38:109-110

13   Dissanayke M, Powell SM. Hioxyl® sensitivity. Contact Dermatitis 1990;22:242-243

14   van Ketel, WG. Allergy to cetylalcohol. Contact Dermatitis 1984;11:125-126

15   van Ketel, WG, Wemer J. Allergy to lanolin and "lanolin-free" creams. Contact Dermatitis 1983;9:420

16   Bandmann H-J, Keilig W. Lanette O—another test substance for lower leg series. Contact Dermatitis 1980;6:227-228

17   Britton JE, Wilkinson SM, English JSC, Gawkrodger DJ, Ormerod AD, Sansom JE, et al. The British standard series of contact dermatitis allergens: validation in clinical practice and value for clinical governance. Br J Dermatol 2003;148:259-264

18   Hasan T, Rantanen T, Alanko K, Harvima RJ, Jolanki R, Kalimo K, et al. Patch test reactions to cosmetic allergens in 1995–1997 and 2000–2002 in Finland –a multicentre study. Contact Dermatitis 2005;53:40-45

19   Uter W, Hegewald J, Aberer W, Ayala F, Bircher AJ, Brasch J, et al. The European standard series in 9 European countries, 2002/2003 –First results of the European Surveillance System on Contact Allergies. Contact Dermatitis 2005;53:136-145

20   Barbaud A, Collet E, Le Coz CJ, Meaume S, Gillois P. Contact allergy in chronic leg ulcers: results of a multicentre study carried out in 423 patients and proposal for an updated series of patch tests. Contact Dermatitis 2009;60:279-287

21   Wilson CC, Cameron J, Powell SM, Cherry G, Ryan TJ. High incidence of contact dermatitis in leg ulcer patients – implications for management. Clin Exp Dermatol 1991;16:250-253

22   Pasche-Koo F, Piletta P-A, Hunziker N, Hauser C. High sensitization rate to emulsifiers in patients with chronic leg ulcers. Contact Dermatitis 1994;31:226-228

23   Tosti A, Guerra L, Morelli R, Bardazzi F. Prevalence and sources of sensitization to emulsifiers: a clinical study. Contact Dermatitis 1990;23:68-72

24   Uter W, Lessmann H, Geier J, Schnuch A. Contact allergy to ingredients of hair cosmetics in female hairdressers and clients: an 8-year analysis of IVDK data. Contact Dermatitis 2003;49:236-240

25   Schnuch A, Uter W, Geier J, Gefeller O (for the IVDK study group). Epidemiology of contact allergy: an estimation of morbidity employing the clinical epidemiology and drug-utilization research (CE-DUR) approach. Contact Dermatitis 2002;47:32-39

26   Schäfer T, Böhler E, Ruhdorfer S, Weigl L, Wessner D, Filipiak B, et al. Epidemiology of contact allergy in adults. Allergy 2001;56:1192-1196

27   Uter W, Ludwig A, Balda BR, Schnuch A, Pfahlberg A, Schäfer T, Wichmann HE, Ring J. The prevalence of contact allergy differed between population-based data and clinic–based data. J Clin Epidemiol 2004;57:627-632

28   Scheman A, Jacob S, Katta R, Nedorost S, Warshaw E, Zirwas M, et al. Part 1 of a 4 part series. Facial cosmetics: trends and alternatives. Data from the American Contact Alternative Group. J Clin Aesthet Dermatol 2011;4:25-30

29   Scheman A, Jacob S, Katta R, Nedorost S, Warshaw E, Zirwas M, et al. Part 2 of a 4 part series. Hair cosmetics: trends and alternatives. Data from the American Contact Alternative Group. J Clin Aesthet Dermatol 2011;4:42-46

30   Scheman A, Jacob S, Katta R, Nedorost S, Warshaw E, Zirwas M, et al. Part 3 of a 4 part series. Lips and common Dental Care products: trends and alternatives. Data from the American Contact Alternative Group. J Clin Aesthet Dermatol 2011;4:50-53

31   Scheman A, Jacob S, Katta R, Nedorost S, Warshaw E, Zirwas M, et al. Part 4 of a 4 part series. Miscellaneous products: trends and alternatives in deodorants, antiperspirants, sunblocks, shaving products, powder, and wipes. Data from the American Contact Alternative Group. J Clin Aesthet Dermatol 2011;4:35-39

32   Toholka R, Wang Y-S, Tate B, Tam M, Cahill J, Palmer A, Nixon R. The first Australian Baseline Series: Recommendations for patch testing in suspected contact dermatitis. Australas J Dermatol 2015;56:107-115

33 Aerts O, Leysen J, Naessens T, Dandelooy J, Apers S, Lambert J. Steareths may sometimes prove problematic in patients contact allergic to cetostearyl alcohol: an example. Contact Dermatitis 2016;75(Suppl.1):54-55

34 Dinkloh A, Worm M, Geier J, Schnuch A, Wollenberg A. Contact sensitization in patients with suspected cosmetic intolerance: results of the IVDK 2006-2011. J Eur Acad Dermatol Venereol 2015;29:1071-1081

35 Uter W, Spiewak R, Cooper SM, Wilkinson M, Sánchez Pérez J, Schnuch A, Schuttelaar M-L. Contact allergy to ingredients of topical medications: results of the European Surveillance System on Contact Allergies (ESSCA), 2009-2012. Pharmacoepidemiol Drug Saf 2016;25:1305-1312

36 Jankićević J, Vesić S, Vukićević J, Gajić M, Adamic M, Pavlović MD. Contact sensitivity in patients with venous leg ulcers in Serbia: comparison with contact dermatitis patients and relationship to ulcer duration. Contact Dermatitis 2008;58:32-36

37 Erfurt-Berge C, Geier J, Mahler V. The current spectrum of contact sensitization in patients with chronic leg ulcers or stasis dermatitis - new data from the Information Network of Departments of Dermatology (IVDK). Contact Dermatitis 2017 Feb 14. doi: 10.1111/cod.12763. [Epub ahead of print]

38 Aschenbeck KA, Warshaw EM. Allergenic ingredients in facial wet wipes. Dermatitis 2017 Mar 23. doi: 10.1097/DER.0000000000000268. [Epub ahead of print]

39 Armengot-Carbo MA, Rodríguez-Serna M, Taberner-Bonastre P, Miquel-Miquel J. Allergic contact dermatitis from cetearyl alcohol in Thrombocid® ointment. Dermatol Online J 2016 Jul 15;22(7). pii: 13030/qt8ht9300r

40 Raulin C, Frosch PJ. Contact allergies to antifungal agents. Z Hautkr 1987;62:1705-1709 (article in German)

41 Gallenkemper G, Rabe E, Bauer R. Contact sensitization in chronic venous insufficiency: modern wound dressings. Contact Dermatitis 1998;38:274-278

42 Aerts O, Naessens T, Dandelooy J, Leysen J, Lambert J, Apers S. Allergic contact dermatitis caused by wet wipes containing steareth-10: Is stearyl alcohol to blame? Contact Dermatitis 2017;77:117-119

43 Ackermann L, Virtanen H, Korhonen L, Laukkanen A, Huilaja L, Riekki R, Hasan T. An epidemic of allergic contact dermatitis caused by a new allergen, caprylhydroxamic acid, in moisturizers. Contact Dermatitis 2017;77:159-162

44 Lynch MD, White JM, McFadden JP, Wang Y, White IR, Banerjee P. A dynamic landscape of allergen associations in delayed-type cutaneous hypersensitivity. Br J Dermatol 2017;176:184-196

2.84 CETEARYL ETHYLHEXANOATE

IDENTIFICATION

Description/definition	: Cetearyl ethylhexanoate is the ester of cetearyl alcohol and 2-ethylhexanoic acid
Chemical class(es)	: Esters
Chemical/IUPAC name	: Hexadecyl 2-ethylhexanoate
Other names	: Cetearyl octanoate; 2-ethylhexanoic acid, cetyl/stearyl ester; perceline oil; hexanoic acid, 2-ethyl-, C16-18 alkyl esters
CAS registry number (s)	: 90411-68-0
EC number(s)	: 291-445-1
CIR review(s)	: J Am Coll Toxicol 1982;1:81-90; Int J Toxicol 2015;34:61-73 (access: www.cir-safety.org/ingredients)
Function(s) in cosmetics	: EU: emollient; hair conditioning; skin conditioning. USA: hair conditioning agents; skin-conditioning agents - emollient
Patch testing	: unknown

GENERAL

Cetearyl ethylhexanoate is a clear, oily liquid that is used in the formulation of a wide variety of cosmetics and personal care products. It acts as a lubricant on the skin's surface to give it a soft and smooth appearance and as a hair conditioning ingredient. It also imparts water-repelling characteristics to cosmetics and personal care products, improves 'spreadability', and is used to improve dry skin conditions.

CONTACT ALLERGY

Case reports and case series

Cetearyl ethylhexanoate was stated to be the (or an) allergen in one patient in a group of 603 individuals suffering from cosmetic dermatitis, seen in the period 2010-2015 in Leuven, Belgium (1). No other data are available.

Presence in cosmetic products and chemical analyses

In the USA, in April 2017, cetearyl ethylhexanoate was present in 545 of 56,714 cosmetic products of which the composition is known in FDA's Voluntary Cosmetic Registration Program (VCRP) (data obtained from FDA, May 2017). In March 2017, cetearyl ethylhexanoate was present in 110 of 64,983 cosmetic products of which the composition is known in EWG's Skin Deep Cosmetics Database, USA (http://www.ewg.org/skindeep/).

LITERATURE

1   Goossens A. Cosmetic contact allergens. Cosmetics 2016, 3, 5; doi:10.3390/cosmetics3010005

2.85 CETEARYL GLUCOSIDE

IDENTIFICATION

Description/definition : Cetearyl glucoside is the product obtained by the condensation of cetearyl alcohol with glucose; it conforms to the formula shown below, wherein R is an alkyl chain 16 or 18 carbons long

Chemical class(es) : Carbohydrates; ethers

Other names : D-Glucopyranose, C16-18 alkyl glycosides

EC number(s) : 246159-33-1

CIR review(s) : Int J Toxicol 2013;32(Suppl.3):22-48 (access: www.cir-safety.org/ingredients)

Function(s) in cosmetics : EU: emulsifying; surfactant. USA: surfactants – emulsifying agents

Patch testing : 20% pet. (8); 10% water (5)

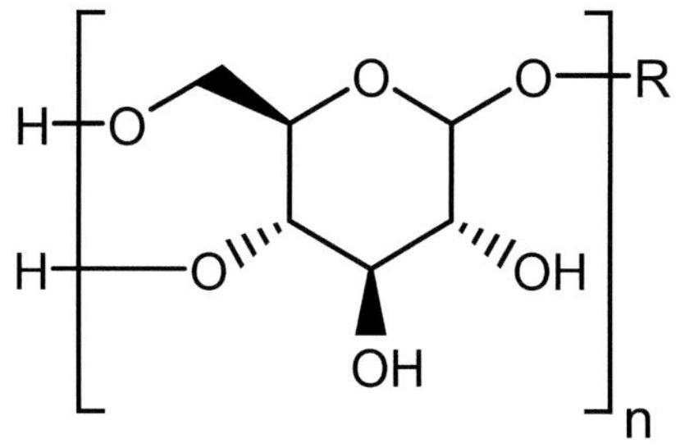

GENERAL

Cetearyl glucoside is one of the alkyl glucosides, a family of organic molecules of vegetal origin. They are produced by the condensation of a sugar, usually a cyclic form of glucose (D-glucopyranose), with a fatty alcohol composed of a linear side chain ranging from 2 to 22 carbons. Fatty alcohol is extracted from palm, coconut, or rapeseed oil, and glucose can be obtained from corn, wheat starch, and potato. The average number of carbon atoms composing the alcohol side chain determines the name of the alkyl glucoside. Members of the alkyl glucoside family include butyl, caprylyl, decyl, lauryl, coco-, cetearyl, undecyl, myristyl, hexadecyl, octadecyl, arachidyl, and caprylyl/capryl glucoside, C10-16, C12-18, C12-20, and C20-22 alkyl glucosides, branched isostearyl glucoside, and octyldodecyl glucoside (9).

Most of the alkyl glucosides are primarily used as mild non-ionic surfactants in cosmetics and cleansing products for human skin, mostly as a mixture of several alkyl glucosides, as it is difficult to obtain individual glucosides at high purity. They can also sometimes function as emulsion stabilizers in sunscreens, skin and hair cleansing agents, and humectants. They can be found in certain baby products such as wipes and cleansers and in antiseptic solutions (3).Other alkyl glucosides which have caused cosmetic allergy include arachidyl glucoside, coco-glucoside, decyl glucoside, lauryl glucoside and myristyl glucoside. These are discussed in their respective chapters. A comprehensive review of contact allergy to alkyl glucosides has been published in 2017 (2,9).

CONTACT ALLERGY

Patch testing in groups of patients

In Italy, in 2015, 310 consecutive patients suspected of contact dermatitis were patch tested with cetearyl glucoside 20% pet. and one individual (0.3%) had a positive patch test reaction. The relevance of this reaction was not stated (8). In the UK, in 2012, 157 patients selected for testing with a facial series were patch tested with cetearyl glucoside 10% water and one (0.6%) had a positive reaction. The relevance of this reaction was not found (5).

Case reports and case series

Cetearyl glucoside was stated to be the (or an) allergen in 2 patients in a group of 603 individuals suffering from cosmetic dermatitis, seen in the period 2010-2015 in Leuven, Belgium (7). Cetearyl glucoside was responsible for 1 out of 959 cases of non-fragrance cosmetic allergy where the causal allergen was identified, Belgium, 2000-2010 (1). During a 19-year period (1993–2012), of 11,842 patients with suspected contact dermatitis patch tested in Leuven, Belgium, 30 patients (24 women and 6 men) presented with a positive reaction to one or more alkyl glucosides. The causal products were shampoos (n=12), skin-cleansing products (n=12, among which were wipes for intimate hygiene), sunscreen products (n=5), skin-care products (n=4), and a deodorant (n=1). Reactions to cetearyl glucoside were seen in 4/30 (13%) of the patients. Co-reactions to other glucosides were as follows: coco-glucoside, decyl glucoside and lauryl glucoside each 3 (75%). Twenty-five of the 30 patients who reacted to alkyl glucosides also had positive test results with non-related chemicals; 16 of these even had multiple sensitivities, defined as three or more contact allergies (6).

A woman who had suffered from ACD caused by hair dye reacted upon patch testing to a cosmetic cream. When tested with its ingredients, there were multiple positive reactions including to cetearyl glucoside 20% pet. (4). A woman reacted to 2 sun sprays out of 13 sun products predictively tested (as is). The only ingredients common to both products were octyl palmitate, cetearyl glucoside and galactorabinan. Since neither cetearyl glucoside nor the other compounds were available, she was tested her coco-glucoside 5% pet. and lauryl glucoside 5% pet., and she reacted to both glucosides. This indicated that cetearyl glucoside was most likely the sensitizer in the sun sprays (10).

Cross-reactions, pseudo-cross-reactions and co-reactions
Often, a mixture of several alkyl glucosides is present in cosmetic products, as it is very difficult to obtain individual glucosides of high purity. Because of this and of their chemical similarity, concomitant reactivity or cross-reactions may occur with the various glucosides.

Presence in cosmetic products and chemical analyses
In the USA, in April 2017, cetearyl glucoside was present in 815 of 56,714 cosmetic products of which the composition is known in FDA's Voluntary Cosmetic Registration Program (VCRP) (data obtained from FDA, May 2017). In February 2017, cetearyl glucoside was present in 640 of 64,631 cosmetic products of which the composition is known in EWG's Skin Deep Cosmetics Database, USA (http://www.ewg.org/skindeep/).

LITERATURE

1   Travassos AR, Claes L, Boey L, Drieghe J, Goossens A. Non-fragrance allergens in specific cosmetic products. Contact Dermatitis 2011;65:276-285
2   Alfalah M, Loranger C, Sasseville D. Contact allergen of the year. Alkyl glucosides. Dermatitis 2017;28:3-4
3   Fiume MM, Heldreth B, Bergfeld WF, Belsito DV, Hill RA, Klaassen CD, et al. Safety assessment of decyl glucoside and other alkyl glucosides as used in cosmetics. Int J Toxicol 2013;32(Suppl.5):22S-48S
4   Madsen JT, Andersen KE. 2-Amino-4-hydroxyethylaminoanisole sulfate – a coupler causing contact allergy from use in hair dyes. Contact Dermatitis 2016;74:102-104
5   Shanmugam S, Wilkinson M, Kirk S. Pitfalls of patch testing with glucosides. Contact Dermatitis 2014;71:108-109
6   Gijbels D, Timmermans A, Serrano P, Verreycken E, Goossens A. Allergic contact dermatitis caused by alkyl glucosides. Contact Dermatitis 2014;70:175-182
7   Goossens A. Cosmetic contact allergens. Cosmetics 2016, 3, 5; doi:10.3390/cosmetics3010005
8   Corazza M, Virgili A, Ricci M, Bianchi A, Borghi A. Contact sensitization to emulsifying agents: an underrated issue? Dermatitis 2016;27:276-281
9   Loranger C, Alfalah M, Ferrier Le Bouedec M-C, Sasseville Denis. Alkyl glucosides in contact dermatitis: a systematic review. Dermatitis 2017;28:5-13
10   Goossens A, Decraene T, Platteaux N, Nardelli A, Rasschaert V. Glucosides as unexpected allergens in cosmetics. Contact Dermatitis 2003;48:164-166

2.86 CETEARYL ISONONANOATE

IDENTIFICATION

Description/definition	: Cetearyl isononanoate is the ester of cetearyl alcohol and a branched chain nonanoic acid
Chemical class(es)	: Esters
Chemical/IUPAC name	: Hexadecyl isononanoate
Other names	: Isononanoic acid, C16-18 alkyl esters
CAS registry number (s)	: 111937-03-2; 84878-33-1
EC number(s)	: 284-424-3
CIR review(s)	: Int J Toxicol 2011;30(Suppl.3):228-269; Final report, March 2013 (access: www.cir-safety.org/ingredients)
Function(s) in cosmetics	: EU: emollient; hair conditioning; skin conditioning. USA: hair conditioning agents; skin-conditioning agents - emollient
Patch testing	: 1% pet. (1); 4% in liquid mineral oil (2)

CONTACT ALLERGY

Case reports and case series

A woman developed acute dermatitis on her legs within two days of application of a urea-based moisturizing cream. Patch testing with the European standard series, additional series and the patient's own emollient showed positive reactions to colophonium, fragrance mix and nickel sulfate (all of past relevance) and to the moisturizing cream. A repeated open application test (ROAT) performed with the cream elicited follicular itching dermatitis within 2 days. Testing with all 24 ingredients provided by the manufacturer, diluted at concentrations identical to that in the product, confirmed the allergic reaction to the cream and to cetearyl isononanoate diluted 4% in liquid mineral oil. The other ingredients, including cetyl alcohol, were negative. A ROAT performed with the cetearyl isononanoate preparation, applied twice daily on the forearm, was positive after 2 days. Ten controls tested with cetearyl isononanoate were negative (2).

Another woman started to use an over-the-counter massage cream on the entire surface of her legs every night. After nine days, she began to wear thigh-high support hose at bedtime to prevent edema. Two days later, pruritic erythema developed on the legs, and this gradually spread over her body; she also developed a high fever. The patient was hospitalized on the same day. On admission, she had dark erythema with purpura on the areas that had been in contact with the support hose. Sharply defined pruritic erythema with target lesions was observed on her forearms and trunk, with swollen inguinal lymph nodes. She was treated with oral prednisone, and her condition improved within two weeks. After she had recovered, patch testing was performed with the cloth of the support hose, the massage cream, and the ingredients of the massage cream. Positive reactions were observed to the massage cream, tested as is, and cetearyl isononanoate 1% pet. The patient was diagnosed with allergic contact dermatitis with a systemic reaction caused by cetearyl isononanoate in massage cream (1).

A 2-year-old boy developed allergic contact dermatitis from cetearyl isononanoate in a sunscreen product and reacted to cetearyl isononanoate 4% pet.; cetearyl alcohol was not tested (4).

Cross-reactions, pseudo-cross-reactions and co-reactions
Not to cetyl alcohol (2).

Presence in cosmetic products and chemical analyses
In the USA, in April 2017, cetearyl isononanoate was present in 215 of 56,714 cosmetic products of which the composition is known in FDA's Voluntary Cosmetic Registration Program (VCRP) (data obtained from FDA, May 2017). In March 2017, cetearyl isononanoate was present in 50 of 64,983 cosmetic products of which the composition is known in EWG's Skin Deep Cosmetics Database, USA (http://www.ewg.org/skindeep/). Cetearyl isononanoate was present in 40 (23%) of 178 facial wipes for which ingredient information was obtained online and from retail stores, USA, 2016 (3).

LITERATURE

1   Ito K, Fujimura N, Uchida T, Ikezawa Z, Aihara M. Contact dermatitis with systemic reactions caused by cetearyl isononanoate. Contact Dermatitis 2013;69:315-316
2   Le Coz C-J, Bressieux A. Allergic contact dermatitis from cetearyl isononanoate. Contact Dermatitis 2003;48:343

3   Aschenbeck KA, Warshaw EM. Allergenic ingredients in facial wet wipes. Dermatitis 2017 Mar 23. doi: 10.1097/DER.0000000000000268. [Epub ahead of print]
4   Sarre ME, Mancel E, Drouet M, Avenel-Audran MJ. Allergic contact dermatitis caused by cetearyl isononanoate in a sunscreen product. Contact Dermatitis 2017;76:357-358

2.87 CETRIMONIUM BROMIDE

IDENTIFICATION

Description/definition	: Cetrimonium bromide is a quaternary ammonium salt that conforms generally to the formula shown below
Chemical class(es)	: Quaternary ammonium compounds
Chemical/IUPAC name	: Hexadecyl(trimethyl)azanium bromide
Other names	: Cetyl trimethyl ammonium bromide; cetrimide; hexadecyltrimethylammonium bromide
CAS registry number (s)	: 57-09-0
EC number(s)	: 200-311-3
CIR review(s)	: Int J Toxicol 1997;16:195-220; Int J Toxicol 2012;31(Suppl.3):296-341 (access: www.cir-safety.org/ingredients)
Merck Index monograph	: 3294
Function(s) in cosmetics	: EU: antimicrobial; antistatic; emulsifying; preservative; surfactant. USA: antistatic agents; cosmetic biocides; surfactants – emulsifying agents
EU cosmetic restrictions	: Regulated in Annex V/44 of the Regulation (EU) No. 866/2014
Patch testing	: 0.5% pet. (Chemotechnique); 1.0% pet. (SmartPracticeCanada)
Molecular formula	: $C_{19}H_{42}BrN$

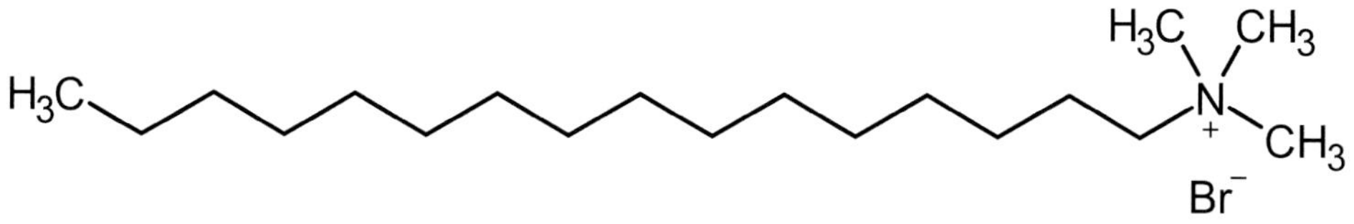

GENERAL

Cetrimide is a mixture of different quaternary ammonium salts, of which the primary surfactant is cetrimonium bromide. It is active against both gram-negative and gram-positive bacteria. In addition, it breaks down surface tension, permitting wetting of the surface, enabling disinfection (6). Although in routine testing and in testing in selected patient groups high rates of sensitization have been reported, cases of proven and relevant contact allergy to cetrimonium bromide are rare. It is very likely that many 'positive' patch test reactions to 0.5% pet. (and certainly to 1% pet., which seems far too high for this type of quaternary ammonium compound, but which is available as commercial patch test preparation) were in fact irritant in nature.

CONTACT ALLERGY

Patch testing in groups of patients
Results of studies patch testing cetrimonium bromide in consecutive patients suspected of contact dermatitis (routine testing) and in groups of selected patients are shown in table 2.87.1. In routine testing, frequencies of sensiti-zation were 0.3% in Singapore in 1985-1987 (10) and 5.5% in India, 1997-2006 (18). In the latter study, almost all reactions were relevant and were caused by an antiseptic product containing cetrimide and chlorhexidine (18). In groups of selected patient (patients suspected of cosmetic dermatitis, patients with leg ulcers, patients suspected of contact allergy to antibacterial agents), very high frequencies of sensitization were noted in both India and in France (12,17,19,20). However, in two studies, commercial creams were tested, so reactions may also have been caused by excipients (19,20), relevance was never mentioned and some authors suggested themselves that some reactions may have been irritant.

Case reports and case series
Cetrimonium bromide was stated to be the (or an) allergen in one patient in a group of 603 individuals suffering from cosmetic dermatitis, seen in the period 2010-2015 in Leuven, Belgium (9). Cetrimonium bromide was responsible for 2 out of 959 cases of non-fragrance cosmetic allergy where the causal allergen was identified, Belgium, 2000-2010 (1). Eighteen positive patch test reactions to cetrimonium bromide were ascribed to cosmetic allergy (2); this can hardly be accurate, most reactions must have been irritant.

One patient reacted 'alarmingly' to a proprietary shampoo containing cetrimonium bromide. When patch tested, the patient strongly reacted to cetrimonium bromide 0.1% and possibly to 0.01% and 0.001% (other patients were also mentioned, but the patch test results were not specified for each individual patient) (15).

Table 2.87.1 Patch testing in groups of patients

Years and Country	Test conc. & vehicle	Number of patients tested	positive (%)		Selection of patients (S); Relevance (R); Comments (C)	Ref.
Routine testing						
1997-2006 India	0.5% pet.	1000	55	(5.5%)	R: 53 reactions were of current relevance, 2 probable; C: all reactions were caused by an antiseptic product containing cetrimide and chlorhexidine	18
1985-1987 Singapore	0.1% water	3145	8	(0.3%)	R: not stated; C: prevalence in men 0.4%, in women 0%	10
Testing in groups of selected patients						
<2014 India		50	14	(28%)	S: patients with suspected cosmetic dermatitis; R: not specified	17
<2005 India	0.5% pet.	50	4	(8%)	S: patients suspected of cosmetic dermatitis; R: not stated	12
2001-2002 France	commercial cream	106	10	(9.4%)	S: patients with leg ulcers; R: not stated; C: as the commercial cream was tested, reactions may have included allergy to excipients in the cream; the authors offered the possibility of (a number of) irritant patch test reactions	20
1980- 1983 India	0.5% comm. cream	247	46	(18.6%)	S: patients suspected of contact allergy to antibacterial agents; R; not stated; C: as the commercial cream was tested, reactions may have included allergy to excipients; high frequency was ascribed to frequent use or 'may not be due to specific allergy' (i.e. irritant patch test reactions)	19

Comm.: commercial

Contact allergy to cetrimonium bromide in non-cosmetic products

A non-atopic man had recently been diagnosed with prostate cancer, and 2 days after a biopsy procedure he developed severe swelling and redness of the scrotal and penile skin. Suspected allergens included the tape from the surgical dressing and chlorhexidine from the antiseptic solution chlorhexidine/cetrimide 0.2%/0.1%. Patch tests with an extended European baseline series, a local anesthetic series, an additional fragrance allergen series, plastic and glue series, and cetrimonium bromide 0.5% pet. gave many positive reactions including to fragrances, to chlorhexidine/cetrimide (0.2%/0.1%) and to cetrimonium bromide 0.5% pet. but there was no reaction to chlorhexidine 0.5% water (6). Cetrimonium bromide in a topical pharmaceutical product caused ACD in one patient; this woman had positive patch tests to the cream and to its ingredient cetrimonium bromide, tested 0.1% water (7). A boy had ACD from cetrimonium bromide in a topical pharmaceutical preparation (14). Forty-six cases of cetrimide sensitivity, seen in a ten-year-period, were described in 1968; the author concluded that the problem was rare (13, data cited in ref. 14).

A young boy seen was given 1% aqueous solution of cetrimide for the cleansing of a mild balanitis. This was followed by an alarming bullous eruption, with shedding of the whole of the skin of the penis and scrotum, and severe dermatitis spreading to the thighs and abdomen. Patch tests were not performed, but the spreading of dermatitis may be in favor of a contact allergic reaction (15). One patient reacted 'alarmingly' to cetrimonium bromide applied to a cut. When patch tested, the patient strongly reacted to cetrimonium bromide 0.1% and possibly to 0.01% and 0.001% (other patients were mentioned also and the patch test results were not specified for each individual patient) (15). Two patients developed eruptions after preoperative skin preparation with cetrimonium bromide, one of them on two separate occasions in the same hospital. They both had strong positive patch test reactions to 0.1% cetrimonium bromide and one or both also to 0.01% and 0.001% (15).

Presence in cosmetic products and chemical analyses

In May 2017, cetrimonium bromide was present in 61 of 66,647 cosmetic products of which the composition is known in EWG's Skin Deep Cosmetics Database, USA (http://www.ewg.org/skindeep/). In the USA, in April 2017, cetrimonium bromide was present in 81 of 56,714 cosmetic products of which the composition is known in FDA's Voluntary Cosmetic Registration Program (VCRP) (data obtained from FDA, May 2017).

OTHER SIDE EFFECTS

Irritant contact dermatitis

Accidental contact with a shampoo containing 12% 'cetrimide' caused a bullous contact dermatitis after approximately 1 day in a child. Upon provocation, a similar eruption developed. This was probably an irritant contact dermatitis (3). Application of pure cetrimide powder under occlusion resulted in extensive necrosis in a 77-year-old woman of the leg and foot, which took 4 months to heal (4). Patch testing with 2% cetrimide has resulted in necrosis (4). Bullous irritant contact dermatitis occurred in a 3-month-old baby from the application of a 17.5% cetrimide solution (5). Eighteen patients presented with irritant contact dermatitis from the use of an undiluted antiseptic solution for pruritic dermatoses, located especially over the flexures and the genitalia; the solution contained 3% cetrimonium bromide and 0.5% chlorhexidine; patch tests were negative (8).

In a man, one week after the skin of the right cheek had been prepared for surgery by washing it with a 3.3% aqueous solution of a preparation containing chlorhexidine gluconate 1.5% and cetrimide 15%, a severe skin eruption over the right cheek developed in an area which corresponded to the region washed with the antiseptic solution. The eruption had an eczematous appearance and was painful to touch. Later, patch tests were positive to the solution and to cetrimonium bromide 5% but not to 1%. It was concluded that the patient was allergic to cetrimonium bromide (16). This may have been a wrong conclusion, as a 5% concentration of cetrimide is obviously irritant in patch testing and 1% should have been positive in a patch test in the case of contact allergy. Why the reaction developed after a week only is unknown, but may be a case of delayed irritancy.

Miscellaneous side effects
Cetrimonium bromide in shampoo was held responsible for irreversible matting of the hair (Bird's nest hair) (11).

LITERATURE

1 Travassos AR, Claes L, Boey L, Drieghe J, Goossens A. Non-fragrance allergens in specific cosmetic products. Contact Dermatitis 2011;65:276-285
2 Kohl L, Blondeel A, Song M. Allergic contact dermatitis from cosmetics: retrospective analysis of 819 patch-tested patients. Dermatology 2002;204:334-337
3 Inman JK. Cetrimide allergy presenting as suspected non-accidental injury. Br Med J (Clin Res Ed) 1982;284:385
4 August P. Cutaneous necrosis due to cetrimide application. Br Med J 1975;1:70
5 Mercer DM. Cetrimide burn in an infant. Postgr Med J 1983;59:472-473
6 Engebretsen KA, Hald M, Johansen JD, Thyssen JP. Allergic contact dermatitis caused by an antiseptic containing cetrimide. Contact Dermatitis 2015;72:60-61
7 Leow Y-H, Tan CS-C. Allergic contact dermatitis from cetrimide and cetearyl alcohol in Burnol-plus ® cream. Contact Dermatitis 2000;43:174-175
8 Lee JY-Y, Wang B-J. Contact dermatitis caused by cetrimide in antiseptics. Contact Dermatitis 1995;33:168-171
9 Goossens A. Cosmetic contact allergens. Cosmetics 2016, 3, 5; doi:10.3390/cosmetics3010005
10 Goh CL. Contact sensitivity to topical antimicrobials. Contact Dermatitis 1989;21:46-48
11 Dawber R. Matting of scalp hair due to shampooing: a hypothesis as to the cause. Clin Exp Dermatol 1984;9:209-211
12 Tomar J, Jain VK, Aggarwal K, Dayal S, Guptaet S. Contact allergies to cosmetics: testing with 52 cosmetic ingredients and personal products. J Dermatol 2005;32:951-955
13 Morgan JK. Iatrogenic epidermal sensitivity. Br J Clin Pract 1968;22:261-264
14 Staniforth P. Allergy to benzalkonium chloride in plaster of Paris after sensitisation to cetrimide. A case report. J Bone Joint Surg Br 1980;62:500-501
15 Sharvill D. Reaction to chlorhexidine and cetrimide. Lancet 1965;1:771
16 Haidar Z. An adverse reaction to a topical antiseptic (Cetrimide). Br J Oral Surg 1977;15:86-89
17 Kumar P, Paulose R. Patch testing in suspected allergic contact dermatitis to cosmetics. Dermatol Res Pract 2014;2014:695387. doi: 10.1155/2014/695387
18 Bajaj AK, Saraswat A, Mukhija G, Rastogi S, Yadav S. Patch testing experience with 1000 patients. Indian J Dermatol Venereol Leprol 2007;73:313-318
19 Bajaj AK, Gupta SC. Contact hypersensitivity to topical antibacterial agents. Int J Dermatol 1986;25:103-105
20 Machet L, Couhé C, Perrinaud A, Hoarau C, Lorette G, Vaillant L. A high prevalence of sensitization still persists in leg ulcer patients: a retrospective series of 106 patients tested between 2001 and 2002 and a meta-analysis of 1975-2003 data. Br J Dermatol 2004;150:929-935

2.88 CETYL ALCOHOL

IDENTIFICATION

Description/definition   : Cetyl alcohol is the fatty alcohol that conforms to the formula shown below
Chemical class(es)   : Fatty alcohols
Chemical/IUPAC name   : Hexadecan-1-ol
Other names   : 1-Hexadecanol
CAS registry number (s)   : 36653-82-4
EC number(s)   : 253-149-0
CIR review(s)   : J Am Coll Toxicol 1988;7:359-413 (access: www.cir-safety.org/ingredients)
Merck Index monograph   : 3297
Function(s) in cosmetics   : EU: emollient; emulsifying; emulsion stabilising; foam boosting; masking; opacifying; surfactant; viscosity controlling. USA: emulsion stabilizers; fragrance ingredients; opacifying agents; surfactants – emulsifying agents; surfactants - foam boosters; viscosity increasing agents – aqueous / nonaqueous
Patch testing   : 5.0% pet. (Chemotechnique)
Molecular formula   : $C_{16}H_{34}O$

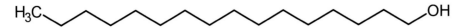

GENERAL

Cetyl alcohol is an emulsifier and stabilizer present in many topical medicaments and cosmetics. Contact allergy from its presence in cosmetics is rare. Allergic contact dermatitis from cetyl alcohol is almost always associated with a previous alteration of the skin barrier that facilitates its absorption. Therefore, most cases of sensitization result from the use of pharmaceutical products containing cetyl alcohol (12,18,26,31), including antifungal (7,9) and corticosteroid preparations (11,13,14,16,29). Patients with leg ulcers and stasis dermatitis are more prone to become sensitized to cetyl alcohol (15,16,31,32,33,34). It should be appreciated that in a number of patients reacting to commercial grade cetyl alcohol, patch tests (8,13) or ROATs (30) with pure cetyl alcohol were negative. In one such report, the actual allergens were n-decyl alcohol and oleyl alcohol (8), which are known impurities in commercial grade cetyl alcohol. Cetyl alcohol used in cosmetics may also contain 30-35% stearyl alcohol, lauryl alcohol and 10% myristyl alcohol (13).

CONTACT ALLERGY

Patch testing in groups of patients

Results of patch testing cetyl alcohol in consecutive patients suspected of contact dermatitis (routine testing) and of testing in groups of *selected* patients (e.g., patients suspected of cosmetic dermatitis) are shown in table 2.88.1. In three studies performing routine testing, the frequencies of sensitization were all very low, ranging from 0.2% to 0.6%. A small minority of the positive patch test reactions were relevant, but causative products were not mentioned (3,4, 21). In three investigations patch testing cetyl alcohol in groups of selected patients (e.g., patients suspected of cosmetic dermatitis), rates of sensitization were also low (0.1%, 0.4%, and 1.5%), the highest frequency being observed in a group of patients suspected of cosmetic or iatrogenic dermatitis. The relevance of the positive patch test reactions in this study was not specified, but 2 of 46 may have been caused by a corticosteroid preparation (11).

Case reports and case series

Cetyl alcohol was stated to be the (or an) allergen in one patient in a group of 603 individuals suffering from cosmetic dermatitis, seen in the period 2010-2015 in Leuven, Belgium (20). Cetyl alcohol was responsible for 5 out of 959 cases of non-fragrance cosmetic allergy where the causal allergen was identified, Belgium, 2000-2010 (1). Cetyl alcohol was responsible for 1 out of 399 cases of cosmetic allergy where the causal allergen was identified in a study of the NACDG, USA, 1977-1983 (2). One patient reacted to cetyl alcohol in a moisturizer containing cetearyl alcohol (10). Two patients had probably allergic contact dermatitis from cetyl alcohol present in various moisturizers and one of them also from a cleanser. Cetyl alcohol itself was possibly not tested, but one patient reacted to cetearyl alcohol and the other to stearyl alcohol, both of which are likely to cross-react to cetyl alcohol (19, also presented as summary [18]). A woman had hand dermatitis from contact allergy to cetyl alcohol in a hand lotion (22).

Table 2.88.1 Patch testing in groups of patients

Years and Country	Test conc. & vehicle	Number of patients tested	positive (%)		Selection of patients (S); Relevance (R); Comments (C)	Ref.
Routine testing						
2015 Italy	30% pet.	310	2	(0.6%)	R: not stated	4
2006-2010 USA	5% pet.	3085		(0.2%)	R: 33%	21
2000-2005 USA	5% pet.	3846		(0.3%)	R: 20%	3
Testing in groups of selected patients						
2000-2007 USA	5% pet.	945	1	(0.1%)	S: patients tested with a supplemental cosmetic screening series; R: 100%; C: weak study: a. high rate of macular erythema and weak reactions; b. relevance figures included 'questionable' and 'past' relevance	24
1990-1999 Belgium	20% pet.	2999	46	(1.5%)	S: patients suspected of cosmetic or iatrogenic dermatitis; R: not specified, 2 reactions were probably from a cortico-steroid preparation	11
1984-1991 USA	30% pet.	3737	16	(0.4%)	S: unknown, possibly routine testing; R: not stated	28

Contact allergy to cetyl alcohol in non-cosmetic products

Of 9 patients allergic to lanette cream, a non-proprietary base for topical pharmaceutical preparations (of who 7 had leg ulcers), all reacted to cetyl alcohol 5% pet. (16). Six leg ulcer patients had contact allergy to a pharmaceutical cream containing cetearyl alcohol; (at least) one reacted to cetyl alcohol 5% pet., (at least) 2 reacted to cetearyl alcohol 20% pet., and (at least) 2 to stearyl alcohol 30% pet. (15). Four middle-aged or older women with leg ulcers and stasis dermatitis had allergic contact dermatitis from cetyl alcohol in silver sulfadiazine cream (31). One individual reacted to commercial cetyl alcohol and stearyl alcohol present in topical pharmaceutical products (antifungal and antibacterial), but not to purified material; the allergens were the impurities n-decyl alcohol and oleyl alcohol (8). Two patients had allergic contact reactions from cetyl alcohol in a corticosteroid preparation (11). One patient may have had allergic contact dermatitis from cetyl alcohol in topical pharmaceuticals for the relief of itching. Cetyl alcohol was not positive (not tested?), but the patient reacted to stearyl alcohol, which was the reason for the authors to conclude that the allergic contact dermatitis was caused by cetyl alcohol (19, also presented as summary [18]). Another individual also had allergic contact dermatitis from cetyl alcohol in a topical pharmaceutical for the relief of itching (12).

One patient reacted to cetyl alcohol present in a topical pharmaceutical corticosteroid-antibiotic combination pharmaceutical product; as he did not react to pure cetyl alcohol, the authors suggest the allergen to have been an unidentified impurity (13). A woman had allergic contact dermatitis, partly resembling urticaria, from cetyl alcohol in an unspecified pharmaceutical preparation. The patch test gave a 3 cm urticarial reaction (probably after 2-3 days, not an immediate-type reaction) (26). There have been various single case reports of patients with contact allergy to cetyl alcohol in antifungal preparations (7,8,9) and corticosteroid preparations (13,14,16,29). One patient had a peculiar allergic reaction to cetyl alcohol in a moisturizing coating on the inside of a rubber glove (5). A woman had allergic contact dermatitis of the left upper eyelid from cetyl alcohol and stearyl alcohol in an antifungal preparation used to treat seborrheic dermatitis (35).

Cross-reactions, pseudo-cross-reactions and co-reactions

Possibly from or to ceteareth-2 and/or ceteareth-3, which are cetearyl alcohols with a variable number of oxyethy-lene molecules (6). Cetyl alcohol used in cosmetics may contain 30-35% stearyl alcohol (C_{18}) and 10% myristyl alcohol (C_{14}); it can also contain lauryl alcohol (C_{12}) (13). Oleyl alcohol and n-decyl alcohol, present in cosmetic grade cetyl alcohol, can be the true sensitizers in some patients with cetyl alcohol contact allergy (14). Hence, pseudo-cross-reactivity may be observed to stearyl alcohol, myristyl alcohol, lauryl alcohol, oleyl alcohol and n-decyl alcohol. Lanolin, lanolin alcohol (13,17,31); cetearyl alcohol (6,17); stearyl alcohol (31).

Presence in cosmetic products and chemical analyses

In June 2017, cetyl alcohol was present in 2965 of 69,510 cosmetic products of which the composition is known in EWG's Skin Deep Cosmetics Database, USA (http://www.ewg.org/skindeep/). In the USA, in April 2017, cetyl alcohol was present in 7388 of 56,714 cosmetic products of which the composition is known in FDA's Voluntary Cosmetic Registration Program (VCRP) (data obtained from FDA, May 2017). Commercial cetyl alcohol in 1988 was found to contain 92.1% C16 alcohol (cetyl alcohol), 3.3% C18 alcohol (stearyl alcohol) and 4.6% lower fatty alcohols and other substances (27).

OTHER SIDE EFFECTS

Other non-eczematous contact reactions
In (somewhat) older literature, cetyl alcohol has been suspected of being comedogenic in 'people with more sensitive complexions or acne-prone problems', based on rabbit ear assays (23). In more recent research using the same test method, however, cetyl alcohol was found to be non-comedogenic (25).

LITERATURE

1   Travassos AR, Claes L, Boey L, Drieghe J, Goossens A. Non-fragrance allergens in specific cosmetic products. Contact Dermatitis 2011;65:276-285

2   Adams RM, Maibach HI, Clendenning WE, Fisher AA, Jordan WJ, Kanof N, et al. A five-year study of cosmetic reactions. J Am Acad Dermatol 1985;13:1062-1069

3   Davis MD, Scalf LA, Yiannias JA, Cheng JF, El-Azhary RA, Rohlinger AL, et al. Changing trends and allergens in the patch test standard series. Arch Dermatol 2008;144:67-72

4   Corazza M, Virgili A, Ricci M, Bianchi A, Borghi A. Contact sensitization to emulsifying agents: an underrated issue? Dermatitis 2016;27:276-281

5   Vanden Broecke K, Zimerson E, Bruze M, Goossens A. Severe allergic contact dermatitis caused by a rubber glove coated with a moisturizer. Contact Dermatitis 2014;71:117-119

6   Corazza M, Zauli S, Bianchi A, Benetti S, Borghi A, Virgili A. Contact dermatitis caused by fatty alcohols: may polyethoxylation of the fatty alcohols influence their sensitizing potential? Contact Dermatitis 2013;68:189-190

7   Garcia-Bravo B, Mazuecos J, Rodriguez-Pichardo A, Navas J, Camacho F. Hypersensitivity to ketoconazole preparations: study of 4 cases. Contact Dermatitis 1989;21:346-348

8   Ishiguro N, Kawishima M. Contact dermatitis from impurities in alcohol. Contact Dermatitis 1991;25:257

9   Soga F, Katoh N, Kishimoto S. Contact dermatitis due to lanoconazole, cetyl alcohol and diethyl sebacate in lanoconazole cream. Contact Dermatitis 2004;50:49-50

10 Kiec-Swierczynska M, Krecisz B, Swierczynska-Machura D. Photoallergic and allergic reaction to 2-hydroxy-4-methoxybenzophenone (sunscreen) and allergy to cetyl alcohol in cosmetic cream. Contact Dermatitis 2005;53:170-171

11 Goossens A, Huygens S, Matura M, Degreef H. Fluticasone propionate: a rare contact sensitizer. Eur J Dermatol 2001;11:29-34

12 Oiso N, Fukai K, Ishii M. Concomitant allergic reaction to cetyl alcohol and crotamiton. Contact Dermatitis 2003;49:261

13 Komamura H, Dor T, Inui S, Yoshikawa K. A case of contact dermatitis due to impurities of cetyl alcohol. Contact Dermatitis 1997;36:44-46

14 Hausen BM, Kulenkamp D. Contact allergy to fludroxycortid and cetyl alcohol. Derm Beruf Umwelt 1985;33:27-28 (article in German)

15 Dissanayke M, Powell SM. Hioxyl® sensitivity. Contact Dermatitis 1990;22:242-243

16 Van Ketel, WG. Allergy to cetylalcohol. Contact Dermatitis 1984;11:125-126

17 Van Ketel, WG, Wemer J. Allergy to lanolin and "lanolin-free" creams. Contact Dermatitis 1983;9:420

18 Aakhus AE. Allergic contact dermatitis to cetyl alcohol. Dermatitis 2011;22:173 (Summary)

19 Aakhus AE, Warshaw EM. Allergic contact dermatitis from cetyl alcohol. Dermatitis 2011;22:56-57

20 Goossens A. Cosmetic contact allergens. Cosmetics 2016, 3, 5; doi:10.3390/cosmetics3010005

21 Wentworth AB, Yiannias JA, Keeling JH, Hall MR, Camilleri MJ, Drage LA, et al. Trends in patch-test results and allergen changes in the standard series: a Mayo Clinic 5-year retrospective review (January 1, 2006, to December 31, 2010). J Am Acad Dermatol 2014;70:269-275

22 Thyresson N, Lodin A, Nilzen A. Eczema of the hands due to triethanolamine in cosmetic handlotions for housewives. Acta Derm Venereol 1956;36:355-359

23 Fulton JE Jr, Pay SR, Fulton JE 3rd. Comedogenicity of current therapeutic products, cosmetics, and ingredients in the rabbit ear. J Am Acad Dermatol 1984;10:96-105

24 Wetter DA, Yiannias JA, Prakash AV, Davis MD, Farmer SA, el-Azhary RA, et al. Results of patch testing to personal care product allergens in a standard series and a supplemental cosmetic series: an analysis of 945 patients from the Mayo Clinic Contact Dermatitis Group, 2000-2007. J Am Acad Dermatol 2010;63:789-798

25 Nguyen SH, Dang TP, Maibach HI. Comedogenicity in rabbit: some cosmetic ingredients/vehicles. Cutan Ocul Toxicol 2007;26:287-292

26 Gaul LE. Dermatitis from cetyl and stearyl alcohols. Arch Dermatol 1969;99:593

27 Hannuksela M. Skin contact allergy to emulsifiers. Int J Cosmet Sci 1988;10:9-14

28 Fransway AF. The problem of preservation in the 1990s. III. Agents with preservative function independent of formaldehyde release. Am J Contact Derm 1991;2:145-174

29 Schmoll M, Hausen BM. Allergic contact dermatitis to prednisolone-21-trimethyl acetate. Z Hautkr 1988;63:311-313 (article in German).

30 Hannuksela M, Salo H. The repeated open application test (ROAT). Contact Dermatitis. 1986;14:221-227

31 Degreef H, Dooms-Goossens A. Patch testing with silver sulfadiazine cream. Contact Dermatitis 1985;12:33-37

32 Bandman H-J, Keilig W. Lanette O. Another test substance for lower leg series. Contact Dermatitis 1980;6:227-228

33 Keilig W. Kontaktallergie auf Cetylstearylalcohol (Lanette O) als therapeutisches Problem bei Stauungsdermatitis und Ulcus cruris. Dermatosen in Beruf und Umwelt 1983;31:50-54

34 Dooms-Goossens A, Degreef H, Parijs M, Maertens M. A retrospective study of patch test results from 163 patients with stasis dermatitis or leg ulcers (II). Retesting of 50 patients. Dermatologica 1979;159:231-238

35 Kang H, Choi J, Lee A Y. Allergic contact dermatitis to white petrolatum. J Dermatol 2004;31:428-430

2.89 CHAMOMILLA RECUTITA (MATRICARIA) EXTRACT

IDENTIFICATION

Description/definition	: Chamomilla recutita extract is the extract of the whole plant of the matricaria, Chamomilla recutita (L.), Asteraceae (Asteraceae is the old name for Compositae)
Chemical class(es)	: Botanical products and botanical derivatives
INCI name USA	: Chamomilla recutita (matricaria) flower/leaf extract
Other names	: Camomille extract; chamomile extract, German; chamomile extract, Hungarian; matricaria extract
CAS registry number (s)	: 84082-60-0
EC number(s)	: 282-006-5
CIR review(s)	: Final report, June 2016 (access: www.cir-safety.org/ingredients)
Merck Index monograph	: 3310 (Chamomile)
Function(s) in cosmetics	: EU: skin conditioning. USA: fragrance ingredients; skin-conditioning agents – miscellaneous; skin-conditioning agents – occlusive (flower extract)
Patch testing	: 1.0% pet. (Chemotechnique); also present in the Compositae mix II (Chemotechnique); 1% physiologic saline for immediate open testing (24)

It should be realized that the colloquial plant name 'Chamomile' (sometimes termed camomile) has been used interchangeably for at least three different species: German chamomile (*Chamomilla recutita* (L.) Rauschert), Roman chamomile (*Chamaemelum nobile* (L.) All.; synonym *Anthemis nobilis* L.) and dog fennel (*Anthemis cotula* L.). German and Roman chamomile are both important medicinal plants, but despite their allegedly similar properties, they differ considerably in their chemical composition (12). Roman chamomile is discussed in Chapter 2.25 Anthemis nobilis flower extract.

GENERAL

The sweet-scented German chamomile (true chamomile) has been used as a medicinal herb worldwide for many centuries and has become increasingly popular in recent decades (12). Chamomile has experimentally supported effects as an anti-inflammatory, spasmolytic, wound-healing and sedative/anxiolytic agent (12,41). German chamomile is found in ointments, tinctures, laxatives, suppositories, medicinal soaps, cough and flu remedies, eye drops, acne lotions, prostate capsules, protective skin sprays, and numerous other products. It is also used widely in cosmetic and sanitary items, especially shampoos, conditioners, and bath additives, as well as in chamomile tea and chamomile vapors (41).

The active constituents are contained in the essential oil of chamomile, which comprises, e.g., anti-inflammatory and spasmolytic sesquiterpene alcohols such as α-bisabolol, chamazulene, farnesene, polyenes and several flavonoids. From a dermatological point of view the content of sensitizing sesquiterpene lactones such as anthecotulide is especially important. The composition of the drug, Matricariae flos, depends on the country of origin. Chamomile imported from Argentina may contain over 7% of the strongly allergenic anthecotulide, and in addition may be contaminated with the morphologically similar dog fennel (*Anthemis cotula* L.), which is a strong sensitizer. In contrast, chamomile of European origin contains only traces of anthecotulide (12).

Common medicinal preparations of chamomile include essential oil, hot-water extract (tea) and a water/alcohol extract. It is very likely that the tea actually contains sesquiterpene lactones (12,16). Apart from anthecotulide, the sesquiterpene lactone matricarin (17) and the coumarin herniarin (31) have been described as possible sensitizers in allergic patients. Contact allergy to German chamomile extract is seen in over 50% of Compositae-sensitive patients (table 2.89.1). However, many positive patch test reactions may in fact be secondary to sensitization to other Compositae, notably chrysanthemum (12,27). Sensitization and elicitation from topical pharmaceutical and cosmetic preparations containing German chamomile appears to be infrequent (12).

Discussion of adverse reactions to German chamomile in this chapter is limited to its extracts and products containing them. Contact allergy to and chemical composition of German chamomile *essential oils* is not presented here but has recently been fully reviewed (39).

CONTACT ALLERGY

Patch testing in groups of patients

There are no recent studies in which consecutive patients suspected of contact dermatitis have been patch tested with German chamomile extract (routine testing). Studies in which groups of *selected* patients have been tested are shown in table 2.89.1. In four of these investigations, patients were sensitive to Compositae and/or had previously reacted to the Compositae mix and were subsequently tested with its 5 ingredients, including chamomile (1,25,26,

28). Between 53% and 75% reacted to chamomile. In a group of 122 patients suspected of contact dermatitis with self-declared adverse reactions to 'botanical products' (cosmetics, detergents, pharmaceutical ointments), only one (0.8%) reacted to German chamomile extract 1% pet. (29). Relevance in the groups of Compositae-sensitive individuals was either not provided or related to the Compositae mix, but was never specified for its ingredient chamomile extract (table 2.89.1).

Table 2.89.1 Patch testing in groups of patients: Selected patient groups

Years and Country	Test conc. & vehicle	Number of patients		Selection of patients (S); Relevance (R); Comments (C)	Ref.
		tested	positive (%)		
2011-2012 Italy	1% pet.	122	1 (0.8%)	S: patients tested with a botanical series, who declared having had adverse reactions to 'botanical' products (cosmetics, detergents, pharmaceutical ointments); R: the reaction was considered to be relevant	29
2000-2004 Denmark	2.5% pet.	76	52 (68%)	S: patients reacting to the Compositae mix 6% (Trolab); R: 80% of positive reactions to all allergens together were considered of current and/or past relevance	1
1996-1999 Germany	?	39	13 (33%)	C: article not read	2
1990-1998 Denmark	2.5% pet.	129	83 (64%)	S: patients sensitive to Compositae; R: not stated	26
1990 Denmark	1% pet.	24	18 (75%)	S: patients reacting to the Compositae mix; R: 75% for 32 patients sensitized to the Compositae mix, not specified for its ingredients including German chamomile	25
1985-1990 Germany	2.5% pet.	85	45 (53%)	S: patients reacting to the Compositae mix; R: nearly all reactions to the Compositae mix were relevant and were most often caused by contact with plants, some by 'natural' cosmetics; C: thirty-three (28%) patients were occupationally sensitized (e.g., florists, gardeners) and 11 (9.3%) had airborne allergic contact dermatitis. The relevance of the reactions to the individual ingredients of the Compositae mix including German chamomile was not specified	28

Case reports and case series

Chamomilla recutita extract was responsible for 1 out of 959 cases of non-fragrance cosmetic allergy where the causal allergen was identified, Belgium, 2000-2010 (3). In a German study performed between 1985 and 1990, a group of 118 patients reacted to the Compositae mix consisting of five ingredients: arnica (*Arnica montana* L.), German chamomile (*Chamomilla recutita*), feverfew (*Tanacetum parthenium*), tansy (*Tanacetum vulgare*) and yarrow (*Achillea millefolium*). In 4 patients, the sensitization was caused by 'natural cosmetics', in 3 by 'natural ointments', in one by a herbal massage oil and in one (probably) by a herbal shampoo, soap and ointment. However, it was not specified, which of the 5 plant extracts was/were the actual sensitizer(s) in these products (28). Contact allergy to German chamomile in cosmetics has been described in 1971, but data are lacking (4, cited in ref. 6).

A woman had a 5-month history of regular flares of a periorbital rash with associated eyelid erythema, eye discomfort and lacrimation. She was patch test positive to parthenolide (a sesquiterpene lactone present in *Tanacetum* species) and later to Chamomilla recutita extract 2.5% pet. The patient admitted drinking chamomile tea (infusion) regularly for the prevention of colds. When she inadvertently used a shampoo containing German chamomile, the facial dermatitis flared (32). A beautician developed occupational allergic contact dermatitis of the hands from working with a herbal beauty mask containing 24% chamomile flowers. She also had a type-I allergy to chamomile resulting in respiratory symptoms (36).

A woman gave a two-week history of three episodes of periorbital swelling, spreading to the cheeks and forehead. Patch tests were positive to 'a cosmetic' containing 12.5% plant extracts. Testing with the individual ingredients produced a positive patch test to bisabolol 1% pet. with a purity of 87-93%. Impurities in the sample of bisabolol were bisabolene, bisabolol oxide, farnesol, nerolidol and chamazulene. Patch tests in 30 controls were negative. It was not specifically mentioned that German chamomile was one of the plant extracts, but this was implied as the entire Discussion section was about chamomile and bisabolol is one of the main components of German chamomile (40).

Contact allergy to Chamomilla recutita extract in non-cosmetic products

Pharmaceutical products

In an early German study of 1000 cases of contact dermatitis, 34% were iatrogenically acquired and chamomile preparations were among the most frequently sensitizing substances (38). There is a lack of information, however, on both details of patch test results to rule out reactions to other constituents of the preparations, and on botanical identification of the chamomile used (38). In another older German study, 200 non-selected patients were patch tested with 11 chamomile-containing products and extracts of (probably German) chamomile. Of 21 (10.5%) persons with positive reactions to the chamomile herbal preparations, 3 tested positive to a chamomile extract and only one reaction was considered relevant due to previous reaction to a chamomile ointment (4).

Kamillosan® is the trade name of a range of botanical pharmaceutical products that contain a water/alcohol extract of *Chamomilla recutita* cultivars 'Degumille' and 'Manzana' which are free of sesquiterpene lactones. It is also filtered to eliminate pollens, which may be the cause of immediate-type reactions (see the section Immediate contact reactions below) (12). Nevertheless, there have been some cases of contact allergy to Kamillosan ointment (6), cream (7), lotion (6), solution (9,10) and concentrate (7,8).

In The Netherlands, in 1988 and 1989, 1032 consecutive or randomly chosen patients were patch tested with Kamillosan (probably the ointment) and 5 reacted to it. Two also reacted to lanolin, a constituent of the ointment, which therefore may have been the culprit, but two others had a positive patch test to a leaf of the German chamomile. Relevance was uncertain (5). In Poland, 982 consecutive patients with contact dermatitis were patch tested, 830 with Kamillosan solution prepared according to manufacturer's instructions and 152 with both Kamillosan cream and Kamillosan ointment. One patient with very high exposure to chamomile tested positive for the solution (10).

The Kamillosan available in the UK contains or contained an extract of the Roman chamomile, *Chamaemelum nobile*, better known as *Anthemis nobilis*. Contact allergy to this preparation, the composition of which must be very different from the extract of the German chamomile, has also been reported (11).

Chamomile tea
Contact allergy to chamomile tea has been reported repeatedly (9,18,19,22,23), including airborne allergic contact dermatitis (18,19) and systemic contact dermatitis (9,19,22). One patient had ACD from topical application of a chamomile fomentation; the dermatitis flared after drinking a cup of chamomile tea (22). One patient had ACD from compresses with German chamomile tea (23). The herbal teas likely contain sesquiterpenes lactones (16).

Cross-reactions, pseudo-cross-reactions and co-reactions
Cross-sensitization between Compositae plants and extracts is frequent (26). It is likely that a large proportion of the positive reactions to German chamomile are due to primary chrysanthemum sensitivity (26,27). Roman chamomile (*Anthemis nobilis*) extract (17).

Provocation tests
Several patients known to be allergic to chamomile extract and patch tested with herbal products and chamomile-containing cosmetics reacted to one or more of these products (that had not been used by the patients) (15). Of 20 patients previously reacting to the sesquiterpene lactone mix, 14 (70%) had positive patch test reactions to tea made of German chamomile (16). Thirty-five patients previously reacting to the sesquiterpene lactone mix were patch tested with German chamomile tea, Roman chamomile tea and strips of the thin-layer chromatograms of German chamomile tea. Thirty patients (86%) reacted to the German chamomile tea, 15 (43%) to Roman chamomile tea and fifteen (43%) tested positively to one or more spots on the thin-layer chromatogram, with many individual reaction patterns. Patch testing with thin-layer chromatograms of German chamomile tea thus showed the presence of several – unidentified – allergens (17).

Presence in cosmetic products and chemical analyses
In August 2017, *Chamomilla recutita* was present in 87 cosmetic products, and its extracts in 11 (leaf extract), 245 (extract) resp. 1245 (flower extract) products of 70,166 cosmetic products of which the composition is known in EWG's Skin Deep Cosmetics Database, USA (http://www.ewg.org/skindeep/).In the USA, in April 2017, Matricaria chamomilla (German chamomile) extract was present in 1059 of 56,714 cosmetic products of which the composition is known in FDA's Voluntary Cosmetic Registration Program (VCRP) (data obtained from FDA, May 2017).

OTHER SIDE EFFECTS

Irritant contact dermatitis
A woman had dermatitis from boiled German chamomile seeds, applied as poultice after it had cooled down, over the knee region to relieve pain. The diagnosis was irritant contact dermatitis, but a patch test to *Chamomilla recutita* was positive (44).

Immediate-type reactions

There have been several cases of immediate-type reactions to chamomile, especially to chamomile tea. It appears that these represent type-1 allergic reactions to chamomile pollens cross-reacting to other pollens, notably from *Artemisia* and *Ambrosia* species (13,34,35,37,42,43).

Chamomile tea

Seven patients using chamomile tea for eye washing suffered from conjunctivitis; two of them also had lid angioedema. All had positive skin prick tests to the chamomile tea extract, to Chamomilla recutita pollen extract and Artemisia vulgaris pollen extract. Positive conjunctival provocations were also observed in all the patients with the chamomile tea. No symptoms were observed after oral challenges with this infusion. IgE-activity against chamomile tea and chamomile and Artemisia extracts was detected by ELISA in the seven patients' sera. Cross-reactivity among these two extracts was observed by an ELISA inhibition study. It was concluded that the chamomile tea eye washing can induce allergic conjunctivitis, chamomile pollens contained in these infusions being the responsible allergens, cross-reacting to Artemisia pollens (13).

An atopic boy experienced hay fever and seasonal asthma caused by a variety of pollen. One night, his mother gave him an infusion of chamomile tea to relieve coughing, dyspnea, and wheezing. Several minutes later the patient's condition suddenly worsened, developing dyspnea, increased coughing, chest tightness and wheezing, abdominal pain, vomiting, and general itchiness of the skin without wheal formation. On arrival in the hospital, he was pale and sweating, became confused, collapsed and lost consciousness. This severe reaction had developed after his first ingestion of chamomile tea. Studies revealed the presence of immediate skin test reactivity and a positive passive transfer test to chamomile tea extract. Moreover, both specific anti-chamomile tea extract and anti-chamomile pollen extract IgE-antibodies were detected by an ELISA technique. Cross-reactivity among chamomile tea extract and the pollens of German chamomile, *Ambrosia trifida* (giant ragweed), and *Artemisia vulgaris* (mugwort) was demonstrated by an ELISA-inhibition study. These findings suggested a type I IgE-mediated immunologic reaction to the pollens of chamomile contained in the chamomile tea, being a cross-reaction to Artemisia pollen to which he was previously sensitized (35).

A woman awoke early one morning with a headache. She drank one cup of chamomile tea and simultaneously ingested two aspirin tablets. Within 20 minutes, she had a severe anaphylactic reaction with generalized hives, upper airway obstruction, and pharyngeal edema. Chamomile was not tested, but she underwent graded oral aspirin challenges and experienced no immediate or delayed allergic reactions, so it was concluded that the chamomile tea had caused the anaphylactic reaction (33).

A woman, suffering from ragweed hay fever, was offered a cup of chamomile tea. Within one to two minutes after several sips of tea, the patient developed abdominal cramps, thickness of her tongue, and a tight sensation in her throat. This was followed by angioedema of her lips and eyes, diffuse pruritus, and a full sensation in her ears. Later, a scratch test with chamomile tea produced a large wheal-and-flare reaction with pseudopod formation. Scratch tests with chamomile tea were applied to 15 additional patients who had positive reactions to ragweed, and 5 of them developed positive reactions to the tea. None gave a history of ingestion of chamomile tea. It was suggested that the reaction to chamomile tea was due to cross-sensitivity to ragweed sensitization: ragweed (Ambrosia spp.) also belongs to the Compositae family (34).

A woman, with a history of seasonal rhinitis, conjunctivitis and exercise-induced asthma, developed eyelid angioedema after applying compresses of chamomile tea to her eyelids in the hope of gaining relief from runny eyes. Prick tests showed a strong positive reaction to *Artemisia vulgaris* and *Artemisia absinthium* and an immediate positive skin response to German chamomile tea extract. IgE-antibodies were positive to chamomile and *Artemisia vulgaris*. Afterwards, an oral challenge test was performed with diluted chamomile tea. The only symptom that the patient developed was pruritus of the entire face (37).

One individual had an episode of severe anaphylaxis with generalized urticaria, angioedema and severe dyspnea one hour after consuming chamomile tea. Laboratory examination demonstrated specific IgE against chamomile. Skin prick test and a labial provocation test with chamomile showed a strong positive reaction (42). An unknown number of patients had systemic allergic reaction from chamomile tea, which were probably caused by an IgE-mediated allergy to Compositae pollen (46).

Other products

Anaphylaxis from a chamomile enema containing glycerol and Kamillosan (an oily extract of chamomile flowers) characterized by nausea, urticaria, larynx edema, tachycardia, and hypotension in a woman while giving birth resulted in the death of her child from asphyxia. The cause was probably an IgE-mediated reaction to a homologue of the birch pollen allergen Bet v1, present in chamomile (20). Another woman had received a chamomile-containing enema in preparation for surgery. Five minutes later, she developed bronchospasm, colicky pains, vomitus and she became unconscious. A skin prick test with chamomile was positive, and specific IgE was demonstrated (14). Anaphylaxis from chamomile tea used as an enema has been reported in another individual (47).

One patient had contact urticaria from chamomile extract in a cosmetic cream; it was not mentioned whether it concerned *Anthemis nobilis* (Roman chamomile) or *Chamomilla recutita* (German chamomile) (21). A woman applied a cosmetic skin mask formulation to her face and noted rapid onset of transient rash, burning, stinging and itching at the application sites. Immediate open testing (without prick, scratch or chamber) to intact forearm skin revealed extensive wheal and flare to many components including chamomile extract 1% physiologic saline (unknown whether it concerned German or Roman chamomile) (24).

A review of contact urticaria caused by ingredients of cosmetics has been provided in ref 30.

Miscellaneous side effects

A beautician had a type-I allergy to chamomile resulting in respiratory symptoms (sneezing, rhinitis, dacryorrhea) and orbital pruritus when having contact with chamomile flowers or a beauty mask containing them. She also had contact allergy to the mask and chamomile flowers resulting in occupational allergic hand dermatitis (36). A 20-year-old woman with a proven allergy to chamomile suffered from short-lasting rhinitis when using a toilet paper scented with chamomile extract. The prick-by-prick test performed with the toilet paper was positive. The diagnosis was confirmed by a challenge test (45).

LITERATURE

1   Paulsen E, Andersen KE. Patch testing with constituents of Compositae mixes. Contact Dermatitis 2012;66:241-246

2   Geier J, Hausen BM. Epikutantesting mit dem Kompositen-mix. Allergologie 2000;23:334-341

3   Travassos AR, Claes L, Boey L, Drieghe J, Goossens A. Non-fragrance allergens in specific cosmetic products. Contact Dermatitis 2011;65:276-285

4   Beetz B, Cramer HJ, Mehlhorn HCh. Zur Häuftigkeit der epidermalen Allergie gegenüber Kamille in kamillenhaltigen Arzneimitteln und Kosmetika. Dermatologische Monatschrift 1971;157:505-510

5   Bruynzeel DP, Van Ketel WG, Young E, Van Joost Th, Smeenk G. Contact sensitization by alternative topical medicaments containing plant extracts. Contact Dermatitis 1992;27:278-279

6   Van Ketel WG. Allergy to *Matricaria chamomilla*. Contact Dermatitis 1982;8:143

7   Klaschka F, Patzelt-Wenczler R. Das allergene Potential der Kamille vom Typ IV in Externa. Allergologie 1988;11:100-103

8   Jablonska S, Rudzki E. Kamillosan® Konzentrat – ein nicht allergisierender Extrakt aus Kamille. Z Hautkrankh 1996;71:542-546

9   Rudzki E, Rebandel P. Positive patch test with Kamillosan® in a patient with hypersensitivity to camomile. Contact Dermatitis 1998;38:164

10 Rudzki E, Jablonska S. Kamillosan® is a safe product of camomile for topical application: results of patch testing consecutive patients with contact dermatitis. J Dermatol Treatment 2000;11:161-163

11 McGeorge BCL, Steele MC. Allergic contact dermatitis of the nipple from Roman chamomile ointment. Contact Dermatitis 1991;24:139-140

12 Paulsen E. Contact sensitization from Compositae-containing herbal remedies and cosmetics. Contact Dermatitis 2002;47:189-198

13 Subiza J, Subiza JL, Alonso M, Hinojosa M, Garcia R, Jerez M, et al. Allergic conjunctivitis to chamomile tea. Ann Allergy 1990;65:127-132

14 Reider N, Sepp N, Fritsch P, Weinlich G, Jensen-Jarolim E. Anaphylaxis to camomile: clinical features and allergen cross-reactivity. Clin Exp Allergy 2000;30:1436-1443

15 Paulsen E, Chistensen LP, Andersen KE. Cosmetics and herbal remedies with Compositae plant extracts – are they tolerated by Compositae-allergic patients?. Contact Dermatitis 2008;58:15-23

16 Lundh K, Hindsén M, Gruvberger B, Möller H, Svensson Å, Bruze M. Contact allergy to herbal teas derived from Asteraceae plants. Contact Dermatitis 2006;54:196-201

17 Lundh K, Gruvberger B, Möller H, Persson L, Hindsén M, Zimerson E, Svensson Å, Bruze, M. Patch testing with thin-layer chromatograms of chamomile tea in patients allergic to sesquiterpene lactones. Contact Dermatitis 2007;57:218-223

18 Anzai A, Vázquez Herrera NE, Tosti A. Airborne allergic contact dermatitis caused by chamomile tea. Contact Dermatitis 2015;72:254-255

19 Rycroft RJG. Recurrent facial dermatitis from chamomile tea. Contact Dermatitis 2003;48:229

20 Jensen-Jarolim E, Reider N, Fritsch R, Breiteneder H. Fatal outcome of anaphylaxis to camomile-containing enema during labor: a case study. J Allergy Clin Immunol 1998;102:1041-1042

21 Rudzki E, Rapiejko EZP, Rebandel P, Jaworski E. Oral allergy syndrome with contact urticaria from cosmetic creams. Contact Dermatitis 1999;40:326

22 Rodriguez-Serna M, Sanchez-Motilla JM, Ramon R, Aliaga A. Allergic and systemic contact dermatitis from Matricaria chamomilla tea. Contact Dermatitis 1998;39:192-193

23 Pereira F, Santos R, Pereira A. Contact dermatitis from chamomile tea. Contact Dermatitis 1997;36:307

24 West I, Maibach HI. Contact urticaria syndrome from multiple cosmetic components. Contact Dermatitis 1995;32:121

25 Paulsen E, Andersen KE, Hausen BM. Compositae dermatitis in a Danish dermatology department in one year. Contact Dermatitis 1993;29:6-10

26 Paulsen E, Andersen KE, Hausen BM. Sensitization and cross-reaction patterns in Danish Compositae-allergic patients. Contact Dermatitis 2001;45:197-204

27 Hausen BM. The sensitizing capacity of Compositae plants. III. Test results and cross-reactions in Compositae-sensitive patients. Dermatologica 1979;159:1-11

28 Hausen BM. A 6-year experience with Compositae mix. Am J Contact Dermatitis 1996;7:94-99

29 Corazza M, Borghi A, Gallo R, Schena D, Pigatto P, Lauriola MM, et al. Topical botanically derived products: use, skin reactions, and usefulness of patch tests. A multicentre Italian study. Contact Dermatitis 2014;70:90-97

30 Verhulst L, Goossens A. Cosmetic components causing contact urticaria: a review and update. Contact Dermatitis 2016;75:333-344

31 Paulsen E, Otkjær A, Andersen KE. The coumarin herniarin as a sensitizer in German chamomile [*Chamomilla recutita* (L.) Rauschert, Compositae]. Contact Dermatitis 2010; 62:338-342

32 Cusack C, Buckley C. Compositae dermatitis in a herbal medicine enthusiast. Contact Dermatitis 2005;53:120-121

33 Casterline CL. Allergy to chamomile tea. JAMA 1990;244:330-331

34 Benner M, Lee H. Anaphylactic reaction to chamomile tea. J Allergy Clin Immunol 1973;52:307

35 Subiza J, Subiza JL, Hinojosa M, Garcia R, Jerez M, Valdivieso R, et al. Anaphylactic reaction after the ingestion of chamomile tea: a study of cross-reactivity with other Compositae pollens. J Allergy Clin Immunol 1989;84:353-358

36 Rudzki E, Rapiejko P, Rebandel P. Occupational contact dermatitis, with asthma and rhinitis, from camomile in a cosmetician also with contact urticaria from both camomile and lime flowers. Contact Dermatitis 2003;49:162

37 Foti C, Nettis E, Panebianco R, Cassano N, Diaferio A, Pia DP. Contact urticaria from *Matricaria chamomilla*. Contact Dermatitis 2000;42:360-361

38 Schubert H. Das iatrogene Kontaktekzem. Allergie Asthma 1967;13:25-30

39 De Groot AC, Schmidt E. Essential oils: Contact allergy and chemical composition. Boca Raton, Fl, USA: CRC Press Taylor and Francis group, 2016:193-204

40 Wilkinson SM, Hausen BM, Beck MH. Allergic contact dermatitis from plant extracts in a cosmetic. Contact Dermatitis 1995;33:58-59

41 Aberer W. Contact allergy and medicinal herbs. J Dtsch Dermatol Ges 2008;6:15-24

42 Andres C, Chen WC, Ollert M, Mempel M, Darsow U, Ring J. Anaphylactic reaction to camomile tea. Allergol Int 2009;58:135-136

43 De la Torre Morín F, Sánchez Machín I, García Robaina JC, Fernández-Caldas E, Sánchez Triviño M. Clinical cross-reactivity between *Artemisia vulgaris* and *Matricaria chamomilla* (chamomile). J Investig Allergol Clin Immunol 2001;11:118-122

44 Duymaz A, Karabekmez FE, Keskin M, Tosun Z. Is it a chemical burn or an irritant contact dermatitis? J Plast Reconstr Aesthet Surg. 2009;62:e663-664

45 Scala G. Acute, short-lasting rhinitis due to camomile-scented toilet paper in patients allergic to compositae. Int Arch Allergy Immunol 2006;139:330-331

46 Florido-Lopez JF, Gonzalez-Delgado P, Saenz de San Pedro B, Perez-Miranda C, Arias de Saavedra JM, Marin-Pozo JF: Allergy to natural honeys and camomile tea. Int Arch Allergy Immunol 1995; 108: 170-174

47 Thien FC. Chamomile tea enema anaphylaxis. Med J Aust 2001;2;175:54

2.90 CHITOSAN GLUCONATE*

Not an INCI name

Chitosan gluconate is neither present in CosIng nor in the Personal Care Products Council Ingredient Database. As the chitosan gluconate in the case reports of contact allergy was indicated by the manufacturer as 'chitin', which must be deacetylated to form chitosan to be useful for incorporation into cosmetic products, the identifiers shown here are those of chitosan.

IDENTIFICATION CHITOSAN

Description/definition	: Chitosan is deacylated chitin
Chemical class(es)	: Biological polymers and their derivatives
Chemical/IUPAC name	: Methyl *N*-[(2*S*,3*R*,4*R*,5*S*,6*R*)-5-[(2*S*,3*R*,4*R*,5*S*,6*R*)-3-amino-5-[(2*S*,3*R*,4*R*,5*S*,6*R*)-3-amino-5-[(2*S*,3*R*,4*R*,5*S*,6*R*)-3-amino-5-[(2*S*,3*R*,4*R*,5*S*,6*R*)-3-amino-5-[(2*S*,3*R*,4*R*,5*S*,6*R*)-3-amino-5-[(2*S*,3*R*,4*R*,5*S*,6*R*)-3-amino-4,5-dihydroxy-6-(hydroxymethyl)oxan-2-yl]oxy-4-hydroxy-6-(hydroxymethyl)oxan-2-yl]oxy-4-hydroxy-6-(hydroxymethyl)oxan-2-yl]oxy-4-hydroxy-6-(hydroxymethyl)oxan-2-yl]oxy-4-hydroxy-6-(hydroxymethyl)oxan-2-yl]oxy-4-hydroxy-6-(hydroxymethyl)oxan-2-yl]oxy-2-[(2*R*,3*S*,4*R*,5*R*,6*S*)-5-amino-6-[(2*R*,3*S*,4*R*,5*R*,6*R*)-5-amino-4,6-dihydroxy-2-(hydroxymethyl)oxan-3-yl]oxy-4-hydroxy-2-(hydroxymethyl)oxan-3-yl]oxy-4-hydroxy-6-(hydroxymethyl)oxan-3-yl]carbamate
Other names	: Poliglusam; deacetylchitin
CAS registry number (s)	: 9012-76-4
EC number(s)	: 618-480-0
Merck Index monograph	: 3335 (Chitin)
Function(s) in cosmetics	: EU: film forming; hair fixing. USA: film formers; hair fixatives
Patch testing	: 10% water (gluconate) (2)
Molecular formula	: $C_{56}H_{103}N_9O_{39}$

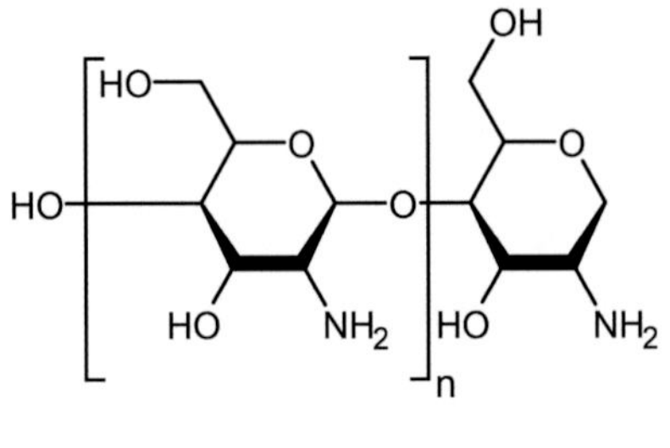

GENERAL

Chitin is a cellulose-like biopolymer, predominantly unbranched chains of β-(1→4)-2-acetamido-2-deoxy-D-glucose (also named *N*-acetyl-D-glucosamine) residues. Being a form of poly-acetyl-glucosamine, it is an important structural element of the integuments of arthropods, particularly crustaceans, molluscs, unicellular organisms, seaweeds, and fungi. As chitin is practically insoluble, except in concentrated acids, it can only be used after partial deacylation. Acetylated groups are replaced by amine groups giving rise to chitosan, a biodegradable polymer with properties of solubility, chelation, dispersion and flocculation. Chitosan is prepared from integuments of crustaceans, mostly shrimps, through deproteinization, demineralization and deacylation. The resulting product is a mixture of polymers from various deacylation and polymerisation levels. Deacylation level and molecular mass influence molecular properties and, along the way, applications (2).

Chitosan is used in cosmetology to make moisturizing creams, after solubilization in certain dilute acids, such as propionic and gluconic acids, since it is insoluble in water. Few laboratories prepare cosmetics with chitosan and even then, they write "with chitin" on the label, perhaps because it looks more ecological. The concentration in moisturizers, soaps and syndets varies from 0.3% to 1% of chitin derivative (2). Other (potential) applications of chitosan can be found in ref. 2

CONTACT ALLERGY

Case reports and case series

A woman presented with papulovesicular dermatitis of the face and neck, with pronounced erythema of the eyelids. She was patch tested with the European standard series and additional allergens, but there were no positive reactions. Later, patch tests were performed with her cosmetic products, which showed a positive reaction to a moisturizing body cream with chitin. When patch tested with the 21 components supplied by the manufacturer at the same concentrations as in the moisturizer, a positive reaction was obtained with chitosan gluconate, the active ingredient of this particular cream. Additional patch testing later showed a positive reaction again to chitosan gluconate 10% water, but patch tests with gluconic acid 5% water, calcium gluconate 2% and 10% water, shrimp and prawn integuments (as is, raw and cooked) were negative. The patient developed neither urticaria nor any clinical symptoms of type I allergy after cutaneous contact with crustaceans or after eating them (2).

Another female patient had a 14-year history of hand eczema. She developed a new episode of hand dermatitis, which worsened when she began applying a cream containing chitin. Patch tests were carried out with the Portuguese standard series, bakery, cosmetic, preservatives and corticosteroid series, and her own topical products. Positive results were obtained with the cream with chitin tested as is. Later, the 23 components of the cream, supplied by the manufacturer at the same concentrations as in the cream, were patch tested, which resulted in positive reactions to 3 ingredients including chitosan gluconate. The test concentration was unknown, but 8 controls were negative (1).

Cross-reactions, pseudo-cross-reactions and co-reactions
Not to gluconic acid or calcium gluconate (2).

Presence in cosmetic products and chemical analyses
In the USA, in April 2017, chitosan gluconate was present in zero of 56,714 cosmetic products of which the composition is known in FDA's Voluntary Cosmetic Registration Program (VCRP) (data obtained from FDA, May 2017). In March 2017, chitosan was present in 30, chitin extract in 2 and chitosan gluconate in zero of 64,983 cosmetic products of which the composition is known in EWG's Skin Deep Cosmetics Database, USA (http://www.ewg.org/skindeep/).

OTHER SIDE EFFECTS

Immediate-type reactions
A woman developed generalized urticaria and difficulty in breathing after oral ingestion of chitosan. Skin tests (prick test and scratch-patch test) were positive to the food. Next, the same tests were done using another commercial source of chitosan, and these were also positive. The patient was diagnosed as having chitosan-induced immediate-type allergy, and was instructed to avoid ingestion of chitosan. She has developed no symptoms thereafter (3).

LITERATURE
1   Pereira F, Pereira C, Lacerda MH. Contact dermatitis due to a cream containing chitin and a Carbitol. Contact Dermatitis 1998;38:290-291
2   Cleenewerck MB, Martin P, Laurent D. Allergic contact dermatitis due to a moisturizing body cream with chitin. Contact Dermatitis 1994;31:196-197
3   Kato Y, Yagami A, Matsunaga K. A case of anaphylaxis caused by the health food chitosan. Arerugi 2005;54:1427-1429 (Article in Japanese)

2.91 CHLORHEXIDINE DIGLUCONATE

IDENTIFICATION

Description/definition	: Chlorhexidine digluconate is a salt of chlorhexidine and gluconic acid, which conforms generally to the formula shown below
Chemical class(es)	: Halogen compounds; organic salts
Chemical/IUPAC name	: (1E)-2-[6-[[Amino-[(E)-[amino-(4-chloroanilino)methylidene]amino]methylidene]amino]hexyl]-1-[amino-(4-chloroanilino)methylidene]guanidine; (2R,3S,4R,5R)-2,3,4,5,6-pentahydroxyhexanoic acid
Other names	: Chlorhexidine gluconate
CAS registry number (s)	: 18472-51-0
EC number(s)	: 242-354-0
CIR review(s)	: J Am Coll Toxicol 1993;12:201-223; Int J Toxicol 1999;18 (Suppl.2):69 (access: www.cir-safety.org/ingredients)
Merck Index monograph	: 3362
Function(s) in cosmetics	: EU: antimicrobial; oral care; preservative. USA: cosmetic biocides; oral care agents; preservatives
EU cosmetic restrictions	: Regulated in Annex V/42 of the Regulation (EC) No. 1223/2009
Patch testing	: 0.5% water (Chemotechnique, SmartPracticeEurope, SmartPracticeCanada); this test conc./vehicle needs improvement (29); 1% water (SmartPracticeCanada); it is advisable to test both with chlorhexidine diacetate and chlorhexidine digluconate (0.5%), as over half of the allergic patients react to the diacetate salt only (63,68); the 1% test concentration is too high and cause irritant reactions, especially the diacetate salt (63,68)
Molecular formula	: $C_{34}H_{54}Cl_2N_{10}O_{14}$

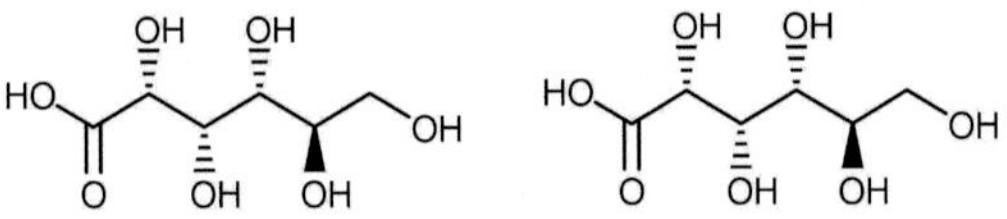

gluconic acid

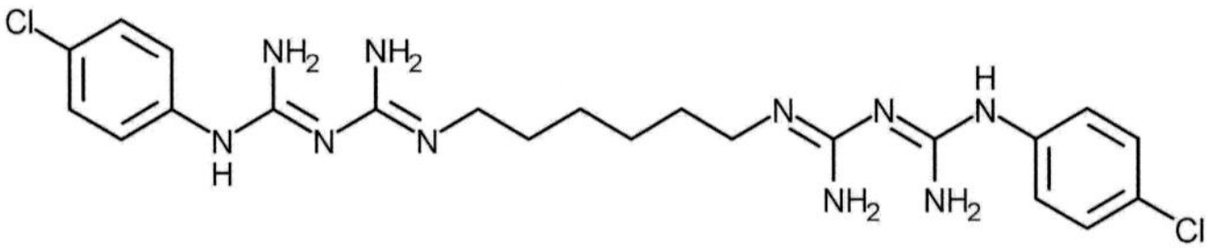

chlorhexidine

GENERAL

Chlorhexidine is a biguanide topical antiseptic which has been in use worldwide since 1954. It is bactericidal against gram-positive and gram-negative bacteria; chlorhexidine is also active against some bacterial spores and viruses and has antifungal activity. With antibiotic-resistant organisms emerging in hospital and community settings, this antiseptic is increasingly recommended in both treatment and prevention protocols. Chlorhexidine, usually in the digluconate formulation and less frequently as a diacetate or dihydrochloride salt, is available in concentrations ranging from 0.05% to 4% in aqueous or alcohol vehicles alone or with other ingredients, such as surfactants, dyes, fragrances, and anesthetics. It is popular for hand washing, daily bathing of intensive care unit patients, nursery neonatal umbilical stump care, preoperative bathing, and surgical site sterilization (74). It is widely used for skin antisepsis before placement of epidural, arterial, and central venous catheters. It has a role in catheter site maintenance, skin cleansing for venipuncture, oropharyngeal decontamination in ventilator patients, burn antisepsis, vaginal sanitation, cleansing before urethral catheter insertion and as a gel for urinary catheterization and vaginal and rectal examinations. Some investigators have advised its use to bathe trauma patients before hospital admission (74). Chlorhexidine has also been impregnated into medical materials, including vascular cannulas and dressings for both vascular and epidural catheters. It has been used for decades by dentists and oral surgeons to control gingivitis and periodontitis (74).

In the home environment, chlorhexidine may be found in products such as mouthwashes, toothpaste, plasters, dressings, ointments, suppositories, disinfectant solutions, antiseptic creams, cleaning fluids, and nose or eye drops. Both the digluconate, and dihydrochloride salts may be found in cosmetic products, but the diacetate salt appears to be used in cosmetics very infrequently, if at all (see the section 'Presence in cosmetic products and chemical analyses' below).

Contact allergy

Related to their widespread use, contact allergy to chlorhexidine is currently infrequent (10,63). In the 1980s, higher prevalence rates 0f 2%-5.4% were found in Denmark (36,65,66). In these studies, it was found that contact allergy to chlorhexidine was primarily diagnosed among patients, especially men, with leg eczema or ulcers (36,65,66). In those days, topical drugs with chlorhexidine were very popular in Denmark. However, in all 3 studies, chlorhexidine digluconate was tested at 1% in water, which we now consider too high as it has irritant properties (63). Indeed, in one study, only 1/14 patients was positive on retesting (65) and in the other, 7 of 16 patients (44%) who had reacted to 1% water only (and not to 1% pet.) was negative on retesting (36).

Contact allergy to chlorhexidine is currently seen in around 0.5% of patients routinely tested for suspected contact dermatitis and most often results from the use of chlorhexidine-containing corticosteroid creams (in Finland), skin disinfectants and oral hygiene products (10,63). People at risk were found to be patients with (atopic) dermatitis, medical staff and patients with leg ulcers and lower leg eczema (27,35). It usually concerns adults, but chlorhexidine sensitization may also be frequent among children with atopic dermatitis (who are treated with chlorhexidine-containing topical corticosteroid preparations) (17). Most patients have multiple contact sensitivities (10).

Chlorhexidine in *cosmetic* products may have caused worsening of skin problems (10), has been listed as cause of cosmetic dermatitis (6,50), and cosmetics with chlorhexidine were – frequently - incriminated by patients allergic to chlorhexidine (unverified) (63), but there is only one (not so very well-) documented case report of cosmetic allergy from chlorhexidine in a cosmetic, a feminine hygiene spray (41).

Immediate-type reactions

IgE-mediated chlorhexidine allergy may lead to type-I allergic reactions, extending from mild local symptoms as itching, erythema, edema and urticaria to – often life-threatening - anaphylaxis in persons with previous immediate-type sensitization. Delayed-type hypersensitivity reactions and immediate-type reactions can sometimes be seen in the same patient (18,19,20,23,116,144). Immediate-type reactions are never caused by cosmetics, but most frequently by urinary catheter gels and skin disinfectants, and to a lesser degree by chlorhexidine-coated central venous lines and disinfectants for the mucosae (see the section 'Immediate-type reactions' below).

In this chapter, both literature on chlorhexidine (di)gluconate (the vast majority), on chlorhexidine (di)acetate and on 'chlorhexidine' (without specification of the salt) is presented. A very useful review article on uses of and adverse reactions to chlorhexidine was published in 2013 (74). The pharmacology and clinical applications of chlorhexidine have been reviewed in 2008 (25). Very useful review articles on type-I allergy to chlorhexidine were published in 2013 (74), 2014 (76) and 2016 (130).

CONTACT ALLERGY

Patch testing in groups of patients
Results of studies testing chlorhexidine digluconate in consecutive patients suspected of contact dermatitis (routine testing) back to 1980 are shown in table 2.91.1. Results of testing in groups of *selected* patients (e.g., patients with suspected cosmetic intolerance, children with atopic dermatitis, patients with leg ulcers, patients tested with a preservative series, individuals suspected of allergy to topical medicaments) back to 1981 are shown in table 2.91.2.

Patch testing in consecutive patients suspected of contact dermatitis: routine testing
In 10 studies in which routine testing with chlorhexidine was performed, rates of sensitization have ranged from 0.5% to 5.4%. With the exception of one small 2003-2005 study from China (48), the higher frequencies have all been observed in the 1980s (36,65,66), when the test concentration used was 1%, which we now consider to be irritant. Relevance has ranged from 31% (65) to 70% (66). Most reactions were caused by topical drugs, topical disinfectants, topical corticosteroid preparations (in Finland [10]) and possibly (not verified by the authors, data based on a questionnaire [63]) by cosmetic products.

Patch testing in groups of selected patients
Results of testing in groups of selected patients (e.g., patients with suspected cosmetic intolerance, children with atopic dermatitis, patients with leg ulcers, patients tested with a preservative series, individuals suspected of allergy to topical medicaments) back to 1981 are shown in table 2.91.2. In 10 investigations, frequencies of sensitization have ranged from 0.3% to 13.1%, but 9 studies scored 3% or lower, of which five had a rate of 1% or lower. The highest frequency (13.1%) was observed in an early study from Denmark, in which patients suspected of allergy to topical medicaments, virtually all of who had leg ulcers / stasis dermatitis, were tested with both chlorhexidine digluconate and chlorhexidine diacetate 1% in water, concentrations which are now considered irritant, which was also mentioned by the authors themselves (for the diacetate preparation) (68). The high frequency of sensitization in this study may be explained by the presence of irritant reactions, testing with both chlorhexidine digluconate and diacetate (which appears to be far more reliable than testing with digluconate alone [63,68]), the selection of patients with leg ulcers / stasis dermatitis (which is a definite risk factor for sensitization) and the popularity of chlorhexidine-containing topical drugs in Denmark at that time. Relevance rates have ranged from 34% to an

unrealistically high 100%, which included 'questionable' and 'past' relevance (5). Culprit products were mentioned in one study only: topical preparations containing chlorhexidine digluconate or diacetate (68).

Table 2.91.1 Patch testing in groups of patients: Routine testing [a]

Years and Country	Test conc. & vehicle	Number of patients tested | positive (%)		Selection of patients (S); Relevance (R); Comments (C)	Ref.
2003-2013 Denmark	1% water, later 0.5%, both diglu- conate and diacetate	8497	82 (1.0%)	R: see specific data in the sections 'Case reports and case series' and 'Contact allergy to chlorhexidine digluconate in non-cosmetic products' below; C: patients were tested with both diacetate and digluconate; of the 82 patients, 43 reacted to diacetate only, 11 to digluconate only and 28 to both; when in 2008 the test concentrations were lowered from 1% to 0.5%, the rate of positive reactions dropped from 1.4% to 0.6%	63
1999-2009 Finland	0.5% water	7610	36 (0.5%)	R: current relevance in 16/36 (44%); most patients had been sensitized from topical corticosteroids containing chlorhexidine and from disinfectants; cosmetic products were suspected of having caused worsening of skin symptoms in 7/36 patients	10
2003-2005 China	0.5% water	599	24 (4.0%)	R: not stated	48
2000-2002 Finland		11,876	(0.5%)	R: not stated	31
1995-1997 Finland		8969	(1.2%)	R: not stated	31
1989-1990 Switzer- land	0.5% water	2295	(2.0%)	R: not stated	34
1985 The Netherlands	1% water	501	4 (0.8%)	R: not stated	51
<1985 Denmark	1% water	2061	48 (2.3%)	R: 15 current relevance, 3 past relevance; C: 15/18 relevant reactions were in patients with leg ulcers / dermatitis; 14 patients were retested after 6 months with chlorhexidine gluconate 1% and only 1 had a positive test; this was ascribed to the 'excited skin syndrome', indicating that most previous reactions had been false-positive	65
1982-1984 Denmark	1% water and pet.	1063	52 (5.4%)	R: about half were considered to be 'truly allergic'; C: 7/16 (44%) reacting to 1% water only were negative upon retesting; 10/27 had a positive ROAT (1 week) to chlorhexidine cream 1%; about half of the relevant reactions were in patients with leg ulcers / stasis dermatitis	36
1978-1980 Denmark	1% water [b]	551	20 (3.6%)	R: 14 were relevant from topical treatment of skin infections (n=4) or of venous or traumatic ulcers (n=10)	66

[a] tested with chlorhexidine *digluconate* unless otherwise indicated
[b] tested with 'chlorhexidine'

Case reports and case series

'Chlorhexidine' was stated to be the (or an) allergen in 3 patients in a group of 603 individuals suffering from cosmetic dermatitis, seen in the period 2010-2015 in Leuven, Belgium (50). Four positive patch test reactions to 'chlorhexidine' were ascribed to cosmetic allergy (6). In a group of 36 individuals with positive patch tests to chlorhexidine, cosmetic products were suspected of having caused worsening of skin symptoms in 7 of the 36 patients (10).

In a retrospective study from Denmark, patients who had previously shown a positive patch test reaction to chlorhexidine diacetate and/or digluconate were contacted and asked in a questionnaire about the cause of the allergy and possible re-exposure. Of 47 responders, 19 (40%) reported knowing the cause of the allergy. Incriminated *cosmetic* products were cream (n=7), hair product (n=5), and make-up or make-up remover (n=1). *Non-cosmetic* products are mentioned in the next section. It should be realized that the causality could not be verified by the investigators, but in many cases, these products had caused symptoms in allergic patients from re-exposure after the diagnosis of contact allergy (63).

Each time a young woman used a 'feminine hygiene spray' (essentially a feminine genital deodorant), dermatitis and itching occurred. When examined, an eczematous, vulvar, and inguinal dermatitis was observed. When tested with the suspected ingredients of the product, the patient had a strongly positive patch test reaction to 'chlorhexidine' (41).

Table 2.91.2 Patch testing in groups of patients: Selected patient groups [a]

Years and Country	Test conc. & vehicle	Number of patients tested	Number of patients positive (%)	Selection of patients (S); Relevance (R); Comments (C)	Ref.
1993-2012 Australia	0.5% water	1565	47 (3.0%)	S: not stated; R: 16/47 (34%); C: tested with digluconate	146
	0.5% water	840	28 (3.3%)	S: not stated; R: 13/28 (46%): C: tested with diacetate; causative products were not mentioned	
2010-2011 Korea	0.5% pet.	584	12 (2.1%)	S: patients suspected of allergic cosmetic dermatitis; R: not stated	49
2006-2011 IVDK	0.5% water	6984	(0.4%)	S: patients suspected of cosmetic intolerance and tested with a preservative series; R: not stated	54
1996-2009 IVDK	0.5% pet.	80,906	368 (0.45%)	S: not specified; R: not specified	7
2004-2008 France	0.5% water	423	10 (2.4%)	S: patients with leg ulcers; R: not stated	47
2000-2007 USA	0.5% water	944	9 (1.0%)	S: patients tested with a supplemental cosmetic screening series; R: 100%; C: weak study: a. high rate of macular erythema and weak reactions; b. relevance figures included 'questionable' and 'past' relevance	5
1997-2007 France	0.5% water [b]	641	17 (2.7%)	S: consecutive children <16 with atopic dermatitis; R: previous use in 5/17 patients, current use in 1/17	17
1990-1994 Germany	0.5% water	11,264	50 (0.4%)	S: patients tested with a preservative series; R: not stated	46
1987-1989 Denmark	1% water, diacetate and digluconate	297	39 (13.1%)	S: patients suspected of allergy to topical medicaments, virtually all had stasis dermatitis / leg ulcers; 3 reactions to digluconate only, 21 to diacetate only, 15 to both; of 31 reactions in leg ulcer patients, 21 were currently relevant, 3 past relevance, from topical preparations (diacetate and digluconate); 1% diacetate was considered to be irritant	68
1980-1981 4 Scandinavian countries	0.5% water [b]	745	2 (0.3%)	S: patients suspected of sun-related skin disease; R: not stated	58

[a] tested with chlorhexidine *digluconate* unless otherwise indicated
[b] tested with 'chlorhexidine'
IVDK: Information Network of Departments of Dermatology, Germany, Austria, Switzerland

Contact allergy to chlorhexidine digluconate in non-cosmetic products

Antiseptics
In a retrospective study from Denmark, patients who had previously shown a positive patch test reaction to chlorhexidine diacetate and/or digluconate were contacted and asked in a questionnaire about the cause of the allergy and possible re-exposure. Of 47 responders, 19 (40%) reported knowing the cause of the allergy. Incriminated *non-cosmetic* products were products used at a hospital, by a doctor or a dentist (n=9), wet wipe or other skin disinfectant (n=5), wound dressing (n=5), mouth wash (n=2), and other products (n=2). Incriminated *cosmetic* products are mentioned in the previous section. It should be realized that the causality could not be verified by the investigators, but in many cases, these products had caused symptoms in allergic patients from re-exposure after the diagnosis of contact allergy (63).

In a 2-year retrospective study, the members of the French Dermato-Allergology Vigilance Network Revidal together found 16 cases of contact allergy to chlorhexidine, i.e., antiseptics containing chlorhexidine; the active principle was probably not tested separately (30). Nine children had allergic contact dermatitis from chlorhexidine gluconate in antiseptic solutions (53). In the period 1983-2002, at St. John's Institute of Dermatology, London, UK, there were only five positive patch tests to chlorhexidine, of which 3 were of current relevance, all caused by antiseptic products (32).

Four (student) nurses had occupational ACD from chlorhexidine in skin disinfecting preparations (146). Three patients had ACD from chlorhexidine digluconate used in 0.05%-0.5% solutions for wound treatment (71). A child of 23 months developed ACD of the face from an antiseptic preparation; he was previously sensitized by disinfection of the umbilical cord for 6 weeks with a disinfecting solution (70). Other single case reports of ACD from chlorhexidine in antiseptic products have been published (23,44,61,62,65,66,67,72,145).

Other products
One of 15 patients with conjunctivitis related to soft contact lenses reacted to chlorhexidine digluconate; it was implied but not verified that the lens solution used contained chlorhexidine digluconate (45). A man had allergic contact balanitis from chlorhexidine in the vaginal lubricating gel used by his wife ('consort' or 'connubial' contact dermatitis (33).

A woman had allergic contact dermatitis of the eyelids from chlorhexidine in a lens cleaning solution (69). A 14-year-old girl experienced a combined delayed- and immediate-type allergy to chlorhexidine. She first developed an eczematous reaction in the face following the long-term application of an antiacne preparation. A use test (Repeated Open Application Test, ROAT) on the forearm was positive. Epicutaneous tests with 1% chlorhexidine gluconate and acetate were both positive (144).

Cross-reactions, pseudo-cross-reactions and co-reactions
Chlorhexidine diacetate (35,36,61,63).

Presence in cosmetic products and chemical analyses
In August 2017, chlorhexidine digluconate was present in 6 (chlorhexidine), 165 (chlorhexidine dihydrochloride), 98 (chlorhexidine digluconate) resp. zero (chlorhexidine diacetate) of 70,516 cosmetic products of which the composition is known in EWG's Skin Deep Cosmetics Database, USA (http://www.ewg.org/skindeep/). In the USA, in April 2017, chlorhexidine digluconate was present in 255 of 56,714 cosmetic products of which the composition is known in FDA's Voluntary Cosmetic Registration Program (VCRP) (data obtained from FDA, May 2017).

Chlorhexidine was present in 42 of 4737 (0.9%) commonly used cosmetic products of which the full composition was known in 2016 in The Contact Allergen Management Program (CAMP) database of the American Contact Dermatitis Society (57). By checking labels for chlorhexidine, chlorhexidine diacetate, chlorhexidine digluconate, and chlorhexidine dihydrochloride, 'chlorhexidine' was found in 80 of 2251 cosmetic products (3.6%) in 2013 in Denmark, in the following categories: hair products (57/760), creams (9/324), face washes (4/24), wet wipes (4/63), skin tonics (3/22), make-up removers (2/25), and mouth washes (1/17). Chlorhexidine concentrations in 10 selected cosmetics were 0.01%-0.15% (42). Later, it was established that 42 of the 80 products contained chlorhexidine digluconate, 33 contained chlorhexidine dihydrochloride, but none contained chlorhexidine diacetate (the salt used could not be identified in five products) (63).

In April 2013, the Hospital Pharmacy in the Capital Region of Denmark, which is the pharmaceutical supplier for all hospitals in the Copenhagen area, was contacted to search for products containing chlorhexidine. The Pharmacy provided a list of all 42 chlorhexidine-containing products supplied to the hospitals by the pharmacy. Product types, application sites, and declared concentrations used in the products were as follows: **Skin**: skin disinfectant (n=19, 0.05-4%); ointment, gel, or cream (n=3; 0.05-1%); powder (n=1, 1%); scrub (n=4, 4%); dressing (n=1, 0.5%). **Mouth**: dental gel (n=2, 1-2%); mouthwash (n=4, 0.1-0.2%); thrush treatment (n=1, 0.1%); tablet for pharyngitis (n=1, 5 mg per tablet). **Urinary tract**: bladder irrigation (n=1, 0.02%); urethral gel in combination with lidocaine (n=3, 0.05%). **Vagina**: cream (n=1, 1%). **Eyes**: eye drops (n=1, 0.02%). The pharmacy also supplied 20 and 85% chlorhexidine solutions, requiring further dilution before use. 27 Products contained chlorhexidine digluconate, six contained chlorhexidine diacetate, and three contained chlorhexidine dihydrochloride (the salt used could not be identified in six products). Products such as central venous catheters and skin cleansing wipes are classified as medical utensils and are not distributed via the Hospital Pharmacy, and thus, they were not identified during this study (64).

In 2009, in the USA, the ingredient lists of 796 hair products from one company were screened for the presence of chlorhexidine digluconate. Chlorhexidine digluconate was present in 0% of 279 shampoos, in 11% of 231 conditioners, and in 1 of 286 styling products (52). In Germany, in 2006-2009, the labels of 4680 cosmetic products were screened for the presence of preservatives. Chlorhexidine was present in 0.2% of the products, according to labelling information (56). Chlorhexidine was present in 0.5% of 204 cosmetic products (92 shampoos, 61 hair conditioners, 34 liquid soaps, 17 wet tissues) in Sweden, 2008 (9). Chlorhexidine was present in 1.9% of 8012 cosmetic products in Finland, 1999-2008; the products included creams, facial liquids, dental products, make-up removers, hair cosmetics and, especially, eye care products (10).

OTHER SIDE EFFECTS

Irritant contact dermatitis
Irritation and irritant contact dermatitis from chlorhexidine antiseptics are far from rare, but may usually be caused by the alcoholic vehicle. Chlorhexidine 1% in alcohol for patch testing was shown to be definitely irritant (60). Chlorhexidine digluconate–impregnated central access catheter dressings may cause irritant dermatitis, especially in neonates and immunocompromised patients. The contribution of chlorhexidine to this adverse effect is unknown; the long contact time, occlusion and ambient temperature and humidity also play a role (96).

Photosensitivity

Photopatch testing in groups of patients
Results of photopatch testing with chlorhexidine in patients suspected of photoallergic contact dermatitis or other photodermatoses are shown in table 2.91.3. In all five investigations, low frequencies of photocontact allergy ranging

from 0.3% to 1.6% have been observed. Relevance rates ranged from 0% (2) to 100% (8), but the number of photoallergic patients in these studies were small (n=2 and n=3). Culprit products were not mentioned.

Table 2.91.3 Photopatch testing in groups of patients [a]

Years and Country	Test conc. & vehicle	Number of patients tested	positive (%)		Selection of patients (S); Relevance (R); Comments (C)	Ref.
2005-2014 China	0.5%	1292	20	(1.6%)	S: patients suspected of photodermatoses; R: not stated	55
2004-2006 Italy	0.1% pet.	1082	3	(0.3%)	S: patients with histories and clinical features suggestive of photoallergic contact dermatitis; 1/3 were cases of photoaugmented contact allergy; R: 100%	8
1993-2006 USA	0.5% water, diacetate	76	1	(1.3%)	S: not stated; R: 94% of all reactions to antimicrobials were considered 'not relevant'	4
1993-1994 France	0.5% water	? (<370)	2	?	S: patients with suspected photodermatitis; R: no relevance	2
1985-1993 Italy	[b]	1050	7	(0.7%)	S: patients suspected of photoallergic contact dermatitis; R: not specified (78% for all photoallergens together)	1

[a] tested with chlorhexidine *digluconate* unless otherwise indicated
[b] tested with 'chlorhexidine'

Case reports and case series
A man developed vesicular dermatitis from chlorhexidine disinfectant used for pre-operative wound cleansing. Both a patch test and a photopatch test with chlorhexidine were positive. The authors suggested that the lights in the operating theatre had augmented the eczematous reaction (3).

Immediate-type reactions
IgE-mediated immediate-type allergic reactions to chlorhexidine (usually digluconate, sometimes acetate [93]) have been reported frequently with symptoms varying from mild local reactions with swelling and localized redness or (contact) urticaria to – often life-threatening - anaphylaxis with generalized urticaria, cardiac problems and anaphylactic shock; respiratory compromise is very infrequently reported (76). The symptoms can develop within a few minutes up to some 45 minutes (99). In some of the cases, urticaria and generalized flushing heralded the drop in blood pressure, but in others, there was no cutaneous indication of the source of the life-threatening hypotension, bradycardia, ventricular fibrillation or cardiac arrest (74). Most reactions have been serious (124) and fatal reactions have been observed (123). The serious reactions have often been reported to be preceded by milder reactions (18); therefore, allergy should be suspected when facing symptoms such as localized swelling or systemic rashes after exposure to chlorhexidine.

Although up to recently considered a rare type-I allergen (at least related to its extremely widespread use), chlorhexidine is increasingly recognized as a cause of perioperative allergy in many countries. Indeed, in Denmark it was recently reported that chlorhexidine caused nearly 10% of all perioperative allergic reactions. In a British study, 104 patients attending four specialist allergy clinics in the United Kingdom following perioperative hypersensitivity reactions to chlorhexidine were seen in a 4-year-period (124), indicating that such reactions are far from rare, at least in absolute numbers.

The allergic reactions may occur after application of chlorhexidine to intact skin, broken skin or after contact with mucosae through oral, vaginal, rectal, or urethral gels or rinses. They may be related to wound cleansing, lubricant gels used in urinary catheterization and cystoscopy, disinfectants before epidural anesthesia or surgery, insertion of chlorhexidine-impregnated central venous catheters or application of impregnated dressings to burns or skin graft and donor sites. Already in 1998, the Food and Drug Administration issued a warning of potential serious hypersensitivity reactions to such impregnated medical devices (75). Likewise, already in 1984, after a high number of reactions to chlorhexidine reported in Japan, the Japanese Ministry of Welfare recommended that the use of chlorhexidine should be prohibited on mucous membranes because of the risk of anaphylactic shock (95).

The most frequently reported causative product is lubricant gel for urinary catheterization, mostly observed in men, followed by skin disinfectants, chlorhexidine-coated central venous lines, disinfectants for mucous membranes and mouthwashes (table 2.91.4). In Finland, patients with immediate-type allergy to chlorhexidine reacted to a corticosteroid cream with chlorhexidine used to treat dermatitis, resulting in immediate itching, burning or redness, (immediate) exacerbation of dermatitis or cough and rhinitis (13). Occupational immediate-type allergy in health care workers has also been observed and has resulted in urticaria (24,77,147) and respiratory symptoms (24,77,147). However, such occupational cases of chlorhexidine allergy appear to be rare (84,118).

The diagnosis can be made by skin prick testing, intradermal tests (only when the prick test is negative [11]) and confirmed by the presence of chlorhexidine-specific IgE (11,43,124). The best diagnostic method is likely the combination of skin prick tests and IgE determination (124).

Table 2.91.4 Products which have caused immediate-type reactions from chlorhexidine

Product	References
Lubricant gel for urinary catheterization / cystoscopy	12,15,16,18,20,37,78,83,88,100,105,106,107,108,109,110, 111,112,115,116,125,132,133,134,136,137,138,140,141,142
Disinfectants for skin	13,15,18,19,23,27,76,79,86,88,89,91,95,98,101,102,108,116, 117,119,120,121,122,129,137,144
Chlorhexidine-coated central venous line	16,22,76,80,81,85,103,104,117,127,128,129,131,135
Disinfectants for mucosae	82,90,92,94,95,122,126,133,139
Mouthwash	13,16,28,121,123
Disinfectant for wounds	97,126
Anti-acne lotion	13
Bath solution	21
Corticosteroid cream	13
Lubricant gel for colonoscopy	13
Lubricant gel for rectal examination	14
Lubricant cream for vaginal examination	87
Toothpaste	77
Wound dressing	93

Very useful review articles on type-I allergy to chlorhexidine were published in 2013 (74), 2014 (76) and 2016 (130). The literature on contact urticaria and other immediate-type reactions caused by any ingredient of cosmetics has been reviewed in 2016 (59).

Miscellaneous side effects

Chlorhexidine in dental care products may cause staining of teeth, tongue and buccal mucosa (39), salivary calculus formation, taste impairment and/or disturbance of taste sensations and desquamation of the oral mucosa (25,40). Chlorhexidine mouthwash has also caused a fixed drug eruption (26). Accidental contact of chlorhexidine with the conjunctiva can cause permanent damage (40). Chlorhexidine is toxic to the middle ear. Animal studies have demonstrated damage to the vestibular nerve and cochlear structures with the loss of vestibular and auditory evoked potentials when chlorhexidine was applied to the middle ear (25). Preoperative disinfection of the ear with chlorhexidine has been associated with deafness after myringoplasty (114). Accidental contact with the middle ear during operation has caused ototoxicity (38). In one publication, bradycardia in a newborn was said to be caused by disinfection of the mother's nipple with chlorhexidine before breastfeeding (40).

Accidental intra-articular irrigation with aqueous 1% chlorhexidine during knee arthroscopy caused persisting pain, swelling, crepitus and stiffness, with partial necrosis of cartilage and fibrosis of synovium (113). Dermal necrosis has been observed from chlorhexidine gluconate disks in adults with complex skin pathology including those with Stevens-Johnson syndrome, toxic epidermal necrolysis, graft-versus-host disease, burns, and anasarca. All patients had a disk placed at a central venous catheter insertion site. Continuous contact of chlorhexidine digluconate is speculated to predispose such patients to local chemical injury secondary to loss of the epithelial tissue barrier, decreased cohesion of the epidermal-dermal junction, and increased tissue permeability (143). Necrosis of the skin from chlorhexidine has also been reported elsewhere (39).

LITERATURE

1   Pigatto PD, Legori A, Bigardi AS, Guarrera M, Tosti A, Santucci B, et al. Gruppo Italiano recerca dermatiti da contatto ed ambientali Italian multicenter study of allergic contact photodermatitis: epidemiological aspects. Am J Contact Dermatitis 1996;7:158-163

2   Journe F, Marguery M-C, Rakotondrazafy J, El Sayed F, Bazex J. Sunscreen sensitization: a 5-year study. Acta Derm Venereol (Stockh) 1999;79:211-213

3   Wahlberg JE, Wennersten G. Hypersensitivity and photosensitivity to chlorhexidine. Dermatologica (Basel) 1971;143:376

4   Victor FC, Cohen DE, Soter NA. A 20-year analysis of previous and emerging allergens that elicit photoallergic contact dermatitis. J Am Acad Dermatol 2010;62:605-610

5   Wetter DA, Yiannias JA, Prakash AV, Davis MD, Farmer SA, el-Azhary RA, et al. Results of patch testing to personal care product allergens in a standard series and a supplemental cosmetic series: an analysis of 945 patients from the Mayo Clinic Contact Dermatitis Group, 2000-2007. J Am Acad Dermatol 2010;63:789-798

6   Kohl L, Blondeel A, Song M. Allergic contact dermatitis from cosmetics: retrospective analysis of 819 patch-tested patients. Dermatology 2002;204:334-337

7 Schnuch A, Lessmann H, Geier J, Uter W. Contact allergy to preservatives. Analysis of IVDK data 1996-2009. Br J Dermatol 2011;164:1316-1325

8 Pigatto PD, Guzzi G, Schena D, Guarrera M, Foti C, Francalanci S, et al. Photopatch tests: an Italian multicentre study from 2004 to 2006. Contact Dermatitis 2008;59:103-108

9 Yazar K, Johnsson S, Lind M-L, Boman A, Lidén C. Preservatives and fragrances in selected consumer-available cosmetics and detergents. Contact Dermatitis 2011;64:265-272

10 Liippo J, Kousa P, Lammintausta K. The relevance of chlorhexidine contact allergy. Contact Dermatitis 2011;64:229-234

11 Garvey LH, Krøigaard M, Poulsen LK, Skov PS, Mosbech H, Venemalm L, et al. IgE-mediated allergy to chlorhexidine. J Allergy Clin Immunol 2007;120:409-415

12 Parkes AW, Harper N, Herwadkar A, Pumphrey R. Anaphylaxis to the chlorhexidine component of Instillagel: a case series. Br J Anesth 2009;102:65-68

13 Aalto-Korte K, Mäkinen-Kiljunen S. Symptoms of immediate chlorhexidine hypersensitivity in patients with a positive prick test. Contact Dermatitis 2006;55:173-177

14 Bae Y-J, Park CS, Lee JK, Jeong E, Kim TB, Cho YS, Moon HB. A case of anaphylaxis to chlorhexidine during digital rectal examination. J Korean Med Sci 2008;23:526-528

15 Ebo DG, Bridts CH, StevensWJ. IgE-mediated anaphylaxis from chlorhexidine: diagnostic possibilities. Contact Dermatitis 2006;55:301-302

16 Nakonechna A, Dore P, Dixon T, Khan S, Deacock S, Holding S, et al. Immediate hypersensitivity to chlorhexidine is increasingly recognized in the United Kingdom. Allergol Immunopathol (Madr) 2014;42:44-49

17 Mailhol C, Lauwers-Cances V, Rancé F, Paul C, Giordano-Labadie F. Prevalence and risk factors for allergic contact dermatitis to topical treatment in atopic dermatitis: a study in 641 children. Allergy 2009:64:801-806

18 Garvey LH, Roed-Petersen J, Husum B. Anaphylactic reactions in anaesthetized patients: four cases of chlorhexidine allergy. Acta Anaesthesiol Scand 2001;45:1290-1294

19 Lauerma AI. Simultaneous immediate and delayed hypersensitivity to chlorhexidine digluconate. Contact Dermatitis 2001;44:59

20 Bergqvist-Karlsson A. Delayed and immediate-type hypersensitivity to chlorhexidine. Contact Dermatitis 1988;18:84-88

21 Snellman E, Rantanen T. Severe anaphylaxis after a chlorhexidine bath. J Am Acad Dermatol 1999;40:771-772

22 Guleri A, Kumar A, Morgan RJ, Hartley M, Roberts DH. Anaphylaxis to chlorhexidine-coated central venous catheters: a case series and review of the literature. Surg Infect (Larchmt) 2012;13:171-174

23 Ebo DG, Stevens WJ, Bridts CH, Matthieu L. Contact allergic dermatitis and life-threatening anaphylaxis to chlorhexidine. J All Clin Immunol 1998;101:128-129

24 Nagendran V, Wicking J, Ekbote A, Onyekwe T, Garvey LH. IgE-mediated chlorhexidine allergy: a new occupational hazard? Occup Med (Lond) 2009;59:270-272

25 Lim K-S, Kam PCA. Chlorhexidine – pharmacology and clinical applications. Anaesth Intensive Care 2008;36:502-512

26 Moghadam BK, Drisko CL, Gier RE. Chlorhexidine mouthwash-induced fixed drug eruption. Case report and review of the literature. Oral Surg Oral Med Oral Pathol 1991;71:431-434

27 Krautheim AM, Jermann THM, Bircher AJ. Chlorhexidine anaphylaxis: case report and review of the literature. Contact Dermatitis 2004;50:113-116

28 Sharma A, Chopra H. Chlorhexidine urticaria: a rare occurrence with a common mouthwash. Indian J Dent Res 2009;20: 377-379

29 Brasch J, Uter W; Information Network of Departments of Dermatology (IVDK); German Contact Dermatitis Group (DKG). Characteristics of patch test reactions to common preservatives incorporated in petrolatum and water, respectively. Contact Dermatitis 2011;64:43-48

30 Barbaud A, Vigan M, Delrous JL, Assier H, Avenel-Audran M, Collet E, et al. Contact allergy to antiseptics: 75 cases analyzed by the dermatoallergovigilance network (Revidal). Ann Dermatol Venereol 2005;132:962-965

31 Hasan T, Rantanen T, Alanko K, Harvima RJ, Jolanki R, Kalimo K, et al. Patch test reactions to cosmetic allergens in 1995-1997 and 2000-2002 in Finland – a multicentre study. Contact Dermatitis 2005;53:40-45

32 Goon AT, White IR, Rycroft RJG, McFadden JP. Allergic contact dermatitis from chlorhexidine. Dermatitis 2004,15:45-47

33 Barrazza V. Connubial allergic contact balanitis due to chlorhexidine. Contact Dermatitis 2001;45;42

34 Perrenoud D, Bircher A, Hunziker T, Suter H, Bruckner-Tuderman L, Stäger J, et al. Frequency of sensitization to 13 common preservatives in Switzerland. Contact Dermatitis 1994;30:276-279

35 Reynolds NJ, Harman RRM. Allergic contact dermatitis from chlorhexidine diacetate in a skin swab. Contact Dermatitis 1990;22:103-104

36 Lasthein Anderson B, Brandrup F. Contact dermatitis from chlorhexidine. Contact Dermatitis 1985;13:307-309

37 Sijbesma T, Röckmann H, Van der Weegen W. Severe anaphylactic reaction to chlorhexidine during total hip arthroplasty surgery: a case report. Hip Int 2011;21:630-632

38 Lai P, Coulson C, Pothier DD, Rutka J. Chlorhexidine ototoxicity in ear surgery, part 1: review of the literature. J Otolaryngol Head Neck Surg 2011;40:437-440

39 De Groot AC. Dermatological drugs, topical agents and cosmetics. In: MNG Dukes, JK Aronson, red. Meyler's side effects of drugs, 14th Edition. Amsterdam: Elsevier, 2000: Chapter 14, pp. 447-480

40 Hackenberger F. Antiseptic drugs and disinfectants. In: MNG Dukes, JK Aronson, red. Meyler's side effects of drugs, 14th Edition. Amsterdam: Elsevier, 2000: Chapter 24, pp. 754-784

41 Fisher AA. Allergic reactions to feminine hygiene sprays. Arch Dermatol 1973;108:801-802

42 Opstrup MS, Johansen JD, Bossi R, Lundov MD, Garvey LH. Chlorhexidine in cosmetic products – a market survey. Contact Dermatitis 2015;72:55-58

43 Opstrup MS, Malling HJ, Krøigaard M, Mosbech H, Skov PS, Poulsen LK, Garvey LH. Standardized testing with chlorhexidine in perioperative allergy--a large single-centre evaluation. Allergy 2014;69:1390-1396

44 De Waard-van der Spek FB, Oranje AP. Allergic contact dermatitis to chlorhexidine and para-amino compounds in a 4-year-old boy: a very rare observation. Contact Dermatitis 2008;58:239-241

45 Van Ketel WG, Melzer-van Riemsdijk FA. Conjunctivitis due to soft lens solutions. Contact Dermatitis 1980;6:321-324

46 Schnuch A, Geier J, Uter W, Frosch PJ. Patch testing with preservatives, antimicrobials and industrial biocides. Results from a multicentre study. Br J Dermatol 1998;138:467-476

47 Barbaud A, Collet E, Le Coz CJ, Meaume S, Gillois P. Contact allergy in chronic leg ulcers: results of a multicentre study carried out in 423 patients and proposal for an updated series of patch tests. Contact Dermatitis 2009;60:279-287

48 Li L-F, Liu G, Wang J. Patch test in Chinese patients with cosmetic allergic contact dermatitis to common cosmetic allergens from a European cosmetic series. Contact Dermatitis 2007;57:50-54

49 Lee SS, Hong DK, Jeong NJ, Lee JH, Choi YS, Lee AY, et al. Multicenter study of preservative sensitivity in patients with suspected cosmetic contact dermatitis in Korea. J Dermatol 2012;39:677-681

50 Goossens A. Cosmetic contact allergens. Cosmetics 2016, 3, 5; doi:10.3390/cosmetics3010005

51 De Groot AC, Bos JD, Jagtman BA, Bruynzeel DP, van Joost T, Weyland JW. Contact allergy to preservatives – II. Contact Dermatitis 1986;15:218-222

52 Scheman A, Jacob S, Katta R, Nedorost S, Warshaw E, Zirwas M, et al. Part 2 of a 4 part series. Hair cosmetics: trends and alternatives. Data from the American Contact Alternative Group. J Clin Aesthet Dermatol 2011;4:42-46

53 Milpied B, Darrigade A-S, Labreze C, Boralevi F. Antiseptic contact dermatitis in children: not just chlorhexidine. Contact Dermatitis 2016;75(Suppl.1):37

54 Dinkloh A, Worm M, Geier J, Schnuch A, Wollenberg A. Contact sensitization in patients with suspected cosmetic intolerance: results of the IVDK 2006-2011. J Eur Acad Dermatol Venereol 2015;29:1071-1081

55 Hu Y, Wang D, Shen Y, Tang H. Photopatch testing in Chinese patients over 10 years. Dermatitis 2016;27:137-142

56 Uter W, Yazar K, Kratz EM, Mildau G, Lidén C. Coupled exposure to ingredients of cosmetic products: II. Preservatives. Contact Dermatitis 2014;70:219-226

57 Beene KM, Scheman A, Severson D, Reeder MJ. Prevalence of preservatives across all product types in the Contact Allergen Management Program. Dermatitis 2017;28:81-87

58 Wennersten G, Thune P, Brodthagen H, Jansen C, Rystedt I, Crames M, et al. The Scandinavian multicenter photopatch study. Contact Dermatitis 1984;10:305-309

59 Verhulst L, Goossens A. Cosmetic components causing contact urticaria: a review and update. Contact Dermatitis 2016;75:333-344

60 Cronin E. Contact Dermatitis. Edinburgh: Churchill Livingstone, 1980:697

61 Calnan CD. Hibitane. Contact Dermatitis Newsletter 1972;11:281

62 Ljunggren B, Möller H. Eczematous contact allergy to chlorhexidine. Acta Derm Venerol 1972;52:308-310

63 Opstrup MS, Johansen JD, Zachariae C, Garvey LH. Contact allergy to chlorhexidine in a tertiary dermatology clinic in Denmark. Contact Dermatitis 2016;74:29-36

64 Opstrup M, Johansen J, Garvey L. Chlorhexidine allergy: sources of exposure in the health-care setting. Br J Anaesth 2015;114:704-705

65 Bechgaard E, Ploug E, Hjorth N. Contact sensitivity to chlorhexidine? Contact Dermatitis 1985;13:53-55

66 Osmundsen P. Contact dermatitis to chlorhexidine. Contact Dermatitis 1982;8:81-83

67 McEnery-Stonelake M, Silvestri DL. Allergic contact dermatitis to chlorhexidine after oral sensitization. Dermatitis 2013;24:92-93

68 Knudsen BB, Avnstrorp C. Chlorhexidine gluconate and acetate in patch testing. Contact Dermatitis 1991;24:45-49

69 Rapaport M. Contact dermatitis secondary to chlorhexidine in contact lens cleansing solutions. Am J Cont Dermat 1991;2:65-66

70 LeCorre Y, Barbarot S, Frot AS, Milpied B. Allergic contact dermatitis to chlorhexidine in a very young child. Pediatr Dermatol 2010;27:485-487

71 Shoji A. Contact dermatitis from chlorhexidine. Contact Dermatitis 1983;9:156

72 Roberts DL, Summerly R, Byrne JPH. Contact dermatitis due to the constituents of Hibiscrub. Contact Dermatitis 1981;7:326-328

73 Sharvill D. Reaction to chlorhexidine and cetrimide. Lancet 1965;1(7388):771

74 Silvestri DL, McEnery-Stonelake M. Chlorhexidine: uses and adverse reactions. Dermatitis 2013;24:112-118

75 Center for Devices and Radiological Health. FDA Public Health Notice: Potential hypersensitivity reactions to chlorhexidine-impregnated medical devices. Food and Drug Administration (cited in ref. 74)

76 Odedra KM, Farooque S. Chlorhexidine: an unrecognised cause of anaphylaxis. Postgrad Med J 2014;90:709-714

77 Wittczak T, Dudek W, Walusiak-Skorupa J, Świerczyńska-Machura D, Pałczyński C. Chlorhexidine – still an underestimated allergic hazard for health care professionals. Occup Med 2013;63:301-305

78 Noel J, Temple A, Laycock GJA. A case report of anaphylaxis to chlorhexidine during urinary catheterisation. Ann R Coll Surg Engl 2012;94:e159-e160

79 Sivathasan N, Goodfellow PB. Skin cleansers: the risks of chlorhexidine. J Clin Pharmacol 2011;51:785-786

80 Khoo A, Oziemski P. Chlorhexidine impregnated central venous catheter inducing an anaphylactic shock in the intensive care unit. Heart Lung Circ 2011;20:669-670

81 Jee R, Nel L, Gnanakumaran G, Williams A, Eren E. Four cases of anaphylaxis to chlorhexidine impregnated central venous catheters: a case cluster or the tip of the iceberg. Br J Anaesth 2009;103: 614-615

82 Thong CL, Lambros M, Stewart MG, Kam PCA. An unexpected cause of an acute hypersensitivity reaction during recovery from anaesthesia. Anaesth Intensive Care 2005;33:521-524

83 Ebo DG, Bridts CH, Stevens WJ. Anaphylaxis to an urethral lubricant: chlorhexidine as the 'hidden' allergen. Acta Clin Belg 2004;59:358-360

84 Garvey LH, Roed-Petersen J, Husum B. Is there a risk of sensitization and allergy to chlorhexidine in health care workers? Acta Anaesthesiol Scand 2003;47:720-724

85 Kluger M. Anaphylaxis to chlorhexidine-impregnated central venous catheter. Anaesth Intensive Care 2003;31:697-698

86 Autegarden J-E, Pecquet C, Huet S, Bayrou O, Leynadier F. Anaphylactic shock after application of chlorhexidine to unbroken skin. Contact Dermatitis 1999;40:215

87 Aalto-Korte K, Kousa M. Välitön klooriheksidiiniallergia. [Immediate type chlorhexidine allergy.] Duodecim 1994;110:2013-2014 (article in Finnish)

88 Stables GI, Turner WH, Prescott S, Wilkinson SM. Generalized urticaria after skin cleansing and urethral instillation with chlorhexidine-containing products. Br J Urol 1998;82:756-757

89 Fisher AA. Contact urticaria from chlorhexidine. Cutis 1989;43:17-18

90 Chisholm DG, Calder I, Peterson D, Powell M, Moult P. Intranasal chlorhexidine resulting in anaphylactic circulatory arrest. BMJ 1997;315:785

91 Torricelli R, Wüthrich B. Life-threatening anaphylactic shock due to skin application of chlorhexidine. Clin Exp Allergy 1996;26:112

92 Okuda T, Funasaka M, Arimitsu M, et al. Anaphylactic shock by ophthalmic wash solution containing chlorhexidine. Masui 1994;43:1352-1355 (article in Japanese)

93 Evans RJ. Acute anaphylaxis due to topical chlorhexidine acetate. Br Med J 1992;304 (6828):686

94 Wong WK, Goh CL, Chan KW. Contact urticaria from chlorhexidine. Contact Dermatitis 1990;22:52

95 Okano M, Nomura M, Hata S, Okada N, Sato K, Kitano Y, et al. Anaphylactic symptoms due to chlorhexidine gluconate. Arch Dermatol 1989;125:50-52

96 Weitz NA, Lauren CT, Weiser JA, LeBoeuf NR, Grossman ME, Biagas K, Garzon MC, Morel KD. Chlorhexidine gluconate–impregnated central access catheter dressings as a cause of erosive contact dermatitis: a report of 7 cases. JAMA Dermatol 2013;149:195-199

97 Ohtoshi T, Yamauchi N, Tadokoro K, Miyachi S, Suzuki S, Miyamoto T, Muranaka M. IgE antibody-mediated shock reaction caused by topical application of chlorhexidine. Clin Allergy 1986;16:155-161

98 Nishioka K, Doi T, Katayama I. Histamine release in contact urticaria. Contact Dermatitis 1984;11:191

99 Beaudouin E, Kanny G, Morisset M, Renaudin JM, Mertes M, Laxenaire MC, et al. Immediate hypersensitivity to chlorhexidine: literature review. Eur Ann Allergy Clin Immunol 2004;36:123-126

100 Knight BA, Puy R, Douglass J, O'Hehir RE, Thien F. Chlorhexidine anaphylaxis: a case report and review of the literature. Intern Med J 2001;31:436-437

101 Conraads VMA, Jorens PG, Ebo DG, Claeys MJ, Bosmans JM, Vrints CJ. Coronary artery spasm complicating anaphylaxis secondary to skin disinfectant. Chest 1998;113:1417-1419

102 Peutrell JM. Anaphylactoid reaction to topical chlorhexidine during anaesthesia. Anaesthesia 1992;47:1013

103 Oda T, Hamasaki J, Kanda N, Mikami K. Anaphylactic shock induced by an antiseptic-coated central venous [correction of nervous] catheter. Anesthesiology 1997;87:1242-1244

104 Stephens R, Mythen M, Kallis P, Davies DW, Egner W, Rickards A. Two episodes of life-threatening anaphylaxis in the same patient to a chlorhexidine-sulphadiazine-coated central venous catheter. Br J Anaesth 2001;87:306-308

105 Pham NH, Weiner JM, Reisner GS, Baldo BA. Anaphylaxis to chlorhexidine. Case report. Implication of immunoglobulin E antibodies and identification of an allergenic determinant. Clin Exp Allergy 2000;30:1001-1007

106 Ramselaar CG, Craenen A, Bijleveld RT. Severe allergic reaction to an intraurethral preparation containing chlorhexidine. Br J Urol 1992;70:451-452

107 Beatty P, Kumar N, Ronald A. A complicated case of chlorhexidine-associated anaphylaxis. Anaesthesia 2011;66:60-61

108 Mitchell DJ, Parker FC. Anaphylaxis following urethral catheterisation. Br J Urol 1993;71:613

109 Russ BR, Maddern PJ. Anaphylactic reaction to chlorhexidine in urinary catheter lubricant. Anaesth Intensive Care 1994;22:611-612

110 Cheung J, O'Leary JJ. Allergic reaction to chlorhexidine in an anaesthetized patient. Anaesth Intensive Care 1985;13:429-430

111 Wicki J, Deluze C, Cirafici L, Desmeules J. Anaphylactic shock induced by intra urethral use of chlorhexidine. Allergy 1999;54:768-769

112 Yong D, Parker C, Foran SM. Severe allergic reactions and intra-urethral chlorhexidine gluconate. Med J Aust 1995;162:257-258

113 Douw CM, Bulstra SK, Vandenbroucke J, Geesink RG, Vermeulen A. Clinical and pathological changes in the knee after accidental chlorhexidine irrigation during arthroscopy. Case reports and review of the literature. J Bone Joint Surg Br 1998;80:437-440

114 Bicknell PG. Sensorineural deafness following myringoplasty operations. J Laryngol Otol 1971;85:957-961

115 Jayathillake A, Mason DF, Broome K. Allergy to chlorhexidine gluconate in urethral gel: report of four cases and review of the literature. Urology 2003;61:835-837

116 Lockhart AS, Harle CC. Anaphylactic reactions due to chlorhexidine allergy. Br J Anaesth 2001; 87:940-941

117 Pittaway A, Ford S. Allergy to chlorhexidine-coated central venous catheters revisited. Br J Anaesth 2002;88:304-305

118 Ibler KS, Jemec GB, Garvey LH, Agner T. Prevalence of delayed-type and immediate-type hypersensitivity in healthcare workers with hand eczema. Contact Dermatitis 2016;75:223-229

119 Hong CC, Wang SM, Nather A, Tan JH, Tay SH, Poon KH. Chlorhexidine anaphylaxis masquerading as septic shock. Int Arch Allergy Immunol 2015;167:16-20

120 Cuervo-Pardo L, Gonzalez-Estrada A, Fernandez J, Pien LC. A rash during surgery: rounding up the usual suspects. BMJ Case Rep 2015 Mar 30;2015. pii: bcr2015209660. doi: 10.1136/bcr-2015-209660

121 Toomey M. Preoperative chlorhexidine anaphylaxis in a patient scheduled for coronary artery bypass graft: a case report. AANA J 2013;81:209-214

122 Teixeira de Abreu AP, Ribeiro de Oliveira LR, Teixeira de Abreu AF, Ribeiro de Oliveira E, Santos de Melo Ireno M, Aarestrup FM, et al. Perioperative anaphylaxis to chlorhexidine during surgery and septoplasty. Case Rep Otolaryngol 2017;2017:9605804. doi: 10.1155/2017/9605804. Epub 2017 Mar 19.

123 Pemberton MN, Gibson J. Chlorhexidine and hypersensitivity reactions in dentistry. Br Dent J 2012;213:547-550

124 Egner W, Helbert M, Sargur R, Swallow K, Harper N, Garcez T, et al. Chlorhexidine allergy in four specialist allergy centres in the United Kingdom, 2009-13: clinical features and diagnostic tests. Clin Exp Immunol 2017;188:380-386

125 Rutkowski K, Wagner A. Chlorhexidine: a new latex? Eur Urol 2015;68:345-347

126 Lasa EM, González C, García-Lirio E, Martínez S, Arroabarren E, Gamboa PM. Anaphylaxis caused by immediate hypersensitivity to topical chlorhexidine in children. Ann Allergy Asthma Immunol 2017;118:118-119

127 Wang ML, Chang CT, Huang HH, Yeh YC, Lee TS, Hung KY. Chlorhexidine-related refractory anaphylactic shock: a case successfully resuscitated with extracorporeal membrane oxygenation. J Clin Anesth 2016;34:654-657

128 Qin Z, Zeng Z. Anaphylaxis to chlorhexidine in a chlorhexidine-coated central venous catheter during general anaesthesia. Anaesth Intensive Care 2016;44:297-298

129 Chen P, Huda W, Levy N. Chlorhexidine anaphylaxis: implications for post-resuscitation management. Anaesthesia 2016;71:242-243

130 Sharp G, Green S, Rose M. Chlorhexidine-induced anaphylaxis in surgical patients: a review of the literature. ANZ J Surg 2016;86:237-243

131 Weng M, Zhu M, Chen W, Miao C. Life-threatening anaphylactic shock due to chlorhexidine on the central venous catheter: a case series. Int J Clin Exp Med 2014;7:5930-5936

132 Buergi A, Jung B, Padevit C, John H, Ganter MT. Severe anaphylaxis: the secret ingredient. A A Case Rep 2014;2:34-36

133 Koch A, Wollina U. Chlorhexidine allergy. Allergo J Int 2014;23:84-86

134 Dyer JE, Nafie S, Mellon JK, Khan MA. Anaphylactic reaction to intraurethral chlorhexidine: sensitisation following previous repeated uneventful administration. Ann R Coll Surg Engl 2013;95:e105-e106

135 Faber M, Leysen J, Bridts C, Sabato V, De Clerck LS, Ebo DG. Allergy to chlorhexidine: beware of the central venous catheter. Acta Anaesthesiol Belg 2012;63:191-194

136 Khan RA, Kazi T, O'Donohoe B. Near fatal intra-operative anaphylaxis to chlorhexidine - is it time to change practice? BMJ Case Rep 2011 Feb 9;2011. pii: bcr0920092300. doi: 10.1136/bcr.09.2009.2300

137 Wills A. Chlorhexidine anaphylaxis in Auckland. Br J Anaesth 2009;102:722-723

138 van Zuuren EJ, Boer F, Lai a Fat EJ, Terreehorst I. Anaphylactic reactions to chlorhexidine during urinary catheterisation. Ned Tijdschr Geneeskd 2007;151:2531-2534 (article in Dutch)

139 Liu SY, Lee JF, Ng SS, Li JC, Yiu RY. Rectal stump lavage: simple procedure resulting in life-threatening complication. Asian J Surg 2007;30:72-74

140 Parker F, Foran S. Chlorhexidine catheter lubricant anaphylaxis. Anaesth Intensive Care 1995;23:126

141 De Groot AC, Weyland JW. Anaphylaxis due to chlorhexidine following cystoscopy or urethral catheterization. Ned Tijdschr Geneeskd 1994;138:1342-1343 (article in Dutch)

142 Visser LE, Veeger JH, Roovers MH, Chan E, Stricker BH. Anaphylaxis caused by chlorhexidine following cystoscopy or urethral catheterization. Ned Tijdschr Geneeskd 1994;138:778-780 (article in Dutch)

143 Wall JB, Divito SJ, Talbot SG. Chlorhexidine gluconate-impregnated central-line dressings and necrosis in complicated skin disorder patients. J Crit Care 2014;29:1130.e1-4

144 Thune P. Two patients with chlorhexidine allergy - anaphylactic reactions and eczema. Tidsskr Nor Laegeforen 1998;118:3295-3296

145 Neering H, van Ketel WG. Contact allergy caused by chlorhexidine. Ned Tijdschr Geneeskd 1972;116:1742-1743

146 Toholka R, Nixon R. Allergic contact dermatitis to chlorhexidine. Australas J Dermatol 2013;54:303-306

147 Vu M, Rajgopal Bala H, Cahill J, Toholka R, Nixon R. Immediate hypersensitivity to chlorhexidine. Australas J Dermatol 2017 Jun 7. doi: 10.1111/ajd.12674. [Epub ahead of print]

2.92 CHLOROACETAMIDE

IDENTIFICATION

Description/definition	: Chloroacetamide is the aliphatic amide that conforms to the formula shown below
Chemical class(es)	: Amides; halogen compounds
Chemical/IUPAC name	: 2-Chloroacetamide
CAS registry number (s)	: 79-07-2
EC number(s)	: 201-174-2
CIR review(s)	: J Am Coll Toxicol 1991;10:21-32 (access: www.cir-safety.org/ingredients)
SCCS opinion(s)	: SCCS/1360/10 (45)
Merck Index monograph	: 3380
Function(s) in cosmetics	: EU: preservative. USA: preservatives
EU cosmetic restrictions	: Regulated in Annex V/41 of the Regulation (EC) No. 1223/2009
Patch testing	: 0.2% pet. (Chemotechnique, SmartPracticeEurope, SmartPracticeCanada)
Molecular formula	: C_2H_4ClNO

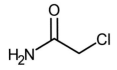

GENERAL

Chloroacetamide, a colorless and odorless powder, is a preservative which has been used in cosmetics, glues, adhesives, the leather and tanning industries, shoe polish, industrial oils, and as a preservative for wood, wax emulsions and technical products (5,8). Currently, chloroacetamide is not used at all in cosmetic products in the USA and probably rarely, if at all, in the EU (see the section 'Presence in cosmetic products and chemical analyses' below). Although chloroacetamide has been reported to be a potent sensitizer (15), sometimes at extremely low concentrations (11), relatively few cases of allergic contact dermatitis have been reported, mostly from its presence in cosmetics, wallpaper glues (13,19), topical pharmaceuticals (12,14,24,27) and paint (5,20).

CONTACT ALLERGY

Patch testing in groups of patients

Results of testing chloroacetamide in consecutive patients suspected of contact dermatitis (routine testing) back to 1980 are shown in table 2.92.1. Results of testing in groups of *selected* patients (e.g., patients suspected of cosmetic allergy, patients with leg ulcers / stasis dermatitis, hairdressers with contact dermatitis) back to 1977 are shown in table 2.92.2.

Patch testing in consecutive patients suspected of contact dermatitis: routine testing

In five studies in which routine testing with chloroacetamide was performed, rates of sensitization have been low, ranging from 0.3% to 1.5%. The high concentration of 1.5% was found in a 1989-1990 Swiss study, but relevance of the positive patch tests was not mentioned (33). In fact, in only one study was this issue addresses and only 20% of 20 reactions were scored as relevant; causative products were not mentioned (30).

Table 2.92.1 Patch testing in groups of patients: Routine testing

Years and Country	Test conc. & vehicle	Number of patients tested	positive (%)	Selection of patients (S); Relevance (R); Comments (C)	Ref.
2003-2005 China		599	4 (0.7%)	R: not stated	34
1992-1994 USA	0.2% pet.	3481	(0.3%)	R: present relevance: 20%	30
1989-90 Switzerland	0.2% pet.	2295	(1.5%)	R: not stated	33
1985 The Netherlands	0.2% pet.	501	3 (0.6%)	R: not stated	37
<1980 Sweden	0.1% pet.	3254	10 (0.3%)	R: not stated	29

Patch testing in groups of selected patients

Results of testing chloroacetamide in groups of selected patients (e.g., patients suspected of cosmetic allergy, patients with leg ulcers / stasis dermatitis, hairdressers with contact dermatitis) back to 1977 are shown in table 2.92.2. In 20 investigations, frequencies of sensitization have ranged from 0.1% to 6%, but 14 had rates of 2% or lower, of which 10 scored <1% positive patch test reactions. The highest frequencies (both 6%) were found in two very small studies (number of tested patients: 36) of patients with chronic venous insufficiency (57) and hairdressers with dermatitis (22), but in neither of these was the relevance of the patch test reactions mentioned. In fact, the issue of relevance was addressed in 5 studies only, in which relevance rates ranged from 19% to 100% (1,19,38,47,59). Where mentioned, the culprit products were cutting oil (one patient only [18]) and glues (19).

Table 2.92.2 Patch testing in groups of patients: Selected patient groups

Years and Country	Test conc. & vehicle	Number of patients tested | positive (%)			Selection of patients (S); Relevance (R); Comments (C)	Ref.
2003-2014 IVDK	0.2% pet.	4216		(1.4%)	S: patients with stasis dermatitis/ chronic leg ulcers; R: not stated	56
2007-2012 IVDK	0.2% pet.	645	1	(0.1%)	S: female hairdressers with current or previous occupational contact dermatitis; R: not stated	51
		1385	5	(0.3%)	S: female patients, clients of hairdressers, in who hair cosmetics were regarded as a cause of dermatitis, and who had never worked as hairdressers; R: not stated	
2010-2011 Korea	0.2% pet.	584	17	(2.9%)	S: patients suspected of allergic cosmetic dermatitis; R: not stated	35
2006-2011 IVDK	0.2% pet	6982		(0.5%)	S: patients suspected of cosmetic intolerance and tested with a preservative series (selection procedure not stated); R: not stated	49
2002-2011 Denmark		302	5	(1.7%)	S: hairdressers with contact dermatitis; R: not stated	50
2001-2010 Australia	0.2% pet.	4576	139	(3.0%)	S: not stated; R: 19%	47
1996-2009 IVDK	0.2% pet.	80,824	717	(0.8%) [a]	S: not specified; R: not specified; C: decrease in prevalence of sensitization during the study period	3
2000-2008 USA	0.2% pet.	210		(0.5%)	S: patients tested with a hairdresser's series; R: 100%	38
2000-2007 USA	0.2% pet.	871	2	(0.2%)	S: patients tested with a supplemental cosmetic screening series; R: 100%; C: weak study: a. high rate of macular erythema and weak reactions; b. relevance figures included 'questionable' and 'past' relevance	1
1993-2006 Australia	0.2% pet.	4451		(2.1%)	S: not stated; R: 53%	59
1999-2004 UK		517	2	(0.4%)	S: patients tested with the hairdressing series; R: only reactions that were of current or past relevance were collected	52
2000-2002 Finland		6524		(0.2%)	S: patients tested with a cosmetic series; R: not stated	31
1996-1997 Germany	0.2% pet.	36	2	(6%)	S: patients with chronic venous insufficiency; R: not stated	57
1995-1996 Finland		5224		(0.3%)	S: patients tested with a cosmetic series; R: not stated	31
1990-1994 Germany	0.2% pet	11,432	142	(1.2%)	S: patients tested with a preservative series; R: not stated	32
1990-1994 Germany	0.2% pet.	1784	9	(0.5%)	S: patients tested with an industrial biocide series; R: not stated	32
1985-1994 Greece	0.2% pet.	106	3	(4.3%)	S: hairdressers with contact dermatitis; R: not specified	53
1974-1993 Finland		36	2	(6%)	S: hairdressers with dermatitis; R: not stated	22
1984-1991 USA	0.2% pet.	913	3	(0.3%)	S: unknown; R: occupational sensitization was suspected in two patients	62
<1986 Italy	2% pet.	51	1	(2%)	S: unknown; R: the patient had occupational ACD from chloroacetamide in a cutting oil; C: curiously high test conc.	18
1977 Sweden	0.1% pet.	190	5	(2.6%)	S: housepainters; R: all 5 had occupational allergic contact dermatitis from glues	19

[a] age-standardized and sex-standardized proportions
IVDK: Information Network of Departments of Dermatology, Germany, Austria, Switzerland

Case reports and case series
Chloroacetamide was stated to be the (or an) allergen in one patient in a group of 603 individuals suffering from cosmetic dermatitis, seen in the period 2010-2015 in Leuven, Belgium (36). In the period 1996-2013, in a tertiary referral center in Valencia, Spain, 5419 patients were patch tested. Of these, 628 individuals had allergic contact dermatitis to cosmetics. Chloroacetamide was the responsible allergen in two cases (48). In a group of 119 patients with allergic contact dermatitis from cosmetics, investigated in The Netherlands in 1986-1987, one case was caused by chloroacetamide in a skin care product (39,40). In a group of 75 patients allergic to cosmetic products, seen in a private practice in The Netherlands in the period 1981-1986, one case was caused by chloroacetamide in an anti-wrinkle serum (41, same patient as in ref. 28). In 3 clinics in Belgium, in the period 1978-1985, 279 patients with allergic contact dermatitis exclusively caused by cosmetics were seen. In this group, there were 7 reactions to chloroacetamide. It was implied that this was the cause of the allergic reactions (46).

Four positive patch test reactions to chloroacetamide were ascribed to cosmetic allergy (2). Two patients were allergic to chloroacetamide in a cream resp. a body lotion (43). One patient reacted to chloroacetamide in a skin care product, another one to the preservative in an eye cream (42). One individual had allergic contact dermatitis from chloroacetamide in an 'anti-wrinkle serum'; the patient also reacted to non-human placental protein, but this proved to be preserved with chloroacetamide (28). A woman residing in the USA had allergic contact dermatitis of the face from chloroacetamide in a spray aerosol facial adstringent. Chloroacetamide at that time (mid 1980s) was not registered or sold for use in cosmetics in the United States, although it was available as an industrial biocidal preservative. However, the product causing the eruption had been imported from France and contained chloroacetamide (58).

A female personal care assistant working in a nursing home had occupational allergic contact dermatitis involving the hands, caused by the cosmetic moisturizing lotion supplied in her workplace (61). Several single case reports of patients with allergic contact dermatitis from chloroacetamide in the following cosmetic products have been published: eye cream (44,54), baby body lotion used for a woman's baby (6), hand lotion (7), two facial cleansing products (8), body cream (10), hair dye (17), tooth-paste (allergic contact cheilitis [25]), and deodorant (60).

Contact allergy to chloroacetamide in non-cosmetic products
One patient had airborne allergic contact dermatitis from chloroacetamide in wall paint (5). Occupational ACD occurred in a patient working in the cosmetics industry from a 0.5% chloroacetamide disinfectant solution (8). At least seventeen patients reacted to chloroacetamide in a topical pharmaceutical product (12,14). Two painters had occupational ACD to chloroacetamide in wallpaper glue (13). A car mechanic had occupational ACD from chloroacetamide in a cutting oil (18). Five housepainters developed occupational ACD from chloroacetamide in glue (19). One woman, who was probably sensitized by a cosmetic cream, developed airborne ACD after painting her wall with a paint containing chloroacetamide (20). A patient reacted to a very low concentration of chloroacetamide in a topical pharmaceutical product (24). Contact allergy to chloroacetamide in leather from shoes was responsible for a bullous allergic contact dermatitis of the feet in one individual (26). One patient reacted to chloroacetamide in two topical pharmaceutical preparations (27).

Cross-reactions, pseudo-cross-reactions and co-reactions
Cross-reactivity with N-methylolchloracetamide has been described several times (9,16,20,21,23). N-methylolchloracetamide is the result of a reaction of 2-chloracetamide with formaldehyde using NaOH as a catalyst and CHCl$_3$ as a solvent (21).

Patch test sensitization
One patient became sensitized from a patch test with chloroacetamide 0.2% in petrolatum (4).

Presence in cosmetic products and chemical analyses
In June 2017, chloroacetamide was present in zero of 69,510 cosmetic products of which the composition is known in EWG's Skin Deep Cosmetics Database, USA (http://www.ewg.org/skindeep/). In the USA, in April 2017, chloroacetamide was present in zero of 56,714 cosmetic products of which the composition is known in FDA's Voluntary Cosmetic Registration Program (VCRP) (data obtained from FDA, May 2017). In Germany, in 2006-2009, the labels of 4680 cosmetic products were screened for the presence of preservatives. Chloroacetamide was present in 0.1% of the products, according to labelling information (55).

LITERATURE

1   Wetter DA, Yiannias JA, Prakash AV, Davis MD, Farmer SA, el-Azhary RA, et al. Results of patch testing to personal care product allergens in a standard series and a supplemental cosmetic series: an analysis of 945 patients from the Mayo Clinic Contact Dermatitis Group, 2000-2007. J Am Acad Dermatol 2010;63:789-798
2   Kohl L, Blondeel A, Song M. Allergic contact dermatitis from cosmetics: retrospective analysis of 819 patch-tested patients. Dermatology 2002;204:334-337
3   Schnuch A, Lessmann H, Geier J, Uter W. Contact allergy to preservatives. Analysis of IVDK data 1996-2009. Br J Dermatol 2011;164:1316-1325
4   Fonia A, White JML, McFadden JP, White IR. Active sensitization to chloroacetamide. Contact Dermatitis 2009;60:58-59
5   Bogenrieder T, Landthaler M, Stolz W. Airborne contact dermatitis due to chloroacetamide in wall paint. Contact Dermatitis 2001;45:55
6   Nater JP. Allergic reactions due to chloracetamide. Dermatologica 1971;142:191-192
7   Suhonen R. Chloracetamide – a hidden contact allergen. Contact Dermatitis 1983;9:161
8   Klaschka F. Contact allergy to chloroacetamide. Contact Dermatitis 1975;1:265-266

9   Hjorth N. *N*-methylol-chloracetamide, a sensitizer in coolant oils and cosmetics. Contact Dermatitis 1979;5:330-334

10 Dooms-Goossens A, Degreef H, Vanhee J, Kerkhofs L, Chrispeels MT. Chlorocresol and chloracetamide: allergens in medications, glues and cosmetics. Contact Dermatitis1981;7:51-52

11 Marzulli, FN, Maibach HI. Antimicrobials: experimental contact sensitization in man. Journal of the Society of Cosmetic Chemists 1973;24:399\

12 Prins FI, Smeenk G. Contacteczeem door Hirudoidzalf. Ned Tijdschr Geneeskd 1971;115:1934-1938

13 Bang Pedersen N, Fregert S. Occupational contact dermatitis from chloracetamide in glue. Contact Dermatitis 1976;2:122-123

14 Smeenk G, Prins F J. Allergic contact eczema due to chloracetamide. Dermatologica 1972;144:108-114

15 Jordan WP, King SE. Delayed hypersensitivity in females. The development of allergic contact dermatitis in females during the comparison of two predictive patch tests. Contact Dermatitis 1977;3:19-26

16 Pereira F, Rafael M, Pereira MA. Occupational allergic contact dermatitis from a glue, containing isothiazolinones and *N*-methylol-chloracetamide, in a carpenter. Contact Dermatitis 1999;40:283-284

17 Assier-Bonnet H, Revuz J. Chloracetamide as a cause of contact dermatitis in hairdressing. Contact Dermatitis 1999;40:284-285

18 Lama L, Vanni D, Barone M, Patrone P, Antonelli C. Occupational contact dermatitis to chloracetamide. Contact Dermatitis1986;15:243

19 Wahlberg JE, Hogberg M, Skare L. Chloracetamide allergy in house painters. Contact Dermatitis 1978;4:116-117

20 Finkbeiner H, Kleinhans D. Airborne allergic contact dermatitis caused by preservatives in home-decorating paints. Contact Dermatitis 1994;31:275-276

21 Farli M, Ginanneschi M, Francalanci S, Martinelli C, Sertoli A. Occupational contact dermatitis to N-methylolchloracetamide. Contact Dermatitis 1987;17:182-184

22 Leino T, Estlander T, Kanerva L. Occupational allergic dermatoses in hairdressers. Contact Dermatitis 1998;38:166-167

23 Jones SK, Kennedy CTC. Chloracetamide as an allergen in the paint industry. Contact Dermatitis 1988;18:304-306

24 Wantke F, Demmer CM, Götz M, Jarisch R. Sensitization to chloroacetamide. Contact Dermatitis 1993;29:213-214

25 Macháćková J, ŠMid P. Allergic contact cheilitis from toothpastes. Contact Dermatitis 1991;24:311

26 Jelen G, Cavelier C, Protois JP, Foussereau J. A new allergen responsible for shoe allergy: chloroacetamide. Contact Dermatitis 1989; 21:110-111

27 Detmar U, Agathos, M. Contact allergy to chloroacetamide. Contact Dermatitis 1988;19:66-67

28 De Groot AC, Weyland JW. Contact allergy to chloroacetamide in an "anti-wrinkle serum". Contact Dermatitis 1986;15:97-98

29 ÅGren S, Dahlquist I, Fregert S, Persson K. Allergic contact dermatitis from the preservative N-methylol-chloracetamide. Contact Dermatitis 1980;6:302-303

30 Marks JG, Belsito DV, DeLeo VA, Fowler JF, Fransway AF, Maibach HI,et al. North American Contact Dermatitis Group standard tray patch test results 1992 through 1994. Am J Contact Dermatitis 1995;6:160-165

31 Hasan T, Rantanen T, Alanko K, Harvima RJ, Jolanki R, Kalimo K, et al. Patch test reactions to cosmetic allergens in 1995–1997 and 2000–2002 in Finland –a multicentre study. Contact Dermatitis 2005;53:40-45

32 Schnuch A, Geier J, Uter W, Frosch PJ. Patch testing with preservatives, antimicrobials and industrial biocides. Results from a multicentre study. Br J Dermatol 1998;138:467-476

33 Perrenoud D, Bircher A, Hunziker T, Suter H, Bruckner-Tuderman L, Stäger J, et al. Frequency of sensitization to 13 common preservatives in Switzerland. Contact Dermatitis 1994;30:276-279

34 Li L-F, Liu G, Wang J. Patch test in Chinese patients with cosmetic allergic contact dermatitis to common cosmetic allergens from a European cosmetic series. Contact Dermatitis 2007;57:50-54

35 Lee SS, Hong DK, Jeong NJ, Lee JH, Choi YS, Lee AY, et al. Multicenter study of preservative sensitivity in patients with suspected cosmetic contact dermatitis in Korea. J Dermatol 2012;39:677-681

36 Goossens A. Cosmetic contact allergens. Cosmetics 2016, 3, 5; doi:10.3390/cosmetics3010005

37 De Groot AC, Bos JD, Jagtman BA, Bruynzeel DP, van Joost T, Weyland JW. Contact allergy to preservatives – II. Contact Dermatitis 1986;15:218-222

38 Wang MZ, Farmer SA, Richardson DM, Davis MDP. Patch-testing with hairdressing chemicals. Dermatitis 2011;22:16-26

39 De Groot AC, Bruynzeel DP, Bos JD, van der Meeren HL, van Joost T, Jagtman BA, Weyland JW. The allergens in cosmetics. Arch Dermatol 1988;124:1525-1529

40 De Groot AC. Adverse reactions to cosmetics. PhD Thesis, University of Groningen, The Netherlands: 1988, chapter 3.4, pp.105-113

41 De Groot AC. Contact allergy to cosmetics: Causative ingredients. Contact Dermatitis 1987;17:26-34

42 Cronin E. Contact Dermatitis. Edinburgh: Churchill Livingstone, 1980:115 and 699

43 Nater JP. Allergic reactions to chloracetamide. Cont Derm Newsl 1970;7:162

44 Calnan CD. Chloracetamide dermatitis from a cosmetic. Cont Derm Newsl 1971;9:215

45 SCCS (Scientific Committee on Consumer Safety). Opinion on chloroacetamide, 22 March 2011, SCCS/1360/10. Available at: http://ec.europa.eu/health/scientific_committees/consumer_safety/docs/sccs_o_053.pdf

46 Dooms-Goossens A, de Boulle K, Dooms M, Degreef H. Imidazolidinyl urea dermatitis. Contact Dermatitis 1986;14:322-324

47 Toholka R, Wang Y-S, Tate B, Tam M, Cahill J, Palmer A, Nixon R. The first Australian Baseline Series: Recommendations for patch testing in suspected contact dermatitis. Australas J Dermatol 2015;56:107-115

48 Zaragoza-Ninet V, Blasco Encinas R, Vilata-Corell JJ, Pérez-Ferriols A, Sierra-Talamantes C, Esteve-Martínez A, de la Cuadra-Oyanguren J. Allergic contact dermatitis due to cosmetics: A clinical and epidemiological study in a tertiary hospital. Actas Dermosifiliogr 2016;107:329-336

49 Dinkloh A, Worm M, Geier J, Schnuch A, Wollenberg A. Contact sensitization in patients with suspected cosmetic intolerance: results of the IVDK 2006-2011. J Eur Acad Dermatol Venereol 2015;29:1071-1081

50 Schwensen JF, Johansen JD, Veien NK, Funding AT, Avnstorp C, Østerballe M, et al. Occupational contact dermatitis in hairdressers: an analysis of patch test data from the Danish Contact Dermatitis Group, 2002–2011. Contact Dermatitis 2014;70:233-237

51 Uter W, Gefeller O, John SM, Schnuch A, Geier J. Contact allergy to ingredients of hair cosmetics – a comparison of female hairdressers and clients based on IVDK 2007–2012 data. Contact Dermatitis 2014;71:13-20

52 Katugampola RP, Statham BN, English JSC, Wilkinson MM, Foulds IS, Green CM, Ormerod AD, et al. A multicentre review of the hairdressing allergens tested in the UK. Contact Dermatitis 2005;53:130-132

53 Katsarou A, Koufou B, Takou K, Kalogeromitros D, Papanayiotou G, Vareltzidis A. Patch test results in hairdressers with contact dermatitis in Greece (1985-1994). Contact Dermatitis 1995;33:347-348

54 Morren MA, Dooms-Goossens A, Delabie J, De Wolf-Peeters C, Mariën K, Degreef H. Contact allergy to isothiazolinone derivatives: unusual clinical presentations. Dermatology 1992;184:260-264

55 Uter W, Yazar K, Kratz EM, Mildau G, Lidén C. Coupled exposure to ingredients of cosmetic products: II. Preservatives. Contact Dermatitis 2014;70:219-226

56 Erfurt-Berge C, Geier J, Mahler V. The current spectrum of contact sensitization in patients with chronic leg ulcers or stasis dermatitis - new data from the Information Network of Departments of Dermatology (IVDK). Contact Dermatitis 2017 Feb 14. doi: 10.1111/cod.12763. [Epub ahead of print]

57 Gallenkemper G, Rabe E, Bauer R. Contact sensitization in chronic venous insufficiency: modern wound dressings. Contact Dermatitis 1998;38:274-278

58 Koch SE, Mathias T, Maibach HI. Chloroacetamide: an unusual cause of allergic cosmetic dermatitis. Arch Dermatol 1985;121:172-173

59 Chow ET, Avolio AM, Lee A, Nixon R. Frequency of positive patch test reactions to preservatives: The Australian experience. Australas J Dermatol 2013;54:31-35

60 Taran J, Delaney T. Contact allergy to chloroacetamide. Australas J Dermatol 1997;38:95-96

61 Sutton T, Nixon R. Allergic contact dermatitis to sodium benzoate chloroacetamide in a sorbolene lotion. Australas J Dermatol 2006;47:209-210

62 Fransway AF. The problem of preservation in the 1990s. III. Agents with preservative function independent of formaldehyde release. Am J Contact Derm 1991;2:145-174

2.93 P-CHLORO-M-CRESOL

IDENTIFICATION

Description/definition : *p*-Chloro-*m*-cresol is the substituted phenol that conforms to the formula shown below
Chemical class(es) : Halogen compounds; phenols
Chemical/IUPAC name : 4-Chloro-3-methylphenol
Other names : Chlorocresol
CAS registry number (s) : 59-50-7
EC number(s) : 200-431-6
CIR review(s) : Int J Toxicol 1997;16(Suppl.3):235-268; Int J Toxicol 2006;25(Suppl.1):29-127
(access: www.cir-safety.org/ingredients)
Merck Index monograph : 3403
Function(s) in cosmetics : EU: preservative. USA: cosmetic biocides; preservatives
EU cosmetic restrictions : Regulated in Annex V/24 of the Regulation (EC) No. 1223/2009
Patch testing : 1.0% pet. (Chemotechnique, SmartPracticeEurope, SmartPracticeCanada)
Molecular formula : C_7H_7ClO

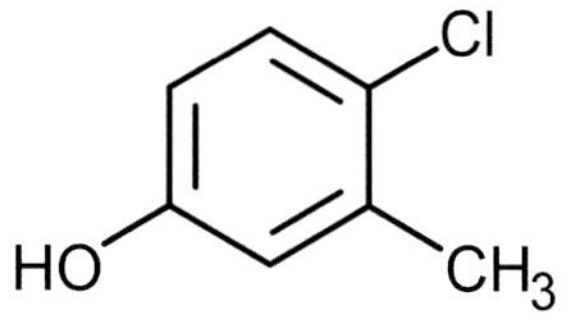

GENERAL

Chlorocresol is a biocide with widespread use in pharmaceutical products such as corticosteroid creams, adhesives, glues, inks, paints, varnishes, textile finishes, packing materials, tanning agents, and metal-working fluids. The use concentration varies from 0.05% to 0.5 % (6,7). It is hardly used in cosmetics as it may interfere with fragrances, but it was an important cause of allergic contact dermatitis in Australia from its presence in a moisturizing cream, that was often advised to patients by dermatologists (34). The literature on contact allergy to *p*-chloro-*m*-cresol up to 1990 has been reviewed (25).

CONTACT ALLERGY

Patch testing in groups of patients
Results of studies patch testing *p*-chloro-*m*-cresol in consecutive patients suspected of contact dermatitis (routine testing) and in groups of selected patients are shown in table 2.93.1. In routine testing, frequencies of sensitization have ranged from 0.3% to 1.3%; only one of the 6 studies had a rate higher than 1% (18). Relevance rates, if mentioned, ranged from 30% to 80%. Causative products were never mentioned.

In studies testing groups of selected patients (hairdressers, patients suspected of allergic cosmetic dermatitis, patients with leg ulcers, patients tested with a preservative series) had no higher rates of sensitization than in routine testing, ranging from 0% to 1.4%. Relevance of positive patch test reactions was mentioned in one study only: 9/9 positive reaction were considered to be relevant, but this included 'questionable' and 'past' relevance (1).

Case reports and case series
A male motor mechanic had persistent hand and foot dermatitis, considered to be endogenous (atopic dermatitis). He frequently applied sorbolene cream, a moisturizing cream widely used in Australia, as a barrier cream. When he quit his job, he stopped using the cream and improvement was noted, though he had sometimes an exacerbation. At one point, he again had an exacerbation of eczema and he also developed dermatitis of the face, where he had also applied the cream. Patch tests showed a strongly positive patch test reaction to sorbolene cream and its ingredient chlorocresol. A ROAT was performed and after only one day, in which he applied the sorbolene cream three times to the flexor surface of his forearm, the patient developed an acute erythematous reaction and ceased the test (34). In Australia, many dermatologists at that time (mid-1990s) frequently advised sorbolene cream as moisturizer. Of 14 top-selling brands of sorbolene cream in Australia, 10 contained *p*-chloro-*m*-cresol (34).

Contact allergy to *p*-chloro-*m*-cresol in non-cosmetic products
A laboratory worker had contact allergy to chlorocresol in disinfectants used at work and from the presence of the antimicrobial in topical corticosteroid preparations. She also had immediate airborne contact reactions with edema, rhinitis and conjunctivitis (3). A secretary had occupational ACD from chlorocresol in glue; she also reacted to the

corticosteroid cream that she was treated with and that also contained chlorocresol (7). A man had occupational allergic contact dermatitis of the hands from p-chloro-m-cresol (and chloroxylenol) in cleansing products used at his work as school custodian (27).

Five patients had ACD from chlorocresol in corticosteroid preparations (single case reports: 5,28,30,31,33). A similar case from a Personal Communication was cited in ref. 6. Another woman also had ACD from p-chloro-m-cresol in a corticosteroid preparation, but also from the active principle itself (26). Eleven cases of sensitivity to chlorocresol incorporated into topical preparations have been reported from Australia; some of these may have been the moisturizing cream described under Case reports and case series (9,10). Two more were published later by the same authors (8). Quite curiously, in 5 of these cases ascribed to chlorocresol allergy, there were only positive patch tests to the cross-reacting chloroxylenol (8).

In the 1950s and early 1960s, chloroxylenol was the second highest cause of contact allergic dermatitis to topical drugs in the United Kingdom (11, data cited in ref. 8).

Table 2.93.1 Patch testing in groups of patients

Years and Country	Test conc. & vehicle	Number of patients tested | positive (%)		Selection of patients (S); Relevance (R); Comments (C)	Ref.
Routine testing					
2001-2010 Australia	1% pet.	5094	53 (1.0%)	R: 30%	21
2003-2005 China		599	8 (1.3%)	R: not stated	18
2000 United Kingdom	1% pet.	3063	(0.6%)	R: 80% (current plus past relevance in one center)	14
1998-2000 USA	2% pet.	611	(0.3%)	R: not stated	13
1979-1996 Australia	1% pet.	4387	35 (0.8%)	R: not stated	34
1992-1994 USA	1% pet.	3471	(0.4%)	R: present relevance: 40%	12
Testing in groups of selected patients					
2010-2011 Korea	1% pet.	584	5 (0.9%)	S: patients suspected of allergic cosmetic dermatitis; R: not stated	19
2002-2011 Denmark		301	1 (0.3%)	S: hairdressers with contact dermatitis; R: not stated	22
2004-2008 France	1% pet.	423	6 (1.4%)	S: patients with leg ulcers; R: not stated	17
2000-2007 USA	1% pet.	943	9 (1.0%)	S: patients tested with a supplemental cosmetic screening series; R: 100%; C: weak study: a. high rate of macular erythema and weak reactions; b. relevance figures included 'questionable' and 'past' relevance	1
2000-2002 Finland		6046	(0.0%)	S: patients tested with a cosmetic series; R: not stated	15
1995-1996 Finland		5369	(0.2%)	S: patients tested with a cosmetic series; R: not stated	15
1990-1994 Germany	1% pet.	11,450	36 (0.3%)	S: patients tested with a preservative series; R: not stated	16

Cross-reactions, pseudo-cross-reactions and co-reactions
Chloroxylenol (2,3,8,34); not to m-cresol (27); possibly to m-cresol (32). It has been speculated that cross-reactivity with chloroxylenol occurs only when the initial sensitization is to chloroxylenol rather than chlorocresol (28). However, is has been demonstrated in animals that bidirectional cross-reactivity can occur, but that a much lower concentration is necessary when the initial sensitization is through chloroxylenol (29).

Presence in cosmetic products and chemical analyses
In the USA, in April 2017, p-chloro-m-cresol was present in 2 of 56,714 cosmetic products of which the composition is known in FDA's Voluntary Cosmetic Registration Program (VCRP) (data obtained from FDA, May 2017). In May 2017, p-chloro-m-cresol was present in 2 of 66,648 cosmetic products of which the composition is known in EWG's Skin Deep Cosmetics Database, USA (http://www.ewg.org/skindeep/).

Other information
Immediate and delayed hypersensitivity reactions to heparin preparations have been ascribed - unconvincingly and by circumstantial evidence - to p-chloro-m-cresol (35,36,37).

OTHER SIDE EFFECTS

Photosensitivity
Photocontact allergy to p-chloro-m-cresol may have been presented in ref. 20 (details unknown, article not read).

Immediate-type reactions

A woman with psoriasis had a history of severe pruritus and redness occurring within 30 minutes of applying certain topical preparations including emollients and corticosteroids creams. She was also aware that perfumes and some cosmetics would induce a similar reaction. Patch tests, removed after 30 minutes, revealed marked urticarial reactions to fragrance mix, cinnamal, eugenol, *p*-chloro-*m*-cresol and to an aqueous cream and three corticosteroid creams containing *p*-chloro-*m*-cresol (24). A laboratory worker had rhinitis, conjunctivitis and lip and eyelid edema within 15-30 minutes after entering a laboratory when disinfectants containing chlorocresol had been used. Prick tests were positive. This was a case of airborne immediate contact reactions. The patient also had contact allergy to chlorocresol in multiple topical corticosteroid preparations (3). A woman working in an aviary had occupational contact urticaria from *p*-chloro-*m*-cresol present in a disinfectant used to wash chicken incubators (4).

A review of contact urticaria caused by ingredients of cosmetics has been provided in ref. 23.

LITERATURE

1   Wetter DA, Yiannias JA, Prakash AV, Davis MD, Farmer SA, el-Azhary RA, et al. Results of patch testing to personal care product allergens in a standard series and a supplemental cosmetic series: an analysis of 945 patients from the Mayo Clinic Contact Dermatitis Group, 2000-2007. J Am Acad Dermatol 2010;63:789-798

2   Hjorth N, Trolle-Lassen C. Skin reactions to ointment bases. Trans St Johns Hosp Dermatol Soc 1963;49:127-140

3   Gonçalo M, Gonçalo S, Moreno, A. Immediate and delayed sensitivity to chlorocresol. Contact Dermatitis 1987;17:46-47

4   Freitas JP, Brandão FM. Contact urticaria to chlorocresol. Contact Dermatitis 1986;15:252

5   Archer CB, MacDonald DM. Chlorocresol sensitivity induced by treatment of allergic contact dermatitis with steroid creams. Contact Dermatitis 1984;11:144-145

6   Andersen KE, Hamann K. How sensitizing is chlorocresol? Contact Dermatitis 1984;11:11-20

7   Dooms-Goossens A, Degreef H, Vanhee J, Kerkhofs L, Chrispeels MT. Chlorocresol and chloracetamide: Allergens in medications, glues, and cosmetics. Contact Dermatitis 1981;7:51

8   Burry JN, Kirk J, Reid JG, Turner T. Chlorocresol sensitivity. Contact Dermatitis 1975;1:41-42

9   Burry, JN. The value of patch testing: A review of 363 cases of allergic contact dermatitis. Medical Journal of Australia 1969;1:1226-1231

10   Burry JN, Kirk J, Reid JG, Turner T. Environmental dermatitis: Patch tests in 1,000 cases of allergic contact dermatitis. Medical Journal of Australia 1973;2: 681-685

11   Calnan CD. Contact dermatitis from drugs. Proceedings of the Royal Society of Medicine 1962;55:39-42

12   Marks JG, Belsito DV, DeLeo VA, Fowler JF, Fransway AF, Maibach HI,et al. North American Contact Dermatitis Group standard tray patch test results 1992 through 1994. Am J Contact Dermatitis 1995;6:160-165

13   Wetter DA, Davis MDP, Yiannias JA, Cheng JF, Connolly SM, el-Azhary RA, et al. Patch test results from the Mayo Contact Dermatitis Group, 1998–2000. J Am Acad Dermatol 2005;53:416-421

14   Britton JE, Wilkinson SM, English JSC, Gawkrodger DJ, Ormerod AD, Sansom JE, et al. The British standard series of contact dermatitis allergens: validation in clinical practice and value for clinical governance. Br J Dermatol 2003;148:259-264

15   Hasan T, Rantanen T, Alanko K, Harvima RJ, Jolanki R, Kalimo K, et al. Patch test reactions to cosmetic allergens in 1995–1997 and 2000–2002 in Finland –a multicentre study. Contact Dermatitis 2005;53:40-45

16   Schnuch A, Geier J, Uter W, Frosch PJ. Patch testing with preservatives, antimicrobials and industrial biocides. Results from a multicentre study. Br J Dermatol 1998;138:467-476

17   Barbaud A, Collet E, Le Coz CJ, Meaume S, Gillois P. Contact allergy in chronic leg ulcers: results of a multicentre study carried out in 423 patients and proposal for an updated series of patch tests. Contact Dermatitis 2009;60:279-287

18   Li L-F, Liu G, Wang J. Patch test in Chinese patients with cosmetic allergic contact dermatitis to common cosmetic allergens from a European cosmetic series. Contact Dermatitis 2007;57:50-54

19   Lee SS, Hong DK, Jeong NJ, Lee JH, Choi YS, Lee AY, et al. Multicenter study of preservative sensitivity in patients with suspected cosmetic contact dermatitis in Korea. J Dermatol 2012;39:677-681

20   Pevny I, Lurz Ch. Photoallergische dermatitis. Allergologie 1985;8:128-138

21   Toholka R, Wang Y-S, Tate B, Tam M, Cahill J, Palmer A, Nixon R. The first Australian Baseline Series: Recommendations for patch testing in suspected contact dermatitis. Australas J Dermatol 2015;56:107-115

22   Schwensen JF, Johansen JD, Veien NK, Funding AT, Avnstorp C, Østerballe M, et al. Occupational contact dermatitis in hairdressers: an analysis of patch test data from the Danish Contact Dermatitis Group, 2002–2011. Contact Dermatitis 2014;70:233-237

23   Verhulst L, Goossens A. Cosmetic components causing contact urticaria: a review and update. Contact Dermatitis 2016;75:333-344

24   Walker SL, Chalmers RJ, Beck MH. Contact urticaria due to p-chloro-*m*-cresol. Br J Dermatol 2004;151:936-937

25 Fransway AF. The problem of preservation in the 1990s. III. Agents with preservative function independent of formaldehyde release. Am J Contact Derm 1991;2:145-174

26 Spiro JG, Lawrence CM. Contact sensitivity to clobetasol propionate. Contact Dermatitis 1986:14:116-117

27 Zemtsov A, Guccione J, Cameron GS, Mattioli F. Evaluation of antigenic determinant in chlorocresol and chloroxylenol contact dermatitis by patch testing with chemically related substances. Am J Cont Dermat 1994;5:19-21

28 Lewis PG, Emmet EA. Irritant dermatitis from tributyl tin oxide and contact allergy from chlorocresol. Contact Dermatitis 1987;17:129-132

29 Yamano T, Shimizu M, Noda T. Allergenicity evaluation of *p*-chloro-*m*-cresol and *p*-chloro-*m*-xylenol by non-radioactive murine local lymph-node assay and multipledose guinea pig maximization test. Toxicology 2003;190:259-266

30 Gómez de la Fuente E, Andreu-Barasoain M, Nuño-González A, López-Estebaranz JL. Allergic contact dermatitis due to chlorocresol in topical corticosteroids. Actas Dermosifiliogr 2013;104:90-92

31 Camarasa JG, Serra-Baldrich E. Dermatitis de contacto por cremas conteniendo propionato de clobetasol. Med Cutan Ibero Lat Am 1988;16:328-330

32 Raipar SF, Foulds IS, Abdullah A, Maheswari M. Severe adverse cutaneous reaction to insulin due to cresol sensitivity. Contact Dermatitis 2006;55:119-120

33 Salim A, Powell S, Wojnarowska F. Allergic contact dermatitis of the vulva - An overlooked diagnosis. J Obstet Gynaecol 2002;22:447

34 MacKenzie-Wood AR, Freeman S. Severe allergy to sorbolene cream. Australas J Dermatol 1997;38:33-34

35 Klein GF, Kofler H, Wolf H, Fritsch PO. Eczema-like, erythematous, infiltrated plaques: a common side effect of subcutaneous heparin therapy. J Am Acad Dermatol 1989;21(4 Pt. 1):703-707

36 Hancock BW, Naysmith A. Hypersensitivity to chlorocresol-preserved heparin. Br Med J 1975;3(5986):746-747

37 Ainley EJ, Mackie IG, Macarthur D. Adverse reaction to chlorocresol-preserved heparin. Lancet 1977;1(8013):705

2.94 2-CHLORO-P-PHENYLENEDIAMINE

IDENTIFICATION

Description/definition   : 2-Chloro-*p*-phenylenediamine is the halogenated aromatic amine that conforms to the formula shown below
Chemical class(es)   : Amines; color additives - hair; halogen compounds
Chemical/IUPAC name   : 2-Chlorobenzene-1,4-diamine
Other names   : 3-Chloro-4-aminoaniline; CI 76065; 2,5-diaminochlorobenzene
CAS registry number (s)   : 615-66-7
EC number(s)   : 210-441-2
CIR review(s)   : J Am Coll Toxicol 1992;11:521-530 (access: www.cir-safety.org/ingredients)
SCCS opinion(s)   : SCCS/1510/13 (3)
Function(s) in cosmetics   : EU: hair dyeing. USA: hair colorants
Patch testing   : 1% pet. (1)
Molecular formula   : $C_6H_7ClN_2$

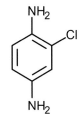

GENERAL

2-Chloro-*p*-phenylenediamine is used as coloring material in semi-permanent and temporary non-oxidative hair dying products.

CONTACT ALLERGY

Case reports and case series

Two women had ACD from 2-chloro-*p*-phenylenediamine in a cream dye used on their eyebrows and -lashes. They both reacted to 2-chloro-*p*-phenylenediamine 1% pet., to the cream dye 'as is' and to *p*-phenylenediamine (1). A man presented with eyelid swelling and conjunctival chemosis a day after having had his eyelashes dyed for the first time and without any history of any earlier exposure to similar compounds. He was treated with oral prednisolone and complete resolution occurred over a week. The authors state that the patient was patch test positive to 2-chloro-*p*-phenylenediamine, but the dilution and methodology were not described (2).

Cross-reactions, pseudo-cross-reactions and co-reactions

2-Chloro-*p*-phenylenediamine may cross-react with structurally related chemicals, notably those with a para-structure. Cross-reactivity between para-compounds is discussed in Chapter 2.359 *p*-Phenylenediamine.

Presence in cosmetic products and chemical analyses

In the USA, in April 2017, 2-chloro-*p*-phenylenediamine was present in zero of 56,714 cosmetic products of which the composition is known in FDA's Voluntary Cosmetic Registration Program (VCRP) (data obtained from FDA, May 2017). In March 2017, 2-chloro-*p*-phenylenediamine was present in zero of 64,983 cosmetic products of which the composition is known in EWG's Skin Deep Cosmetics Database, USA (http://www.ewg.org/skindeep/).

Miscellaneous side effects

A woman known to be allergic to *p*-phenylenediamine reported that she had lost all her eyelashes after using a mascara containing 2-chloro-*p*-phenylenediamine. She had had no associated dermatitis or blepharitis (4).

LITERATURE

1   Hansson C, Thorneby-Andersson K. Allergic contact dermatitis from 2-chloro-*p*-phenylenediamine in a cream dye for eyelashes and eyebrows. Contact Dermatitis 2001;45:235-236

2	Awan MA, Lockinton D, Ramaesh. Severe allergic blepharoconjunctivitis after eyelash colouring (letter). Eye 2010;24:200-201

3	SCCS (Scientific Committee on Consumer Safety). Opinion on -2-chloro-*p*-phenylenediamine, SCCS/1510/13, 19 September 2013 available at:
http://ec.europa.eu/health//sites/health/files/scientific_committees/consumer_safety/docs/sccs_o_139.pdf

4	Wachsmuth R, Wilkinson M. Loss of eyelashes after use of a tinting mascara containing PPD. Contact Dermatitis 2006;54:169-170

2.95 CHLOROXYLENOL

IDENTIFICATION

Description/definition	: Chloroxylenol is the organic compound that conforms to the formula shown below
Chemical class(es)	: Halogen compounds; phenols
Chemical/IUPAC name	: 4-Chloro-3,5-dimethylphenol
Other names	: Chlorodimethylhydroxybenzene; *p*-chloro-*m*-xylenol
CAS registry number (s)	: 88-04-0; 1321-23-9
EC number(s)	: 201-793-8; 215-316-6
CIR review(s)	: J Am Coll Toxicol 1985;4:147-169 (access: www.cir-safety.org/ingredients)
Merck Index monograph	: 3452
Function(s) in cosmetics	: EU: antimicrobial; deodorant; preservative. USA: cosmetic biocides; deodorant agents; preservatives
EU cosmetic restrictions	: Regulated in Annex V/26 of the Regulation (EC) No. 1223/2009
Patch testing	: 0.5% pet. (Chemotechnique); 1.0% pet. (Chemotechnique, SmartPracticeEurope, SmartPracticeCanada)
Molecular formula	: C_8H_9ClO

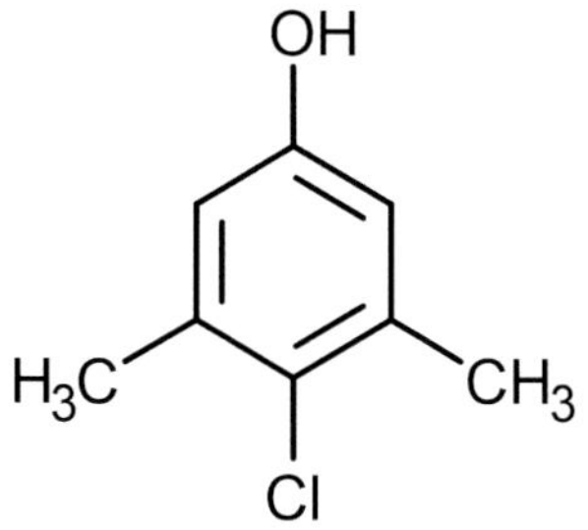

GENERAL

Chloroxylenol is a halogenated phenolic compound, which was first introduced in Germany in 1927 and is produced as a stable white crystalline powder with a phenolic odor (40). It is used as antimicrobial and preservative in cosmetics, hand soaps, topical medications, antiseptics, metalworking fluids and electrocardiograph pastes. One of its major uses in the United States is as an ingredient in antimicrobial soaps used in the health care and food service industries (38). Chloroxylenol has a broad spectrum of antibacterial activity, with good *in vitro* activity against gram-positive organisms and moderate activity against gram-negative organisms (but not to *Pseudomonas aeruginosa*) and mycobacteria.

Currently, contact allergy to chloroxylenol occurs infrequently, although it used to be a frequent cause of dermatitis medicamentosa in the UK at the beginning of the 1960s and it caused many reactions from antiseptics in the 1980s in the Manchester area, UK, from widespread use of 2 brands of antiseptics containing high concentrations of chloroxylenol. Most sensitizations have been caused by topical pharmaceuticals including Carbolated Vaseline (12,16), disinfectant hand soaps (11,36,38,40,42,43), other antiseptic preparations (36,39,41,44) and electrocardiography paste (14,16,43). Sensitization is usually not suspected on the basis of patient history and clinical examination (49). It has been suggested that the antigenic component is the chloride atom in the para position of the phenol ring (41).

CONTACT ALLERGY

Patch testing in groups of patients

Results of testing chloroxylenol in consecutive patients suspected of contact dermatitis (routine testing) back to 1976 are shown in table 2.95.1. Results of testing in groups of *selected* patients (e.g., patients suspected of cosmetic dermatitis, individuals with eyelid dermatitis, hairdressers with contact dermatitis, health care workers) back to 1990 are shown in table 2.95.2.

Patch testing in consecutive patients suspected of contact dermatitis: routine testing

Chloroxylenol has been part of the North American Contact Dermatitis Group (NACDG) screening series since 1992, so there is much information available from the USA and Canada, where the NACDG publishes its results biannually. In twenty studies in which routine testing with chloroxylenol was performed, rates of sensitization have generally been low, ranging from 0.3% to 3.3%; in 14 studies, they were below 1%. The high concentration of 3.3% was found in a 1998-2000 USA study, but relevance of the positive patch tests was not mentioned (23). In studies that did address the issue of relevance, rates have varied greatly, ranging from 13% to 90%. In most NACDG studies, 'definite' or 'probable' relevance was found in 30-40% of the positive patch test reactions. In only one study were the causative products mentioned, which were over-the-counter antiseptics with high concentrations of chloroxylenol widely used in that part of the UK (44).

Table 2.95.1 Patch testing in groups of patients: Routine testing

Years and Country	Test conc. & vehicle	Number of patients tested	positive (%)	Selection of patients (S); Relevance (R); Comments (C)	Ref.
2013-14 USA, Canada	1% pet.	4859	22 (0.5%)	R: definite + probable relevance: 32%	33
2011-12 USA, Canada	1% pet.	4230	23 (0.5%)	R: definite + probable relevance: 57%	8
2009-10 USA, Canada	1% pet.	4304	22 (0.5%)	R: definite + probable relevance: 32%	9
2006-2010 USA	1% pet.	3087	(0.7%)	R: 48%	30
2007-8 USA, Canada	1% pet.	5083	(0.4%)	R: definite + probable relevance: 29%	5
2005-6 USA, Canada	1% pet.	4436	(0.5%)	R: definite + probable relevance: 38%	4
2004-2005 UK	0.5% pet.	6958	(1.9%)	R: not stated	22
2003-2005 China		599	3 (0.5%)	R: not stated	26
2000-2005 USA	1% pet.	3845	(0.7%)	R: 50%	3
2003-4 USA, Canada	1% pet.	5141	36 (0.7%)	R: not stated	6
2001-2 USA, Canada	1% pet.	4898	(0.6%)	R: definite + probable relevance: 25%	17
2000 United Kingdom	1% pet.	3063	(0.4%)	R: 80% (current and past relevance in one centre)	24
1998-00 USA, Canada	1% pet.	5800	(0.8%)	R: definite + probable relevance: 13%	18
1998-00 USA, Canada	1% pet.	1039	(3.3%)	R: not stated	23
1996-8 USA, Canada	1% pet.	4093	(1%)	R: definite + probable + possible relevance: 63%	19
1994-6 USA, Canada	1% pet.	3074	(1.2%)	R: definite + probable relevance: 41%	20
1992-4 USA, Canada	1% pet.	3506	(1.4%)	R: present relevance: 90%	21
1985 The Netherlands	1% pet.	627	2 (0.3%)	R: not stated	28
<1985 UK	2% pet.	951	17 (1.8%)	R: 7 relevant, 6 probably past relevance, 4 unknown, all from 2 antiseptics containing high concentrations of chloroxylenol; C: the antiseptics were in that area of the UK widely used, e.g., by >50% of patient s with hand and/or foot dermatitis	44
1975-6 USA, Canada	1% pet.		(1.3%)	R: not stated	29

Patch testing in groups of selected patients
Results of testing chloroxylenol in groups of selected patients (e.g., patients suspected of cosmetic dermatitis, individuals with eyelid dermatitis, hairdressers with contact dermatitis, health care workers) back to 1990 are shown in table 2.95.2. In 9 investigations, frequencies of sensitization have ranged from 0.3% to 3%, but rates were higher than 1.7% in only 2 studies (27,35). In neither of these studies were relevance data provided, as was the case in all but 3 investigations. One of these had a 30% score (32), the second considered all 7 reactions to be relevant, but this study had certain weaknesses (1). In the third study, performed by the NACDG, only relevant reactions were presented; the causative products were mostly soaps, cleansers and disinfectants (36).

Case reports and case series
Chloroxylenol was responsible for 1 out of 399 cases of cosmetic allergy where the causal allergen was identified in a study of the NACDG, USA, 1977-1983 (2). Two patients reacted to chloroxylenol in a hand lotion (31). A woman had allergic contact dermatitis superimposed on irritant hand dermatitis from treating it with a moisturizer containing chloroxylenol (38). A restaurant manager had worsening of hand dermatitis from contact allergy to chloroxylenol in hand soap (38). A cleaner had occupational allergic contact dermatitis from chloroxylenol in handwashing soap (11). A plumber had occupational allergic contact dermatitis of the hands from chloroxylenol in a liquid hand soap (40). A physical therapy aid and a man working in a food processing plant developed occupational allergic contact dermatitis from a disinfecting soap and hand cleanser (42). Another individual also developed hand dermatitis from chloroxylenol in a liquid soap (43).

Contact allergy to chloroxylenol in non-cosmetic products
Four patients (12) and five more (16) developed allergic contact dermatitis from chloroxylenol in Carbolated Vaseline. One patient had contact allergy to chloroxylenol in another topical pharmaceutical product (16). One individual reacted to chloroxylenol in an electrode gel (14, data cited in ref. 13). A man had allergic contact dermatitis from chloroxylenol in an antimycotic cream. Later, while being a surgical intern, he had occupational allergic contact dermatitis from the hand caused by chloroxylenol in an electrocardiography paste (16). One more patient allergic to ECG paste has been reported (unknown whether occupational or in an individual who underwent

electrocardiography) (16). A woman had allergic contact dermatitis of the chest from chloroxylenol in an ECG electrode, which in the center contained a gel-soaked pad containing the bacteriostatic agent (43). One patient developed allergic contact dermatitis from a paste containing chlorocresol while undergoing an ECG; this individual had previously been sensitized to chloroxylenol in Carbolated Vaseline (16).

A machinist in a jet turbine plant had occupational allergic contact dermatitis of the dorsal aspects of the fingers from chloroxylenol in a barrier cream used in the workplace (37). Two other machinists developed occupational allergic contact dermatitis from chloroxylenol in coolants (15). A young man had generalized allergic contact dermatitis from taking a bath to which an antiseptic containing 4.8% chloroxylenol had been added (39). A high school custodian had allergic hand dermatitis from chloroxylenol in cleansing solutions (41). A machinist had hand dermatitis and contact allergy to chloroxylenol. After avoidance of products containing chloroxylenol, the dermatitis improved considerably, but culprit products (metalworking fluids?) were not mentioned (42).

Table 2.95.2 Patch testing in groups of patients: Selected patient groups

Years and Country	Test conc. & vehicle	Number of patients tested	positive (%)		Selection of patients (S); Relevance (R); Comments (C)	Ref.
2010-2011 Korea	0.5% pet.	584	15	(2.6%)	S: patients suspected of allergic cosmetic dermatitis; R: not stated	27
2002-2011 Denmark		283	1	(0.4%)	S: hairdressers with contact dermatitis; R: not stated	34
2006-2010 USA	1% pet.	100	1	(1%)	S: patients with eyelid dermatitis; R: not stated	7
2001-2010 Australia	0.5% pet.	1598	27	(1.7%)	S: not stated; R: 30%	32
2000-2007 USA	1% pet.	944	7	(0.7%)	S: patients tested with a supplemental cosmetic screening series; R: 100%; C: weak study: a. high rate of macular erythema and weak reactions; b. relevance figures included 'questionable' and 'past' relevance	1
1998-04 USA, Canada	1% pet.	1250	11	(0.9%)	S: health care workers; R: only occupation-related (=relevant) reactions were recorded; C: because of this selection, the frequency of sensitization is low; the frequency was significantly higher than the rate of occupation-related reactions in non-health care workers (0.1%); the causative products were mostly soaps, cleansers and disinfectants	36
1990-1994 Germany	1% pet.	11,436	32	(0.3%)	S: patients tested with a preservative series; R: not stated	25
1990-1994 Germany	1% pet.	1776	6	(0.3%)	S: patients tested with an industrial biocide series; R: not stated	25
1984-1991 USA	0.5% pet.	4399	47	(1.1%)	S: unknown, possibly routine testing; R: not stated	47
<1990 India	0.5% pet.	69	2	(3%)	S: patients, with features suggestive of allergic contact dermatitis and histories of prolonged use of numerous topical preparations, or of exacerbation or spread of dermatitis following the use of such preparations; R: not stated	35

Cross-reactions, pseudo-cross-reactions and co-reactions
Cross-reactions to *p*-chloro-*m*-cresol in 4 patients (10,43); cresol (10,16); dichloro-*m*-xylenol (43); only one of 17 patients reacting to chloroxylenol co-reacted to *p*-chloro-*m*-cresol (44).

Presence in cosmetic products and chemical analyses
In June 2017, chloroxylenol was present in 5 of 69,510 cosmetic products of which the composition is known in EWG's Skin Deep Cosmetics Database, USA (http://www.ewg.org/skindeep/). In the USA, in April 2017, chloroxylenol was present in 119 of 56,714 cosmetic products of which the composition is known in FDA's Voluntary Cosmetic Registration Program (VCRP) (data obtained from FDA, May 2017).

OTHER SIDE EFFECTS

Miscellaneous side effects
A young man took a bath with an antiseptic containing chloroxylenol on two consecutive days to treat a widespread pustular eruption on his body. As soon as the second bath was finished, the patient developed itching, stinging and burning. This was followed by the sequential development of erythema, hyperpigmentation, blackening and depigmentation. The sequence of events took place in 1 week. Three months later, depigmentation was found to be generalized including the palms and face, but perifollicular repigmentation was apparent at many places. Patch tests gave a positive reaction to chloroxylenol, and depigmentation occurred at the test site. The antiseptic was a popular over-the-counter antiseptic containing chloroxylenol 4.8% w/v, terpinol 9% w/v and absolute alcohol 13.1% v/v (39). A man developed irritant dermatitis from an antiseptic containing 4.8% chloroxylenol followed by depigmentation

(chemical leukoderma). The causative role of chloroxylenol was claimed, but not proven, as the antiseptic contains other ingredients, although it must be admitted that the phenolic compound chloroxylenol is indeed the most likely candidate as cause for the observed depigmentation (48).

LITERATURE

1   Wetter DA, Yiannias JA, Prakash AV, Davis MD, Farmer SA, el-Azhary RA, et al. Results of patch testing to personal care product allergens in a standard series and a supplemental cosmetic series: an analysis of 945 patients from the Mayo Clinic Contact Dermatitis Group, 2000-2007. J Am Acad Dermatol 2010;63:789-798

2   Adams RM, Maibach HI, Clendenning WE, Fisher AA, Jordan WJ, Kanof N, et al. A five-year study of cosmetic reactions. J Am Acad Dermatol 1985;13:1062-1069

3   Davis MD, Scalf LA, Yiannias JA, Cheng JF, El-Azhary RA, Rohlinger AL, et al. Changing trends and allergens in the patch test standard series. Arch Dermatol 2008;144:67-72

4   Zug KA, Warshaw EM, Fowler JF Jr, Maibach HI, Belsito DL, Pratt MD, et al. Patch-test results of the North American Contact Dermatitis Group 2005-2006. Dermatitis 2009;20:149-160

5   Fransway AF, Zug KA, Belsito DV, Deleo VA, Fowler JF Jr, Maibach HI, et al. North American Contact Dermatitis Group patch test results for 2007-2008. Dermatitis 2013;24:10-21

6   Warshaw EM, Belsito DV, DeLeo VA, Fowler JF Jr, Maibach HI, Marks JG, et al. North American Contact Dermatitis Group patch-test results, 2003-2004 study period. Dermatitis 2008;19:129-136

7   Wenk KS, Ehrlich AE. Fragrance series testing in eyelid dermatitis. Dermatitis 2012;23:22-26

8   Warshaw EM, Maibach HI, Taylor JS, Sasseville D, DeKoven JG, Zirwas MJ, et al. North American Contact Dermatitis Group patch test results: 2011-2012. Dermatitis 2015;26:49-59

9   Warshaw EM, Belsito DV, Taylor JS, Sasseville D, DeKoven JG, Zirwas MJ, et al. North American Contact Dermatitis Group patch test results: 2009 to 2010. Dermatitis 2013;24:50-59

10   Hjorth N, Trolle-Lassen C. Skin reactions to ointment bases. Trans St Johns Hosp Dermatol Soc 1963;49:127-140

11   Libow, LF, Ruszkowski AM, Deleo VA. Allergic contact dermatitis from para-chloro-meta-xylenol in Lurosep soap. Contact Dermatitis 1989;20:67-68

12   Rubin MB, Pirozzi DJ. Contact dermatitis from carbolated Vaseline. Cutis 1973;12:52-55

13   Tomb RR, Rivara G, Foussereau J. Contact dermatitis after ultrasonography and electrocardiography. Contact Dermatitis 1987;17:149-152

14   Fisher AA. Dermatologic hazards of electrocardiography. Cutis 1977;20:686 (further pages unknown, data cited in ref. 13)

15   Adams RM. p-Chloro-m-xylenol in cutting fluids: Two cases of allergic contact dermatitis in machinists. Contact Dermatitis 1981;7:341-343

16   Storrs FJ. Para-chloro-meta-xylenol allergic contact dermatitis in seven individuals. Contact Dermatitis 1975;1:211-213

17   Pratt MD, Belsito DV, DeLeo VA, Fowler JF Jr, Fransway AF, Maibach HI, et al. North American Contact Dermatitis Group patch-test results, 2001–2002 study period. Dermatitis 2004;15:176-183

18   Marks JG Jr, Belsito DV, DeLeo VA, Fowler JF Jr, Fransway AF, Maibach HI, et al. North American Contact Dermatitis Group patch-test results, 1998–2000. Am J Contact Dermat 2003;14:59-62

19   Marks JG Jr, Belsito DV, DeLeo VA, Fowler JF Jr, Fransway AF, Maibach HI, et al. North American Contact Dermatitis Group patch test results, 1996–1998. Arch Dermatol 2000;136:272-273

20   Marks JG Jr, Belsito DV, DeLeo VA, Fowler JF Jr, Fransway AF, Maibach HI,et al. North American Contact Dermatitis Group patch test results for the detection of delayed-type hypersensitivity to topical allergens. J Am Acad Dermatol 1998;38:911-918

21   Marks JG, Belsito DV, DeLeo VA, Fowler JF, Fransway AF, Maibach HI,et al. North American Contact Dermatitis Group standard tray patch test results 1992 through 1994. Am J Contact Dermatitis 1995;6:160-165

22   Jong CT, Statham BN, Green CM, King CM, Gawkrodger DJ, Sansom JE, et al. Contact sensitivity to preservatives in the UK 2004–2005: results of a multicenter study. Contact Dermatitis 2007;57:165-168

23   Wetter DA, Davis MDP, Yiannias JA, Cheng JF, Connolly SM, el-Azhary RA, et al. Patch test results from the Mayo Contact Dermatitis Group, 1998–2000. J Am Acad Dermatol 2005;53:416-421

24   Britton JE, Wilkinson SM, English JSC, Gawkrodger DJ, Ormerod AD, Sansom JE, et al. The British standard series of contact dermatitis allergens: validation in clinical practice and value for clinical governance. Br J Dermatol 2003;148:259-264

25   Schnuch A, Geier J, Uter W, Frosch PJ. Patch testing with preservatives, antimicrobials and industrial biocides. Results from a multicentre study. Br J Dermatol 1998;138:467-476

26   Li L-F, Liu G, Wang J. Patch test in Chinese patients with cosmetic allergic contact dermatitis to common cosmetic allergens from a European cosmetic series. Contact Dermatitis 2007;57:50-54

27 Lee SS, Hong DK, Jeong NJ, Lee JH, Choi YS, Lee AY, et al. Multicenter study of preservative sensitivity in patients with suspected cosmetic contact dermatitis in Korea. J Dermatol 2012;39:677-681

28 De Groot AC, Weyland JW, Bos JD, Jagtman BA. Contact allergy to preservatives (I). Contact Dermatitis 1986;14:120-122

29 Rudner EJ. North American Group Results. Contact Dermatitis 1977;3:208-209

30 Wentworth AB, Yiannias JA, Keeling JH, Hall MR, Camilleri MJ, Drage LA, et al. Trends in patch-test results and allergen changes in the standard series: a Mayo Clinic 5-year retrospective review (January 1, 2006, to December 31, 2010). J Am Acad Dermatol 2014;70:269-275

31 Cronin E. Contact Dermatitis. Edinburgh: Churchill Livingstone, 1980:676

32 Toholka R, Wang Y-S, Tate B, Tam M, Cahill J, Palmer A, Nixon R. The first Australian Baseline Series: Recommendations for patch testing in suspected contact dermatitis. Australas J Dermatol 2015;56:107-115

33 DeKoven JG, Warshaw EM, Belsito DV, Sasseville D, Maibach HI, Taylor JS, et al. North American Contact Dermatitis Group Patch Test Results: 2013-2014. Dermatitis 2017;28:33-46

34 Schwensen JF, Johansen JD, Veien NK, Funding AT, Avnstorp C, Østerballe M, et al. Occupational contact dermatitis in hairdressers: an analysis of patch test data from the Danish Contact Dermatitis Group, 2002–2011. Contact Dermatitis 2014;70:233-237

35 George ND, Srinivas CR, Balachandran C, Shenoi SD. Sensitivity to various ingredients of topical preparations following prolonged use. Contact Dermatitis 1990;23:367-368

36 Warshaw EM, Schram SE, Maibach HI, Belsito DV, Marks JG Jr, Fowler JF Jr, et al. Occupation-related contact dermatitis in North American health care workers referred for patch testing: cross-sectional data, 1998 to 2004. Dermatitis 2008;19:261-274

37 Madden SD, Thiboutot DM, Marks JG. Occupationally induced allergic contact dermatitis to methylchloro-isothiazolinone/methylisothiazolinone among machinists. J Am Acad Dermatol 1994;30:272-277

38 Berthelot C, Zirwas MJ. Allergic contact dermatitis to chloroxylenol. Dermatitis 2006;17:156-159

39 Malakar S, Panda S. Post-inflammatory depigmentation following allergic contact dermatitis to chloroxylenol. Br J Dermatol 2001;144:1275-1276

40 Mowad C. Chloroxylenol causing hand dermatitis in a plumber. Am J Cont Derm 1998;9:128-129

41 Zemtsov A, Guccione J, Cameron GS, Mattioli F. Evaluation of antigenic determinant in chlorocresol and chloroxylenol contact dermatitis by patch testing with chemically related substances. Am J Cont Derm 1994;5:19-21

42 Fowler JF Jr. Para-chloro-meta-xylenol allergy and hand eczema. Am J Cont Derm 1993;4:53-54

43 Ranchoff RE, Steck WD, Taylor JS, Evey P. Electrocardiograph electrode and hand dermatitis from parachlorometaxylenol. J Am Acad Dermatol 1986;15:348-350

44 Myatt AE, Beck MH. Contact sensitivity to parachlorometaxylenol (PCMX). Clin Exp Dermatol 1985;10:491-494

45 Calcan CD. Contact Dermatitis from drugs. Proc Royal Soc Med 1962;55:39-42

46 Fransway AF. The problem of preservation in the 1990s. III. Agents with preservative function independent of formaldehyde release. Am J Contact Derm 1991;2:145-174

47 Verma GK, Mahajan VK, Shanker V, Tegta GR, Jindal N, Minhas S. Contact depigmentation following irritant contact dermatitis to chloroxylenol (Dettol). Indian J Dermatol Venereol Leprol 2011;77:612-614

48 Verma GK, Mahajan VK, Shanker V, Tegta GR, Jindal N, Minhas S. Contact depigmentation following irritant contact dermatitis to chloroxylenol (Dettol). Indian J Dermatol Venereol Leprol 2011;77:612-614

49 Wilson M, Mowad C. Chloroxylenol. Dermatitis 2007;18:120-121

2.96 CHLORPHENESIN

IDENTIFICATION

Description/definition	: Chlorphenesin is the organic compound that conforms to the formula shown below
Chemical class(es)	: Alcohols; ethers
Chemical/IUPAC name	: 3-(4-Chlorophenoxy)propane-1,2-diol
CAS registry number (s)	: 104-29-0
EC number(s)	: 203-192-6
CIR review(s)	: Int J Toxicol 2014;33(Suppl.2):5-15 (access: www.cir-safety.org/ingredients)
Merck Index monograph	: 3454
Function(s) in cosmetics	: EU: antimicrobial; preservative. USA: cosmetic biocides
EU cosmetic restrictions	: Regulated in Annex V/50 of the Regulation (EC) No. 1223/2009
Patch testing	: Chlorphenesin 1% and 0.5% pet. Both may cause irritant reactions (11)
Molecular formula	: $C_9H_{11}ClO_3$

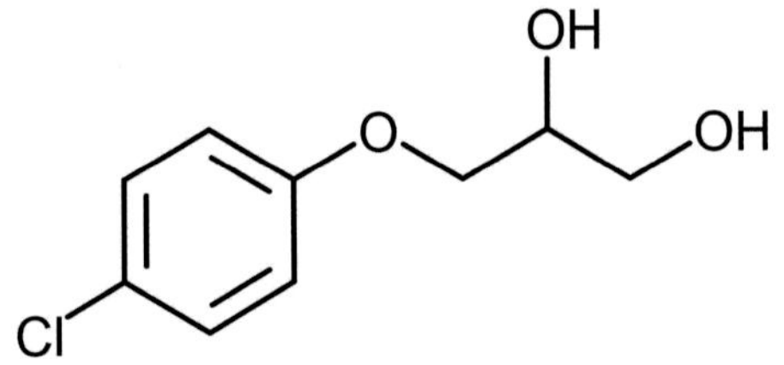

GENERAL

Chlorphenesin is an antimicrobial agent with antifungal, antibacterial and anticandidal activity. It has been included in preparations to treat dermatophytosis of the feet for more than 70 years and may also be present in cosmetics as a biocide and preservative. It is a rare cause of contact allergy and allergic reactions were seen especially when it was still used for fungal infections of the feet.

CONTACT ALLERGY

Patch testing in groups of patients

In Korea, in 2010-2011, 584 patients suspected of allergic cosmetic dermatitis were patch tested with chlorphenesin 1% pet. and 24 (4.1%) had a positive reaction. The relevance of these reactions was not mentioned (11). It should be appreciated, however, that the test concentration of 1% pet. may result in false-positive, irritant, patch test reactions.

Case reports and case series

Chlorphenesin was stated to be the (or an) allergen in one patient in a group of 603 individuals suffering from cosmetic dermatitis, seen in the period 2010-2015 in Leuven, Belgium (12). Chlorphenesin was responsible for 5 out of 959 cases of non-fragrance cosmetic allergy where the causal allergen was identified, Belgium, 2000-2010 (1). One patient had allergic contact dermatitis of the axillae from chlorphenesin in a deodorant (6) and another from its presence in a facial moisturizer (7). One individual had dermatitis from contact allergy to chlorphenesin in a face and body cream (8). Two other patients were also sensitized to chlorphenesin in cosmetics, one from a foundation make-up, the other from a moisturizer (10).

Contact allergy to chlorphenesin in non-cosmetic products

Two patients (3) and two more individuals (4,5) had allergic contact dermatitis from chlorphenesin in antifungal preparations.

Presence in cosmetic products and chemical analyses

In the USA, in April 2017, chlorphenesin was present in 2468 of 56,714 cosmetic products of which the composition is known in FDA's Voluntary Cosmetic Registration Program (VCRP) (data obtained from FDA, May 2017). In March 2017, chlorphenesin was present in 725 of 64,983 cosmetic products of which the composition is known in EWG's Skin Deep Cosmetics Database, USA (http://www.ewg.org/skindeep/). Chlorphenesin was present in 136 of 4737 (2.9%) commonly used cosmetic products of which the full composition was known in 2016 in The Contact Allergen Management Program (CAMP) database of the American Contact Dermatitis Society (13). Chlorphenesin was present in one (0.5%) of 204 cosmetic products (92 shampoos, 61 hair conditioners, 34 liquid soaps, 17 wet tissues) collected in Sweden, 2008 (2). According to the Voluntary Cosmetic Registration Program, chlorphenesin was used in more than 1300 cosmetic products in 2012 in the USA (9).

LITERATURE

1   Travassos AR, Claes L, Boey L, Drieghe J, Goossens A. Non-fragrance allergens in specific cosmetic products. Contact Dermatitis 2011;65:276-285
2   Yazar K, Johnsson S, Lind M-L, Boman A, Lidén C. Preservatives and fragrances in selected consumer-available cosmetics and detergents. Contact Dermatitis 2011;64:265-272
3   Cronin E. Contact Dermatitis. Edinburgh: Churchill Livingstone, 1980: 227
4   Brown R. Chlorphenesin sensitivity. Contact Dermatitis 1981;7:162
5   Burns DA. Allergic contact sensitivity to chlorphenesin. Contact Dermatitis 1986;14:246
6   Goh CL. Dermatitis from chlorphenesin in a deodorant. Contact Dermatitis 1987;16:287
7   Wakelin SH, White IR. Dermatitis from chlorphenesin in a facial cosmetic. Contact Dermatitis 1997;37:138-139
8   Dyring-Andersen B, Elberling J, Johansen JD, Zachariae C. Contact allergy to chlorphenesin. JEADV 2015;29:1019
9   Johnson W. On behalf of the 2012 Cosmetic Ingredient Review Expert Panel members, Safety assessment of chlorphenesin as used in cosmetics. 2012. http://online.personalcarecouncil.org/jsp/CIRList.jsp?id=5002
10 Brown VL, Orton DI. Two cases of facial dermatitis due to chlorphenesin in cosmetics. Contact Dermatitis 2005;52:48-49
11 Lee SS, Hong DK, Jeong NJ, Lee JH, Choi YS, Lee AY, et al. Multicenter study of preservative sensitivity in patients with suspected cosmetic contact dermatitis in Korea. J Dermatol 2012;39:677-681
12 Goossens A. Cosmetic contact allergens. Cosmetics 2016, 3, 5; doi:10.3390/cosmetics3010005
13 Beene KM, Scheman A, Severson D, Reeder MJ. Prevalence of preservatives across all product types in the Contact Allergen Management Program. Dermatitis 2017;28:81-87

2.97 CI 11680

IDENTIFICATION

Description/definition : CI 11680 is a monoazo color that conforms to the structural formula shown below
Chemical class(es) : Color additives - miscellaneous
INCI name USA : Pigment yellow 1
Chemical/IUPAC name : (2Z)-2-[(4-Methyl-2-nitrophenyl)hydrazinylidene]-3-oxo-N-phenylbutanamide
Other names : 2-[(4-Methyl-2-nitrophenyl)azo]-3-oxo-N-phenylbutyramide; pigment yellow 1; fast yellow G; hansa yellow
CAS registry number (s) : 2512-29-0
EC number(s) : 219-730-8
Function(s) in cosmetics : EU: cosmetic colorant. USA: colorants
EU cosmetic restrictions : Regulated in Annex IV/40 of the Regulation (EC) No. 1223/2009
Patch testing : 5% polyethylene glycol (1)
Molecular formula : $C_{17}H_{16}N_4O_4$

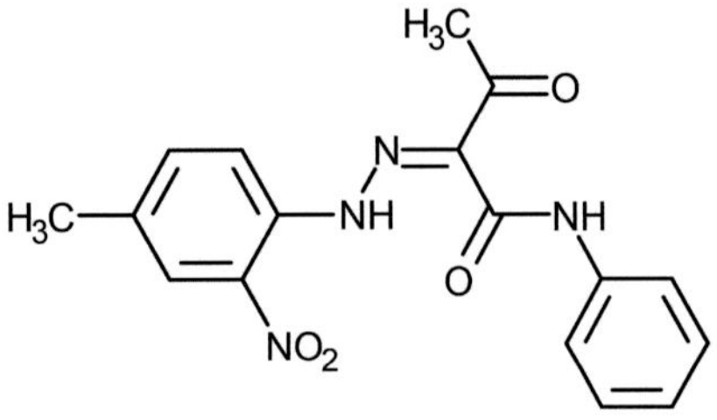

CONTACT ALLERGY

Patch testing in groups of patients
Of 38 Japanese patients with pigmented cosmetic dermatitis, patch tested and photopatch tested with coal tar dyes in 1975-1976, two had positive patch tests CI 11680. It was not mentioned (and probably unknown) whether this color was present in the cosmetics used by the patients (1).

Cross-reactions, pseudo-cross-reactions and co-reactions
Other coal tar dyes (1).

Presence in cosmetic products and chemical analyses
In the USA, in April 2017, CI 11680 was present in zero of 56,714 cosmetic products of which the composition is known in FDA's Voluntary Cosmetic Registration Program (VCRP) (data obtained from FDA, May 2017). In March 2017, CI 11680 was present in 3 of 64,983 cosmetic products of which the composition is known in EWG's Skin Deep Cosmetics Database, USA (http://www.ewg.org/skindeep/).

OTHER SIDE EFFECTS

Photosensitivity
Of 38 Japanese patients with pigmented cosmetic dermatitis, patch tested and photopatch tested with coal tar dyes in 1975-1976, one had a positive photopatch test to CI 11680. It was not mentioned (and probably unknown) whether this color was present in the cosmetics used by the patient (1).

LITERATURE
1   Sugai T, Takahashi Y, Tagaki T. Pigmented cosmetic dermatitis and coal tar dyes. Contact Dermatitis 1977;3:249-256

2.98 CI 12010

IDENTIFICATION

Description/definition : CI 12010 is a monoazo color, which conforms to the formula shown below
Chemical class(es) : Color additives - miscellaneous
INCI name USA : Solvent red 3
Chemical/IUPAC name : (4E)-4-[(4-Ethoxyphenyl)hydrazinylidene]naphthalen-1-one
Other names : Solvent red 3; 4-[(4-ethoxyphenyl)azo]naphthol; Sudan brown B
CAS registry number (s) : 6535-42-8
EC number(s) : 229-439-8
Function(s) in cosmetics : EU: cosmetic colorant. USA: colorants
EU cosmetic restrictions : Regulated in Annex II/1344 of the Regulation (EC) No. 344/2013 (prohibited in hair dye products) and in Annex IV/8 of the Regulation (EC) No. 1223/2009
Patch testing : 1% pet.
Molecular formula : $C_{18}H_{16}N_2O_2$

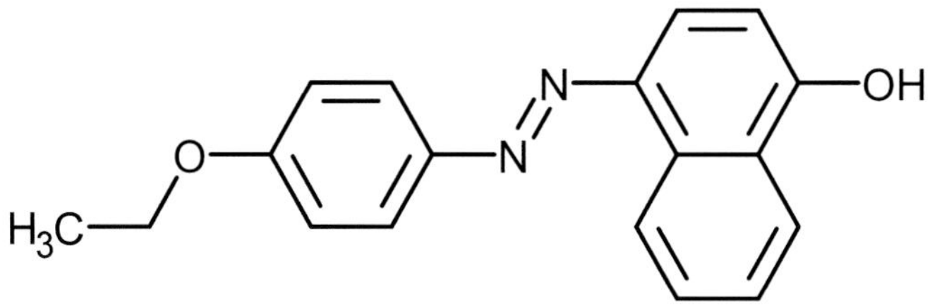

CONTACT ALLERGY

Case reports and case series

A woman with no prior skin problems had a cosmetic face mask applied and then a soothing oil. Three to four hours later, she experienced itching, swelling and redness of her face, which lasted for several days. On the 4th day, she still had gross edema, redness and scaling of the face, especially around the eyelids. Patch testing with a standard series, common constituents of ointments, with the face mask, and the cosmetic oil gave a positive result only to the oil. Additional testing of its constituents gave a positive reaction to CI Solvent red 3 1% pet. Control tests in 10 persons were negative (3).

A man had an itchy red scaly dermatitis for one year, involving the scalp, face and neck (particularly behind the ears, sparing under the chin), upper chest and backs of the hands, later spreading to the thighs and becoming darker, especially in the summer. He used a popular brand of brilliantine to make his hair glossy and smooth. Patch tests with the GIRDCA standard series, a textile dye series, a cosmetics series, the brilliantine as is, and its different components showed positive reactions to disperse yellow 3, disperse black 1, the brilliantine as is and its ingredient CI solvent red 3 (tested 0.1% and 1% pet.). Control tests with the dye were negative in 10 subjects (2).

One patient had allergic contact dermatitis from CI 12010 in a sun tan cream (1) and another individual reacted to solvent red 3 in a sunscreen product (4).

Cross-reactions, pseudo-cross-reactions and co-reactions
Possibly to disperse yellow 3 and disperse black 1 (2).

Presence in cosmetic products and chemical analyses
In the USA, in April 2017, CI 12010 was present in zero of 56,714 cosmetic products of which the composition is known in FDA's Voluntary Cosmetic Registration Program (VCRP) (data obtained from FDA, May 2017). In March 2017, CI 12010 was present in zero of 64,983 cosmetic products of which the composition is known in EWG's Skin Deep Cosmetics Database, USA (http://www.ewg.org/skindeep/).

LITERATURE
1   Wantke F, Gotz MM, Jarisch R. Contact dermatitis due to henna, Solvent Red 1 and Solvent Red 3 A case report. Contact Dermatitis 1992;27:346-347
2   Guarrera M, Saino M, Rivara G, Crovato F. Allergic contact dermatitis from brilliantine. Contact Dermatitis 1991;25:130
3   Gollhausen R, Pryzbilla B, Ring J. Contact allergy to C.I. Solvent Red 3. Contact Dermatitis 1986;14:123-125
4   Thune P. Contact and photocontact allergy to sunscreens. Photodermatol 1984;1:5-9

2.99 CI 12055*
Not an INCI name

IDENTIFICATION

Description/definition	: CI 12055 is a monoazo color that conforms to the formula shown below
Chemical class(es)	: Color additives
INCI name USA	: Neither in CosIng nor in the Personal Care Products Council Ingredient Database
Chemical/IUPAC name	: 1-(Phenyldiazenyl)naphthalen-2-ol
Other names	: Sudan 1; 1-phenylazo-2-naphthol; solvent yellow 14
CAS registry number (s)	: 842-07-9
EINECS number(s)	: 212-668-2
Patch testing	: 1% pet.
Molecular formula	: $C_{16}H_{12}N_2O$

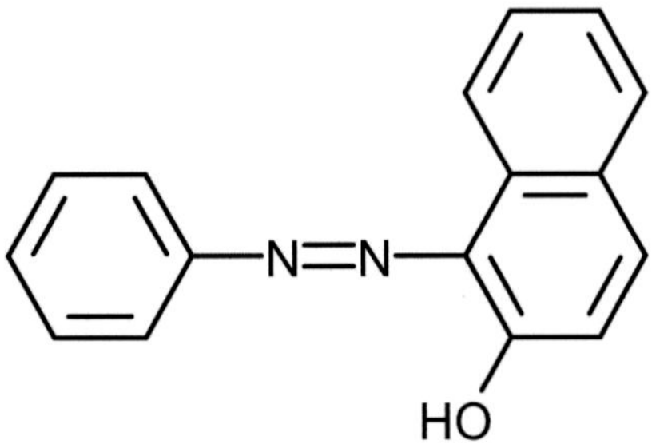

GENERAL

CI 12055 (Sudan I) is a monoazo color that is not used in cosmetics in the EU and the USA, but may be used as dye for hydrocarbon solvents, oils, fats, waxes, shoe and floor polishes, gasoline, soap, colored smokes, cellulose ether varnishes and styrene resins (www.chemicalbook.com). It is an impurity in commercial samples of brilliant lake red R (CI 15800) (see Chapter 2.103 CI 15800), which was formerly used in cosmetics in Japan and was one of the main causes of 'pigmented cosmetic dermatitis' in the 1970s in that country (2,3). The cases of allergic contact dermatitis from CI 12055 described here are caused by 'kum-kum', colored materials which are considered (and used) as cosmetic products in India (1).

CONTACT ALLERGY

Case reports and case series

'Kum-kum' (also called 'kumkum', 'sindhoor' or 'tilak') are colored cosmetics applied to the forehead by Indian women for socio-religious purposes. Kum-kum is held in high esteem by the South Indians, especially the married women who apply it on their forehead as a sign of their marital status and these cosmetics are sold as powders or liquids. Contact dermatitis and pigmented cosmetic dermatitis to kum-kum is a common cosmetic problem in India (5,6). It presents as erythema, papular and vesicular lesions at the site of kum-kum on the forehead, near the hair margin, and on the surrounding skin where it may trickle with sweat. The abdomen and the neck may also be involved (6). However, in by far most cases, the composition of the kum-kum and the allergenic ingredient(s) remain unknown (5,6,7). The pigmented variety is seen only with red kum-kum, presumably because they may contain azo dyes such as brilliant lake red R (CI 15800) and its impurity Sudan I (CI 12055), which are capable of producing pigmented cosmetic dermatitis (6,7).

One product and a refill pack were analyzed with thin layer chromatography and found to contain brilliant lake red R, Sudan I, *p*-aminoazobenzene and cananga oil. Twenty patients suspected of dermatitis from kum-kum were patch tested with their own products and with these chemicals (test concentrations and vehicles not mentioned) and all 20 reacted to the product itself, brilliant lake red R, Sudan I, *p*-aminoazobenzene and cananga oil. There were no reactions to any of the chemicals in the standard series (1). These results appear to be too good to be true and the identification of cananga oil with thin layer chromatography is impossible as it may contain over 150 chemicals which are also present in (many) other essential oils.

In one patient, pigmented allergic contact dermatitis to kum-kum may have been associated with contact allergy to brilliant Lake Red R and Sudan I (7).

Presence in cosmetic products and chemical analyses
Three of 7 brands of red kum-kums analyzed by gas chromatography - mass spectrophotometry were found to contain CI 12055 (Sudan I), ranging from 2.789 mg/gm to 8.694 mg/gm. The authors suggested that Sudan I is probably the cause of pigmented allergic contact dermatitis in red kum-kum (4).

LITERATURE

1   Kumar JV, Moideen R, Murugesh SB. Contactants in 'Kum-Kum' dermatitis. Indian J Dermatol Venereol Leprol 1996;62:220-221

2   Kozuka T, Tashiro M, Sano S, Fujimoto K, Nakamura Y, Hashimoto S, Nakaminami G. Brilliant Lake Red R as a cause of pigmented contact dermatitis. Contact Dermatitis 1979;5:297-304

3   Sugai T, Takahashi Y, Tagaki T. Pigmented cosmetic dermatitis and coal tar dyes. Contact Dermatitis 1977;3:249-256

4   Kozuka I, Goh CL, Doi T, Yioshikawa K. Sudan I as a cause of pigmented contact dermatitis in "kumkum" (an Indian cosmetic). Ann Acad Med Singapore 1988;17:492-494

5   Nath AK, Thappa DM. Clinical spectrum of dermatoses caused by cosmetics in south India: high prevalence of kumkum dermatitis. Indian J Dermatol Venereol Leprol 2007;73:195-196

6   Nath AK, Thappa DM. Kumkum-induced dermatitis: an analysis of 46 cases. Clin Exp Dermatol 2007;32:385-387

7   Goh CL, Kozuka T. Pigmented contact dermatitis from 'kumkum'. Clin Exp Dermatol 1986;11:603-606

2.100   CI 12085

IDENTIFICATION

Description/definition	: CI 12085 is a monoazo color which conforms to the formula shown below
Chemical class(es)	: Color additives
INCI name USA	: Pigment red 4 (non-certified batches); red 36 (certified batches)
Chemical/IUPAC name	: 1-[(2-Chloro-4-nitrophenyl)azo]-2-naphthol
Other names	: Pigment red 4; red 36; D&C red no. 36
CAS registry number (s)	: 2814-77-9
EC number(s)	: 220-562-2
Function(s) in cosmetics	: EU: cosmetic colorant. USA: colorants
EU cosmetic restrictions	: Regulated in Annex II/1345 of the Regulation (EC) No. 344/2013 (prohibited in hair dyes) and in Annex IV/9 of the Regulation (EC) No. 1223/2009
Patch testing	: 1% pet. (1)
Molecular formula	: $C_{16}H_{10}ClN_3O_3$

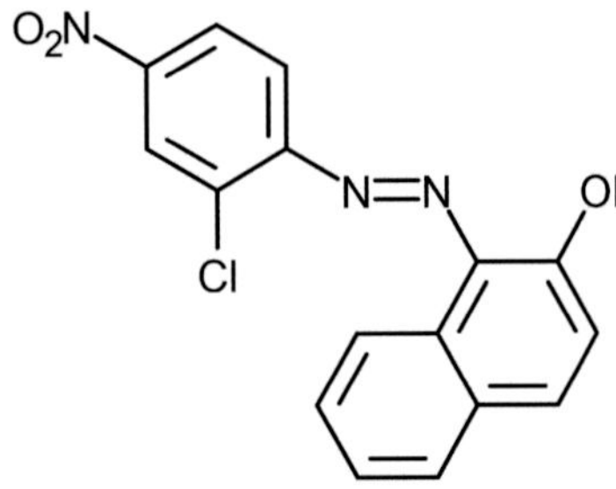

CONTACT ALLERGY

Case reports and case series

A woman with a past history of atopy presented with an 18-month history of an intermittent rash affecting her eyelids. She had red edematous upper eyelids and a mild patchy eczema on her cheeks and sides of the neck. Patch tests to the standard and facial series produced no reactions. However, testing with her cosmetics revealed an allergic reaction to her blusher. Further tests to the constituents showed that she was sensitive to D&C no. 36 pigment (1% pet.). Another woman was sensitized to CI 12085 from its presence in a facial make-up (2). One patient (3) and two other women (2) had allergic contact cheilitis from CI 12085 in lipsticks

Presence in cosmetic products and chemical analyses

In the USA, in April 2017, CI 12085 was (apparently) present in zero of 56,714 cosmetic products of which the composition is known in FDA's Voluntary Cosmetic Registration Program (VCRP) (data obtained from FDA, May 2017). In March 2017, CI 12085 (D&C red 36) was present in 79 of 64,983 cosmetic products of which the composition is known in EWG's Skin Deep Cosmetics Database, USA (http://www.ewg.org/skindeep/).

LITERATURE
1   English JSC, White IR. Dermatitis from D & C Red no. 36. Contact Dermatitis 1985;13:335
2   Calnan CD. Reactions to artificial colouring materials. J Soc Cosm Chem 1967;18:215-223
3   Cronin E. Contact Dermatitis. Edinburgh: Churchill Livingstone, 1980:144

2.101   CI 12120

IDENTIFICATION

Description/definition	: CI 12120 is a nitroso color, which conforms to the formula shown below
Chemical class(es)	: Color additives – approved in the EU
INCI name USA	: CI 12120 (not approved in the USA)
Chemical/IUPAC name	: 1-[(4-Methyl-2-nitrophenyl)azo]-2-naphthalenol
Other names	: Pigment red 3; toluidine red
CAS registry number (s)	: 2425-85-6
EC number(s)	: 219-372-2
Function(s) in cosmetics	: EU: cosmetic colorant
EU cosmetic restrictions	: Regulated in Annex IV/10 of the Regulation (EC) No. 1223/2009
Patch testing	: 1% pet. (2)
Molecular formula	: $C_{17}H_{13}N_3O_3$

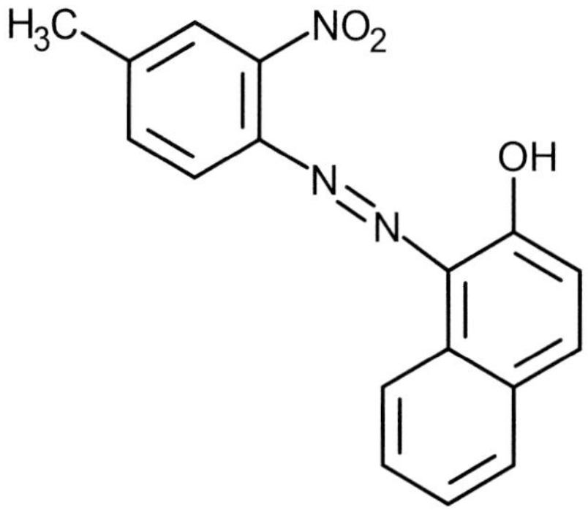

CONTACT ALLERGY

Patch testing in groups of patients
Of 38 Japanese patients with pigmented cosmetic dermatitis, patch tested and photopatch tested with coal tar dyes in 1975-1976, 10 had positive patch tests to CI 12120. It was not mentioned (and probably unknown) whether this color was present in the cosmetics used by the patients (1).

Cross-reactions, pseudo-cross-reactions and co-reactions
Other coal tar dyes (1).

Presence in cosmetic products and chemical analyses
In the USA, in April 2017, CI 12120 was present in zero of 56,714 cosmetic products of which the composition is known in FDA's Voluntary Cosmetic Registration Program (VCRP) (data obtained from FDA, May 2017). In March 2017, CI 12120 was present in zero of 64,983 cosmetic products of which the composition is known in EWG's Skin Deep Cosmetics Database, USA (not allowed in the USA) (http://www.ewg.org/skindeep/).

OTHER SIDE EFFECTS

Photosensitivity
Of 38 Japanese patients with pigmented cosmetic dermatitis, patch tested and photopatch tested with coal tar dyes in 1975-1976, three had positive photopatch tests to CI 12120. It was not mentioned (and probably unknown) whether this color was present in the cosmetics used by the patients (1).

LITERATURE
1   Sugai T, Takahashi Y, Tagaki T. Pigmented cosmetic dermatitis and coal tar dyes. Contact Dermatitis 1977;3:249-256
2   De Groot AC. Patch Testing, 3rd Edition. Wapserveen, The Netherlands: acdegroot publishing, 2008 (ISBN 978-90-813233-1-4)

2.102   CI 12150

IDENTIFICATION

Description/definition   : CI 12150 is a monoazo color, which conforms to the formula shown below
Chemical class(es)   : Color additives - miscellaneous
INCI name USA   : Solvent red 1
Chemical/IUPAC name   : (1Z)-1-[(2-Methoxyphenyl)hydrazinylidene]naphthalen-2-one
Other names   : Solvent red 1; anisole-2-azo-β-naphthol; 1-[(2-methoxyphenyl)azo]-2-naphthol
CAS registry number (s)   : 1229-55-6
EC number(s)   : 214-968-9
Function(s) in cosmetics   : EU: formerly used for hair dyeing and as cosmetic colorant; USA: colorants
EU cosmetic restrictions   : Regulated in Annex II/1231 of the Regulation (EC) No. 1223/2009 (prohibited)
Patch testing   : 0.0003% pet. (same concentration as in the product) (1); 0.5% pet. (3); suggested:
                               1% pet.
Molecular formula   : $C_{17}H_{14}N_2O_2$

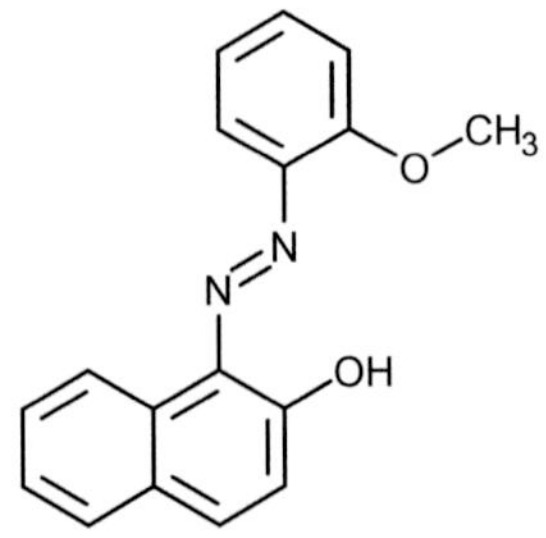

CONTACT ALLERGY

Case reports and case series

A man had used a particular suntan cream for 10 years on his body in summer and on his face from spring to autumn when hiking. Two years before presentation, he had developed dermatitis on the cheeks and forehead, which appeared within hours of using the suntan cream, increasing in severity from application to application. One year later, the dermatitis had started to spread to his chest. Two weeks before presentation, the patient applied the suntan cream again. Dermatitis occurred on the cheeks and forehead, both eyelids showing swelling several hours later. Patch tests were performed with the European standard series, an ointment series, the suntan cream and a series of sunscreens. The patient had a positive reaction to the suntan cream and later to its ingredient solvent red 1 (1). Another individual reacted to solvent red 1 in a sunscreen product (2).

Presence in cosmetic products and chemical analyses

In the USA, in April 2017, CI 12150 was present in zero of 56,714 cosmetic products of which the composition is known in FDA's Voluntary Cosmetic Registration Program (VCRP) (data obtained from FDA, May 2017). In March 2017, CI 12150 was present in zero of 64,983 cosmetic products of which the composition is known in EWG's Skin Deep Cosmetics Database, USA (http://www.ewg.org/skindeep/).

Other information

Tests using the local lymph node assay (LLNA) and a modified mouse ear swelling test (MEST) have shown that CI 12150 has weak sensitizing properties (4).

LITERATURE

1   Wantke F, Gotz MM, Jarisch R. Contact dermatitis due to henna, Solvent Red 1 and Solvent Red 3. A case report. Contact Dermatitis 1992;27:346-347
2   Thune P. Contact and photocontact allergy to sunscreens. Photodermatol 1984;1:5-9
3   De Groot AC. Patch Testing, 3rd Edition. Wapserveen, The Netherlands: acdegroot publishing, 2008 (ISBN 978-90-813233-1-4)
4   Sailstad DM, Tepper JS, Doerfler DL, Qasim M, Selgrade MK. Evaluation of an azo and two anthraquinone dyes for allergic potential. Fundam Appl Toxicol 1994;23:569-577

2.103 CI 15800

IDENTIFICATION

Description/definition : CI 15800 is the monoazo color, which conforms to the formula shown below
Chemical class(es) : Color additives
INCI name USA : Pigment red 64:1 (non-certified batches); red 31 (certified batches)
Chemical/IUPAC name : 3-Hydroxy-4-(phenylazo)-2-naphthalenecarboxylic acid, calcium salt (2:1)
Other names : Calcium bis[3-hydroxy-4-(phenylazo)-2-naphthoate]; D&C red no. 31; brilliant lake red R; pigment red 64:1 (calcium salt)
CAS registry number (s) : 6371-76-2; 27757-79-5 (parent molecule)
EC number(s) : 228-899-7; 248-638-0
Function(s) in cosmetics : EU: cosmetic colorant. USA: colorants
EU cosmetic restrictions : Regulated in Annex II/1331 of the Regulation (EC) No. 344/2013 and in Annex IV/26 of the Regulation (EC) No. 1223/2009
Patch testing : 1% pet.
Molecular formula : $C_{34}H_{22}CaN_4O_6$

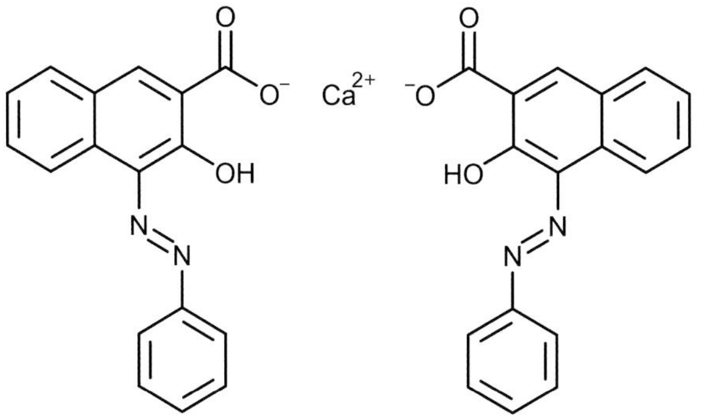

GENERAL

In this chapter, the name Brilliant lake red R is used instead of its INCI name CI 15800, as this was the common name in publications on adverse effects caused by cosmetics containing this color in the past. Brilliant lake red R is an azo dye which was used in many rouges and lipsticks in Japan. However, it caused many cases of pigmented cosmetic dermatitis (3). As the initial symptom, some patients complained of moderate pruritus without an eruption, while some showed recurrent attacks of considerable edema with severe pruritus. Pigmentation developed within several weeks to months. The hue of the pigmentation was brown to dark brown and its pattern reticulated or diffuse (3).

Commercial samples of Brilliant lake red R used for cosmetics and patch testing contained many impurities of which Sudan I (CI 12055) was the major one. Its use in Japan was abandoned in 1976 (3). Brilliant lake red R and Sudan I may still be used in 'kum-kum' (see Chapter 2.99 CI 12055).

CONTACT ALLERGY

Case reports and case series
Brilliant lake red R was found to be an important contact allergen in 'kum-kum' (7). Kum-Kum (also called 'sindhoor' or 'tilak') are colored cosmetics applied to the forehead by Indian women for socio-religious purposes. Kum-Kum is held in high esteem by the South Indians, especially the married women who apply it on their forehead as a sign of their marital status and these cosmetics are sold as powders or liquids (7). Contact dermatitis to Kum-Kum is a common cosmetic problem. It presents as erythema, papular and vesicular lesions at the site of Kum-Kum on forehead, near the hair margin, and on the surrounding skin where it may trickle with sweat. One product and a refill pack were analyzed with thin layer chromatography and found to contain brilliant lake red R, Sudan I, *p*-aminoazobenzene and cananga oil. Twenty patients suspected of dermatitis from Kum-kum were patch tested with their own products and with these chemicals (test concentrations and vehicles not mentioned) and all 20 reacted to the product itself, brilliant lake red R, Sudan I, *p*-aminoazobenzene and cananga oil. There were no reactions to any of the chemicals in the standard series (7). These results appear to be too good to be true and the identification of cananga oil with thin layer chromatography is virtually impossible as it contains over 150 chemicals which are also present in (many) other essential oils (8).

In a period of 3 years , 23 patients with pigmented cosmetic dermatitis from contact allergy to Brilliant lake red R were seen in 2 hospitals in Osaka, Japan (3). Five patients were described in some detail; they were all women who had diffuse or reticulated pigmentation on the face and/or the lips from rouges and lipsticks (3). A study of the Mid-

Japan Contact Dermatitis Research Group revealed that brilliant lake red R was the most important causative agent of pigmented contact dermatitis. This dye was one of the azo dyes which had been widely used in cosmetics in Japan until 1976 (2). Of 38 Japanese patients with pigmented cosmetic dermatitis, patch tested and photopatch tested with coal tar dyes in 1975-1976, 21 had positive patch tests to brilliant lake red R. It was not mentioned (and probably unknown) whether this color was present in the cosmetics used by the patients, but brilliant lake red R was considered to be a major allergen responsible for pigmented cosmetic dermatitis (4). One female patient (5) and two other women (6) had contact allergy to brilliant lake R in lipsticks. Two patients suffered from allergic contact cheilitis caused by 'D&C red no.31 lake' in lipsticks (6).

Kum-Kum (also called 'sindhoor' or 'tilak') are colored cosmetics applied to the forehead by Indian women for socio-religious purposes. Kum-Kum is held in high esteem by the South Indians, especially the married women who apply it on their forehead as a sign of their marital status and these cosmetics are sold as powders or liquids (9). Contact dermatitis to Kum-Kum is a common cosmetic problem. It presents as erythema, papular and vesicular lesions at the site of Kum-Kum on the forehead, near the hair margin, and on the surrounding skin where it may trickle with sweat. One product and a refill pack were analyzed with thin layer chromatography and found to contain brilliant lake red R, Sudan I, p-aminoazobenzene and cananga oil. Twenty patients suspected of dermatitis from Kum-kum were patch tested with their own products and with these chemicals (test concentrations and vehicles not mentioned) and all 20 reacted to the product itself, brilliant lake red R, Sudan I, p-aminoazobenzene and cananga oil. There were no reactions to any of the chemicals in the standard series (9). These results appear to be too good to be true and the identification of cananga oil with thin layer chromatography is impossible as it contains over 150 chemicals which are also present in (many) other essential oils.

Cross-reactions, pseudo-cross-reactions and co-reactions

Eight patients with pigmented cosmetic dermatitis from commercial brilliant lake red R were tested with purified brilliant lake red R and other related azo dyes. All 8 reacted to Sudan I (CI 12055) and to orange SS (CI 12100), 7 to the purified brilliant lake red R (CI 15800), 6 to vacanceine red (CI 12175), 5 to yellow OB (CI 11390) and 2 to Sudan II (CI 12140) (1). Other coal tar dyes may co- or cross-react (4), including Sudan I (7). Twenty patients with 'kum-kum' dermatitis all had co-reactions to brilliant lake red R and p-aminoazobenzene (7).

Presence in cosmetic products and chemical analyses

In the USA, in April 2017, CI 15800 was present in zero of 56,714 cosmetic products of which the composition is known in FDA's Voluntary Cosmetic Registration Program (VCRP) (data obtained from FDA, May 2017). In April 2017, CI 15800 / red 31 was present in one of 65,521 cosmetic products of which the composition is known in EWG's Skin Deep Cosmetics Database, USA (http://www.ewg.org/skindeep/).

Commercial samples of brilliant lake red R used for cosmetics and patch testing were chemically analyzed and found to contain many impurities of which Sudan I (CI 12055) was the major one (3). These authors concluded – on the basis of insufficient evidence – that the sensitizer in commercial brilliant lake red R is Sudan I and that brilliant lake red R (CI 15800) is either a weaker sensitizer or a cross-reacting chemical (3).

OTHER SIDE EFFECTS

Photosensitivity

Of 38 Japanese patients with pigmented cosmetic dermatitis, patch tested and photopatch tested with coal tar dyes in 1975-1976, one had a positive photopatch test. It was not mentioned (and probably unknown) whether this color was present in the cosmetics used by the patient, but brilliant lake red R was considered to be a major allergen responsible for pigmented cosmetic dermatitis (4).

LITERATURE

1   Kozuka, T, Tashiro M, Sano S, Fujimoto K, Nakamura Y, Hashimoto S, Nakaminami G. Pigmented contact dermatitis from azo dyes. I, Cross-sensitivity in humans. Contact Dermatitis 1980;6:330-336
2   Mid-Japan Contact Dermatitis Research Group. Incidence of allergic reactions to coal tar dyes in patients with cosmetic dermatitis. J Dermatol (Tokyo) 1978;5:291-295 (in Japanese)
3   Kozuka T, Tashiro M, Sano S, Fujimoto K, Nakamura Y, Hashimoto S, Nakaminami G. Brilliant Lake Red R as a cause of pigmented contact dermatitis. Contact Dermatitis 1979;5:297-304
4   Sugai T, Takahashi Y, Tagaki T. Pigmented cosmetic dermatitis and coal tar dyes. Contact Dermatitis 1977;3:249-256

5   Cronin E. Contact Dermatitis. Edinburgh: Churchill Livingstone, 1980:145

6   Cronin E. Contact dermatitis from cosmetics. J Soc Cosm Chem 1967;18:681-691

7   Kumar JV, Moideen R, Murugesh SB. Contactants in 'Kum-Kum' dermatitis. Indian J Dermatol Venereol Leprol 1996;62:220-221

8   De Groot AC, Schmidt E. Essential oils: contact allergy and chemical composition. Boca Raton, Fl., USA: CRC Press, Taylor and Francis Group, 2016 (ISBN 9781482246407)

9   Kumar JV, Moideen R, Murugesh SB. Contactants in 'Kum-Kum' dermatitis. Indian J Dermatol Venereol Leprol 1996;62:220-221

2.104   CI 26100

IDENTIFICATION

Description/definition	: CI 26100 is a disazo color, that conforms the formula shown below
Chemical class(es)	: Color additives – miscellaneous
INCI name USA	: Solvent red 23 (non-certified batches); red 17 (certified batches)
Chemical/IUPAC name	: 1-(4-(Phenylazo)phenylazo)-2-naphthol
Other names	: Sudan III; D&C red no. 17
CAS registry number (s)	: 85-86-9
EC number(s)	: 201-638-4
SCCS opinion(s)	: SCCP/0902/05 (10)
Function(s) in cosmetics	: EU: cosmetic colorant. USA: the name CI 26100 is not used for labeling purposes
EU cosmetic restrictions	: Regulated in Annex II/1353 of the Regulation (EC) No. 344/2013 and in Annex IV/51 of the Regulation (EC) No. 1223/2009
Patch testing	: 1% pet.
Molecular formula	: $C_{22}H_{16}N_4O$

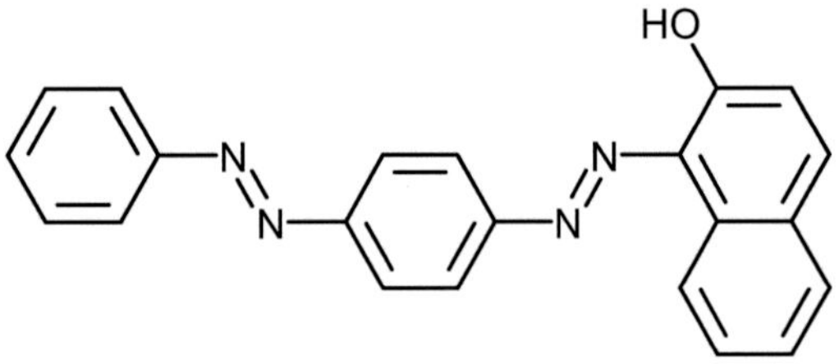

CONTACT ALLERGY

Case reports and case series

Two women had allergic contact cheilitis from CI 26100 in lipstick, another one had dermatitis of the face from the color present in rouge (1). The patient allergic to rouge had been described previously (2). A woman had allergic contact dermatitis of the eyelids from CI 26100 in an eye cream (3). Six dermatitis patients had positive patch test reactions to commercial Sudan III, but not to the purified CI 26100; the causative products were unknown, but were thought to be cosmetics (5).

Cross-reactions, pseudo-cross-reactions and co-reactions

Patients sensitized to *p*-phenylenediamine may cross-react to CI 26100 (4); positive patch test reactions to Sudan III in hairdressers (8,9) were the result of primary *p*-phenylenediamine sensitization (4).

Presence in cosmetic products and chemical analyses

In April 2017, CI 26100 was present in 10 and D&C red 17 in 58 of 65,521 cosmetic products of which the composition is known in EWG's Skin Deep Cosmetics Database, USA (http://www.ewg.org/skindeep/). In the USA, in April 2017, CI 26100 was present in zero of 56,714 cosmetic products of which the composition is known in FDA's Voluntary Cosmetic Registration Program (VCRP) (data obtained from FDA, May 2017).

Six patients had positive patch test reactions to commercial Sudan III, but not to purified CI 26100, so the authors suggested the allergen to be an impurity (5). Indeed, it was found that guinea pigs could be sensitized to the commercial products but not to purified CI 26100 (4,6,7). By conducting chemical analyses, 2-naphthol (82 ppm), azobenzene (48 ppm), Sudan I (570 ppm) and many unknown impurities, as well as the main constituent Sudan III (87%), were found (4). The chemical structure of one unknown impurity was identified as an isomer of Sudan III. The investigators found that purified Sudan III showed no positive reaction in the guinea pig maximization test, while the isomer elicited 30% positive reactions, in the same guinea pig test. Furthermore, cross-sensitization with *p*-phenylenediamine was investigated using the guinea pig test. Animals sensitized with *p*-phenylenediamine also showed positive elicitation reactions with purified Sudan III. From these results, the contact allergenicity of CI 26100 is considered to be due to impurities, including the isomer of Sudan III, 1-(*o*-phenylazophenylazo)-2-naphthol (4).

LITERATURE

1   Calnan CD. Quinazoline Yellow SS in cosmetics. Contact Dermatitis 1976;2:160-166.
2   Calnan CD. Allergy to D & C Red 17 and D & C Yellow 11. Contact Dermatitis Newsletter 1973:14:405
3   Calnan CD. Quinazoline yellow dermatitis (D & C Yellow 11) in an eye cream. Contact Dermatitis 1981;7:271

4   Okada J, Kanbe R, Kuzukawa M, Ikeda Y, Yoshimura K, Haykawa R, Matsunaga K. Identification of contact allergens in C.I. Solvent Red 23 (commercial Sudan III) by chemical analysis and animal testing. Contact Dermatitis 1991;25:313-318

5   Kozuka T, Tashiro M, Fujimoto K, Nakamura Y. Hashimoto S, Nakaminami G. Positive patch test by commercial Sudan III. Skin Research 1979;21 293-296 (in Japanese) (data cited in ref. 4)

6   Sato Y, Katsumura Y, Ichikawa H, Kobayashi T. Experimental method of contact sensitivity using guinea pig. Skin Research 1981;23:461-467 (in Japanese) (data cited in ref. 4)

7   Sato Y, Katsumura Y, Ichikawa H, Kobayashi T, Kozuka T, Morikawa F, Ohta S. A modified technic of guinea pig testing to identify delayed hypersensitivity allergens. Contact Dermatitis 1981;7:225-237

8   Matsunaga K, Hayakawa R, Suzuki M, Kawaguchi K, Ogino Y, Hirose O. allergic contact dermatitis in hairdressers and barbers. Skin Research 1989:31 (supplement 7):167-175 (in Japanese) (data cited in ref. 4)

9   Matsunaga K, Ogino Y, Suzuki M, Arisu K, Hayakawa R, Yoshimura K, Okada J, Kuzukawa M. Patch test positive reactions to Solvent Red 23 in hairdressers. Skin Research 1990;32 (supplement 9):244-251 (in Japanese) (data cited in ref. 4)

10 SCCP (Scientific Committee on Consumer Products). Opinion on the use of CI 26100 (CI Solvent Red 23) as a colorant in cosmetic products, 21 June 2005, SCCP/0902/05. Available at: http://ec.europa.eu/health/ph_risk/committees/04_sccp/docs/sccp_o_013.pdf

2.105 CI 45380

IDENTIFICATION

Description/definition	: CI 45380 is a xanthene color, that conforms to the formula shown below
Chemical class(es)	: Color additives – miscellaneous
INCI names USA	: Red 21 (certified batches, acid form); red 43 (non-certified batches, acid form); solvent red 22 (certified batches); acid red 87 (non-certified batches)
Chemical/IUPAC name	: Disodium 2-(2,4,5,7-tetrabromo-6-oxido-3-oxoxanthen-9-yl)benzoate
Other names	: Eosin; bromofluorescein; tetrabromofluorescein
CAS registry number(s)	: 17372-87-1; 548-26-5
EC number(s)	: 241-409-6
Merck Index monograph	: 4928
Function(s) in cosmetics	: EU: cosmetic colorant. USA: CI 45380 is not approved for labeling purposes in the USA
EU cosmetic restrictions	: Regulated in Annex II/1334 of the Regulation (EC) No. 344/2013 and in Annex IV/76 of the Regulation (EC) No. 1223/2009
Patch testing	: 5.0% pet. (Chemotechnique)
Molecular formula	: $C_{20}H_6Br_4Na_2O_5$

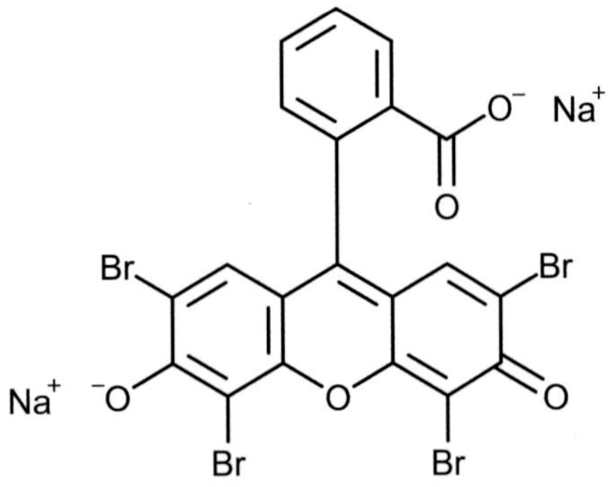

GENERAL

CI 45380 (better known as eosin) is a red dye belonging to the xanthene group. Usually, it is prepared by bromination of fluorescein. Most often its disodium salt is manufactured. Formerly, especially in the 1920s and 1930s, it was used in high concentrations in lipsticks. It may also be used as coloring agent in nail polish, wool, silk and paper. Furthermore, it has applications in inks, drugs, cosmetics except for the eye area, and as a topical antiseptic in low concentrations (1 to 2%, in aqueous or alcoholic solution) (3).

Lipstick cheilitis from eosin, first reported from eosin in 1928 (4), was a common finding before World War II (5,6). Between 1947 and 1995, about 160-172 cases of specific eosin hypersensitivity from topical preparations have been described, mostly caused by eosin in cosmetics (7,8,9,10,11) (data cited in ref. 3). At the St. John's hospital, London, UK, for example, 110 patients allergic to eosin in lip sticks were seen in a period of 5 years (11).

There has always been controversy on the exact allergenic chemical. In 1939, it was suggested that the allergen was an impurity, or a by-product of the manufacturing process, rather than the substance itself. However, some reactions were considered as possibly being due to the pure dye, though this could not be proven with certainty (1,2, cited in ref. 3). It is well known that patients allergic to eosin from one source may well tolerate products containing the color from another manufacturer (3,11,12), which suggests a role for chemicals other than the dye itself. However, contact allergy to the pure CI 45380 has been established (3).

The incidence of eosin sensitivity fell rapidly after 1960, because paler shades of lipsticks, not requiring the routine addition of eosin, became more fashionable and much purer (and consequently less allergenic) eosin became available (13).

CONTACT ALLERGY

Case reports and case series
See under GENERAL.

Contact allergy to CI 45380 in non-cosmetic products
One patient reacted to eosin solution she used as a bacteriostatic agent to treat leg ulcers, prepared by the hospital pharmacy (3). She did not react to eosin from other sources. The pharmacy product was analysed with thin-layer

chromatography. The patient was patch tested again and reacted to pure CI 45380; she also had a weak positive reaction to one of three impurities (3).

Presence in cosmetic products and chemical analyses
In the USA, in April 2017, CI 45380 was present in an unknown number of 56,714 cosmetic products of which the composition is known in FDA's Voluntary Cosmetic Registration Program (VCRP) (data accidentally not requested from FDA). In April 2017, CI 45380 (including its other name AKA223) was present in 36 of 65,536 cosmetic products of which the composition is known in EWG's Skin Deep Cosmetics Database, USA (http://www.ewg.org/skindeep/).

LITERATURE
1   Hecht R, Schwarzschild L, Sulzberger MB. Sensitization to simple chemicals. Comparison between reactions to commercial and to purified dyes. New York State Journal of Medicine 1939;39:2170-2173
2   Sulzberger MB, Hecht R. Acquired specific hypersensitivity to simple chemicals. Further studies on the· purification of dyes in relation to allergic reactions. J Allergy 1941;12:129-137
3   Koch P, Bahmer FA, Hausen BM. Allergic contact dermatitis from purified eosin. Contact Dermatitis 1995;32:92-95
4   Audry C, Valdiguie. Sur le role de l'eosine dans la cheilite du rouge. Bull Soc Franc Dermatol 1928;35:623-624
5   Sezary A, Horowitz A. La cheilite du rouge. Presse MM 1937;45:137-138
6   Sulzberger MB, Goodman J, Byrne L A, Mallozzi ED. Acquired specific hypersensitivity to simple chemicals. Cheilitis with special reference to sensitivity to lipsticks. Arch Dermatol 1938;37:597-615
7   Tomb E. Allergic contact dermatitis from eosin. Contact Dermatitis 1991;24:27-29
8   Cronin E. Contact dermatitis from cosmetics. J Soc Cosm Chem 1967;18:681-691
9   Broeckx W, Blondeel A, Dooms-Goossens A, Achten G. Cosmetic intolerance. Contact Dermatitis 1987;16:189-194
10 Voldanova A. A detailed analysis of I 000 cases of eczema of external origin hospitalized on the skin service at Bulovka Hospital from 1953 to 1955. Csl Derm 1957;32:60-71
11 Calnan CD, Sarkany I. Studies in contact dermatitis (II). Lipstick cheilitis. Transactions of the St. John's Hospital Dermatological Society 1957;39:28-36
12 Calnan CD. Allergic sensitivity to eosin. Acta Allergol 1959;13:493-499
13 Cronin E. Contact Dermatitis. Edinburgh: Churchill Livingstone, 1980:142-143

2.106   CI 47000

IDENTIFICATION

Description/definition	: CI 47000 is a quinoline color which conforms to the formula shown below
Chemical class(es)	: Color additives
INCI name USA	: Solvent yellow 33 (non-certified batches); yellow 11 (certified batches)
Chemical/IUPAC name	: 2-Quinolin-2-ylindene-1,3-dione
Other names	: Quinophthalone; D&C yellow no. 11; yellow 11; solvent yellow 33; quinoline yellow SS
CAS registry number (s)	: 8003-22-3
EC number(s)	: 232-318-2
Merck Index number	: 9459 (Quinoline yellow spirit soluble)
Function(s) in cosmetics	: EU: cosmetic colorant. USA: colorants
EU cosmetic restrictions	: Regulated in Annex II/1358 of the Regulation (EC) No. 344/2013 in Annex IV/81 of the Regulation (EC) No. 1223/2009
Patch testing	: 0.1% pet.
Molecular formula	: $C_{18}H_{11}NO_2$

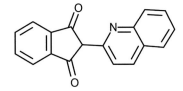

CONTACT ALLERGY

Patch testing in groups of patients

Before 1980, in Sweden, 88 consecutive patients suspected of contact dermatitis were patch tested (routine testing) with CI 47000 1% in PEG (polyethylene glycol) and there were 3 (3.4%) positive reactions. The relevance of the positive tests was unknown. One of the patients became sensitized from the patch test (17).

Case reports and case series

In a group of 146 patients patch tested for cheilitis in Amersham, UK, between 1982 and 2001, there was one positive patch test reaction to CI 47000 considered to be relevant for the lip dermatitis. The causative product was not mentioned, but over half of the reactions in the entire group were ascribed to lipsticks and lip salves (5). One patient had allergic contact dermatitis from CI 47000 in a shampoo (1). A woman developed generalized dermatitis from contact allergy to CI 47000 in a yellow soap bar after using it in three to five showers. The patient had previously become sensitized to the color by a modified Draize test (3). A female patient had recurrent desquamative cheilitis from allergy to the yellow color present in 2 lip balms (4). A young woman presented with an acute contact dermatitis of the face primarily around the eyes. She had used a new rouge 2 days previously. She had positive reactions to the rouge and its ingredient CI 47000 (9). Another female patient (9) and one more (13, also reported in ref. 12) also had facial dermatitis from the color present in rouge. A woman had allergic contact dermatitis of the face from CI 47000 in a lipstick, which she had used as rouge on the face (14, also reported in ref. 12).

   Five patients were allergic to CI 47000, 3 from lipstick and 2 from rouge (12); two of these patient had been reported separately before (13,14). A female patient had dermatitis of the eyelids from contact allergy to CI 47000, present in a concentration of 0.004% in an eye cream (15). A man presented with an acute dermatitis of the scalp, forehead, hair margin and ears, which proved to be caused by contact allergy to CI 47000 in a hair cream (16). Another man, diagnosed as having seborrheic dermatitis, was patch tested with his hair preparations and he reacted to a hair stick. Among its ingredients, D&C yellow no. 11, from 0.0001% to 0.1% showed positive reactions. The color was found to consist only of quinophthalone by chemical analyses. The concentration of quinophthalone in the hair stick was determined as 9.41 ppm w/w by high-performance liquid chromatography (19). Two patients had developed 'vesicular dermatoses' from CI 47000 in a soap bar, present in a concentration of 0.006% (20).

Contact allergy to CI 47000 in non-cosmetic products

One individual working in an explosives factory developed occupational allergic contact dermatitis from CI 47000 used for colored smokes in detonators. The dye was is a mixture of 67% unsubstituted quinophthalone and 33% 6-methylquinophthalone (21).

Cross-reactions, pseudo-cross-reactions and co-reactions

Patients who react to CI 47000 may also react to CI 47005 (D&C yellow no. 10) (2,6), but this has been attributed to impurities present in the latter (2). *Not* to CI 47005 (D&C yellow no. 10) in 9 patients allergic to CI 47000, who had become sensitized to the color by repeated insult patch tests with pure CI 47000 (22).

Provocation tests

Nine subjects allergic to CI 47000 used cosmetics containing the color in approximately 0.001% concentrations. The cosmetics were self-applied liberally on a twice-daily basis to the appropriate body areas. Hand creams, soaps, bath oils, and body and facial moisturizers were used. No subject showed any dermatitis to any of the cosmetics after using them for one month. No subjective pruritus or stinging was noted. All subjects used 4, 5, or 6 different preparations on this twice-daily basis. All preparations were different, and almost all of the body was covered by material (22).

Patch test sensitization

One patient was sensitized from a patch test with CI 47000 1% in petrolatum (12). Another became allergic to CI 47000 from the test substance 1% in polyethylene glycol (17); this patient became so sensitive that D&C yellow no. 11 diluted down to 0.00001% gave a positive test reaction (17).

Presence in cosmetic products and chemical analyses

In the USA, in April 2017, DC yellow #11 was present in 233 of 56,714 cosmetic products of which the composition is known in FDA's Voluntary Cosmetic Registration Program (VCRP) (data obtained from FDA, May 2017). In April 2017, CI 47000 (as D&C yellow 11) was present in 232 of 65,521 cosmetic products of which the composition is known in EWG's Skin Deep Cosmetics Database, USA (http://www.ewg.org/skindeep/). D&C yellow no. 11, produced by condensing quinaldine and 6-methylquinaldine with phthalic anhydride at 190-220°C, was found to be composed of a mixture of 2 parts of unsubstituted quinophthalone and one part of 6-methylquinophtalone (6). Other investigators found >98% quinophthalone but no 6-methylquinophthalone (18).

OTHER SIDE EFFECTS

Other non-eczematous contact reactions

In one patient, a patch test with CI 47000 apparently worsened lupus erythematosus (H. Nakayama, personal communication, cited in ref. 17).

OTHER INFORMATION

CI 47000 was found to be a potent sensitizer in guinea pig (2,7,8,18) and human (10,11) test models.

LITERATURE

1   Fisher AA. Allergic reactions to D&C Yellow no.11 dye. Cutis 1984;34:344,346,350
2   Sato Y, Kutsuna H, Kobayashi T, Mitsui T. D&C nos. 10 and 11: Chemical composition analysis and delayed contact hypersensitivity testing in the guinea pig. Contact Dermatitis 1984;10:30-38
3   Jordan WE. Contact dermatitis from D&C Yellow 11 dye in a toilet bar soap. J Am Acad Dermatol 1981;4:613-614
4   Sasseville D, Joncas V. Allergic contact cheilitis from D & C Yellow 11. Contact Dermatitis 2009;60:294-295
5   Strauss RM, Orton DI. Allergic contact cheilitis in the United Kingdom: a retrospective study. Am J Contact Dermat 2003;14:75-77
6   Björkner B, Niklasson B. Contact allergic reaction to D & C Yellow No. 11 and Quinoline Yellow. Contact Dermatitis 1983;9:263-268
7   Lamson SA, Kong BM, De Salva SJ. D & C Yellow Nos. 10 and 11: delayed contact hypersensitivity in the guinea pig. Contact Dermatitis 1982;8:200-203
8   Palazzolo MJ, DiPasquale LC. The sensitization potential of D & C Yellow No. 11 in guinea pigs. Contact Dermatitis 1983;9:367-371
9   Larsen WG. Cosmetic dermatitis due to a dye (D and C Yellow # 11). Contact Dermatitis 1975;1:61
10 Rapaport MJ. Allergy to D and C yellow dye # 11. Contact Dermatitis 1980;6:364-365
11 Kita S, Kobayashi T, Kutsuna H, Kligman A M. Human maximization testing of D&C Yellow no. 10 and Yellow no. 11. Contact Dermatitis 1984;11:210-213
12 Calnan CD. Quinazoline Yellow SS in cosmetics. Contact Dermatitis 1976;2:160-166. One of these 5 patients was already reported in ref. 13, another in ref. 14
13 Calnan CD. Allergy to D & C Red 17 and D & C Yellow 11. Contact Dermatitis Newsletter 1973:14:405. Also reported in ref. 12
14 Calnan CD. D and C Yellow 11 in a lipstick. Contact Dermatitis 1975;1:121

15 Calnan CD. Quinazoline yellow dermatitis (D & C Yellow 11) in an eye cream. Contact Dermatitis 1981;7:271

16 Monk B. Allergic contact dermatitis to D & C Yellow 11 in a hair cream. Contact Dermatitis 1987;17:57-58

17 Björkner B, Magnusson B. Patch test sensitization to D & C Yellow No. 11 and simultaneous reaction to Quinoline Yellow. Contact Dermatitis 1981;7:1-4

18 Sato Y, Kutsuna H, Kobayashi T, Mitsui T. D&C nos. 10 and 11: chemical composition analysis and delayed contact hypersensitivity testing in the guinea pig. Contact Dermatitis 1984;10:30-38

19 Komamura H, Kozuka T, Ishii M, Yoshikawa K, Iyoda M. Allergic contact sensitivity to quinophthalone. Contact Dermatitis 1989;20:177-181

20 Weaver JE. Dose response relationships in delayed hypersensitivity to quinoline dyes. Contact Dermatitis 1983;9:309-312

21 Noster U, Hausen BM. Berufsbedingtes Kontaktekzem durch gelben Chinophthalonfarbstoff (Solvent Yellow 33: C.I. 47000). Hautarzt 1978;29:153-157

22 Rapaport MJ. Allergy to yellow dyes. Arch Dermatol 1984;120:535-536

2.107   CI 69825

IDENTIFICATION

Description/definition	: CI 69825 is an anthraquinone color, which conform to the formula shown below
Chemical class(es)	: Color additives
Chemical/IUPAC name	: 5,9,14,18-Anthrazinetetrone, 7,16-dichloro-6,15-dihydro-,
Other names	: 7,16-Dichloro-6,15-dihydroanthrazine-5,9,14,18-tetrone; D&C blue no. 9; carbanthrene blue; vat blue 6; 3,3'-dichloroindanthrene
CAS registry number (s)	: 130-20-1
EC number(s)	: 204-980-2
Function(s) in cosmetics	: EU: cosmetic colorant. USA: not allowed in cosmetics in the USA
EU cosmetic restrictions	: Regulated in Annex IV/96 of the Regulation (EC) No. 1223/2009
Patch testing	: 5% polyethylene glycol (1); 1% pet. (2)
Molecular formula	: $C_{28}H_{12}Cl_2N_2O_4$

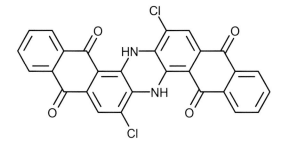

CONTACT ALLERGY

Patch testing in groups of patients
Of 28 Japanese patients with pigmented cosmetic dermatitis, patch tested and photopatch tested with coal tar dyes in 1975-1976, 3 had positive patch tests to carbanthrene blue. It was not mentioned (and probably unknown) whether this color was present in the cosmetics used by the patients (1).

Cross-reactions, pseudo-cross-reactions and co-reactions
Other coal tar dyes (1).

Presence in cosmetic products and chemical analyses
In the USA, in April 2017, CI 69825 was present in zero of 56,714 cosmetic products of which the composition is known in FDA's Voluntary Cosmetic Registration Program (VCRP) (data obtained from FDA, May 2017). In March 2017, CI 69825 was present in zero of 64,983 cosmetic products of which the composition is known in EWG's Skin Deep Cosmetics Database, USA (not allowed in the USA) (http://www.ewg.org/skindeep/).

LITERATURE
1   Sugai T, Takahashi Y, Tagaki T. Pigmented cosmetic dermatitis and coal tar dyes. Contact Dermatitis 1977;3:249-256
2   De Groot AC. Patch Testing, 3rd Edition. Wapserveen, The Netherlands: acdegroot publishing, 2008 (ISBN 978-90-813233-1-4)

2.108   CI 75470

IDENTIFICATION

Description/definition	: CI 75470 is the aluminum lake of the coloring agent cochineal; cochineal is a natural pigment derived from the dried female insect *Coccus cacti*
Chemical class(es)	: Color additives
INCI name USA	: Carmine
Chemical/IUPAC name	: 3,5,6,8-Tetrahydroxy-1-methyl-9,10-dioxo-7-[3,4,5-trihydroxy-6-(hydroxymethyl)oxan-2-yl]anthracene-2-carboxylic acid
Other names	: Carmine; natural red 4; carminic acid aluminium lake; cochineal; E120 (food additive in EU); cochineal red
CAS registry number (s)	: 1390-65-4; 1260-17-9; 1328-60-5; 1343-78-8
EC number(s)	: 215-023-3; 215-527-3; 215-680-6; 215-724-4
Merck Index monograph	: 3712 (Cochineal)
Function(s) in cosmetics	: EU: cosmetic colorant. USA: colorants; fragrance ingredients
EU cosmetic restrictions	: Regulated in Annex IV/115 of the Regulation (EC) No. 1223/2009
Patch testing	: 0.5% water (SmartPracticeCanada); 2.5% pet. (SmartPracticeCanada)
Molecular formula	: $C_{22}H_{20}O_{13}$

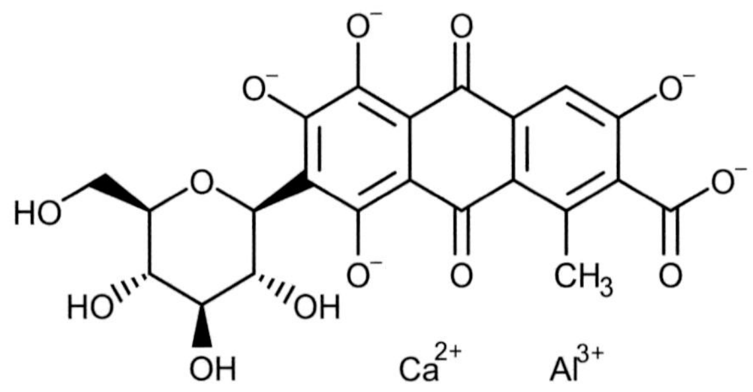

GENERAL

CI 75470 is a naturally derived red pigment or dye that is extracted from cochineal. Cochineal is the dried, pulverized bodies of a female mealybug *Dactylopius coccus* (or *Coccus cacti*) that lives on the prickly pear *Opuntia coccinellifera*. The brilliant red color of carmine is due to carminic acid secreted into intracellular vesicles of the insects. Carmine is used in foods, beverages, drugs, cosmetics, textiles, inks, paints, and biologic stains (1,8,31). The cochineal mealybug is cultivated in the Canary Islands, Algeria, Spain, Honduras, Peru, and Mexico. It requires about 70,000 insects to make 500 g of cochineal, which contains about 10% pure carminic acid (1).

Contact allergy to carmine has rarely been reported, but there are many publications on immediate-type hypersensitivity reactions, immunoglobulin E-mediated reactions directed against cochineal insect proteins in carmine.

CONTACT ALLERGY

Contact allergy to carmine is rare and has been reported in a small number of case reports only. Because carmine is a natural pigment from cochineal extracts, it contains several proteins (which may cause immediate reactions) as well as the main pigment. The nature of the allergen has not been identified, no patients have been patch tested with purified carminic acid (5,8).

Patch testing in groups of patients

In the period 2011-2012, the members of the North American Contact Dermatitis group (NACDG) patch tested 4230 consecutive patients suspected of contact dermatitis (routine testing) with carmine 2.5% pet. and 131 (3.1%) had a positive reactions. Only 15% of these were considered to be of either 'definite' or 'probable' relevance, but the causative products were not mentioned (26).

Case reports and case series

Three women had allergic contact cheilitis from carmine in lip salve (2). A woman had itchy redness of her cheeks since half a year. Two years earlier, she had exhibited the same symptoms, which improved after she stopped using her cosmetics. On examination, a scaly erythema was seen on her cheeks where blush had been applied. Patch tests with her personal cosmetics and a series of cosmetic allergens gave a positive reaction to the blush, tested 30% in petrolatum. Later, when tested with its ingredients, the patient now reacted to a mixture of carmine and talc (1% pet.) but not to talc alone. Carmine from another supplier was patch tested at concentrations of 0.1%, 0.2%, 0.3%,

0.4%, and 0.5% in petrolatum and positive reactions were seen to all materials except the 0.1% concentration (5). One patient had allergic contact cheilitis from CI 75470 in a lip product (6). Two women had allergic contact cheilitis from CI 75470 in lipsticks. They were patch tested with three kinds of carmine; one had positive reactions to all three carmines, the other reacted to only two. It was suspected that an impurity in the carmine reagent was responsible for causing the delayed-type hypersensitivity (7).

A woman suffered from recurrent dermatitis that usually began within 6 to 24 hours after she used various eye shadows and lipsticks. Products that had, according to the patient, caused contact dermatitis included a lip balm and 12 different eye shadows. According to the ingredient lists of the implicated eye shadows, carmine, iron oxides, and mica were present in nearly all of the products. Patch tests with the North American Contact Dermatitis Group standard series, carmine 2.5% in petrolatum, iron oxides 1% pet., mica 5% pet., and several of the patient's implicated eye shadows showed a positive reaction to carmine, but not to the cosmetic products. Next, a repeated open application test (ROAT) was performed with a small quantity of carmine 2.5% pet. twice daily to one antecubital fossa. A few isolated papules first appeared after 12 days of applications which became semi-confluent at D16. Since avoiding carmine-free products, the patient has not had further dermatitis (8).

Another woman had allergic contact dermatitis from carmine in her lip balm (33).

Contact allergy to CI 75470 in non-cosmetic products
A woman had ACD from carmine in in her lip balm and chewable multivitamin. The presence of carmine in the multivitamin may have caused additional systemic contact dermatitis (33).

Presence in cosmetic products and chemical analyses
In May 2017, carmine was present in 2427 of 66,647 cosmetic products of which the composition is known in EWG's Skin Deep Cosmetics Database, USA (http://www.ewg.org/skindeep/). In the USA, in April 2017, carmine was present in 3980 of 56,714 cosmetic products of which the composition is known in FDA's Voluntary Cosmetic Registration Program (VCRP) (data obtained from FDA, May 2017).

OTHER SIDE EFFECTS

Immediate-type reactions
In contrast to the rarity of reports of contact allergic reactions to carmine, there are many published descriptions of patients with immediate hypersensitivity to carmine (1,3,4,9,11-24,28,30,32). In Finland, 3164 patients with putative food or food additive-related cutaneous or intestinal symptoms were tested with carmine 5 mg/ml skin prick tests and 94 (3.0%) had a positive reaction. At the time of testing, the diagnosis of the patients with positive SPT reactions to carmine was urticaria, angioedema or anaphylaxis in 51/94 patients, atopic dermatitis without earlier urticaria or angioedema in 28/94, non-atopic dermatitis in 3/94 and asthma or allergic rhinitis, pruritus cutis or diarrhea in 12/94 patients (27). As summarized in recent reports (9,24) in about half of the patients, allergy is caused by occupational exposures, including exposures in carmine manufacturing, cosmetic blending, spice blending in a sausage factory, and among butchers handling additives to sausages, burgers, and salami. Symptoms include asthma, rhinitis, and conjunctivitis (32). In other patients, allergic reactions are non-occupational; many of these reactions are anaphylactic and mostly due to ingestion of foods or beverages colored with carmine. These included the alcoholic beverage Campari (1,3,17,23), juices (19,23), yogurt (12,17,24), artificial crab (17,19), fish paste (22) and a popsicle (4). Many of these patients also describe immediate itching, an erythematous eruption, urticaria, or intense rhinorrhea within minutes of their using carmine-containing cosmetics (1,4,17,19,24).

It has been suggested that the application of cosmetics may have been the primary route of sensitization in adult female patients with food- or drink-related hypersensitivity reactions (25). One case of carmine allergy was caused by the ingestion of azithromycin tablets (24). These immediate hypersensitivity reactions to carmine are immunoglobulin E—mediated and directed against cochineal proteins (9,10,16,18,19,21, 23,28). An oral challenge test with carmine in skin prick test-positive patients is positive only in about 20% of the patients and has been advised as a valuable *in vivo* tool to better inform patients with positive skin prick tests, to avoid unnecessary allergy diets (29).

LITERATURE
1   Kägi MK, Wüthrich B, Johansson SGO. Campari-Orange anaphylaxis due to carmine allergy. Lancet 1994;344:60-61
2   Sarkany I, Meara RH, Everall J. Cheilitis due to carmine in lip salve. Trans Ann Rep St John's Hosp Dermatol Soc 1961;46:39
3   Wüthrich B, Kägi MK, Stücker W. Anaphylactic reactions to ingested carmine (E120). Allergy 1997;52:1133-1137

4   Baldwin JL, Chou AH, Solomon WR. Popsicle-induced anaphylaxis due to carmine dye allergy. An Allergy Asthma Immunol 1997;79:415-419

5   Suzuki K, Hirokawa K, Yagami A, Matsunaga K. Allergic contact dermatitis from carmine in cosmetic blush. Dermatitis 2011;22:348-349

6   Yamamoto A, Kono T, Kato A, et al. Contact dermatitis due to cochineal carmine. Environ Dermatol 1999;6:185-189 (in Japanese)

7   Endo Y, Onozawa N, Tamura A, Ishikawa O. Positive patch test reaction to carmine in lipstick. Environ Dermatol 2003;10:75-78 (in Japanese)

8   Shaw DW. Allergic contact dermatitis from carmine. Dermatitis 2009;20:292-295

9   Ferrer A, Marco FM, Andreu C, Sempere JM. Occupational asthma to carmine in a butcher. Int Arch Allergy Immunol 2005;138:243-250

10   Ohgiya Y, Arakawa F, Akiyama H, Yoshioka Y, Hayashi Y, Sakai S, et al. Molecular cloning, expression, and characterization of a major 38-kd cochineal allergen. J Allergy Clin Immunol 2009;123:1157-1162

11   Burge PS, O'Brien IM, Harries MG, Pepys J. Occupational asthma due to inhaled carmine. Clin Allergy 1979;9:185-189

12   Beaudouin E, Kanny G, Lambert H, Fremont S, Moneret-Vautrin DA. Food anaphylaxis following ingestion of carmine. Ann Allergy Asthma Immunol 1995;74:427-430

13   Stücker W, Roggenbuck D, von Kirchbach G. Schweres Asthma nach beruflicher Exposition gegenüber dem Lebensmittelfarbstoff Kochenille/Karmin. Allergo J 1996;5:143-146

14   Tenabene A, Bessot JC, Lenz D, et al. Asthme professionnel au carmin de cochenille. Arch Mal Prof 1987;48:569-571

15   Quirce S, Cuevas M, Olaguibel JM, Tabar AI. Occupational asthma and immunologic responses induced by inhaled carmine among employees at a factory making natural dyes. J Allergy Clin Immunol 1994;93:44-52

16   Acero S, Tabar AI, Alvarez MJ, Garcia BE, Olaguibel JM, Moneo I. Occupational asthma and food allergy due to carmine. Allergy 1998;53:897-901

17   DiCello MC, Myc A, Baker JR Jr, Baldwin JL. Anaphylaxis after ingestion of carmine colored foods: two case reports and a review of the literature. Allergy Asthma Proc 1999;20:377-382

18   Lizaso MT, Moneo I, García BE, Acero S, Quirce S, Tabar AI. Identification of allergens involved in occupational asthma due to carmine dye. Ann Allergy Asthma Immunol 2000;84:549-552

19   Chung K, Baker JR, Baldwin JL, Chou A. Identification of carmine allergens among three carmine allergy patients. Allergy 2001;56:73-77

20   Tabar-Purroy AI, Alvarez-Puebla MJ, Acero-Sainz S, García-Figueroa BE, Echechipía-Madoz S, Olaguibel-Rivera JM, et al. Carmine (E-120)-induced occupational asthma revisited. J Allergy Clin Immunol 2003;111:415-419

21   Añíbarro B, Seoane J, Vila C, Múgica V, Lombardero M. Occupational asthma induced by inhaled carmine among butchers. Int J Occup Med Environ Health 2003;16:133-137

22   Kotobuki Y, Azukizawa H, Nishida Y, et al. Case of urticaria due to cochineal dye in red-colored diet. Arerugi 2007;56:1510-1514 (in Japanese)

23   Yamakawa Y, Oosuna H, Yamakawa T, Aihara M, Ikezawa Z. Cochineal extract-induced immediate allergy. J Dermatol 2009;36:72-74

24   Greenhawt M, McMorris M, Baldwin J. Carmine hypersensitivity masquerading as azithromycin hypersensitivity. Allergy Asthma Proc 2009;30:95-101

25   Greenhawt MJ, Baldwin JL. Carmine dye and cochineal extract: hidden allergens no more. Ann Allergy Asthma Immunol 2009;103:73-75

26   Warshaw EM, Maibach HI, Taylor JS, Sasseville D, DeKoven JG, Zirwas MJ, et al. North American Contact Dermatitis Group patch test results: 2011-2012. Dermatitis 2015;26:49-59

27   Lippo J, Lammintausta K. Allergy to carmine red (E120) is not dependant on concurrent mite allergy. Int Arch Allergy Immunol 2009;150:179-183

28   De Pasquale T, Buonomo A, Illuminati I, D'Alò S, Pucci S. Recurrent anaphylaxis: A case of IgE-mediated allergy to carmine red (E120). J Investig Allergol Clin Immunol 2015;25:440-441

29   Liippo J, Lammintausta K. An oral challenge test with carmine red (E120) in skin prick test positive patients. Eur Ann Allergy Clin Immunol 2015;47:206-210

30   Voltolini S, Pellegrini S, Contatore M, Bignardi D, Minale P. New risks from ancient food dyes: cochineal red allergy. Eur Ann Allergy Clin Immunol 2014;46:232-233

31   Pecquet C. Allergic reactions to insect secretions. Eur J Dermatol 2013;23:767-773

32   Cox CE, Ebo DG. Carmine red (E-120)-induced occupational respiratory allergy in a screen-printing worker: a case report. B-ENT 2012;8:229-232

33   Ferris GJ, Wat M, Nedorost S. Multifactorial dermatitis with probable systemic contact dermatitis to carmine. Dermatitis 2017;28:293-294

2.109   CI 77163

IDENTIFICATION

Description/definition	: CI 77163 is an inorganic color, which conforms generally to the formula shown below
Chemical class(es)	: Color additives – miscellaneous; inorganics
INCI name USA	: Bismuth oxychloride
Chemical/IUPAC name	: Oxobismuth hydrochloride
Other names	: Bismuth oxychloride; bismuth chloride oxide; pigment white 14
CAS registry number (s)	: 7787-59-9
EC number(s)	: 232-122-7
Merck Index monograph	: 2544
Function(s) in cosmetics	: EU: colorant. USA: colorants
EU cosmetic restrictions	: Regulated in Annex IV/123 of the Regulation (EC) No. 1223/2009
Patch testing	: pure (3)
Molecular formula	: BiClO

$$Cl-Bi=O$$

CONTACT ALLERGY

Case reports and case series

Bismuth oxychloride was responsible for 1 out of 399 cases of cosmetic allergy where the causal allergen was identified in a study of the NACDG, USA, 1977-1983 (1). One patient had ACD from bismuth oxychloride in eye shadow (2).

Presence in cosmetic products and chemical analyses

In the USA, in April 2017, bismuth oxychloride was present in 2795 of 56,714 cosmetic products of which the composition is known in FDA's Voluntary Cosmetic Registration Program (VCRP) (data obtained from FDA, May 2017). In March 2017, CI 77163 was present in 1076 of 64,983 cosmetic products of which the composition is known in EWG's Skin Deep Cosmetics Database, USA (http://www.ewg.org/skindeep/).

LITERATURE

1   Adams RM, Maibach HI, Clendenning WE, Fisher AA, Jordan WJ, Kanof N, et al. A five-year study of cosmetic reactions. J Am Acad Dermatol 1985;13:1062-1069
2   Fisher AA. Contact Dermatitis, 3rd Edition. Philadelphia: Lea and Febiger, 1986:379
3   De Groot AC. Patch Testing, 3rd Edition. Wapserveen, The Netherlands: acdegroot publishing, 2008 (ISBN 978-90-813233-1-4)

2.110   CI 77288

IDENTIFICATION

Description/definition	: CI 77288 is the inorganic color, that conforms generally to the formula Cr_2O_3
Chemical class(es)	: Color additives; inorganic materials
INCI name(s) USA	: Chromium oxide greens
Chemical/IUPAC name	: Oxo(oxochromiooxy)chromium
Other names	: Dichromium trioxide; chromic oxide; chromium (III) oxide; green chromic oxide; green oxide of chromium; pigment green 17
CAS registry number (s)	: 1308-38-9; 11118-57-3
EC number(s)	: 215-160-9; 234-361-2
Merck Index monograph	: 3508
Function(s) in cosmetics	: EU: cosmetic colorant. USA: colorants
EU cosmetic restrictions	: Regulated in Annex IV/129 of the Regulation (EC) No. 1223/2009
Patch testing	: Potassium dichromate 0.25% pet. (Chemotechnique; SmartPracticeCanada); potassium dichromate 0.5% pet. (Chemotechnique; SmartPracticeEurope.com; SmartPracticeCanada.com)
Molecular formula	: Cr_2O_3

GENERAL

The USA name Chromium oxide greens also has an entry in CosIng (CAS 308-38-9; EC 15-160-9) with Hair dyeing as function and regulated in Annex IV/129 of the Regulation (EC) No. 1223/2009. Discussion of CI 77288 in this chapter is limited to side effects from its presence in cosmetic products.

CONTACT ALLERGY

Case reports and case series

A woman had periorbital dermatitis and was allergic to chromate and cobalt. She used a brown eyeliner and a metallic eye shadow. The metallic eyeshadow contained the pigments green 17 (CI 77288) and green 18 (CI 77289), which are chromium (III) oxide and chromium hydroxide, respectively. These two cosmetic products were analyzed with inductively coupled plasma mass spectrometry and proved to contain 13 and 34 ppm chromium and 7 and 120 ppm cobalt, resp. Chromium and cobalt, to which the patient had positive patch tests, were suspected to be the allergens. Quite curiously, the authors did not state whether the dermatitis disappeared after stopping the use of the incriminated products (1).

Presence in cosmetic products and chemical analyses

In the USA, in April 2017, chromium oxide greens was present in 1987 of 56,714 cosmetic products of which the composition is known in FDA's Voluntary Cosmetic Registration Program (VCRP) (data obtained from FDA, May 2017). In April 2017, CI 77288 was present in 885 of 65,521 cosmetic products of which the composition is known in EWG's Skin Deep Cosmetics Database, USA (http://www.ewg.org/skindeep/). In Finland, in 1997, 88 samples of eyeshadows purchased in Helsinki were analyzed by electrothermal atomic absorption spectroscopy for the presence of metals. Chromium was present in all products in amounts ranging from 0.3 ppm to 5470 ppm (0,547%). The levels of *soluble* chromium were determined only in products with total chromium content exceeding 10 ppm. Nine of the 88 eyeshadows contained more than 2 ppm of soluble chromium, but only 2 more than 10 ppm, of which the highest content was 318 ppm (2). Chromium (VI) (hexavalent chromium, the allergenic form of the metal) was analyzed in 22 eye shadow samples by ion chromatography and post column derivatization. Two products contained more than 5 mg l^{-1} (5 ppm), which is, according to the authors, the threshold for allergic reactivity to Cr(VI) (4). A thorough review of the literature on studies analysing the amounts of chromium in cosmetic products has been published in 2014 (3).

LITERATURE

1.   Lee HJ, Byun JY, Choi YW, Choi HY. Two cases of eyelid dermatitis caused by cobalt in colour cosmetics. Contact Dermatitis 2016;75:390-392
2.   Sainio EL, Jolanki R, Hakala E, Kanerva L. Metals and arsenic in eye shadows. Contact Dermatitis 2000; 42:5-10
3.   Bocca B, Pino A, Alimonti A, Forte G. Toxic metals contained in cosmetics. A status report. Regul Toxicol Pharmacol 2014;68:447-462
4.   Kang EK, Lee S, Park JH, Joo KM, Jeong HJ, Chang IS. Determination of hexavalent chromium in cosmetic products by ion chromatography and postcolumn derivatization. Contact Dermatitis 2006;54:244-248

2.111 CI 77289

IDENTIFICATION

Description/definition	: CI 77289 is the hydrated oxide of chromium (III)
Chemical class(es)	: Inorganic compounds; color additives
Chemical/IUPAC name	: Chromium; trihydrate
Other names	: Chromic (III) hydroxide; chromic oxide hydrated; chromium hydroxide green
CAS registry number (s)	: 1308-14-1; 12001-99-9
EC number(s)	: 215-158-8
Merck Index monograph	: 3499
Function(s) in cosmetics	: EU: cosmetic colorant. USA: colorants
EU cosmetic restrictions	: Regulated in Annex IV/130 of the Regulation (EC) No. 1223/2009
Patch testing	: Potassium dichromate 0.25% pet. (Chemotechnique; SmartPracticeCanada); potassium dichromate 0.5% pet. (Chemotechnique; SmartPracticeEurope.com; SmartPracticeCanada.com)
Molecular formula	: CrH_6O_3

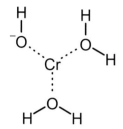

CONTACT ALLERGY

Case reports

One patient had pigmented allergic cosmetic dermatitis from chromium hydroxide in a toilet soap bar. The chromium hydroxide was added as a green pigment. Analysis showed the cosmetic product to contain 110 µg/gr (ppm) elemental chromium (1). A woman had periorbital dermatitis and was allergic to chromate and cobalt . She used a brown eyeliner and a metallic eye shadow. The metallic eyeshadow contained the pigments green 18 (CI 77289) and green 17 (CI 77288), which are chromium hydroxide and chromium oxide, respectively. These two cosmetic products were analyzed with inductively coupled plasma mass spectrometry and proved to contain 13 and 34 ppm chromium and 7 and 120 ppm cobalt, resp. Chromium and cobalt were suspected to be the allergens. Quite curiously, the authors did not state whether the dermatitis disappeared after stopping the use of the incriminated products (2).

Presence in cosmetic products and chemical analyses

In the USA, in April 2017, chromium hydroxide green was present in 1708 of 56,714 cosmetic products of which the composition is known in FDA's Voluntary Cosmetic Registration Program (VCRP) (data obtained from FDA, May 2017). In April 2017, CI 77289 was present in 576 of 65,521 cosmetic products of which the composition is known in EWG's Skin Deep Cosmetics Database, USA (http://www.ewg.org/skindeep/). In Finland, in 1997, 88 samples of eyeshadows purchased in Helsinki were analyzed by electrothermal atomic absorption spectroscopy for the presence of metals. Chromium was present in all products in amounts ranging from 0.3 ppm to 5470 ppm (0,547%). The levels of *soluble* chromium were determined only in products with total chromium content exceeding 10 ppm. Nine of the 88 eyeshadows contained more than 2 ppm of soluble chromium, but only 2 more than 10 ppm, of which the highest content was 318 ppm (3). Chromium (VI) (hexavalent chromium, the allergenic form of the metal) was analyzed in 22 eye shadow samples by ion chromatography and post column derivatization. Two products contained more than 5 mg l^{-1} (5 ppm), which is, according to the authors, the threshold for allergic reactivity to Cr(VI) (5). A thorough review of the literature on studies analysing the amounts of chromium in cosmetic products has been published in 2014 (4).

LITERATURE

1   Mathias CGT. Pigmented cosmetic dermatitis from contact allergy to a toilet soap containing chromium. Contact Dermatitis 1982;8:29-31

2   Lee HJ, Byun JY, Choi YW, Choi HY. Two cases of eyelid dermatitis caused by cobalt in colour cosmetics. Contact Dermatitis 2016;75:390-392

3   Sainio EL, Jolanki R, Hakala E, Kanerva L. Metals and arsenic in eye shadows. Contact Dermatitis 2000; 42:5-10

4   Bocca B, Pino A, Alimonti A, Forte G. Toxic metals contained in cosmetics. A status report. Regul Toxicol Pharmacol 2014;68:447-462

5   Kang EK, Lee S, Park JH, Joo KM, Jeong HJ, Chang IS. Determination of hexavalent chromium in cosmetic products by ion chromatography and postcolumn derivatization. Contact Dermatitis 2006;54:244-248

2.112 CINOXATE

IDENTIFICATION

Description/definition	: Cinoxate is the aromatic ether that conforms to the formula shown below
Chemical class(es)	: Esters; ethers
Chemical/IUPAC name	: 2-Ethoxyethyl (*E*)-3-(4-methoxyphenyl)prop-2-enoate
Other names	: 2-Ethoxyethyl-*p*-methoxycinnamate
CAS registry number (s)	: 104-28-9
EC number(s)	: 203-191-0
Merck Index monograph	: 3580
Function(s) in cosmetics	: EU: UV-absorber. USA: light stabilizers; sunscreen agents
EU cosmetic restrictions	: Not in Annex VI of the Regulation (EC) No. 1223/2009 (List of UV filters allowed in cosmetic products in the European Union)
Patch testing	: 2% pet.
Molecular formula	: $C_{14}H_{18}O_4$

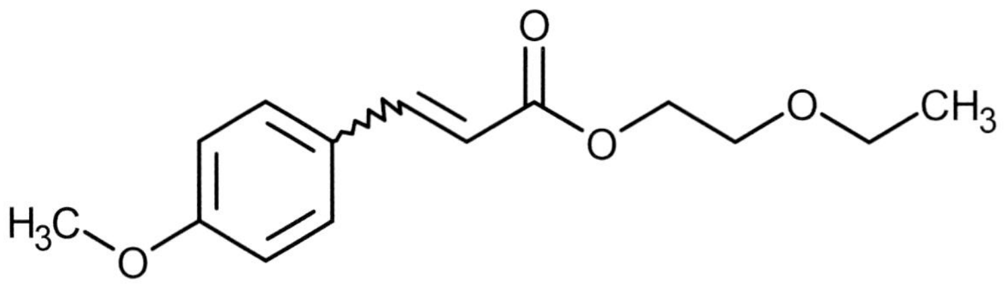

GENERAL

Cinoxate is a UVB filter with UV absorbance maximum (λ_{max}) at 308 nm (23). It is currently hardly, if at all, used in sunscreens or cosmetic products. It is not included in Annex VI of the Regulation (EC) No. 1223/2009, the list of UV filters allowed in cosmetic products in the European Union. All reports of adverse reactions to cinoxate date from before 1998. The literature on adverse reactions to sunscreens has been reviewed in several recent and older publications (5,14-18,25). A review of photocontact allergy to sunscreens was published in 2010 (1).

CONTACT ALLERGY

Patch testing in groups of patients

There have been no studies in which cinoxate has been patch tested in consecutive patients suspected of contact dermatitis (routine testing). Results of testing cinoxate in *selected* patients (patients with photosensitivity dermatitis / actinic reticuloid syndrome, polymorphic light eruption, with photosensitivity or suspected of sunscreen derma-titis) are shown in table 2.112.1. In two studies, the frequencies of sensitization were 1% (3) and >0.4% (exact number of patients tested not mentioned) (11), but in both cases, there was only 1 positive patch test. One reaction was relevant and was caused by the use of a sunscreen containing cinoxate (11).

Table 2.112.1 Patch testing in groups of patients: Selected patient groups

Years and Country	Test conc. & vehicle	Number of patients tested | positive (%)			Selection of patients (S); Relevance (R); Comments (C)	Ref.
1989-1991 UK	2% pet.	99	1	(1%)	S: 45 patients with photosensitivity dermatitis/actinic reticuloid syndrome and 54 with polymorphic light eruption; R: not specified	3
1985-1987 UK	2% pet.	<280	1	(>0.4%)	S: patients with photosensitivity and other patients suspected of sunscreen dermatitis; R: the patient used a sunscreen con-taining cinoxate; C: the patient had chronic actinic dermatitis	11

Case reports and case series

In a 4-month-period in 1996, 475 patients with contact allergy to 'cosmetic ingredients' were collected in 5 centers in Belgium, UK and Germany. There was one reaction to cinoxate; relevance was not stated (19). Four patients became sensitized to cinoxate in sunscreen preparations (20,21). One more individual suffered from allergic contact dermatitis caused by cinoxate in a sunscreen (7).

Cross-reactions, pseudo-cross-reactions and co-reactions

Benzyl cinnamate, methyl cinnamate, cinnamyl alcohol (20).

Presence in cosmetic products and chemical analyses

In June 2017, cinoxate was present in 1 of 68,864 cosmetic products of which the composition is known in EWG's Skin Deep Cosmetics Database, USA (http://www.ewg.org/skindeep/). It should be realized that sunscreen products containing UV-filters are classified as drugs in the USA, not as cosmetics; the number mentioned here, therefore, is that of cosmetics containing the UV-filter, but it does *not* include their presence in sunscreens. In the USA, in April 2017, cinoxate was present in zero of 56,714 cosmetic products of which the composition is known in FDA's Voluntary Cosmetic Registration Program (VCRP) (data obtained from FDA, May 2017). In The Netherlands, in 1978, 197 sunscreen products of 48 brands were investigated for the presence of UV-filters. Cinoxate was present in 9 brands (number of products not mentioned) in a concentration range of 0.4-4.8%. Cinoxate was at that time the most prevalent UV-absorber in sunscreen products after ethylhexyl methoxycinnamate (19 brands) and phenylbenzimidazole sulfonic acid (11 brands) (22).

OTHER SIDE EFFECTS

Photosensitivity

Photopatch testing in groups of patients

Results of photopatch testing cinoxate in selected patients (patients suspected of photoallergic contact dermatitis, with photosensitivity or suspected of sunscreen dermatitis) are shown in table 2.112.2. In two studies, frequencies of photosensitization were 0.3% (2) and >0.4% (exact number of patients tested not mentioned). In a large study from Italy, the relevance of the 3 photopatch test reactions to cinoxate was not specified (78% for all photoallergens together) (2) and in the other study, the one reacting patient had used a sunscreen containing cinoxate (11).

Table 2.112.2 Photopatch testing in groups of patients

Years and Country	Test conc. & vehicle	Number of patients tested | positive (%)		Selection of patients (S); Relevance (R); Comments (C)	Ref.
1985-1993 Italy		1050	3 (0.3%)	S: patients suspected of photoallergic contact dermatitis; R: not specified (78% for all photoallergens together)	2
1985-1987 UK	2% pet.	<280	1 (>0.4%)	S: patients with photosensitivity and other patients suspected of sunscreen dermatitis; R: the patient used a sunscreen containing cinoxate; C: the patient had chronic actinic dermatitis	11

Case reports and series

Several single case reports of photoallergic contact dermatitis from cinoxate in sunscreens have been published (4,6,10,12,13,24). In another article, two patients with photocontact allergy to cinoxate in sunscreens were presented (7).

Other non-eczematous contact reactions

A stinging sensation from a face powder was –unconvincingly – ascribed to cinoxate (9). Two patients had possible photo*toxic* reactions to cinoxate with erythema and blisters after 12 hours, leaving streaky hyperpigmentation (8).

LITERATURE

1   Shaw T, Simpson B, Wilson B, Oostman H, Rainey D, Storrs F. True photoallergy to sunscreens is rare despite popular belief. Dermatitis 2010;21:185-198

2   Pigatto PD, Legori A, Bigardi AS, Guarrera M, Tosti A, Santucci B, et al. Gruppo Italiano recerca dermatiti da contatto ed ambientali Italian multicenter study of allergic contact photodermatitis: epidemiological aspects. Am J Contact Dermatitis 1996;17:158-163

3   Bilsland D, Ferguson J. Contact allergy to sunscreen chemicals in photosensitivity dermatitis/actinic reticuloid syndrome (PD/AR) and polymorphic light eruption. Contact Dermatitis 1993;29:70-73

4   Goodman T Jr. Photodermatitis from a sunscreening agent (Letter). Arch Dermatol 1970;102:563

5   Dromgoole SH, Maibach HI. Sunscreening agent intolerance: Contact and photocontact sensitization and contact urticaria. J Am Acad Dermatol 1990;22:1068-1078

6   Murphy GM, White IR. Photoallergic contact dermatitis to 2-ethoxyethyl-p-methoxycinnamate. Contact Dermatitis 1987;16:296

7   Thune P. Contact and photocontact allergy to sunscreens. Photodermatology 1984;1:5-9

8   Davies MG, Hawk JLM, Rycroft RJG. Acute photosensitivity from the sunscreen 2-ethoxyethyl-p-methoxycinnamate. Contact Dermatitis 1982; 8:190-192

9   Calnan CD. Stinging sensation from elhoxyethyl – methoxy cinnamate. Contact Dermatitis 1978;4:294

10 Gonçalo M, Ruas E, Figueiredo A, Gonçalo S. Contact and photocontact sensitivity to sunscreens. Contact Dermatitis 1995;33:278-280

11 English JSC, White IR, Cronin K. Sensitivity to sunscreens. Contact Dermatitis 1987;17:159-162

12 Ang P, Ng SK, Goh CL. Sunscreen allergy in Singapore. Am J Cont Derm 1998;9:42-44

13 Freeman S, Frederiksen P. Sunscreen allergy. Am J Cont Derm 1990;1:240-243

14 Heurung AR, Raju SI, Warshaw EM. Adverse reactions to sunscreen agents: epidemiology, responsible irritants and allergens, clinical characteristics, and management. Dermatitis 2014;25:289-326

15 Heurung AR, Raju SI, Warshaw EM. Contact allergen of the year. Benzophenones. Dermatitis 2014;25:3-10 (contains many mistakes; Erratum in Dermatitis 2014;25:92-95)

16 Avenel-Audran M. Sunscreen products: finding the allergen. Eur J Dermatol 2010;20:161-166

17 Scheuer E, Warshaw E. Sunscreen allergy: a review of epidemiology, clinical characteristics, and responsible allergens. Dermatitis 2006;17:3-11

18 Funk JO, Dromgoole SH, Maibach HI. Sunscreen intolerance: contact sensitization, photocontact sensitization, and irritancy of sunscreen agents. Dermatol Clin 1995;13:473-481

19 Goossens A, Beck MH, Haneke E, McFadden JP, Nolting S, Durupt G, Ries G. Adverse cutaneous reactions to cosmetic allergens. Contact Dermatitis 1999;40:112-113

20 Cronin E. Contact Dermatitis. Edinburgh: Churchill Livingstone, 1980:454

21 Cronin E. Contact dermatitis from cinnamate. Cont Derm Newsl 1971;9:216

22 Liem DH, Hilderink LT. UV absorbers in sun cosmetics 1978. Int J Cosmet Sci 1979;1:341-361

23 Shaath NA. Ultraviolet filters. Photochem Photobiol Sci 2010;9:464-469

24 Fagerlund VL, Kalimo K, Jansen CH. Photokontakallergie durch Lichtschutzmittel (Valonsurjaaineet fotokontaktallergien aiheuttajin). Duodecim 1983;99:146-150 (article in Finnish)

25 Schauder S. Survey of the literature on adverse reactions to preparations containing UV filters (1947-1989) (Literaturübersicht über Unverträglichkeitsreaktionen auf lichtfilterhaltige Produkte von 1947 bis 1989). Z Hautkr 1990;65:982-998 (article in German)

2.113   CI PIGMENT RED 53:1

IDENTIFICATION

Description/definition	: CI Pigment red 53:1 is a monoazo color, which conforms to the formula shown below
Chemical class(es)	: Color additives - miscellaneous; halogen compounds
INCI name USA	: Pigment red 53:1
Chemical/IUPAC name	: Barium(2+);5-chloro-4-methyl-2-[(2Z)-2-(2-oxonaphthalen-1-ylidene)hydra-zinyl]benzenesulfonate
Other names	: Benzenesulfonic acid, 5-chloro-2-(2-(2-hydroxy-1-naphthalenyl)diazenyl)-4-methyl-, barium salt (2:1); red lake CBA; D&C red no. 9; CI 15585:1; brilliant red
CAS registry number (s)	: 5160-02-1
EC number(s)	: 225-935-3
Function(s) in cosmetics	: EU: prohibited. USA: colorants
EU cosmetic restrictions	: Regulated in Annex II/401 of the Regulation (EC) No. 1223/2009 (prohibited)
Patch testing	: 5% polyethylene glycol (1)
Molecular formula	: $C_{34}H_{24}BaCl_2N_4O_8S_2$

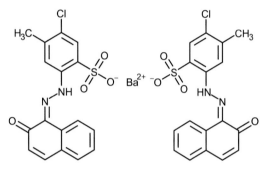

CONTACT ALLERGY

Patch testing in groups of patients
Of 28 Japanese patients with pigmented cosmetic dermatitis, patch tested and photopatch tested with coal tar dyes in 1975-1976, five had positive patch tests to Red Lake CBA. It was not mentioned (and probably unknown) whether this color was present in the cosmetics used by the patients (1).

Cross-reactions, pseudo-cross-reactions and co-reactions
Other coal tar dyes (1).

Presence in cosmetic products and chemical analyses
In the USA, in April 2017, CI pigment red 53:1 was present in zero of 56,714 cosmetic products of which the composition is known in FDA's Voluntary Cosmetic Registration Program (VCRP) (data obtained from FDA, May 2017). In March 2017, CI pigment red 53:1 was present in zero of 64,983 cosmetic products of which the composition is known in EWG's Skin Deep Cosmetics Database, USA (http://www.ewg.org/skindeep/).

Other information
The prohibited color, which is a suspected carcinogen, was found to be present in 40% of 42 German flag-colored face paints offered during the soccer world cup in 2014 (2).

LITERATURE

1   Sugai T, Takahashi Y, Tagaki T. Pigmented cosmetic dermatitis and coal tar dyes. Contact Dermatitis 1977;3:249-256
2   Keck-Wilhelm A, Kratz E, Mildau G, Ilse M, Schlee C, Lachenmeier DW. Chemical analysis and risk assessment of prohibited colouring agents in face paint with special regard to CI 15585 (D&C Red No. 9, Pigment Red 53:1). Int J Cosmet Sci 2015;37:187-195

2.114 COAL TAR

IDENTIFICATION

Description/definition	: Coal tar is a thick liquid or semi-solid obtained as a by-product in the destructive distillation of bituminous coal
Chemical class(es)	: Hydrocarbons
Other names	: Tar, coal; pix lithanthracis
CAS registry number (s)	: 8007-45-2
EC number(s)	: 232-361-7
CIR review(s)	: Int J Toxicol 2008;27(Suppl.2):1-24 (access: www.cir-safety.org/ingredients)
SCCS opinion(s)	: SCCNFP/0330/00 (2)
Merck Index monograph	: 3679
Function(s) in cosmetics	: EU: formerly used as antimicrobial; antidandruff; denaturant. USA: antidandruff agents; cosmetic biocides; denaturants
EU cosmetic restrictions	: Regulated in Annex II/420 of the Regulation (EC) No. 1223/2009 (prohibited)
Patch testing	: 5.0% pet. (Chemotechnique, SmartPracticeEurope, SmartPracticeCanada)

GENERAL

Topical coal tar products are widely used in the treatment of psoriasis and atopic dermatitis, although the level of evidence of their efficacy is not strong (3) and people dislike their odor, messy application, and staining of clothing. The short-term side effects of coal tar pharmaceutical preparations are folliculitis, irritation, phototoxicity and contact allergy. Coal tar contains carcinogens. The carcinogenicity of coal tar has been shown in animal studies and studies in occupational settings. Yet, there is no clear evidence of an increased risk of skin tumors or internal tumors in patients treated with coal tar (4).

Shampoos with coal tar were formerly widely used in the treatment of dandruff and seborrheic dermatitis of the scalp, but, because of the known carcinogenicity of coal tar, its use in the EU is prohibited. In this chapter, only side effects of coal tar from its presence in cosmetic products are presented.

CONTACT ALLERGY

Case reports and case series
Coal tar was responsible for 1 out of 399 cases of cosmetic allergy where the causal allergen was identified in a study of the NACDG, USA, 1977-1983 (1).

A woman had dermatitis of both hands, arms, back and the periorbital area of her face. Patch tests were positive to an 'udderfat' and a shampoo containing coal tar. When tested with their ingredients, the patient reacted to Osmaron B 1% in the udderfat and to coal tar 0.1%, present in the shampoo, with a co-reaction to birch tar (5).

Presence in cosmetic products and chemical analyses
In the USA, in April 2017, coal tar was present in 2 of 56,714 cosmetic products of which the composition is known in FDA's Voluntary Cosmetic Registration Program (VCRP) (data obtained from FDA, May 2017). In April 2017, coal tar was present in 12 of 65,521 cosmetic products of which the composition is known in EWG's Skin Deep Cosmetics Database, USA (http://www.ewg.org/skindeep/).

LITERATURE

1 Adams RM, Maibach HI, Clendenning WE, Fisher AA, Jordan WJ, Kanof N, et al. A five-year study of cosmetic reactions. J Am Acad Dermatol 1985;13:1062-1069
2 SCCNFP (Scientific Committee on Cosmetics and Non Food Products). Opinion concerning refined coal tar by bi-distillation, 28 June 2000, SCCNFP/0330/00. Available at: http://ec.europa.eu/health/archive/ph_risk/committees/sccp/documents/out119_en.pdf
3 Slutsky JB, Clark RA, Remedios AA, Klein PA. An evidence-based review of the efficacy of coal tar preparations in the treatment of psoriasis and atopic dermatitis. J Drugs Dermatol 2010;9:1258-1264
4 Roelofzen JH, Aben KK, van der Valk PG, van Houtum JL, van de Kerkhof PC, Kiemeney LA. Coal tar in dermatology. J Dermatolog Treat 2007;18:329-334
5 Goldermann R, Scharffetter-Kochanek K, Brunner M, Merk H, Goerz G. 3 cases of contact dermatitis from alkylammonium amidobenzoate (Osmaron BA). Contact Dermatitis 1992;27:337-339

2.115   COBALT*
Not an INCI name

IDENTIFICATION

Description/definition	: Cobalt is a metal, which may be present in pigmented make-up products as a contaminant
Chemical class(es)	: Elements, transition metals
INCI name USA	: Neither in CosIng nor in the Personal Care Products Council Ingredient Database
CAS registry number (s)	: 7440-48-4
EC number(s)	: 231-158-0
Merck Index monograph	: 3681
Patch testing	: Cobalt(II)chloride hexahydrate 1.0% pet. (Chemotechnique, SmartPracticeCanada); cobalt chloride 1% pet. (SmartPracticeEurope)

GENERAL

Discussion of cobalt in this chapter is limited to adverse reactions from its presence in cosmetic products.

CONTACT ALLERGY

Case reports and case series

Two women had periorbital dermatitis. When patch tested, they reacted to chromate and to cobalt. The first patient used a brow liner, the second a brown eyeliner and a metallic eye shadow. These cosmetic products were analyzed with inductively coupled plasma mass spectrometry and proved to contain 7-120 ppm cobalt. Cobalt was suspected to be the allergen in patient one, and cobalt and chromium in the second (the cosmetics of this patient also contained chromium colors: CI 77288 and CI 77289).   Quite curiously, the authors did not state whether the dermatitis disappeared after stopping the use of the incriminated products (1).

A woman presented with multiple, intensely itchy, eczematous periungual and palmar lesions on both hands. She had undergone a nail-art procedure by a professional beautician 9 months before, and had repeated the procedure herself at home several times. The 'nail gel' used was labeled 'acrylic', but the ingredients were not listed. Patch tests were performed with the baseline series, a (meth)acrylates series and the ingredients of the nail gel, but there was a reaction only to cobalt chloride, which was not present in the nail gel. The patient then told that she had added a 'glitter color' to the original top coat gel. The label of the additional product revealed that it contained cobalt. Removal of all products from her nails led to complete resolution in 4 weeks (4).

A beauty therapist had severe hand dermatitis. Patch tests showed her to be allergic to nickel, cobalt and two 'galvanic gels', both containing 0.1% cobaltous chloride. These gels are used as a facial massage in combination with iontophoresis, which is assisted by the cobalt. Since avoiding these products, the patient has been completely free of hand dermatitis (5).

Analysis of allergen in products

In Finland, in 1997, 88 samples of eyeshadows purchased in Helsinki were analyzed by electrothermal atomic absorption spectroscopy for the presence of metals. Cobalt was found in all samples in amounts ranging from <0.5 to 41.2 ppm (2). A thorough review of the literature on studies analysing the amounts of cobalt in cosmetic products has been published in 2014 (3).

LITERATURE

1   Lee HJ, Byun JY, Choi YW, Choi HY. Two cases of eyelid dermatitis caused by cobalt in colour cosmetics. Contact Dermatitis 2016;75:390-392
2   Sainio EL, Jolanki R, Hakala E, Kanerva L. Metals and arsenic in eye shadows. Contact Dermatitis 2000; 42:5-10
3   Bocca B, Pino A, Alimonti A, Forte G. Toxic metals contained in cosmetics. A status report. Regul Toxicol Pharmacol 2014;68:447-462
4   Guarneri F, Guarneri C, Cannavò SP. Nail-art and cobalt allergy. Contact Dermatitis 2010; 62:320-321
5   Chave TA, Warin AP. Allergic contact dermatitis from cobalt in a beauty product. Contact Dermatitis 1999;41:236

2.116 COCAMIDE

IDENTIFICATION

Description/definition : Cocamide is the aliphatic amide that conforms generally to the formula shown below, where RCO- represents the fatty acids derived from coconut oil
Chemical class(es) : Amides
Other names : Amides, coco
CAS registry number (s) : 61789-19-3
EC number(s) : 263-039-4
Function(s) in cosmetics : EU: emulsifying; emulsion stabilizing; surfactant; viscosity controlling. USA: not reported
Patch testing : 3% water (1)

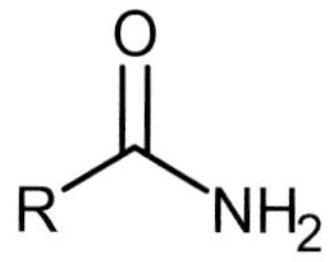

CONTACT ALLERGY

Case reports and case series

A man had suffered from intense outbreaks of seborrheic dermatitis, which improved with topical corticosteroids and ketoconazole but recurred on ceasing medication. For the past 3 months, papular, erythematous, intensely pruriginous lesions had been appearing on sun-exposed areas of the face, neck and hands. Patch tests and photopatch tests with the standard series were negative at 2 and 4 days, as were his cosmetics and toiletries with the single exception of a shaving foam, as is, which gave a strongly positive patch test reaction at both readings. Patch and photopatch tests were then carried out with the ingredients of this product supplied by the manufacturer and he had positive patch test reactions to 6 ingredients including cocamide 3% in water. There were no positive reactions in 25 controls. The patient was retested 7 months later to all 6 allergens previously positive and reacted again at 2 and 4 days to cocamide (1).

Presence in cosmetic products and chemical analyses

In the USA, in April 2017, cocamide was present in 9 of 56,714 cosmetic products of which the composition is known in FDA's Voluntary Cosmetic Registration Program (VCRP) (data obtained from FDA, May 2017). In March 2017, cocamide was present in 2 older products of 64,983 cosmetic products of which the composition is known in EWG's Skin Deep Cosmetics Database, USA (http://www.ewg.org/skindeep/).

LITERATURE

1 Vilaplana J, Lecha M, Romaguera C, Alsina A, Mascaro JM, Castel, T. A polysensitized HIV-positive patient. Contact Dermatitis 1993;29:101-102

2.117   COCAMIDE DEA

IDENTIFICATION

Description/definition	: Cocamide DEA is a mixture of ethanolamides of coconut acid. It conforms generally to the formula shown below, where RCO- represents the fatty acids derived from *Cocos nucifera* (coconut) oil
Chemical class(es)	: Alkanolamides
Chemical/IUPAC name	: Amides, coco, *N,N*-bis(hydroxyethyl)
Other names	: Coconut diethanolamide; cocamine diethanolamine; coconut fatty acids diethanolamide
CAS registry number (s)	: 68603-42-9; 61791-31-9
EC number(s)	: 271-657-0; 263-163-9
CIR review(s)	: J Am Coll Toxicol 1986;5:415-454; J Am Coll Toxicol 1996;15:527-542; Int J Toxicol 2013;32(Suppl.3):36-58 (access: www.cir-safety.org/ingredients)
Function(s) in cosmetics	: EU: emulsifying; emulsion stabilising; foam boosting; surfactant; viscosity controlling. USA: surfactants – foam boosters; viscosity increasing agents – aqueous
EU cosmetic restrictions	: Regulated in Annex III/60 of the Regulation (EC) No. 1223/2009
Patch testing	: 0.5% pet. (Chemotechnique, SmartPracticeEurope, SmartPracticeCanada); the test material may sometimes cause irritant reactions (11)

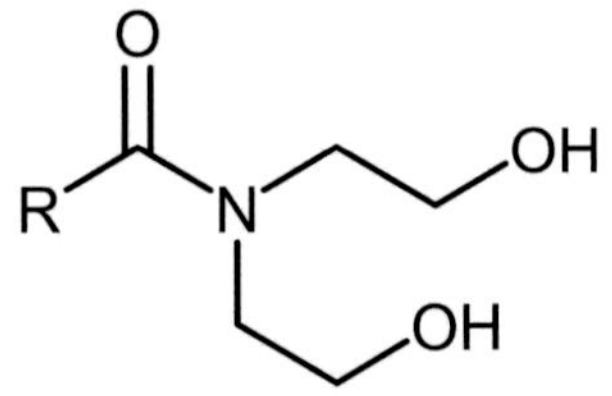

GENERAL

Cocamide DEA is an agent with surface-active properties; it is frequently used in cleansers, hair shampoos, hand gels and hand-washing liquids for its foam-producing and stabilizing properties (1). It also functions as corrosion inhibitor and cleansing agent in industrial and household products such as cleaning agents, waxes and wax removers, cutting fluids, industrial hand cleansers and protective creams (11). Cocamide DEA is synthesized from coconut oil and DEA (diethanolamine). Coconut oil is composed of fatty acids with varying chain lengths of C6-C20 (table 2.117.1), the main com ponent being lauric acid (C12). Cocamide DEA therefore is a mixture of DEA derivatives of the fatty acids of coco-nut oil, and its main component is accordingly lauramide DEA (lauric acid diethanolamide, lauramide diethanolamine; CAS no. 120-40-1), the derivative of lauric acid (11).

Allergic contact dermatitis from cocamide DEA is relatively rare. Most patients sensitized to cocamide DEA have an impaired skin barrier due to atopic dermatitis and/or previous contact dermatitis (8). Many are occupationally related and most patients have hand dermatitis (8,11,13). Occupations at risk are metalworkers (11), hairdressers (8) and health care workers (8,38). The majority also has other contact allergies. Liquid hand soaps and hand cleansers and shampoos (in hairdressers) are the most important sources of exposure to cocamide DEA (8,11,13).

Table 2.117.1 Fatty acid composition of coconut oil and names of the corresponding diethanolamine derivatives (11)

Fatty acid	Number of carbons (chain length)	Coconut oil (%)	Corresponding DEA (diethanolamine) derivatives
Lauric	12	47.5	Lauramide DEA
Myristic	14	18.1	Myristamide DEA
Palmitic	16	8.8	Palmitamide DEA
Caprylic	8	7.8	Caprylamide DEA
Capric	10	6.7	Capramide DEA
Oleic (monounsaturated)	18	6.2	Oleamide DEA
Stearic	18	2.6	Stearamide DEA
Linoleic (polyunsaturated)	18	1.6	Linolamide DEA
Caproic	6	0.5	Caproamide DEA
Arachidic	20	0.1	Arachidamide DEA

CONTACT ALLERGY

Patch testing in groups of patients
Results of testing cocamide DEA in consecutive patients suspected of contact dermatitis (routine testing) back to 2004 are shown in table 2.117.2. Results of testing in groups of *selected* patients (e.g., patients suspected of cosmetic dermatitis, patients with allergic contact cheilitis, individuals tested with a metalworking fluid series, healthcare workers) back to 2004 are shown in table 2.117.3.

Patch testing in consecutive patients suspected of contact dermatitis: routine testing
Cocamide DEA has been present in the North American Contact Dermatitis Group screening series since 2003 and all studies but one (a 2001-2010 study from Australia [30]) are from the United States (mostly plus Canada), where the NACDG publishes their results biannually. In 10 studies from the NACDG or other US centers, in which routine testing with cocamide DEA was performed, rates of sensitization have been consistently fairly low, ranging from 0.8% to 1.7%. Relevance scores were usually in the 30%-50% range. In an Australian study, there were 2.7% positive reactions of which 31% were scored as relevant, but culprit products were not mentioned (30).

Table 2.117.2 Patch testing in groups of patients: Routine testing

Years and Country	Test conc. & vehicle	Number of patients tested | positive (%)		Selection of patients (S); Relevance (R); Comments (C)	Ref.
2013-14 USA, Canada	0.5% pet.	4859	42 (0.9%)	R: definite + probable relevance: 33%	32
2009-14 USA, Canada	0.5% pet.	10,877	92 (0.8%)	R: not stated	23
2001-2013 USA	0.5% pet.	1674	28 (1.7%)	R: not stated; C: contact allergy rates in atopics and non-atopics did not differ significantly; significant association with cocamidopropyl betaine reactions	20
2011-12 USA, Canada	0.5% pet.	4230	36 (0.9%)	R: definite + probable relevance: 42%	21
2009-10 USA, Canada	0.5% pet.	4304	39 (0.9%)	R: definite + probable relevance: 34%	22
2006-2010 USA	0.5% pet.	3085	(1.2%)	R: 45%	26
2001-2010 Australia	0.5% pet.	5088	139 (2.7%)	R: 31%	30
2007-8 USA, Canada	0.5% pet.	5082	(1.2%)	R: definite + probable relevance: 45%	7
2005-6 USA, Canada	0.5% pet.	4437	(1.0%)	R: definite + probable relevance: 51%	6
2000-2005 USA	0.5% pet.	410	(1.5%)	R: 17%	3
2003-4 USA, Canada	0.5% pet.	5137	56 (1.1%)	R: not stated	9

Patch testing in groups of selected patients
Results of testing cocamide DEA in groups of selected patients (e.g., patients suspected of cosmetic dermatitis, patients with allergic contact cheilitis, individuals tested with a metalworking fluid series, healthcare workers) back to 2004 are shown in table 2.117.3. In 9 investigations, frequencies of sensitization have ranged from 0.7% to 9%, all but two scored 2.5% or lower. A high percentage of 8% was seen in a very small study of 25 patients with allergic contact cheilitis. Both positive reactions were apparently relevant, but causative products were not mentioned (36). The highest 9% sensitization frequency has been observed in a small study of a highly selected group of 47 patients, who had previously reacted to one or more surfactants present in the NACDG screening series. There were 4 positive reactions, but their relevance was not mentioned (31).

Case reports and case series
Cocamide DEA was stated to be the (or an) allergen in 2 patients in a group of 603 individuals suffering from cosmetic dermatitis, seen in the period 2010-2015 in Leuven, Belgium (25). Cocamide DEA was responsible for 4 out of 959 cases of non-fragrance cosmetic allergy where the causal allergen was identified, Belgium, 2000-2010 (1). In the same center in Leuven, Belgium, between 1990 and 2015, 1767 patients were tested with cocamide DEA on the basis of the patient history and clinical signs, and the label of the cosmetic products used. Eighteen individuals (1%) had a mostly weak, but clearly allergic positive reaction. Fourteen reactions were currently relevant, one was of past relevance, and in 3 cases no relevance could be found. Many of the sensitized patients also had a (considerable) number of other contact allergies. All patients suffered from hand dermatitis; some also had dermatitis on other body parts, such as the arms, chest, legs, and feet. Of the 18 patients with positive patch test reactions to cocamide DEA, 11 had occupational exposure and one past occupational exposures: 6 hairdressers, 3 healthcare workers, two car mechanics, and a workman in the rubber industry. The most common sources of occupational cocamide DEA exposure were shampoos for the hairdressers and hand cleansers/liquid soaps for the other patients.

In a group of 611 men with (presumed) cosmetic allergy, 17 reactions (2.8%) were caused by cocamide DEA in a study of the NACDG, 2001-2004 (4). In a group of 119 patients with allergic contact dermatitis from cosmetics, inves-

Table 2.117.3 Patch testing in groups of patients: Selected patient groups

Years and Country	Test conc. & vehicle	Number of patients tested	positive (%)		Selection of patients (S); Relevance (R); Comments (C)	Ref.
2015-2016 USA	0.5% pet.	47	4	(9%)	S: patients previously reacting to one or more surfactants present in the NACDG screening series; R: not stated; C: there were also 2 doubtful reactions	31
2009-2015 Belgium	0.5% pet.	1767	18	(1%)	S: patients were selected on the basis of the patient history and clinical signs, and the label of the cosmetic products used; R: 14/18 (78%) relevant, one past relevance, 3 unknown; C: 2/3 were from occupational exposure, notably in hairdressers and healthcare workers; the most common causative products were shampoos, liquid hand cleansers and liquid soaps	8
2006-2011 IVDK	0.5% pet.	7719		(0.7%)	S: patients suspected of cosmetic intolerance and tested with an ointment base series (selection procedure not stated); R: not stated	33
2001-2011 USA	0.5% pet.	25	2	(8%)	S: patients with allergic contact cheilitis; R: 2/2 relevant	36
1993-2011 Finland	0.5% pet.	2572	25	(1.0%)	S: not specified; R: 19 patients (76%) had occupational allergic contact dermatitis, mostly from industrial hand cleansers, one patient had dermatitis from hand soap; C: the study was performed in an occupational Health Clinic	11
1994-2010 USA, Canada	0.5% pet.	?	?	(?)	S: hairdressers/cosmetologists; R: in the group of 131 patients who had at least one relevant occupationally related reaction, 7 (5.3%) reacted to cocamide DEA	34
2000-2007 USA	0.5% pet.	939	20	(2.1%)	S: patients tested with a supplemental cosmetic screening series; R: 80%; C: weak study: a. high rate of macular erythema and weak reactions; b. relevance figures included 'questionable' and 'past' relevance	2
2004-2005 Germany	0.5% pet.	120	3	(2.5%)	S: patients tested with a metalworking fluid series; R: not stated	24
1998-04 USA, Canada	0.5% pet.	788	7	(0.9%)	S: health care workers; R: only occupation-related (=relevant) reactions were recorded; C: the frequency was significantly higher than the rate of occupation-related reactions in non-health care workers (0.1%); the causative products were cosmetics and a disinfectant	37

IVDK: Information Network of Departments of Dermatology, Germany, Austria, Switzerland

tigated in The Netherlands in 1986-1987, two cases were caused by cocamide DEA, one in a hair conditioner, the other in a bath foam (27,28). Five positive patch test reactions to cocamide DEA were ascribed to cosmetic allergy (5). One patient had hand dermatitis from cocamide DEA in liquid soap (12). Another individual suffered from eyelid dermatitis caused by contact allergy to cocamide DEA in shampoo (15). A man experienced worsening of scalp psoriasis and eyelid dermatitis from cocamide DEA and zinc pyrithione in an anti-dandruff shampoo (16).

A woman and a man both had allergic contact dermatitis from cocamide DEA in several personal care products (19). A woman working in a printing works had occupational hand dermatitis from cocamide DEA in a hand gel (17). Three other individuals had non-occupational exposure to liquid hand soap (8). One patient suffered from hand dermatitis from cocamide DEA in hand washing liquid (12).

Some reports of sensitization to cocamide DEA in – amongst others - hand cleansers are discussed in the next section.

Contact allergy to cocamide DEA in non-cosmetic products

In a 2-year retrospective study, the members of the French Dermato-Allergology Vigilance network Revidal together found 17 cases of contact allergy to an antiseptic cream containing triclocarban. However, triclocarban itself was the allergen in none of these cases, all were caused by excipients including cocamide DEA in one case. Cocamide DEA was also the allergenic culprit in another antiseptic in one patient in the same investigation (35).

In a Finnish occupational contact dermatitis clinic, in the period 1993-2011, cocamide DEA was tested on 2572 patients and 25 (1%) had an allergic reaction. Of these 25, 19 patients had occupational exposure to cocamide DEA or its component oleamide DEA and they were diagnosed with occupational allergic contact dermatitis. Eleven patients worked in the metal industry. All had hand dermatitis and most had also other contact allergies. The most common source of cocamide DEA sensitization was hand cleansers at work; others were barrier cream, dishwashing liquid and metalworking fluid in one patient each (11).

Six non-occupational cases of allergic contact dermatitis from cocamide DEA were reported from France. Three patients reacted to cocamide DEA in an antifungal cream, one to an antiseptic solution and two patients had ACD from both products (10). In one center in Finland, during 1985-1992, 6 patients were diagnosed with occupational allergic contact dermatitis caused by cocamide DEA. Two of them became sensitized from a barrier cream, 3 from a hand-washing liquid, and 1 had been exposed both to a hand-washing liquid and to a metalworking fluid (13). A coal miner had occupational ACD from cocamide DEA in a hydraulic oil used as a lubricant (18). A metalworker had allergic contact dermatitis from cocamide DEA in a metalworking fluid (14).

Some reports of sensitization to cocamide DEA in – amongst others - hand cleansers have been discussed in the previous section.

Cross-reactions, pseudo-cross-reactions and co-reactions

Monoethanolamine (11); diethanolamine (a contaminant in cocamide DEA [11]); lauramide DEA (16); cocamide MEA (8); cocamidopropyl betaine (8,20). *Not* to triethanolamine (11).

Presence in cosmetic products and chemical analyses

In June 2017, cocamide DEA was present in 139 of 69,510 cosmetic products of which the composition is known in EWG's Skin Deep Cosmetics Database, USA (http://www.ewg.org/skindeep/). In the USA, in April 2017, cocamide DEA was present in 950 of 56,714 cosmetic products of which the composition is known in FDA's Voluntary Cosmetic Registration Program (VCRP) (data obtained from FDA, May 2017). In the cosmetics database from one center in Leuven, Belgium, which contains ingredient information on ~1300 cosmetic products distributed in pharmacies, cocamide DEA in 2016 was found to be present in nine bath, shower or hand wash oils, in one anti-dandruff shampoo, and in one bar soap (8). In 2009, in the USA, the ingredient lists of 796 hair products from one company were screened for the presence of cocamide DEA. Cocamide DEA was present in 11% of 279 shampoos, in 2% of 231 conditioners, and in 0% of 286 styling products (29).

LITERATURE

1   Travassos AR, Claes L, Boey L, Drieghe J, Goossens A. Non-fragrance allergens in specific cosmetic products. Contact Dermatitis 2011;65:276-285
2   Wetter DA, Yiannias JA, Prakash AV, Davis MD, Farmer SA, el-Azhary RA, et al. Results of patch testing to personal care product allergens in a standard series and a supplemental cosmetic series: an analysis of 945 patients from the Mayo Clinic Contact Dermatitis Group, 2000-2007. J Am Acad Dermatol 2010;63:789-798
3   Davis MD, Scalf LA, Yiannias JA, Cheng JF, El-Azhary RA, Rohlinger AL, et al. Changing trends and allergens in the patch test standard series. Arch Dermatol 2008;144:67-72
4   Warshaw EM, Buchholz HJ, Belsito DV, Maibach HI, Fowler JF Jr, Rietschel RL, et al. Allergic patch test reactions associated with cosmetics: Retrospective analysis of cross-sectional data from the North American Contact Dermatitis Group, 2001-2004. J Am Acad Dermatol 2009;60:23-38
5   Kohl L, Blondeel A, Song M. Allergic contact dermatitis from cosmetics: retrospective analysis of 819 patch-tested patients. Dermatology 2002;204:334-337
6   Zug KA, Warshaw EM, Fowler JF Jr, Maibach HI, Belsito DL, Pratt MD, et al. Patch-test results of the North American Contact Dermatitis Group 2005-2006. Dermatitis 2009;20:149-160
7   Fransway AF, Zug KA, Belsito DV, Deleo VA, Fowler JF Jr, Maibach HI, et al. North American Contact Dermatitis Group patch test results for 2007-2008. Dermatitis 2013;24:10-21
8   Mertens S, Gilissen L, Goossens A. Allergic contact dermatitis caused by cocamide diethanolamine. Contact Dermatitis 2016;75:20-24
9   Warshaw EM, Belsito DV, DeLeo VA, Fowler JF Jr, Maibach HI, Marks JG, et al. North American Contact Dermatitis Group patch-test results, 2003-2004 study period. Dermatitis 2008;19:129-136
10   Badaoui A, Amsler E, Raison-Peyron N, Vigan M, Pecquet C, Frances C, et al. An outbreak of contact allergy to cocamide diethanolamide? Contact Dermatitis 2015;72:407-409
11   Aalto-Korte K, Pesonen M, Kuuliala O, Suuronen K. Occupational allergic contact dermatitis caused by coconut fatty acids diethanolamide. Contact Dermatitis 2014;70:169-174
12   Kanerva L, Jolanki R, Estlander T. Dentist's occupational allergic contact dermatitis caused by coconut diethanolamide, N-ethyl-4-toluene sulfonamide and 4-tolyldiethanolamine. Acta Derm Venereol 1993;73:126-129
13   Pinola A, Estlander T, Jolanki R, Tarvainen K, Kanerva L. Occupational allergic contact dermatitis due to coconut diethanolamide (cocamide DEA). Contact Dermatitis 1993;29:262-265
14   De Boer EM, van Ketel WG, Bruynzeel DP. Dermatoses in metal workers. Contact Dermatitis 1989;20:280-286
15   Dejobert Y, Delaporte E, Piette F, Thomas P. Eyelid dermatitis with positive patch test to coconut diethanolamide. Contact Dermatitis 2005;52:173
16   De Groot AC, de Wit FS, Bos JD, Weyland JW. Contact allergy to cocamide DEA and lauramide DEA in shampoos. Contact Dermatitis 1987;16:117-118
17   Nurse DS. Sensitivity to coconut diethanolamide. Contact Dermatitis 1980;6:502

18 Hindson C, Lawlor F. Coconut diethanolamide in a hydraulic mining oil. Contact Dermatitis 1983;9:168

19 Fowler JF Jr. Allergy to cocamide DEA. Am J Contact Dermat 1998;9:40-41

20 Shaughnessy CN, Malajian D, Belsito DV. Cutaneous delayed-type hypersensitivity in patients with atopic dermatitis: reactivity to surfactants. J Am Acad Dermatol 2014;70:704-708

21 Warshaw EM, Maibach HI, Taylor JS, Sasseville D, DeKoven JG, Zirwas MJ, et al. North American Contact Dermatitis Group patch test results: 2011-2012. Dermatitis 2015;26:49-59

22 Warshaw EM, Belsito DV, Taylor JS, Sasseville D, DeKoven JG, Zirwas MJ, et al. North American Contact Dermatitis Group patch test results: 2009 to 2010. Dermatitis 2013;24:50-59

23 Fowler JF Jr, Shaughnessy CN, Belsito DV, DeKoven JG, Deleo VA, Fransway AF, et al. Cutaneous delayed-type hypersensitivity to surfactants. Dermatitis 2015;26:268-270

24 Geier J, Lessmann H, Becker D, Bruze M, Frosch PJ, Fuchs T, et al. Patch testing with components of water-based metalworking fluids: results of a multicentre study with a second series. Contact Dermatitis 2006;55:322-329

25 Goossens A. Cosmetic contact allergens. Cosmetics 2016, 3, 5; doi:10.3390/cosmetics3010005

26 Wentworth AB, Yiannias JA, Keeling JH, Hall MR, Camilleri MJ, Drage LA, et al. Trends in patch-test results and allergen changes in the standard series: a Mayo Clinic 5-year retrospective review (January 1, 2006, to December 31, 2010). J Am Acad Dermatol 2014;70:269-275

27 De Groot AC, Bruynzeel DP, Bos JD, van der Meeren HL, van Joost T, Jagtman BA, Weyland JW. The allergens in cosmetics. Arch Dermatol 1988;124:1525-1529

28 De Groot AC. Adverse reactions to cosmetics. PhD Thesis, University of Groningen, The Netherlands: 1988, chapter 3.4, pp.105-113

29 Scheman A, Jacob S, Katta R, Nedorost S, Warshaw E, Zirwas M, et al. Part 2 of a 4 part series. Hair cosmetics: trends and alternatives. Data from the American Contact Alternative Group. J Clin Aesthet Dermatol 2011;4:42-46

30 Toholka R, Wang Y-S, Tate B, Tam M, Cahill J, Palmer A, Nixon R. The first Australian Baseline Series: Recommendations for patch testing in suspected contact dermatitis. Australas J Dermatol 2015;56:107-115

31 Grey KR, Hanson J, Hagen SL, Hylwa SA, Warshaw EM. Epidemiology and co-reactivity of novel surfactant allergens: a double-blind randomized controlled study. Dermatitis 2016;27:348-354

32 DeKoven JG, Warshaw EM, Belsito DV, Sasseville D, Maibach HI, Taylor JS, et al. North American Contact Dermatitis Group Patch Test Results: 2013-2014. Dermatitis 2017;28:33-46

33 Dinkloh A, Worm M, Geier J, Schnuch A, Wollenberg A. Contact sensitization in patients with suspected cosmetic intolerance: results of the IVDK 2006-2011. J Eur Acad Dermatol Venereol 2015;29:1071-1081

34 Warshaw EM, Wang MZ, Mathias CGT, Maibach HI, Belsito DV, Zug KA, et al. Occupational contact dermatitis in hairdressers/cosmetologists; retrospective analysis of North American Contact Dermatitis Group data, 1994 to 2010. Dermatitis 2012;23:258-268

35 Barbaud A, Vigan M, Delrous JL, et al. Contact allergy to antiseptics: 75 cases analyzed by the dermato-allergovigilance network (Revidal). Ann Dermatol Venereol 2005;132:962-965

36 O'Gorman SM, Torgerson RR. Contact allergy in cheilitis. Int J Dermatol 2016;55:e386-e391

37 Warshaw EM, Schram SE, Maibach HI, Belsito DV, Marks JG Jr, Fowler JF Jr, et al. Occupation-related contact dermatitis in North American health care workers referred for patch testing: cross-sectional data, 1998 to 2004. Dermatitis 2008;19:261-274

38 Kadivar S, Belsito D V. Occupational dermatitis in health care workers evaluated for suspected allergic contact dermatitis. Dermatitis 2015;26:177-183

2.118 COCAMIDOPROPYLAMINE OXIDE

IDENTIFICATION

Description/definition	: Cocamidopropylamine oxide is the tertiary amine oxide that conforms generally to the formula shown below, where RCO- represents the fatty acids from coconut oil
Chemical class(es)	: Amine oxides
Other names	: N-(3-(Dimethylamino)propyl)coco amides-N-oxide; amides, coco, N-[3-(dimethylamino)propyl], N-oxides
CAS registry number (s)	: 68155-09-9
EC number(s)	: 268-938-5; 931-324-9
CIR review(s)	: Int J Toxicol 2000;19(Suppl.2):1-5; Int J Toxicol 2008;27(Suppl.1):55-62 (access: www.cir-safety.org/ingredients)
Function(s) in cosmetics	: EU: cleansing; foam boosting; hair conditioning; hydrotrope; surfactant. USA: hair conditioning agents; surfactants – cleansing agent; surfactants – foam boosters; surfactants – hydrotropes
Patch testing	: Commercial cocamidopropylamine oxide (30% active matter) 1% water (1,2)

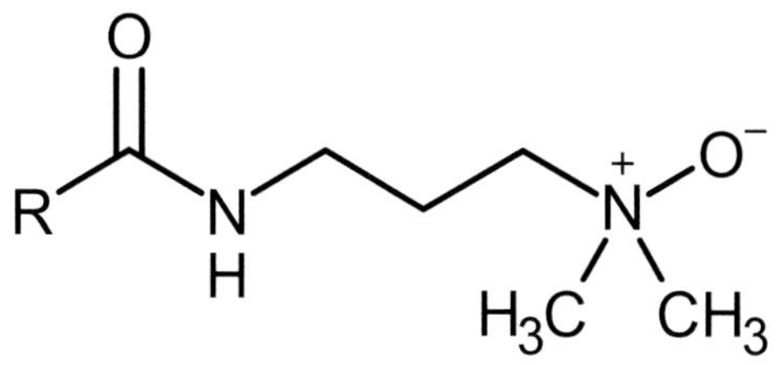

GENERAL

Cocamidopropylamine oxide (CPAO) is a tertiary amine oxide and the result of the reaction of hydrogenated coconut oil with dimethylaminopropylamine (DMAPA), and subsequently with hydrogen peroxide. It is available as a 30% aqueous solution, and is used by the cosmetics industry in a wide range of products, including skin cleansers, eye makeup removers, deodorants, and hair and nail care products, in concentrations ranging from 0.07% to 4.0% (2). This coconut oil derivative is itself considered to be a mild skin irritant and a non-sensitizer in animal models, but, owing to its impurities cocamidopropyl dimethylamine ('amidoamine') and DMAPA (levels of, respectively, ≤3000 and ≤5 ppm), it may cause skin sensitization (2).

CONTACT ALLERGY

Testing in groups of patients

In 2002, in the USA, 12 patients previously reacting to cocamidopropyl betaine (CAPB) were retested with CAPB and with a number of coconut oil derivatives including cocamidopropylamine oxide 1% water. Only 3 patients had positive reactions to CAPB on retesting, and all were doubtful. There was one positive reaction in this group to cocamidopropylamine oxide 1% water and three dubious reactions (relevance not mentioned), and one dubious reaction in a control group of 10 patients (3).

Case reports and case series

A woman had chronic hand dermatitis for 1.5 years, related to her job in a children's nursery. The patient was convinced that a specific, unscented hand cleanser that she used at the workplace, was the cause of her dermatitis. Patch tests were performed with the Belgian baseline series and a cosmetic series; the suspected liquid soap was tested semi-open, undiluted. At day 2, a doubtful reaction was seen to the semi-open test with the soap; this evolved to become an itchy, follicular eruption at D4. Also at D4, a positive reaction was scored for dimethylamino-propylamine (DMAPA), whereas the patch test for (purified) cocamidopropyl betaine remained negative. Subsequently, additional patch tests were performed with oleamidopropyl dimethylamine and cocamidopropyl dimethylamine ('amidoamine'). These showed weak positive reactions at D2, which persisted at D4.

The manufacturer of the soap provided a sample of cocamidopropylamine oxide (CPAO) as a 30% aqueous solution, which was further diluted to 1% and 0.1% water for patch testing. Only the former gave a weakly positive reaction. As some controls were positive to CPAO at day two, the patient was retested with cocamidopropyl dimethylamine, oleamidopropyl dimethylamine and CPAO 1% and 0.1%, and this now produced reactions to the first three preparations that were compatible with a contact allergic response. A repeated open application test (ROAT) with the patch test preparation of CPAO 1% water, applied twice daily in an elbow fold, was positive after 3 days, as was a provocation test with the undiluted liquid soap after one day (2).

Other information
Of 34 patients known to be allergic to dimethylaminopropylamine (DMAPA) (1% water) from the use of shampoos containing detergents with DMAPA as impurity, 12 (35%) had a positive patch test to commercial cocamidopropyl-amine oxide (30-35% active matter) 1% in water (1). The test substance contained 2.4 ppm DMAPA (1).

Cross-reactions, pseudo-cross-reactions and co-reactions
DMAPA (1,2); oleamidopropyl dimethylamine, cocamidopropyl dimethylamine (amidoamine), possibly from the presence of the impurity dimethylaminopropylamine (DMAPA) (2). Not to *purified* cocamidopropyl betaine, which contains <0.1 ppm DMAPA (2).

Presence in cosmetic products and chemical analyses
In the USA, in April 2017, cocamidopropylamine oxide was present in 64 of 56,714 cosmetic products of which the composition is known in FDA's Voluntary Cosmetic Registration Program (VCRP) (data obtained from FDA, May 2017). In March 2017, cocamidopropylamine oxide was present in 53 of 64,983 cosmetic products of which the composition is known in EWG's Skin Deep Cosmetics Database, USA (http://www.ewg.org/skindeep/).

LITERATURE
1   Angelini G, Rigano L, Foti C, Vena GA, Grandolfo M. Contact allergy to impurities in structures: amount, chemical structure, and carrier effect in reactions to 3-dimethylaminopropylamine. Contact Dermatitis 1996;34:248-252
2   Aerts O, van Dyck F, van Tichelen W, Lambert J. The many faces of coconut oil derivatives: occupational hand dermatitis caused by a liquid soap containing cocamidopropylamine oxide. Contact Dermatitis 2016;74:248-251
3   Shaffer KK, Jaimes JP, Hordinsky MK, Zielke GR, Warshaw EM. Allergenicity and cross-reactivity of coconut oil derivatives: A double-blind randomized controlled pilot study. Dermatitis 2006;17:71-76

2.119   COCAMIDOPROPYL BETAINE

IDENTIFICATION

Description/definition   : Cocamidopropyl betaine is the pseudo-amphoteric zwitterion (inner salt) that conforms generally to the formula shown below, where RCO- represents the fatty acids derived from coconut oil
Chemical class(es)   : Betaines
Chemical/IUPAC name   : 2-[Diamino(3-formamidopropyl)azaniumyl]acetate
Other names   : Cocamido betaine; coconut oil amidopropylbetaine
CAS registry number (s) : 61789-40-0; 70851-07-9; 83138-08-3
EC number(s)   : 263-058-8; 274-923-4
CIR review(s)   : J Am Coll Toxicol 1991;10:33-52; Int J Toxicol 2012;31(Suppl.1):77-111 (access: www.cir-safety.org/ingredients)
Function(s) in cosmetics : EU: antistatic; cleansing; foam boosting; hair conditioning; surfactant; viscosity controlling. USA: antistatic agents; hair conditioning agents; skin-conditioning agents – miscellaneous; surfactants – cleansing agents; surfactants – foam boosters; viscosity increasing agents – aqueous
Patch testing   : 1.0% water (Chemotechnique, SmartPracticeEurope, SmartPracticeCanada)

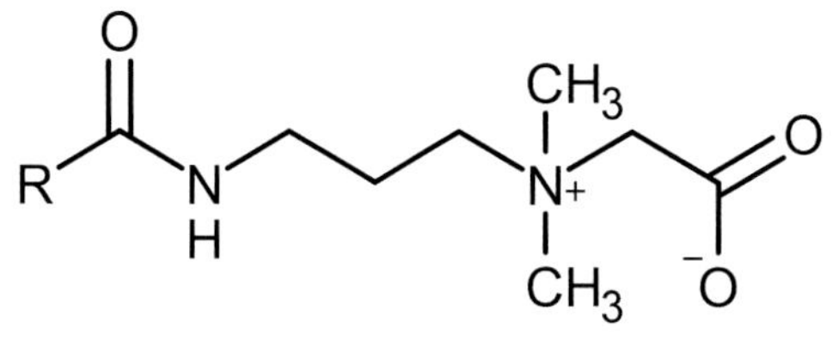

GENERAL

What is cocamidopropyl betaine?

Cocamidopropyl betaine (CAPB) is an amphoteric surfactant used in cosmetics, mainly in rinse-off products such as shampoos, but also in roll-on deodorants, toothpaste detergents, makeup removers, bath gels, skin care products, cleansers, liquid soaps, and hair spray products (15). Reported use concentrations vary from 0.2% to 25% (18). Non-cosmetic uses include contact lens solutions, antiseptics, and household cleaning products, including laundry detergents, hand dishwashing liquids, and hard surface cleaners (18).

CAPB is derived from long-chain alkylbetaines. The first step in its synthesis consists of the reaction of coconut fatty acids (with chain lengths varying between C-8 and C-18) with 3,3-dimethylaminopropylamine (DMAPA, synonym: *N,N*-dimethyl-1,3-propanediamine, CAS 109-55-7), giving cocamidopropyl dimethylamine (synonym: 'amidoamine'; this name will from here on be used for convenience). This 'amidoamine' is converted to CAPB by the reaction with sodium monochloroacetate (figure 1 [18]). Thus, CAPB is a mixture of several compounds with the same basic structure and different lipophilic ends.

Cosmetic grade CAPB is an aqueous solution, which normally contains about 30-35% solids (18). Depending on the quality of the commercial material, varying amounts of the reactants and intermediates involved in its synthesis can remain in CAPB as impurities. In the 1990s and the beginning of the 21st century, impurities in commercial CAPB were monochloroacetic acid (0.1%-0.2%), glycolic acids, coconut fatty acids (traces), unreacted DMAPA (0.1%-0.5% [3,42]; 0.0003%-0.03% [6,59]) and amidoamine (0.3%-3%) (3,6,35,42). Current cosmetic grade CAPC contains 4-6% sodium chloride and may contain a maximum of 3% glycerin (18).

Contact allergy

In predictive animal testing, some studies indicated commercial cocamidopropyl betaine to be a sensitizer (45,62), but in human studies (HRIPT, Human Repeat Insult Patch tests, summarized in ref. 18), no sensitization to CAPB was observed. Since its first clinical description as a contact allergen in 1983 (21), there have been many case reports of allergic contact dermatitis to CAPB in cosmetic products such as shampoo, shower gel, (liquid) soap, cleansing products (eye, face), skin care products, anal hygiene products, toothpaste, make-up removers and deodorant. Non-cosmetic sources of contact dermatitis to CAPB have included antiseptics and contact lens fluids (see the sections 'Case reports' and 'Contact allergy to cocamidopropyl betaine in non-cosmetic products' below).

Patients with contact dermatitis from CAPB often have dermatitis in the head and neck region (mostly facial or scalp dermatitis) (4,19,29,41) or sometimes scattered, extensive or generalized dermatitis (4,19); hand dermatitis is seen in occupational contact allergy to CAPB, especially in hairdressers (24,56,61,62)l it has also been observed in a nurse (29). In patients routinely tested with CAPB 1% in water, up to 4.5% have had positive patch tests. A summary of patch test studies in unselected and selected patients is shown below in the section 'Patch testing in groups of patients'.

Figure 1 Synthesis of cocamidopropyl betaine (adapted from ref. 18)

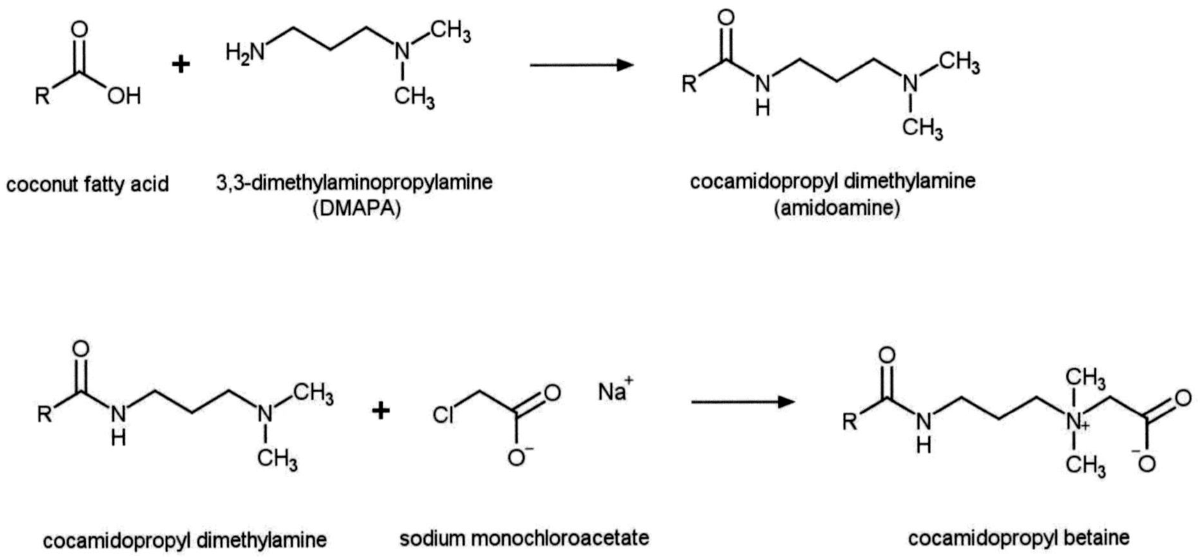

R represents the coconut fatty acid chain that varies between C-8 and C-18 (18)

The allergenic ingredients in cocamidopropyl betaine

It has repeatedly been shown that patients reacting to commercial grade CAPB do not (or infrequently) react to highly purified CAPB (3,5,17,26,34). In patch test studies using contaminated CAPB, sensitization rates are much higher (19,20,42), which suggests that contact allergy is not caused by CAPB itself, but by impurities. Indeed, several studies have pointed to DMAPA, amidoamine or both as the sensitizers. The issue of which one (or both) is the real sensitizer has been a matter of controversy for many years, with amidoamine 'favorite' in the USA and DMAPA in Europe (6,41). Some studies have demonstrated that DMAPA (which has strong allergenic properties, 44,45) was the sensitizer (3,26,34,42). In one Italian study, for example, all 15 patients reacting to CAPB 1% water (containing 200 ppm DMAPA) also reacted to DMAPA and this chemical was identified in causative products at levels varying from 50 to 150 ppm (26). DMAPA being the sensitizer was, however, not confirmed by others (5,17,22,55), although sometimes a too low concentration may have been used for patch testing (17,43).

Other investigators have suggested that amidoamine is the allergenic impurity in CAPB (4,5,17,35). One group found that all patients allergic to commercial CAPB (negative to a more purified commercial test substance) also reacted to DMAPA *and* to amidoamine. The simultaneous allergic reaction to DMAPA and amidoamine was considered to represent cross-reactivity and it was hypothesized that DMAPA is in fact the true sensitizing substance, while amidoamine, which may release DMAPA *in vivo* as a result of enzymatic hydrolysis, may favor the transepi-dermal penetration of the sensitizing agent DMAPA (3). Thus, reactions to CAPB in the past may have been caused by both DMAPA and amidoamine, depending on the source of the commercial CAPB products and the nature and amount of impurities they contained.

Currently, according to the main manufacturers, commercial CAPB raw material typically contains 5-20 ppm DMAPA and up to 0.3% cocamidopropyl dimethylamine (amidoamine) (1,2,7). The maximum recommended dose of CAPB in rinse-off and leave-on products is 3.0% (2). Thus, the concentrations of DMAPA to be expected would be <0.6 ppm; these concentrations are most likely below any induction or elicitation threshold (2,46,55,59). However, the concentrations of amidoamine to be expected would be 90 ppm in products, at which concentration induction and elicitation in highly susceptible individuals cannot be excluded (2). It should also be realized that a 2007 Personal Care Products Council survey with suppliers has indicated (far) higher levels of amidoamine, ranging from 0.5% to 5%, with 0.5% as the typical value and 1.5% as the suggested maximum level (58).

Interpretation of patch test results

The current patch test materials contain very small amounts of the impurities (0.1 ppm of DMAPA and 30 ppm of cocamidopropyl dimethylamine (amidoamine) in the Chemotechnique test substance) (1). CAPB is a known irritant (summary of studies: ref. 18) and irritant patch test reactions to CAPB 1% in water occur frequently (1,2,6,12,50,98).

Reproducibility on synchronous patch testing is poor and the reactions upon retesting are very often non-reproducible (2,20). Thus, it has been postulated that the majority of positive patch test reactions to CAPB are false-positive and that true allergic reactions are, in fact, quite infrequent, in the order of 0.2-0.3% of patients routinely tested (2). It is assumed that the 30 ppm of amidoamine present in the Chemotechnique CAPB patch test material may be capable of inducing a positive patch test reaction in highly sensitized individuals (2). In the light of the irritant potential of CAPB 1% in water, positive patch test reactions must always be very carefully interpreted and be followed by a meticulous relevancy assessment.

Review articles on CABP are provided in refs. 2,15 and 52. The format of this chapter is slightly different from (most of) the other chapters.

CONTACT ALLERGY

Patch testing in groups of patients
Results of studies testing cocamidopropyl betaine in consecutive patients suspected of contact dermatitis (routine testing) back to 1998 are shown in table 2.119.1. Results of testing in groups of *selected* patients (e.g., female hairdressers with occupational contact dermatitis, children with dermatitis, patients with stasis dermatitis / leg ulcers, individuals suspected of cosmetic intolerance, patients with scalp or pure eyelid dermatitis) back to 1993 are shown in table 2.119.2.

Patch testing in consecutive patients suspected of contact dermatitis: routine testing
Virtually all studies in which routine testing with CAPB has been performed come from the USA + Canada, where cocamidopropyl betaine has been part of the North American Contact Dermatitis Group (NACDG) screening series since 2001. The NACDG publishes their results biannually. There are also large studies from the IVDK (IVDK: Information Network of Dermatological Departments, Germany, Austria, Switzerland) (2), Italy (3) and from the UK (19). In 16 investigations, frequencies of sensitization have ranged from 0.3% to 4.5%. In the NACDG studies, since 2003, rates have been fairly constant in the 1.1%-1.8% range, after a higher percentage of 2.8 in 2001-2002 (71). In other US centers, higher frequencies of sensitization (4% and 4.5%) were found (10,75). In other countries, rates were high in Italy (3.4% [3]), low in the UK (0.3% [19]) and intermediate in the IVDK countries (2.2% [2]). In the IVDK study, 17 patients with a weak positive (+) reactions were retested with CAPB 1% water and only 2 had again a positive result. It was concluded that many of these weak positive reactions are in fact false-positive irritant responses (2).

In the USA, relevance rates (in the NACDG studies 'definite' and 'probable' relevance combined) were mostly between 35% and 60%. In the Italian study (3), 70% of the positive patch tests were considered to be relevant. Most relevant reactions concerned patients with dermatitis of the face, axillae and/or genitals from CAPB in detergents (soap, shampoo, shower gel *et cetera*). This was the only study in which culprit products were mentioned (3).

Table 2.119.1 Patch testing in groups of patients: Routine testing

Years and Country	Test conc. & vehicle	Number of patients tested | positive (%)		Selection of patients (S); Relevance (R); Comments (C)	Ref.
2013-14 USA, Canada	1% water	4859	77 (1.6%)	R: definite + probable relevance: 44%	84
2009-14 USA, Canada	1% water	10877	152 (1.4%)	R: not stated	70
2001-2013 USA	1% water	1674	39 (2.3%)	R: not stated; C: the contact allergy rate in atopics (3.97%) was significantly higher than in non-atopics (2.04%)	97
2011-12 USA, Canada	1% water	4232	61 (1.5%)	R: definite + probable relevance: 69%	67
2009-10 USA, Canada	1% water	4304	60 (1.4%)	R: definite + probable relevance: 48%	68
2006-2010 USA	1% water	3003	(4.0%)	R: 40%	75
1996-2009 IVDK	1% water	83,864	1812 (2.2%)	R: not stated. C: only 2 of 17 patients with a + reaction had again a + reaction upon retesting; in patients with duplicate testing, of 227 with a positive reaction to one of the patch tests, only 42 had a + reaction to both patch tests	2
2007-8 USA, Canada	1% water	5081	(1.1%)	R: definite + probable relevance: 51%	57
2005-6 USA, Canada	1% water	4436	(1.8%)	R: definite + probable relevance: 32%	14
2000-2005 USA	1% water	1093	(4.5%)	R: 59%	10
2003-4 USA, Canada	1% water	5137	94 (1.8%)	R: not stated	64
2001-2 USA, Canada	1% water	4887	(2.8%)	R: definite + probable relevance: 34%	71
	0.5% pet.	4888	(1.3%)	R: definite + probable relevance: 22%	
1996-2002 Italy	1% water	13,642	(3.4%)	R: 70%; C: patients with dermatitis of the face, axillae and genitals, reactions mostly from detergents	3
2001 USA, Canada	1% water	975	33 (3.4%)	R: 48% definite + probable relevance; 18 of these patients	4

Table 2.119.1 Patch testing in groups of patients: Routine testing (*continued*)

Years and Country	Test conc. & vehicle	Number of patients tested | positive (%)		Selection of patients (S); Relevance (R); Comments (C)	Ref.
2001 USA	1% water	957	32 (3.3%)	also reacted to amidoamine 0.1% water R: definite 56%, probable 26%; C: 11 of these patients also reacted to amidoamine	35
1991-1998 UK	1% water	10,798	29 (0.3%)	R: current or past relevance: 79%; the prevalence dropped from 0.40% to 0.11% when purer grade CAPB was used for patch testing	19

IVDK: Information Network of Dermatological Departments, Germany, Austria, Switzerland

Patch testing in groups of selected patients

Results of testing CAPB in groups of selected patients (e.g., female hairdressers with occupational contact dermatitis, children with dermatitis, patients with stasis dermatitis / leg ulcers, individuals suspected of cosmetic intolerance, patients with scalp or pure eyelid dermatitis) back to 1993 are shown in table 2.119.2. In 25 investigations, frequencies of sensitization have ranged from 0.2% to 15.9%. The latter rate was found in a Dutch study in which a group of 339 children of 0-17 years with dermatitis were tested with CAPB 1% water between 1996 and 2013 (90). This is unrealistically high and may be explained by many false-positive reactions to CAPB in these children, many of who must have had atopic dermatitis, a disorder in which the skin is very sensitive to irritation. In two other series of children also, high percentages of 6.5 (96) and 7.2 (32) were observed. Other patient groups in which rates of >5% positives were found include patients previously reacting to one or more surfactants present in the NACDG screening series (83, easy to explain), patients suspected of cosmetic dermatitis (5.7% [29]), hairdressers (5.5% [87]), and a group with unknown selection criteria from Australia (6.8% [81]). Patients with scalp dermatitis were found to have a 2.4 odds ratio for patch test positivity versus patients with non-scalp dermatitis, which can easily be explained by the presence of CAPB in shampoos (53).

In 16 of the 25 studies, no relevance data were provided. In investigations that did address the issue, the relevance rate was mostly between 60% and 100%. In 2 Australian studies, however, relevance was found for 12% resp. 11% of the positive reactions only (81,87). Culprit products were never mentioned.

Table 2.119.2 Patch testing in groups of patients: Selected patient groups

Years and Country	Test conc. & vehicle	Number of patients tested | positive (%)		Selection of patients (S); Relevance (R); Comments (C)	Ref.
2015-2016 USA	1% water	47	5 (11%)	S: patients previously reacting to one or more surfactants present in the NACDG screening series; R: not stated; C: there were also 10 doubtful reactions	83
2013-2015 USA		818	53 (6.5%)	S: children 0-18 years suspected of contact dermatitis; R: 72%	96
2003-2014 IVDK	1% water	4756	(2.6%)	S: patients with stasis dermatitis / chronic leg ulcers; R: not stated	91
2002-2013 Italy	1% water	2614	89 (3.4%)	S: children younger than 11 suspected of contact dermatitis; R: n=61 (69%)	95
1996-2013 Nether- lands	1% water	339	54 (15.9%)	S: children aged 0-17 years; R: not stated; C: unrealistically high prevalence, must include many irritant reactions	90
2007-2012 IVDK	1% water	744	22 (3.4%)	S: female hairdressers with current or previous occupational contact dermatitis; R: not stated	88
		1903	37 (1.9%)	S: female patients, clients of hairdressers, in who hair cosmetics were regarded as a cause of dermatitis, and who had never worked as hairdressers; R: not stated	
2003-2012 IVDK		1723	41 (2.4%)	S: nurses with occupational contact dermatitis; R: not stated	66
2011 China	1% water	201	4 (2.0%)	S: healthy student volunteers 19-30 years; R: not stated	82
2006-2011 IVDK	1% water	7721	(2.6%)	S: patients suspected of cosmetic intolerance and tested with an ointment base series; R: not stated	86
2001-2010 Australia	1% water	4297	292 (6.8%)	S: not stated; R: 12%	81
2000-2010 IVDK		3576	55 (1.5%)	S: patients with periorbital dermatitis; R: not stated	69
1994-2010 USA, Canada	1% water	?	? (?)	S: hairdressers / cosmetologists; R: in the group of 131 patients who had at least one relevant occupationally rela- ted reaction, 5 (3.8%) reacted to cocamidopropyl betaine	89
1993-2010 Australia		164	9 (5.5%)	S: hairdressers and apprentice hairdressers presenting at an occupational dermatology clinic; R: 11%	87
2002-2009 Finland	1% water	1092	2 (0.2%)	S: patients suspected of occupational contact dermatitis and tested with a 'coconut series'; R: both reactions were relevant and caused by liquid soap and shower gel; C: there	1

Table 2.119.2 Patch testing in groups of patients: Selected patient groups (*continued*)

Years and Country	Test conc. & vehicle	Number of patients tested	positive (%)	Selection of patients (S); Relevance (R); Comments (C)	Ref.
				were 166 (15%) *irritant* patch test reactions	
2002-2008 Italy	1% water	321	23 (7.2%)	S: children with dermatitis <3 years; R: present + past relevance in 18 (78%)	32
2000-2007 USA	1% water	935	32 (3.4%)	S: patients tested with a supplemental cosmetic screening series; R: 100%; C: weak study: a. high rate of macular erythema and weak reactions; b. relevance figures included 'questionable' and 'past' relevance	9
2003-2006 IVDK	1% water	432	(3.4%)	S: (former) female hairdressers with (former) occupational dermatitis; biannual prevalence 2.2%-4.1%; R: not stated	61
	1% water	614	(2.9%)	S: female clients of hairdressers with dermatitis where hair cosmetics were considered a potential cause; biannual prevalence 2.7%-3.1%; R: not stated	
2003-2004 USA	1% water	268	5 (1.9%)	S: patients with pure eyelid dermatitis; R: this was the number of relevant reactions	76
1999-2003 IVDK	1% water	1021	48 (4.7%)	S: patients with scalp dermatitis; R: not stated; C: odds ratio 2.37 versus patients with non-scalp dermatitis	53
2001-2002 Sweden	1% water	1075	(2.8%)	S: patients referred for routine testing willing to participate in a study on cosmetic use and adverse reactions; R: not stated	12
1995-2002 IVDK	1% water	884	(3.1%)	S: (former) female hairdressers with (former) occupational contact dermatitis; annual prevalences 1.9%-4.4%; decreasing trend; R: not stated	60
	1% water	1217	(2.0%)	S: 1217 female clients of hairdressers with contact dermatitis considered to have been caused by hairdressing cosmetics and hair care products; R: nor stated	
2000-2002 Finland		1672	(1.5%)	S: patients tested with a hairdressing series; R: not stated	72
1995-1999 IVDK	1% water	716	(2.8%)	S: patients with allergic periorbital contact dermatitis; R: not stated	77
1995-1996 Finland		364	(1.4%)	S: patients tested with a hairdressing series; R: not stated	72
1992-1993 USA	1% water	210	12 (5.7%)	S: patients suspected of cosmetic dermatitis and patients with head and neck dermatitis; 58% definitely relevant	29

IVDK: Information Network of Dermatological Departments, Germany, Austria, Switzerland

Case reports and case series

Case series

Cocamidopropyl betaine was stated to be the (or an) allergen in 4 patients in a group of 603 individuals suffering from cosmetic dermatitis, seen in the period 2010-2015 in Leuven, Belgium (74). In the period 1996-2013, in a tertiary referral center in Valencia, Spain, 5419 patients were patch tested. Of these, 628 individuals had allergic contact dermatitis to cosmetics. Cocamidopropyl betaine was the responsible allergen in 15 cases (85, overlap with ref. 80). Cocamidopropyl betaine was responsible for 15 out of 959 cases of non-fragrance cosmetic allergy where the causal allergen was identified, Belgium, 2000-2010 (8). In the period 2000-2007, 202 patients with allergic contact dermatitis caused by cosmetics were seen in Valencia, Spain. In this group, 7 individuals reacted to cocamidopropyl betaine from its presence in shampoo (n=4) and in gel/soap (n=3) (80, overlap with ref. 85).

In a group of 2193 patients (1582 women, 611 men) with (presumed) cosmetic allergy, 147 reactions (7%) were caused by cocamidopropyl betaine in a study of the NACDG, 2001-2004, cocamidopropyl betaine ranking 7th in the list of most frequent allergens (11). In a group of 46 patients with allergic contact dermatitis of the eyelids seen in Kansas City, USA, between 1994 and 2004, one case (2.2%) was caused by contact allergy to CAPB; the source of sensitization was not mentioned (73). Ten patients had positive patch test reactions to CAPB, of which six were relevant (no further details known [65]).

Case reports

Reports on contact allergic reactions to cocamidopropyl betaine from its presence in cosmetic products are summarized in table 2.119.3.

Table 2.119.3 Case reports of contact allergy to cocamidopropyl betaine in cosmetic products

Product	Number of patients (reference)
Anal hygiene products	2 (26)
Cleansing products (eyes)	1 (39); 4 (48)
Cleansing products (face)	? (38); 1 (63); 2 (37)
Deodorant	? (38)
Liquid soap	1 (5); 1 (40); 1 (48); 6 (26)
Make-up remover	4 (5)
Shampoo	? (38); ? (42); 1 (23); 1 (24); 1 (25); 1 (33); 1 (41); 2 (36); 2 (37); 3 (26); 4 (13); 6 (29)
Shampoo and / or shower gel	20 (24)
Shower gel / bath foam /soap	? (42); 2 (24); 2 (26); 2 (29)
Skin care products	1 (24); 3 (47)
Toothpaste	1 (28); 1 (54)

? number of allergic patients unknown

DMAPA and/or amidoamine *may* have caused chronic eyelid dermatitis in a woman using a baby shampoo to scrub her eyelids daily. The shampoo contained CAPB. The patch tests to DMAPA and amidoamine were positive, but there was no reaction to CAPB (100).

Contact allergy to cocamidopropyl betaine in non-cosmetic products
Non-cosmetic products that have caused dermatitis from contact allergy to CAPB present in them include antiseptics (26,51,92), contact lens fluid (27,30), anal detergent (apparently different from soap [26]), and possibly shoe refresher spray (93)

Cross-reactions, pseudo-cross-reactions and co-reactions
Amidoamine (3,4,5,17,35,83); cocamide DEA (35,70); cocamide MEA (38); coco-betaine (21); disodium lauroampho-diacetate (83); DMAPA (3,26,34,42); isostearamidopropyl morpholine lactate (83); oleamidopropyl dimethylamine (1,6,49,70,83); sodium lauroyl sarcosinate (83); stearamidopropyl dimethylamine (70); TEA-PEG-3 cocamide sulfate (20).

Presence in cosmetic products and chemical analyses
In August 2017, cocamidopropyl betaine was present in 2517 of 70,534 cosmetic products of which the composition is known in EWG's Skin Deep Cosmetics Database, USA (http://www.ewg.org/skindeep/). In the USA, in April 2017, cocamidopropyl betaine was present in 5155 of 56,714 cosmetic products of which the composition is known in FDA's Voluntary Cosmetic Registration Program (VCRP) (data obtained from FDA, May 2017). In the USA, in 2015-2016, 63 diaper wipes and 41 topical diaper preparations from a large retailer were screened for the presence of potential sensitizers. Cocamidopropyl betaine was found in 2/63 (3%) disposable diaper wipes and in none of 41 topical diaper preparations (94). In 2009, in the USA, the ingredient lists of 796 hair products from one company were screened for the presence of cocamidopropyl betaine. CAPB was present in 63% of 279 shampoos, in 35% of 231 conditioners, and in 5% of 286 styling products (78).

In 2009, in the USA, the ingredient lists of 730 lip cosmetics and dental care products from one company were screened for the presence of cocamidopropyl betaine. CAPB was present only in 14% of 153 toothpastes (79). A 2007 analysis of data provided by a US pharmacy company revealed that 95 of 179 shampoos (53%) contained CAPB (16). In October 2005, 1242 of 22,016 products (5.6%) cosmetics were listed as containing CAPB according to the Food and Drug Administration Data Voluntary Cosmetic Registration Program in the USA (15).

Other side effects
There is an unexplained high frequency of positive patch tests to cocamidopropyl betaine (27%) in patients reacting to ascaridole, an allergen in Melaleuca alternifolia (tea tree) oil (31).

OTHER INFORMATION
In this chapter, 'Amidoamine' is the term coined by the NACDG for cocamidopropyl dimethylamine, an intermediate in the synthesis of cocamidopropyl betaine. The test substance 'amidoamine' provided by Chemotechnique is currently and has always been cocamidopropyl dimethylamine. Another provider, Allergeaze/SmartPracticeCanada, also sells 'amidoamine' for patch testing, but this is *stearamido*propyl dimethylamine (stearic acid instead of coconut fatty acids). Up to 2008, the NACDG purchased 'amidoamine' from Chemotechnique, and from 2009 on from Allergeaze/SmartPracticeCanada. This means that, in the publications of the NACDG, up to 2008, 'amidoamine' was

cocamidopropyl dimethylamine and from 2009 on, stearamidopropyl dimethylamine. This may easily lead to confusion and possibly to mistakes (84,99). The term amidoamine was also somewhat unfortunately chosen as it refers to a class of chemicals rather to a specific compound.

LITERATURE

1   Suuronen K, Pesonen M, Aalto-Korte K. Occupational contact allergy to cocamidopropyl betaine. Contact Dermatitis 2012;66:286-292

2   Schnuch A, Lessmann H, Geier J, Uter W. Is cocamidopropyl betaine a contact allergen? Analysis of network data and short review of the literature. Contact Dermatitis 2011;64:203-211

3   Foti C, Bonamonte D, Mascolo G, Corcelli A, Lobasso S, Rigano L, et al. The role of 3-dimethylaminopropylamine and amidoamine in contact allergy to cocamidopropyl betaine. Contact Dermatitis 2003;48:194-198

4   Fowler JF Jr, Zug KM, Taylor JS, Storrs FJ, Sherertz EA, Sasseville DA, et al. Allergy to cocamidopropyl betaine and amidoamine in North America. Dermatitis 2004;15:5-6

5   McFadden JP, Ross JS, White IR, Basketter DA. Clinical allergy to cocamidopropyl betaine: reactivity to cocamidopropylamine and lack of reactivity to 3-dimethylaminopropylamine. Contact Dermatitis 2001;45:72-74

6   Moreau L, Sasseville D. Allergic contact dermatitis from cocamidopropyl betaine, cocamidoamine, 3-(dimethylamino)propylamine, and oleamidopropyl dimethylamine: co-reactions or cross-reactions? Dermatitis 2004;15:146-149

7   Grüning B, Käseborn D, Leidreiter HI. Cocamidopropyl betaine; methods for producing CAPB and new analytical methods for determining purity and side product composition. Cosmet Toiletries 1997;112: 67-76

8   Travassos AR, Claes L, Boey L, Drieghe J, Goossens A. Non-fragrance allergens in specific cosmetic products. Contact Dermatitis 2011;65:276-285

9   Wetter DA, Yiannias JA, Prakash AV, Davis MD, Farmer SA, el-Azhary RA, et al. Results of patch testing to personal care product allergens in a standard series and a supplemental cosmetic series: an analysis of 945 patients from the Mayo Clinic Contact Dermatitis Group, 2000-2007. J Am Acad Dermatol 2010;63:789-798

10 Davis MD, Scalf LA, Yiannias JA, Cheng JF, El-Azhary RA, Rohlinger AL, et al. Changing trends and allergens in the patch test standard series. Arch Dermatol 2008;144:67-72

11 Warshaw EM, Buchholz HJ, Belsito DV et al. Allergic patch test reactions associated with cosmetics: Retrospective analysis of cross-sectional data from the North American Contact Dermatitis Group, 2001-2004. J Am Acad Dermatol 2009;60:23-38

12 Lindberg M, Tammela M, Bostrom A, Fischer T, Inerot A, Sundberg K, et al. Are adverse skin reactions to cosmetics underestimated in the clinical assessment of contact dermatitis? A prospective study among 1075 patients attending Swedish patch test clinics. Acta Derm Venereol 2004;84:291-295

13 Korting WC, Parsch EM, Enders F, Przybilla B. Allergic contact dermatitis to cocamidopropyl betaine in shampoo. J Am Acad Dermatol 1992;27:1013-1015

14 Zug KA, Warshaw EM, Fowler JF Jr, Maibach HI, Belsito DL, Pratt MD, et al. Patch-test results of the North American Contact Dermatitis Group 2005-2006. Dermatitis 2009;20:149-160

15 Jacob SE, Amini S. Cocamidopropyl betaine. Dermatitis 2008;19:157-160

16 Zirwas M, Moennich J. Shampoos. Dermatitis 2009;20:106-110

17 Fowler JF, Fowler LM, Hunter JE. Allergy to cocamidopropyl betaine may be due to amidoamine: a patch test and product use test study. Contact Dermatitis 1997;37:276-281

18 Burnett CL, Bergfeld WF, Belsito DV, Hill RA, Klaassen CD, Liebler D, et al. Final report of the Cosmetic Ingredient Review Expert Panel on the safety assessment of cocamidopropyl betaine (CAPB). Int J Toxicol 2012;31(suppl. 1):77S-111S

19 Armstrong DKB, Smith HR, Ross JS, White IR. Sensitization to cocamidopropyl betaine: an 8-year review. Contact Dermatitis 1999;40:335-336

20 Shaffer KK, Jaimes JP, Hordinsky MK, Zielke GR, Warshaw EM. Allergenicity and cross-reactivity of coconut oil derivatives: a double-blind randomized controlled pilot study. Dermatitis 2006;17:71-76

21 Van Haute N, Dooms-Goossens A. Shampoo dermatitis due to cocobetaine and sodium lauryl ether sulphate. Contact Dermatitis 1983;9:169

22 Uter W. Lack of patch test reactivity to 3-dimethylaminopropylamine in German hairdressers. Contact Dermatitis 1999;41:231

23 Mowad CM. Cocamidopropyl betaine allergy. Am J Contact Dermatitis 2001;12:223-224

24 De Groot AC, van der Walle HB, Weyland JW. Contact allergy to cocamidopropyl betaine. Contact Dermatitis 1995;33:419-422

25 Taniguchi S, Katoh J, Hisa T, Tabata M, Hamada T. Shampoo dermatitis due to cocamidopropyl betaine. Contact Dermatitis 1992;26:139

26 Pigatto PD, Bigardi AS, Cusano F. Contact dermatitis to cocamidopropyl-betaine is caused by residual amines: relevance, clinical characteristics and review of the literature. Am J Contact Dermatitis 1995;6:13-16

27   Sertoli A, Lombardi P, Palleschi GM, Gola M, Giorgini S. Tegobetaine in contact lens solutions. Contact Dermatitis 1987;16:111-112

28   Herlofson BB, Barkvoll P. The effect of two toothpaste detergents on the frequency of recurrent aphthous ulcers. Acta Odontol Scand 1996;54:150-153

29   Fowler JF. Cocamidopropyl betaine: the significance of positive patch test results in twelve patients. Cutis 1993;52:281-284

30   Cameli N, Tosti G, Venturo N, Tosti A. Eyelid dermatitis due to cocamidopropyl betaine in a hard contact lens solution. Contact Dermatitis 1991;25:261-262

31   Bakker C, Blömeke B, Coenraads PJ, Schuttelaar M-L. Ascaridole, a sensitizing component of tea tree oil, patch tested at 1% and 5% in two series of patients. Contact Dermatitis 2012;65:240-241

32   Fortina AB, Romano I, Peserico A, Eichenfeld LE. Contact sensitization in very young children. J Am Acad Dermatol 2011;65:772-779

33   Brand R, Delaney TA. Allergic contact dermatitis to cocamidopropylbetaine in hair shampoo. Australas J Dermatol 1998;39:121-122

34   Angelini G, Rigano L, Foti C, Rossi P, Vena GA. Pure cocamidopropylbetaine is not the allergen in patients with positive reactions to commercial cocamidopropylbetaine. Contact Dermatitis 1996;35:252-253

35   Brey NL, Fowler JF. Relevance of positive patch-test reactions to cocamidopropyl betaine and amidoamine. Dermatitis 2004;15:7-9

36   Andersen KE, Roed-Petersen J, Kamp P. Contact allergy related to TEA-PEG-3 cocamide sulfate and cocamidopropyl betaine in a shampoo. Contact Dermatitis 1984;11:192-193

37   Vilaplana J, Grimalt F, Romaguera C. Contact dermatitis from cocamidopropyl betaine. Contact Dermatitis 1990;23:274

38   Peter C, Hoting E. Contact allergy to cocamidopropyl betaine (CAPB). Contact Dermatitis 1992;26:282-283

39   Ross JS, White IR. Eyelid dermatitis due to cocamidopropyl betaine in an eye make-up remover. Contact Dermatitis 1991;25:64

40   Yepes-Nuñez JJ, Rendón G, Nuñez-Rinta R. Allergic contact dermatitis to cocamidopropyl betaine in Colombia. Allergol Immunopathol (Madrid) 2012;40:126-128

41   Fowler JF. Contact allergen of the year. Cocamidopropyl betaine. Dermatitis 2004;15:3-4

42   Angelini G, Foti C, Rigano L, Vena GA. 3-Dimethylaminopropylamine: a key substance in contact allergy to cocamidopropylbetaine? Contact Dermatitis 1995;32:96-99

43   Angelini G, Rigano L. The allergen cocamidopropyl betaine. Contact Dermatitis 1998;39:210-211

44   Guinea pig maximization test of *N,N*-dimethyl-1,3-propanediamine. Air Products and Chem, data on file (data cited in ref. 3)

45   Basketter DA, Lea LJ, Cooper K, Stocks J, Dickens A, Pate I, et al. Threshold for classification as a skin sensitizer in the local lymph node assay: a statistical evaluation. Food Chem Toxicol 1999; 37:1167-1174

46   Angelini G, Rigano L, Foti C, Grandolfo M, Grüning B. Carrier and inhibitory effects of surfactants on allergic contact reaction to 3-dimethylaminopropylamine. Contact Dermatitis 1998;39:152-153

47   De Groot AC, Bruynzeel DP, Bos JD, van der Meeren HL, van Joost T, Jagtman BA, Weyland JW. The allergens in cosmetics. Arch Dermatol 1988;124:1525-1529

48   Ross JS, White IR. Contact sensitivity to cocamidopropyl betaine and amido amine in patients reacting to the commercially available surfactant TegoBetaine L7. Proceedings of the 1st Congress of the European Society of Contact Dermatitis, Brussels, 1992:70 (abstract)

49   Foti C, Rigano L, Vena GA, Grandolfo M, Liguori G, Angelini G. Contact allergy to oleamidopropyl dimethylamine and related substances. Contact Dermatitis 1995;33:132-133

50   Warshaw EM, Nelsen DD, Sasseville D, Belsito DV, Maibach HI, Zug KA, et al. Positivity ratio and reaction index: patch-test quality-control metrics applied to the North American contact dermatitis group database. Dermatitis 2010;21:91-97

51   Calow T, Oberle K, Bruckner-Tuderman L, Jakob T, Schumann H. Contact dermatitis due to use of Octenisept in wound care. J Dtsch Dermatol Ges 2009;7:759-765

52   De Groot AC. Cocamidopropyl betaine: a "new" important cosmetic allergen. Derm Beruf Umwelt 1997;45:60-63

53   Hillen U, Grabbe S, Uter W. Patch test results in patients with scalp dermatitis: analysis of data of the Information Network of Departments of Dermatology. Contact Dermatitis 2007;56:87-93

54   Agar N, Freeman S. Cheilitis caused by contact allergy to cocamidopropyl betaine in '2-in-1 toothpaste and mouthwash'. Australas J Dermatol 2005;46:15-17

55   Fartasch M, Diepgen TL, Kuhn M, Basketter DA. Provocative use tests in CAPB-allergic subjects with CAPB-containing product. Contact Dermatitis 1999;41:30-34

56   Van der Walle HB, Brunsveld VM. Dermatitis in hairdressers. (I). The experience of the past 4 years. Contact Dermatitis 1994;30:217-221

57 Fransway AF, Zug KA, Belsito DV, Deleo VA, Fowler JF Jr, Maibach HI, et al. North American Contact Dermatitis Group patch test results for 2007-2008. Dermatitis 2013;24:10-21

58 Cosmetic, Toiletry and Fragrance Association. Levels of DMAPA and amidoamine in Cocamidopropyl Betaine. (CTFA, Unpublished data, 2007:2)

59 Angelini G, Rigano L, Foti C, Vena GA, Grandolfo M, et al. Contact allergy to impurities in structures: amount, chemical structure, and carrier effect in reactions to 3-dimethylaminopropylamine. Contact Dermatitis 1996;34:248-252

60 Uter W, Lessmann H, Geier J, Schnuch A. Contact allergy to ingredients of hair cosmetics in female hairdressers and clients – an 8-year analysis of IVDK data. Contact Dermatitis 2003;49:236-240

61 Uter W, Lessmann H, Geier J, Schnuch A. Contact allergy to hairdressing allergens in female hairdressers and clients – current data from the IVDK, 2003-2006. J Dtsch Dermatol Ges 2007;5:993-1001

62 Rantuccio F, Coviello C, Sinisi D, Scardigno A, Conte A. Experimental sensitization of guinea pigs by drugs. Comparison of the maximization test with the wholly intradermal test. Contact Dermatitis 1983;9:479-483

63 Solomon I, Lutuc R, Haiducu L. Facial contact dermatitis with mixed mechanism caused by cosmetic products. Contact Dermatitis 2016;75(Suppl.1):83-84

64 Warshaw EM, Belsito DV, DeLeo VA, Fowler JF Jr, Maibach HI, Marks JG, et al. North American Contact Dermatitis Group patch-test results, 2003-2004 study period. Dermatitis 2008;19:129-136

65 Dailey A. Cocamidopropyl betaine allergy. Presented at the American Contact Dermatitis Society, Texas, December 1991.

66 Molin S, Bauer A, Schnuch A, Geier J. Occupational contact allergy in nurses: results from the Information Network of Departments of Dermatology 2003–2012. Contact Dermatitis 2015;72:164-171

67 Warshaw EM, Maibach HI, Taylor JS, Sasseville D, DeKoven JG, Zirwas MJ, et al. North American Contact Dermatitis Group patch test results: 2011-2012. Dermatitis 2015;26:49-59

68 Warshaw EM, Belsito DV, Taylor JS, Sasseville D, DeKoven JG, Zirwas MJ, et al. North American Contact Dermatitis Group patch test results: 2009 to 2010. Dermatitis 2013;24:50-59

69 Landeck L, John SM, Geier J. Periorbital dermatitis in 4779 patients – patch test results during a 10-year period. Contact Dermatitis 2014;70:205-212

70 Fowler JF Jr, Shaughnessy CN, Belsito DV, DeKoven JG, Deleo VA, Fransway AF, et al. Cutaneous delayed-type hypersensitivity to surfactants. Dermatitis 2015;26:268-270

71 Pratt MD, Belsito DV, DeLeo VA, Fowler JF Jr, Fransway AF, Maibach HI, et al. North American Contact Dermatitis Group patch-test results, 2001–2002 study period. Dermatitis 2004;15:176-183

72 Hasan T, Rantanen T, Alanko K, Harvima RJ, Jolanki R, Kalimo K, et al. Patch test reactions to cosmetic allergens in 1995–1997 and 2000–2002 in Finland –a multicentre study. Contact Dermatitis 2005;53:40-45

73 Amin KA, Belsito DV. The aetiology of eyelid dermatitis: a 10-year retrospective analysis. Contact Dermatitis 2006;55:280-285

74 Goossens A. Cosmetic contact allergens. Cosmetics 2016, 3, 5; doi:10.3390/cosmetics3010005

75 Wentworth AB, Yiannias JA, Keeling JH, Hall MR, Camilleri MJ, Drage LA, et al. Trends in patch-test results and allergen changes in the standard series: a Mayo Clinic 5-year retrospective review (January 1, 2006, to December 31, 2010). J Am Acad Dermatol 2014;70:269-275

76 Rietschel RL, Warshaw EM, Sasseville D, Fowler JF Jr, DeLeo VA. Belsito DV, et al. Common contact allergens associated with eyelid dermatitis: data from the North American Contact Dermatitis Group 2003-2004 study period. Dermatitis 2007;18:78-81

77 Herbst RA, Uter W, Pirker C, Geier J, Frosch PJ. Allergic and non-allergic periorbital dermatitis: patch test results of the Information Network of the Departments of Dermatology during a 5-year period. Contact Dermatitis 2004;51:13-19

78 Scheman A, Jacob S, Katta R, Nedorost S, Warshaw E, Zirwas M, et al. Part 2 of a 4 part series. Hair cosmetics: trends and alternatives. Data from the American Contact Alternative Group. J Clin Aesthet Dermatol 2011;4:42-46

79 Scheman A, Jacob S, Katta R, Nedorost S, Warshaw E, Zirwas M, et al. Part 3 of a 4 part series. Lips and common Dental Care products: trends and alternatives. Data from the American Contact Alternative Group. J Clin Aesthet Dermatol 2011;4:50-53

80 Laguna C, de la Cuadra J, Martín-González B, Zaragoza V, Martínez-Casimiro L, Alegre V. Allergic contact dermatitis to cosmetics. Actas Dermosifiliogr 2009;100:53-60

81 Toholka R, Wang Y-S, Tate B, Tam M, Cahill J, Palmer A, Nixon R. The first Australian Baseline Series: Recommendations for patch testing in suspected contact dermatitis. Australas J Dermatol 2015;56:107-115

82 Zhao J, Li LF. Contact sensitization to cosmetic series of allergens in a general population in Beijing. J Cosmet Dermatol 2014;13:68-71

83 Grey KR, Hanson J, Hagen SL, Hylwa SA, Warshaw EM. Epidemiology and co-reactivity of novel surfactant allergens: a double-blind randomized controlled study. Dermatitis 2016;27:348-354

84 DeKoven JG, Warshaw EM, Belsito DV, Sasseville D, Maibach HI, Taylor JS, et al. North American Contact Dermatitis Group Patch Test Results: 2013-2014. Dermatitis 2017;28:33-46

85 Zaragoza-Ninet V, Blasco Encinas R, Vilata-Corell JJ, Pérez-Ferriols A, Sierra-Talamantes C, Esteve-Martínez A, de la Cuadra-Oyanguren J. Allergic contact dermatitis due to cosmetics: A clinical and epidemiological study in a tertiary hospital. Actas Dermosifiliogr 2016;107:329-336

86 Dinkloh A, Worm M, Geier J, Schnuch A, Wollenberg A. Contact sensitization in patients with suspected cosmetic intolerance: results of the IVDK 2006-2011. J Eur Acad Dermatol Venereol 2015;29:1071-1081

87 Lyons G, Roberts H, Palmer A, Matheson M, Nixon R. Hairdressers presenting to an occupational dermatology clinic in Melbourne, Australia. Contact Dermatitis 2013;68:300-306

88 Uter W, Gefeller O, John SM, Schnuch A, Geier J. Contact allergy to ingredients of hair cosmetics – a comparison of female hairdressers and clients based on IVDK 2007–2012 data. Contact Dermatitis 2014;71:13-20

89 Warshaw EM, Wang MZ, Mathias CGT, Maibach HI, Belsito DV, Zug KA, et al. Occupational contact dermatitis in hairdressers/cosmetologists; retrospective analysis of North American Contact Dermatitis Group data, 1994 to 2010. Dermatitis 2012;23:258-268

90 Lubbes S, Rustemeyer T, Sillevis Smitt JH, Schuttelaar ML, Middelkamp-Hup MA. Contact sensitization in Dutch children and adolescents with and without atopic dermatitis - a retrospective analysis. Contact Dermatitis 2017;76:151-159

91 Erfurt-Berge C, Geier J, Mahler V. The current spectrum of contact sensitization in patients with chronic leg ulcers or stasis dermatitis - new data from the Information Network of Departments of Dermatology (IVDK). Contact Dermatitis 2017;77:151-158

92 Barbaud A, Vigan M, Delrous JL, Asiier H, Avenel-Audran M, Collet E, et al. Contact allergy to antiseptics: 75 cases analyzed by the dermato-allergovigilance network (Revidal). Ann Dermatol Venereol 2005;132:962-965 (article in French)

93 Mowitz M, Pontén A. Foot dermatitis caused by didecyldimethylammonium chloride in a shoe refresher spray. Contact Dermatitis 2015;73:374-376

94 Yu J, Treat J, Chaney K, Brod B. Potential allergens in disposable diaper wipes, topical diaper preparations, and disposable diapers: under-recognized etiology of pediatric perineal dermatitis. Dermatitis 2016;27:110-118

95 Belloni Fortina A, Fontana E, Peserico A. Contact sensitization in children: A retrospective study of 2,614 children from a single center. Pediatr Dermatol 2016;33:399-404

96 Goldenberg A, Mousdicas N, Silverberg N, Powell D, Pelletier JL, Silverberg JI, et al. Pediatric Contact Dermatitis Registry inaugural case data. Dermatitis 2016;27:293-302

97 Shaughnessy CN, Malajian D, Belsito DV. Cutaneous delayed-type hypersensitivity in patients with atopic dermatitis: reactivity to surfactants. J Am Acad Dermatol 2014;70:704-708

98 Grey KR, Hanson J, Hagen SL, Hylwa SA, Warshaw EM. Epidemiology and co-reactivity of novel surfactant allergens: a double-blind randomized controlled study. Dermatitis 2016;27:348-354

99 Fowler JF Jr, Shaughnessy CN, Belsito DV, DeKoven JG, Deleo VA, Fransway AF, et al. Cutaneous delayed-type hypersensitivity to surfactants. Dermatitis 2015;26:268-270

100 Welling JD, Mauger TF, Schoenfield LR, Hendershot AJ. Chronic eyelid dermatitis secondary to cocamidopropyl betaine allergy in a patient using baby shampoo eyelid scrubs. JAMA Ophthalmol 2014;132:357-359

2.120 COCAMIDOPROPYL DIMETHYLAMINE

IDENTIFICATION

Description/definition	: Cocamidopropyl dimethylamine is the amidoamine that conforms generally to the formula shown below, where RCO- represents the fatty acids derived from coconut oil.
Chemical class(es)	: Amines
Other names	: Amides, coco, *N*-[3-(dimethylamino)propyl]; cocamidopropylamine ; coconut fatty acid, dimethylaminopropylamide; Amidoamine (term used by the NACDG); after 2008, 'Amidoamine' probably was stearamidopropyl dimethylamine
CAS registry number (s)	: 68140-01-2
EC number(s)	: 268-771-8; 930-947-3
CIR review(s)	: Final report, June 2014 (access: www.cir-safety.org/ingredients)
Function(s) in cosmetics	: EU: antistatic; emulsifying; hair conditioning; surfactant. USA: antistatic agents
Patch testing	: 0.1% water (Chemotechnique); test concentrations of 0.1% and 0.05% may be irritant (1), but a concentration of 0.01% leads to false-negative reactions (10); 0.1% of purified cocamidopropyl dimethylamine may be too low to detect all cases of sensitization (3)

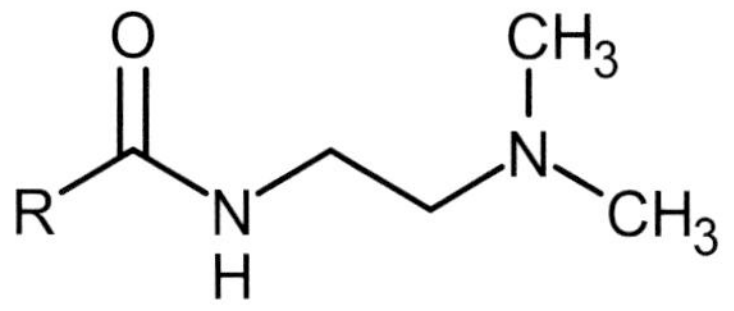

CONTACT ALLERGY

Cocamidopropyl dimethylamine is an intermediate in the synthesis of cocamidopropyl betaine and possibly an important cause of allergic reactions to commercial cocamidopropyl betaine (1,3,4,10,11,12, see also Chapter 2.119 Cocamidopropyl betaine). The other allergen in commercial cocamidopropyl betaine, 3-dimethylaminopropylamine, may also be present in cocamidopropyl dimethylamine (0.06% [1]). Cocamidopropyl dimethylamine, which is called 'Amidoamine' by the NACDG (which is strictly speaking incorrect, as Amidoamines are a class of chemicals) is also used in cosmetics *per se*, but no convincing case reports of cosmetic allergic contact dermatitis from such use have as yet been reported. However, 'Amidoamine' (as cocamidopropyl dimethylamine) has been present in the NACDG screening series from 1998 to 2009 and caused 1.6% to 4.4% positive reactions, some of which were definitely relevant. As criteria for definite relevance implies a positive patch test or use test to a product containing cocamidopropyl dimethylamine, this would suggest that some cases of contact allergy to cocamidopropyl dimethylamine in cosmetic products must have been observed (4,8,9,14,15) (although some may have been from its presence as impurity rather than from its intentional formulation by the cosmetics manufacturer).

It should be appreciated that, from 2009 on, the members of the NACDG purchased 'Amidoamine' from another supplier of patch test materials. This Amidoamine is not cocamidopropyl dimethylamine, but stearamidopropyl dimethylamine!

Patch testing in groups of patients
Results of studies patch testing cocamidopropyl dimethylamine in consecutive patients suspected of contact dermatitis (routine testing) back to 2000 are shown in table 2.120.1. Results of testing in groups of *selected* patients (patients previously reacting to one or more surfactants, patients suspected of occupational contact dermatitis, patients with pure eyelid dermatitis, patients tested with a cosmetic screening series) back to 2004 are shown in table 2.120.2.

Patch testing in consecutive patients suspected of contact dermatitis: routine testing
Results of studies patch testing cocamidopropyl dimethylamine in consecutive patients suspected of contact dermatitis (routine testing) are shown in table 2.1
20.1. In routine testing, frequencies of sensitization have ranged from 1.3% to 4.4%. In the studies of the NACDG, relevance rates for either 'definite' or 'probable' relevance ranged from 21% to 37%, with very low 'definite' scores. In another USA study, 'definite' relevance was 60%, 'probable' 30% (12). Causative products were never mentioned.

Patch testing in groups of selected patients
In groups of selected patients (patients previously reacting to one or more surfactants, patients suspected of occupational contact dermatitis, patients with pure eyelid dermatitis, patients tested with a cosmetic screening series),'frequencies of sensitization to cocamidopropyl dimethylamine were mostly low (table 2.120.2). In one study,

there were 5 (11%) reactions in a small group of 47 individuals who had previously reacted to surfactants present in the NACDG screening series, but relevance was not mentioned and there were also 8 doubtful reactions (19).

Table 2.120.1 Patch testing in groups of patients: Routine testing

Years and Country	Test conc. & vehicle	Number of patients tested | positive (%)		Selection of patients (S); Relevance (R); Comments (C)	Ref.
2001-2013 USA	0.1% water	1674	22 (1.3%)	R: not stated; from 2001-2007, 'Amidoamine' was cocamidopropyl dimethylamine, from 2008-2013 it was most likely stearamidopropyl dimethylamine	5
2006-2010 USA	0.1% water	2988	(2.0%)	R: 49%; C: as it was not specified from which supplier the 'amidoamine' had been purchased, it is uncertain whether it was cocamidopropyl dimethylamine or stearamidopropyl dimethylamine	17
2007-8 USA, Canada	0.1% water	5081	81 (1.6%)	R: definite relevance: 2%, probable 24%	8
2005-6 USA, Canada	0.1% water	4434	89 (2.0%)	R: definite relevance 2.3%, probable 31%	9
2003-4 USA, Canada	0.1% water	5139	86 (1.7%)	R: not stated	13
2001-2002 USA	0.1% water	4897	(2.3%)	R: definite + probable relevance: 21%	14
2001 USA, Canada	0.1% water	975	43 (4.4%)	R: definite + probable relevance: 37%; of the 43, 18 also reacted to cocamidopropyl betaine	4
2001 USA	0.1% water	957	28 (2.9%)	R: definite 60%, probable 30%; C: 11 of these patients also reacted to cocamidopropyl betaine	12
1998-2000 USA, Canada	0.1% water	5773	(3.4%)	R: definite + probable relevance: 22%	15

Table 2.120.2 Patch testing in groups of patients: Selected patient groups

Years and Country	Test conc. & vehicle	Number of patients tested | positive (%)		Selection of patients (S); Relevance (R); Comments (C)	Ref.
2015-2016 USA	0.1% water	47	5 (11%)	S: patients previously reacting to one or more surfactants present in the NACDG screening series; R: not stated; C: there were also 8 doubtful reactions	19
2002-2009 Finland	0.05%, 0.16% & 0.5% water	1092	11 (1.0%)	S: patients suspected of occupational contact dermatitis and tested with a 'coconut series'; R: most reactions were relevant and caused by liquid soap and shampoo; C: there were 7% (test substance 0.05% water) to 25% (test substance 0.5% water) *irritant* patch test reactions	1
2000-2007 USA	0.1% water	412	11 (2.7%)	S: patients tested with a supplemental cosmetic screening series; R: 100%; C: weak study: a. high rate of macular erythema and weak reactions; b. relevance figures included 'questionable' and 'past' relevance	20
2003-2004 USA	0.1% water	268	5 (1.9%)	S: patients with pure eyelid dermatitis; R: this was the number of relevant reactions	18

Case reports and case series

In a group of 2193 patients (1582 women, 611 men) with (presumed) cosmetic allergy, 104 reactions (5%) were caused by cocamidopropyl dimethylamine ('amidoamine') in a study of the NACDG, 2001-2004, cocamidopropyl dimethylamine ranking 13th in the list of most frequent allergens (7). Of 11 patients suspected of occupational contact dermatitis and tested with a 'coconut series', eleven had positive reactions to cocamidopropyl dimethylamine. Most of these were relevant and caused by its presence in liquid soaps and shampoos (1). In a group of 46 patients with allergic contact dermatitis of the eyelids seen in Kansas City, USA, between 1994 and 2004, two cases (4.3%) were caused by contact allergy to cocamidopropyl dimethylamine (source not mentioned) (16). One patient probably had allergic contact dermatitis from cocamidopropyl dimethylamine present in hair cosmetics (6).

Cross-reactions, pseudo-cross-reactions and co-reactions

3-Dimethylaminopropylamine (which may also be present in cocamidopropyl dimethylamine) (3,6); oleamidopropyl dimethylamine (1,2). Co-reactions to chemically related surfactants (oleamidopropyl dimethylamine, cocamidopropyl betaine, sodium lauroyl sarcosinate, isostearamidopropyl morpholine lactate, disodium lauroamphodiacetate) have been observed (19). Cocamidopropyl betaine (4).

Presence in cosmetic products and chemical analyses
In May 2017, cocamidopropyl dimethylamine was present in 25 older products of 66,648 cosmetic products of which the composition is known in EWG's Skin Deep Cosmetics Database, USA (http://www.ewg.org/skindeep/). In the USA, in April 2017, cocamidopropyl dimethylamine was present in 26 of 56,714 cosmetic products of which the composition is known in FDA's Voluntary Cosmetic Registration Program (VCRP) (data obtained from FDA, May 2017).

LITERATURE

1   Suuronen K, Pesonen M, Aalto-Korte K. Occupational contact allergy to cocamidopropyl betaine. Contact Dermatitis 2012;66:286-292

2   De Groot AC, Jagtman BA, van der Meeren HLM, Bruynzeel DP, Bos JD, den Hengst CW, et al. Cross-reaction pattern of the cationic emulsifier oleamidopropyl dimethylamine. Contact Dermatitis 1988;19:284-289

3   Foti C, Bonamonte D, Mascolo G, Corcelli A, Lobasso S, Rigano L, et al. The role of 3-dimethylaminopropylamine and amidoamine in contact allergy to cocamidopropyl betaine. Contact Dermatitis 2003;48:194-198

4   Fowler JF Jr, Zug KM, Taylor JS, Storrs FJ, Sherertz EA, Sasseville DA, et al. Allergy to cocamidopropyl betaine and amidoamine in North America. Dermatitis 2004;15:5-6

5   Shaughnessy CN, Malajian D, Belsito DV. Cutaneous delayed-type hypersensitivity in patients with atopic dermatitis: reactivity to surfactants. J Am Acad Dermatol 2014;70:704-708

6   Moreau L, Sasseville D. Allergic contact dermatitis from cocamidopropyl betaine, cocamidoamine, 3-(dimethylamino)propylamine, and oleamidopropyl dimethylamine: co-reactions or cross-reactions? Dermatitis 2004;15:146-149

7   Warshaw EM, Buchholz HJ, Belsito DV, Maibach HI, Fowler JF Jr, Rietschel RL, et al. Allergic patch test reactions associated with cosmetics: Retrospective analysis of cross-sectional data from the North American Contact Dermatitis Group, 2001-2004. J Am Acad Dermatol 2009;60:23-38

8   Fransway AF, Zug KA, Belsito DV, Deleo VA, Fowler JF Jr, Maibach HI, et al. North American Contact Dermatitis Group patch test results for 2007-2008. Dermatitis 2013;24:10-21

9   Zug KA, Warshaw EM, Fowler JF Jr, Maibach HI, Belsito DL, Pratt MD, et al. Patch-test results of the North American Contact Dermatitis Group 2005-2006. Dermatitis 2009;20:149-160

10 McFadden JP, Ross JS, White IR, Basketter DA. Clinical allergy to cocamidopropyl betaine: reactivity to cocamidopropylamine and lack of reactivity to 3-dimethylaminopropylamine. Contact Dermatitis 2001;45:72-74

11 Fowler JF, Fowler LM, Hunter JE. Allergy to cocamidopropyl betaine may be due to amidoamine: a patch test and product use test study. Contact Dermatitis 1997;37:276-281

12 Brey NL, Fowler JF. Relevance of positive patch-test reactions to cocamidopropyl betaine and amidoamine. Dermatitis 2004;15:7-9

13 Warshaw EM, Belsito DV, DeLeo VA, Fowler JF Jr, Maibach HI, Marks JG, et al. North American Contact Dermatitis Group patch-test results, 2003-2004 study period. Dermatitis 2008;19:129-136

14 Pratt MD, Belsito DV, DeLeo VA, Fowler JF Jr, Fransway AF, Maibach HI, et al. North American Contact Dermatitis Group patch-test results, 2001–2002 study period. Dermatitis 2004;15:176-183

15 Marks JG Jr, Belsito DV, DeLeo VA, Fowler JF Jr, Fransway AF, Maibach HI, et al. North American Contact Dermatitis Group patch-test results, 1998–2000. Am J Contact Dermat 2003;14:59-62

16 Amin KA, Belsito DV. The aetiology of eyelid dermatitis: a 10-year retrospective analysis. Contact Dermatitis 2006;55:280-285

17 Wentworth AB, Yiannias JA, Keeling JH, Hall MR, Camilleri MJ, Drage LA, et al. Trends in patch-test results and allergen changes in the standard series: a Mayo Clinic 5-year retrospective review (January 1, 2006, to December 31, 2010). J Am Acad Dermatol 2014;70:269-275

18 Rietschel RL, Warshaw EM, Sasseville D, Fowler JF Jr, DeLeo VA, Belsito DV, et al. Common contact allergens associated with eyelid dermatitis: data from the North American Contact Dermatitis Group 2003-2004 study period. Dermatitis 2007;18:78-81

19 Grey KR, Hanson J, Hagen SL, Hylwa SA, Warshaw EM. Epidemiology and co-reactivity of novel surfactant allergens: a double-blind randomized controlled study. Dermatitis 2016;27:348-354

20 Wetter DA, Yiannias JA, Prakash AV, Davis MD, Farmer SA, el-Azhary RA, et al. Results of patch testing to personal care product allergens in a standard series and a supplemental cosmetic series: an analysis of 945 patients from the Mayo Clinic Contact Dermatitis Group, 2000-2007. J Am Acad Dermatol 2010;63:789-798

2.121   COCAMIDOPROPYL HYDROXYSULTAINE

IDENTIFICATION

Description/definition	: Cocamidopropyl hydroxysultaine is the zwitterion (inner salt) that conforms generally to the formula shown below, where RCO- represents the fatty acids derived from coconut oil
Chemical class(es)	: Betaines
Chemical/IUPAC name	: 3-[3-(Dodecanoylamino)propyl-dimethylazaniumyl]-2-hydroxypropane-1-sulfonate
Other names	: 1-Propanaminium, N-(3-aminopropyl)-2-hydroxy-N,N-dimethyl-3-sulfo-, N-coco acyl derivatives, hydroxides, inner salts
CAS registry number (s)	: 68139-30-0
EC number(s)	: 268-761-3
Function(s) in cosmetics	: EU: antistatic; cleansing; foam boosting; hair conditioning; skin conditioning; surfactant; viscosity controlling. USA: antistatic agents; hair conditioning agents; skin-conditioning agents - miscellaneous; surfactants - cleansing agents; surfactants - foam boosters; viscosity increasing agents - aqueous
Patch testing	: 1% water (1)

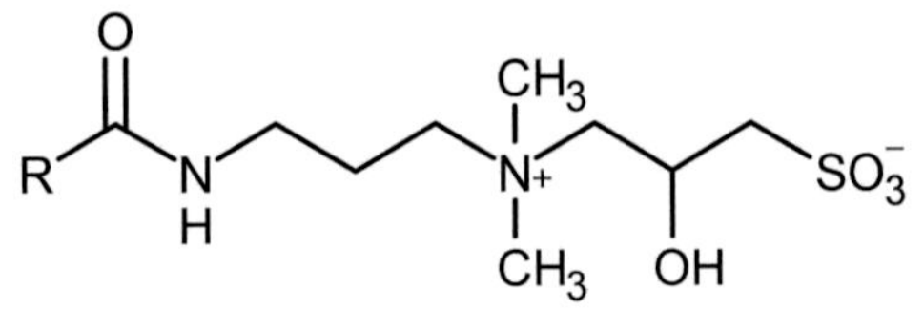

CONTACT ALLERGY

Patch testing in groups of patients

In 2002, in the USA, 12 patients previously reacting to cocamidopropyl betaine (CAPB) were retested with CAPB and with a number of coconut oil derivatives including cocamidopropyl hydroxysultaine 2% water. Only 3 patients had positive reactions to CAPB on retesting, and all were doubtful. There was one positive reaction in this group to cocamidopropyl hydroxysultaine 2% water (relevance not mentioned) and one dubious reaction in a control group of 10 patients (2).

Case reports and case series

A man presented with an eczema of 2 months' duration on the forehead, back of neck, ears and surrounding areas. He had used 2 different shampoos that included botanical materials, and recalled previous reactivity to a massage product. Patch tests to 40 screening agents and corticosteroids revealed positive reactions to formaldehyde, quaternium-15, DMDM hydantoin, and methylchloro- and methylisothiazolinone, and to cocamidopropyl hydroxysultaine, tested 1% in water. There was no reaction to cocamidopropyl betaine. There were no positive patch test reactions to cocamidopropyl hydroxysultaine 1% in water in five control patients. Because of the difficulty in finding a shampoo lacking all agents to which he was sensitive, the patient used a synthetic detergent bar as a shampoo, and the eruption cleared, except for mild residual erythema, after only 3 days (1).

Cross-reactions, pseudo-cross-reactions and co-reactions

Not to cocamidopropyl betaine (1).

Presence in cosmetic products and chemical analyses

In August 2017, cocamidopropyl hydroxysultaine was present in 336 of 70,366 cosmetic products of which the composition is known in EWG's Skin Deep Cosmetics Database, USA (http://www.ewg.org/skindeep/). In the USA, in April 2017, cocamidopropyl hydroxysultaine was present in 310 of 56,714 cosmetic products of which the composition is known in FDA's Voluntary Cosmetic Registration Program (VCRP) (data obtained from FDA, May 2017).

LITERATURE

1   Guin JD. Reaction to cocamidopropyl hydroxysultaine, an amphoteric surfactant and conditioner. Contact Dermatitis 2000;42:284
2   Shaffer KK, Jaimes JP, Hordinsky MK, Zielke GR, Warshaw EM. Allergenicity and cross-reactivity of coconut oil derivatives: A double-blind randomized controlled pilot study. Dermatitis 2006;17:71-76

2.122 COCAMIDOPROPYL PG-DIMONIUM CHLORIDE PHOSPHATE

IDENTIFICATION

Description/definition : Cocamidopropyl PG-dimonium chloride phosphate is the quaternary ammonium salt that conforms generally to the formula shown below, where RCO- represents the fatty acids derived from coconut oil

Chemical class(es) : Phosphorus compounds; quaternary ammonium compounds

Chemical/IUPAC name : 1-Propanaminium, 3,3',3''-[phosphinylidynetris(oxy)]tris[N-(3-aminopropyl)-2-hydroxy-N,N-dimethyl-, N,N',N''-tri-C6-18 acyl derivs. trichlorides

CAS registry number (s) : 83682-78-4

EC number(s) : 280-518-3

Function(s) in cosmetics : EU: antistatic; hair conditioning. USA: antistatic agents; hair conditioning agents

Patch testing : 2.5% water (2,3)

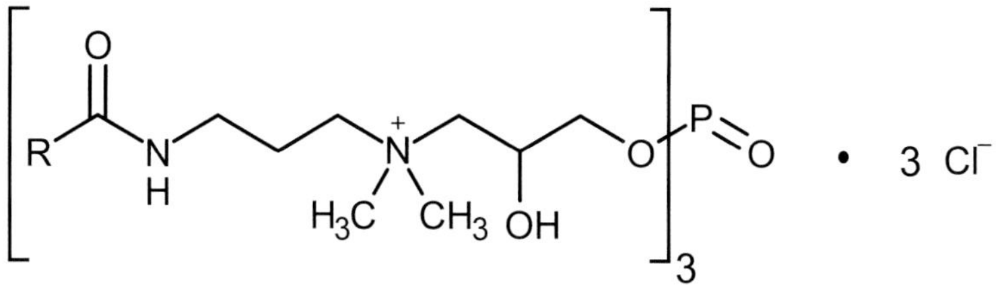

CONTACT ALLERGY

Case reports and case series

Cocamidopropyl PG-dimonium chloride phosphate was responsible for 1 out of 959 cases of non-fragrance cosmetic allergy where the causal allergen was identified, Belgium, 2000-2010 (1).

A woman had suffered from three episodes of severe erythema and swelling of the face, eyelids, and neck. Each episode lasted approximately four days and responded rapidly to short courses of oral corticosteroids. Patch tests to a modified European standard series, supplementary, cosmetic, and hairdressing series, were all negative. Patch testing to the patient's own cosmetics revealed a weak positive reaction to a hydrating lotion. When tested with its individual ingredients, a positive patch test reaction was observed to cocamidopropyl PG dimonium chloride phosphate 2.5% water. Repeat testing with the lotion was again positive (2), but control testing with cocamidopropyl PG dimonium chloride phosphate to exclude irritancy was not performed.

A woman had a 3-month history of dermatitis on the eyelids and neck. She was patch tested with the GIRDCA standard series and her own cosmetics, with a positive reaction to a moisturizing cream. She was then patched tested with its individual constituents and the patient had a positive reaction to cocamidopropyl PG-dimonium chloride phosphate 2.5% water; 20 volunteers did not react to the test material (3). The authors stated that the manufacturer was aware of similar cases of allergy from the same cosmetic cream and that cocamidopropyl PG-dimonium chloride phosphate had been removed from that particular product (3).

Cross-reactions, pseudo-cross-reactions and co-reactions

Not to cocamidopropyl betaine (3).

Presence in cosmetic products and chemical analyses

In the USA, in April 2017, cocamidopropyl PG-dimonium chloride phosphate was present in 79 of 56,714 cosmetic products of which the composition is known in FDA's Voluntary Cosmetic Registration Program (VCRP) (data obtained from FDA, May 2017). In March 2017, cocamidopropyl PG-dimonium chloride phosphate was present in 66 of 64,983 cosmetic products of which the composition is known in EWG's Skin Deep Cosmetics Database, USA (http://www.ewg.org/skindeep/). Cocamidopropyl PG-dimonium chloride phosphate was present in 6 (11%) of 54 personal hygiene wet wipes for which ingredient information was obtained online and from retail stores, USA, 2016 (4).

LITERATURE

1   Travassos AR, Claes L, Boey L, Drieghe J, Goossens A. Non-fragrance allergens in specific cosmetic products. Contact Dermatitis 2011;65:276-285

2   Roberts H, Williams J, Tate B. Allergic contact dermatitis to panthenol and cocamidopropyl PG dimonium chloride phosphate in a facial hydrating lotion. Contact Dermatitis 2006;55:369-370

3   Lorenzi S, Placucci F, Vincenzi C, Tosti A. Contact sensitization to cocamidopropyl PG-dimonium chloride phosphate in a cosmetic cream. Contact Dermatitis 1996;34:149-150

4   Aschenbeck KA, Warshaw EM. Allergenic ingredients in personal hygiene wet wipes. Dermatitis 2017 Mar 23. doi: 10.1097/DER.0000000000000275. [Epub ahead of print]

2.123 COCO-BETAINE

IDENTIFICATION

Description/definition : Coco-betaine is the zwitterion (inner salt) that conforms generally to the formula shown below, where R represents the alkyl groups derived from coconut oil
Chemical class(es) : Betaines
Chemical/IUPAC name : Betaines, coco alkyldimethyl
CAS registry number (s) : 68424-94-2
EC number(s) : 270-329-4
CIR review(s) : Final report, March 2014 (access: www.cir-safety.org/ingredients)
Function(s) in cosmetics : EU: antistatic; cleansing; foam boosting; hair conditioning; skin conditioning; surfactant; viscosity controlling. USA: antistatic agents; hair conditioning agents; skin-conditioning agents - miscellaneous; surfactants – cleansing agents; surfactants- foam boosters; viscosity increasing agents – aqueous
Patch testing : 2% water (1)

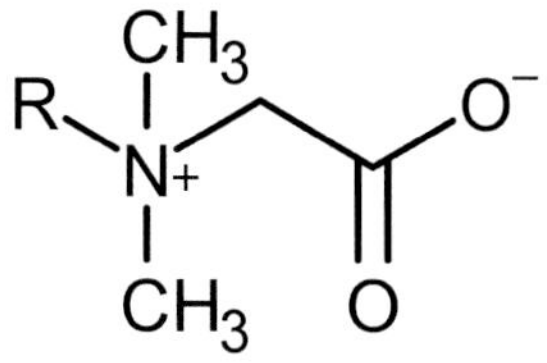

CONTACT ALLERGY

Patch testing in groups of patients

In 2002, in the USA, 12 patients previously reacting to cocamidopropyl betaine (CAPB) were retested with CAPB and with a number of coconut oil derivatives including coco-betaine 1.5% water. Only 3 patients had positive reactions to CAPB on retesting, and all were doubtful. There were three weak positive reactions in this group to coco-betaine 1.5% water and six doubtful ones (relevance not mentioned). This obviously points at irritancy of the test material, and, indeed, in a control group of 10 patients, there were 5 doubtful reactions and one weak positive result (2).

Case reports and case series

A woman presented with acute eczematous lesions with erythema, edema, and vesiculation on the backs and palms of her hands. Her scalp also itched and was slightly red. Patch tests 2 years previously had shown positive reactions to p-phenylenediamine, benzocaine, wool alcohols, parabens, chinoform, perfumes, nickel sulphate and cobalt chloride. A few days prior to the present acute attack, she had used a shampoo based on chestnut leaf extract. Patch tests with the shampoo and the individual components showed positive reactions to the shampoo (open test as is and patch test 2% water) and to its ingredient coco-betaine 2% water (1).

In the same report, another woman was presented with a red, swollen face with weeping eczematous lesions. There were also red, oozing and crusted acute lesions on her shoulders and scalp. Two days previously she had washed her hair with a new shampoo. Patch tests were performed with the shampoo, the individual ingredients and all the topical agents and cosmetics used. A strongly positive reaction was found to the shampoo (open test, as is, and patch test 2% water), and a positive reaction to coco-betaine (2% water). Three controls were negative to coco-betaine 2% in water (1).

Cross-reactions, pseudo-cross-reactions and co-reactions

Co-reaction to cocamidopropyl betaine in one patient (1).

Presence in cosmetic products and chemical analyses

In the USA, in April 2017, coco-betaine was present in 227 of 56,714 cosmetic products of which the composition is known in FDA's Voluntary Cosmetic Registration Program (VCRP) (data obtained from FDA, May 2017). In March 2017, coco-betaine was present in 128 of 64,983 cosmetic products of which the composition is known in EWG's Skin Deep Cosmetics Database, USA (http://www.ewg.org/skindeep/).

LITERATURE

1 Van Haute N, Dooms-Goossens A. Shampoo dermatitis due to cocobetaine and sodium lauryl ether sulphate. Contact Dermatitis 1983;9:169

2 Shaffer KK, Jaimes JP, Hordinsky MK, Zielke GR, Warshaw EM. Allergenicity and cross-reactivity of coconut oil derivatives: A double-blind randomized controlled pilot study. Dermatitis 2006;17:71-76

2.124 COCO-GLUCOSIDE

IDENTIFICATION

Description/definition : Coco-glucoside is the product obtained by the condensation of coconut alcohol with glucose; it conforms generally to the formula shown below, wherein R is an alkyl chain residue of fatty alcohols derived from coconut acid
Chemical class(es) : Carbohydrates
Other names : Alcohols, coco, reaction products with glucose
CAS registry number (s) : 110615-47-9 (generic: **D-glucopyranose, oligomeric, C10-16-alkyl glycosides**)
CIR review(s) : Int J Toxicol 2013;32(Suppl.3):22-48 (access: www.cir-safety.org/ingredients)
Function(s) in cosmetics : EU: cleansing; foaming; surfactant. USA: surfactants – cleansing agents
Patch testing : 5% pet. (1,7)

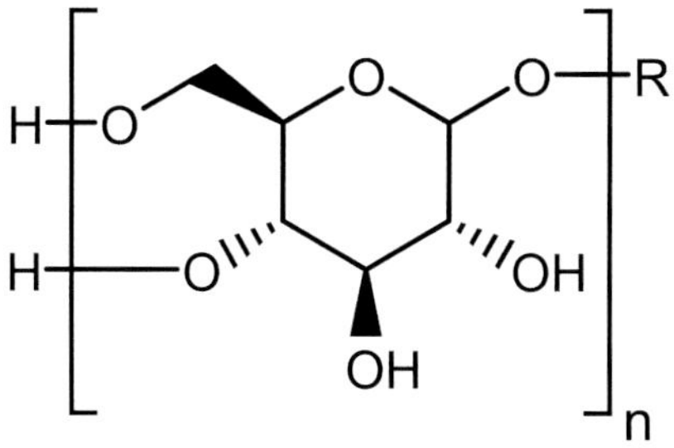

GENERAL

Coco-glucoside is one of the alkyl glucosides, a family of organic molecules of vegetal origin. They are produced by the condensation of a sugar, usually a cyclic form of glucose (D-glucopyranose), with a fatty alcohol composed of a linear side chain ranging from 2 to 22 carbons. Fatty alcohol is extracted from palm, coconut, or rapeseed oil, and glucose can be obtained from corn, wheat starch, and potato. The average number of carbon atoms composing the alcohol side chain determines the name of the alkyl glucoside. Members of the alkyl glucoside family include butyl, caprylyl, decyl, lauryl, coco-, cetearyl, undecyl, myristyl, hexadecyl, octadecyl, arachidyl, and caprylyl/capryl glucoside, C10-16, C12-18, C12-20, and C20-22 alkyl glucosides, branched isostearyl glucoside, and octyldodecyl glucoside.

Most of the alkyl glucosides are primarily used as mild non-ionic surfactants in cosmetics and cleansing products for human skin, mostly as a mixture of several alkyl glucosides, as it is difficult to obtain individual glucosides at high purity. They can also sometimes function as emulsion stabilizers in sunscreens, skin and hair cleansing agents, and humectants. They can be found in certain baby products such as wipes and cleansers and in antiseptic solutions (12). Other alkyl glucosides which have caused cosmetic allergy include arachidyl glucoside, cetearyl glucoside, decyl glucoside, lauryl glucoside and myristyl glucoside. These are discussed in their respective chapters. A comprehensive review of contact allergy to alkyl glucosides has been published in 2017 (10,11).

CONTACT ALLERGY

Case reports and case series

Coco-glucoside was stated to be the (or an) allergen in 14 patients in a group of 603 individuals suffering from cosmetic dermatitis, seen in the period 2010-2015 in Leuven, Belgium (8). Coco-glucoside was responsible for 5 out of 959 cases of non-fragrance cosmetic allergy where the causal allergen was identified, Belgium, 2000-2010 (1). During a 19-year period (1993–2012), of 11,842 patients with suspected contact dermatitis patch tested in Leuven, Belgium, 30 patients (24 women and 6 men) presented with a positive reaction to one or more alkyl glucosides. The causal products were shampoos (n=12), skin-cleansing products (n=12, among which were wipes for intimate hygiene), sunscreen products (n=5), skin-care products (n=4), and a deodorant (n=1) (7). Reactions to coco-glucoside were seen in 22/30 (73%) of the patients. Co-reactions to other glucosides were as follows: lauryl glucoside 18 (82%), decyl glucoside 16 (72%), and cetearyl glucoside 3 (14%) (7). Twenty-five of the 30 patients who reacted to alkyl glucosides also had positive test results with non-related chemicals; 16 of these even had multiple sensitivities, defined as three or more contact allergies (7).

A patient was predictively tested with 6 different shower gels (semi-open, to determine their irritant potential), and reacted positively to all products tested. The common ingredient in all 6 was coco-glucoside, and in 5 out of 6 lauryl glucoside as well. When tested with their ingredients, the patient showed positive reactions to both coco-glucoside and lauryl glucoside (3). A woman had ACD of the hands from coco-glucoside and lauryl glucoside in a body lotion and a sunscreen that she applied to her child's skin (3). Two nurses had occupational allergic contact dermatitis from coco-glucoside in liquid soap and a hairdresser from this glucoside present in a shampoo (7). A patient known to be allergic to decyl glucoside in Tinosorb® M had positive patch test reactions to his facial cosmetics containing coco-glucoside (2).

Contact allergy to coco-glucoside in non-cosmetic products
A nurse had ACD of the hands from contact allergy to coco-glucoside in a lotion she used for cleaning her hands (3).

Cross-reactions, pseudo-cross-reactions and co-reactions
Other glucosides such as lauryl glucoside, decyl glucoside, cetearyl glucoside and myristyl glucoside (2,3,4,5,7). In commercial batches of decyl, coco- and lauryl glucoside about 500 ng/g isobornyl acrylate was found as an impurity. It has been suggested, that this chemical may play a role in the simultaneous reactions to various alkyl glucosides (9). Often, a mixture of several alkyl glucosides is present in cosmetic products, as it is very difficult to obtain individual glucosides of high purity (6). Because of this and of their chemical similarity, concomitant reactivity or cross-reactions may occur with the various glucosides (2).

Presence in cosmetic products and chemical analyses
In the USA, in April 2017, coco-glucoside was present in 703 of 56,714 cosmetic products of which the composition is known in FDA's Voluntary Cosmetic Registration Program (VCRP) (data obtained from FDA, May 2017). In August 2017, coco-glucoside was present in 656 of 70,366 cosmetic products of which the composition is known in EWG's Skin Deep Cosmetics Database, USA (http://www.ewg.org/skindeep/). Coco-glucoside was present in 6 (3%) of 178 facial wipes for which ingredient information was obtained online and from retail stores, USA, 2016 (13).

LITERATURE
1   Travassos AR, Claes L, Boey L, Drieghe J, Goossens A. Non-fragrance allergens in specific cosmetic products. Contact Dermatitis 2011;65:276-285
2   Pereira N, Coutinho I, Andrade P, Gonçalo M. The UV filter Tinosorb M, containing decyl glucoside, is a frequent cause of allergic contact dermatitis. Dermatitis 2013;24:41-43
3   Goossens A, Decraene T, Platteaux N, Nardelli A, Rasschaert V. Glucosides as unexpected allergens in cosmetics. Contact Dermatitis 2003;48:164-166
4   Andrade P, Gonçalo M, Figueiredo A. Allergic contact dermatitis to decyl glucoside in Tinosorb® M. Contact Dermatitis 2010;62:119-120
5   Blondeel A. Contact allergy to the mild surfactant decylglucoside. Contact Dermatitis 2003;49:304-305
6   Le Coz CJ, Meyer MT. Contact allergy to decyl glucoside in antiseptic after body piercing. Contact Dermatitis 2003:48:279-280
7   Gijbels D, Timmermans A, Serrano P, Verreycken E, Goossens A. Allergic contact dermatitis caused by alkyl glucosides. Contact Dermatitis 2014;70:175-182
8   Goossens A. Cosmetic contact allergens. Cosmetics 2016, 3, 5; doi:10.3390/cosmetics3010005
9   Foti C, Romita P, Rigano L, Zimerson E, Sicilia M, Ballini A, et al. Isobornyl acrylate: an impurity in alkyl glucosides. Cutan Ocul Toxicol 2016;35:115-119
10   Loranger C, Alfalah M, Ferrier Le Bouedec M-C, Sasseville Denis. Alkyl glucosides in contact dermatitis: a systematic review. Dermatitis Dermatitis 2017;28:5-13
11   Alfalah M, Loranger C, Sasseville D. Contact allergen of the year. Alkyl glucosides. Dermatitis 2017;28:3-4
12   Fiume MM, Heldreth B, Bergfeld WF, Belsito DV, Hill RA, Klaassen CD, et al. Safety assessment of decyl glucoside and other alkyl glucosides as used in cosmetics. Int J Toxicol 2013;32(Suppl.5):22S-48S
13   Aschenbeck KA, Warshaw EM. Allergenic ingredients in facial wet wipes. Dermatitis 2017 Mar 23. doi: 10.1097/DER.0000000000000268. [Epub ahead of print]

2.125   COD LIVER OIL

IDENTIFICATION

Description/definition : Cod liver oil is the fixed oil expressed from the fresh livers of *Gadus morrhua* and other Gadidae species of codfish
Chemical class(es) : Fats and oils
Other names : Gadidae oil; gadi lecur; gadi lecur oil
CAS registry number (s) : 8001-69-2
EC number(s) : 232-289-6
Merck Index monograph : 3719
Function(s) in cosmetics : EU: masking; skin conditioning; skin protecting. USA: fragrance ingredients; skin protectants; skin-conditioning agents - occlusive
Patch testing : 40%, 20%, 10% and 5% pet. (1); 10 controls were negative to all concentrations

CONTACT ALLERGY

Case reports and case series

One patient reacted to cod liver oil in a topical multivitamin ointment; there were no reactions to either vitamin A acetate or vitamin D_3 (1). This is a cosmeceutical rather than a pure cosmetic. Cod liver oil is used topically for dressing of wounds, burns, hemorrhoids, and abrasions because it is thought to accelerate the epithelial and the vascular component of wound healing. Moreover, topical cod liver oil is used in diaper rash (2) and contact dermatitis and in other skin disorders because of the bland and soothing effects associated with its oily nature and for its alleged eutrophic and epithelialization properties presumed to be related to vitamin A and D, which have markedly high concentrations in cod liver oil (1).

Presence in cosmetic products and chemical analyses

In June 2017, cod liver oil was present in 9 of 69,283 cosmetic products of which the composition is known in EWG's Skin Deep Cosmetics Database, USA (http://www.ewg.org/skindeep/). In the USA, in April 2017, cod liver oil was present in 12 of 56,714 cosmetic products of which the composition is known in FDA's Voluntary Cosmetic Registration Program (VCRP) (data obtained from FDA, May 2017).

LITERATURE

1   Foti C, Bonamonte D, Conserva A, Pepe ML, Angelini G. Allergic contact dermatitis to cod liver oil contained in a topical ointment. Contact Dermatitis 2007;57:281-282
2   Gozen D, Caglar S, Bayraktar S, Atici F. Diaper dermatitis care of newborns human breast milk or barrier cream. J Clin Nurs 2014;23:515-523

2.126   COLOPHONIUM

IDENTIFICATION

Description/definition	: Colophonium is the residue left after distilling off the volatile oil from the oleoresin obtained from *Pinus palustris* and other species of Pinaceae
Chemical class(es)	: Botanical products and derivatives
INCI name USA	: Rosin
Other names	: Gum rosin; colophony
CAS registry number (s)	: 8050-09-7
EC number(s)	: 232-475-7
Merck Index monograph	: 9667
Function(s) in cosmetics	: EU: binding; depilatory; film forming; viscosity controlling. USA: binders; epilating agents; film formers; viscosity increasing agents - nonaqueous
Patch testing	: 20% pet. (Chemotechnique, SmartPracticeEurope, SmartPracticeCanada); this test substance often does *not* detect contact allergy to modified (hydrogenated, esterified *et cetera*) colophony products and sometimes to colophony itself, when the allergen is in the neutral fraction (167)

GENERAL

The word colophony is derived from Colophon, an ancient town on the west coast of Asia Minor, once famous for its colophony production . The term colophony is widely used in Europe, whereas rosin is the preferred name in North America, and the INCI name is colophonium. Here, the term colophony will be used.

Table 2.126.1 Examples of products that may contain colophony (17,33,40,91,185) [a]

Adhesives	Metalworking fluids
Adhesive tapes	Neoprene rubber
Asphalt products	Newspapers
Band aids	Oils
Chewing gum	Paints
Cleaning products	Paper
Coated or glossy paper	Permanent markers
Coatings	Pine oil cleaners
Colophony products to enhance grip in sports (racket, bowling ball)	Pine sawdust
Colophony products for string instruments	Pine trees
Colored pencils	Pine wood
Cosmetics (mascara, eye shadow, eyeliner, lipstick)	Polishes
Cutting fluids (metalworking fluids)	Printing inks
Dental products	Putties used in iron foundries
Depilating products	Sanitary napkins / pads
Diapers	Sealants
Eyeliners	Shoes
Eyeshadows	Soaps
Floor polishes	Soldering fluxes
Furniture polishes	Solvents
Glues	Stamps
Greases	Surgical neoprene gloves
Inks	Surgical tapes
Insulation materials	Synthetic rubber (neoprene) products
Lacquers	Tapes
Linoleum	Topical pharmaceutical products
Lipsticks	Varnishes
Marking inks	Wart treatment products
Mascaras	Waterproofing products
Medicated ointments	Waxes
Menstrual pads (sanitary napkins)	Wood fillers

[a] Case reports of cosmetic allergy from colophony are shown below in the section 'Case reports and case series'; contact allergy to colophony in other products is discussed in the section 'Contact allergy to colophony in non-cosmetic products' below

There are several types of colophony: gum rosin, wood rosin and tall oil rosin. Gum rosin is manufactured from crude rosin tapped directly from the pine tree *Pinus palustris* and other species of Pinaceae. This oleoresin is steam distilled to separate it into turpentine and a yellowish residue, the colophony. Wood rosin is made from rotted pine tree stumps. These are chipped into small pieces and boiled in aliphatic solvents to extract the crude rosin. The solution is distilled to release a product with a high percentage of oxidized resin acids. Tall oil rosin (liquid rosin) is a by-product of paper manufacturing. Pine wood chips are acid digested to extract cellulose and the crude tall oil is obtained by fractional distillation of the residue. The major producers of gum rosin are China, Portugal, Finland, USA, Russia and Brazil; Sweden, Finland, USA, Russia and Japan (also) produce tall oil rosin (17,40,91).

Applications

Colophony is widely distributed and has three main properties: it has good tackifying qualities, it can be used as an emulsifier, and it has acid properties without causing corrosion (55). Colophony is used in a large range of products. Examples are given in table 2.126.1. The largest users of colophony are the paper, adhesive, and printing industries. Contact with colophony may be both occupational and non-occupational.

Resin acids in colophony may also be hydrogenated, esterified or otherwise modified in the presence of for example glycerin, pentaerythritol, maleic anhydride, fumaric acid, formaldehyde or ethylene glycol, or modified by salt formation or polymerization, to form modified colophony compounds, Modified colophonies are rarely pure substances and will almost certainly contain a percentage of the unmodified product. Modified colophony products are widely used in industry; in fact, most of the colophony used today is modified. As a consequence, exposure to (modified) colophony is universal (17,33,91).

Composition of colophony

Colophony is a heterogeneous mixture of >100 chemicals, consisting of approximately 90% resin acids and 10% neutral substances. The neutral fraction consists of terpenes, terpene alcohols, sesquiterpenes and diterpene hydrocarbons, aldehydes and alcohols. The chemical composition is variable and depends on the species extracted, climate, extraction method, storing method and many other parameters. The resin acids can be divided into abietic types (abietic acid [the most important constituent], palustric, levopimaric and dehydroabietic acids) and pimaric types (pimaric, isopimaric and sandarapimaric acids), the former being characterized by a double conjugated bond that is missing in the latter.

The most important resin acid in colophony is abietic acid. Pure abietc acid and other resin acids are not allergenic according to some (137,151), but others claim that pure abietic acid does have sensitizing properties (169). Undisputed is that the acids are very prone to oxidation in the atmosphere (auto-oxidation), and that this results in the formation of stronger allergenic products (28,39), the most potent of which are 15-hydroperoxyabietic acid and 7-oxodehydroabietic acid (54,169). Also, peroxides, epoxides, ketones, and alcohols of abietic acid and dehydroabietic acid have been identified in oxidized colophony (55). The major chemicals in colophony identified as contact allergens are shown in table 2.126.2. The neutral fraction may also contain sensitizing constituents (138,167,206).

Table 2.126.2 Chemicals identified as contact allergens in colophony (40,55,95,132,140,169)

Chemical	Comments
Unmodified colophony	
Oxidation products	
Di-(dehydroabietic acid 15-yl)peroxide	Oxidation product of dehydroabietic acid
Di(methyl dehydroabietate-15-yl)peroxide	Oxidation product of dehydroabietic acid (203)
13,14(α)-Epoxyabietic acid	Oxidation product of abietic acid (132)
13,14(β)-Epoxyabietic acid	Oxidation product of abietic acid (111,132)
15-Hydroperoxyabietic acid	Oxidation product of abietic acid, unstable
15-Hydroperoxydehydroabietic acid	Oxidation product of dehydroabietic acid, low concentration
12α-Hydroxyabietic acid	Oxidation product of levopimaric acid; only tested in guinea pigs (122)
15-Hydroxydehydroabietic acid	Oxidation product of dehydroabietic acid (141)
15-Hydroxy-7-oxodehydroabietic acid	Oxidation product of dehydroabietic acid
7-Oxodehydroabietic acid	Oxidation product of dehydroabietic acid (111,132,141)
18,12-Peroxo-7,8-dihydroabietic acid	Oxidation product of resin acids; only tested in guinea pigs (122)

Table 2.126.2 Chemicals identified as contact allergens in colophony (40,55,95,132,140,169) (*continued*)

Chemical	Comments
Unmodified colophony	
Other chemicals	
Pure abietic acid	See ref. 169
Other pure resin acids	Levopimaric, neoabietic, palustric and pimaric acids; infrequent sensitizers (169)
Modified colophony	
Fumaropimaric acid	Minor constituent of fumaric acid modification: weak sensitizer
Glyceryl-1-monoabietate	Main constituent of glycerin modification; does not cross-react with unmodified colophony (109,121)
Maleopimaric acid	Main constituent of maleic anhydride or fumaric acid modification; does not cross-react with unmodified colophony (100,109,135,214)
Pentaerythritol esterified colophony	Complex mixture of compounds: does not cross-react with unmodified colophony

Miscellaneous information

In patients reacting to modified colophony compounds, the unmodified colophony 20% in petrolatum in the baseline series is often negative. The modified products appear to be more potent sensitizers than the unmodified material (84). Colophony is an – albeit weak - indicator of fragrance sensitization (10). In 1992, the International Fragrance Association (IFRA) recommended that crude colophony no longer be used in fragrance compositions due to its sensitizing potential (18). Important articles and theses on chemistry, allergenic activity and uses of (modified) colophony not discussed in this chapter include refs. 97 and 251-255.

CONTACT ALLERGY

Contact allergy in the general population and subgroups

There have been investigations in several European countries, in which random samples of the population of certain age groups have been patch tested with colophony (table 2.126.3). Frequencies of sensitization have ranged from 0.6% to 1.2% (52,68,171,233,235). In two Danish studies, the patch tests were read only at day 2, which may have resulted in underestimation of the actual rate of sensitization (233,235). The frequencies in women were higher than in men in 4/5 studies (table 2.126.3).

In subgroups of the general population, somewhat higher rates of sensitization to colophonium have been observed of 1.6% in German adults aged 28-78 years, comprising a large percentage (>50%) of atopic individuals (56,231) and of 2% in a follow-up study of a group of 442 unselected 8th grade schoolchildren in Denmark, 15 years later (170). In all subgroup studies, women had higher prevalence scores than men, which may be explained by the relationship of colophony to fragrances and fragrance allergy being more prevalent in the female population.

Table 2.126.3   Contact allergy in the general population and in subgroups

Year and country	Selection and number tested	Prevalence of contact allergy			Comments	Ref.
		Total	Women	Men		
General population						
2008-11 five European countries	general population, random sample, 18-74 years, n=3119	0.9%	1.4%	0.4%		171
2008 Denmark	general population, random sample, 15-41 years, n=469		1.4%	0%	patch tests were read on day 2 only	235
2006 Denmark	general population, random sample, 18-69 years, n=3460	0.6%	0.5%	0.7%	patch tests were read on day 2 only	233
2005 Norway	general population, random sample, 18-69 years, n=1236	1.2%	1.4%	0.9%		68
1990 Denmark	general population, random sample, 18-69 years, n=543	0.7%	1.1%	0.4%	patch tests were read on day 2 only; data from 15-17 years old excluded in the data presented here	52

Table 2.126.3   Contact allergy in the general population and in subgroups (*continued*)

Year and country	Selection and number tested	Prevalence of contact allergy			Comments	Ref.
		Total	Women	Men		
Subgroups						
2010 Denmark	unselected population of 8th grade schoolchildren in Denmark, 15 years later; n=442	2.0%	2.2%	0.8%	follow-up study	170
1997-1998 Germany	adults 28-78 year, with a large percentage (>50%) of atopic individuals, n=1141	1.6%	2.2%	1.6%		56, 231
1995-1996 Denmark	8th grade school children, 12-16 years, n=1146	1.0%	1.3%	0.8%		234, 236
1989 Italy	male soldiers without skin disease, 18-28 years, n=593	0.2%				232

A 10-year prevalence (1992-2002) of contact allergy to colophony in the population in Germany based on the positive reactions to the baseline series in 78,067 dermatitis patients was estimated to be 1.4-0.6% (57). Using the same CE-DUR method, a prevalence of 0.84-0.62% of colophony allergy was later (2006) calculated in the Danish population (58).

Patch testing in groups of patients

Results of studies testing colophony in consecutive patients suspected of contact dermatitis (routine testing) back to 2000 are shown in table 2.126.4. Results of testing in groups of *selected* patients (e.g., children with dermatitis, patients with stasis dermatitis / leg ulcers, individuals suspected of cosmetic dermatitis, patients with periorbital dermatitis or cheilitis) back to 1994 are shown in table 2.126.5.

Patch testing in consecutive patients suspected of contact dermatitis: routine testing

As colophony is included in the European Baseline Series, the screening tray of the North American Contact Dermatitis Group (NACDG) and most other national series routinely tested in consecutive patients suspected of contact dermatitis, there are many data on colophony contact allergy available, notably from European countries and from the USA + Canada, where the NACDG publishes their patch test results biannually.

In 29 studies in which routine testing with colophony was performed, prevalences of sensitization have ranged from 0.8% to 7.5%, the majority being between 2% and 3%. The highest frequency of 7.5% was observed in a 2001-2010 Australian study; 29% of the 388 positive patch test reactions to colophony were considered to be relevant, the causative products were not mentioned (257). In the studies of the ESSCA (European Surveillance System on Contact Allergies), with participants from 10-12 European countries, there was a wide variation between the centers in sensitization rates of 0.3% to 9.3% (1,9,32,73,247,263).

In 16/29 studies, no relevance data were provided. In the NACDG studies, 'definite' + 'probably' relevance rates were invariably low, ranging from 9% to 28% (15,16,30,31,222,223,259). In other investigations, some 30-65% were considered to be relevant (104,179,226,230,257), but culprit products were mentioned in one study only. In this 1999-2008 study from Brazil, there were 50 positive reactions to colophonium in a group of 1672 routinely tested patients, of which 65% (n=33) were scored as relevant. 35 Percent of cases were occupational (construction workers 15%, kitchen workers 6%, cleaners 4%, hairdressers 4%) and 10% were due to home activities (e.g., cleaning products); 33% of the culprit products were cosmetics and 17% shoes (179).

Table 2.126.4 Patch testing in groups of patients: Routine testing

Years and Country	Test conc. & vehicle	Number of patients tested | positive (%)		Selection of patients (S); Relevance (R); Comments (C)	Ref.
2013-2014 12 European countries, 46 departments [b]	20% pet.	26,991	(2.9%)	R: not stated; C: results of 6 occupational dermatology clinics and one pediatric clinic not included in these figures; range of positive reactions: 0.3%-5.2%	247
2013-14 USA, Canada	20% pet.	4858	92 (1.9%)	R: definite + probable relevance: 15%	259
2011-12 USA, Canada	20% pet.	4236	96 (2.3%)	R: definite + probable relevance: 22%	30
2009-2012 12 European countries [b]	20% pet.	57,123	(2.6%) [a]	R: not stated; prevalences ranged from 1.2% (Italy) to 4.8% (Austria)	32
2009-10 USA, Canada	20% pet.	4306	116 (2.7%)	R: definite + probable relevance: 28%	31
2006-2010 USA	20% pet.	3076	(2.6%)	R: 51%	230
2001-2010 Australia	20% pet.	5148	388 (7.5%)	R: 29%	257
2009 Sweden	20% pet.	3112	(2.4%)	R: not stated	183

Table 2.126.4 Patch testing in groups of patients: Routine testing (*continued*)

Years and Country	Test conc. & vehicle	Number of patients tested | positive (%)		Selection of patients (S); Relevance (R); Comments (C)	Ref.
2007-2008, 11 European countries [b]	20% pet.	25,181	666 (2.6%)	R: not stated; prevalences ranged from 1.5% (Italy) to 6.1% (Austria)	1
2007-8 USA, Canada	20% pet.	5083	(2.8%)	R: definite + probable relevance: 24%	16
2005-2008 Denmark	20% pet.	12,302	262 (2.1%)	R: 47%	104
2004-2008 IVDK	20% pet.	37,011	(4.2%) [a]	R: not stated	34
1999-2008 Brazil		1672	(3%)	R: 65%; 35% occupational (construction workers 15%, kitchen workers 6%, cleaners 4%, hairdressers 4%) and 10% due to home activities (e.g., cleaning products); 33% cosmetics, 17% shoes; C: frequent co-reactivity to turpentine (8%), balsam of Peru (15%) and the perfume mix I (33%)	179
2005-6 USA, Canada	20% pet.	4447	(2.2%)	R: definite + probable relevance: 20%	15
2005-6 10 European countries [b]	20% pet.	18,537	672 (3.6%)	R: not stated; C: prevalences in the four regions (Central, West, Northeast and South Europe) ranged from 1.7% to 3.8%	263
2000-2005 USA	20% pet.	3842	(2.6%)	R: 59%	6
2004, 11 European countries [b]	20% pet.	9973	378 (3.8%)	R: not stated; C: range positives: 0.6%-9.3%	9
2000-04 Switzerland	20% pet.	4094	120 (2.9%)	R: not stated	29
1998-2004 Israel	20% pet.	2156	18 (0.8%)	R: not stated	70
1992-2004 Turkey	20% pet.	1038	11 (1.0%)	R: not stated; C: prevalence in women 0.9%, in men 1.2%	228
2002-2003 11 European countries [b]	20% pet.	9676	(3.6%)	R: not stated; C: range of positives 0.6% (Italy) to 6.2% (Germany)	73
2001-2 USA, Canada	20% pet.	4908	(2.6%)	R: definite + probable relevance: 9%	222
2000-2002 Finland		11,802	(3.5%)	R: not stated	227
1999-2001 Sweden	20% pet.	3790	(3.4%)	R: not stated; C: prevalence in women 3.6%, in men 3.1% (standardized prevalences)	224
1997-2001 Czech Rep.	20% pet.	12,058	346 (2.9%)	R: not stated	74
2000 United Kingdom	20% pet.	3063	(5.2%)	R: 60% (current and past relevance in one center)	226
1998-00 USA, Canada	20% pet.	5833	(2.5%)	R: definite + probable relevance: 12%	223
1998-2000 USA	20% pet.	1322	(2.5%)	R: not stated	225
1996-2000 Europe	20% pet.	26,210	(4.0%)	R: not stated; C: prevalence in women 4.5%, in men 3.2%; C: ten centers, seven countries, EECDRG study	229

[a] age-standardized and sex-standardized percentage
[b] study of the ESSCA (European Surveillance System on Contact Allergies)
EECDRG: European Environmental and Contact Dermatitis Research Group
IVDK: Information Network of Departments of Dermatology, Germany, Austria, Switzerland

Patch testing in groups of selected patients

Results of testing colophonium in groups of selected patients (e.g., children with dermatitis, patients with stasis dermatitis / leg ulcers, individuals suspected of cosmetic dermatitis, patients with periorbital dermatitis or cheilitis) back to 1994 are shown in table 2.126.5. In 25 investigations, frequencies of sensitization have ranged from 0.6% to 13%. Rates of >5% positive reactions have been observed in patients with leg ulcers / stasis dermatitis (13% [271], 11% [67], 7.6% [177], and 6.6% [246]), in children referred for patch testing (9.1% [250]), in patients with eyelid dermatitis (7% [26]), and in (apprentice) hairdressers presenting at an occupational dermatology clinic (6.1% [264]).

In 13/25 investigations, no relevance data were provided. In most studies that did address the relevancy issue, 80-100% of the positive patch tests were considered to be relevant, but in not a single instance were culprit products mentioned (5,249,250,264,268)..

Case reports and case series

Case series

Colophony was stated to be the (or an) allergen in 23 patients in a group of 603 individuals suffering from cosmetic dermatitis, seen in the period 2010-2015 in Leuven, Belgium (37). In the period 1996-2013, in a tertiary referral center in Valencia, Spain, 5419 patients were patch tested. Of these, 628 individuals had allergic contact dermatitis to cosmetics. Colophony was the responsible allergen in five cases (260, overlap with ref. 244). Colophony was responsible for 1 out of 959 cases of non-fragrance cosmetic allergy where the causal allergen was identified, Leuven, Belgium, 2000-2010 (4). In one-third of 51 patients reacting to colophony between 1999 and 2008 in a clinic in Brazil, the sensitization/dermatitis was cosmetic-related (not further specified (179)). In the period 2000-2007, 202 patients with allergic contact dermatitis caused by cosmetics were seen in Valencia, Spain. In this group, three individuals reacted to colophony from its presence in hair removal wax, of which one was a beautician with occupational allergic had dermatitis (244, overlap with ref. 260).

Table 2.126.5 Patch testing in groups of patients: Selected patient groups

Years and Country	Test conc. & vehicle	Number of patients tested	positive (%)	Selection of patients (S); Relevance (R); Comments (C)	Ref.
2013-2015 USA		1109	29 (2.6%)	S: children 0-18 years suspected of contact dermatitis; R: 86%	268
2000-2015 Spain		265	24 (9.1%)	S: children 0-16 years referred for patch testing; R: 100%	250
2003-2014 IVDK	20% pet.	5202	(6.6%)	S: patients with stasis dermatitis/ chronic leg ulcers; R: not stated; C: percentage of reactions significantly higher than in a control group of routine testing	246
2002-2013 Italy	20% pet.	2614	15 (0.6%)	S: children younger than 11 suspected of contact dermatitis; R: 2/15 (13%)	269
1996-2013 Nether-lands	20% pet.	1001	21 (2.1%)	S: children aged 0-17 years; R: not stated	245
2011-2012 Italy		122	1 (0.8%)	S: patients tested with a botanical series, who declared having had adverse reactions to 'botanical' products (cosmetics, detergents, pharmaceutical ointments); R: the reaction was considered to be relevant	270
2006-2011 IVDK	20% pet.	10,124	389 (4.1%)	S: patients suspected of cosmetic intolerance; R: not stated	261
2003-2011 Denmark	20% pet.	2594	62 (2.4%)	S: children 1-17 years old; R: 61%	180
2002-2011 Denmark		399	6 (1.5%)	S: hairdressers with contact dermatitis; R: not stated	265
2006-2010 USA	20% pet.	100	7 (7%)	S: patients with eyelid dermatitis; R: not stated	26
2000-2010 IVDK		4386	155 (3.5%)	S: patients with periorbital dermatitis; R: not stated	35
1993-2010 Australia		164	10 (6.1%)	S: hairdressers and apprentice hairdressers presenting at an occupational dermatology clinic; R: 90%	264
<2010 China	20% pet.	205	(1.5%)	S: healthy Chinese student volunteers; R: not stated	46
<2010 China	20% pet.	327	(4.6%)	S: Chinese students with dermatitis; R: not stated	46
2004-2008 France	20% pet.	423	32 (7.6%)	S: patients with chronic leg ulcers; R: not stated; C: there was an association with reactions to one brand of transparent dressings	177
2000-2007 USA	20% pet.	942	24 (2.5%)	S: patients tested with a supplemental cosmetic screening series; R: 92%; C: weak study: a. high rate of macular erythema and weak reactions; b. relevance figures included 'questionable' and 'past' relevance	5
2005-2006 Singapore	20% pet.	44	5 (11%)	S: patients with chronic venous (or mixed venous and arterial) leg ulcers; R: not stated	67
2005-2006 Thailand		1178	(2.0%)	S: adult volunteers 18-55 years, recruited by advertising R: not stated; C: patch tests read at D2 only; prevalence in women 2.7%, in men 1.4%	24
2001-2006 Italy	20% pet.	129	4 (3.1%)	S: patients with chronic cheilitis; R: 1 reaction was relevant	267
1998-04 USA, Canada	20% pet.	1253	3 (0.2%)	S: health care workers; R: only occupation-related (=relevant) reactions were recorded; C: considering this selection, the frequency of sensitization is low; the frequency was not signi-ficantly higher than the rate of occupation-related reactions in non-health care workers (0.2%)	258
1995-2004 UK	20% pet.	500	9 (1.8%)	S:children 0-16 years with dermatitis; R: 7/9 (78%)	249
1994-2004 USA	20% pet.	46	2 (4%)	S: patients with allergic contact dermatitis of the eyelids; R: both reactions were relevant, products not mentioned	69
2000-2002 Serbia	20% pet.	75	10 (13%)	S: patients with venous leg ulcers and dermatitis of the surrounding skin; R: not stated	271
1995-1999 IVDK	20% pet.	967	(3.3%)	S: patients with allergic periorbital contact dermatitis; R: not stated	241
1990-1994 IVDK		587	18 (3.1%)	S: patients with periorbital eczema; R: not stated	266

IVDK: Information Network of Departments of Dermatology, Germany, Austria, Switzerland

Five patients reacting to colophony in a makeup source were identified by the NACDG in 1582 female patients with (presumed) cosmetic allergy between 2001 and 2004 (7). In a group of 146 patients patch tested for cheilitis in Amersham, UK, between 1982 and 2001, there were 4 positive patch test reactions to colophony considered to be relevant for the lip dermatitis. Over half of the reactions in the entire group were ascribed to lipsticks and lip salves (221). In a group of 119 patients with allergic contact dermatitis from cosmetics, investigated in The Netherlands in 1986-1987, one case was caused by colophony in a mascara (237,238). In 3 clinics in Belgium, in the period 1978-

1985, 279 patients with allergic contact dermatitis exclusively caused by cosmetics were seen. In this group, there were 11 reactions to colophony. It was implied that this was the cause of the allergic reaction (256).

Case reports
A female patient had contact allergy to colophony in eye shadow and mascara (8). Another woman reacted to a lipstick sealant (27). One patient had cheilitis and perioral dermatitis from a lipstick containing 0.07% colophony (103). One individual had facial dermatitis from colophony in rouge (164), another one reacted to colophony in soap (165). Two women had ACD from colophony in eyeshadow (240), another one reacted to colophony in an eye shadow (239). An unknown number of patients had cosmetic dermatitis caused by colophony, probably in mascaras (61). An early publication reported an outbreak of dermatitis from colophony in hair lacquer (93).

Contact allergy to colophony in non-cosmetic products
Colophony has caused many cases of allergic contact dermatitis from a great variety of products other than cosmetics, both in occupational and non-occupational settings (partial literature review up to 1999: ref. 40). Airborne allergic contact dermatitis has been reported frequently, especially from contact with pine sawdust and from the fumes of colophony released from soldering flux. Responsible published product categories are shown in table 2.126.6 and are discussed below. Products containing the pentaerythritol ester of colophony, which have caused allergic contact dermatitis, notably hydrocolloid dressings, are discussed in Chapter 2.347 Pentaerythrityl rosinate.

Table 2.126.6 Non-cosmetic colophony-containing product categories reported as causes of allergic contact dermatitis

Adhesives and adhesive materials	Paper and paper products
Colophony (products) used for string instruments	Pine trees, pine sawdust and pine wood
Colophony (products) used in sports	Soldering fluxes
Dental products	Topical pharmaceutical products
Inks	Waxes, polishes and depilatory products
Metalworking fluids	Miscellaneous products

Adhesives and adhesive materials
Many patients allergic to colophony know that they may react to certain plasters or adhesive tapes. Single case reports can be found in refs. 33,77,123,130,139,161,193,197,198,212 and 218. Four cases of contact allergy to colophony in surgical adhesives have been described (204) as was a single case of a reaction to bindi adhesive (118). Sometimes the adhesive was sprayed to help secure tapes, underwrap and elastic wraps (48) or colophony-containing benzoin was sprayed on dressings (186). Airborne allergic contact dermatitis from colophony used as adhesive in car door linings has also been observed (98).

Topical pharmaceutical products
Seven patients with contact allergy to colophony in topical pharmaceutical products were seen in one clinic in Belgium between 1978 and 2008 (2). There have been several single case reports on contact allergy to wart treatments (124,131,178,198,205,217) and one publication describing 3 such cases (142). Other products have included an alternative remedy (19), nitroglycerin transdermal therapeutic system (134), and ointment (188). No cases of *occupational* allergic contact dermatitis to colophony in topical pharmaceutical products appear to have been published.

Soldering fluxes
Soldering flux is a well-known cause of occupational allergic contact dermatitis from colophony. Two (153) and three (155) cases have been described. During soldering, fumes are released from the colophony by the high temperature, which may result in airborne contact dermatitis (108 [2 cases], 136, 146). In one patient, the allergic contact dermatitis was accompanied by phototoxicity (136). Much more frequent than allergic contact dermatitis is occupational asthma from inhaling the fumes (see below in the section 'Miscellaneous side effects').

Inks
Allergic contact dermatitis from colophony-containing permanent markers has been described several times (20,21,45,180), sometimes from its use in patch testing (20,220). In one case, a patient reacted to the marker for patch testing and to colophony and abietic acid, but the presence of colophony in the ink could not be ascertained (219).

Dental products

Colophony may be present in dental materials such as periodontal dressings, impression materials, cements, fix adhesives and varnishes (62). Occupational allergic contact dermatitis in dental personnel has been reported from colophony in dental fluoride varnish (87,96), baseplate molding material (88), impression material (162), and dental paste (96). Some reports of contact stomatitis and lichen oris from dental material containing colophony have also been published (62). Causative products were dental fluoride varnish (62,87) and periodontal dressing (208). Contact allergy to colophony in dental floss and interdens toothpicks has caused allergic contact cheilitis (210). Widespread dermatitis from colophony in a dental product was attributed to systemic exposure (201).

Pine trees, pine sawdust and pine wood

Pine trees, pine wood and pine sawdust contain oleoresin, the source material of colophony, and may cause contact dermatitis in colophony-sensitive individuals. The dermatitis may both be occupational (e.g., in carpenters, mill workers, cabinet makers, woodwork teachers, horticulturists) and non-occupational. Exposure to pine dust frequently results in airborne contact dermatitis on the face.

Occupational allergic contact dermatitis from sawdust was reported in refs. 85,159 (2 patients) and 86 (5 cases), non-occupational cases in refs. 76 and 149. For cases of *airborne* occupational allergic contact dermatitis see refs. 75,89,105,106,107 (2 patients), and 90 (4 cases). Occupational dermatitis from contact with pine wood was reported in ref. 114 (woodwork teacher) and with trees in 125 (horticulturalist transplanting young pine trees) and in 138 (carpenter). For non-occupational cases see refs. 77 (trees) and 192 (chair made of untreated pine wood).

Paper

Paper may be an important, but probably underdiagnosed, source of colophony contact dermatitis. Twelve patients with known allergy to colophony all reacted to patch tests with extracts of newsprint paper (63). Ten individuals with established colophony allergy all reacted to paper extracts in a similar study (176). Of a group of 27 patients having frequent contact with paper at work, only those 8 who proved to be allergic to colophony (and one not reacting to colophony) had positive tests to paper extracts. None of ten healthy controls reacted to the paper extracts, attesting to the specificity of the test (176). Occupational allergic contact dermatitis has been the result of colophony allergy in lottery tickets (102), banknote paper (116), newspaper (154) and various sorts of paper (136, 6 patients). Non-occupational cases have been reported from newspaper (63,126) and cigarette paper (138).

Paper products

Occupational allergic contact dermatitis has been reported from carton dust (109) and paper-based surgical clothing in a surgeon (119). Colophony in sanitary napkins/pads may cause vulvar dermatitis (20,41).

Metalworking fluids

Metalworkers working with metalworking fluids have an eight times higher risk of sensitization to colophony than metalworkers with occupational allergic contact dermatitis not working with these products (50). Cases are reported in refs. 53 (airborne contact dermatitis) and 64 (4 patients).

Colophony (products) used for string instruments

Colophony ('string players' colophony') is commonly applied to the strings of string instruments like violins and violoncello's in order to increase the attrition between the bow and the strings, which influences the production of sound and stabilizes bow contact (82). However, colophony may cause dermatitis of the fingers and hands, as well as of the face and neck in colophony-allergic individuals. This is seen especially in professional string musicians such as violinists and cellists (79,80,82,173), sometimes in amateur players (33,81,120 [causing vulvar dermatitis], 61 [specifics unknown], 174 [specifics unknown]). Contact dermatitis and other skin conditions in instrumental musicians have been reviewed (175)

Colophony (products) used in sports

As colophony exhibits the property of tackiness, colophony and colophony bags are used in multiple sports to enhance grip. Such sports include baseball, rock-climbing, weight lifting, gymnastics, tennis, golf, and bowling. Allergic contact dermatitis from 'bowlers' grip' has been reported repeatedly: refs. 200 (2 patients), 209 (not absolutely certain the material contained colophony) and 191 (dermatitis not on the hand but on the face, 'ectopic' dermatitis). Pure colophony to get more grip on a squash racket handle has caused hand dermatitis (163).

Waxes, polishes and depilatory products

Depilatory products containing colophony have caused allergic contact dermatitis in consumers (22,25,33) and in patients handling the material professionally: refs. 113, 138 (beautician), 216 (beautician), 213 (cosmetologist; from self-prepared depilatory containing colophony), and 161 (depilatory to remove hair from pigs). Other incriminated products have included floor polish (109, occupational airborne contact dermatitis), wax for polishing spectacle frames (199), garage door wax (33) and beeswax, to which colophony had been added to improve adherence, used by an accordion repairer (202).

Miscellaneous products

Miscellaneous colophony-containing products that have caused published cases of allergic contact dermatitis are shown in table 2.126.7.

Table 2.126.7 Miscellaneous colophony-containing products that have caused published cases of allergic contact dermatitis

Occupational allergic contact dermatitis	Non-occupational allergic contact dermatitis
Colophony powder applied to the surface of a machine operating leather belt (166)	Detergent (163)
Colophony used by dancers, dermatitis in their masseur (147)	ECG electrodes (from soldering during manufacturing) (66,190)
Compound mixture of petrol, pitch, colophony, and antirust oil (143)	Flexible collodion BP used to immobilize traumatized fingers and toes (157)
Crude colophony in extractors (47,184)	Lubricant used on leather belts (161)
Linoleum floor (109, airborne)	Neoprene rubber in thermal sauna short (189)
Paint (126)	Outbreak from fabric finishes (94)
Print protective coating (211) (details unknown)	Toilet seat, probably the varnish (182)
Sand cores (158)	Shoes (leather tanning, linings, tackifiers) (51,83,215)
Violin lacquer, dermatitis in a violinist (78)	Swelling of the lips from chewing gum (99)

Cross-reactions, pseudo-cross-reactions and co-reactions

Compounds causing possible cross- or pseudo-cross-reactions from or to colophony and co-reactions are shown in table 2.126.8.

Table 2.126.8 Compounds causing possible cross-reactions or pseudo-cross-reactions to and from colophony and co-reactions

β-Caryophyllene	Fragrance mix I/*Juniperus chinensis* L. Hetzii
Compositae plants	Mastix (mastic)
Compound tincture of benzoin	*Myroxylon pereirae* resin
Cupressus × leylandii	Oxidized limonene
Essential oils (incl. oil of turpentine)	Oxidized linalool
Evernia furfuracea extract (tree moss)	Propolis
Evernia prunastri (oak moss absolute)	Wood tar

It is well known that there are frequent co-reactivities between colophony and the fragrance mix I (34,168,248) and FM II (104,248). Other chemicals that co-react more often than expected by chance include *Myroxylon pereirae* resin (10,248), propolis (10,248), essential oils (72,172) including oil of turpentine (which can be expected as colophony and oil of turpentine are prepared from the same source material, pine oleoresin) (34), wood tar (86,168), β-caryophyllene (72) and Compositae plants (72,172). There are also frequent co-reactions between colophony and both oxidized limonene (59) and oxidized linalool (60). Besides concomitant sensitization this could be caused by the allergenic hydroperoxides forming nonspecific antigens (55). Then, cross-reactions between hydroperoxides with significantly different structures could be observed (55). Primary sensitization to FM1, FM2 or *Myroxylon pereirae* is *not* often accompanied by co-reactivity to colophony (248).

Many patients reacting to *Evernia furfuracea* extract (tree moss) co-react to colophony. This is caused by contamination of *E. furfuracea* by relevant quantities of pieces of bark of the host trees, mainly pine and fir trees. In a recent analysis, 2.2-4.8% wt./wt. total resin acids have been analytically identified in typical samples of *E. furfuracea* raw material (38), including allergens (oxidized resin acids) found in colophony such as the oxidation product 7-oxo-dehydroabietic acid (11). Previously, approximately 5.2-5.6% dehydroabietic acid has been found in tree moss by leading producers of tree moss (cited in ref. 36). Thus, the concomitant reactions of colophony and tree moss probably are the result of common allergens, presumably oxidized resin acids (36). A (non-binding) industry IFRA standard indicates that 'tree moss extracts shall not contain more than 0.8% of dehydroabietic acid ... (about 40% of the total resin acids)' (cited in ref. 36), which means that co-reactivities can be anticipated.

Concomitant reactivity between oak moss absolute (*Evernia prunastri*) and colophony, which could be regarded as indicative of contamination by (oxidized) resin acids, has been previously identified in a number of patients (11).

In later studies, however, this phenomenon was found to be rather limited in extensive clinical patch testing (12, 13), although significant in one study (14). Formerly, many of the oak moss absolutes were deliberately mixed with tree moss absolute, for cost reasons, which may have explained a certain degree of co-reactivity (34).

Concomitant reactions between colophony and extract of the leylandcypress *Cupressus × leylandii* (150), between colophony and *Juniperus chinensis* L. Hetzii (152) and between colophony and mastix, also known as mastic, the resin of the mastic tree *Pistacia lentiscus* (71,117) may point at common constituents or cross-reacting allergenic substances. Of 45 patients reacting to compound tincture of benzoin (benzoin 10%, aloe 2%, styrax 8%, Tolu balsam 4% in alcohol 95%), nine (20%) co-reacted to colophony (194).

Presence in cosmetic and non-cosmetic products and chemical analyses

Cosmetics

In August 2017, colophony was present in 25 (colophony) and 14 (rosin) of 70,676 cosmetic products of which the composition is known in EWG's Skin Deep Cosmetics Database, USA (http://www.ewg.org/skindeep/). In 2009, in the USA, the ingredient lists of 796 hair products from one company were screened for the presence of colophony. Colophony was present in 7% of 279 shampoos, in 4% of 231 conditioners, and in 0% of 286 styling products (243). Of eight mascaras analysed with High Performance Liquid Chromatography (HPLC), colophony was found in 3. These contained 0.017-1.14% abietic acid, corresponding to about 0.05-3% colophony. The higher concentrations elicited allergic patch test reactions in 10 out of 11 colophony-sensitive individuals (3). Of 22 mascaras purchased in Finland, 3 contained resin acids in the concentration range 0.25-0.7%, corresponding to about 0.4-1% colophony (112).

Non-cosmetic products

Colophony was present in 9 out of 370 topical pharmaceutical products marketed in Belgium (2). Resin acids of colophony were detected in seven out of 17 investigated metalworking fluids from Finland in concentrations ranging from 0.41% to 3.8% (49). The adhesive material of 25 out of 30 types of bindi investigated contained abietic acid (range: 0.05-0.83 µg) and 27 contained dehydroabietic acid in amounts ranging from 0.02µg to 1.53 µg (118).

Of 5 types neoprene gloves, 4 contained dehydroabietic acid in amounts ranging from 7 to 31 mg/kg (181). Colophony was demonstrated in 3 of 5 patch test adhesive materials (207). In sanitary pads, the highest content of resin acids found was 0.056%, corresponding to approximately 0.08% colophony (42). Analysis of abietic acid and dehydroabietic acid in topical (traditional Chinese) medicaments has been performed in ref. 101 and in technical products of Swedish origin in ref. 133. Analyses of linoleum and of floor dust can be found in ref. 109.

Other information

Some mascaras contain enough colophony to produce a positive patch test in colophony-allergic patients (3).

OTHER SIDE EFFECTS

Photosensitivity

Combined airborne allergic contact dermatitis and phototoxicity to colophony from vaporized colophony in soldering flux has been reported (136). A patient with chronic actinic dermatitis and extreme contact allergy to colophony also had photosensitivity to colophony, which was neither phototoxic nor photoallergic; the relevance of the reactions remained uncertain (195). In a study in China performed between 2005 and 2014, 5298 patients with suspected photodermatoses were photopatch tested with colophony (test concentration 2% ??) and 64 (1.2%) had a positive photopatch test; the relevance of the reactions was not mentioned (262).

Immediate-type reactions

One patient developed contact urticaria from abietic acid in an adhesive (115). Occupational allergic airborne contact urticaria from colophony released from soldering flux has been observed (144). In a group of 664 patch tested patients, there were 3 (0.5%) immediate contact reactions to colophony as shown by 'well distinguished erythema' after 30 minutes (242).

Other non-eczematous contact reactions

Oral ulcers and burning mouth from chewing colophony-containing chewing gum has been described (99). One patient had lichen planus oris ascribed to contact allergy to colophony in an adhesive used to glue a broken dental prosthesis (128)

Systemic side effects

Colophony in a dental product may have caused widespread dermatitis (systemic contact dermatitis) from absorption through the oral mucosa (201).

Miscellaneous side effects

Colophony is a common cause of occupational asthma, ranking in the top five causes in the UK (196). The problem is seen especially in employees soldering conductive connections in the electrical or electronic industry who inhale colophony fumes; prevalences of 5 to 20% have been mentioned (17,65,91,145,156). Specific IgE antibodies to colophony have been detected in the serum of some such patients (65), but the asthma is usually considered to be caused by nonspecific irritation. Occupational asthma is mostly caused by the fumes of heated colophony from soldering and occasionally from hot melt glues or depilatory mixtures (196). However, sporadic cases caused by unheated material have been described, e.g., in a violin player (187), from colophony added as a deodorant to coolant oils (196), floor cleaning products (196) and from colophony in sealing wax (92).

Rhinitis, eye irritation and, perhaps, headache and allergic alveolitis may also be caused by exposure to colophony (17). One patient developed urticaria after the application of colophony and eugenol following gingivectomy (129). In another individual, contact allergy to colophony may have been the result of passive transfer through an allogenic bone-marrow transplantation (139). Rhinoconjunctivitis in a cosmetologist was caused by colophony fumes emerging from heated depilatory wax (213).

LITERATURE

1　Uter W, Aberer W, Armario-Hita JC, Fernandez-Vozmediano JM, Ayala F, Balato A, et al. Current patch test results with the European baseline series and extensions to it from the 'European Surveillance System on Contact Allergy' network, 2007-2008. Contact Dermatitis 2012;67:9-19

2　Nardelli A, D'Hooge E, Drieghe J, Dooms M, Goossens A. Allergic contact dermatitis from fragrance components in specific topical pharmaceutical products in Belgium. Contact Dermatitis 2009;60:303-313

3　Karlberg A-T, Lidén C, Ehrin E. Colophony in mascara as a cause of eyelid dermatitis. Chemical analyses and patch testing. Acta Derm Venereol 1991;71:445-447

4　Travassos AR, Claes L, Boey L, Drieghe J, Goossens A. Non-fragrance allergens in specific cosmetic products. Contact Dermatitis 2011;65:276-285

5　Wetter DA, Yiannias JA, Prakash AV, Davis MD, Farmer SA, el-Azhary RA. Results of patch testing to personal care product allergens in a standard series and a supplemental cosmetic series: an analysis of 945 patients from the Mayo Clinic Contact Dermatitis Group, 2000-2007. J Am Acad Dermatol 2010;63:789-798

6　Davis MDP, Scalf LA, Yiannias JA, Cheng JF, El-Azhary RA, Rohlinger AL, et al. Changing trends and allergens in the patch test standard series. Arch Dermatol 2008;144:67-72

7　Warshaw EM, Buchholz HJ, Belsito DV, Maibach HI, Fowler JF Jr, Rietschel RL, et al. Allergic patch test reactions associated with cosmetics: Retrospective analysis of cross-sectional data from the North American Contact Dermatitis Group, 2001-2004. J Am Acad Dermatol 2009;60:23-38

8　Fisher AA. Allergic contact dermatitis to rosin (colophony) in eyeshadow and mascara. Cutis 1988;42:507-508

9　ESSCA Writing Group. The European Surveillance System of Contact Allergies (ESSCA): results of patch testing the standard series, 2004. J Eur Acad Dermatol Venereol 2008;22:174-181

10　Wöhrl S, Hemmer W, Focke M, Götz M, Jarisch R. The significance of fragrance mix, balsam of Peru, colophonium and propolis as screening tools in the detection of fragrance allergy. Br J Dermatol 2001;145:268-273

11　Lepoittevin JP, Meschkat E, Huygens S, Goossens A. Presence of resin acids in 'oakmoss' patch test materials: a source of misdiagnosis? J Invest Dermatol 2000;115:129-130

12　UterW, Gefeller O, Geier J, Schnuch A. Limited concordance between 'oakmoss' and colophony in clinical patch testing. J Invest Dermatol 2001;116:478-480

13　Buckley DA, Rycroft RJ,White IR, McFadden JP. Contaminating resin acids have not caused the high rate of sensitivity to oak moss. Contact Dermatitis 2002;47:19-20

14　Johansen JD, Heydorn S, Menné T. Oak moss extracts in the diagnosis of fragrance contact allergy. Contact Dermatitis 2002;46:157-161

15　Zug KA, Warshaw EM, Fowler JF jr, Maibach HI, Belsito DL, Pratt MD, et al. Patch-test results of the North American Contact Dermatitis Group 2005-2006. Dermatitis 2009;20:149-160

16　Fransway AF, Zug KA, Belsito DV, Deleo VA, Fowler JF Jr, Maibach HI, et al. North American Contact Dermatitis Group patch test results for 2007-2008. Dermatitis 2013;24:10-21

17　Keira T, Aizawa Y, Karube H, Niituya M, Shinohara S, Kuwashima A, et al. Adverse effects of colophony. Industrial Health 1997;35:1-7

18　International Fragrance Association. Code of Practice. Colophonium. Geneva, Switzerland: IFRA, 1992

19 Doukaki S, Pistone G, Aricò M, Bongiorno MR. Allergic contact dermatitis with contact urticaria to colophony from an alternative remedy. Dermatitis 2012;23:298-299

20 Rademaker M. Allergic contact dermatitis to a sanitary pad. Australas J Dermatol 2004;45:234-235

21 Martin-Garcia C, Conde Salazar L, Gonzalez-Mendioca R, Hinojosa M, Sanchez-Cano H. Contact dermatitis due to Edding 3000. Allergy 2004;59:235-236

22 Quain RD, Militello G, Crawford GH. Allergic contact dermatitis caused by colophony in an epilating product. Dermatitis 2007;18:96-88

23 Karlberg AT. Pure abietic acid is not allergenic. Contact Dermatitis 1989;21:282-285

24 White JML, Gilmour NJ, Jeffries D, Duangdeeden I, Kullavanijaya P, Basketter DA, et al. A general population from Thailand: incidence of common allergens with emphasis on para-phenylenediamine. Clin Exp Allergy 2007;37:1848-1853

25 Lauriola MM, De Bitonto A, Ermini G, Lenzi O, Pigatto PD. Allergic contact dermatitis from depilatory wax. Dermatitis 2012;23:126-127

26 Wenk KS, Ehrlich AE. Fragrance series testing in eyelid dermatitis. Dermatitis 2012;23:22-26

27 Rademaker M, Kirby JD, White IR. Contact cheilitis to shellac, Lanpol 5 and colophony. Contact Dermatitis 1986;15:307-308

28 Gafvert E, Shao LP, Karlberg AT, Nilsson U, Nilsson JL. Contact allergy to resin acid hydroperoxides. Hapten binding via free radicals and epoxides. Chem Res Toxicol 1994;7:260-266

29 Janach, M, Kühne A, Seifert B, French LE, Ballmer-Weber B, Hofbauer GFL. Changing delayed-type sensitizations to the baseline series allergens over a decade at the Zurich University Hospital. Contact Dermatitis 2010;63:42-48

30 Warshaw EM, Maibach HI, Taylor JS, Sasseville D, DeKoven JG, Zirwas MJ, et al. North American Contact Dermatitis Group patch test results: 2011-2012. Dermatitis 2015;26:49-59

31 Warshaw EM, Belsito DV, Taylor JS, Sasseville D, DeKoven JG, Zirwas MJ, et al. North American Contact Dermatitis Group patch test results: 2009 to 2010. Dermatitis 2013;24:50-59

32 Frosch PJ, Johansen JD, Schuttelaar M-LA, Silvestre JF, Sánchez-Pérez J, Weisshaar E, Uter W (on behalf of the ESSCA network). Patch test results with fragrance markers of the baseline series – analysis of the European Surveillance System on Contact Allergies (ESSCA) network 2009–2012. Contact Dermatitis 2015;73:163-171

33 Vandebuerie L, Aerts C, Goossens A. Allergic contact dermatitis resulting from multiple colophonium-related allergen sources. Contact Dermatitis 2014;70:117-119

34 Uter W, Geier J, Frosch P, Schnuch A. Contact allergy to fragrances: current patch test results (2005–2008) from the Information Network of Departments of Dermatology. Contact Dermatitis 2010;63:254-261

35 Landeck L, John SM, Geier J. Periorbital dermatitis in 4779 patients – patch test results during a 10-year period. Contact Dermatitis 2014;70:205-212

36 Uter W, Schmidt E, Lessmann H, Schnuch A. Contact sensitization to tree moss (*Evernia furfuracea* extract, INCI) is heterogeneous. Contact Dermatitis 2012;67:36-41

37 Goossens A. Cosmetic contact allergens. Cosmetics 2016;3. doi: 10.3390/cosmetics3010005

38 Joulain D, Tabacchi R. Lichen extracts as raw materials in perfumery. Part 2: treemoss. Flavour Fragance J 2009;24:105-116

39 Karlberg AT. Contact allergy to colophony. Chemical identifications of allergens, sensitization experiments and clinical experiences. Acta Derm Venereol Suppl (Stockh) 1988:139:1-43

40 Downs AMR, Sansom JE. Colophony allergy: a review. Contact Dermatitis 1999;41:305-310

41 Wujanto L, Wakelin S. Allergic contact dermatitis to colophonium in a sanitary pad–an overlooked allergen?. Contact Dermatitis 2012;66:161-162

42 Kanerva L, Rintala H, Henriks-Eckerman K, Engström K. Colophonium in sanitary pads. Contact Dermatitis 2001;44:53-54

43 McKenna KE, Burrows D. Allergy to patch test marking ink. Contact Dermatitis 1994;30:182-183

44 Karlberg AT, Magnusson K. Rosin components identified in diapers. Contact Dermatitis 1996;34:176-180

45 Fesquet E, Guillot B, Raison-Peyron N. Allergic contact dermatitis to rosin after a single accidental permanent marker skin contact. Contact Dermatitis 2006;55:58-59

46 Li LF. Contact sensitization to European baseline series of allergens in university students in Beijing. Contact Dermatitis 2010;62:371-372

47 Scherrer M, Francisca Junqueira A. Allergic contact dermatitis to natural resin rare among gum rosin extractors? Contact Dermatitis 2010;62:64-65

48 Sasseville D, Saber M, Lessard L. Allergic contact dermatitis from tincture of benzoin with multiple concomitant reactions. Contact Dermatitis 2009;61:358-360

49 Henriks-Eckerman M-L, Suuronen K, Jolanki R. Analysis of allergens in metalworking fluids. Contact Dermatitis 2008;59:261-267

50   Geier J, Lessmann H, Schnuch A, Uter W. Contact sensitizations in metalworkers with occupational dermatitis exposed to water-based metalworking fluids: results of the research project "FaSt". Int Arch Occup Environ Health 2004;77:543-551

51   Bugnet LD, Sanchez-Politta S, Sorg O, Piletta P. Allergic contact dermatitis to colophonium-contaminated socks. Contact Dermatitis 2008;59:127-128

52   Nielsen SH, Menné T. Allergic contact sensitization in an unselected Danish population. The Glostrup Allergy Study, Denmark. Acta Derm Venereol 1992;72:456- 460

53   Corazza M, Borghi A, Virgili A. A medicolegal controversy due to a hidden allergen in cutting oils. Contact Dermatitis 2004;50:254-255

54   Karlberg A-T, Bråred-Christensson J, Börje A, Harambasic E, Matura M. Methyl esterification of 15-hydroperoxyabietic acid does not affect the patch-test result in colophonium allergic patients. Contact Dermatitis 2007;56:355-356

55   Karlberg A-T. Colophony: Rosin in unmodified and modified form. In: Th Rustemeyer, P Elsner, SM John and HI Maibach, eds. Kanerva's occupational dermatology, second edition. Berlin Heidelberg: Springer Verlag: 2012, section 3, chapter 41: 467-480

56   Schäfer T, Böhler E, Ruhdorfer S, Weigl L, Wessner D, Filipiak B, et al. Epidemiology of contact allergy in adults. Allergy 2001;56:1192-1196

57   Schnuch A, Uter W, Geier J, Gefeller O (for the IVDK study group). Epidemiology of contact allergy: an estimation of morbidity employing the clinical epidemiology and drug-utilization research (CE-DUR) approach. Contact Dermatitis 2002;47:32-39

58   Thyssen JP, Linneberg A, Menné T, Johansen JD. The epidemiology of contact allergy in the general population-prevalence and main findings. Contact Dermatitis 2007;57:287-299

59   Matura M, Goossens A, Bordalo O, Garcia-Bravo B, Magnusson K, Wrangsjö K, Karlberg AT. Patch testing with oxidized R-(+)-limonene and its hydroperoxide fraction. Contact Dermatitis 2003;49:15-21

60   Matura M, Sköld M, Börje A, Andersen KE, Bruze M, Frosch P, et al. Selected oxidized fragrance terpenes are common contact allergens. Contact Dermatitis 2005;52:320-328

61   Färm G. Contact allergy to colophony. Clinical and experimental studies with emphasis on clinical relevance. Acta Derm Venereol Suppl (Stockh) 1998;201:1-42

62   Sharma PR. Allergic contact stomatitis from colophony. Dent Update 2006;33:440-442

63   Karlberg A-T, Lidén C. Colophony (rosin) in newspapers may contribute to hand eczema. Br J Dermatol 1992;126:161-165

64   Suuronen K, Aalto-Korte K, Piipari R, Tuomi T, Jolanki R. Occupational dermatitis and allergic respiratory diseases in Finnish metalworking machinists. Occup Med (Lond) 2007;57:277-283

65   Elms J, Fishwick D, Robinson E, Burge S, Huggins V, Barber C, et al. Specific IgE to colophony? Occup Med (Lond) 2005;55:234-237

66   Oestmann E, Philipp S, Zuberbier T, Worm M. Colophony-induced contact dermatitis due to ECG electrodes in an infant. Contact Dermatitis 2007;56:177-178

67   Lim K-S, Tang MBY, Goon ATJ, Leow YH. Contact sensitization in patients with chronic venous leg ulcers in Singapore. Contact Dermatitis 2007;56:94-98

68   Dotterud LK, Smith-Sivertsen T. Allergic contact sensitization in the general adult population: a population-based study from Northern Norway. Contact Dermatitis 2007;56:10-15

69   Amin KA, Belsito DV. The aetiology of eyelid dermatitis: a 10-year retrospective analysis. Contact Dermatitis 2006;55:280-285

70   Lazarov A. European Standard Series patch test results from a contact dermatitis clinic in Israel during the 7-year period from 1998 to 2004. Contact Dermatitis 2006;55:73-76

71   Volz A, Pfister-Wartha A, Bruckner-Tuderman L, Nashan D, Radny P. Mastix, a known herbal allergen, as causative agent in occupation-related dermatitis. Contact Dermatitis 2006;54:346-347

72   Paulsen E, Andersen KE. Colophonium and Compositae mix as markers of fragrance allergy: Cross-reactivity between fragrance terpenes, colophonium and Compositae plant extracts. Contact Dermatitis 2005;53:285-291

73   Uter W, Hegewald J, Aberer W, Ayala F, Bircher A, Brasch J, et al. The European standard series in 9 European countries, 2002/2003 – First results of the European Surveillance System on Contact Allergies. Contact Dermatitis 2005;53:136-145

74   Machovcova A, Dastychova E, Kostalova D, Vojtechovska A, Reslova J, et al. Common contact sensitizers in the Czech Republic. Patch test results in 12,058 patients with suspected contact dermatitis. Contact Dermatitis 2005;53:162-166

75   Majamaa H, Viljanen P. Occupational facial allergic contact dermatitis caused by Finnish pine and spruce wood dusts. Contact Dermatitis 2004;51:157-158

76   Cook DK, Freeman S. Allergic contact dermatitis to multiple sawdust allergens. Australas J Dermatol 1997;38:77-79

77 Miranda-Romero A, Gonzàles-Lòpez A, Esquivias JL Allergic contact dermatitis to pine dust. J Eur Acad Dermatol Venereol 1999;12: 69-70

78 Kuner N, Jappe U. Allergic contact dermatitis from colophonium, turpentine and ebony in a violinist presenting as fiddler's neck. Contact Dermatitis 2004;50:258-259

79 Fisher AA. Allergic contact dermatitis in a violinist. The role of abietic acid- a sensitizer in rosin (colophony) – as the causative agent. Cutis 1981;27: 466, 468, 473

80 Murphy J, Clark C, Kenicer K, Green C. Allergic contact dermatitis from colophony and compositae in a violinist. Contact Dermatitis 1999;40:334

81 Angelini G, Vena GA. Allergic contact dermatitis to colophony in a violoncellist. Contact Dermatitis 1986;15:108

82 Alvarez MS, Brancaccio RR. Multiple contact allergens in a violinist. Contact Dermatitis 2003;49: 43-44

83 Strauss RM, Wilkinson SM. Shoe dermatitis due to colophonium used as leather tanning or finishing agent in Portuguese shoes. Contact Dermatitis 2002; 47:59

84 Goossens A, Armingaud P, Avenel-Audran M, Begon-Bagdassarian I, Constandt L, Giordano-Labadie F, et al. An epidemic of allergic contact dermatitis due to epilating products. Contact Dermatitis 2002;47:67-70

85 Álvarez-Cuesta CC, López FV, Aguado CR, López MAG, Oliva NP. Allergic contact dermatitis from colophonium in the sawdust of Asturian cider-bars. Contact Dermatitis 2001;45:57

86 Estlander T, Jolanki R, Alanko K, Kanerva L. Occupational allergic contact dermatitis caused by wood dusts. Contact Dermatitis 2001;44:213-217

87 Isaksson M, Bruze M, Björkner B , Niklasson B. Contact allergy to Duraphat. Scand J Dent Res 1993;101:49-51

88 Cockayne, SE, Murphy R, Gawkrodger DJ. Occupational contact dermatitis from colophonium in a dental technician. Contact Dermatitis 2001;44:60

89 de Cock P, van Ginkel CJW, Faber WR, Bruynzeel DP. Occupational airborne allergic contact dermatitis from sawdust in livestock sheds. Contact Dermatitis 2000;42:113

90 Watsky KL. Airborne allergic contact dermatitis from pine dust. Am J Contact Dermatitis 1997;8:118-120

91 Sadhra S, Foulds IS, Gray C N, Koh D, Gardiner K. Colophony – uses, health effects, airborne measurement and analysis. Ann Occ Hygiene 1994;38:385-396

92 Mariano A, Paredes I, Nuti R, Innocenti A. Occupational asthma due to colophony in non-industrial environments. Medicina del Lavoro 1993;84:459-462

93 Schwartz L. An outbreak of dermatitis from hair lacquer. J Am Med Assoc 1943;121:1623-1625

94 Schwartz L, Spolyar LW, Gastineau FM, Dalton JE, Loveman AB, Sulzberger MB, et al. An outbreak of dermatitis from new resin fabric finishes. J Am Med Assoc 1940;115:906-911

95 Karlberg A T, Bohlinder K, Boman, Hacksell U, Hermansson J, Jacobsson S, Nilsson JL. Identification of 15-hydroperoxyabietic acid as a contact allergen in Portuguese colophony. J Pharm Pharmacol 1988;40: 42-47

96 Kanerva L, Estlander T. Occupational allergic contact dermatitis from colophony in 2 dental nurses Contact Dermatitis 1999;41:342-343

97 Hausen BM, Kuhlwein A, Schulz KH. Colophony allergy. A contribution to the origin, chemistry, and uses of colophony and modified colophony products. 1. Derm Beruf Umwelt 1982;30:107-115 (in German)

98 Danielsen H. Airborne allergic contact dermatitis from colophony in a car. Contact Dermatitis 1999;41:51

99 Gupta G, Forsyth A. Allergic contact reactions to colophony presenting as oral disease. Contact Dermatitis 1999;40:332-333

100 Kanerva L, Gäfvert E, Alanko K, Estlander T, Jolanki R. Patch testing with maleopimaric acid in an occupational dermatology clinic. Contact Dermatitis 1998;39:329-330

101 Koh D, Lee BL, Ong HY, Ong CN. Colophony in topical traditional Chinese medicaments. Contact Dermatitis 1997;37:243

102 Peretra F, Mamuel R, Gäfvert E, Helena Lacerda M. Relapse of colophony dermatitis from lottery tickets. Contact Dermatitis 1997;37:43

103 Batta K, Bourke JF, Foulds IS. Allergic contact dermatitis from colophony in lipsticks. Contact Dermatitis 1997;36:171-172

104 Heisterberg MV, Andersen KE, Avnstorp C, Kristensen B, Kristensen O, Kaaber K, et al. Fragrance mix II in the baseline series contributes significantly to detection of fragrance allergy. Contact Dermatitis 2010; 63:270-276

105 Mackey SA, Marks JG. Allergic contact dermatitis to white pine saw dust. Arch Dermatol 1992;128:1660

106 Hinnen U, Willa-Craps C, Elsner P. Allergic contact dermatitis from iroko and pine wood dust. Contact Dermatitis 1995;33:428-430

107 Meding B, Ahman M, Karlberg A-T. Skin symptoms in woodwork teachers. Contact Dermatitis 1996;34:176-180

108 Mathias CGT, Adams RM. Allergic contact dermatitis from rosin used as soldering flux. J Am Acad Dermatol 1984;10:454-456

109 Karlberg A-T, Gäfvert E, Meding B, Stenberg B. Airborne contact dermatitis from unexpected exposure to rosin (colophony) : Rosin sources revealed with chemical analyses. Contact Dermatitis 1996;35:272-278

110 Gäfvert, Bordalo O, Karlberg A-T. Patch testing with allergens from modified rosin (colophony) discloses additional cases of contact allergy. Contact Dermatitis 1996;35:290-298

111 Karlberg A-T, Gäfvert E. Isolated colophony allergens as screening substances for contact allergy. Contact Dermatitis 1996;35:201-207

112 Sainio EL, Henriks-Eckerman M-L, Kanerva L. Colophony, formaldehyde and mercury in mascaras. Contact Dermatitis 1996;34:364-365

113 de Argila D, Ortiz-Frutos J, Iglesias L. Occupational allergic contact dermatitis from colophony in depilatory wax. Contact Dermatitis 1996;34:369

114 Meding B, Haman M, Karlberg A-T. Skin symptoms and contact allergy in woodwork teachers. Contact Dermatitis 1996;34:185-190

115 el Sayed F, Manzur F, Bayle P, Marguery MS, Bazex J. Contact urticaria from abietic acid. Contact Dermatitis 1995;32:361-362

116 Koch P. Occupational contact dermatitis from colophony and formaldehyde in banknote paper. Contact Dermatitis 1995;32:371-372

117 Färm G, Karlberg A-T, Lidén C. Are opera-house artistes afflicted with contact allergy to colophony and cosmetics? Contact Dermatitis 1995;32:273-280

118 Koh D, Lee BL, Ong HY, Ong CN, Wong WK, Ng SK, Goh CL. Colophony in bindi adhesive. Contact Dermatitis 1995;32:186

119 Bergh M, Menné T, Karlberg A-T. Colophony in paper-based surgical clothing. Contact Dermatitis 1994;31:332-333

120 Lewis FM, Gawkrodger DJ, Harrington CI. Colophony: an unusual factor in pruritus vulvae. Contact Dermatitis 1994;31:119

121 Gäfvert E, Shao LP, Karlberg A-T, Nilsson U, Nilsson JLG. Allergenicity of rosin (colophony) esters : (II). Glyceryl monoabietate identified as contact allergen. Contact Dermatitis 1994;31:11-17

122 Hausen BM, Böurries M, Budianto E, Krohn K. Contact allergy due to colophony : (IX). Sensitization studies with further products isolated after oxidative degradation of resin acids and colophony. Contact Dermatitis 1993;29:234-240

123 Dooms-Goossens A, Boden G, Aupaix F, Bruze M. Allergic contact dermatitis from adhesive plaster due to colophony and epoxy resin. Contact Dermatitis 1993;28:120-121

124 Lodi A, Leuchi S, Mancini L, Chiarelli G, Crosti C. Allergy to castor oil and colophony in a wart remover. Contact Dermatitis 1992;26: 266-267

125 Castiglioni G, Carosso A, Nebiolo F. Contact dermatitis from colophony in a horticulturalist. Contact Dermatitis 1992;26:271

126 Lidén C, Kariberg A-T. Colophony in paper as a cause of hand eczema. Contact Dermatitis 1992;26:272-273

127 Wickstrom K. Allergic contact dermatitis caused by paper. Acta Dermato-venereologica 1969;49:547-551

128 Garcia-Bravo B, Pons A, Rodreguez-Pichardo A. Oral lichen planus from colophony. Contact Dermatitis 1992;26:279

129 Koch G, Magnusson B, Nyquist G. Contact allergy to medicaments and materials used in dentistry. Odontologisk Revy 1971;22:275

130 Barbaud A, Mougeolle JM, Tang JQ, Protois JC. Contact allergy to colophony in Chinese Musk and Tiger-Bone Plaster®. Contact Dermatitis 1991;25:324-326

131 Cameli N, Vassilopoulou A, Vincenzi C. Contact allergy to colophony in a wart remover. Contact Dermatitis 1991;24:315

132 Hausen BM, Krohn K, Budianto E. Contact allergy due to colophony (VII). Sensitizing studies with oxidation products of abietic and related acids. Contact Dermatitis 1990;23:352-358

133 Ehrin E, Karlberg A-T. Detection of rosin (colophony) components in technical products using an HPLC technique. Contact Dermatitis 1990;23:359-366

134 Tennstedt D, Lachapelle J-M. Allergic contact dermatitis from colophony in a nitroglycerin transdermal therapeutic system. Contact Dermatitis 1990;23 254-255

135 Karlberg A-T, Gäfvert E, Hagelthorn G, Nilsson JLG. Maleopimaric acid – a potent sensitizer in modified rosin Contact Dermatitis 1990;22:193-201

136 Krutmann J, Rzany B, Schöpf E, Kapp A. Airborne contact dermatitis from colophony: phototoxic reaction? Contact Dermatitis 1989;21:275-276

137 Karlberg A-T. Pure abietic acid is not allergenic. Contact Dermatitis 1989;21:282-284

138 Hausen BM, Mohnert J. Contact allergy due to colophony : (V). Patch test results with different types of colophony and modified–colophony products. Contact Dermatitis 1989;20:295-301

139 Olaguibel J, Almodovar A, Giner A, Serrano G, Martinez J, Basomba A. Passive transfer of contact sensitivity to colophony as a complication of an allogenic bone-marrow transplant. Contact Dermatitis 1989;20:182-184

140 Hausen BM, Krueger A, Mohnert A, Hahn H, König WA. Contact allergy due to colophony : (III). Sensitizing potency of resin acids and some related products. Contact Dermatitis 1989;20:41-50

141 Karlberg A-T, Boman A, Hacksell U, Jacobsson S, Nilsson LG. Contact allergy to dehydroabietic acid derivatives isolated from Portuguese colophony. Contact Dermatitis 1988;19:166-174

142 Monk B. Allergic contact dermatitis to colophony in a wart remover. Contact Dermatitis 1987;17:242

143 Matos J, Mariano A, Goncalo S, Freitas JD, Oliveira J. Occupational dermatitis from colophony. Contact Dermatitis 1988;18:53-54

144 Rivers JK, Rycroft RJG. Occupational allergic contact urticaria from colophony. Contact Dermatitis 1987;17:181

145 Fawcett IW, Newman Taylor AJ, Pepys J. Asthma due to inhaled chemical agents – fumes from 'Multicore' soldering flux and colophony resin. Clinical Allergy 1976;6:577

146 Goh CL, Ng SK. Airborne contact dermatitis to colophony in soldering flux. Contact Dermatitis 1987;17:89-91

147 Aberer W. Allergy to colophony acquired backstage. Contact Dermatitis 1987;16:34-36

148 Schlewet G, Chabeau G, Retmennger A, Fousserau J. Etude des allergènes de type colophane et dérivés, utilisés dans des sparadraps. Dermatosen 1979;27:170-172

149 Burry JN. Colophony, perfumes and paper handkerchiefs. Contact Dermatitis 1986;15:304-305

150 Lovell CR, Dannaker CJ, White IR. Dermatitis from X Cupressocyparis leylandii and concomitant sensitivity to colophony. Contact Dermatitis 1985;13:344-345

151 Karlberg A-T, Bergstedt E, Boman A, Bohlinder K, Lidén C, Nilsson LJ, et al. Is abietic acid the allergenic component of colophony?. Contact Dermatitis 1985;13:209-215

152 Dooms-Goosens A, Maertens M, van Lint L, Ruys-Catlender RM, Scheffer JJC. Colophony-induced sensitivity to Juniperus chinensis L. "Hetzii"? Contact Dermatitis 1984;10:185-187

153 Lidén C. Patch testing with soldering fluxes. Contact Dermatitis 1984;10:119-120

154 Bergmark G, Meding B. Allergic contact dermatitis from newsprint paper. Contact Dermatitis 1983;9:330

155 Widström L. Contact allergy to colophony in soldering flux. Contact Dermatitis 1983;9:205-207

156 Burge PS, Harries MG, O'Brien I, Pepys J. Bronchial provocation studies in workers exposed to the fumes of electronic soldering fluxes. Clin Allergy 1980;10:137-149

157 Barth JH. Colophony sensitivity – A regional variant. Contact Dermatitis 1981;7:165-166

158 Dahlquist I. Contact allergy to colophony and formaldehyde from sand cores. Contact Dermatitis 1981;7:167-168

159 Hjorth N. Contact dermatitis from sawdust. Contact Dermatitis 1979;5:339-340

160 Fregert S. Colophony in cutting oil and in soap water used as cutting fluid. Contact Dermatitis 1979;5:52

161 Ducombs G. Allergy to colophony. Contact Dermatitis 1978;4:118-119

162 Dawson TAJ. Colophony sensitivity in dentistry. Contact Dermatitis 1977;3:343

163 Kirk J. Colophony collar dermatitis. Contact Dermatitis 1976;2:294-295

164 Foussereau J. A case of allergy to colophony in a facial cosmetic. Contact Dermatitis 1975;1:259

165 Cooke MA, Kurwa AR. Colophony sensitivity. Contact Dermatitis 1975;1:192

166 Wilkinson DS, Calnan CD. Rosin used for belt-drive machine. Contact Dermatitis 1975;1:64

167 Sadhra S, Foulds IS. Allergic potential of neutrals in unmodified colophony, and a method for their separation from resin acids. Brit J Dermatol 1995;132:69-73

168 Karlberg A-T, Lidén C. Colophony from different sources. Brit J Dermatology 1985;113:475-481

169 Sadhra S, Foulds IS, Gray CN. Identification of contact allergens in unmodified rosin using a combination of patch testing and analytical chemistry techniques. Br J Dermatol 1996;134: 662- 668

170 Mortz CG, Bindslev-Jensen C, Andersen KE. Prevalence, incidence rates and persistence of contact allergy and allergic contact dermatitis in The Odense Adolescence Cohort Study: a 15-year follow-up. Brit J Dermatol 2013;168: 318-325

171 Diepgen TL, Ofenloch RF, Bruze M, Bertuccio P, Cazzaniga S, Coenraads P-J, et al. Prevalence of contact allergy in the general population in different European regions. Br J Dermatol 2016;174:319-329

172 Nardelli A, Carbonez A, Drieghe J, Goossens A. Results of patch testing with fragrance mix 1, fragrance mix 2, and their ingredients, and Myroxylon pereirae and colophonium, over a 21-year period. Contact Dermatitis 2013;68:307-313

173 Ramirez MA, Eller JJ. The patch test in contact dermatitis. J Allergy 1930;1:489-495

174 Fisher AA. Allergic contact dermatitis from musical instruments. Cutis 1993;51:75-76

175 Gambichler T, Boms S, Freitag M. Contact dermatitis and other skin conditions in instrumental musicians. BMC Dermatol 2004;4:3

176 Karlberg A-T, Gäfvert E, Lidén C. Environmentally friendly paper may increase risk of hand eczema in rosin-sensitive persons. J Am Acad Dermatol 1995;33:427-432

177 Barbaud A, Collet E, Le Coz CJ, Meaume S, Gillois P. Contact allergy in chronic leg ulcers: results of a multicentre study carried out in 423 patients and proposal for an updated series of patch tests. Contact Dermatitis 2009;60:279-287

178 Lachapelle JM, Leroy B. Allergic contact dermatitis to colophony included in the formulation of flexible collodion BP, the vehicle of a salicylic and lactic acid wart paint. Dermatol Clin 1990;8:143-146

179 Scherrer M, Resende A. Allergic contact dermatitis to colophony (rosin): A retrospective study from 1999 to 2008. Dermatitis 2009;20:235

180 Simonsen AB, Deleuran M, Mortz CG, Johansen JD, Sommerlund M. Allergic contact dermatitis in Danish children referred for patch testing – a nationwide multicentre study. Contact Dermatitis 2014;70:104–111

181 Siegel PD, Law BF, Fowler JF, Fowler LM. Disproportionated rosin dehydroabietic acid in neoprene surgical gloves. Dermatitis 2010;21:157-159

182 Raison-Peyron N, Nilsson U, Du-Thanh Aurélie, Karlberg A-T. Contact dermatitis from unexpected exposure to rosin from a toilet seat. Dermatitis 2013;24:149-150

183 Fall S, Bruze M, Isaksson M, Lidén C, Matura M, Stenberg B, Lindberg M. Contact allergy trends in Sweden – a retrospective comparison of patch test data from 1992, 2000, and 2009. Contact Dermatitis 2015;72:297-304

184 Scherrer M, Junqueira A. Occupational allergic contact dermatitis (oacd) in a gum rosin extractor. Dermatitis 2009;20:235-236

185 Hood CR Jr, Cornell RS, Greenfield B. Liquid adhesive contact dermatitis after bunionectomy: a case report and literature review. J Foot Ankle Surg. 2016;55:209-214

186 Han JS. Benzoin spray: cause of allergic contact dermatitis due to its rosin content. Ann Dermatol 2014;26:524-525

187 Hanon S, Rongé R, Potvin M, Schuermans D, Vincken W. Occupational asthma due to colophony in a violin player. J Allergy Clin Immunol Pract 2014;2):624-625

188 Tsuruta D, Sowa J, Tsuruta K, Ishii M, Kobayashi H. Allergic contact dermatitis caused by gum rosin and wood rosin in Tako-no-Suidashi ointment. J Dermatol 2011;38:993-995

189 Özkaya E, Elinç-Aslan MS, Mirzoyeva L. Allergic contact dermatitis caused by p-tert-butylphenol formaldehyde resin and colophonium in neoprene thermal sauna shorts. Contact Dermatitis 2010;63:230-232

190 Machovcova A. Colophony, a hidden allergen on ECG electrodes in a boy after cardiovascular surgery. Pediatr Dermatol 2011;28:345-347

191 Aboutalebi A, Chan CS, Katta R. Transfer contact dermatitis caused by rosin use in bowling. Dermatol Online J 2009;15(12):11

192 Booken D, Velten FW, Utikal J, Goerdt S, Bayerl C. Allergic contact dermatitis from colophony and turpentine in resins of untreated pine wood. Hautarzt 2006;57:1013-1015 (article in German)

193 Calnan CD. Quinazoline Yellow SS in cosmetics. Contact Dermatitis 1976;2:160-166

194 Scardamaglia L, Nixon R, Fewings J. Compound tincture of benzoin: A common contact allergen? Australas J Dermatol 2003;44:180-184

195 Kuno Y, Kato M. Photosensitivity from colophony in a case of chronic actinic dermatitis associated with contact allergy from colophony. Acta Derm Venereol 2001;81:442-443

196 Burge PS. Colophony hypersensitivity revisited. Clin Exp Allergy 2000;30:158-159

197 Dwyer P, Freeman S. Allergic contact dermatitis to adhesive tape and contrived disease. Australas J Dermatol 1997;38:141-144

198 Moss C, Berry K. Allergy to colophony. BMJ 1995;310(6979):603

199 Thörneby-Andersson K, Hansson C. Allergic contact dermatitis from colophony in waxes for polishing spectacle frames. Contact Dermatitis 1994;31:126-127

200 Paterson BC, White MI, Cowen PS. Further observations on adverse reactions to a bowler's grip. Contact Dermatitis 1993;29:278

201 Bruze M. Systemically induced contact dermatitis from dental rosin. Scand J Dent Res 1994;102:376-378

202 van Ketel WG, Bruynzeel DP. Occupational dermatitis in an accordion repairer. Contact Dermatitis 1992;27:186

203 Gäfvert E, Nilsson U, Karlberg A-T, Magnusson K, Nilsson JL. Rosin allergy: identification of a dehydroabietic acid peroxide with allergenic properties. Arch Dermatol Res 1992;284:409-413

204 Hindson C, Sinclair S. Contact allergy to self-adhesive dressings. Lancet 1988;1(8596):1224

205 O'Brien TJ. Colophony in collodion. Australas J Dermatol 1986;27:142-143

206 Karlberg A-T, Boman A, Holmbom B, Lidén C. Contact allergy to acid and neutral fractions of rosins. Sensitization experiments in guinea pigs and patch testing in patients. Derm Beruf Umwelt 1986;34:31-36

207 Schlewer G, Chabeau G, Reimeringer A, Foussereau J. Allergy to rosin caused by patch tests. Derm Beruf Umwelt 1980;28:16-1 7 (article in French, German)

208 Lysell L. Contact allergy to rosin in a periodontal dressing. A case report. J Oral Med 1976;31:24-25

209 Blair C. The dermatological hazards of bowling, contact dermatitis to resin in a bowlsgrip. Contact Dermatitis 1982;8:138-139

210 Freeman S, Stephens R. Cheilitis: analysis of 75 cases referred to a contact dermatitis clinic. Am J Contact Dermat 1999;10:198-200

211 Fregert S. Contact dermatitis from colophony used as print protective coating. Contact Dermatitis   Newsletter 1968;nr.4:58

212 Kulozik M, Powell SM, Cherry G, Ryan T J. Contact sensitivity in community-based leg ulcer patients. Clin Exp Dermatol 1988;13:82-84

213 Krakowiak A, Krêcisz B, Pas-Wyroślak A, Dudek W, Kieć-Świerzyñska M, Pałczyñski C. Occupational contact dermatitis with rhinoconjunctivitis due to *Tilia cordata* and colophonium exposure in a cosmetician. Contact Dermatitis 2004;51:34

214 Nilsson A-M, Gäfvert E, Nilsson JLG, Karlberg A-T. Different physical forms of maleopimaric acid give different allergic responses. Contact Dermatitis 2002;46:38-43

215 Lyon CC, Tucker SC, Gäfvert E, Karlberg A-T., Beck MH. Contact dermatitis from modified rosin in footwear. Contact Dermatitis 1999;41:102-103

216 O'Reilly FM, Murphy GM. Occupational contact dermatitis in a beautician. Contact Dermatitis 1996;35:47-48

217 Di Landro A, Pansera B, Valsecchi R, Cainelli T. Allergic contact dermatitis from a wart remover solution. Contact Dermatitis 1995;32:178-179

218 Van Ketel WG, Tan-Lim KN. Contact dermatitis from ethanol. Contact Dermatitis 1975;1:7-10

219 Sánchez-Pedreño P, Martínez-Menchón T, Frías-Iniesta J. Contact allergy to a permanent marker. Dermatitis 2012;23:96-97

220 Romaguera C, Vilaplana J, Grimalt R. Allergic contact dermatitis from a permanent marker. Dermatitis 2010;21:60-61

221 Strauss RM, Orton DI. Allergic contact cheilitis in the United Kingdom: a retrospective study. Am J Contact Dermat 2003;14:75-77

222 Pratt MD, Belsito DV, DeLeo VA, Fowler JF Jr, Fransway AF, Maibach HI, et al. North American Contact Dermatitis Group patch-test results, 2001–2002 study period. Dermatitis 2004;15:176-183

223 Marks JG Jr, Belsito DV, DeLeo VA, Fowler JF Jr, Fransway AF, Maibach HI, et al. North American Contact Dermatitis Group patch-test results, 1998–2000. Am J Contact Dermat 2003;14:59-62

224 Lindberg M, Edman B, Fischer T, Stenberg B. Time trends in Swedish patch test data from 1992 to 2000. A multi-centre study based on age- and sex-adjusted results of the Swedish standard series. Contact Dermatitis 2007;56:205-210

225 Wetter DA, Davis MDP, Yiannias JA, Cheng JF, Connolly SM, el-Azhary RA, et al. Patch test results from the Mayo Contact Dermatitis Group, 1998–2000. J Am Acad Dermatol 2005;53:416-421

226 Britton JE, Wilkinson SM, English JSC, Gawkrodger DJ, Ormerod AD, Sansom JE, et al. The British standard series of contact dermatitis allergens: validation in clinical practice and value for clinical governance. Br J Dermatol 2003;148:259-264

227 Hasan T, Rantanen T, Alanko K, Harvima RJ, Jolanki R, Kalimo K, et al. Patch test reactions to cosmetic allergens in 1995–1997 and 2000–2002 in Finland –a multicentre study. Contact Dermatitis 2005;53:40-45

228 Akyol A, Boyvat A, Peksari Y, Gurgey E. Contact sensitivity to standard series allergens in 1038 patients with contact dermatitis in Turkey. Contact Dermatitis 2005;52:333-337

229 Bruynzeel DP, Diepgen TL, Andersen KE, Brandão FM, Bruze M, Frosch PJ, et al (EECDRG). Monitoring the European Standard Series in 10 centres 1996–2000. Contact Dermatitis 2005;53:146-152

230 Wentworth AB, Yiannias JA, Keeling JH, Hall MR, Camilleri MJ, Drage LA, et al. Trends in patch-test results and allergen changes in the standard series: a Mayo Clinic 5-year retrospective review (January 1, 2006, to December 31, 2010). J Am Acad Dermatol 2014;70:269-275

231 Uter W, Ludwig A, Balda BR, Schnuch A, Pfahlberg A, Schäfer T, Wichmann HE, Ring J. The prevalence of contact allergy differed between population-based data and clinic–based data. J Clin Epidemiol 2004;57:627-632

232 Seidenari S, Manzini BM, Danese P, Motolese A. Patch and prick test study of 593 healthy subjects. Contact Dermatitis 1990; 23:162-167

233 Thyssen JP, Linneberg A, Menné T, Nielsen NH, Johansen JD. Contact allergy to allergens of the TRUE-test (panels 1 and 2) has decreased modestly in the general population. Br J Dermatol 2009;161:1124-1129

234 Mortz CG, Lauritsen JM, Bindslev-Jensen C, Andersen KE. Prevalence of atopic dermatitis, asthma, allergic rhinitis, and hand and contact dermatitis in adolescents. The Odense Adolescence Cohort Study on Atopic Diseases and Dermatitis. Br J Dermatol 2001;144:523-532

235 Nielsen NH, Linneberg A, Menné T, Madsen F, Frølund L, Dirksen A, et al. Allergic contact sensitization in an adult Danish population: two cross-sectional surveys eight years apart (the Copenhagen Allergy Study). Acta Derm Venereol 2001;81:31-34

236 Mortz CG, Lauritsen JM, Bindslev-Jensen C, Andersen KE. Contact allergy and allergic contact dermatitis in adolescents: prevalence measures and associations. Acta Derm Venereol 2002;82:352-358

237 De Groot AC, Bruynzeel DP, Bos JD, van der Meeren HL, van Joost T, Jagtman BA, Weyland JW. The allergens in cosmetics. Arch Dermatol 1988;124:1525-1529

238 De Groot AC. Adverse reactions to cosmetics. PhD Thesis, University of Groningen, The Netherlands: 1988, chapter 3.4, pp.105-113

239 Calnan CD. Colophony in eye-shadow. Cont Derm Newsl 1971;10:235

240 Cronin E. Contact Dermatitis. Edinburgh: Churchill Livingstone, 1980:113

241 Herbst RA, Uter W, Pirker C, Geier J, Frosch PJ. Allergic and non-allergic periorbital dermatitis: patch test results of the Information Network of the Departments of Dermatology during a 5-year period. Contact Dermatitis 2004;51:13-19

242 Katsarou A, Armenaka M, Ale I, Koufou V, Kalogeromitros, D. Frequency of immediate reactions to the European standard series. Contact Dermatitis 1999;41:276-279

243 Scheman A, Jacob S, Katta R, Nedorost S, Warshaw E, Zirwas M, et al. Part 2 of a 4 part series. Hair cosmetics: trends and alternatives. Data from the American Contact Alternative Group. J Clin Aesthet Dermatol 2011;4:42-46

244 Laguna C, de la Cuadra J, Martín-González B, Zaragoza V, Martínez-Casimiro L, Alegre V. Allergic contact dermatitis to cosmetics. Actas Dermosifiliogr 2009;100:53-60

245 Lubbes S, Rustemeyer T, Sillevis Smitt JH, Schuttelaar ML, Middelkamp-Hup MA. Contact sensitization in Dutch children and adolescents with and without atopic dermatitis - a retrospective analysis. Contact Dermatitis 2017;76:151-159

246 Erfurt-Berge C, Geier J, Mahler V. The current spectrum of contact sensitization in patients with chronic leg ulcers or stasis dermatitis - new data from the Information Network of Departments of Dermatology (IVDK). Contact Dermatitis 2017;77:151-158

247 Uter W, Amario-Hita JC, Balato A, Ballmer-Weber B, Bauer A, Belloni Fortina A, et al. European Surveillance System on Contact Allergies (ESSCA): results with the European baseline series, 2013/14. J Eur Acad Dermatol Venereol 2017 Jun 19. doi: 10.1111/jdv.14423. [Epub ahead of print]

248 Shi Y, Nedorost S, Scheman L, Scheman A. Propolis, colophony, and fragrance cross-reactivity and allergic contact dermatitis. Dermatitis 2016;27:123-126

249 Clayton TH, Wilkinson SM, Rawcliffe C, Pollock B, Clark SM. Allergic contact dermatitis in children: should pattern of dermatitis determine referral? A retrospective study of 500 children tested between 1995 and 2004 in one U.K. centre. Br J Dermatol 2006;154:114-117

250 Ortiz Salvador JM, Esteve Martínez A, Subiabre Ferrer D, Victoria Martínez AM, de la Cuadra Oyanguren J, Zaragoza Ninet V. Pediatric allergic contact dermatitis: Clinical and epidemiological study in a tertiary hospital. Actas Dermosifiliogr 2017;108:571-578

251 Färm G. Contact allergy to colophony. Clinical and experimental studies with emphasis on clinical relevance. Acta Derm Venereol (Stockh) 1998;201 (Suppl.):S1-42

252 Gafvert E. Allergenic components in modified and unmodified rosin. Chemical characterization and studies of allergenic activity. Acta Derm Venereol (Stockh) 1994;184 (Suppl.):S1-36

253 Sadhra S. Chromatographic investigations of contact allergens in colophony (rosin). PhD Thesis, 1991. Institute of Occupational Health, University of Birmingham.

254 Karlberg A-T. Contact allergy to colophony. Chemical identifications of allergens, sensitization experiments and clinical experiences. Acta Derm Venereol (Stockh) 1988;139 (Suppl.):S1-43

255 Hausen BM, Kuhlwein A, Schulz KH. Colophony-induced allergy. Origin, chemistry and use of colophony and modified colophony products. 2. Derm Beruf Umwelt 1982;30:145-152 (in German)

256 Dooms-Goossens A, de Boulle K, Dooms M, Degreef H. Imidazolidinyl urea dermatitis. Contact Dermatitis 1986;14:322-324

257 Toholka R, Wang Y-S, Tate B, Tam M, Cahill J, Palmer A, Nixon R. The first Australian Baseline Series: Recommendations for patch testing in suspected contact dermatitis. Australas J Dermatol 2015;56:107-115

258 Warshaw EM, Schram SE, Maibach HI, Belsito DV, Marks JG Jr, Fowler JF Jr, et al. Occupation-related contact dermatitis in North American health care workers referred for patch testing: cross-sectional data, 1998 to 2004. Dermatitis 2008;19:261-274

259 DeKoven JG, Warshaw EM, Belsito DV, Sasseville D, Maibach HI, Taylor JS, et al. North American Contact Dermatitis Group Patch Test Results: 2013-2014. Dermatitis. 2016 Oct 21. [Epub ahead of print]

260 Zaragoza-Ninet V, Blasco Encinas R, Vilata-Corell JJ, Pérez-Ferriols A, Sierra-Talamantes C, Esteve-Martínez A, de la Cuadra-Oyanguren J. Allergic contact dermatitis due to cosmetics: A clinical and epidemiological study in a tertiary hospital. Actas Dermosifiliogr 2016;107:329-336

261 Dinkloh A, Worm M, Geier J, Schnuch A, Wollenberg A. Contact sensitization in patients with suspected cosmetic intolerance: results of the IVDK 2006-2011. J Eur Acad Dermatol Venereol 2015;29:1071-1081

262 Hu Y, Wang D, Shen Y, Tang H. Photopatch testing in Chinese patients over 10 years. Dermatitis 2016;27:137-142

263 Uter W, Rämsch C, Aberer, W, Ayala F, Balato A, Beliauskiene A, et al. The European baseline series in 10 European Countries, 2005/2006 – Results of the European Surveillance System on Contact Allergies (ESSCA). Contact Dermatitis 2009;61:31-38

264 Lyons G, Roberts H, Palmer A, Matheson M, Nixon R. Hairdressers presenting to an occupational dermatology clinic in Melbourne, Australia. Contact Dermatitis 2013;68:300-306

265 Schwensen JF, Johansen JD, Veien NK, Funding AT, Avnstorp C, Østerballe M, et al. Occupational contact dermatitis in hairdressers: an analysis of patch test data from the Danish Contact Dermatitis Group, 2002–2011. Contact Dermatitis 2014;70:233-237

266 Ockenfels H, Seemann U, Goos M. Contact allergy in patients with periorbital eczema: an analysis of allergens. Dermatology 1997;195:119-124

267 Schena D, Fantuzzi F, Girolomoni G. Contact allergy in chronic eczematous lip dermatitis. Eur J Dermatol 2008;18:688-692

268 Goldenberg A, Mousdicas N, Silverberg N, Powell D, Pelletier JL, Silverberg JI, et al. Pediatric Contact Dermatitis Registry inaugural case data. Dermatitis 2016;27:293-302

269 Belloni Fortina A, Fontana E, Peserico A. Contact sensitization in children: A retrospective study of 2,614 children from a single center. Pediatr Dermatol 2016;33:399-404

270 Corazza M, Borghi A, Gallo R, Schena D, Pigatto P, Lauriola MM, et al. Topical botanically derived products: use, skin reactions, and usefulness of patch tests. A multicentre Italian study. Contact Dermatitis 2014;70:90-97

271 Jankićević J, Vesić S, Vukićević J, Gajić M, Adamic M, Pavlović MD. Contact sensitivity in patients with venous leg ulcers in Serbia: comparison with contact dermatitis patients and relationship to ulcer duration. Contact Dermatitis 2008;58:32-36

2.127   COMMIPHORA MUKUL RESIN EXTRACT

IDENTIFICATION

Description/definition	: Commiphora mukul resin extract is an extract of the resin of *Commiphora mukul*, Burseraceae
Chemical class(es)	: Botanical products and botanical derivatives
Other names	: Guggul
CAS registry number (s)	: 93165-11-8
EC number(s)	: 296-895-2
Merck Index monograph	: 5879 (Guggulu)
Function(s) in cosmetics	: EU: skin conditioning; tonic. USA: skin-conditioning agents - miscellaneous
Patch testing	: Extract 1% pet. and water (4)

GENERAL

Commiphora mukul resin extract (guggul) is a gum resin extracted from the mukul myrrh tree *Commiphora mukul*, Burseraecae. The correct scientific name of this species is *Commiphora wightii* (Arn.) Bhandari. The tree is commonly found in Pakistan and India and widely used for nearly 3000 years in Ayurvedic medicine. The extract is a complex mixture of various chemical compounds such as lignans, lipids, diterpenoids and steroids. Among the latter, *E*- and *Z*-guggulsterones (4,17(20)-pregnadiene-3,16-dione) are the major ones. Oral guggullipid preparations are often standardized to contain 2.5%-5% of guggulsterones. Its use is recommended in adults for its lipid-lowering effects; however, its impact on cholesterol levels is controversial. Guggul has also been proposed for the treatment of acne, obesity and arthritis. Topical administration is rarely reported for skin wound care (1).

CONTACT ALLERGY

Case reports and case series

After 15 days of application of an anticellulite cream on her thighs, a woman experienced recurrent itchy maculopapular lesions on her legs, buttocks, arms and abdomen. Patch tests to the European standard and cosmetic series were all negative. Contact allergy to the patient's cream was suspected and confirmed by patch testing to the product 'as is'. When tested with its ingredients, there was a positive reaction to guggul extract 1% pet. and water. The same ingredient gave negative results in five controls (4). Another female patient reacted to Commiphora mukul resin extract in a 'slimming cream' (1).

Cross-reactions, pseudo-cross-reactions and co-reactions

Not to colophonium or *Myroxylon pereirae* resin (1,4).

Presence in cosmetic products and chemical analyses

In the USA, in April 2017, Commiphora mukul resin extract was present in 41 of 56,714 cosmetic products of which the composition is known in FDA's Voluntary Cosmetic Registration Program (VCRP) (data obtained from FDA, May 2017). In March 2017, Commiphora mukul resin extract was present in 6 of 64,983 cosmetic products of which the composition is known in EWG's Skin Deep Cosmetics Database, USA (http://www.ewg.org/skindeep/).

Miscellaneous side effects

Hypersensitivity skin reactions have been noted in 3 to 15% of patients treated with oral guggul supplements depending on the dosage. In all cases, the skin rash occurred within 2 days after starting therapy and spontaneously resolved over 2 days to 30 days after therapy discontinuation. One patient required oral steroids. Cutaneous lesions were a morbilliform eruption, swelling and erythema of the face, erythematous papules and macules or bullous lesions of the legs (2,3).

LITERATURE

1. Salavert M, Amarger S, Ferrier Le Bouedec MC, Roger H, Souteyrand P, D'Incan M. Allergic contact dermatitis to guggul in a slimming cream. Contact Dermatitis 2007;56:286-287
2. Szapary PO, Wolfe ML, Bloedon LT, Cucchiara AJ, DerMarderosian AH, Cirigliano MD, Rader DJ. Guggullipid for the treatment of hypercholesterolemia: a randomized controlled trial. JAMA 2003;290: 765-772

3   Gelfand JM, Crawford GH, Brod BA, Szapary PO. Adverse cutaneous reactions to guggullipid. J Am Acad Dermatol 2005;52:533-534

4   Kölönte A, Guillot B, Raison-Peyron N. Allergic contact dermatitis to guggul extract contained in an anticellulite gel-cream. Contact Dermatitis 2006;54:226-227

2.128 COPERNICIA CERIFERA (CARNAUBA) WAX

IDENTIFICATION

Description/definition	: Copernicia cerifera wax is a wax obtained from the leaves and leaf buds of *Copernicia cerifera*, Palmaceae
Chemical class(es)	: Waxes
INCI name USA	: Copernicia cerifera (carnauba) wax
Other names	: Carnauba wax; Brazil wax
CAS registry number (s)	: 8015-86-9
EC number(s)	: 232-399-4
CIR review(s)	: J Am Coll Toxicol 1984;3:1-41 (access: www.cir-safety.org/ingredients)
Function(s) in cosmetics	: EU: depilatory. USA: epilating agents; film formers; skin-conditioning agents - emollient
Patch testing	: Pure (1); 50% mineral oil (2)

GENERAL

Copernicia cerifera wax (carnauba wax) is obtained from the Brazilian carnauba palm, *Copernicia cerifera*. It is a solid that becomes fluid when rubbed in a circular motion. The wax is used in automobile, floor and furniture waxes, shoe polishes, and as a filming and coating agent for confectionaries and tablets. Carnauba wax can also be found in old phonograph records, candles, and electrical insulation. It is a common ingredient in many cosmetic products, such as mascaras, lipsticks, eye shadows, and eyeliners, because of its emollient properties and a high glossy finish (1,2). The main classes of constituents are fatty acids, ω-hydroxy fatty acids, alcohols, α,ω-diols and cinnamic acids (4).

CONTACT ALLERGY

Case reports and case series

One patient had cheilitis from contact allergy to Copernicia cerifera (carnauba) wax in a lip balm (1). Another woman suffered from eyelid dermatitis from prime yellow carnauba wax in mascara (2). A third patient was presented with allergic contact cheilitis from carnauba wax in a lip balm; consuming chewable multivitamins containing carnauba wax may have worsened the cheilitis and caused dermatitis of the face and arms. However, this case report is rather unconvincing, as contact allergy to carnauba wax was not demonstrated by patch testing and its presence in the lip balm not ascertained (3).

Contact allergy to Copernicia cerifera wax in non-cosmetic products

Chewable multivitamins may have caused dermatitis of the face and arms in a patient with contact cheilitis from carnauba wax in a lip balm; this case report is rather unconvincing, as contact allergy to carnauba wax was not demonstrated by patch testing and its presence in the lip balm not ascertained (3).

Cross-reactions, pseudo-cross-reactions and co-reactions

Possibly pseudo-cross-reactivity to and from propolis from their common constituent cinnamic acid (3).

Presence in cosmetic products and chemical analyses

In the USA, in April 2017, Copernicia cerifera (carnauba) wax was present in 2299 of 56,714 cosmetic products of which the composition is known in FDA's Voluntary Cosmetic Registration Program (VCRP) (data obtained from FDA, May 2017). In March 2017, Copernia cerifera (carnauba) wax was present in 1944 of 64,983 cosmetic products of which the composition is known in EWG's Skin Deep Cosmetics Database, USA (http://www.ewg.org/skindeep/).

LITERATURE

1. Alrowaishdi F, Colomb S, Guillot B, Raison-Peyron N. Allergic contact cheilitis caused by carnauba wax in a lip balm. Contact Dermatitis 2013;69:318-319
2. Chowdhury MM. Allergic contact dermatitis from prime yellow carnauba wax and coathylene in mascara. Contact Dermatitis 2002;46:244
3. Jacob SE, Chimento S, Castanedo-Tardan MP. Allergic contact dermatitis to propolis and carnauba wax from lip balm and chewable vitamins in a child. Contact Dermatitis 2008;58:242-243
4. Wang L, Ando S, Ishida Y, Ohtani H, Tsuge S, Nakayama T. Quantitative and discriminative analysis of carnauba waxes by reactive pyrolysis-GC in the presence of organic alkali using a vertical microfurnace pyrolyzer. J Anal Appl Pyrolysis 2001;58-59:525-537

2.129   CUCUMIS SATIVUS (CUCUMBER) EXTRACT

IDENTIFICATION

Description/definition	: Cucumis sativus extract is the extract obtained from the whole plant of the cucumber, *Cucumis sativus* L., Cucurbitaceae (CosIng)
	Cucumis sativus (cucumber) fruit extract is the extract of the fruit of *Cucumis sativus* (Personal Care Products Council Ingredient Database)
Chemical class(es)	: Botanical products and botanical derivatives
INCI name USA	: Cucumis sativus (cucumber) fruit extract
Other names	: Cucumber extract; cucumber fruit extract
CAS registry number (s)	: 89998-01-6
EC number(s)	: 289-738-4
CIR review(s)	: Int J Toxicol 2014;33(Suppl.2):47-64 (access: www.cir-safety.org/ingredients)
Function(s) in cosmetics	: EU: skin conditioning. USA: skin-conditioning agents - emollient; skin-conditioning agents - miscellaneous
Patch testing	: Extract, undiluted (1)

CONTACT ALLERGY

Case reports and case series

A woman was treated with 1% hydrocortisone-17-butyrate for dermatitis of the lower limbs. At the same time, she started to use a new eye gel, after which edema developed around the eyes within one week. She stopped using the eye gel, but instead started to use alternative remedies. Over the following days, edema spread to the rest of the face and neck and became eczema. She was treated systemically with corticosteroids and was advised not to use any cosmetics or alternative remedies. The dermatitis disappeared and did not relapse. Patch tests were performed with an extended European standard series, corticosteroid, preservative and topical medicament series, and various acrylates.

She was further patch tested with her cosmetics and, later, with selected ingredients of her eye gel, provided by the manufacturer. The patient had positive reactions to 2 corticosteroids, witch hazel distillate (several reactions in a dilution series) and to cucumber extract as is. However, she did *not* react to a dilution series 50%, 10%, 5% and 1% in alcohol. Thus, it may be considered doubtful whether this individual was really contact allergic to the cucumber extract, which was also the opinion of the author (1).

Presence in cosmetic products and chemical analyses

In the USA, in April 2017, Cucumis sativus (cucumber) extract was present in 56 of 56,714 cosmetic products of which the composition is known in FDA's Voluntary Cosmetic Registration Program (VCRP) (data obtained from FDA, May 2017). In March 2017, Cucumis sativus fruit extract was present in 696 of 64,983 cosmetic products of which the composition is known in EWG's Skin Deep Cosmetics Database, USA (http://www.ewg.org/skindeep/). *Cucumis sativus* (cucumber) was present in (%) of 178 facial wipes for which ingredient information was obtained online and from retail stores, USA, 2016 (2).

LITERATURE

1   Granlund H. Contact allergy to witch hazel. Contact Dermatitis 1994;31:195
2   Aschenbeck KA, Warshaw EM. Allergenic ingredients in facial wet wipes. Dermatitis 2017 Mar 23. doi: 10.1097/DER.0000000000000268. [Epub ahead of print]

2.130   CYCLOMETHICONE

IDENTIFICATION

Description/definition	: Cyclomethicone is a mixture of low molecular weight volatile cyclic siloxanes, the principal ingredients of which are octamethylcyclotetrasiloxane (D4), decamethylcyclopentasiloxane (D5) and dodecamethylcyclohexasiloxane (D6), in varying proportions
Chemical class(es)	: Siloxanes and silanes
CAS registry number (s)	: 69430-24-6; 556-67-2; 541-02-6; 540-97-6
EC number(s)	: 209-136-7; 208-764-9; 208-762-8
CIR review(s)	: J Am Coll Toxicol 1991;10:9-19; Int J Toxicol 2011;30(Suppl.3):149-227 (access: www.cir-safety.org/ingredients)
SCCS opinion(s)	: SCCS/1549/15 (4); SCCP/0893/05 (3)
Merck Index monograph	: 8106 (octamethylcyclotetrasiloxane); 4122 (decamethyltrisiloxane)
Function(s) in cosmetics	: EU: antistatic; emollient; hair conditioning; humectant; solvent; viscosity controlling. USA: hair conditioning agents; skin-conditioning agents - emollient; solvents
Patch testing	: pure (5)
Molecular formula	: $C_8H_{24}O_2Si_3$ (octamethylcyclotetrasiloxane); $C_{10}H_{30}O_5Si_5$ (decamethylcyclopentasiloxane); $C_{12}H_{36}O_6Si_6$ (dodecamethylcyclohexasiloxane)

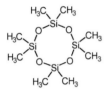

octamethylcyclotetrasiloxane

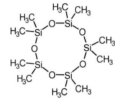

decamethylcyclopentasiloxane

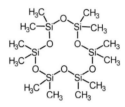

dodecamethylcyclohexasiloxane

CONTACT ALLERGY

Case reports and case series

In a group of 119 patients with allergic contact dermatitis from cosmetics, investigated in The Netherlands in 1986-1987, one case was caused by cyclomethicone in a skin care product (1,2).

Presence in cosmetic products and chemical analyses

In the USA, in April 2017, Cyclomethicone was present in 1312 of 56,714 cosmetic products of which the composition is known in FDA's Voluntary Cosmetic Registration Program (VCRP) (data obtained from FDA, May 2017). In March 2017, cyclomethicone was present in 643 of 64,983 cosmetic products of which the composition is known in EWG's Skin Deep Cosmetics Database, USA (http://www.ewg.org/skindeep/). Silicones / siloxanes were present in 38 (21%) of 178 facial wipes for which ingredient information was obtained online and from retail stores, USA, 2016 (6).

LITERATURE

1   De Groot AC, Bruynzeel DP, Bos JD, van der Meeren HL, van Joost T, Jagtman BA, Weyland JW. The allergens in cosmetics. Arch Dermatol 1988;124:1525-1529
2   De Groot AC. Adverse reactions to cosmetics. PhD Thesis, University of Groningen, The Netherlands: 1988, chapter 3.4, pp.105-113
3   SCCP (Scientific Committee on Consumer Products). Opinion on Octamethylcyclotetrasiloxane (D4) Cyclomethicone (INCI name), December 2005, SCCP/0893/05. Available at: http://ec.europa.eu/health/archive/ph_risk/committees/04_sccp/docs/sccp_o_035.pdf
4   SCCS (Scientific Committee on Consumer Safety). Opinion on decamethylcyclopentasiloxane (cyclopentasiloxane, D5) in cosmetic products, March 2015, SCCS/1549/15. Final version available at: http://ec.europa.eu/health/scientific_committees/consumer_safety/docs/sccs_o_174.pdf (29-7-2016)
5   De Groot AC. Patch Testing, 3rd Edition. Wapserveen, The Netherlands: acdegroot publishing, 2008 (ISBN 978-90-813233-1-4)
6   Aschenbeck KA, Warshaw EM. Allergenic ingredients in facial wet wipes. Dermatitis 2017 Mar 23. doi: 10.1097/DER.0000000000000268. [Epub ahead of print]

2.131 CYSTAMINE BIS-LACTAMIDE*

Not an INCI name

IDENTIFICATION

Description/definition : Cystamine bis-lactamide is an amide, that conforms to the formula shown below
Chemical class(es) : Amides
INCI name EU/USA : Neither in CosIng nor in the Personal Care Products Council Ingredient Database
Patch testing : 0.2% water (1,2,3)
Molecular formula : $C_{10}H_{26}N_4O_4S_2$

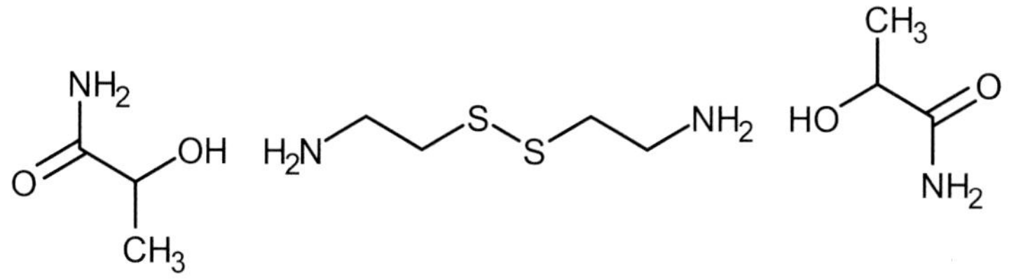

GENERAL

Cystamine bis-lactamide is a chemical designed to retain lactic acid within the stratum corneum. Extensive testing on humans had not revealed any allergenic potential. Once incorporated into skin care products, however, reports of people reacting to these creams came to light. Further investigation revealed that it was the 'designer chemical' cystamine bis-lactamide that patients were sensitized and reacting to. Contact allergy to it was reported in 1997, and once identified as an allergen, the chemical was withdrawn the same year (1,3).

CONTACT ALLERGY

Case reports and case series

In the first half of 1997, contact sensitisation to a cosmetic product was observed independently by two Swiss clinics in Zürich and Geneva. The single components of the product, prepared by the manufacturer, were tested in a double-blind fashion in fourteen women with suspected contact dermatitis of the eyelids or the face. Women with contact dermatitis showed sensitisation to the original cosmetic product, confirmed in 12 patients who agreed to further testing. Eight of these patients had positive patch test reactions to cystamine bis-lactamide at a concentration of 0.2% in water. No controls had positive reactions to cystamine bis-lactamide. In all women, dermatitis healed immediately after discontinued use of the incriminated skin care product (3).

A woman presented with florid facial eczema. Patch tests to an extended European standard and facial series were negative, but there was a positive reaction to her facial moisturizer. Further patch testing to this cream, together with its individual ingredients, again showed a positive reaction to the whole product and also to cystamine bis-lactamide 0.2% water. Twenty control patients did not react when tested with the same patch test material (1).

Another female patient developed facial eczema 4 days after applying 5 new face cosmetics (a facial wash, 3 creams and an eye gel). She had 3 repeated episodes within 12 hours of reapplying the products. The patient was patch tested to an extended European standard and a facial and cosmetic series, which were negative. A repeated open application test with the 5 products showed a strong reaction to one of the creams, a moisturizer that she had bought in 2001 in the USA, although it was from a batch made in 1996. She was patch tested to the 27 components provided by the moisturizer manufacturer and showed a positive reaction on day 3 and D5 to cystamine bis-lactamide 0.2% water. She had no further skin problems since avoiding this product (2).

Presence in cosmetic products and chemical analyses

In the USA, in April 2017, cystamine bis-lactamide was present in zero of 56,714 cosmetic products of which the composition is known in FDA's Voluntary Cosmetic Registration Program (VCRP) (data obtained from FDA, May 2017). In March 2017, cystamine bis-lactamide was present in zero of 64,983 cosmetic products of which the composition is known in EWG's Skin Deep Cosmetics Database, USA (http://www.ewg.org/skindeep/).

LITERATURE

1 Ross JS, White IR. Human studies fail to detect the allergenic potential of cystamine bis-lactamide. Contact Dermatitis 1997;39:139
2 Ostlere L. Contact allergy to cystamine bis-lactamide. Contact Dermatitis 2003;48:340
3 Borelli S, Piletta P, Fritz MG, Elsner P, Nestle FO. Cystamine bislactamide: a cosmetic allergen. Lancet 1998;351:1861-1862

2.132 CYSTEAMINE HCL

IDENTIFICATION

Description/definition	: Cysteamine HCl is the amine salt that conforms to the formula shown below
Chemical class(es)	: Organic salts; thio compounds
Chemical/IUPAC name	: 2-Aminoethanethiol;hydrochloride
Other names	: Cysteamine hydrochloride; mercaptamine hydrochloride; mercaptoethylamine
CAS registry number (s)	: 156-57-0
EC number(s)	: 205-858-1
Merck Index monograph	: 4046 (Cysteamine)
Function(s) in cosmetics	: EU: antioxidant; hair waving or straightening. USA: hair-waving/straightening agents; reducing agents
Patch testing	: 0.5% pet. (Chemotechnique)
Molecular formula	: C_2H_8ClNS

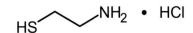

CONTACT ALLERGY

Patch testing in groups of patients

In Denmark, in 2002-2011, twelve hairdressers with contact dermatitis were patch tested with cysteamine HCl (test concentration unknown) and one had a positive patch test reaction. Its relevance was not mentioned (3). In the period 1994-2004, in a clinic specialized in contact dermatitis in hairdressers in The Netherland, 1347 hairdressers were patch tested with cysteamine HCl 0.5% in petrolatum. There were 16 (1.2%) positive reactions, all of which were considered to be relevant. All patients had been exposed to cysteamine HCl in one brand of permanent wave products. After 2004, no new case reports have been published, the cause of which is unknown, but it was suggested that the supplier may have lowered the concentration of cysteamine HCl in the perms (1).

Nevertheless, in 2012-2014, in Japan, 192 patients suspected of allergic contact dermatitis from hair dyes or perming solutions, of who 13% were hairdressers, were patch tested with cysteamine HCl 0.5% and 1% pet. and 26 (13.5%) had a positive reaction. In hairdressers, the frequency of sensitization was 31%, in the non-occupational group 10.8%. Unfortunately, the relevance of the observed positive patch test reactions was not mentioned (4). It should be realized that the rate of sensitization to 0.5% was far lower (4.5%) than to cysteamine HCl tested 1% pet. (12.6%). This may indicate some degree of irritancy of (at least) the higher test concentration.

Case reports and case series

An atopic female hairdresser had had recurrent hand dermatitis on the hypothenar eminences since 15 years. Four months prior to presentation, she suddenly developed erythematous and edematous fingers accompanied by burning and stinging, later followed by desquamation. Wearing protective gloves ameliorated the skin symptoms. Patch tests with the standard, hairdressers and cosmetics series and her own working materials gave a positive reaction to one of her permanent waving solutions 2% and 0.2% in water, but the reactions to glyceryl and ammonium thioglycolate were negative. In a later patch test session, ingredients of the cosmetic product were tested, which yielded a positive reaction to cysteamine HCl 1% pet. The concentration of this material in the perm was 5%. After avoidance of permanent wave solutions containing the chemical combined with wearing protective gloves, her dermatitis cleared (1). Another hairdresser also developed occupational allergic contact dermatitis from cysteamine HCl in permanent wave solution (2).

Presence in cosmetic products and chemical analyses

In the USA, in April 2017, cysteamine HCl was present in zero of 56,714 cosmetic products of which the composition is known in FDA's Voluntary Cosmetic Registration Program (VCRP) (data obtained from FDA, May 2017). In April 2017, cysteamine HCl was present in 2 of 65,521 cosmetic products of which the composition is known in EWG's Skin Deep Cosmetics Database, USA (http://www.ewg.org/skindeep/).

LITERATURE

1 Isaksson M, Van der Walle H. Occupational contact allergy to cysteamine hydrochloride in permanent-wave solutions. Contact Dermatitis 2007;56:295-296
2 Landers M, Law S, Storrs FJ. Permanent–wave dermatitis: contact allergy to cysteamine hydrochloride. Am J Contact Dermat 2003;14:157-160

3   Schwensen JF, Johansen JD, Veien NK, Funding AT, Avnstorp C, Østerballe M, et al. Occupational contact dermatitis in hairdressers: an analysis of patch test data from the Danish Contact Dermatitis Group, 2002–2011. Contact Dermatitis 2014;70:233-237

4   Ito A, Nishioka K, Kanto H, Yagami A, Yamada S, Sugiura M, et al. A multi-institutional joint study of contact dermatitis related to hair colouring and perming agents in Japan. Contact Dermatitis 2017;77:42-48

2.133   DEA-DIHYDROXYPALMITYL PHOSPHATE*
Not an INCI name

IDENTIFICATION

Description/definition : DEA-dihydroxypalmityl phosphate is the organic ammonium phosphate that conforms to the structural formula shown below
Chemical class(es) : Organic phosphates; ammonium salts
INCI name USA : Neither in CosIng nor in the Personal Care Products Council Ingredient Database
Chemical/IUPAC name : bis(2-Hydroxyethyl)ammonium bis(2-hydroxyhexadecyl) phosphate
CAS registry number (s) : 93777-69-6
EC number(s) : 298-103-0
Patch testing : Parent emulsifier 2.5% water, containing both DEA-dihydroxypalmityl phosphate and isopropyl hydroxypalmityl ether
Molecular formula : $C_{36}H_{78}NO_8P$

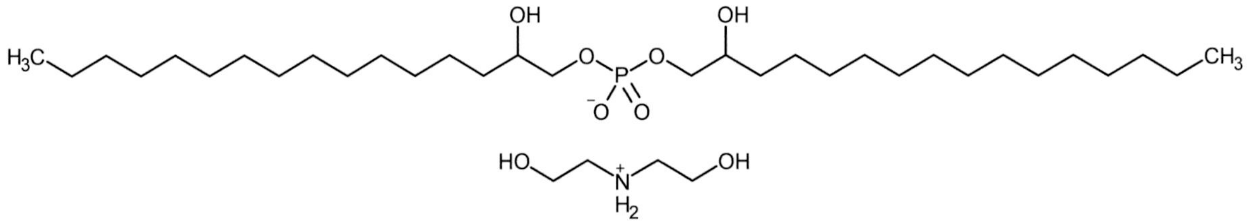

GENERAL

The emulsifier mentioned under Case reports and case series is an anionic oil-in-water emulsifier containing DEA-dihydroxypalmityl phosphate and isopropyl hydroxypalmityl ether and is available only as a mixture. It is (or at least was at the time of publication, the end of the 1980s) used in concentrations of 2% to 5% in cosmetics. Previous predictive testing had revealed no sensitizing potential (2).

CONTACT ALLERGY

Case reports and case series

A non-atopic woman had a one month history of acute itchy dermatitis on the face with edema of the eyelids. She was patch test positive to a facial beauty lotion which the patient had suspected. Patch testing with the ingredients gave a positive reaction to the water phase, which was a mixture of propylene glycol (3%) and an emulsifier. The emulsifier, tested at 2.5% water, produced a positive reaction after 3 days; propylene glycol gave no reaction. The emulsifier proved to be a mixture of isopropyl hydroxypalmityl ether and DEA-dihydroxypalmityl phosphate. The chemicals were not tested separately (1).

Another woman had an itchy erythematosquamous eruption on both eyelids that had appeared after a month's use of the same facial beauty lotion. Patch tests were positive to the facial beauty lotion, the water phase of the beauty lotion and the emulsifier of the product. A repeated open application test (ROAT) (1x/day) with the emulsifier 2.5% water on the right upper arm gave a slight eczematous response after 3 days. The emulsifier in the same concentration produced no skin reactions in 10 control subjects (1).

A third female patient allergic to the same cosmetic product and to the emulsifier was mentioned in the article (personal communication in ref. 1). A woman who reacted to sodium dihydroxycetyl phosphate in a herbal moisturizing cream was patch test positive to the emulsifier described above, which was now termed 'a mixture of DEA-hydroxypalmitylether and palmityl phosphate' (3).

Presence in cosmetic products and chemical analyses

In May 2017, DEA-dihydroxypalmityl phosphate was present in zero of 66,975 cosmetic products of which the composition is known in EWG's Skin Deep Cosmetics Database, USA (http://www.ewg.org/skindeep/). In the USA, in April 2017, DEA-dihydroxypalmityl phosphate was present in zero of 56,714 cosmetic products of which the composition is known in FDA's Voluntary Cosmetic Registration Program (VCRP) (data obtained from FDA, May 2017).

LITERATURE

1 Dooms-Goossens A, Debusschere K, Gladys K, Degreef H. Contact allergy to an emulsifier in a cosmetic lotion. Contact Dermatitis 1988;18:249-250

2 Fiedler HP. Lexikon der Hilfstoffe für Pharmazie, Kosmetik und angrenzende Gebiete, 2nd Edition. Aulendorf, Germany: Editio Cantor Verlag GmbH, 1981:320

3 Lomholt H, Rastogi SC, Andersen KE. Allergic contact dermatitis from sodium dihydroxycetyl phosphate, a new cosmetic allergen? Contact Dermatitis 2001;45:143-145

2.134   DECYL GLUCOSIDE

IDENTIFICATION

Description/definition	: Decyl glucoside is the product obtained from the condensation of decyl alcohol with glucose, which generally conforms to the formula shown below
Chemical class(es)	: Carbohydrates; ethers
Chemical/IUPAC name	: (3R,4S,5S,6R)-2-Decoxy-6-(hydroxymethyl)oxane-3,4,5-triol
Other names	: Decyl D-glucopyranoside
CAS registry number (s)	: 54549-25-6; 68515-73-1
EC number(s)	: 259-218-1
CIR review(s)	: Int J Toxicol 2013;32(Suppl.3):22-48 (access: www.cir-safety.org/ingredients)
Function(s) in cosmetics	: EU: cleansing; emulsion stabilising; surfactant. USA: surfactants – cleansing agents
Patch testing	: 5.0% pet. (Chemotechnique, SmartPracticeCanada); 10% in water is not irritant (9)
Molecular formula	: $C_{16}H_{32}O_6$

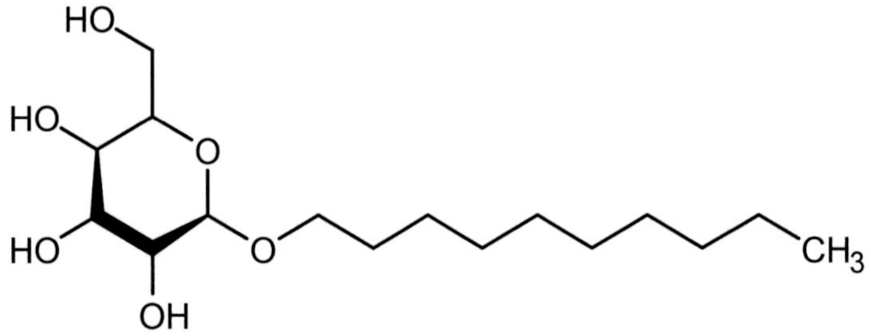

GENERAL

Decyl glucoside is one of the alkyl glucosides, a family of organic molecules of vegetal origin. They are produced by the condensation of a sugar, usually a cyclic form of glucose (D-glucopyranose), with a fatty alcohol composed of a linear side chain ranging from 2 to 22 carbons. Fatty alcohol is extracted from palm, coconut, or rapeseed oil, and glucose can be obtained from corn, wheat starch, and potato. The average number of carbon atoms composing the alcohol side chain determines the name of the alkyl glucoside. Members of the alkyl glucoside family include butyl, caprylyl, decyl, lauryl, coco-, cetearyl, undecyl, myristyl, hexadecyl, octadecyl, arachidyl, and caprylyl/capryl glucoside, C10-16, C12-18, C12-20, and C20-22 alkyl glucosides, branched isostearyl glucoside, and octyldodecyl glucoside.

Most of the alkyl glucosides are primarily used as mild non-ionic surfactants in cosmetics and cleansing products for human skin, mostly as a mixture of several alkyl glucosides, as it is difficult to obtain individual glucosides at high purity. They can also sometimes function as emulsion stabilizers in sunscreens, skin and hair cleansing agents, and humectants. They can be found in certain baby products such as wipes and cleansers and in antiseptic solutions (22). Decyl glucoside is present as a solubilizer in the UV-filter Tinosorb® M (containing methylene bis-benzotriazolyl tetramethylbutylphenol) and is probably the main cause of allergic reactions to this UV-filter (2,3,4,5,7,11,16).

Other alkyl glucosides which have caused cosmetic allergy include arachidyl glucoside, cetearyl glucoside, coco-glucoside, lauryl glucoside and myristyl glucoside. These are discussed in their respective chapters. A comprehensive review of contact allergy to alkyl glucosides has been published in 2017 (21,23).

CONTACT ALLERGY

Patch testing in groups of patients

Decyl glucoside has been added to the screening series of the NACDG in 2009, which is tested in all consecutive patients suspected of contact dermatitis (routine testing). The results of routine testing with decyl glucoside are shown in table 2.134.1. In their 3 biannual reports (2009-2014), the members of the North American Contact Dermatitis group found a stable frequency of sensitization of 1.5%-1.7%. 'Definite + probable relevance ranged from 20% to 33% (13,14,25). In a study from Canada, a rate of sensitization of 0.6% was found in the period 2009-2016. All 20 reactions were considered to be relevant. Over 70% of the patients were women who mostly had dermatitis of the face and hands; moisturizers and hand creams were most frequently implicated (23). In some studies, the rates of positive reactions to decyl glucoside has been found rising in recent years (23,24)

The results of testing groups of *selected* patients with decyl glucoside are shown in table 2.134.1. A high percentage of positive reactions (13%) was observed in a small group of 47 patients, who had previously reacted to one or more surfactants present in the NACDG screening series. The relevance of these reactions was not stated (20).

Table 2.134.1 Patch testing in groups of patients

Years and Country	Test conc. & vehicle	Number of patients tested | positive (%)		Selection of patients (S); Relevance (R); Comments (C)	Ref.
Routine testing					
2009-2016 Canada	5% pet.	3095	20 (0.6%)	R: all reactions were relevant; C: >70% were women who mostly had dermatitis of the face and hands; moisturizers and hand creams were most frequently implicated; the frequency of sensitization to decyl glucoside and/or lauryl glucoside rose to 2.2% in the first 6 months of 2016	23
2013-14 USA, Canada	5% pet.	4859	85 (1.7%)	R: definite + probable relevance: 33%	25
2012-2014 France, Belgium, Switzerland	5% pet.	?	?	R: unknown; C: the frequency of sensitization was 2% in 2012, 1,6% in 2013 and 2.6% in 2014	24
2011-12 USA, Canada	5% pet.	4231	66 (1.6%)	R: definite + probable relevance: 20%	13
2009-10 USA, Canada	5% pet.	4302	65 (1.5%)	R: definite + probable relevance: 32%	14
Testing in groups of selected patients					
2015-2016 USA	5.0% pet.	47	6 (13%)	S: patients previously reacting to one or more surfactants present in the NACDG screening series; R: not stated; C: there were also 4 doubtful reactions	20
2002-2004 Belgium	10% pet.	329	8 (2.4%)	S: patients tested with a pharmacocosmetic series; R: not stated	7

Case reports and case series

Decyl glucoside was stated to be the (or an) allergen in 11 patients in a group of 603 individuals suffering from cosmetic dermatitis, seen in the period 2010-2015 in Leuven, Belgium (15). During a 19-year period (1993-2012), of 11,842 patients with suspected contact dermatitis patch tested in Leuven, Belgium, 30 patients (24 women and 6 men) presented with a positive reaction to one or more alkyl glucosides. The causal products were shampoos (n=12), skin-cleansing products (n=12, among which were wipes for intimate hygiene), sunscreen products (n=5), skin-care products (n=4), and a deodorant (n=1). Reactions to decyl glucoside were seen in 21/30 (70%) of the patients. In two patients, decyl glucoside was present in the UV-filter mixture Tinosorb M® (see there). Co-reactions to other gluco-sides were as follows: lauryl glucoside 15 (71%), coco-glucoside 15 (71%) and cetearyl glucoside 3 (14%) (12). Twenty-five of the 30 patients who reacted to alkyl glucosides also had positive test results with non-related chemicals; 16 of these even had multiple sensitivities, defined as three or more contact allergies (12). Decyl glucoside was responsible for 8 out of 959 cases of non-fragrance cosmetic allergy where the causal allergen was identified, Belgium, 2000-2010 (1).

Ten patients had allergic contact dermatitis from to decyl glucoside in the sunscreen Tinosorb® M (containing methylene bis-benzotriazolyl tetramethylbutylphenol as UV-filter) present in sunscreen products (2,3,4,5,7,11,16); in some, decyl glucoside was not tested, but there were positive reactions to lauryl glucoside. One patient had ACD of the scalp and trunk from decyl glucoside in a shampoo (7). A woman developed eczematous patches on her arms and confluent eczema of the neck, upper chest and face. Subsequently, there was also acute eczema of the scalp and associated hair loss. Inflammation of the upper chest was sharply demarcated at the lower margin and confined to skin which came into contact with the patient's shoulder length hair. Contact allergy to her customary hair mousse was suspected and confirmed by patch testing to the mousse 'as is'. The responsible ingredient proved to be decyl glucoside (8). A patient suffering from lymphomatoid ACD caused by methylisothiazolinone in a floor-cleaning detergent had positive patch test reactions to a sunscreen cream and its component decyl glucoside (26). A man with facial dermatitis, allergic to methylisothiazolinone in a designer spectacle frame, reacted on patch testing to decyl glucoside. This reaction was considered relevant by the authors, as the patient had used a sunscreen cream and a shampoo containing 'glucosides' (27).

Occupational allergic contact dermatitis

Two hairdressers reacted to decyl glucoside in shampoos and hair care products (12). An apprentice hairdresser had occupational ACD of the hands from decyl glucoside in shampoos (7). A nurse had occupational ACD of the hands from decyl glucoside present in a hand soap (12).

Contact allergy to decyl glucoside in non-cosmetic products

A woman had acute allergic contact dermatitis of the umbilical area spreading to the whole abdomen caused by decyl glucoside in a chlorhexidine gluconate antiseptic gel used for wound care after an umbilical piercing (9). Two similar cases caused by decyl glucoside in an antiseptic lotion were reported from France; both patients co-reacted to chlorhexidine digluconate (10).

Cross-reactions, pseudo-cross-reactions and co-reactions

Other glucosides like lauryl glucoside, coco-glucoside, myristyl glucoside and ceteraryl glucoside (3,4,5,6,7,11,12,23). Possibly cross-reactivity to methyl glucose dioleate (7). In commercial batches of decyl, coco- and lauryl glucoside about 500 ng/g isobornyl acrylate was found as an impurity. It has been suggested, that this chemical may play a role in the simultaneous reactions to various alkyl glucosides (19).

Often, a mixture of several alkyl glucosides is present in cosmetic products, as it is very difficult to obtain individual glucosides of high purity (9). Because of this and of their chemical similarity, concomitant reactivity or cross-reactions may occur with the various glucosides (5).

Presence in cosmetic products and chemical analyses

In the USA, in April 2017, decyl glucoside was present in 977 of 56,714 cosmetic products of which the composition is known in FDA's Voluntary Cosmetic Registration Program (VCRP) (data obtained from FDA, May 2017). In February 2017, decyl glucoside was present in 675 of 64,631 cosmetic products of which the composition is known in EWG's Skin Deep Cosmetics Database, USA (http://www.ewg.org/skindeep/). Decyl glucoside was present in 14 (8%) of 178 facial wipes for which ingredient information was obtained online and from retail stores, USA, 2016 (28). In the USA, in 2015-2016, 63 diaper wipes and 41 topical diaper preparations from a large retailer were screened for the presence of potential sensitizers. Decyl glucoside was found in 5/63 (8%) disposable diaper wipes and in none of 41 topical diaper preparations (29).

In 2011, in the USA, according to information from the Voluntary Cosmetic Registration Program database, decyl glucoside was reported to be an ingredient in 492 cosmetic formulations, mainly rinse-off products (22). In 2009, in the USA, the ingredient lists of 796 hair products from one company were screened for the presence of decyl glucoside. Decyl glucoside was labeled in 6% of 279 shampoos, in 0% of 231 conditioners, and in 0% of 286 styling products (17). In 2009, in the USA, the ingredient lists of 657 miscellaneous cosmetics from one company were screened for the presence of decyl glucoside. Decyl glucoside was found to be present in 9% of 53 wipes only, not in other product categories (18).

LITERATURE

1   Travassos AR, Claes L, Boey L, Drieghe J, Goossens A. Non-fragrance allergens in specific cosmetic products. Contact Dermatitis 2011;65:276-285
2   O'Connell M, Kirk S, Wilkinson MS. Allergic contact dermatitis caused by Tinosorb® M. Contact Dermatitis 2011;65:48-49
3   Andrade P, Gonçalo M, Figueiredo A. Allergic contact dermatitis to decyl glucoside in Tinosorb® M. Contact Dermatitis 2010;62:119-120
4   Andersen KE, Goossens A. Decyl glucoside contact allergy from a sunscreen product. Contact Dermatitis 2006;54:349-350
5   Pereira N, Coutinho I, Andrade P, Gonçalo M. The UV filter Tinosorb M, containing decyl glucoside, is a frequent cause of allergic contact dermatitis. Dermatitis 2013;24:41-43
6   Goossens A, Decraene T, Platteaux N, Nardelli A, Rasschaert V. Glucosides as unexpected allergens in cosmetics. Contact Dermatitis 2003;48:164-166
7   Blondeel A. Contact allergy to the mild surfactant decylglucoside. Contact Dermatitis 2003;49:304-305
8   Horn HM, Murray C, Aldridge RD. Contact allergy to decyl glucoside. Contact Dermatitis 2005;52:227
9   Le Coz CJ, Meyer MT. Contact allergy to decyl glucoside in antiseptic after body piercing. Contact Dermatitis 2003;48:279-280
10 Krehic M, Avenel-Audran M. Allergic contact dermatitis from decyl glucoside in an antiseptic lotion. Contact Dermatitis 2009;61:349-350
11 Liuti F, Borrego L. Contact dermatitis caused by Tinosorb® M: the importance of patch testing with pure methylene bis-benzotriazolyl tetramethylbutylphenol. Contact Dermatitis 2015;73:192-193
12 Gijbels D, Timmermans A, Serrano P, Verreycken E, Goossens A. Allergic contact dermatitis caused by alkyl glucosides. Contact Dermatitis 2014;70:175-182
13 Warshaw EM, Maibach HI, Taylor JS, Sasseville D, DeKoven JG, Zirwas MJ, et al. North American Contact Dermatitis Group patch test results: 2011-2012. Dermatitis 2015;26:49-59
14 Warshaw EM, Belsito DV, Taylor JS, Sasseville D, DeKoven JG, Zirwas MJ, et al. North American Contact Dermatitis Group patch test results: 2009 to 2010. Dermatitis 2013;24:50-59
15 Goossens A. Cosmetic contact allergens. Cosmetics 2016, 3, 5; doi:10.3390/cosmetics3010005
16 Giordano-Labadie F, Marguery MC, Viraben R. Décylglucoside: un nouvel allergène cosmétique. Revue Française d'Allergologie et d'Immunologie Clinique 2005;45:74–82
17 Scheman A, Jacob S, Katta R, Nedorost S, Warshaw E, Zirwas M, et al. Part 2 of a 4 part series. Hair cosmetics: trends and alternatives. Data from the American Contact Alternative Group. J Clin Aesthet Dermatol 2011;4:42-46

18 Scheman A, Jacob S, Katta R, Nedorost S, Warshaw E, Zirwas M, et al. Part 4 of a 4 part series. Miscellaneous products: trends and alternatives in deodorants, antiperspirants, sunblocks, shaving products, powder, and wipes. Data from the American Contact Alternative Group. J Clin Aesthet Dermatol 2011;4:35-39

19 Foti C, Romita P, Rigano L, Zimerson E, Sicilia M, Ballini A, et al. Isobornyl acrylate: an impurity in alkyl glucosides. Cutan Ocul Toxicol 2016;35:115-119

20 Grey KR, Hanson J, Hagen SL, Hylwa SA, Warshaw EM. Epidemiology and co-reactivity of novel surfactant allergens: a double-blind randomized controlled study. Dermatitis 2016;27:348-354

21 Alfalah M, Loranger C, Sasseville D. Contact allergen of the year. Alkyl glucosides. Dermatitis 2017;28:3-4

22 Fiume MM, Heldreth B, Bergfeld WF, et al. Safety assessment of decyl glucoside and other alkyl glucosides as used in cosmetics. Int J Toxicol 2013;32(Suppl.5):22-48

23 Loranger C, Alfalah M, Ferrier Le Bouedec M-C, Sasseville Denis. Alkyl glucosides in contact dermatitis: a systematic review. Dermatitis Dermatitis 2017;28:5-13

24 Castelain M, Castelain F. Les ajouts à la batterie standard: utiles ou inutiles? In: Tennstedt D, Goossens A, Baeck M, eds. Progrès en Dermato-Allergologie: Bruxelles 2015. Montrouge, France: John Libbey Eurotext, 2015:275-286

25 DeKoven JG, Warshaw EM, Belsito DV, Sasseville D, Maibach HI, Taylor JS, et al. North American Contact Dermatitis Group Patch Test Results: 2013-2014. Dermatitis 2017;28:33-46

26 Van Steenkiste E, Goossens A, Meert H, Apers S, Aerts O. Airborne-induced lymphomatoid contact dermatitis caused by methylisothiazolinone. Contact Dermatitis 2015;72:237-240

27 El-Houri R, Christensen L. Persson C, et al. Methylisothiazolinone in a designer spectacle frame - a surprising finding. Contact Dermatitis 2016;75:310-312

28 Aschenbeck KA, Warshaw EM. Allergenic ingredients in facial wet wipes. Dermatitis 2017 Mar 23. doi: 10.1097/DER.0000000000000268. [Epub ahead of print]

29 Yu J, Treat J, Chaney K, Brod B. Potential allergens in disposable diaper wipes, topical diaper preparations, and disposable diapers: under-recognized etiology of pediatric perineal dermatitis. Dermatitis 2016;27:110-118

2.135   DECYL OLEATE

IDENTIFICATION

Description/definition	: Decyl oleate is the ester of decyl alcohol and oleic acid, which conforms to the formula shown below
Chemical class(es)	: Esthers
Chemical/IUPAC name	: Decyl (Z)-octadec-9-enoate
Other names	: Oleic acid decyl ester; (Z)-9-octadecenoic acid decyl ester
CAS registry number (s)	: 3687-46-5
EC number(s)	: 222-981-6
CIR review(s)	: J Am Coll Toxicol 1982;1:85-95; Final report, March 2013 (access: www.cir-safety.org/ingredients)
Function(s) in cosmetics	: EU: emollient; skin conditioning. USA: skin-conditioning agents - emollient
Patch testing	: 1% pet. (1)
Molecular formula	: $C_{28}H_{54}O_2$

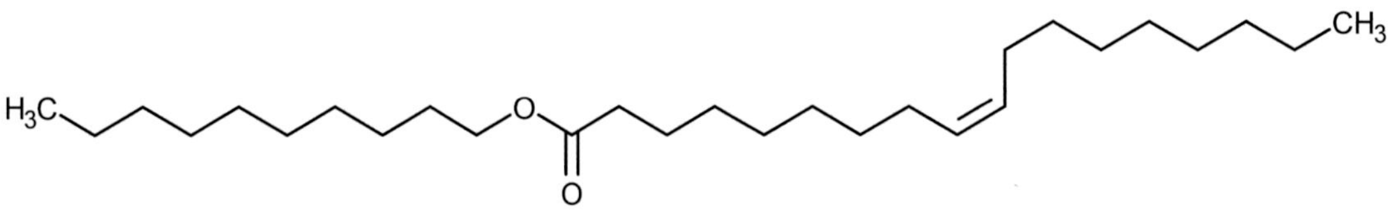

CONTACT ALLERGY

Case reports and case series

A man with a personal and family history of atopic dermatitis presented with acute generalized dermatitis after the application of 'natural' creams (one containing propolis). After recovery from this outbreak, he used a soapy oats lotion and a urea moisturizing lotion, developing a fresh outbreak of acute generalized eczema. He was patch tested with the GEIDC standard series, excipients and fragrances, all being negative. Patch tests with the three 'natural' creams, the soapy oats lotion and the urea moisturizing lotion were all positive after 2 and 4 days. The ingredients of the latter 2 were tested, showing positive reactions to decyl oleate (1% pet.) in the moisturizing lotion (1). Control tests were not performed, but decyl oleate at 1% seems unlikely to be irritant. The patient was also allergic to tocopheryl acetate in the soapy oats lotion. It was impossible to obtain the composition of the three 'natural' creams (1).

Presence in cosmetic products and chemical analyses

In the USA, in April 2017, decyl oleate was present in 294 of 56,714 cosmetic products of which the composition is known in FDA's Voluntary Cosmetic Registration Program (VCRP) (data obtained from FDA, May 2017). In March 2017, decyl oleate was present in 52 of 64,983 cosmetic products of which the composition is known in EWG's Skin Deep Cosmetics Database, USA (http://www.ewg.org/skindeep/).

OTHER SIDE EFFECTS

Other non-eczematous contact reactions

In (somewhat) older (3,4), but also more recent literature (5), decyl oleate has been suspected of being comedogenic in 'people with more sensitive complexions or acne-prone problems', based on rabbit ear assays.

LITERATURE

1   Garcia-Bravo B, Mozo P. Generalized contact dermatitis from vitamin E. Contact Dermatitis 1992;26:280
2   Mitchell JC, Adams RM, Glendenning WE, Fisher A, Kanof N, Larsen W, et al. Results of standard patch tests with substances abandoned. Contact Dermatitis 1982;8:336-337
3   Fulton JE Jr, Pay SR, Fulton JE 3rd. Comedogenicity of current therapeutic products, cosmetics, and ingredients in the rabbit ear. J Am Acad Dermatol 1984;10:96-105
4   Lanzet M. Comedogenic effects of cosmetic raw materials. Cosmetics & Toiletries 1986;101:63-72
5   Nguyen SH, Dang TP, Maibach HI. Comedogenicity in rabbit: some cosmetic ingredients/vehicles. Cutan Ocul Toxicol 2007;26:287-292

2.136   2,4-DIAMINOPHENOXYETHANOL HCL

IDENTIFICATION

Description/definition   : 2,4-Diaminophenoxyethanol HCl is the aromatic amine salt that conforms to the formula shown below
Chemical class(es)   : Amines; color additives - hair
Chemical/IUPAC name   : 2-(2,4-Diaminophenoxy)ethanol; dihydrochloride
CAS registry number (s)   : 66422-95-5
EC number(s)   : 266-357-1
CIR review(s)   : J Am Coll Toxicol 1991;10:113-134; Final report, December 2007 (access: www.cir-safety.org/ingredients)
Function(s) in cosmetics   : EU: hair dyeing. USA: hair colorants
EU cosmetic restrictions   : Regulated in Annex III/242 of the Regulation (EC) No. 1197/2013
Patch testing   : 1% pet. (5)
Molecular formula   : $C_8H_{14}Cl_2N_2O_2$

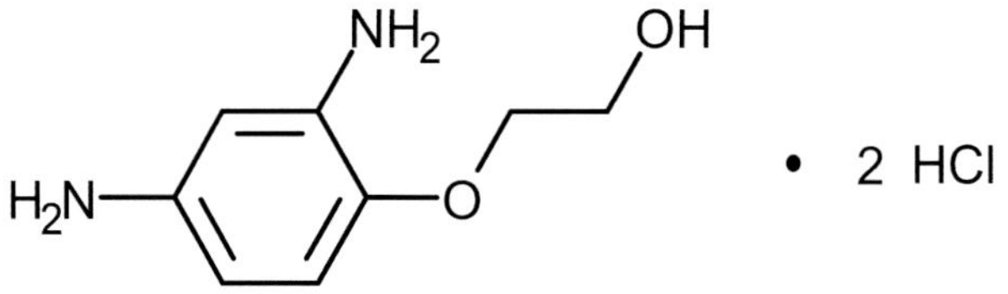

GENERAL

2,4-Diaminophenoxyethanol HCl is used as a coupler in oxidative hair dying products. For the chemistry of hair dying see Chapter 2.359 *p*-Phenylenediamine.

CONTACT ALLERGY

Patch testing in groups of patients

In 2007-2008, 2,4-diaminophenoxyethanol HCl 1% pet. was patch tested in 3 European countries (Denmark, Germany, Belgium) in 847 consecutive patients suspected of contact dermatitis (routine testing). There were 4 (0.5%) positive patch test reactions. Their relevance was not specified (5). In 2012-2014, in Japan, 195 patients suspected of allergic contact dermatitis from hair dyes or perming solutions, of who 13% were hairdressers, were patch tested with 2,4-diaminophenoxyethanol HCl 1% pet. and 5 (2.6%), all consumers of hair products, had a positive reaction. Relevance was not mentioned (13).

Case reports and case series

Diaminophenoxyethanol HCl was stated to be the (or an) allergen in one patient in a group of 603 individuals suffering from cosmetic dermatitis, seen in the period 2010-2015 in Leuven, Belgium (2).

Cross-reactions, pseudo-cross-reactions and co-reactions

2,4-Diaminophenoxyethanol HCl may probably cross-react with structurally related chemicals, notably those with a para-structure. Cross-reactivity between para-compounds is discussed in Chapter 2.359 *p*-Phenylenediamine.

Presence in cosmetic products and chemical analyses

In July 2017, 2,4-diaminophenoxyethanol HCl was present in 61 of 69,545 cosmetic products of which the composition is known in EWG's Skin Deep Cosmetics Database, USA (http://www.ewg.org/skindeep/). In the USA, in April 2017, 2,4-diaminophenoxyethanol HCl was present in an unknown number of 56,714 cosmetic products of which the composition is known in FDA's Voluntary Cosmetic Registration Program (VCRP) (data accidentally not requested from FDA). In 2016, in Sweden, the labels of 26 oxidative hair dye products advertised with the signal words organic, natural or similar, or sold/used at a hair dressing salon advertised with the same terminology, were screened for the presence of known contact allergens. 2,4-Diaminophenoxyethanol HCl was present in 7 (27%) products (4).

Of 15 hair dyes advertised as 'hypoallergenic', 'para-phenylenediamine-free', or 'non-allergenic', purchased in South Korea in 2015, 3 (20%) proved to contain 2,4-diaminophenoxyethanol HCl (9). In 2013-2014 labeled ingredient information from 252 home use and professional hair dye products (210 permanent and 42 non-permanent dyes) from 48 brands sold in Bangkok, Thailand, was collected to identify the type and frequency of potent contact sensitizers. 2,4-Diaminophenoxyethanol HCl was present in 55 (21.8%) products (3).

In southern Germany, in 2013-2014, the labels of 924 permanent oxidative hair dyes were checked for the presence of hair dye components. There were 334 retail products (of seven different brands) and 590 professional products (of six different brands). The 924 products analyzed revealed a total of 58 different hair dye components, with retail products containing 32 and professional products 52. 2,4-Diaminophenoxyethanol HCl was present in 27% of the 924 products (7).

In 2013, in Korea, the labels of 99 oxidative hair dyes produced by Korean domestic manufacturers were examined for potent skin sensitizers. 4-Amino-2-hydroxytoluene was found to be present in 29 (29%) of the hair dyes (11). In the USA, in 2012, ingredient labels of 107 different consumer oxidative hair dyes from 10 different companies were assessed in stores across the city of Phoenix, Arizona. 2,4-Diaminophenoxyethanol (as free base, sulfate, or HCl) was present in 36% of the products (8). In 2011, labels and other information on 365 hair dye products (282 permanent dyes, 79 semi-permanent dyes, 4 direct dyes) available on the Danish market (159 hair dyes for private use, 206 for professional use by hairdressers) were collected to identify the presence of sensitizers. 2,4-Diaminophenoxyethanol HCl was present in 72 (20%) products (6).

In April 2010, in Spain, 111 consumer-available oxidative hair dye products of 19 brands were purchased to check the labeling for sensitizers. A systematic selection of products to be purchased from each hair dye brand was applied, including the darkest blonde shade available, one 'regular' light brown shade, one 'regular' dark brown shade, one 'regular' black shade, and two further shades with different colours (red, blue, purple, etc.). In this group of 111 hair dyes, 2,4-diaminophenoxyethanol HCl was present in 30% of the products (10). In August - October 2008, the labels of 122 oxidative hair dye products on the Swedish market were examined for the presence of hair dye substances categorized as potent skin sensitizers. 2,4-Diaminophenoxyethanol HCl was present in 31 (25%) of these products (12).

OTHER SIDE EFFECTS

Immediate-type reactions

A female patient experienced dermatitis of the scalp and neck after each hair coloring, which was carried out every 6 weeks. Following a subsequent hair dying procedure, a severe reaction occurred, with generalized pruritus and erythema, dyspnea, vomiting, and hypotonia. The symptoms disappeared over a 2-hr period at home. The usual contact dermatitis appeared thereafter, and lasted for 8 days. The allergic contact dermatitis was caused by *p*-phenylenediamine, the immediate contact reaction by oxidized 2,4-diaminophenoxyethanol HCl, which showed a positive direct skin test (1).

LITERATURE

1   Nosbaum A, Dupin C, Nicolas J-F, Bérard F. Severe immediate hypersensitivity and allergic contact dermatitis caused by hair dye. Contact Dermatitis 2012;67:52-53
2   Goossens A. Cosmetic contact allergens. Cosmetics 2016, 3, 5; doi:10.3390/cosmetics3010005
3   Boonchai W, Bunyavaree M, Winayanuwattikun W, Kasemsarn P. Contact sensitizers in commercial hair dye products sold in Thailand. Contact Dermatitis 2016;74:222-229
4   Thorén S, Yazar K. Contact allergens in 'natural' hair dyes. Contact Dermatitis 2016;74:302-304
5   Søsted H, Rustemeyer T, Gonçalo M, Bruze M, Goossens A, Giménez-Arnau AM, et al. Contact allergy to common ingredients in hair dyes. Contact Dermatitis 2013;69:32-39
6   The Danish Environmental Protection Agency. Survey and occurrence of PPD, PTD and other allergenic hair dye substances in hair dyes. Copenhagen, Denmark: The Danish Environmental Protection Agency, 2013 (ISBN 978-87-92903-92-1). Available at: http://www2.mst.dk/Udgiv/publications/2013/02/978-87-92903-92-1.pdf
7   Kirchlecher S, Hübner A, Uter W. Survey of sensitizing constituents of oxidative hair dyes (retail and professional products) in Germany. J Dtsch Dermatol Ges 2016;14:707-715
8   Hamann D, Yazar K, Hamann CR, Thyssen JP, Lidén C. p-Phenylenediamine and other allergens in hair dye products in the United States: a consumer exposure study. Contact Dermatitis 2014;70:213-218
9   Lee HJ, Kim WJ, Kim JY, Kim HS, Kim BS, Kim MB, Ko HC. Patch tests with commercial hair dye products in patients with allergic contact dermatitis to para-phenylenediamine. Indian J Dermatol Venereol Leprol 2016;82:645-650
10   Yazar K, Boman A, Lidén C. Potent skin sensitizers in oxidative hair dye products on the Swedish market. Contact Dermatitis 2009;61:269-275

11 Kim H, Kim K. Prevalence of potent skin sensitizers in oxidative hair dye products in Korea. Cutan Ocul Toxicol 2016;35:204-207

12 Yazar K, Boman A, Lidén C. *p*-Phenylenediamine and other hair dye sensitizers in Spain. Contact Dermatitis 2012;66:27-32

13 Ito A, Nishioka K, Kanto H, Yagami A, Yamada S, Sugiura M, et al. A multi-institutional joint study of contact dermatitis related to hair colouring and perming agents in Japan. Contact Dermatitis 2017;77:42-48

2.137   DIAZOLIDINYL UREA

IDENTIFICATION

Description/definition	: Diazolidinyl urea is the heterocyclic substituted urea that conforms to the formula shown below
Chemical class(es)	: Amides; heterocyclic compounds
Chemical/IUPAC name	: 1-[1,3-bis(Hydroxymethyl)-2,5-dioxoimidazolidin-4-yl]-1,3-bis(hydroxymethyl)urea
Other names	: N,N'-bis(hydroxymethyl)urea; Germall® II
CAS registry number (s)	: 78491-02-8
EC number(s)	: 278-928-2
Merck Index monograph	: 4273
CIR review(s)	: J Am Coll Toxicol 1990;9:229-245 (access: www.cir-safety.org/ingredients) (95)
Function(s) in cosmetics	: EU: preservative. USA: preservatives
EU cosmetic restrictions	: Regulated in Annex V/46 of the Regulation (EC) No. 1223/2009
Patch testing	: 1.0% pet. (Chemotechnique, SmartPracticeCanada); 2.0% pet. (Chemotechnique, SmartPracticeCanada); 2.0% water (Chemotechnique); in the studies of the North American Contact Dermatitis Group (NACDG), the petrolatum-based diazolidinyl urea test material was significantly more sensitive than diazolidinyl urea in an aqueous base (23)
Molecular formula	: $C_8H_{14}N_4O_7$

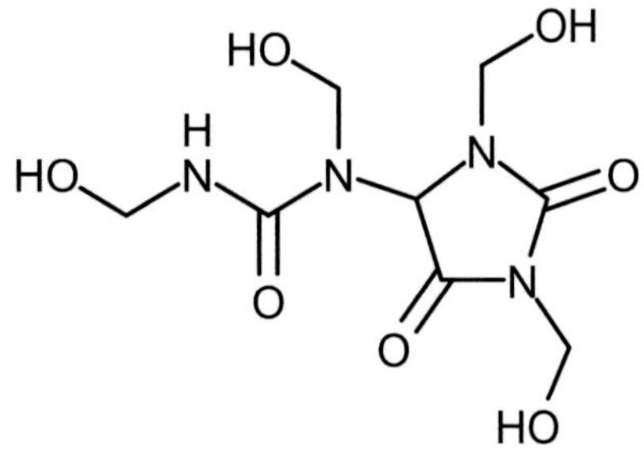

GENERAL

Diazolidinyl urea was first introduced in 1982 (9,10). It is a colorless, odorless, stable, and water-soluble preservative (8,10). Diazolidinyl urea is reported to have a wider antimicrobial spectrum than the structurally related imidazolidinyl urea and over a wider pH range (8). It is effective in a typical use concentration of 0.1-0.3% against gram-negative and gram-positive bacteria, molds, and yeast. However, it has limited activity against fungi, and therefore it is often combined with parabens (10,34,71). Diazolidinyl urea is used mostly in cosmetics, but may also be applied in topical drugs, contact lens solutions, cleaning products, detergents and as a preservative in a chemical compound used in the water of aquaria to promote the healing of damaged tissue of tropical and cold water fish (95,109).

Diazolidinyl urea is a formaldehyde-releaser, which releases formaldehyde through decomposition. In cosmetics and aqueous patch test materials, the major decomposition products are (4-hydroxymethyl-2,5-dioxo-imidazolidine-4-yl)-urea (HU) and (3,4-bis-hydroxymethyl-2,5-dioxo-imidazolidine-4-yl)-urea (3,4-BHU) (13). Although it is often stated that contact allergy to diazolidinyl urea may result from sensitization to the parent molecule per se, sensitization to its decomposition products is more likely. Of course, contact allergy may also occur from the formaldehyde released by this preservative. In fact, virtually all cases of sensitization to diazolidinyl urea are from its presence in cosmetics (7). The chemistry of diazolidinyl urea has been discussed (11,13,36). The literature on formaldehyde-releasers in cosmetic products including diazolidinyl urea up to 2009-2010 has been reviewed by the author (24,25). The literature on preservative allergy up to 1990 has been reviewed in refs. 50 and 51. Other useful preservative allergy reviews have appeared in 2014 (109) and 2004 (71).

CONTACT ALLERGY

General population and subgroups

The results of patch test studies with diazolidinyl urea in (subgroups of) the general population are shown in table 2.137.1. In a random sample of 3119 adults from five European countries, 6 (0.2%) had a positive patch test to diazolidinyl urea (65). A follow-up study of 8th grade schoolchildren in Denmark, with a mean age of 29 years, showed a 0.5% prevalence of sensitization to diazolidinyl urea (66). In the original study of 15 years earlier (96), the preservative had not been tested. In a group of 201 healthy Chinese volunteers, one (0.5%) reacted to diazolidinyl urea. There were no data on relevance of the positive patch test reactions in any of the studies (65,66,97).

Table 2.137.1 Contact allergy in the general population and in subgroups

Year and country	Selection and number tested	Prevalence of contact allergy			Comments	Ref.
		Total	Women	Men		
General population						
2008-11 five European countries	general population, random sample, 18-74 years, n=3119	0.2%	0.2%	0.1%		65
Subgroups						
2011 China	healthy Chinese volunteer students, 19-30 years; n=201	0.5%	0%	1.6%	one positive reaction in 60 men	97
2010 Denmark	unselected population of 8th grade schoolchildren in Denmark, 15 years later; n=442	0.5%	0.4%	0.6%	follow-up study; mean age 29 years; in the previous 1995-1996 study, diazolidinyl urea had not been tested (96)	66

Patch testing in groups of patients

Results of testing in consecutive patients suspected of contact dermatitis (routine testing) back to 1988 are shown in table 2.137.2. Results of testing in groups of *selected* patients (e.g., patients with eyelid dermatitis or individuals suspected of cosmetic allergy) back to 1989 are shown in table 2.137.3.

Patch testing in consecutive patients suspected of contact dermatitis: routine testing

Diazolidinyl urea is not routinely tested in Europe (it has been added to the Spanish standard patch test series in 2016 [91]), but has been part of the screening series of the North American Contact Dermatitis Group (NACDG) for over 25 years. Their results have been published biannually (table 2.137.2). Since 1992, the preservative has been tested in a concentration of 1% both in petrolatum and in water. The petrolatum-based diazolidinyl urea test material was statistically significantly more sensitive than the same allergen in an aqueous base (23); in the more recent NACDG studies (20,21,98), the water-based preparation has not been tested anymore. In these NADG studies, frequencies of sensitization (to the petrolatum-based material) have ranged from 2.1% to 3.7% (14-16,20,21,41,46-49) with the lowest rates (2.2%, 2.1% and 1.6%) in the most recent 2009-2014 period (20,21,98). Similar results were obtained in other US centers (5,62). In European countries, prevalences have been consistently lower, ranging from 0.5% to 1.4%, mostly being below 1% (1,19,42,43,45,57,103). In two Australian studies, frequencies of 2.4% and 2.7% positive patch test reactions were reported (77,81).

In many investigations, no relevance figures were provided. In the NACDG studies, 'definite' + 'probable' relevance has ranged from 24% to 48% (mean 36% [the 2013-2014 period excluded]). Current relevance in other studies ranged from 43 to 77 per cent. The incriminated products were hardly ever mentioned, but contact allergy to diazolidinyl urea is virtually always the result of its presence in cosmetic products.

Table 2.137.2 Patch testing in groups of patients: Routine testing

Years and Country	Test conc. & vehicle	Number of patients tested | positive (%)		Selection of patients (S); Relevance (R); Comments (C)	Ref.
2013-14 USA, Canada	1% pet.	4858	76 (1.6%)	R: definite + probable relevance: 28%	98
2011-12 USA, Canada	1% pet.	4232	90 (2.1%)	R: definite + probable relevance: 33%	20
2009-2012, 12 European countries [b]	2% pet.	16,673	(0.7%) [a]	R: not stated; C: range per country 0-0.8%	103
2009-10 USA, Canada	1% pet.	4304	95 (2.2%)	R: definite + probable relevance: 40%	21
2006-2010 USA	1% pet.	3091	(2.5%)	R: 55%	62
	1% water	3086	(1.3%)	R: 63%	
2001-2010 Australia	2% pet.	5139	140 (2.7%)	R: 43%	77
2009 Sweden	2% pet.	3112	(0.5%)	R: not stated	57
2007-2008, 7 European countries [b]	2% pet.	13,785	120 (0.9%) [a]	R: not stated; prevalences ranged from 0.7% (Netherlands) to 1.8% (Finland)	1
2007-8 USA, Canada	1% pet.	5082	(3.1%)	R: definite + probable relevance: 33%	15
	1% water	5081	(1.7%)	R: definite + probable relevance: 45%	
2005-6 USA, Canada	1% pet.	4439	(3.7%)	R: definite + probable relevance: 43%	14
	1% water	4433	(2.2%)	R: definite + probable relevance: 51%	

Table 2.137.2 Patch testing in groups of patients: Routine testing (continued)

Years and Country	Test conc. & vehicle	Number of patients tested | positive (%)		Selection of patients (S); Relevance (R); Comments (C)	Ref.
1993-2006 Australia	2% pet.	5215	(2.4%)	R: 55%	81
2005 United Kingdom	2% pet.	6958	(1.1%)	R: not stated; C: prevalence 1.2% in women, 0.9% in men	42
2000-2005 USA	1% pet.	3842	(3.5%)	R: 77%	5
	1% water	3840	(2.4%)	R: 73%	
2003-4 USA, Canada	1% pet.	5139	180 (3.5%)	R: not stated	16
	1% water	5141	131 (2.5%)	R: not stated	
2001-2 USA, Canada	1% pet.	4897	(3.1%)	R: definite + probable relevance: 31%	41
	1% water	4897	(3.2%)	R: definite + probable relevance: 33%	
2000 Sweden	1% pet.	3790	(1.4%)	R: not stated	43
2000 United Kingdom	2% pet.	3062	(0.7%)	R: 90% (in one center present and past relevance)	45
1998-2000 USA	1% pet.	1033	(2.9%)	R: not stated	44
	1% water	1319	(2.5%)	R: not stated	
1998-00 USA, Canada	1% pet.	5802	(3.0%)	R: definite + probable relevance: 24%	46
	1% water	5778	(2.6%)	R: definite + probable relevance: 28%	
1996-8 USA, Canada	1% pet.	4096	(3.7%)	R: 92%, including 'possible relevance'	47
	1% water	4094	(2.9%)	R: 85%, including 'possible relevance'	
1994-1996 USA	1% pet.	3085	(3.7%)	R: definite + probable relevance: 48%	48
	1% water	3060	(3.7%)	R: definite + probable relevance: 44%	
1992-1994 USA	1% pet.	3481	(3.0%)	R: 65%, including 'possible relevance'	49
	1% water	3471	(3.1%)	R: 65%, including 'possible relevance'	
1984-1988 Nether-lands	2% water	2400	13 (0.5%)	R: one patient had ACD from a body milk, rest unknown; 6/13 co-reacted to formaldehyde and other formaldehyde-releasers	19

[a] age-standardized and sex-standardized proportions
[b] study of the ESSCA (European Surveillance System on Contact Allergy' network)

Patch testing in groups of selected patients

Data on patch testing with diazolidinyl urea in groups of selected patients back to 1989 are summarized in table 2.137.3. Despite selection for possible reactions to cosmetics, a high prevalence rate has been observed in two investigation only (44,64). One was a small study of 57 patients with proven facial allergic contact dermatitis, of who 4 (7%) reacted to diazolidinyl urea (64). In a study by the Mayo clinic, 285 selected patients were tested and 4.9% had a positive patch test to diazolidinyl urea. However, it was neither mentioned how the patients were selected, not were relevance data provided (44). In fact, relevance data have been lacking or unspecified in all but three publications (4,38,60,64). In one study from the USA, relevance was given as 90-100%, but this included 'questionable' and 'past' relevance (4). Culprit products were never mentioned.

Table 2.137.3 Patch testing in groups of patients: Selected patient groups

Years and Country	Test conc. & vehicle	Number of patients tested | positive (%)		Selection of patients (S); Relevance (R); Comments (C)	Ref.
1996-2013 Nether-lands	2% pet.	438	1 (0.2%)	S: children aged 0-17 years; R: not stated	107
1994-2013 USA		342	13 (3.8%)	S: patients with atopic dermatitis as subgroup of 2453 successive patients suspected of contact dermatitis; R: not stated; C: in the non-atopic group, the frequency was 2.8%; there was no significant difference between the 2 groups	92
2010-2011 Korea	2% pet.	584	8 (1.4%)	S: patients suspected of allergic cosmetic dermatitis; R: not stated	59
2006-2011 Singapore	2% pet.	366	5 (1.4%)	S: not specified; R: not stated; C: prevalence in men was 0.7%, in women 1.8%	63
2006-2011 IVDK	2% pet.	6979	(0.7%)	S: patients suspected of cosmetic intolerance and tested with a preservative series; R: not stated	100
2006-2010 USA	2% pet.	100	1 (1%)	S: patients with eyelid dermatitis; R: not stated	17
1994-2010 USA, Canada	1% pet.	432	? (?)	S: hairdressers/cosmetologists; R: in the group of 187 patients who had at least one relevant occupationally rela-ted reaction, 8 (4.3%) reacted to diazolidinyl urea	101
2005-2009 Spain	2% water	3900	31 (0.8%)	S: patients allergic to formaldehyde or quaternium-15, or suspicion of cosmetic or industrial contact dermatitis; R: not specified	2
1996-2009 IVDK	2% pet.	78,711	587 (0.7%) [a]	S: not specified; R: not specified	7

Table 2.137.3 Patch testing in groups of patients: Selected patient groups (*continued*)

Years and Country	Test conc. & vehicle	Number of patients tested	positive (%)	Selection of patients (S); Relevance (R); Comments (C)	Ref.
2000-2007 USA	1% pet. 1% water	942 940	29 (3.1%) 19 (2.0%)	S: patients tested with a supplemental cosmetic screening series; R: 90% (1% pet.), 100% (1% water); C: weak study: a. high rate of macular erythema and weak reactions; b. relevance figures included 'questionable' and 'past' relevance	4
2000-2002 Finland	1% pet.	6539	(0.9%)	S: not stated; R: not stated; C: selected from approximately 11,800 patients	52
1998-2000 USA	2% pet.	285	(4.9%)	S: not stated; R: not stated	44
1994-1998 UK	2% pet.	232	7 (3.0%)	S: patients with eyelid dermatitis; R: all were currently relevant	60
1995-1997 USA		57	4 (7%)	S: patients with facial allergic contact dermatitis; R: only relevant reactions were mentioned	64
1995-1996 Finland	1% pet.	2911	(1.2%)	S: not stated; R: not stated; C: selected from approx. 9400 patients	52
1992-1995 IVDK [b]		14,881	(1.0%)	S: not stated; R: not stated; C: selected from 35,062 patients	54
1990-1994 IVDK [b]	2% pet.	7812	(1.3%)	S: not stated; R: not stated; C: selected from 28,349 patients	53
1988-1989 Italy	1% water	270	3 (1.1%)	S: probably patients tested with a preservative series; R: two patients had used stay-on cosmetics preserved with diazolidinyl urea	38

[a] age-standardized and sex-standardized proportions
[b] it may be assumed that there is an overlap in the patient populations in these IVDK studies
IVDK: Information Network of Departments of Dermatology, Germany, Austria, Switzerland

Case reports and case series

Diazolidinyl urea was stated to be the (or an) allergen in 13 patients in a group of 603 individuals suffering from cosmetic dermatitis, seen in the period 2010-2015 in Leuven, Belgium (61). In the period 1996-2013, in a tertiary referral center in Valencia, Spain, 5419 patients were patch tested. Of these, 628 individuals had allergic contact dermatitis to cosmetics. Diazolidinyl urea was the responsible allergen in four cases (99). Diazolidinyl urea was responsible for 29 out of 959 cases of non-fragrance cosmetic allergy where the causal allergen was identified, Belgium, 2000-2010 (3). In a group of 2193 patients (1582 women, 611 men) with (presumed) cosmetic allergy, 146 reactions (7%) were caused by diazolidinyl urea in a study of the NACDG, 2001-2004, diazolidinyl urea (in petrolatum) ranking 8th in the list of most frequent allergens (6). In a group of 46 patients with allergic contact dermatitis of the eyelids seen in Kansas City, USA, between 1994 and 2004, two cases (4.3%) were caused by contact allergy to diazolidinyl urea (source not mentioned) (58). In a group of 119 patients with allergic contact dermatitis from cosmetics, investigated in The Netherlands in 1986-1987, three cases were caused by diazolidinyl urea in skin care products (68,69).

The first report of contact allergy to diazolidinyl urea was in 1985 from its presence in a hair gel (8). One patient reacted to diazolidinyl urea in a shampoo (18), another to the preservative in a hand cream (26). A woman had ACD of the hands from a liquid soap containing diazolidinyl urea and formaldehyde (27). An unknown number of patients reacted to diazolidinyl urea in sunscreen products (28). A female patient had allergic contact dermatitis from diazolidinyl urea in 4 skin care products (29). A girl had ACD from 3 cosmetic creams of the same brand. She was probably sensitized to a cream containing diazolidinyl urea and later also reacted to another cream with diazolidinyl urea and - probably from cross-reactivity - to a cream preserved with imidazolidinyl urea; she was not allergic to formaldehyde (30). Two masseurs developed occupational ACD from formaldehyde, which was probably induced by formaldehyde released by diazolidinyl urea present in massage cream, massage oil and cold cream; however, the patch test to diazolidinyl urea itself was negative (33).

A woman had dermatitis of the face and reacted to diazolidinyl urea and 2-bromo-2-nitropropane-1,3-diol. It was implied that this was the cause of her dermatitis, but apparently she did not use any cosmetics and no products were tested or even mentioned (37). Three patients from Italy had positive patch tests to diazolidinyl urea, of who 2 also to imidazolidinyl urea; however, the reaction to formaldehyde was negative in all. One of these patients had used 'some leave-on cosmetics' preserved with diazolidinyl urea, a second (reacting to both preservatives) had used cosmetics containing both diazolidinyl urea and imidazolidinyl urea and in the third, the relevance was uncertain (38). One individual allergic to diazolidinyl urea and formaldehyde had ACD from diazolidinyl urea in a body milk (19). Four patients had allergic contact dermatitis from several leave-on products of a 'hypoallergenic' brand of cosmetics. One also had seborrheic-like scalp dermatitis from a shampoo of the same brand. Two of the patients were not allergic to formaldehyde, the other 2 did react to formaldehyde and also to imidazolidinyl urea (39). One patient had relevant positive patch test reactions to a moisturizer and to its ingredient diazolidinyl urea, another reacted to a shaving product and its component diazolidinyl urea (73). Three patients had positive patch test reactions to resp. a cream, 2 nail lacquers and another cosmetic cream containing diazolidinyl urea. Diazolidinyl urea itself was not tested, but all had positive patch test reactions to imidazolidinyl urea and several cosmetics containing this preservative (80).

Contact allergy to diazolidinyl urea in non-cosmetic products
A female nurse working in a neonatal intensive care unit developed occupational allergic contact dermatitis of the hands from diazolidinyl urea in an antimicrobial hand gel (93). Two patients had positive patch tests to some hydrogels used to treat leg ulcers, to diazolidinyl urea and to imidazolidinyl urea. Because the patients did not react to propylene glycol, the usual allergen in such gels, the authors suggested diazolidinyl urea and/or imidazolidinyl urea to be the allergenic culprit. However, the composition of the gels was unknown to them (94).

Cross-reactions, pseudo-cross-reactions and co-reactions
Diazolidinyl urea is a formaldehyde-releaser. In a number of patients, contact allergy to the preservative is the result of sensitivity to formaldehyde. In these cases, pseudo-cross-reactions may be observed to formaldehyde and other formaldehyde-releasers including DMDM hydantoin, imidazolidinyl urea, quaternium-15 and – to a lesser degree – 2-bromo-2-nitropropane-1,3-diol (7,79,110). The subject is summarized in Chapter 2.188 Formaldehyde and discussed in detail in a review article by the author (24). Cross-reactivity to and from imidazolidinyl urea independent of formaldehyde contact allergy is seen frequently (29,30,38,40,110). In a number of cases, this may be explained by the presence of two common (decomposition) compounds: (4-hydroxymethyl-2,5-dioxo-imidazolidine-4-yl)-urea (HU) and (3,4-bis-hydroxymethyl-2,5-dioxo-imidazolidine-4-yl)-urea (3,4-BHU) (11). Cross-reactivity to imidazolidinyl urea has been confirmed by animal (56) and human (40) sensitization experiments. Contact allergies to diazolidinyl urea and to the preservative methylchloroisothiazolinone/methylisothiazolinone has been observed to be significantly associated. This probably results from concomitant or successive sensitization to these chemicals in the same or different products rather than from cross-reactivity (78).

Provocation tests
A group of 40 patients allergic to formaldehyde was divided into 4 groups of 10, and they were exposed to creams containing resp. 0.05%, 0.15%, 0.3% and 0.6% diazolidinyl urea (34). The creams were applied twice daily for 2 weeks to three locations: the flexor aspect of the mid upper arm, followed by the side of the neck (if there was no reaction to the arm) and finally the face (if there were no reactions to either the arm or the neck). In the group exposed to the lowest concentration (0.05%), there were no positive reactions. In the group treated with the cream containing 0.15% diazolidinyl urea, dermatitis appeared in 2 (20%); 7 (70%) reacted to the cream containing 0.3% and also 7 (70%) to the 0.6% cream. In the total group of 40 formaldehyde-allergic patients, there was only one positive reaction to the arm. Eleven patients reacted positively to the cream applied to the neck and four had a positive test to the face (34). It was concluded that the concentration of 0.05%, containing 130 ppm formaldehyde, did not elicit allergic contact dermatitis . With an increasing concentration of diazolidinyl urea from 0.15% to 0.6% (corresponding to formaldehyde concentrations of 370 ppm to 1500 ppm, respectively), a dose-dependent increase in patients' reactivity was seen (34). In the same investigation, 10 patients who had a positive patch test to diazolidinyl urea (of which 7 co-reacted to formaldehyde) were provoked with the cream containing 0.15% diazolidinyl urea and 9 (90%) had a positive test, 6 on the arm and another 3 on the neck (34). The morphology of early allergic contact dermatitis reactions in this study was also reported (35). On the arm and neck, the early lesions were scattered papules and/or vesicles, which later became confluent with areas of homogenous redness and infiltration. The morphology on the face differed in the sense that it appeared as homogenous erythema at the beginning, followed by infiltration (35).

Fifteen patients with contact allergy to formaldehyde (n=7) and/or the formaldehyde-releasers quaternium-15 (n= 8), DMDM hydantoin (n=1), imidazolidinyl urea (n=2), and/or 2-bromo-2-nitropropane-1,3-diol (n=6) but patch test negative to diazolidinyl urea performed a ROAT (twice daily application to the underarm for 2 weeks) with a moisturizer preserved with 0.2% diazolidinyl urea. In only one patient, the ROAT was clearly positive. It was con-cluded that in patients allergic to formaldehyde and/or one or more formaldehyde-releasers, complete avoidance of other formaldehyde-releasers to which the patient is patch test negative, is not always necessary (84). In the light of the study discussed earlier in this section (34), it may be assumed that, in the latter investigation (84), false-negative reactions to the cream may have occurred.

Presence in cosmetic products and chemical analyses
In July 2017, diazolidinyl urea was present in 820 of 69,545 cosmetic products of which the composition is known in EWG's Skin Deep Cosmetics Database, USA (http://www.ewg.org/skindeep/). In the USA, in April 2017, diazolidinyl urea was present in 2387 of 56,714 cosmetic products of which the composition is known in FDA's Voluntary Cosmetic Registration Program (VCRP) (data obtained from FDA, May 2017). Diazolidinyl urea was present in 139 of 4737 (2.9%) commonly used cosmetic products of which the full composition was known in 2016 in The Contact Allergen Management Program (CAMP) database of the American Contact Dermatitis Society (104). In the USA, in

2015-2016, 63 diaper wipes and 41 topical diaper preparations from a large retailer were screened for the presence of potential sensitizers. Diazolidinyl urea was found in none of 63 disposable diaper wipes and in 1/41 (2%) topical diaper preparations (108). In 2014, in Thailand, the labels of 1000 cosmetic products (593 leave-on, 407 rinse-off products) were examined for the presence of preservatives. These were partly purchased in shops and on markets and partly brought in by patients. Diazolidinyl urea was present in 34 products (3.4%); in the leave-on products, the percentage was 4.6 and in the rinse-off products 1.7 (105). Of 179 emollients available in Poland in 2014, 9 (5.0%) contained diazolidinyl urea (106).

In 2013, 60 cosmetic products manufactured and purchased in Israel (40 stay-on and 20 rinse-off products) were investigated for preservatives. According to the labelling, 3 (5%) cosmetics contained diazolidinyl urea. In the stay-on products (hand and body creams), the percentage was 8, whereas none of the 20 shampoos and soaps was preserved with diazolidinyl urea (83). In 2009, in the USA, the ingredient lists of 1591 facial cosmetics from one company were screened for the presence of diazolidinyl urea. Diazolidinyl urea was present in 0% of 132 blushers and 38 bronzers, in 0% of 90 concealers, in 0% of 174 eyeliners, in 0% of 304 eyeshadows, in 12% of 457 foundations, in 3% of 140 loose and pressed powders, and in 5% of 256 mascaras (74). In 2009, in the USA, the ingredient lists of 796 hair products from one company were screened for the presence of diazolidinyl urea. Diazolidinyl urea was present in 3% of 279 shampoos, in 0% of 231 conditioners, and in 0% of 286 styling products (75). In 2009, in the USA, the ingredient lists of 657 miscellaneous cosmetics from one company were screened for the presence of diazolidinyl urea. Diazolidinyl urea was present in 0% of 195 antiperspirants/deodorants, in 0% of 41 powders, in 5% of 167 shaving products, in 7% of 201 sunblocks, and in 0% of 53 wipes (76). Diazolidinyl urea was present in 65 out of 3541 (1.7%) randomly sampled leave-on cosmetic products, Germany, 2006-2009 (12).

In Germany, in 2006-2009, the labels of 4680 cosmetic products were screened for the presence of preservatives. Diazolidinyl urea was present in 1.9% of the products, according to labelling information (102). In 2008, 19.5% of 33,212 cosmetics and toiletries registered in the USA Food and Drug Administration (FDA) Voluntary Cosmetic Registration Database contained a formaldehyde-releaser. They were more frequently used in rinse-off products (27.3%) than in stay-on cosmetics (16.9%). Diazolidinyl urea was present in 4.5% of all products; in stay-on cosmetics, the percentage was 4.2 and in rinse-off products 5.3 (31). In the same period, of 496 stay-on cosmetic products present in a local drugstore in The Netherlands and investigated by checking the ingredient labelling, 40 products (8.1%) proved to contain this preservative. Any formaldehyde-releaser was found in 122 of this group of stay-on products (24.6%) (31). Of 23 brands of moist toilet paper marketed in 2006 in Italy, 2 (9%) contained diazolidinyl urea (70). Diazolidinyl urea was present in 35 of 1774 (2.0%) cosmetics and toiletries in 2002 resp. in 6 of 1170 (0.5%) such products in 2005, filed in the Danish Product Register Database (PROBAS) (72). In 1998, 100 moisturizers sold in Sweden were analyzed for the presence and amount of preservatives. Thirty-five products contained a formaldehyde-releaser, of which three diazolidinyl urea (67). In 1996, in the USA, diazolidinyl urea was present in 3.6% of approximately 20,000 formulae voluntarily registered by cosmetic companies in the FDA Voluntary Cosmetic Registration Database (32).

Amounts of free formaldehyde released by diazolidinyl urea and chemical analyses
Diazolidinyl urea is produced from 4 mole of formaldehyde and 1 mole of allantoin. From each molecule of diazolidinyl urea, four formaldehyde molecules can be released (4 mole formaldehyde/mole diazolidinyl urea). However, only about 50% of the theoretical amount of formaldehyde in diazolidinyl urea can be released upon complete hydrolysis (25). The actual amounts of free formaldehyde released by diazolidinyl urea in products depend on its concentration, the pH of the product, the temperature (the higher the temperature the more formaldehyde is present in solution after constant time) (82,86), the age of the product (upon storage, increased levels of formaldehyde will be released [82]), the level of microbial contamination, and the other constituents of the products preserved with diazolidinyl urea (54,86,87,88).

The pH may greatly influence the release of formaldehyde. Diazolidinyl urea releases formaldehyde foremost in an alkaline product, i.e. with high pH value (49,89). The presence of protein in shampoo significantly decreased the amount of free formaldehyde compared to the same shampoo without protein (table 2.137.4), indicating that free formaldehyde was complexed by the protein introduced (85). Some examples of reports of free formaldehyde concentrations in products containing diazolidinyl urea are shown in table 2.137.4. Results of analysis of free formaldehyde in diazolidinyl urea patch test preparations are presented in Chapter 2.188 Formaldehyde (22). A 2% aqueous solution prepared by a supplier of patch test materials at pH 6.0 contained 0.29% (2900 ppm) free formaldehyde (22). In recent experiments, diazolidinyl urea in cosmetics released - after paraformaldehyde - the highest amount of formaldehyde of all formaldehyde-releasers investigated (paraformaldehyde, diazolidinyl urea, DMDM hydantoin, quaternium-15 , imidazolidinyl urea, methenamine and 2-bromo-2-nitropropane-1,3-diol) (82).

Table 2.137.4 Reports of free formaldehyde released from products containing diazolidinyl urea (adapted from [24])

Product	Conc. of diazolidinyl urea	Free formaldehyde (ppm)	Ref.
Shampoo containing protein	0.1%	58	85
	0.2%	125	
	0.4%	235	
	0.8%	384	
Shampoo *not* containing protein	0.1%	150	85
	0.2%	262	
	0.4%	452	
	0.8%	740	
Diluted cream	0.02%	40	90
	0.08%	140	
	0.16%	240	
	0.24%	350	

LITERATURE

1   Uter W, Aberer W, Armario-Hita JC, Fernandez-Vozmediano JM, Ayala F, Balato A, et al. Current patch test results with the European baseline series and extensions to it from the 'European Surveillance System on Contact Allergy' network, 2007-2008. Contact Dermatitis 2012;67:9-19

2   Latorre N, Borrego L, Fernández-Redondo V, García-Bravo B, Giménez-Arnau AM, Sánchez J, et al. Patch testing with formaldehyde and formaldehyde-releasers: multicenter study in Spain (2005-2009). Contact Dermatitis 2011;65:286-292

3   Travassos AR, Claes L, Boey L, Drieghe J, Goossens A. Non-fragrance allergens in specific cosmetic products. Contact Dermatitis 2011;65:276-285

4   Wetter DA, Yiannias JA, Prakash AV, Davis MD, Farmer SA, el-Azhary RA, et al. Results of patch testing to personal care product allergens in a standard series and a supplemental cosmetic series: an analysis of 945 patients from the Mayo Clinic Contact Dermatitis Group, 2000-2007. J Am Acad Dermatol 2010;63:789-798

5   Davis MD, Scalf LA, Yiannias JA, Cheng JF, El-Azhary RA, Rohlinger AL, et al. Changing trends and allergens in the patch test standard series. Arch Dermatol 2008;144:67-72

6   Warshaw EM, Buchholz HJ, Belsito DV et al. Allergic patch test reactions associated with cosmetics: Retrospective analysis of cross-sectional data from the North American Contact Dermatitis Group, 2001-2004. J Am Acad Dermatol 2009;60:23-38

7   Schnuch A, Lessmann H, Geier J, Uter W. Contact allergy to preservatives. Analysis of IVDK data 1996-2009. Br J Dermatol 2011;164:1316-1325

8   Kantor GR, Taylor JS, Ratz RL, Evey PL. Acute allergic contact dermatitis from diazolidinyl urea (Germall II) in a hair gel. J Am Acad Dermatol 1985;13:116-119

9   Brancaccio RR. What's new in contact dermatitis. Am J Contact Dermatitis 1993;4:55-57

10 Hectorne KJ, Fransway AF. Diazolidinyl urea: incidence of sensitivity, patterns of cross-reactivity and clinical relevance. Contact Dermatitis 1994;30:16-19

11 Doi T, Takeda A, Asada A, Kajimura K. Characterization of the decomposition of compounds derived from imidazolidinyl urea in cosmetics and patch test materials. Contact Dermatitis 2012;67:284-292

12 Schnuch A, Mildau G, Kratz E-M, Uter W. Risk of sensitization to preservatives estimated on the basis of patch test data and exposure, according to a sample of 3541 leave-on products. Contact Dermatitis 2011;65:167-174

13 Doi T, Kajimura K, Taguchi S. The different decomposition properties of diazolidinyl urea in cosmetics and patch test materials. Contact Dermatitis 2011;65:81-91

14 Zug KA, Warshaw EM, Fowler JF Jr, Maibach HI, Belsito DL, Pratt MD, et al. Patch-test results of the North American Contact Dermatitis Group 2005-2006. Dermatitis 2009;20:149-160

15 Fransway AF, Zug KA, Belsito DV, Deleo VA, Fowler JF Jr, Maibach HI, et al. North American Contact Dermatitis Group patch test results for 2007-2008. Dermatitis 2013;24:10-21

16 Warshaw EM, Belsito DV, DeLeo VA, Fowler JF Jr, Maibach HI, Marks JG, et al. North American Contact Dermatitis Group patch-test results, 2003-2004 study period. Dermatitis 2008;19:129-136

17 Wenk KS, Ehrlich AE. Fragrance series testing in eyelid dermatitis. Dermatitis 2012;23:22-26

18 Blondeel A. Contact allergy to the mild surfactant decylglucoside. Contact Dermatitis 2003;49:304-305

19 Perret CM, Happle R. Contact sensitivity to diazolidinyl urea (Germall II). Arch Dermatol Res 1989;281:57-59

20 Warshaw EM, Maibach HI, Taylor JS, Sasseville D, DeKoven JG, Zirwas MJ, et al. North American Contact Dermatitis Group patch test results: 2011-2012. Dermatitis 2015;26:49-59

21 Warshaw EM, Belsito DV, Taylor JS, Sasseville D, DeKoven JG, Zirwas MJ, et al. North American Contact Dermatitis Group patch test results: 2009 to 2010. Dermatitis 2013;24:50-59

22 Emeis D, De Groot AC, Brinkmann J. Determination of formaldehyde in formaldehyde-releaser patch test preparations. Contact Dermatitis 2010;63:57-62

23 Rietschel RL, Warshaw EM, Sasseville D, Fowler JF Jr, DeLeo VA, Belsito DV, Taylor JS, et al; North American Contact Dermatitis Group. Sensitivity of petrolatum and aqueous vehicles for detecting allergy to imidazolidinylurea, diazolidinylurea, and DMDM hydantoin: a retrospective analysis from the North American Contact Dermatitis Group. Dermatitis 2007;18:155-162

24 De Groot AC, White IR, Flyvholm M-A, Lensen G, Coenraads P-J. Formaldehyde-releasers in cosmetics: relationship to formaldehyde contact allergy. Part 2. Patch test relationship to formaldehyde contact allergy, experimental provocation tests, amount of formaldehyde released and assessment of risk to consumers allergic to formaldehyde. Contact Dermatitis 2010;62:18-31

25 De Groot AC, White IR, Flyvholm M-A, Lensen G, Coenraads P-J. Formaldehyde-releasers: relationship to formaldehyde contact allergy. II. Formaldehyde-releasers used in cosmetics. Part 1. Characterization, frequency and relevance of sensitization, and frequency of use in cosmetics. Contact Dermatitis 2010;62:2-17

26 Timmermans A, De Hertog S, Gladys K, Vanacker H, Goossens A. 'Dermatologically tested' baby toilet tissues: a cause of allergic contact dermatitis in adults. Contact Dermatitis 2007;57:97-99

27 Zaugg T, Hunziker T. Germall II and triclosan. Contact Dermatitis 1987;17:262-263

28 Cook N, Freeman S. Report of 19 cases of photoallergic contact dermatitis to sunscreens seen at the Skin and Cancer Foundation. Austral J Dermatol 2001;42:257-259

29 Jagtman BA, de Groot AC, Bakker M. Allergisch contacteczeem door propolis in een cosmeticum. Het nut van aanvullende epicutane tests met een cosmeticareeks. Ned Tijdschr Derm Venereol 2016;26:339-341 (article in Dutch)

30 García-Gavín J, González-Vilas D, Fernández-Redondo V, Toribo J. Allergic contact dermatitis in a girl due to several cosmetics containing diazolidinyl-urea or imidazolidinyl-urea. Contact Dermatitis 2010;63:49-50

31 De Groot AC, Veenstra M. Formaldehyde-releasers in cosmetics in the USA and in Europe. Contact Dermatitis 2010;62:221-224

32 Steinberg D. Frequency of use of preservatives in the United States. Paper given at Preservatech, Paris, 1996. www.creative-developments.co.uk/papers/Preservatives%201999.htm

33 Aalto-Korte K, Kuuliala O, Suuronen K, Alanko K. Occupational contact allergy to formaldehyde and formaldehyde releasers. Contact Dermatitis 2008;59:280-289

34 Zachariae C, Hall B, Cottin M, Cupferman S, Andersen KE, Menné T. Experimental elicitation of contact allergy from a diazolidinyl urea-preserved cream in relation to anatomical region, exposure time and concentration. Contact Dermatitis 2005;53:268-277

35 Zachariae C, Hall B, Cupferman S, Andersen KE, Menné T. ROAT: morphology of ROAT on arm, neck and face in formaldehyde and diazolidinyl urea sensitive individuals. Contact Dermatitis 2006;54:21-24

36 Lehmann SV, Hoeck U, Breinholdt J, Olsen CE, Kreilgaard B. Characterization and chemistry of imidazolidinyl urea and diazolidinyl urea. Contact Dermatitis 2006;54:50-58

37 Fowler JF Jr, Skinner SL. Contact dermatitis due to cosmetic preservatives. Am J Contact Dermatitis 1991;2:143-144

38 Tosti A, Ristanti S, Lanzarini M. Contact sensitization to diazolidinyl urea: report of 3 cases. Contact Dermatitis 1990;22:127-128

39 De Groot AC, Bruynzeel DP, Jagtman BA, Weyland JW. Contact allergy to diazolidinyl urea (Germall II®). Contact Dermatitis 1988;18:202-205

40 Jordan WP. Human studies that determine the sensitizing potential of haptens. Experimental allergic contact dermatitis. Dermatologic Clinics 1984;2:533-538

41 Pratt MD, Belsito DV, DeLeo VA, Fowler JF Jr, Fransway AF, Maibach HI, et al. North American Contact Dermatitis Group patch-test results, 2001–2002 study period. Dermatitis 2004;15:176-183

42 Jong CT, Statham BN, Green CM, King CM, Gawkrodger DJ, Sansom JE, et al. Contact sensitivity to preservatives in the UK 2004–2005: results of a multicenter study. Contact Dermatitis 2007;57:165-168

43 Lindberg M, Edman B, Fischer T, Stenberg B. Time trends in Swedish patch test data from 1992 to 2000. A multi-centre study based on age- and sex-adjusted results of the Swedish standard series. Contact Dermatitis 2007;56:205-210

44 Wetter DA, Davis MDP, Yiannias JA, Cheng JF, Connolly SM, el-Azhary RA, et al. Patch test results from the Mayo Contact Dermatitis Group, 1998–2000. J Am Acad Dermatol 2005;53:416-421

45 Britton JE, Wilkinson SM, English JSC, Gawkrodger DJ, Ormerod AD, Sansom JE, et al. The British standard series of contact dermatitis allergens: validation in clinical practice and value for clinical governance. Br J Dermatol 2003;148:259-264

46   Marks JG Jr, Belsito DV, DeLeo VA, Fowler JF Jr, Fransway AF, Maibach HI, et al. North American Contact Dermatitis Group patch-test results, 1998–2000. Am J Contact Dermat 2003;14:59-68

47   Marks JG Jr, Belsito DV, DeLeo VA, Fowler JF Jr, Fransway AF, Maibach HI, et al. North American Contact Dermatitis Group patch test results, 1996–1998. Arch Dermatol 2000;136:272-273

48   Marks JG Jr, Belsito DV, DeLeo VA, Fowler JF Jr, Fransway AF, Maibach HI,et al. North American Contact Dermatitis Group patch test results for the detection of delayed-type hypersensitivity to topical allergens. J Am Acad Dermatol 1998;38:911-918

49   Marks JG, Belsito DV, DeLeo VA, Fowler JF, Fransway AF, Maibach HI,et al. North American Contact Dermatitis Group standard tray patch test results 1992 through 1994. Am J Contact Dermatitis 1995;6:160-165

50   Fransway AF. The problem of preservation in the 1990s: I. Statement of the problem. Solution(s) of the industry, and the current use of formaldehyde and formaldehyde-releasing biocides. Am J Contact Dermatitis 1991;2:6-23

51   Fransway AF, Schmitz NA. The problem of preservation in the 1990s: II. Formaldehyde and formaldehyde-releasing biocides: incidences of cross-reactivity and the significance of the positive response to formaldehyde. Am J Contact Dermatitis 1991;2:78-88

52   Hasan T, Rantanen T, Alanko K, Harvima RJ, Jolanki R, Kalimo K, et al. Patch test reactions to cosmetic allergens in 1995–1997 and 2000–2002 in Finland –a multicentre study. Contact Dermatitis 2005;53:40-45

53   Schnuch A, Geier J, Uter W, Frosch PJ. Patch testing with preservatives, antimicrobials and industrial biocides. Results from a multicentre study. Br J Dermatol 1998;138:467-476

54   Geier J, Lessmann H, Schuch A, Fuchs Th. Kontaktallergien durch formaldehydabspaltende Biozide. Allergologie 1997;20:215-224 (article in German)

55   De Groot AC, White IR, Flyvholm M-A, Lensen G, Coenraads P-J. Formaldehyde-releasers in cosmetics: relationship to formaldehyde contact allergy. Part 1. Characterization, frequency and relevance of sensitization, and frequency of use in cosmetics. Contact Dermatitis 2010;62:2-17

56   Stephens TJ, Drake KD, Drotman RB. Experimental delayed contact sensitization to diazolidinyl urea (Germall II) in guinea pigs. Contact Dermatitis 1987;16:164-168

57   Fall S, Bruze M, Isaksson M, Lidén C, Matura M, Stenberg B, Lindberg M. Contact allergy trends in Sweden – a retrospective comparison of patch test data from 1992, 2000, and 2009. Contact Dermatitis 2015;72:297-304

58   Amin KA, Belsito DV. The aetiology of eyelid dermatitis: a 10-year retrospective analysis. Contact Dermatitis 2006;55:280-285

59   Lee SS, Hong DK, Jeong NJ, Lee JH, Choi YS, Lee AY, et al. Multicenter study of preservative sensitivity in patients with suspected cosmetic contact dermatitis in Korea. J Dermatol 2012;39:677-681

60   Cooper SM, Shaw S. Eyelid dermatitis: an evaluation of 232 patch test patients over 5 years. Contact Dermatitis 2000: 42;291-293

61   Goossens A. Cosmetic contact allergens. Cosmetics 2016, 3, 5; doi:10.3390/cosmetics3010005

62   Wentworth AB, Yiannias JA, Keeling JH, Hall MR, Camilleri MJ, Drage LA, et al. Trends in patch-test results and allergen changes in the standard series: a Mayo Clinic 5-year retrospective review (January 1, 2006, to December 31, 2010). J Am Acad Dermatol 2014;70:269-275

63   Cheng S, Leow YH, Goh CL, Goon A. contact sensitivity to preservatives in Singapore: frequency of sensitization to 11 common preservatives 2006–2011. Dermatitis 2014;25:77-82

64   Katz AS, Sherertz EF. Facial dermatitis: Patch test results and final diagnoses. Am J Cont Dermat 1999;10:153-156

65   Diepgen TL, Ofenloch RF, Bruze M, Bertuccio P, Cazzaniga S, Coenraads P-J, et al. Prevalence of contact allergy in the general population in different European regions. Br J Dermatol 2016;174:319-329

66   Mortz CG, Bindslev-Jensen C, Andersen KE. Prevalence, incidence rates and persistence of contact allergy and allergic contact dermatitis in The Odense Adolescence Cohort Study: a 15-year follow-up. Brit J Dermatol 2013;168:318-325

67   Gruvberger B, Bruze M, Tammela M. Preservatives in moisturizers on the Swedish market. Acta Derm Venereol 1998;78:52-56

68   De Groot AC, Bruynzeel DP, Bos JD, van der Meeren HL, van Joost T, Jagtman BA, Weyland JW. The allergens in cosmetics. Arch Dermatol 1988;124:1525-1529

69   De Groot AC. Adverse reactions to cosmetics. PhD Thesis, University of Groningen, The Netherlands: 1988, chapter 3.4, pp.105-113

70   Zoli V, Tosti A, Silvani S, Vincenzi C. Moist toilet papers as possible sensitizers: review of the literature and evaluation of commercial products in Italy. Contact Dermatitis 2006;55:252-254

71   Sasseville D. Hypersensitivity to preservatives. Dermatol Ther 2004;17:251-263

72   Flyvholm, MA. Preservatives in registered chemical products. Contact Dermatitis 2005;53:27-32

73   Held E, Johansen JD, Agner T, Menné T. Contact allergy to cosmetics: testing with patients' own products. Contact Dermatitis 1999;40:310-315

74   Scheman A, Jacob S, Katta R, Nedorost S, Warshaw E, Zirwas M, et al. Part 1 of a 4 part series. Facial cosmetics: trends and alternatives. Data from the American Contact Alternative Group. J Clin Aesthet Dermatol 2011;4:25-30

75   Scheman A, Jacob S, Katta R, Nedorost S, Warshaw E, Zirwas M, et al. Part 2 of a 4 part series. Hair cosmetics: trends and alternatives. Data from the American Contact Alternative Group. J Clin Aesthet Dermatol 2011;4:42-46

76   Scheman A, Jacob S, Katta R, Nedorost S, Warshaw E, Zirwas M, et al. Part 4 of a 4 part series. Miscellaneous products: trends and alternatives in deodorants, antiperspirants, sunblocks, shaving products, powder, and wipes. Data from the American Contact Alternative Group. J Clin Aesthet Dermatol 2011;4:35-39

77   Toholka R, Wang Y-S, Tate B, Tam M, Cahill J, Palmer A, Nixon R. The first Australian Baseline Series: Recommendations for patch testing in suspected contact dermatitis. Australas J Dermatol 2015;56:107-115

78   Statham BN, Smith EV, Bodger OG, Green CM, King CM, Ormerod AD, et al. Concomitant contact allergy to methylchloroisothiazolinone/ methylisothiazolinone and formaldehyde-releasing preservatives. Contact Dermatitis 2010;62:56-57

79   Isaksson M, Bråred-Christensson J, Engfeldt M, Lindberg M, Matura M, Möller H, et al. Swedish Contact Dermatitis Research Group. Patch testing with formaldehyde 2.0% in parallel with 1.0% by the Swedish contact dermatitis research group. Acta Derm Venereol 2014;94:408-410

80   Okkerse A, Thijssen-Vermijs ME, Geursen-Reitsma AM, van Joost T. Sensibilisatie voor hypoallergene cosmetica. Sensitization to hypoallergenic cosmetics. Ned Tijdschr Geneeskd 1994;138:2377-2380 (article in Dutch)

81   Chow ET, Avolio AM, Lee A, Nixon R. Frequency of positive patch test reactions to preservatives: The Australian experience. Australas J Dermatol 2013;54:31-35

82   Lv C, Hou J, Xie W, Cheng H. Investigation on formaldehyde release from preservatives in cosmetics. Int J Cosm Sci 2015;37:474-478

83   Horev L, Isaksson M, Engfeldt M, Persson L, Ingber A, Bruze M. Preservatives in cosmetics in the Israeli market conform well to the EU legislation. J Eur Acad Dermatol Venereol 2015;29:761-766

84   Herbert C, Rietschel RL. Formaldehyde and formaldehyde releasers: How much avoidance of cross-reacting agents is required? Contact Dermatitis 2004;50:371-373

85   Rosen M, McFarland A. Free formaldehyde in anionic shampoos. J Soc Cosmet Chem 1984;35:157-169

86   Engelhardt H, Klinkner R. Determination of free formaldehyde in the presence of donators in cosmetics by HPLC and post-column derivation. Chromatographia 1985;20:559-565

87   Geier J, Lessmann H, Schnuch A, Uter W. Contact sensitizations in metalworkers with occupational dermatitis exposed to water-based metalworking fluids: results of the research project 'FaSt'. Int Arch Occup Environ Health 2004;77:543-551

88   Geier J, Lessmann H, Becker D, et al. Formaldehydabspalter. Dermatol Beruf Umwelt 2008;56:34-36 (article in German)

89   Emeis D, Anker W, Wittern K-P. Quantitative 13C NMR spectroscopic studies on the equilibrium of formaldehyde with its releasing preservatives. Anal Chem 2007;79:2096-2100

90   Karlberg A-T, Skare L, Lindberg I, Nyhammer E. A method for quantification of formaldehyde in the presence of formaldehyde donors in skin-care products. Contact Dermatitis 1998;38:20-28

91   Hervella-Garcés M, García-Gavín J, Silvestre-Salvador JF; en representación del Grupo Español de Investigación en Dermatitis de Contacto y Alergia Cutánea (GEIDAC). The Spanish standard patch test series: 2016 update by the Spanish Contact Dermatitis and Skin Allergy Research Group (GEIDAC). Actas Dermosifiliogr 2016;107:559-566 (article in Spanish)

92   Shaughnessy CN, Malajian D, Belsito DV. Cutaneous delayed-type hypersensitivity in patients with atopic dermatitis: reactivity to topical preservatives. J Am Acad Dermatol 2014;70:102-107

93   Cahill JL, Nixon RL. Allergic contact dermatitis in health care workers to diazolidinyl urea present in antimicrobial hand gel. Med J Aust 2011;194:664-665

94   Carvalho R, Maio P, Amaro C, Santos R, Cardoso J. Hydrogel allergic contact dermatitis and imidazolidinyl urea/diazolidinyl urea. Cutan Ocul Toxicol 2011;30:331-332

95   CIR Expert Panel. Final report on the safety assessment of diazolidinyl urea. J Am Coll Toxicol 1990;9:229-245

96   Mortz CG, Lauritsen JM, Bindslev-Jensen C, Andersen KE. Prevalence of atopic dermatitis, asthma, allergic rhinitis, and hand and contact dermatitis in adolescents. The Odense Adolescence Cohort Study on Atopic Diseases and Dermatitis. Br J Dermatol 2001;144:523-532

97   Zhao J, Li LF. Contact sensitization to cosmetic series of allergens in a general population in Beijing. J Cosmet Dermatol 2014;13:68-71

98   DeKoven JG, Warshaw EM, Belsito DV, Sasseville D, Maibach HI, Taylor JS, et al. North American Contact Dermatitis Group Patch Test Results: 2013-2014. Dermatitis 2017;28:33-46

99   Zaragoza-Ninet V, Blasco Encinas R, Vilata-Corell JJ, Pérez-Ferriols A, Sierra-Talamantes C, Esteve-Martínez A, de la Cuadra-Oyanguren J. Allergic contact dermatitis due to cosmetics: A clinical and epidemiological study in a tertiary hospital. Actas Dermosifiliogr 2016;107:329-336

100 Dinkloh A, Worm M, Geier J, Schnuch A, Wollenberg A. Contact sensitization in patients with suspected cosmetic intolerance: results of the IVDK 2006-2011. J Eur Acad Dermatol Venereol 2015;29:1071-1081

101 Warshaw EM, Wang MZ, Mathias CGT, Maibach HI, Belsito DV, Zug KA, et al. Occupational contact dermatitis in hairdressers/cosmetologists; retrospective analysis of North American Contact Dermatitis Group data, 1994 to 2010. Dermatitis 2012;23:258-268

102 Uter W, Yazar K, Kratz EM, Mildau G, Lidén C. Coupled exposure to ingredients of cosmetic products: II. Preservatives. Contact Dermatitis 2014;70:219-226

103 Giménez-Arnau AM, Deza G, Bauer A, Johnston GA, Mahler V, Schuttelaar ML, et al. Contact allergy to preservatives: ESSCA* results with the baseline series, 2009-2012. J Eur Acad Dermatol Venereol 2017;31:664-671

104 Beene KM, Scheman A, Severson D, Reeder MJ. Prevalence of preservatives across all product types in the Contact Allergen Management Program. Dermatitis 2017;28:81-87

105 Bunyavaree M, Kasemsarn P, Boonchai W. Cosmetic preservative labelling on the Thai market. Contact Dermatitis 2016;74:217-221

106 Osinka K, Karczmarz A, Krauze A, Feleszko W. Contact allergens in cosmetics used in atopic dermatitis: analysis of product composition. Contact Dermatitis 2016;75:241-243

107 Lubbes S, Rustemeyer T, Sillevis Smitt JH, Schuttelaar ML, Middelkamp-Hup MA. Contact sensitization in Dutch children and adolescents with and without atopic dermatitis - a retrospective analysis. Contact Dermatitis 2017;76:151-159

108 Yu J, Treat J, Chaney K, Brod B. Potential allergens in disposable diaper wipes, topical diaper preparations, and disposable diapers: under-recognized etiology of pediatric perineal dermatitis. Dermatitis 2016;27:110-118

109 Yim E, Baquerizo Nole KL, Tosti A. Contact dermatitis caused by preservatives. Dermatitis 2014;25:215-231

110 Lynch MD, White JM, McFadden JP, Wang Y, White IR, Banerjee P. A dynamic landscape of allergen associations in delayed-type cutaneous hypersensitivity. Br J Dermatol 2017;176:184-196

2.138   4',5-DIBROMOSALICYLANILIDE*

Not an INCI name

IDENTIFICATION

Description/definition	: 4',5-Dibromosalicylanilide is the brominated aromatic amide that conform to the structural formula shown below
Chemical class(es)	: Organobromine compounds; aromatic compounds; amides
INCI name USA	: Not in the Personal Care Products Council Ingredient Database
Chemical/IUPAC name	: 5-Bromo-N-(4-bromophenyl)-2-hydroxybenzamide
Other names	: Dibromsalan
CAS registry number (s)	: 87-12-7
EINECS number(s)	: 201-724-1
Function(s) in cosmetics	: EU: prohibited. USA: formerly used as antimicrobial
EU cosmetic restrictions	: Regulated in Annex II/351 of the Regulation (EC) No. 1223/2009 (prohibited)
USA cosmetic restrictions	: Prohibited (FDA)
Patch testing	: 1% pet.
Molecular formula	: $C_{13}H_9Br_2NO_2$

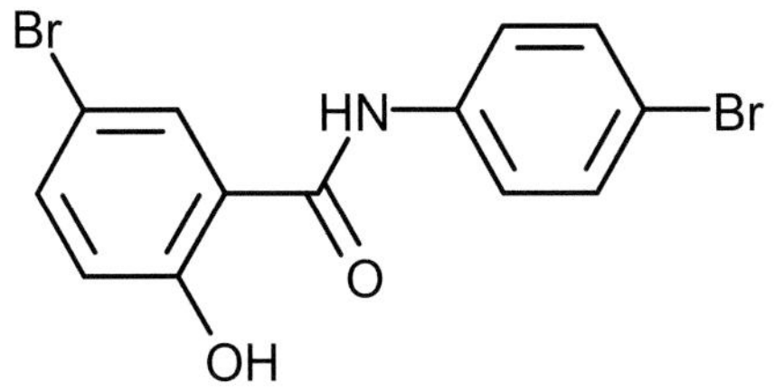

GENERAL

4'5-Dibromosalicylanilide (from here: dibromosalicylanilide) is a halogenated salicylanilide which was used in the 1960s and 1970s as an antimicrobial in germicidal soaps in certain countries, notably the USA. This chemical caused a small number of cases of photosensitization from its presence in soap (1,5,9) and hair lotions (2). When tested, it not infrequently caused positive photopatch tests (12), but most of these probably were the result of photocross-reactivity to primary photosensitization to tribromosalicylanilide or tetrachlorosalicylanilide. The United States Food and Drug Administration (FDA) prohibited the use of halogenated salicylanilides in cosmetics in 1975 (13) and it is also prohibited in the EU. It may be assumed that dibromosalicylanilide is not in use anymore.

A general introduction to the halogenated salicylanilides and related chemicals (halogenated phenols) can be found in Chapter 2.450 Tetrachlorosalicylanilide. In assessing the data from early studies, and notably in the distinction between contact allergy and photocontact allergy, it should be realized that, in those days, experience with photopatch tests was limited and such tests may not always have been reliable.

CONTACT ALLERGY

Cross-reactions, pseudo-cross-reactions and co-reactions (including photo-reactions)

Patients primarily photosensitized to tribromosalicylanilide frequently showed photocross-sensitization (3,5,11) and occasional plain contact allergy as cross-reaction (3). Cross-reactions and photocross-reactions from tetrachlorosalicylanilide to dibromosalicylanilide have also been reported (6,7). Patients photosensitized to dibromosalicylanilide have photocross-reacted to tribromosalicylanilide and tetrachlorosalicylanilide (5, primary sensitizer unknown). Photocross-reactivity between 2',3,4',5-tetrabromosalicylanilide, tribromosalicylanilide, dibromosalicylanilide, 3,5-dibromosalicylanilide and 3,5-dibromosalicylic acid has been observed (8).

Presence in cosmetic products and chemical analyses

In May 2017, dibromosalicylanilide was present in zero of 66,975 cosmetic products of which the composition is known in EWG's Skin Deep Cosmetics Database, USA (http://www.ewg.org/skindeep/).In the USA, in April 2017, dibromosalicylanilide was present in zero of 56,714 cosmetic products of which the composition is known in FDA's Voluntary Cosmetic Registration Program (VCRP) (data obtained from FDA, May 2017).

OTHER SIDE EFFECTS

Photosensitivity

Photopatch testing in groups of patients

In the period 1967 to 1975, in one center in the USA, 133 patients with a history suggestive of a photosensitivity problem or an eruption involving sun-exposed areas were photopatch tested with dibromosalicylanilide and 12 (9%) had a positive photopatch test. The relevance of the reactions was not mentioned, most were probably photocross-reactions (12).

Case reports and case series

Two patients (1) and one more (5) had photoallergic contact dermatitis from primary photosensitization to dibromosalicylanilide in soaps (1). Occupational dermatitis in hairdressers from dibromosalicylanilide in hair lotions has been reported from Germany (2). An unspecified number of patients had photoallergic contact dermatitis from dibromosalicylanilide in soaps (9). Twelve patients with photosensitive reactions due to soaps had positive photopatch tests to either dibromosalicylanilide or tribromosalicylanilide, or a soap solution containing these substances, but tests were negative if soap solutions free of halogenated salicylanilides were used (10).

In a period of 1.5 year (1966-1967), in a university center in San Francisco, USA, 26 patients suspected of photosensitivity were investigated with photopatch tests with halogenated salicylanilides and related compounds. Tetrachlorosalicylanilide was the most frequent photosensitizer (21/22 tested), followed by dibromosalicylanilide (n=17), bithionol (10/26), tribromosalicylanilide (9/22), hexachlorophene (n=4), triclocarban (n=3) and dichlorophene (n=3). Six patients became persistent light reactors. The relevance of the reactions was not specified. In fact, the authors stated that it was generally impossible to determine which was the original photosensitizer and which positive photopatch tests were the result of photocross-sensitivity (4).

LITERATURE

1   Molloy JF, Mayer JA. Photodermatitis from dibromsalan. Arch Derm 1966;93:329-331
2   Behrbohm P, Schzunke E. Arbeitsbedingtes Ekzem durch 5,4'-Dibromsalicylanilid in Haarkosmetische Präparaten. Berufsdermatosen 1966;14:169 (article in German)
3   Osmundsen PE. Contact photoallergy to tribromsalicylanilide. Br J Dermatol 1969;81:429-434
4   Epstein JH, Wuepper KD, Maibach HI. Photocontact dermatitis to halogenated salicylanilides and related compounds: A clinical and histologic review of 26 patients. Arch Dermatol 1968;97:236-244
5   Epstein S. Photosensitizers in soaps. JAMA 1966;195:878
6   Wilkinson DS. Further experiences with halogenated salicylanilides. Br J Dermatol 1962;74:295-301
7   Wilkinson DS. Patch test reactions to certain halogenated salicylanilides. Br J Dermatol 1962;74:302-306
8   Harber LC, Harris H, Baer RL. Photoallergic contact dermatitis due to halogenated salicylanilides and related compounds. Arch Dermatol 1966;94:255-262
9   Harber LC, Targovnik SE, Baer RL. Contact photosensitivity patterns to halogenated salicylanilides in man and guinea pigs. Arch Dermatol 1967;96:646-656
10   Ison AE, Tucker JB. Photosensitive dermatitis from soaps. N Eng J Med 1968;278:81
11   Emmett EA. The nature of tribromosalicylanilide photoallergy. J Invest Dermatol 1974;63:227-230
12   Smith SZ, Epstein JH. Photocontact dermatitis to halogenated salicylanilides and related compounds. Our experience between 1967 and 1975. Arch Dermatol 1977;113:1372-1374
13   Wolverton JE, Soter NA, Cohen DE. Fentichlor photocontact dermatitis: A persistent enigma. Dermatitis 2013;24:77-81

2.139 DIBUTYL PHTHALATE

IDENTIFICATION

Description/definition   : Dibutyl phthalate is the aromatic diester of butyl alcohol and phthalic acid, which
                             conforms to the formula shown below
Chemical class(es)   : Esters
Chemical/IUPAC name   : Dibutyl benzene-1,2-dicarboxylate
Other names   : Butyl phthalate
CAS registry number (s)   : 84-74-2
EC number(s)   : 201-557-4
CIR review(s)   : J Am Coll Toxicol 1985;4:267-303 (access: www.cir-safety.org/ingredients)
SCCS opinion(s)   : SCCP/1016/06 (9); SCCNFP/0833/04 (10)
Merck Index monograph   : 4314
Function(s) in cosmetics   : EU: formerly used for masking; perfuming; plasticizer; solvent; delisted in 2005.
                             USA: fragrance ingredients; plasticizers; solvents
EU cosmetic restrictions   : Regulated in Annex II/675 of the Regulation (EC) No. 1223/2009 (prohibited)
Patch testing   : 5.0% pet. (Chemotechnique, SmartPracticeEurope, SmartPracticeCanada)
Molecular formula   : $C_{16}H_{22}O_4$

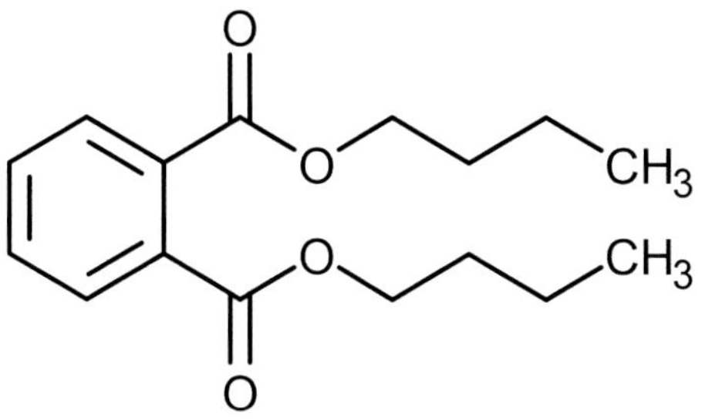

GENERAL

Dibutyl phthalate is used in pharmaceutical manufacturing as a plasticizer in films covering tablets, dragées and capsules, as a softener for adding to plastics and in thermoplastic resins. It may also be used as insect repellent (12).

CONTACT ALLERGY

Patch testing in groups of patients

In the period 2000-2007, in the USA, 944 selected patients tested with a supplemental cosmetic screening series were patch tested with dibutyl phthalate 5% pet. and 5 (0.5%) had a positive reaction. Four of the 5 reactions were considered to be relevant, but these included 'questionable' and 'past' relevance (2).

Case reports and case series

Dibutyl phthalate was responsible for 1 out of 399 cases of cosmetic allergy where the causal allergen was identified in a study of the NACDG, USA, 1977-1983 (1). One individual had allergic contact dermatitis from dibutyl phthalate in an aerosol antiperspirant and a deodorant (3).

Contact allergy to dibutyl phthalate in non-cosmetic products

A man had an acute erythematous rash in his groins and anogenital region from contact allergy to dibutyl phthalate (and benzalkonium chloride) in a pharmaceutical cream, that he had used for treatment of itching in the perianal area (11). Another patient had a similar rash from the same cream, used to treat chronic intertrigo. This patient was allergic to its ingredients dibutyl phthalate, propyl gallate and hydrocortisone (8).

Presence in cosmetic products and chemical analyses

In the USA, in April 2017, dibutyl phthalate was present in 29 of 56,714 cosmetic products of which the composition is known in FDA's Voluntary Cosmetic Registration Program (VCRP) (data obtained from FDA, May 2017). In April 2017, dibutyl phthalate was present in 2 of 65,521 cosmetic products of which the composition is known in EWG's Skin Deep Cosmetics Database, USA (http://www.ewg.org/skindeep/). In 1980, it was reported that dibutyl phthalate was contained in 553 (2.9%) of 19,000 cosmetic formulations held by the American Food and Drug Administration (7). Recent analyses of phthalates in cosmetic products can be found in refs. 4-6. Gas chromatography - mass spectrometry analysis to search for hazardous compounds was performed on 14 different commercially available black tattoo ink samples. All inks contained dibutyl phthalate in amounts ranging from 0.12 to 691 µg/g (ppm) (13).

OTHER SIDE EFFECTS

Immediate-type reactions

A patient had taken a capsule with a mucolytic product, containing various herbal extracts, predominantly myrrhe, plus 7.5 mg dibutyl phthalate per capsule, for the first time. Twenty minutes later, itching, urticaria and respiratory distress occurred and culminated in anaphylactic shock, making emergency treatment in the hospital necessary. Later, prick tests were carried out on the volar aspect of the arm with all the individual substances from the capsule. At the test site of dibutyl phthalate, tested undiluted, a weal of 3 centimeter diameter developed which, in the further course, expanded to cover the entire lower arm. At the same time, the patient developed generalized urticaria and rhinoconjunctivitis. A mucolytic solution of the same brand and the other individual substances of the capsule gave negative results. Prick tests with dibutyl phthalate in 10 control persons were negative (12).

LITERATURE

1   Adams RM, Maibach HI, Clendenning WE, Fisher AA, Jordan WJ, Kanof N, et al. A five-year study of cosmetic reactions. J Am Acad Dermatol 1985;13:1062-1069

2   Wetter DA, Yiannias JA, Prakash AV, Davis MD, Farmer SA, el-Azhary RA, et al. Results of patch testing to personal care product allergens in a standard series and a supplemental cosmetic series: an analysis of 945 patients from the Mayo Clinic Contact Dermatitis Group, 2000-2007. J Am Acad Dermatol 2010;63:789-798

3   Sneddon I. Dermatitis from dibutyl phthalate in an aerosol antiperspirant and deodorant. Contact Dermatitis Newsl 1972;12:308

4   Hubinger JC, Harvey DC. Analysis of consumer cosmetic products for phthalate esters. J Cosmet Sci 2006;57:127-137

5   Koniecki D, Wang R, Moody RP, Zhu J. Phthalates in cosmetic and personal care products: concentrations and possible dermal exposure. Environ Res 2011;111:329-336

6   Hubinger JC. A survey of phthalate esters in consumer cosmetic products. J Cosm Sc 2010;61:457-465

7   Maibach HI, Akerson JN, Marzulli FN, Wenninger J, Greif M, Hjorth N, Andersen KE, Wilkinson DS. Test concentrations and vehicles for dermatological testing of cosmetic ingredients. Contact Dermatitis 1980;6:369-404

8   Wilkinson SM, Beck MH. Allergic contact dermatitis from dibutyl phthalate, propyl gallate and hydrocortisone in Timodine®. Contact Dermatitis 1992;27:197

9   SCCP (Scientific Committee on Consumer Products). Opinion on phthalates in cosmetic products, 21 March 2007, SCCP/1016/06. Available at:
http://ec.europa.eu/health/archive/ph_risk/committees/04_sccp/docs/sccp_o_106.pdf

10 SCCNFP (Scientific Committee on Cosmetics and Non Food Products). Opinion concerning dibutylphthalate, 1 July 2004, SCCNFP/0833/04. Available at:
http://ec.europa.eu/health/archive/ph_risk/committees/sccp/documents/out287_en.pdf

11 Chowdhury MM, Statham BN. Allergic contact dermatitis from dibutyl phthalate and benzalkonium chloride in Timodine cream. Contact Dermatitis 2002;46:57

12 Gall H, Köhler A, Peter RU. Anaphylactic shock reaction to dibutyl-phthalate-containing capsules. Dermatology 1999;199:169-170

13 Lehner K, Santarelli F, Vasold R, König B, Landthaler M, Bäumler W. Black tattoo inks are a source of problematic substances such as dibutyl phthalate. Contact Dermatitis 2011;65:231-238

2.140   DICAPRYLYL MALEATE

IDENTIFICATION

Description/definition   : Dicaprylyl maleate is the diester of capryl alcohol and maleic acid, which conforms to
the formula shown below
Chemical class(es)   : Esters
Chemical/IUPAC name : Dioctyl (Z)-but-2-enedioate
Other names   : Dioctyl maleate
CAS registry number (s) : 2915-53-9
EC number(s)   : 220-835-6
Function(s) in cosmetics : EU: emollient; skin conditioning; solvent. USA: skin-conditioning agents - emollient
Patch testing   : 10% pet. (1,4); preferably use aged material for patch testing (1)
Molecular formula   : $C_{20}H_{36}O_4$

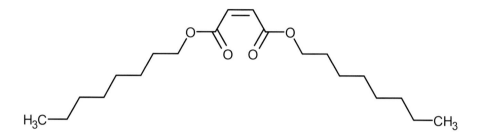

GENERAL

Dicaprylyl maleate is a synthetic, lipophilic diester, produced by reacting caprylyl alcohol and maleic acid, the latter
being a dicarboxylic acid. Cosmetically, it imparts a silky, non-greasy feel and is used as an emollient in various skin
and hair care products such as cleansers, moisturizers, sunscreens, eye shadows, hair relaxers, and hair styling
products. In industry, it is categorized as a plasticizer and used in emulsion-type paints, paper, textile coating,
adhesives, and oil additives. It is also used in surfactants and wetting agents (1,4).

CONTACT ALLERGY

Case reports and case series

Two patient had allergic contact dermatitis from dicaprylyl maleate (DCM) in cucumber lotion (2,3), another
individual reacted to DCM in a moisturizer (4). In the period 2001-2005, in 18 dermatology clinics in the UK and
Finland, twenty-two patients allergic to dicaprylyl maleate, reacting to 26 cosmetic products including moisturizing
products, fake tanning lotions, foundation and sunscreen products were seen (1). Five of the 22 patients did not
react to DCM prepared by the manufacturer from concurrent factory stock, but did have positive reactions to a
deliberately aged batch of DCM. On the basis of the positive patch test results to DCM, one large cosmetics
manufacturing company (the producer of 23 of the 26 products) began the process of withdrawing DCM from its
products in 2003. By early 2006, the reports from clinicians to this company regarding suspected contact dermatitis
to the previously identified products had almost ceased, implying that the withdrawal of DCM from the products has
reduced the problem of contact dermatitis (1).

Cross-reactions, pseudo-cross-reactions and co-reactions

Co-reactivity with or (pseudo)cross-reactivity to or from caprylic/capric triglycerides (2).

Presence in cosmetic products and chemical analyses

In the USA, in April 2017, dicaprylyl maleate was present in 60 of 56,714 cosmetic products of which the composition
is known in FDA's Voluntary Cosmetic Registration Program (VCRP) (data obtained from FDA, May 2017). In March
2017, dicaprylyl maleate was present in 24 of 64,983 cosmetic products of which the composition is known in EWG's
Skin Deep Cosmetics Database, USA (http://www.ewg.org/skindeep/).

LITERATURE

1   Lotery H, Kirk S, Beck M, Burova E, Crone M, Curley R, et al. Dicaprylyl maleate – an emerging cosmetic allergen. Contact Dermatitis 2007;57:169-172
2   Laube S, Davies MG, Prais L, Foulds IS. Allergic contact dermatitis from medium-chain triglycerides in a moisturizing lotion. Contact Dermatitis 2002;47:171
3   Laube S. Allergic contact dermatitis from medium-chain triglycerides. Contact Dermatitis 2003;48:350
4   Chan I, Wakelin S H. Allergic contact dermatitis from dioctyl maleate in a moisturizer. Contact Dermatitis 2006;55:250

2.141 DICHLOROBENZYL ALCOHOL

IDENTIFICATION

Description/definition : Dichlorobenzyl alcohol is the substituted aromatic compound that conforms to the formula shown below
Chemical class(es) : Alcohols; halogen compounds
Chemical/IUPAC name : (2,4-Dichlorophenyl)methanol
Other name(s) : 2,4-Dichlorobenzenemethanol
CAS registry number (s) : 1777-82-8; 12041-76-8
EC number(s) : 217-210-5
Merck Index monograph : 4339
Function(s) in cosmetics : EU: antimicrobial; preservative. USA: cosmetic biocides
SCCP opinion(s) : SCCNFP/0604/02 (5)
EU cosmetic restrictions : Regulated in Annex V/22 of the Regulation (EC) No. 1223/2009
Patch testing : 1% pet. (4); 2% pet. (3,6)
Molecular formula : $C_7H_6Cl_2O$

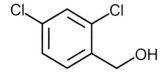

CONTACT ALLERGY

Patch testing in groups of patients
In Switzerland, in 1989-1990, 2295 consecutive patients suspected of contact dermatitis (routine testing) were patch tested with dichlorobenzyl alcohol and 9 (0.4%) had a positive reaction. The relevance of these reactions was not mentioned (4).

Case reports and case series
Dichlorobenzyl alcohol was responsible for 3 out of 959 cases of non-fragrance cosmetic allergy where the causal allergen was identified, Belgium, 2000-2010 (1). Two positive patch test reactions were ascribed to cosmetic allergy (2). One patient had allergic contact dermatitis from a moisturizing cream and reacted to the cream and to its ingredient dichlorobenzyl alcohol 2% pet. Twenty-six controls were negative to the test material. Repeated open application tests (ROAT) with dichlorobenzyl alcohol 2% pet. and the moisturizer as is were positive on day five (3).

Presence in cosmetic products and chemical analyses
In the USA, in April 2017, dichlorobenzyl alcohol was present in 12 of 56,714 cosmetic products of which the composition is known in FDA's Voluntary Cosmetic Registration Program (VCRP) (data obtained from FDA, May 2017). In March 2017, dichlorobenzyl alcohol was present in one of 64,983 cosmetic products of which the composition is known in EWG's Skin Deep Cosmetics Database, USA (http://www.ewg.org/skindeep/).

LITERATURE
1   Travassos AR, Claes L, Boey L, Drieghe J, Goossens A. Non-fragrance allergens in specific cosmetic products. Contact Dermatitis 2011;65:276-285
2   Kohl L, Blondeel A, Song M. Allergic contact dermatitis from cosmetics: retrospective analysis of 819 patch-tested patients. Dermatology 2002;204:334-337
3   Thormann H, Kollander M, Andersen KE. Allergic contact dermatitis from dichlorobenzyl alcohol in a patient with multiple contact allergies. Contact Dermatitis 2009;60:295-296
4   Perrenoud D, Bircher A, Hunziker T, Suter H, Bruckner-Tuderman L, Stäger J, et al. Frequency of sensitization to 13 common preservatives in Switzerland. Contact Dermatitis 1994;30:276-279
5   (SCCFNP) Scientific Committee on Cosmetic Products and Non-Food Products Intended for Consumers. Opinion Concerning 2,4-dichlorobenzyl alcohol (DCBA), 10 January 2003, SCCNFP/0604/02. Available at: http://ec.europa.eu/health/archive/ph_risk/committees/sccp/documents/out189_en.pdf
6   De Groot AC. Patch Testing, 3rd Edition. Wapserveen, The Netherlands: acdegroot publishing, 2008 (ISBN 978-90-813233-1-4)

2.142 DICHLORODIFLUOROMETHANE[*]

Not an INCI name

IDENTIFICATION

Description/definition	: Dichlorodifluoromethane is the halogen-substituted hydrocarbon that conforms to the structural formula shown below
Chemical class(es)	: Organohalogen compounds
INCI name USA	: Neither in CosIng nor in the Personal Care Products Council Ingredient Database
Chemical/IUPAC name	: Dichloro(difluoro)methane
Other names	: Freon® 12
CAS registry number (s)	: 75-71-8
EC number(s)	: 200-893-9
Merck Index monograph	: 4343
EU cosmetic restrictions	: Prohibited (Regulation (EC) No. 1005/2009 of the European parliament and of the Council of 16 September 2009 on substances that deplete the ozone layer; Official Journal of the European Union L 286/1-30, 31-10-2009)
USA cosmetic restrictions	: Prohibited (FDA)
Patch testing	: pure, open and closed (1)
Molecular formula	: CCl_2F_2

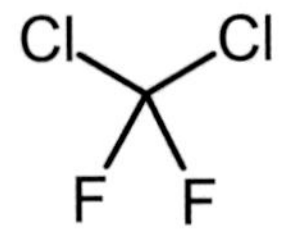

GENERAL

The chlorofluorocarbons are liquefied gases of low molecular weight which have been in use as propellants since 1940. For several decades, they were considered the best propellants available, because of their physicochemical properties, and were used in personal care products such as hair sprays, deodorants, antiperspirants, perfumes, and medicated aerosols. Due to their ozone-depleting potential, dichlorodifluoromethane and other chlorofluorocarbons are not used anymore. Discussion of adverse reactions to dichlorodifluoromethane in this chapter is limited to those caused by its presence in cosmetic products.

CONTACT ALLERGY

Case reports and case series

A man using a deodorant spray presented with a one-year history of recurrent episodes of axillary dermatitis. The same brand of deodorants in the form of bars or roll-on was tolerated perfectly. Several months before, he had used a medicated antimycotic aerosol, and observed a new eruption affecting the area. Patch testing was performed with the standard series and three different deodorant sprays, as well as the individual components of each mark separately. Freon® 11 (CCl_3F), Freon® 12 (CCl_2F_2) and Freon® 114 ($CClF_2$-$CClF_2$) were tested in open and closed patch tests. The patient reacted to the three aerosol deodorants and to dichlorodifluoromethane (Freon® 12) in the closed patch test, but the open test with Freon® 12 was negative (1).

A female patient had hand dermatitis, but was tested with a large battery of aerosol deodorants, and to dichlorodifluoromethane and the related trichlorofluoromethane (Freon® 11) because of a history of axillary dermatitis from the use of aerosol deodorants. She reacted positively to all deodorants and to both dichlorodifluoromethane and trichlorofluoromethane. It was not mentioned, which of these had been present in the deodorants previously used by the patient and causing the axillary dermatitis (2).

A woman reported that she had never tolerated deodorants, female hygiene sprays and medical 'wound sprays'. She developed an allergic reaction to ethyl chloride used for anesthesia during removal of mollusca contagiosa (4). When patch tested, she reacted to both ethyl chloride and to dichlorodifluoromethane. It was not mentioned whether the deodorants and female hygiene sprays that she had previously used and that caused skin reactions, had contained dichlorodifluoromethane or related propellants (4).

Cross-reactions, pseudo-cross-reactions and co-reactions

Not to Freon® 11 (CCl_3F) and probably not to Freon 114® ($CClF_2$-$CClF_2$; the patch test reaction was irritant) (1). Co-reactivity to trichlorofluoromethane (Freon® 11) and ethyl chloride; the latter was not considered to be cross-sensitization, the former was (2). However, co-reactivity between ethyl chloride and dichlorodifluoromethane has been observed by other authors also (3,4).

Presence in cosmetic products and chemical analyses

In May 2017, dichlorodifluoromethane was present in zero of 66,975 cosmetic products of which the composition is known in EWG's Skin Deep Cosmetics Database, USA (http://www.ewg.org/skindeep/). In the USA, in April 2017, dichlorodifluoromethane was present in zero of 56,714 cosmetic products of which the composition is known in FDA's Voluntary Cosmetic Registration Program (VCRP) (data obtained from FDA, May 2017).

LITERATURE

1   Valdivieso R, Pola J, Zapata C, Cuesta J, Puyana J, Martin C, Losada E. Contact allergic dermatitis caused by Freon 12 in deodorants. Contact Dermatitis 1987;17:243-245
2   Van Ketel WG. Allergic contact dermatitis from propellants in deodorant sprays in combination with allergy to ethyl chloride. Contact Dermatitis 1976;2:115-119
3   Bircher AJ, Hampl K, Hirsbrunner P, Buechner SA, Schneider M. Allergic contact dermatitis from ethyl chloride and sensitization to dichlorodifluoromethane (CFC 12). Contact Dermatitis 1994;31:41-44
4   Aberer W, Zonzits E. Allergy to ethyl chloride does occur, and might frequently be misdiagnosed. Contact Dermatitis 1989;21:352-353

2.143 DICHLOROPHENE

IDENTIFICATION

Description/definition   : Dichlorophene is the halogenated phenolic compound that conforms to the formula
                          shown below
Chemical class(es)   : Halogen compounds; phenols
Chemical/IUPAC name   : 4-Chloro-2-[(5-chloro-2-hydroxyphenyl)methyl]phenol
Other name(s)   : 2,2'-Methylenebis(4-chlorophenol); dichlorophen
CAS registry number (s) : 97-23-4
EC number(s)   : 202-567-1
CIR review(s)   : Int J Toxicol 2004;23(Suppl.1):1-27 (access: www.cir-safety.org/ingredients)
Merck Index monograph   : 4351
Function(s) in cosmetics : EU: antimicrobial; deodorant. USA: cosmetic biocides; deodorant agents; pesticides
EU cosmetic restrictions : Regulated in Annex III/11 of the Regulation (EC) No. 1223/2009
Patch testing   : 1.0% pet. (Chemotechnique); 0.5% pet. (SmartPracticeEurope, SmartPracticeCanada)
Molecular formula   : $C_{13}H_{10}Cl_2O_2$

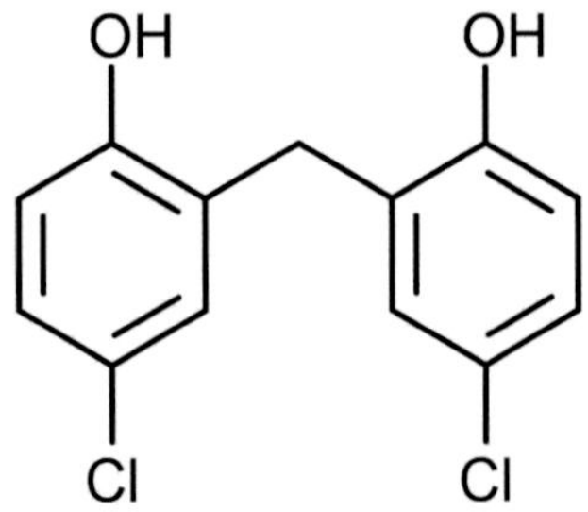

GENERAL

Dichlorophene is a halogenated phenolic bactericide and fungicide used as an anthelmintic drug in veterinary medicine and as an anti-moss product in horticulture. Dichlorophene has been used to preserve cotton textiles, woollen textiles, and other materials from the mold, mildew, rot, and mustiness commonly caused by fungi and bacteria. The antimicrobial is or was also used to prevent growth of microorganisms in cutting oils, disinfectants, felt products, paper mill products, rug backing, canvas lawn and beach furniture, and rubber-coated fabrics (16,22). Although it is allowed both in the EU and the USA for use in cosmetic products, it is highly unlikely that cosmetic manufacturers still make use of dichlorophene. Indeed, in two databases of cosmetic ingredients in the USA, not a single of over 64,000 and 56,000 cosmetic products contained dichlorophene (see the section 'Presence in cosmetic products and chemical analyses' below).

CONTACT ALLERGY

Patch testing in groups of patients

There are no studies in which dichlorophene has been tested in consecutive patients suspected of contact dermatitis (routine testing, possible exception: ref. 22). Results of patch testing dichlorophene in groups of *selected* patients (e.g., patients suspected of photosensitivity, patients suspected to react to topical drugs or cosmetics) back to 1970 are shown in table 2.143.1. Frequencies of sensitization have ranged from 1.2% to 11.3%. The study reporting an 11.3% sensitization rate had certain weaknesses and the relevance of the 18 positive reactions was not mentioned (5). A similar high percentage (11%) of positive reactions was seen in 1970 by the members of the North American Contact Dermatitis Group; neither the selection nor the relevance of the positive reactions was mentioned (7)

Case reports and case series

Three patients had cheilitis and/or perioral eczema and/or glossitis and/or stomatitis from contact allergy to dichlorophene in one brand of toothpastes. The authors mentioned having seen 4 more such patients, but details were not provided (8). A similar patient was the first case of toothpaste allergy from dichlorophene reported (9). A patient was described in a US journal with the title 'Eczematous contact dermatitis of the palm due to toothpaste' (10). The allergen was cited as formaldehyde in ref. 11. However, the authors of ref. 12 mentioned that it was a toothpaste 'that contained compound G-4' (which is dichlorophene) and Cronin in her book states that 'patch testing with the toothpaste was positive' (13).

A woman had eczema from contact allergy to dichlorophene present in a hand lotion (16). Three patients had allergic contact dermatitis from dichlorophene. In two, the allergic dermatitis apparently was caused by liquid or cream cosmetic bases. The third patient was probably previously sensitized by hexachlorophene in a spray deodorant, and the dichlorophene allergy may have represented cross-sensitivity (18, data cited in ref. 16, article not read; in ref. 22 it is stated that the culprit products were topical medicaments).

Table 2.143.1 Patch testing in groups of patients: Selected patient groups

Years and Country	Test conc. & vehicle	Number of patients tested	positive (%)		Selection of patients (S); Relevance (R); Comments (C)	Ref.
2001-2010 Canada		160	18	(11.3%)	S: patients with suspected photosensitivity and patients who developed pruritus or a rash after sunscreen application; R: not stated; C: weak study: inadequate reading of test results, erythema only was considered to represent a positive patch test reaction	5
2000-2005 USA	1% pet.	178	3	(1.7%)	S: patients photopatch tested for suspected photodermatitis; R: 2 reactions were relevant	18
1984-1991 USA	1% pet.	3781	46	(1.2%)	S: unknown, possibly routine testing; R: not stated	22
1981 France	1% pet.	465	8	(1.7%)	S: patients suspected of allergy to cosmetics, drugs, industrial products, or clothes; R: not stated	14
1975-6 USA, Canada	1% pet.	173		(11%)	S: not stated; R: not stated	7
1970 USA	1% pet.	100	2	(2%)	S: patients suspected to react to topical medication; R: not stated	6

Contact allergy to dichlorophene in non-cosmetic products
One individual had allergic contact dermatitis from dichlorophene in a proprietary ointment for treating 'athlete's foot' (17). In a period of one year, in 1969, one author saw two women and one man suffering from allergic reactions to dichlorophene present as an antimicrobial in a 0.25% concentration in a modification of Unna's boots, applied to the lower legs for stasis dermatitis, ulcers, or both (16). One patient had ACD from dichlorophene (19, cited in ref. 18, details unknown, article not read). Another individual had allergic contact dermatitis of the dorsal aspects of the feet from dichlorophene present in his shoes (21).

Cross-reactions, pseudo-cross-reactions and co-reactions
Not to hexachlorophene (8,9,16). Possible cross-reaction from hexachlorophene (18). Bithionol (18); tetrachlorosalicylanilide (18).

Patch test sensitization
A man developed a positive patch test reaction to dichlorophene 1% pet. at day 10. When retested, he had again this late reaction, indicating that the first one was *not* indicative of patch test sensitization (21).

Presence in cosmetic products and chemical analyses
In June 2016, dichlorophene was present in zero of 69,045 cosmetic products of which the composition is known in EWG's Skin Deep Cosmetics Database, USA (http://www.ewg.org/skindeep/). In the USA, in April 2017, dichlorophene was present in zero of 56,714 cosmetic products of which the composition is known in FDA's Voluntary Cosmetic Registration Program (VCRP) (data obtained from FDA, May 2017).

OTHER SIDE EFFECTS

Photosensitivity

Photopatch testing in groups of patients
Results of photopatch testing with dichlorophene in groups of selected patients (usually based on suspicion of photosensitivity) back to 1985 are shown in table 2.143.2. In 6 studies, frequencies of photosensitization have ranged from 0.4% to 3.8%. The study with the highest concentration had certain weaknesses and the relevance of the 6 positive photopatch tests was not mentioned (5). In three studies, the reactions were not relevant, but the number of positive photopatch tests were only 1 or 2 (2,3,15). In a 2004-2006 study from Italy, 2 of 4 positive photopatch tests were scored as positive, but culprit products were not mentioned (4).

Case reports and case series
An unknown number of patients from Germany had positive photopatch tests to dichlorophene (20, details unknown, article not read). In a period of 1.5 year (1966-1967), in a university center in San Francisco, USA, 26 patients suspected of photosensitivity were investigated with photopatch tests with halogenated salicylanilides and

related compounds. Tetrachlorosalicylanilide was the most frequent photosensitizer (21/22 tested), followed by bithionol (10/26), tribromosalicylanilide (9/22), hexachlorophene (n=4), triclocarban (n=3) and dichlorophene (n=3). Six patients became persistent light reactors. The relevance of the reactions was not specified. In fact, the authors stated that it was generally impossible to determine which was the original photosensitizer and which positive photopatch tests were the result of photocross-sensitivity (23).

Table 2.143.2 Photopatch testing in groups of patients

Years and Country	Test conc. & vehicle	Number of patients tested | positive (%)		Selection of patients (S); Relevance (R); Comments (C)	Ref.
2001-2010 Canada		160	6 (3.8%)	S: patients with suspected photosensitivity and patients who developed pruritus or a rash after sunscreen application; R: not stated; C: weak study: inadequate reading of test results, erythema only was considered to represent a positive patch test reaction	5
2004-2006 Italy	10% pet.	1082	4 (0.4%)	S: patients with histories and clinical features suggestive of photoallergic contact dermatitis; 3/4 were cases of photoaugmented contact allergy; R: 50%	4
1993-2006 USA	1% pet.	76	1 (1.3%)	S: not stated; R: 94% of all reactions to antimicrobials were considered 'not relevant'	3
2000-2005 USA	1% pet.	178	1 (0.6%)	S: patients photopatch tested for suspected photodermatitis; R: the reaction was not relevant	15
1985-1990 USA	1% pet.	176	2 (1.2%)	S: patients with a history of photosensitivity; R: not relevant	2
1980-1985 USA	1% pet.	70	2 (3%)	S: not stated; R: not stated	1
1967-1975 USA		352	13 (3.7%)	S: patients with a history suggestive of a photosensitivity problem or an eruption involving sun-exposed areas	24

LITERATURE

1   Menz J, Muller SA, Connnolly SM. Photopatch testing: A six year experience. J Am Acad Dermatol 1988;18:1044-1047
2   DeLeo VA, Suarez SM, Maso MJ. Photoallergic contact dermatitis. Results of photopatch testing in New York, 1985 to 1990. Arch Dermatol 1992;128:1513-1518
3   Victor FC, Cohen DE, Soter NA. A 20-year analysis of previous and emerging allergens that elicit photoallergic contact dermatitis. J Am Acad Dermatol 2010;62:605-610
4   Pigatto PD, Guzzi G, Schena D, Guarrera M, Foti C, Francalanci S, et al. Photopatch tests: an Italian multicentre study from 2004 to 2006. Contact Dermatitis 2008;59:103-108
5   Greenspoon J, Ahluwalia R, Juma N, Rosen CF. Allergic and photoallergic contact dermatitis: A 10-year experience. Dermatitis 2013;24:29-32
6   Fisher AA, Pascher F, Kanof NB. Allergic contact dermatitis due to ingredients of vehicles. A "vehicle tray" for patch testing. Arch Dermatol 1971;104:286-290
7   Rudner EJ. North American Group Results. Contact Dermatitis 1977;3:208-209
8   Fisher AA, Tobin I. Sensitivity to compound G-4 ('Dichlorophene') in dentifrices. JAMA 1953;151:998-999
9   Fisher AA, Lipton M. Allergic stomatitis due to "baxin" in a dentifrice. Arch Derm Syph 1951;64:640-641
10   Löwenthal K. Eczematous contact dermatitis of the palm due to toothpaste. New York State J Med 1952;53:1437-1438 (data cited in refs. 11,12 and 13)
11   De Groot AC, Weyland JW, Nater JP. Unwanted effects of cosmetics and drugs used in dermatology. 3rd edition. Amsterdam: Elsevier Science BV, 1994:187-189
12   Fisher AA, Tobin I. Sensitivity to compound G-4 ('Dichlorophene') in dentifrices. JAMA 1953;151:998-999.
13   Cronin E. Contact Dermatitis. Edinburgh London new York: Churchill Livingstone; 1980: 678
14   Meynadier JM, Meynadier J, Colmas A, Castelain PY, Ducombs G, Chabeau G, et al. Allergy to preservatives. Ann Dermatol Venereol 1982;109:1017-1023
15   Scalf LA, Davis MDP, Rohlinger AL, Connolly SM. Photopatch testing of 182 patients: A 6-year experience at the Mayo Clinic. Dermatitis 2009;20:44-52
16   Schorr WF. Dichlorophene (G-4) allergy. Arch Dermatol 1970;102;515-520
17   Gaul LE, Underwood GB. The cutaneous toxicity of dihydroxydichlordiphenylmethane: A new fungicide for athlete's foot. J Indiana Med Assoc 1949;42:22-24
18   Epstein E. Dichlorophene allergy. Ann Allergy 1966;24:437-439
19   Bier AG. Allergie gegen ein Diphenylmethan Derivat. Berufsdermatosen 1958;6:40-43
20   Pevny I, Lurz Ch. Photoallergische dermatitis. Allergologie 1985;8:128-138

21 Barbuzza O, Guarneri F, Galtieri G, Vaccaro M. Late patch test reaction to dichlorophene. J Investig Allergol Clin Immunol 2008;18:317-318

22 Fransway AF. The problem of preservation in the 1990s. III. Agents with preservative function independent of formaldehyde release. Am J Contact Derm 1991;2:145-174

23 Epstein JH, Wuepper KD, Maibach HI. Photocontact dermatitis to halogenated salicylanilides and related compounds: A clinical and histologic review of 26 patients. Arch Dermatol 1968;97:236-244

24 Smith SZ, Epstein JH. Photocontact dermatitis to halogenated salicylanilides and related compounds. Our experience between 1967 and 1975. Arch Dermatol 1977;113:1372-1374

2.144 DIDECYLDIMONIUM CHLORIDE

IDENTIFICATION

Description/definition   : Didecyldimonium chloride is the quaternary ammonium salt that conforms generally to the formula shown below

Chemical class(es)   : Quaternary ammonium compounds

Chemical/IUPAC name   : Didecyl(dimethyl)azanium chloride

Other names   : Didecyl dimethyl ammonium chloride; didecyldimethylammonium chloride; quaternium-12

CAS registry number (s)   : 7173-51-5

EC number(s)   : 230-525-2

Merck Index monograph   : 4380

Function(s) in cosmetics   : EU: antistatic; emulsifying; hair conditioning; surfactant. USA: antistatic agents; hair conditioning agents

Patch testing   : 0.01% and 0.1% pet. (2); risk of irritant reactions with the higher concentration (7,10); risk of false-negative reaction to 0.01% pet. (10); recent advice: 0.03% pet., 0.05% pet. and/or 0.05% water (10)

Molecular formula   : $C_{22}H_{48}ClN$

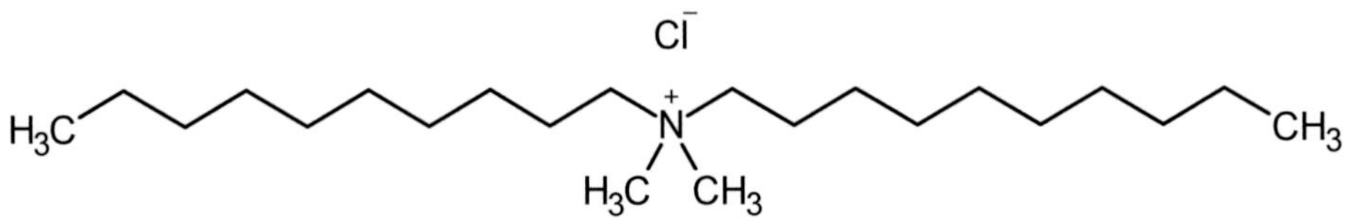

GENERAL

Didecyldimonium chloride is a quaternary ammonium compound with bactericidal, virucidal (against hepatitis B virus and human immunodeficiency virus), fungicidal and mildewcidal properties (5). The chemical is widely used in surface and instrument disinfectants. It can also be used for protecting cellulose string from microbial attack, as a wood preservative against termites, as a fungicide for wood and as an algistatic and algicide in swimming pools (2).

CONTACT ALLERGY

Case reports and case series

Didecyldimonium chloride was responsible for 1 out of 959 cases of non-fragrance cosmetic allergy where the causal allergen was identified, Belgium, 2000-2010 (1).

Contact allergy to didecyldimonium chloride in non-cosmetic products

A female hospital employee had suffered from dermatitis of the dorsum of the hands and wrists, which occurred during the course of her work, for 2 months. She had also presented with dermatitis of the face with involvement of the eyelids and conjunctivitis one month before. Patch tests showed her to be allergic to a detergent-disinfectant used at work. Later, when working in a new location, where she had no more direct contact with the detergent-disinfectant, she developed dermatitis of the eyelids, face, and arms (exposed parts). The day before, her colleagues had used the disinfectant product, to which she was allergic. She had to wait for the floor to be completely dry, or she would develop new episodes of this airborne allergic contact dermatitis. The culprit proved to be didecyldimonium chloride in the disinfectant product (2).

A female nurse working for more than 20 years in the department of surgery of a university hospital developeddermatitis on the dorsa of her hands and arms shortly after coming into contact with a newly-introduced detergent-disinfectant. Despite protective measures (including gloves and masks), the skin lesions persisted, and she had to change workplace, after which the dermatitis healed. The patient had positive patch tests to the detergent-disinfectant product 10% in water and to its ingredient didecyldimonium chloride 0.01% water (3).

A woman, who had previously worked as a saleswoman of shoes, and who had a history of atopic dermatitis and chronic hand eczema, was seen because of dermatitis on the dorsal aspects of the feet, spreading to the lower legs, which were swollen, and to the arms. Before using shoes, the patient would spray a 'refreshing spray' on the inside. Patch tests with the Swedish baseline series, an extended baseline and shoe series and the shoe refresher 10% water gave several positive reactions including to potassium dichromate and to the shoe refresher. A dilution series of the shoe refresher was positive down to 1.3% water. Patch tests with its ingredient revealed didecyldimonium chloride to be the culprit allergen (6). A geriatric nurse had occupational airborne allergic contact dermatitis from didecyldimonium chloride in a bath and a surface disinfectant (7).

Presence in cosmetic products and chemical analyses
In May 2017, didecyldimonium chloride (quaternium-12) was present in 6 of 66,648 cosmetic products of which the composition is known in EWG's Skin Deep Cosmetics Database, USA (http://www.ewg.org/skindeep/). In the USA, in April 2017, dodecyl dimethyl ammonium chloride was present in 9 of 56,714 cosmetic products of which the composition is known in FDA's Voluntary Cosmetic Registration Program (VCRP) (data obtained from FDA, May 2017).

OTHER SIDE EFFECTS

Immediate contact reactions
A female laboratory technician had recurrent rashes on her face, neck, and chest for 6 months. She attributed it to a disinfectant product with didecyldimonium chloride at a concentration of 10% used at a sterile bench where she worked. Patch testing with the disinfectant provoked an urticarial reaction with swelling of the hands and feet and a sensation of stinging, burning and itchiness after 8-10 hours. An open epicutaneous test with 15 µl of 1:1 million (unit exposure) didecyldimonium chloride dripped onto the right forearm and rinsed with water after 20 minutes gave an urticarial rash, which spread to the elbow, face and back after 2 hours (5). A young woman working in a catering school developed occupational immediate-type hypersensitivity with urticaria, facial angioedema, and dyspnea from didecyldimonium chloride in a cleaning product (4).

Miscellaneous side effects
Occupational asthma from didecyldimonium chloride has been observed (8,9).

LITERATURE

1   Travassos AR, Claes L, Boey L, Drieghe J, Goossens A. Non-fragrance allergens in specific cosmetic products. Contact Dermatitis 2011;65:276-285
2   Dejobert Y, Martin P, Piette F, Thomas P, Bergoend H. Contact dermatitis from didecyldimethylammonium chloride and bis-(aminopropyl)-lauryl amine in a detergent-disinfectant used in hospital. Contact Dermatitis 1997;37:95-96
3   Dibo M, Brasch J. Occupational allergic contact dermatitis from N,N-bis(3-aminopropyl)dodecylamine and dimethyldidecylammonium chloride in 2 hospital staff. Contact Dermatitis 2001;45:40
4   Houtappel M, Bruijnzeel-Koomen CAFM, Röckmann H. Immediate-type allergy by occupational exposure to didecyl dimethyl ammonium chloride. Contact Dermatitis 2008;59:116-117
5   Ruiz Oropeza A, Friis UF, Johansen JD. Occupational contact urticaria caused by didecyl dimethyl ammonium chloride. Contact Dermatitis 2011;64:297-298
6   Mowitz M, Pontén A. Foot dermatitis caused by didecyldimethylammonium chloride in a shoe refresher spray. Contact Dermatitis 2015;73:374-376
7   Geier J, Lessmann H, Krautheim A, Fuchs T. Airborne allergic contact dermatitis caused by didecyldimethylammonium chloride in a geriatric nurse. Contact Dermatitis 2013;68:123-125
8   Purohit A, Kopferschmitt-Kubler MC, Moreau C, Popin E, Blaumeiser M, Pauli G. Quaternary ammonium compounds and occupational asthma. Int Arch Occup Environ Health 2000;73:423-427
9   Nielsen GD, Larsen ST, Olsen O, Lovik M, Poulsen LK, Glue C, Wolkoff P. Do indoor chemicals promote development of airway allergy? Indoor Air 2007;17:236-255
10 Geier J, Lessmann H, Cevik N, Fuchs T, Buhl T. Patch testing with didecyldimethylammonium chloride. Contact Dermatitis 2016;74:374-376

2.145   DIETHYLAMINO HYDROXYBENZOYL HEXYL BENZOATE

IDENTIFICATION

Description/definition   : Diethylamino hydroxybenzoyl hexyl benzoate is the organic compound that conforms to
                              the formula shown below
Chemical class(es)   : Amines; esters; phenols
Chemical/IUPAC name   : Benzoic acid, 2-[4-(diethylamino)-2-hydroxybenzoyl]-, hexyl ester
Other names   : 2-Hydroxy-4-diethylamino-2'-hexyloxycarbonylbenzophenone
CAS registry number (s)   : 302776-68-7
EC number(s)   : 443-860-6
SCCS opinion(s)   : SCCP/1166/08 (11)
Merck Index monograph   : 11780
Function(s) in cosmetics   : EU: UV-filter. USA: light stabilizers
EU cosmetic restrictions   : Regulated in Annex VI/28 of the Regulation (EC) No. 344/2013
Patch testing   : 10% pet. (1)
Molecular formula   : $C_{24}H_{31}NO_4$

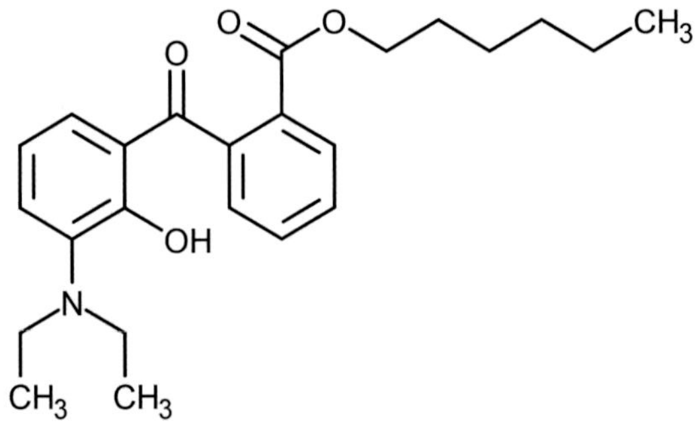

GENERAL

Diethylamino hydroxy benzoyl hexyl benzoate is a relatively new UVA filter with UV absorbance maximum (λ_{max}) at 354 nm (3,16). The literature on adverse reactions to sunscreens has been reviewed in several recent and older publications (5-10,18). A review of photocontact allergy to sunscreens was published in 2010 (17).

CONTACT ALLERGY

Patch testing in groups of patients

In 2008-2011, in 12 European countries, 1031 patients with exposed site dermatitis or history of a reaction to a sunscreen or topical NSAID were patch tested with diethylamino hydroxybenzoyl hexyl benzoate 10% pet. and 1 individual (0.1%) had a positive reaction. The relevance of this reaction was not specified (1).

Presence in cosmetic products and chemical analyses

In the USA, in April 2017, diethylamino hydroxybenzoyl hexyl benzoate was present in 230 of 56,714 cosmetic products of which the composition is known in FDA's Voluntary Cosmetic Registration Program (VCRP) (data obtained from FDA, May 2017). In March 2017, diethylamino hydroxybenzoyl hexyl benzoate was present in 5 of 64,983 cosmetic products of which the composition is known in EWG's Skin Deep Cosmetics Database, USA (http://www.ewg.org/skindeep/). It should be realized that sunscreen products containing UV-filters are classified as drugs in the USA, not as cosmetics; the number mentioned here, therefore, is that of cosmetics containing the UV-filter, but it does *not* include their presence in sunscreens.

Diethylamino hydroxybenzoyl hexyl benzoate was present in 1.8% of 4447 cosmetic products collected in Germany, 2006-2009 (2). In a sample of 337 sunscreens marketed in the UK in 2010, diethylaminohydroxybenzoyl hexyl benzoate was present in 17 (5%) products (4). Diethylamino hydroxybenzoyl hexyl benzoate was present in 1% of 329 sunscreen products (incl. 21 lipstick sunscreens) marketed in the UK in 2005 (3).

OTHER SIDE EFFECTS

Photosensitivity

Photopatch testing in groups of patients
In 2008-2011, in 12 European countries, 1031 patients with exposed site dermatitis or history of a reaction to a sunscreen or topical NSAID were photopatch tested with diethylamino hydroxybenzoyl hexyl benzoate 10% pet. and 4 individuals (0.4%) had a positive reaction. The relevance of these reactions was not specified, but for all photoallergens together, 44% of the positive photopatch tests were of current relevance and 11% of past relevance (1).

LITERATURE

1   The European Multicentre Photopatch Test Study (EMCPPTS) Taskforce. A European multicentre photopatch test study. Br J Dermatol 2012;166:1002-1009
2   Uter W, Gonçalo M, Yazar K, Kratz E-M, Mildau G, Lidén C. Coupled exposure to ingredients of cosmetic products: III. Ultraviolet filters. Contact Dermatitis 2014;71:162-169
3   Wahie S, Lloyd JJ, Farr PM. Sunscreen ingredients and labelling: a survey of products available in the U.K. Clin Exp Dermatol 2007;32:359-364
4   Kerr AC. A survey of the availability of sunscreen filters in the U.K. Clin Exp Dermatol 2011;36:541-543
5   Heurung AR, Raju SI, Warshaw EM. Adverse reactions to sunscreen agents: epidemiology, responsible irritants and allergens, clinical characteristics, and management. Dermatitis 2014;25:289-326
6   Heurung AR, Raju SI, Warshaw EM. Contact allergen of the year. Benzophenones. Dermatitis 2014;25:3-10 (contains many mistakes; Erratum in Dermatitis 2014;25:92-95)
7   Avenel-Audran M. Sunscreen products: finding the allergen. Eur J Dermatol 2010;20:161-166
8   Scheuer E, Warshaw E. Sunscreen allergy: a review of epidemiology, clinical characteristics, and responsible allergens. Dermatitis 2006;17:3-11
9   Funk JO, Dromgoole SH, Maibach HI. Sunscreen intolerance: contact sensitization, photocontact sensitization, and irritancy of sunscreen agents. Dermatol Clin 1995;13:473-481
10   Dromgoole SH, Maibach HI. Sunscreening agent intolerance: Contact and photocontact sensitization and contact urticaria. J Am Acad Dermatol 1990;22:1068-1078
11   SCCP (Scientific Committee on Consumer Products). Opinion on Diethylamino hydroxybenzoyl hexyl benzoate, 15 April 2008, SCCP/1166/08. Available at: http://ec.europa.eu/health/archive/ph_risk/committees/04_sccp/docs/sccp_o_130.pdf
16   Shaath NA. Ultraviolet filters. Photochem Photobiol Sci 2010;9:464-469
17   Shaw T, Simpson B, Wilson B, Oostman H, Rainey D, Storrs F. True photoallergy to sunscreens is rare despite popular belief. Dermatitis 2010;21:185-198
18   Schauder S. Survey of the literature on adverse reactions to preparations containing UV filters (1947-1989) (Literaturübersicht über Unverträglichkeitsreaktionen auf lichtfilterhaltige Produkte von 1947 bis 1989). Z Hautkr 1990;65:982-998 (article in German)

2.146 DIETHYLENE GLYCOL DIMETHACRYLATE

IDENTIFICATION

Description/definition   : Diethylene glycol dimethacrylate is the organic compound that conforms to the formula shown below
Chemical class(es)   : Esters
Chemical/IUPAC name   : 2-[2-(2-Methylprop-2-enoyloxy)ethoxy]ethyl 2-methylprop-2-enoate
Other names   : Diethylene glycol bis(methacrylate)
CAS registry number (s)   : 2358-84-1
EC number(s)   : 219-099-9
Function(s) in cosmetics : EU: film forming; nail conditioning. USA: artificial nail builders; film formers
Patch testing   : 1% pet. (2)
Molecular formula   : $C_{12}H_{18}O_5$

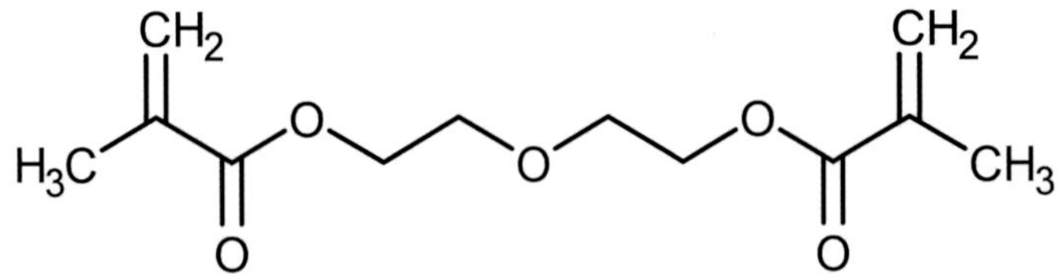

GENERAL

Discussion of contact allergy to (meth)acrylates *from non-cosmetic sources* is considered to fall outside the scope of this book. Therefore, only contact allergy from their presence in cosmetics is presented, which virtually always is from artificial nails. There are many reports of contact allergy to artificial nails, but the specific sensitizers have rarely been identified and – consequently - such publications are not presented in this and other acrylate and methacrylate monographs. Discussion is limited to publications in which the culprit (meth)acrylates have been identified, e.g., from information found in Material Data Safety Sheets, data obtained from the manufacturer or from chemical analyses. Patients often react to many (meth)acrylates on patch testing. Primary sensitization to methacrylates may result in both methacrylate and acrylate cross-sensitization. Conversely, patients sensitized to acrylates are unlikely to show cross-sensitization to methacrylates (3).

General aspects of acrylates and methacrylates are presented in Chapter 2.219 HEMA (hydroxyethyl methacrylate). A discussion of general aspects of artificial nails, contact allergy to these products, the clinical picture of allergic contact dermatitis and other side effects of sculptured nails can also be found there. A very useful review of contact sensitization to allergens in nail cosmetics, with emphasis on acrylic manicures, was published in 2017 (4).

CONTACT ALLERGY

Patch testing in groups of patients

Studies in which consecutive patients suspected of contact dermatitis have been tested with diethylene glycol dimethacrylate (routine testing) and studies testing groups of selected patients are planned to be discussed in a future publication.

Case reports and case series

Diethylene glycol dimethacrylate was responsible for 1 out of 399 cases of cosmetic allergy where the causal allergen was identified in a study of the NACDG, USA, 1977-1983 (1). One patient had onychia and paronychia from contact allergy to diethylene glycol dimethacrylate in a nail extender (cold-curing artificial nails) (2).

Presence in cosmetic products and chemical analyses

In the USA, in April 2017, diethylene glycol dimethacrylate was present in 2 of 56,714 cosmetic products of which the composition is known in FDA's Voluntary Cosmetic Registration Program (VCRP) (data obtained from FDA, May 2017). In February 2017, diethylene glycol dimethacrylate was present in zero of 64,445 cosmetic products of which the composition is known in EWG's Skin Deep Cosmetics Database, USA (http://www.ewg.org/skindeep/).

LITERATURE

1 Adams RM, Maibach HI, Clendenning WE, Fisher AA, Jordan WJ, Kanof N, et al. A five-year study of cosmetic reactions. J Am Acad Dermatol 1985;13:1062-1069
2 Fisher AA. Cross reactions between methyl methacrylate monomer and acrylic monomers presently used in acrylic nail preparations. Contact Dermatitis 1980;6:345-347
3 Aalto-Korte K, Henriks-Eckerman M-L, Kuuliala O, Jolanki R. Occupational methacrylate and acrylate allergy – cross-reactions and possible screening allergens. Contact Dermatitis 2010;63:301-312
4 Chou M, Dhingra N, Strugar TL. Contact sensitization to allergens in nail cosmetics. Dermatitis 2017;28:231-240

2.147   DIETHYL SEBACATE

IDENTIFICATION

Description/definition	: Diethyl sebacate is the diester of ethyl alcohol and sebacic acid, which conforms to the formula shown below
Chemical class(es)	: Esters
Chemical/IUPAC name	: Diethyl decanedioate
Other names	: Ethyl sebacate; sebacic acid diethyl ester; decanedioic acid diethyl ester
CAS registry number (s)	: 110-40-7
EC number(s)	: 203-764-5
CIR review(s)	: Int J Toxicol 2012;31(Suppl.1):5-76 (access: www.cir-safety.org/ingredients)
Merck Index monograph	: 9822 (sebacic acid)
Function(s) in cosmetics	: EU: emollient; masking; plasticiser; skin conditioning; solvent. USA: fragrance ingredients; plasticizers; skin-conditioning agents - emollient; solvents
Patch testing	: 5% pet. (1,6); 20-30% alc. (3)
Molecular formula	: $C_{14}H_{26}O_4$

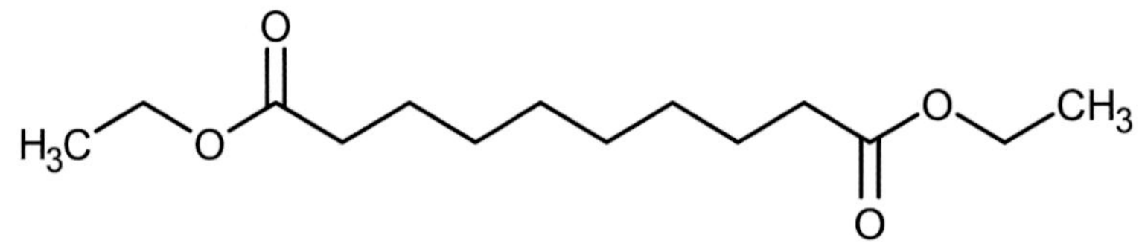

CONTACT ALLERGY

Case reports and case series

A woman was seen with pruritic erythematous macules on the dorsa of hands, where she had applied a hand cream containing 10% urea. The lesions were only observed on the applied area. A patch test to the cream was positive and later she reacted to its ingredient diethyl sebacate 5% pet. (1).

Contact allergy to diethyl sebacate in non-cosmetic products

Two patients reacted to ethyl sebacate in an antifungal preparation in one study (2). Six similar reports of single patients allergic to diethyl sebacate in antifungal topical pharmaceuticals have been published (3-8). A girl had ACD from diethyl sebacate (ethyl sebacate) from a corticosteroid ointment containing 10% ethyl sebacate (9).

Presence in cosmetic products and chemical analyses

In the USA, in April 2017, diethyl sebacate was present in zero of 56,714 cosmetic products of which the composition is known in FDA's Voluntary Cosmetic Registration Program (VCRP) (data obtained from FDA, May 2017). In March 2017, diethyl sebacate was present in zero of 64,983 cosmetic products of which the composition is known in EWG's Skin Deep Cosmetics Database, USA (http://www.ewg.org/skindeep/).

LITERATURE

1   Narita T, Oiso N, Ota T, Kawara S, Kawada A. Allergic contact dermatitis due to diethyl sebacate in a hand cream. Contact Dermatitis 2006;55:117
2   Schneider KW. Contact dermatitis due to diethyl sebacate. Contact Dermatitis 1980;6:506-507
3   Sasaki E, Hata M, Aramaki J, Honda M. Allergic contact dermatitis due to diethyl sebacate. Contact Dermatitis 1997;36:172
4   Kimura M, Kawada A. Contact dermatitis due to diethyl sebacate. Contact Dermatitis 1999;40:48-49
5   Tanaka M, Kobayashi S, Murata T, Tanikawa A, Nishikawa T. Allergic contact dermatitis from diethyl sebacate in lanoconazole cream. Contact Dermatitis 2000;43:233-234
6   Soga F, Katoh N, Kishimoto S. Contact dermatitis due to lanoconazole, cetyl alcohol and diethyl sebacate in lanoconazole cream. Contact Dermatitis 2004;50:49-50
7   Moss HV. Allergic contact dermatitis due to Halotex solution. Arch Dermatol 1974;109:572
8   Berlin AR, Miller OF. Allergic contact dermatitis from ethyl sebacate in haloprogin cream. Arch Dermatol 1976;112:1563-1564
9   Kabasawa Y, Kanzaki T. Allergic contact dermatitis from ethyl sebacate. Contact Dermatitis 1990;22:226

2.148 DIETHYLSTILBESTROL[*]

Not an INCI name

IDENTIFICATION

Description/definition	: Diethylstilbestrol is the aromatic organic compound that conforms to the structural formula shown below
Chemical class(es)	: Unsaturated organic compounds; aromatic compounds; alcohols
INCI name USA	: Not in the Personal Care Products Council Ingredient Database
Chemical/IUPAC name	: 4-[(E)-4-(4-Hydroxyphenyl)hex-3-en-3-yl]phenol
CAS registry number (s)	: 56-53-1
EC number(s)	: 200-278-5
Merck Index monograph	: 4418
Function(s) in cosmetics	: EU: Delisted in 1979
EU cosmetic restrictions	: Regulated in Annex II/260 of the Regulation (EC) No. 1223/2009 (prohibited)
Patch testing	: 1% pet. or 0.1% alc. (2)
Molecular formula	: $C_{18}H_{20}O_2$

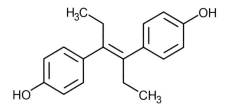

CONTACT ALLERGY

Case reports and case series
One patient had allergic contact dermatitis from diethylstilbestrol used as a hair growth stimulant in a hair lotion (1).

Cross-reactions, pseudo-cross-reactions and co-reactions
Benzestrol (3); dienestrol, hexestrol, bisphenol A, *p*-benzylphenol, monobenzone, benzylparaben (1).

Presence in cosmetic products and chemical analyses
In May 2017, diethylstilbestrol was present in zero of 66,975 cosmetic products of which the composition is known in EWG's Skin Deep Cosmetics Database, USA (http://www.ewg.org/skindeep/). In the USA, in April 2017, diethylstilbestrol was present in zero of 56,714 cosmetic products of which the composition is known in FDA's Voluntary Cosmetic Registration Program (VCRP) (data obtained from FDA, May 2017).

OTHER SIDE EFFECTS

Photosensitivity
Photosensitivity from diethylstilbestrol is cited in ref. 2.

Immediate-type reactions
Contact urticaria from diethylstilbestrol is cited in ref. 2

LITERATURE

1   Fregert S, Rorsman H. Hypersensitivity to diethyldtilbestrol. Cross-sensitization to dienestrol, hexestrol, bisphenol A, *p*-benzylphenol, hydroquinone-monobenzylether, and p-hydroxybenzoic-benzylester. Acta Derm Venereol 1960;40:206-219
2   De Groot AC. Patch Testing, 3rd Edition. Wapserveen, The Netherlands: acdegroot publishing, 2008 (ISBN 978-90-813233-1-4)
3   Fregert S, Rorsman H. Hypersensitivity to diethylstilbestrol with cross-sensitization to benzestrol. Acta Derm Venereol 1962;42:290-293

2.149   BIS-DIGLYCERYL POLYACYLADIPATE-2

IDENTIFICATION

Description/definition	: bis-Diglyceryl polyacyladipate-2 is the adipic acid diester of a mixed diglyceryl ester of caprylic, capric, stearic, isostearic and hydroxystearic acids
Chemical class(es)	: Glyceryl esters and derivatives
Other names	: Hexanedioic acid, 3-(2,3-dihydroxypropyloxy)-2-hydroxypropyl diester, esters from reaction with a mixture of octanoic, decanoic, isooctadecanoic, octadecanoic and 12-hydroxyoctadecanoic acids; Softisan® 649
CAS registry number (s)	: 82249-33-0
EC number(s)	: 406-144-4
CIR review(s)	: Int J Toxicol 2013;32(Suppl.3):56-64 (access: www.cir-safety.org/ingredients)
Function(s) in cosmetics	: EU: emollient; skin conditioning. USA: skin-conditioning agents - emollient
Patch testing	: Softisan® 649 pure (Chemotechnique)

GENERAL

bis-Diglyceryl polyacyladipate-2 (trade name: Softisan® 649) is an ointment base and lanolin substitute. It is described by the manufacturer as a partial ester of diglycerin with several fatty acids, including 10-30% adipic acid, 20-50% stearic acid, 5-10% hydroxystearic acid, and 1-10% each of caprylic, capric, palmitic and isostearic acids (1).

CONTACT ALLERGY

Case reports and case series

An atopic woman was seen because of eczema of the lips (cheilitis) and on her cheeks. She had been applying a lipstick for 1 week before the onset of the dermatitis. Patch tests with the European baseline series and her personal cosmetics were negative. The patient then performed a repeated open application test (ROAT) on the forearm with her lipstick, where an eczematous reaction at the application site developed after one week. Later, the lipstick was again tested as were all its ingredients, which yielded positive reactions to the lipstick and to bis-diglyceryl polyacyladipate-2, tested 16% in petrolatum. Ten controls were negative for this test material. Later, the patient experienced a second eczematous reaction on her eyelids 3 days after the use of an eye shadow, which also proved to contain bis-diglyceryl polyacyladipate-2. A ROAT with this eye shadow was already positive on day 3 (3).

A man had allergic contact dermatitis caused by a lip balm containing 4% bis-diglyceryl polyacyladipate-2 and 7% 12-hydroxystearic acid. Patch tests were positive to bis-diglyceryl polyacyladipate-2 at 5% pet. and with 99.7% pure 12-hydroxystearic acid in serial dilution patch testing from 10% to 0.001% pet. There were also positive reactions to hydrogenated castor oil (in which 12-hydroxystearic acid is the main fatty acid), castor oil and ricinoleic acid (the main fatty acid in castor oil). As patch tests were negative with glycerin and with capric, palmitic and stearic acids and 12-hydroxystearic acid is present in bis-diglyceryl polyacyladipate-2, the authors concluded that the patient's patch test reaction to bis-diglyceryl polyacyladipate-2 was caused by its component 12-hydroxystearic acid (1,2).

Presence in cosmetic products and chemical analyses

In the USA, in April 2017, bis-diglyceryl polyacyladipate-2 was present in 955 of 56,714 cosmetic products of which the composition is known in FDA's Voluntary Cosmetic Registration Program (VCRP) (data obtained from FDA, May 2017). In April 2017, bis-diglyceryl polyacyladipate-2 was present in 565 of 65,521 cosmetic products of which the composition is known in EWG's Skin Deep Cosmetics Database, USA (http://www.ewg.org/skindeep/).

Other information

Softisan® 649 is used by Chemotechnique as vehicle for the benzyl alcohol and anisyl alcohol patch test materials.

LITERATURE

1   Shaw DW. Allergic contact dermatitis caused by bis-diglycerylpolyacyladipate-2 (Softisan® 649) owing to its 12-hydroxystearic acid content. Contact Dermatitis 2011;65:369-370
2   Shaw DW. Allergic contact dermatitis from 12-hydroxystearic acid, the principal fatty acid in hydrogenated castor oil. Dermatitis 2009;20:236 (Abstract)
3   Du-Thanh A, Raison-Peyron N, Guillot B. Bis-diglycerylpolyacyladipate-2: An emergent allergen in cosmetics? Contact Dermatitis 2011;64:358-359

2.150 DIGLYCERYL SEBACATE/ISOPALMITATE

IDENTIFICATION

Description/definition : Diglyceryl sebacate/isopalmitate is the mixed ester of sebacic acid and isopalmitic acid with diglycerin

Chemical/IUPAC name : Esters

Other names : Isopalmityl diglyceryl sebacate; Salacos DGS 16 ®

CAS registry number (s) : 208265-85-4

EC number(s) : 450-370-6

Function(s) in cosmetics : EU: emollient; skin conditioning. USA: skin-conditioning agents - emollient

Patch testing : 10% pet. (3); 30% pet. (2)

Molecular formula : $C_{32}H_{62}O_{10}$

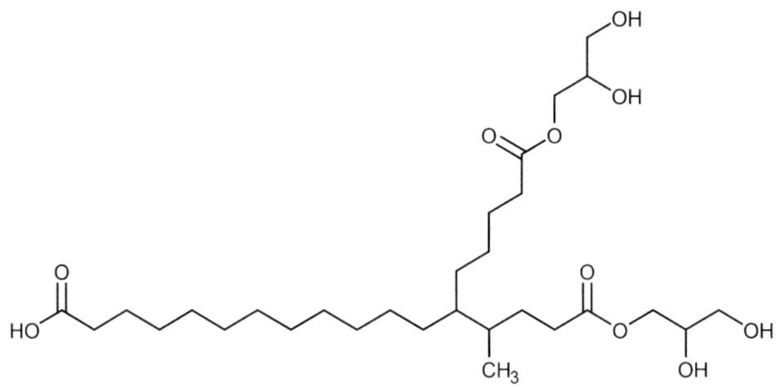

GENERAL

In all reports of contact allergy to diglyceryl sebacate/isopalmitate, that originate without exception from Japan, the name isopalmityl diglyceryl sebacate has been used. Diglyceryl sebacate/isopalmitate was developed as an ingredient of lipsticks in 1994 (2). It is an oily base that has hygroscopic water-holding capacity and water-releasing ability. Diglyceryl sebacate/isopalmitate was formulated mainly for lipsticks, but also for creams, emulsions, foundation creams *et cetera*. The cosmetics containing this material are produced only in Japan. They are exported to Taiwan and Korea, but not to Europe (2). The concentrations of diglyceryl sebacate/isopalmitate in lipsticks are 3-29%, in lip gloss about 60%, and in foundation creams are about 3% (2). The precise allergens are as yet unknown, but are likely to be impurities such as low molecular weight oligomers or incompletely esterified substances. Several manufacturers have withdrawn diglyceryl sebacate/isopalmitate from their lipsticks (6).

CONTACT ALLERGY

Case reports and case series

Two patients had allergic contact cheilitis from diglyceryl sebacate/isopalmitate in lipsticks (1). Two and another two similar cases were reported in refs. 4 and 6. Two more (probably unreported) patients with cheilitis from diglyceryl sebacate/isopalmitate were cited in ref. 6. Four patients reacted to various lipsticks and one of them also to a cream containing diglyceryl sebacate/isopalmitate (2). One woman (3) and an unknown number of patients (5,7) suffered from dermatitis of the lips due to diglyceryl sebacate/isopalmitate contact allergy.

Presence in cosmetic products and chemical analyses

In May 2017, diglyceryl sebacate/isopalmitate was present in zero of 64,655 cosmetic products of which the composition is known in EWG's Skin Deep Cosmetics Database, USA (http://www.ewg.org/skindeep/). In the USA, in April 2017, diglyceryl sebacate/isopalmitate was present in 6 of 56,714 cosmetic products of which the composition is known in FDA's Voluntary Cosmetic Registration Program (VCRP) (data obtained from FDA, May 2017).

LITERATURE

1   Adachi A, Yamada Y. Allergic contact cheilitis due to isopalmityl diglyceryl sebacate and pentaerythritol rosinate in the lipsticks. Environ Dermatol 2003;10:70-74 (in Japanese)
2   Sugiura M, Hayakawa R, Sugiura K. Contact dermatitis due to lipsticks and a cream containing isopalmityl diglyceryl sebacate (DGS). Contact Dermatitis 2006;54:213-214
3   Suzuki K, Matsunaga K, Suzuki M. Allergic contact dermatitis due to isopalmityl diglyceryl sebacate in a lipstick. Contact Dermatitis 1999;41:110
4   Watanabe Y. Two cases of contact dermatitis from lipsticks. Nishinihon J Dermatol 2001;63:668 (in Japanese)

5   Sugiura K, Sugiura M, Kato Y, Hayakawa R. Lip dermatitis due to isopalmityl diglyceryl sebacate. Environ Dermatol 2002;9 (Suppl. 1):44

6   Shono M. Allergic contact dermatitis from isopalmityl diglyceryl sebacate in lipsticks. Contact Dermatitis 2003;48:48-49

7   Sugaya N, Harada T, Suzuki K, Matsunaga K. Allergic contact cheilitis due to isopalmityl diglyceryl sebacate in a lipstick. J Environ Dermatol Cutan Allergol 2007;1:43-46

2.151 DI-HEMA TRIMETHYLHEXYL DICARBAMATE

IDENTIFICATION

Description/definition : Di-HEMA trimethylhexyl dicarbamate is the organic compound that conforms to the formula shown below
Chemical class(es) : Amides; esters
Chemical/IUPAC name : 2-Propenoic acid, 2-methyl-, 7,7,9(or 7,9,9)-trimethyl-4,13-dioxo-3,14-dioxa-5,12-diazahexadecane-1,16-diyl ester
Other names : Diurethane dimethacrylate
CAS registry number (s) : 41137-60-4; 72869-86-4
EC number(s) : 276-957-5
CIR review(s) : Int J Toxicol 2005;24(Suppl.5):53-100 (access: www.cir-safety.org/ingredients)
Function(s) in cosmetics : EU: film forming. USA: artificial nail builders
Patch testing : 2% pet. (1)
Molecular formula : $C_{23}H_{38}N_2O_8$

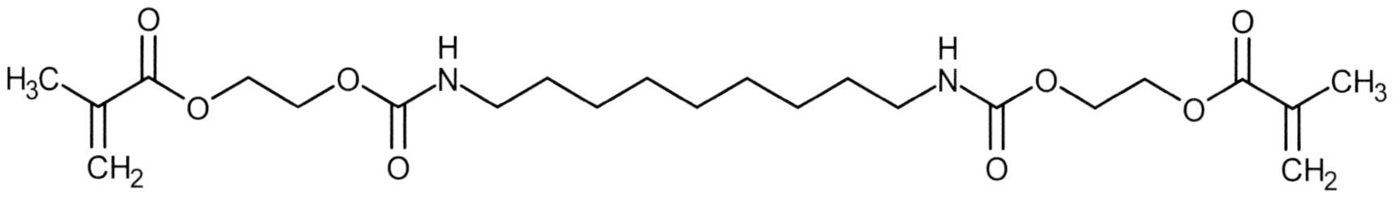

GENERAL

Discussion of contact allergy to (meth)acrylates *from non-cosmetic sources* is considered to fall outside the scope of this book. Therefore, only contact allergy from their presence in cosmetics is presented, which virtually always is from artificial nails. There are many reports of contact allergy to artificial nails, but the specific sensitizers have rarely been identified and – consequently - such publications are not presented in this and other acrylate and methacrylate monographs. Discussion is limited to publications in which the culprit (meth)acrylates have been identified, e.g., from information found in Material Data Safety Sheets, data obtained from the manufacturer or from chemical analyses.

Patients often react to many (meth)acrylates on patch testing. Primary sensitization to methacrylates may result in both methacrylate and acrylate cross-sensitization. Conversely, patients sensitized to acrylates are unlikely to show cross-sensitization to methacrylates (2).

General aspects of acrylates and methacrylates are presented in Chapter 2.219 HEMA (hydroxyethyl methacrylate). A discussion of general aspects of artificial nails, contact allergy to these products, the clinical picture of allergic contact dermatitis and other side effects of sculptured nails can also be found there. A very useful review of contact sensitization to allergens in nail cosmetics, with emphasis on acrylic manicures, was published in 2017 (4).

CONTACT ALLERGY

Patch testing in groups of patients

Studies in which consecutive patients suspected of contact dermatitis have been tested with di-HEMA trimethylhexyl dicarbamate (routine testing) and studies testing groups of selected patients are planned to be discussed in a future publication.

Case reports and case series

Di-HEMA trimethylhexyl dicarbamate was stated to be the (or an) allergen in one patient in a group of 603 individuals suffering from cosmetic dermatitis, seen in the period 2010-2015 in Leuven, Belgium (3). Six women who had experience adverse reactions from an UV-cured nail polish had positive patch tests to its ingredient di-HEMA trimethylhexyl dicarbamate. As 5 of the 6 patients also reacted to HEMA, this may have been the allergen (1).

Presence in cosmetic products and chemical analyses

In the USA, in April 2017, di-HEMA trimethylhexyl dicarbamate was present in 124 of 56,714 cosmetic products of which the composition is known in FDA's Voluntary Cosmetic Registration Program (VCRP) (data obtained from FDA, May 2017). In February 2016, di-HEMA trimethylhexyl dicarbamate was present in 71 of 64,445 cosmetic products of which the composition is known in EWG's Skin Deep Cosmetics Database, USA (http://www.ewg.org/skindeep/).

LITERATURE

1   Dahlin J, Berne B, Dunér K, Hosseiny S, Matura M, Nyman G, et al. Several cases of undesirable effects caused by methacrylate ultraviolet-curing nail polish for non-professional use. Contact Dermatitis 2016;75:151-156

2   Aalto-Korte K, Henriks-Eckerman M-L, Kuuliala O, Jolanki R. Occupational methacrylate and acrylate allergy – cross-reactions and possible screening allergens. Contact Dermatitis 2010;63:301-312

3   Goossens A. Cosmetic contact allergens. Cosmetics 2016, 3, 5; doi:10.3390/cosmetics3010005

4   Chou M, Dhingra N, Strugar TL. Contact sensitization to allergens in nail cosmetics. Dermatitis 2017;28:231-240

2.152 DIHYDROXYACETONE

IDENTIFICATION

Description/definition   : Dihydroxyacetone is the aliphatic ketone that conforms to the formula shown below
Chemical class(es)   : Alcohols; ketones; color additives
Chemical/IUPAC name   : 1,3-Dihydroxypropan-2-one
Other names   : 1,3-Dihydroxydimethyl ketone
CAS registry number (s)   : 96-26-4
EC number(s)   : 202-494-5
SCCS opinion(s)   : SCCS/1347/10 (8)
Merck Index monograph   : 4470
Function(s) in cosmetics : EU: reducing; skin conditioning; tanning. USA: colorants; skin-conditioning agents –
                            miscellaneous
Patch testing   : 7% and 10% water (5); 10% alcohol (2); 10% water (4)
Molecular formula   : $C_3H_6O_3$

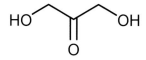

GENERAL

Dihydroxyacetone (DHA) is a triose carbohydrate. It is a white powder, with a sweet cooling taste and a characteristic odor. It is derived by the fermentation of glycerin. Dihydroxyacetone was first coincidentally recognized as a skin coloring agent in the 1920s by German scientists. DHA is non-toxic in nature and is approved for use as a sunless tanning solution. The higher the concentration of DHA in the product, the deeper the tan that will be produced. Concentrations of DHA can usually range from 2.5% to 10% or more (mostly 3-5%) in products that list shades as light, medium, or dark. The pigment is formed by the interaction of dihydroxyacetone with amino acids in the stratum corneum and can be removed by tape stripping. Various amino acids react differently to DHA, producing different tones of coloration from yellow to brown. The resulting pigments are called melanoidins. The tan color remains for 4-6 days in the skin and resists removal by water and detergents. Topical agents containing dihydroxyacetone are safe and effective in camouflage treatment of vitiligo. However, there is no proven photoprotective effect of the melanoidins (2,5).

CONTACT ALLERGY

Case reports and case series

Dihydroxyacetone was responsible for 1 out of 959 cases of non-fragrance cosmetic allergy where the causal allergen was identified, Belgium, 2000-2010 (1). In a 4-month-period in 1996, 475 patients with contact allergy to 'cosmetic ingredients' were collected in 5 centers in Belgium, UK and Germany. There were 12 reactions to dihydroxyacetone; relevance was not stated (7).

A woman developed edematous red plaques on the limbs and trunk where she had repeatedly applied a self-tanning product and an after-sun lotion. The lesions disappeared spontaneously when she ceased using these. She had positive patch tests to the two cosmetics and, when later tested with their ingredients, to dihydroxyacetone 10% water, which was present in both products (4). Another female patient presented with an itchy dermatitis of both legs of 2 weeks duration. There were erythematous papules and erythematosquamous macules in her knee folds, extending to the extensor aspects. On her legs, she had used a cream for venous problems as well as a self-tanning product. Patch testing revealed contact allergy to the self-tanning cosmetic and its component dihydroxyacetone, tested 10% in water (4).

A healthy, atopic woman had sequentially used three self-tanning products. Instead of getting a bronzed skin, she developed an itchy, red, scaly rash at the sites of application. The skin lesions typically appeared 1-2 days after the use of the self-tanning products and cleared within a few days of stopping their use. Patch tests were positive to all three product and their common ingredient dihydroxyacetone, tested at 7% and 10% water, which were their use concentrations in two of the products (5). Two women had a history of intermittent dermatitis affecting the trunk, arms, legs and hands, which improved with the use of topical steroids. Both patients were using numerous cosmetic creams and sunless tanning products, both lotions and sprays. They were patch tested with the extended British baseline series of allergens, as well as their own cosmetics and toiletries. At D4, both patients had positive reactions to the tanning products. Later, they were tested with dihydroxyacetone in alcohol and in water (0.1%, 1%, and 10%) and showed multiple positive reactions, the strongest to the chemical 10% in alcohol. Ten controls tested with the

10% alcoholic solution of dihydroxyacetone were negative. Since stopping the use of tanning products, neither patient has suffered from further episodes of dermatitis (2). From London, UK, an unknown number of (probably allergic) contact reactions have been reported at the beginning of the 1960s (3).

Presence in cosmetic products and chemical analyses
In the USA, in April 2017, dihydroxyacetone was present in 295 of 56,714 cosmetic products of which the composition is known in FDA's Voluntary Cosmetic Registration Program (VCRP) (data obtained from FDA, May 2017). In April 2017, dihydroxyacetone was present in 83 of 65,52 cosmetic products of which the composition is known in EWG's Skin Deep Cosmetics Database, USA (http://www.ewg.org/skindeep/).

Other non-eczematous contact reactions
Application of dihydroxyacetone containing self-tanning lotions may cause orange discolouration of the nails (6). It may also turn hair yellow (xanthotrichia) (9).

LITERATURE
1   Travassos AR, Claes L, Boey L, Drieghe J, Goossens A. Non-fragrance allergens in specific cosmetic products. Contact Dermatitis 2011;65:276-285
2   Zokaie S, Singh S, Wakelin SH. Allergic contact dermatitis caused by dihydroxyacetone – optimal concentration and vehicle for testing. Contact Dermatitis 2011;64:291-292
3   Harman RR. Severe contact reaction to dihydroxyacetone. Trans St Johns Dermatol Soc 1961;47:157-159
4   Morren M, Dooms-Goossens A, Heidbuchel M, Sente F, Damas MC. Contact allergy to dihydroxyacetone. Contact Dermatitis 1991;25:326-327
5   Bovenschen HJ, Körver JEM, van der Valk PGM. Contact dermatitis to self-tanning products. Contact Dermatitis 2009;60:290-291
6   Herskovitz I, Nolan BV, Tosti A. Orange chromonychia due to dihydroxyacetone. Dermatitis 2014;25:43-44
7   Goossens A, Beck MH, Haneke E, McFadden JP, Nolting S, Durupt G, Ries G. Adverse cutaneous reactions to cosmetic allergens. Contact Dermatitis 1999;40:112-113
8   SCCS (Scientific Committee on Consumer Safety). Opinion on dihydroxyacetone, 14 December 2010, SCCS/1347/10. Available at:
    http://ec.europa.eu/health/scientific_committees/consumer_safety/docs/sccs_o_048.pdf
9   Prevost N, English JC 3rd. Xanthotrichia (yellow hair) due to selenium sulfide and dihydroxyacetone. J Drugs Dermatol 2008;7:689-691

2.153 DIISOPROPANOLAMINE

IDENTIFICATION

Description/definition : Diisopropanolamine is the aliphatic amine that conforms to the formula shown below
Chemical class(es) : Alkanolamines
Chemical/IUPAC name : 1-(2-Hydroxypropylamino)propan-2-ol
CAS registry number (s) : 110-97-4
EC number(s) : 203-820-9
CIR review(s) : J Am Coll Toxicol 1987;6:53-76 (access: www.cir-safety.org/ingredients)
Merck Index monograph : 4484
Function(s) in cosmetics : EU: formerly used for buffering; delisted in 2005. USA: pH adjusters
EU cosmetic restrictions : Regulated in Annex II/411 of the Regulation (EC) No. 1223/2009 (prohibited)
Patch testing : 1% pet. (1,2,6)
Molecular formula : $C_6H_{15}NO_2$

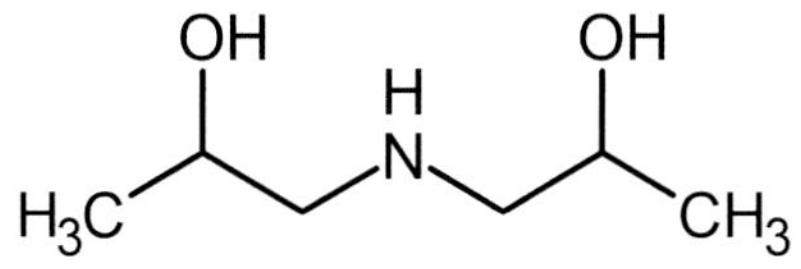

CONTACT ALLERGY

Case reports and case series
One patient had allergic contact dermatitis from diisopropanolamine in eye gloss (3), another from blushing gel (4), a third from and eye shadow (5).

Contact allergy to diisopropanolamine in non-cosmetic products
One patient reacted to diisopropanolamine in a pharmaceutical ointment (2), another one had ACD from the chemical present in an NSAID lotion (9). A man had allergic contact dermatitis from diisopropanolamine present in a compress used for lumbago (6). One (1), one (8) and two (7) more individuals reacted to diisopropanolamine in a compress containing the NSAID felbinac.

Presence in cosmetic products and chemical analyses
In the USA, in April 2017, diisopropanolamine was present in 5 of 56,714 cosmetic products of which the composition is known in FDA's Voluntary Cosmetic Registration Program (VCRP) (data obtained from FDA, May 2017). In March 2017, diisopropanolamine was present in 3 older products of 64,983 cosmetic products of which the composition is known in EWG's Skin Deep Cosmetics Database, USA (http://www.ewg.org/skindeep/).

LITERATURE
1   Oiso N, Fukai K, Ishii M. Triple allergic contact sensitivities due to ferbinac, crotamiton and diisopropanolamine. Contact Dermatitis 2003;49:261-263
2   Fujimoto K, Hashimoto S, Kozuka T, Yoshikawa K. Contact dermatitis due to diisopropanolamine. Contact Dermatitis 1989;21:56
3   Cronin E. Contact dermatitis. Edinburgh: Churchill Livingstone, 1980:114
4   Cronin E. Contact dermatitis. Edinburgh: Churchill Livingstone, 1980:149
5   Cronin E. Di-isopropanolamine in an eyeshadow. Cont Derm Newsletter 1973;13:364
6   Rind T, Oiso N, Hirao A, Kawada A. Allergic contact dermatitis with diffuse erythematous reaction from diisopropanolamine in a compress. Case Rep Dermatol 2010;2:50-54
7   Umebayashi Y. Two cases of contact dermatitis due to diisopropanolamine. J Dermatol 2005;32:145-146 (article in Japanese) (data cited in ref. 6)
8   Umebayashi Y. Contact dermatitis due to diisopropanolamine. Rinsho Derma (Tokyo) 2000;42:526-527 (article in Japanese) (data cited in ref. 6)
9   Hosokawa K, Mitsuya K, Nishijima S, Horio T, Asada Y. Photocontact dermatitis from a non-steroidal anti-inflammatory drug (Sector Lotion). Skin Research 1993;35:26-32 (article in Japanese) (data cited in ref. 6)

2.154   DIISOSTEARYL MALATE

IDENTIFICATION

Description/definition	: Diisostearyl malate is the diester of isostearyl alcohol and malic acid, which conforms generally to the formula shown below
Chemical class(es)	: Esters
Chemical/IUPAC name	: bis(16-Methylheptadecyl) 2-hydroxybutanedioate
Other names	: bis(16-Methylheptadecyl) malate
CAS registry number (s)	: 67763-18-2; 81230-05-9
EC number(s)	: 267-041-6
CIR review(s)	: Int J Toxicol 2015;34(Suppl.1):5-17 (access: www.cir-safety.org/ingredients)
Function(s) in cosmetics	: EU: emollient; skin conditioning; surfactant. USA: skin-conditioning agents - emollient
Patch testing	: 40% pet. (1); 7.7% pet. (2)
Molecular formula	: $C_{40}H_{78}O_5$

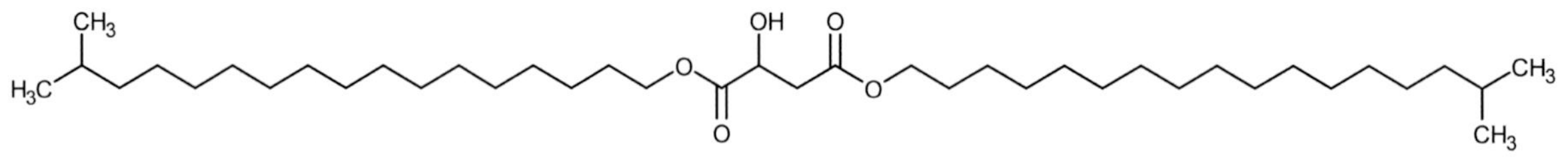

CONTACT ALLERGY

Case reports and case series

One patient (2), another one (4) and three more women (5) had allergic contact cheilitis from diisostearyl malate in lipsticks. One patient had allergic contact cheilitis from diisostearyl malate in lipsticks (1); in this publication, the name diisostearyl maleate was used, which is probably incorrect, because CosIng (the EU database of cosmetic ingredients) does not know this name. Also, the authors refer to a similar previously reported case, which is diisostearyl malate.

A patient had allergic contact cheilitis from 2 lipsticks. She was patch test positive to the lipsticks, to glyceryl diisostearate in both lipsticks and to diisostearyl malate in one. Glyceryl diisostearate from the manufacturer was investigated by gas chromatography and proved to have the following composition: glyceryl diisostearate 66%, glyceryl triisostearate 29%, glyceryl (mono)isostearate 0.43%, isostearic acid 0.21% and unknown 4%. The commercial diisostearyl malate was also analyzed and proved to contain diisostearyl malate 93.3%, isostearyl alcohol 3.91% and unknown 2.79%. Next, the patient was patch tested with all chemicals including purified glyceryl diisostearate and diisostearyl malate. The patient now reacted to all chemicals except isostearic acid. However, the purified glyceryl diisostearate and isosteary malate only had weak positive reactions when tested undiluted, whereas glyceryl (mono)isostearate 0.01% pet. and isostearyl alcohol 0.25% pet. showed strong patch test reactions. It was concluded that these impurities were the most important sensitizers in the lipstick(s) (3).

Cross-reactions, pseudo-cross-reactions and co-reactions
Glyceryl isostearate (1). See also under Case reports, ref. 3.

Presence in cosmetic products and chemical analyses
In the USA, in April 2017, diisostearyl malate was present in 1099 of 56,714 cosmetic products of which the composition is known in FDA's Voluntary Cosmetic Registration Program (VCRP) (data obtained from FDA, May 2017). In March 2017, diisostearyl malate was present in 347 of 64,983 cosmetic products of which the composition is known in EWG's Skin Deep Cosmetics Database, USA (http://www.ewg.org/skindeep/).

LITERATURE
1   Inui S, Azukizawa H, Katayama I. Recurrent contact cheilitis because of glyceryl isostearate, diisostearyl maleate, oleyl alcohol, and Lithol Rubine BCA in lipsticks. Contact Dermatitis 2009;60:231-232
2   Guin JD. Allergic contact cheilitis from di-isostearyl malate in lipstick. Contact Dermatitis 2001;44:375
3   Hayakawa R, Matsunaga K, Suzuki M, Arima Y, Ohkido Y. Lipstick dermatitis due to C18 aliphatic compounds. Contact Dermatitis 1987;16:215-219
4   Sugiura K, Sugiura M. Di-isostearyl malate and macademia nut oil in lipstick caused cheilitis. J Eur Acad Dermatol Venereol 2009;23:606-607
5   Sugiura M, Hayakawa R, Kato Y, Sugiura K, Hashimoto R, Shamoto M. Three cases of lip dermatitis due to diisostearyl malate. Environ Dermatol 2001; 8: 6-10 (article in Japanese) (data cited in ref. 4)

2.155 DIMETHYL OXAZOLIDINE

IDENTIFICATION

Description/definition   : Dimethyl oxazolidine is the heterocyclic compound that conforms to the formula shown below
Chemical class(es)   : Heterocyclic compounds
Chemical/IUPAC name   : 4,4-Dimethyl-1,3-oxazolidine
Other names   : Oxazolidine A; present in Bioban® CS 1135® with 3,4,4-trimethyloxazolidine (CAS **75673-43-7)**
CAS registry number (s)   : 51200-87-4
EC number(s)   : 257-048-2
Function(s) in cosmetics   : EU: preservative. USA: preservatives
EU cosmetic restrictions   : Regulated in Annex V/45 of the Regulation (EC) No. 1223/2009
Patch testing   : Bioban® CS 1135 1% pet. (Chemotechnique, SmartPracticeCanada, SmartPracticeEurope); this test concentration may be slightly irritant; dimethyl oxazolidine is not commercially available as single hapten
Molecular formula   : $C_5H_{11}NO$

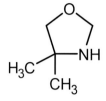

GENERAL

Dimethyl oxazolidine is used together with 3,4,4-trimethyloxazolidine in Bioban® CS 1135 as bactericide in metal-working fluids and many other industrial applications. The literature on contact allergy to Bioban® CS 1135 has been reviewed in 2010 (2,3). Dimethyl oxazolidine has never been tested as single chemical. It is a formaldehyde-releaser and most patients with positive patch tests to Bioban® CS 1135 also react to formaldehyde, which may be the actual allergen (3). Dimethyl oxazolidine is hardly used in cosmetics.

CONTACT ALLERGY

Case reports and case series

A plastic worker allergic to formaldehyde had occupational allergic contact dermatitis from the formaldehyde-releaser dimethyl oxazolidine present in a hand-washing liquid. He had positive patch tests to formaldehyde, and the other formaldehyde releasers benzylhemiformal, 2-bromo-2-nitropropane-1,3-diol, and Bioban® CS 1135. The latter product contains dimethyl oxazolidine and 3,4,4-trimethyloxazolidine. According to the sales representative, the hand-washing liquid contained dimethyl oxazolidine (and 2-bromo-2-nitropropane-1,3-diol (1).

Cross-reactions, pseudo-cross-reactions and co-reactions

Pseudo-cross-reactions with formaldehyde and formaldehyde-releasers are possible (review: ref. 3).

Presence in cosmetic products and chemical analyses

In May 2017, dimethyl oxazolidine was present in one of 66,648 cosmetic products of which the composition is known in EWG's Skin Deep Cosmetics Database, USA (http://www.ewg.org/skindeep/). In the USA, in April 2017, dimethyl oxazolidine was present in zero of 56,714 cosmetic products of which the composition is known in FDA's Voluntary Cosmetic Registration Program (VCRP) (data obtained from FDA, May 2017).

LITERATURE

1   Aalto-Korte K, Kuuliala O, Suuronen K, Alanko K. Occupational contact allergy to formaldehyde and formaldehyde releasers. Contact Dermatitis 2008;59:280-289
2   De Groot AC, Geier J, Flyvholm MA, Lensen G, Coenraads PJ. Formaldehyde-releasers: relationship to formaldehyde contact allergy. Metalworking fluids and remainder. Part 1. Contact Dermatitis 2010;63:117-128
3   De Groot AC, Geier J, Flyvholm MA, Lensen G, Coenraads PJ. Formaldehyde-releasers: relationship to formaldehyde contact allergy. Part 2: Metalworking fluids and remainder. Contact Dermatitis 2010;63:129-139

2.156   DIPENTAERYTHRITYL HEXAHYDROXYSTEARATE/HEXASTEARATE /HEXAROSINATE

IDENTIFICATION

Description/definition	: Dipentaerythrityl hexahydroxystearate/hexastearate/hexarosinate is the hexaester of 6-hydroxystearic acid, stearic acid, the acids derived from colophony and a dimer of pentaerythritol
Chemical class(es)	: Esters
Other names	: Dipentaerythritol, esters with hexahydroxystearate, stearate, and rosinate; dipentaerythritol fatty acid ester
CAS registry number (s)	: 208126-52-7
Function(s) in cosmetics	: EU: emollient; skin conditioning. USA: skin-conditioning agents - occlusive; viscosity increasing agents – nonaqueous
Patch testing	: 1% pet. (1)

CONTACT ALLERGY

Case reports and case series

A Japanese woman was seen with darkened lips associated with vesicles and scales that had been present for four months. The patient had been using a new lipstick since six months and began to notice burning and itchy swelling on her lips after about two months. Herpes simplex was suspected, and she was treated with vidarabine ointment, but her cheilitis persisted. She had continued to use the same lipstick to cover the darkened lips until recently. After she stopped using the lipstick, the vesicles and scales subsided within a few weeks, leaving a dirty purplish brown pigmentation on her lips. She had no previously taken medication with tetracycline.

The patient was patch tested with the Japanese standard allergen series and her own lipstick. At the D2 and D3 readings, the lipstick, tested as is, showed a positive reaction. There were no positive reactions to other patch tests. Further testing with 13 constituents of the lipstick provided by the manufacturer yielded a positive patch test only to dipentaerythritol fatty acid ester (dipentaerythritol, esters with hexahydroxystearate, stearate, and rosinate) 1% pet. Retesting with dipentaerythritol fatty acid ester 1% pet., 0.1% pet. and 0.01% pet. confirmed the previous positive reaction. Five normal controls showed negative responses to pentaerythritol fatty acid ester 1% pet. The patient stopped using the incriminated lipstick for a year and in that period, the pigmentation on her lips faded spontaneously. There was no recurrence in the following 16 months (1).

Presence in cosmetic products and chemical analyses

In the USA, in April 2017, dipentaerythrityl hexahydroxystearate/hexastearate/hexarosinate was present in 154 of 56,714 cosmetic products of which the composition is known in FDA's Voluntary Cosmetic Registration Program (VCRP) (data obtained from FDA, May 2017). In March 2017, dipentaerythrityl hexahydroxystearate/hexastearate/ hexarosinate was present in 13 of 64,983 cosmetic products of which the composition is known in EWG's Skin Deep Cosmetics Database, USA (http://www.ewg.org/skindeep/).

LITERATURE

1   Ido T, Nishikawa M, Kiyohara T, Ishiguro K, Kumakiri M. Pigmented contact cheilitis from dipentaerythritol fatty acid ester. Contact Dermatitis 2008;59:117-118

2.157 DIPOTASSIUM GLYCYRRHIZATE

IDENTIFICATION

Description/definition	: Dipotassium glycyrrhizate is the dipotassium salt of glycyrrhizic acid
Chemical class(es)	: Carbohydrates; organic salts; sterols
Chemical/IUPAC name	: dipotassium;(2S,3S,4S,5R,6R)-6-[(2S,3R,4S,5S,6S)-2-[[(3S,4aR,6aR,6bS,8aS,11S, 12aR,14aR,14bS)-11-carboxy-4,4,6a,6b,8a,11,14b-heptamethyl-14-oxo-2,3,4a,5,6, 7,8,9,10,12,12a,14a-dodecahydro-1H-picen-3-yl]oxy]-6-carboxylato-4,5-dihydroxyoxan-3-yl]oxy-3,4,5-trihydroxyoxane-2-carboxylate
Other names	: α-D-Glucopyranosiduronic acid, (3β,20β)-20-Carboxy-11-oxo-30-norolean-12-en-3-yl-2-O-β-D-glucopyranuronosyl-, dipotassium salt
CAS registry number (s)	: 68797-35-3
EC number(s)	: 272-296-1
Function(s) in cosmetics	: EU: humectant; skin conditioning. USA: flavoring agents; skin-conditioning agents – miscellaneous
Patch testing	: 0.1% water
Molecular formula	: $C_{42}H_{60}K_2O_{16}$

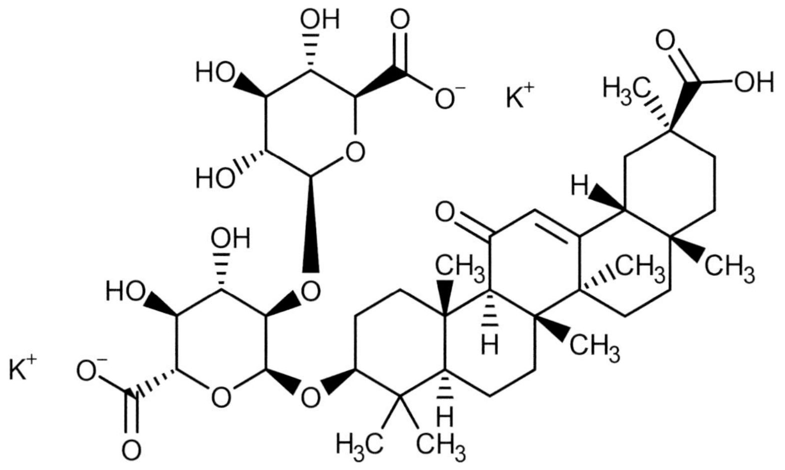

CONTACT ALLERGY

Case reports and case series
A Japanese woman was referred for patch testing. Pruritic erythematous macules and vesicles had recurrently developed on the face during the use of 15 different products. When patch tested, the patient reacted to 2 skin-lightening products. When tested with their ingredients, the patient had positive patch test reactions to arbutin in both products and to dipotassium glycyrrhizate 0.1% water in one of these. The other product also contained dipotassium glycyrrhizate, but the test concentration (probably the same as in the product) was presumably too low to elicit a positive response. Control tests were not performed (1).

Presence in cosmetic products and chemical analyses
In July 2017, dipotassium glycyrrhizate was present in 197 of 69,548 cosmetic products of which the composition is known in EWG's Skin Deep Cosmetics Database, USA (http://www.ewg.org/skindeep/).

LITERATURE
1   Oiso N, Tatebayashi M, Hoshiyama Y, Kawada A. Allergic contact dermatitis caused by arbutin and dipotassium glycyrrhizate in skin-lightening products. Contact Dermatitis 2017;77:51-53

2.158   DIPROPYLENE GLYCOL

IDENTIFICATION

Description/definition   : Dipropylene glycol is a mixture of diol stereoisomers; their structures are shown below
Chemical class(es)   : Alcohols; ethers
Chemical/IUPAC name   : 1-(2-Hydroxypropoxy)propan-2-ol
Other names   : Hydroxypropyloxypropanol
CAS registry number (s)   : 110-98-5; 25265-71-8; 106-62-7; 108-61-2
EC number(s)   : 203-821-4; 246-770-3; 203-416-2; 203-599-9
CIR review(s)   : J Am Coll Toxicol 1985;4:223-248 (access: www.cir-safety.org/ingredients)
Function(s) in cosmetics : EU: masking; perfuming; solvent; viscosity controlling. USA: fragrance ingredients;
solvents; viscosity decreasing agents
Patch testing   : 10% water (1); the test concentration is marginally irritant; 0.5% pet. (2)
Molecular formula   : $C_6H_{14}O_3$

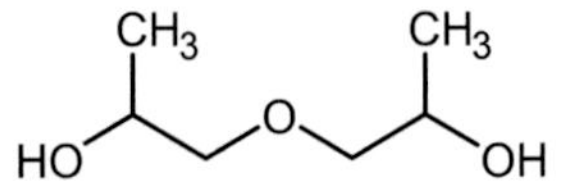

1-(2-hydroxypropoxy)propan-2-ol 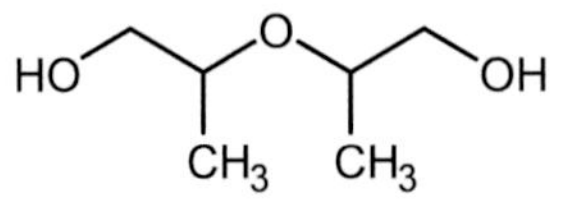   2-[(1-hydroxypropan-2-yl)oxy]propan-1-ol 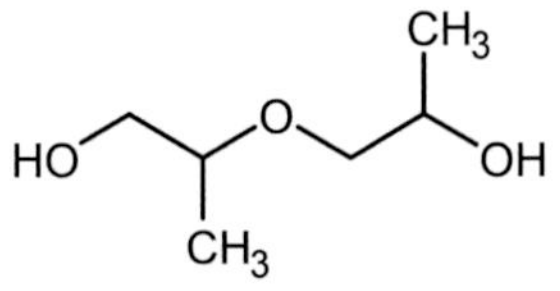   2-(2-hydroxypropoxy)propan-1-ol

CONTACT ALLERGY

Patch testing in groups of patients

In Denmark, in 1994, 503 consecutive patients suspected of contact dermatitis (routine testing) were patch tested with dipropylene glycol 10% water and 1 (0.2%) had a positive patch test reactions. It's relevance could not be established. There were many ?+ reactions, which probably means that the used test concentration of 10% in water is marginally irritant (1).

Case reports and case series

A woman was admitted to hospital with infected generalized eczema. Ten days before, the patient had started to use a new antiseptic hand lotion recommended for fry skin. After a few days of use, her hands became swollen and red. The patient kept using the lotion, and the eczematous reaction spread to the rest of her body. At admission, her hands were severely affected with extensive blisters and edema. Four months later, when clear of dermatitis, the patient was tested with the routine series, the hand lotion and – later – the components of the lotion. The patient reacted to the hand lotion, the fragrance mix, Myroxylon pereirae, lanolin alcohol and the perfume formulation of the product. No reactions to the single components of the fragrance mix from the standard series were found. The perfume from the product consisted of 16 different substances: 15 fragrance materials and the solvent dipropylene glycol, which comprised 91.5% of the formulation. The patient was tested with all of these chemicals and reacted to dipropylene glycol 0.5% pet. and coumarin 0.5% pet. When retested with other vehicles, both materials again gave a positive patch test. Twenty control tests were negative (2).

Cross-reactions, pseudo-cross-reactions and co-reactions

Not to propylene glycol (2)

Presence in cosmetic products and chemical analyses

In the USA, in April 2017, dipropylene glycol was present in 2484 of 56,714 cosmetic products of which the composition is known in FDA's Voluntary Cosmetic Registration Program (VCRP) (data obtained from FDA, May 2017). In March 2017, dipropylene glycol was present in 515 of 64,983 cosmetic products of which the composition is known in EWG's Skin Deep Cosmetics Database, USA (http://www.ewg.org/skindeep/).

LITERATURE

1   Johansen JD, Jemec GBE, Rastogi SC. Contact sensitization to dipropylene glycol in an eczema population. Contact Dermatitis 1995;33:211-212
2   Johansen JD, Rastogi SC, Jemec GBE. Dipropylene glycol allergy: a hidden cause of perfume contact dermatitis. Am J Cont Derm 1994;5:98-101

2.159 DISODIUM EDTA

IDENTIFICATION

Description/definition : Disodium EDTA is the substituted diamine that conforms to the formula shown below
Chemical class(es) : Alkyl-substituted aminoacids
Chemical/IUPAC name : Disodium 2-[2-[carboxylatomethyl(carboxymethyl)amino]ethyl-(carboxymethyl) amino]acetate
Other names : Edetate disodium; disodium edetate; disodium ethylenediaminetetraacetate
CAS registry number (s) : 139-33-3; 6381-92-6
EC number(s) : 205-358-3
CIR review(s) : Int J Toxicol 2002;21(Suppl.2):95-142 (access: www.cir-safety.org/ingredients)
Merck Index monograph : 4835 (EDTA)
Function(s) in cosmetics : EU: chelating; viscosity controlling. USA: chelating agents
Patch testing : 1.0% pet. (Chemotechnique, SmartPracticeCanada)
Molecular formula : $C_{10}H_{14}N_2Na_2O_8$

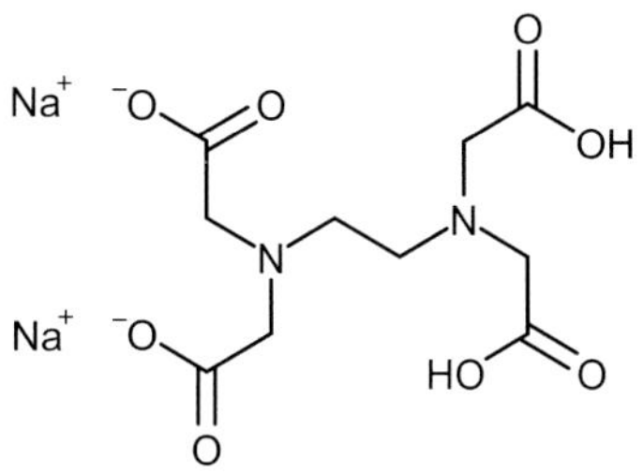

CONTACT ALLERGY

Patch testing in groups of patients
In the period 2005-2008, in France, 423 patients with leg ulcers were patch tested with disodium EDTA 1% pet. and one patient (0.2%) had a positive reaction; its relevance was not mentioned (8).

Case reports and case series
Disodium EDTA was responsible for 1 out of 959 cases of non-fragrance cosmetic allergy where the causal allergen was identified, Belgium, 2000-2010 (1).

A woman had a 3-year history of recurrent itchy redness on her scalp, face and neck. Her symptoms gradually worsened in spite of topical corticosteroid treatment. Patch testing with her cosmetic products and shampoo revealed positive reactions to a cosmetic lotion, a cream and the shampoo at D2 and D3. Later, when tested with the ingredients of the shampoo, there were positive reactions to disodium EDTA 0.1 and 1% water. The cream and the lotion also proved to contain disodium EDTA. After avoidance of these products, the skin eruption rapidly improved and did not recur (2). Another female patient, who had suffered from allergic contact dermatitis caused by hair dye, reacted upon patch testing to a cosmetic cream. When tested with its ingredients, there were multiple positive reactions including to disodium EDTA 10% water (10).

Contact allergy to disodium EDTA in non-cosmetic products
A man purchased a popular ophthalmic solution containing disodium EDTA 0.1% to treat a minor eye irritation. This preparation had been used by the patient previously without difficulty. Over the next two days, he experienced increasing redness and burning of the eyes. His family physician prescribed an ophthalmic solution containing an antibiotic, a decongestant, and a corticosteroid but also EDTA. After one day's use of this solution, his eyes became worse and he developed periorbital edema with vesiculation of the eyelids. This responded well to treatment with cool compresses and systemic steroids. Re-administration of the two solutions, each to one eye, produced an exacerbation of the dermatitis bilaterally within four hours. Patch tests were positive to both ophthalmic solutions and to calcium disodium EDTA, but not to ethylenediamine (3).

A man had a history of foot dermatitis and recurrent otitis externa. In addition, he had suffered from swelling and redness of the face on two separate occasions one day after receiving a local anaesthetic prior to dental treatment. The swelling resolved both times within 36 hours. Patch testing with the standard series, dental and ear series gave positive reactions to disodium EDTA 1% pet., gentamicin sulfate 20% pet. (relevant to the otitis externa) and potassium dichromate 0.5% pet. (explaining the foot dermatitis). There was no reaction to ethylenediamine 1% pet. The local anesthetic itself was not tested, but it did contain EDTA (5).

A man suffered from episodic erythematous eruptions occurring primarily over the buttocks for 9 months and lasting a week before desquamating. With each episode he felt malaise and fatigue the evening before rash onset. The cause proved to be disodium EDTA in nasal spray. Patch tests were negative, but the symptoms of this systemic contact dermatitis were reproduced by patch tests with the nasal spray containing disodium EDTA, with disodium EDTA itself, but not with the nasal spray without disodium EDTA (11).

In a 2-year retrospective study, the members of the French Dermato-Allergology Vigilance network Revidal together found 17 cases of contact allergy to Septivon®, an antiseptic preparation containing triclocarban. However, triclocarban itself was the allergen in none of these cases, all were caused by excipients including disodium EDTA in 4 cases (14).

Cross-reactions, pseudo-cross-reactions and co-reactions
Possible (but inconsistent) cross-reactions to (3) but probably not *from* ethylenediamine (4); trisodium EDTA (6); tetrasodium EDTA (6).

Presence in cosmetic products and chemical analyses
In the USA, in April 2017, disodium EDTA was present in 11313 of 56,714 cosmetic products of which the composition is known in FDA's Voluntary Cosmetic Registration Program (VCRP) (data obtained from FDA, May 2017). In April 2017, disodium EDTA was present in 3843 of 65,522 cosmetic products of which the composition is known in EWG's Skin Deep Cosmetics Database, USA (http://www.ewg.org/skindeep/). Of 38 cosmetic products marketed for babies in the UK in 2007, 29 (76 %) contained disodium EDTA (9). Disodium EDTA was present in 79 (44%) of 178 facial wipes for which ingredient information was obtained online and from retail stores, USA, 2016 (15). Disodium EDTA was present in 23 (43%) of 54 personal hygiene wet wipes for which ingredient information was obtained online and from retail stores, USA, 2016 (16).

OTHER SIDE EFFECTS

Immediate-type reactions
Within minutes of receiving a subcutaneous injection of a local anesthetic, a man developed palmoplantar pruritus, intense facial urticaria, and mild facial swelling, with a feeling of panic but no systemic effects. The reaction proved to be caused by type-I allergy to disodium EDTA; a prick test was strongly positive (12).

Miscellaneous side effects
Detergents and disinfectants containing disodium EDTA may cause occupational rhinitis and/or asthma in (mostly) cleaners and healthcare workers, using spray formulations of cleaning products. An irritant mechanism is unlikely and it is unknown whether the respiratory effects are caused by an immunoallergic or a pharmacological mechanism (13).

LITERATURE
1   Travassos AR, Claes L, Boey L, Drieghe J, Goossens A. Non-fragrance allergens in specific cosmetic products. Contact Dermatitis 2011;65:276-285
2   Soga F, Izawa K, Inoue T, Katoh N, Kishimoto S. Contact dermatitis due to disodium ethylenediamine- tetraacetic acid in cosmetics and shampoo. Contact Dermatitis 2003;49:105
3   Raymond J Z, Gross P R. EDTA preservative dermatitis. Arch Dermatol 1969;100:436-440
4   Provost TT, Jillson OF. Ethylenediamine contact dermatitis. Arch Derm 1967;96:231-234
5   Bhushan M, Beck MH. Allergic contact dermatitis from disodium ethylenediamine tetra-acetic acid (EDTA) in a local anaesthetic. Contact Dermatitis 1998;38:183
6   Kimura M, Kawada A. Contact dermatitis due to trisodium ethylenediaminetetra-acetic acid (EDTA) in a cosmetic lotion. Contact Dermatitis 1999: 41: 341.
7   Sánchez-Pedreño P, García-Bravo B, Frías-Iniesta J. Contact allergy to tetrasodium EDTA in a sunscreen. Contact Dermatitis 2009;61:125-126
8   Barbaud A, Collet E, Le Coz CJ, Meaume S, Gillois P. Contact allergy in chronic leg ulcers: results of a multicentre study carried out in 423 patients and proposal for an updated series of patch tests. Contact Dermatitis 2009;60:279-287
9   White JML, McFadden JP. Exposure to haptens/contact allergens in baby cosmetic products. Contact Dermatitis 2008;59:176-177
10 Madsen JT, Andersen KE. 2-Amino-4-hydroxyethylaminoanisole sulfate – a coupler causing contact allergy from use in hair dyes. Contact Dermatitis 2016;74:102-104

11 Rajan JP, Cornell R, White AA. A case of systemic contact dermatitis secondary to edetate disodium. J Allergy Clin Immunol Pract 2015;3:607-608

12 Russo PA, Banovic T, Wiese MD, Whyte AF, Smith WB. Systemic allergy to EDTA in local anesthetic and radiocontrast media. J Allergy Clin Immunol Pract 2014;2:225-229

13 Laborde-Castérot H, Villa AF, Rosenberg N, Dupont P, Lee HM, Garnier R. Occupational rhinitis and asthma due to EDTA-containing detergents or disinfectants. Am J Ind Med 2012;55:677-682

14 Barbaud A, Vigan M, Delrous JL, et al. Contact allergy to antiseptics: 75 cases analyzed by the dermato-allergovigilance network (Revidal). Ann Dermatol Venereol 2005;132:962-965

15 Aschenbeck KA, Warshaw EM. Allergenic ingredients in facial wet wipes. Dermatitis 2017 Mar 23. doi: 10.1097/DER.0000000000000268. [Epub ahead of print]

16 Aschenbeck KA, Warshaw EM. Allergenic ingredients in personal hygiene wet wipes. Dermatitis 2017 Mar 23. doi: 10.1097/DER.0000000000000275. [Epub ahead of print]

2.160   DISODIUM LAUROAMPHODIACETATE

IDENTIFICATION

Description/definition : Disodium lauroamphodiacetate is the amphoteric organic compound that conforms
generally to the formula shown below
Chemical class(es) : Alkylamido alkylamines
Chemical/IUPAC name : Disodium;2-[1-[2-(carboxylatomethoxy)ethyl]-2-undecyl-4,5-dihydroimidazol-1-ium-1-
yl]acetate;hydroxide
Other name(s) : Lauroamphocarboxyglycinate
CAS registry number (s) : 14350-97-1
EC number(s) : 238-306-3
Function(s) in cosmetics : EU: antistatic; cleansing; foam boosting; foaming; hair conditioning; hydrotrope
surfactant; viscosity controlling. USA: hair conditioning agents; surfactants – cleansing
agents; surfactants - foam boosters; surfactants - hydrotropes
Patch testing : 1% and 2% water (1,3); these concentrations are probably marginally irritant (3)
Molecular formula : $C_{20}H_{36}N_2Na_2O_6$

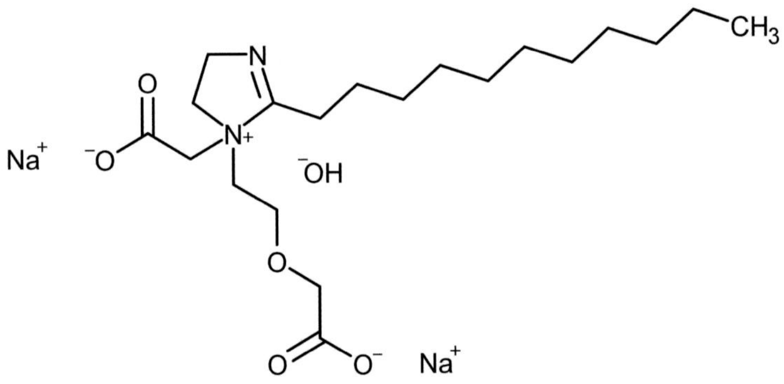

CONTACT ALLERGY

Patch testing in groups of patients

In the USA, in 2015-2016, 47 patients previously reacting to one or more surfactants in the NACDG screening series were patch
tested with disodium lauroamphodiacetate 1% and 2% water and three (6.4%) had a positive reaction. The relevance
of these 3 reactions was not mentioned. There were also 7 doubtful reactions, suggesting that the concentration is
marginally irritant (3).

Case reports and case series

Two women had hand dermatitis from contact allergy to disodium lauroamphodiacetate in a liquid hand cleanser;
one of them, a massage therapist, had occupational ACD (1). The semi-open test with the cleanser pure was positive
in both individuals on two occasions. Later, they both had positive reactions to its ingredient disodium lauroamphodiacetate 1% and 2% water. Ten controls were negative (1). The massage therapist was probably again presented
one year later in an Abstract (2).

Cross-reactions, pseudo-cross-reactions and co-reactions

Sodium lauroyl sarcosinate, isostearamidopropyl morpholine lactate, oleamidopropyl dimethylamine,
cocamidopropyl dimethylamine ('amidoamine') and cocamidopropyl betaine (1,3). The authors suggested cross-
sensitivity. However, another likely explanation is pseudo-cross-reactivity to common ingredients (e.g.,
contaminants) in these chemicals, most of which are amide-type surfactants.

Presence in cosmetic products and chemical analyses

In the USA, in April 2017, disodium lauroamphodiacetate e was present in 71 of 56,714 cosmetic products of which
the composition is known in FDA's Voluntary Cosmetic Registration Program (VCRP) (data obtained from FDA, May
2017). In March 2017, disodium lauroamphodiacetate was present in 43 of 64,983 cosmetic products of which the
composition is known in EWG's Skin Deep Cosmetics Database, USA (http://www.ewg.org/skindeep/).

LITERATURE

1   Hanson JL, Warshaw EM. Contact allergy to surfactants in a hypoallergenic liquid cleanser. Dermatitis 2015;26:284-286
2   Hanson JL, Warshaw EM. Contact allergy to surfactants in a liquid cleanser. Dermatitis 2016;27(5):e2
3   Grey KR, Hanson J, Hagen SL, Hylwa SA, Warshaw EM. Epidemiology and co-reactivity of novel surfactant allergens: a double-blind randomized controlled study. Dermatitis 2016;27:348-354

2.161   DISODIUM OLEAMIDO MEA-SULFOSUCCINATE

IDENTIFICATION

Description/definition	: Disodium oleamido MEA-sulfosuccinate is the disodium salt of a substituted ethanolamide half ester of sulfosuccinic acid, which conforms to the formula shown below
Chemical class(es)	: Sulfosuccinates and sulfosuccinamates
Chemical/IUPAC name	: Disodium;4-[2-(octadec-9-enoylamino)ethoxy]-4-oxo-3-sulfonatobutanoate
Other names	: Disodium (Z)-[2-[(1-oxooctadec-9-enyl)amino]ethyl] 2-sulphonatosuccinate; disodium mono-oleamidosulfosuccinate (incorrect name used in ref. 1)
CAS registry number (s)	: 68479-64-1; 79702-63-9
EC number(s)	: 270-864-3
Function(s) in cosmetics	: EU: cleansing; foam boosting; hydrotrope; surfactant. USA: surfactants – cleansing agents; surfactants - foam boosters; surfactants - hydrotropes
Patch testing	: No data available
Molecular formula	: $C_{24}H_{41}NNa_2O_8S$

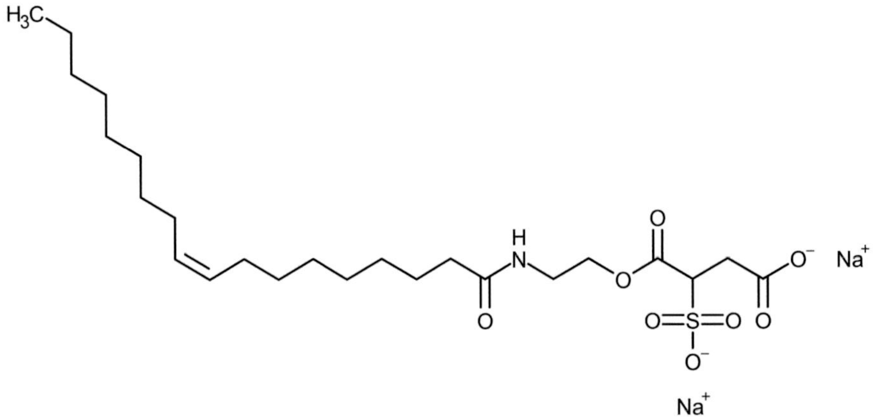

GENERAL
The (incorrect) name used for this compound in ref. 1 was disodium mono-oleamidosulfosuccinate.

CONTACT ALLERGY

Case reports and case series
Disodium oleamido MEA-sulfosuccinate was responsible for 1 out of 399 cases of cosmetic allergy where the causal allergen was identified in a study of the NACDG, USA, 1977-1983 (1).

Presence in cosmetic products and chemical analyses
In the USA, in April 2017, disodium monooleamidosulfosuccinate was present in 4 of 56,714 cosmetic products of which the composition is known in FDA's Voluntary Cosmetic Registration Program (VCRP) (data obtained from FDA, May 2017). In March 2017, disodium oleamido MEA-sulfosuccinate was present in one of 64,983 cosmetic products of which the composition is known in EWG's Skin Deep Cosmetics Database, USA (http://www.ewg.org/skindeep/).

LITERATURE
1   Adams RM, Maibach HI, Clendenning WE, Fisher AA, Jordan WJ, Kanof N, et al. A five-year study of cosmetic reactions. J Am Acad Dermatol 1985;13:1062-1069

2.162   DISODIUM PHENYL DIBENZIMIDAZOLE TETRASULFONATE

IDENTIFICATION

Description/definition   : Disodium phenyl dibenzimidazole tetrasulfonate is the heterocyclic compound that
                            conforms to the formula shown below
Chemical class(es)   : Heterocyclic compounds; sulfonic acids
Chemical/IUPAC name   : Disodium 2-[4-(4,6-disulfobenzimidazol-3-id-2-yl)phenyl]benzimidazol-3-ide-4,
                            6-disulfonic acid
Other names   : Bisdisulizole disodium; NeoHeliopan® AP
CAS registry number (s)   : 180898-37-7
Function(s) in cosmetics : EU: UV-absorber; UV-filter. USA: light stabilizers
EU cosmetic restrictions : Regulated in Annex VI/24 of the Regulation (EC) No. 1223/2009
Patch testing   : 10.0% pet. (Chemotechnique)
Molecular formula   : $C_{20}H_{12}N_4Na_2O_{12}S_4$

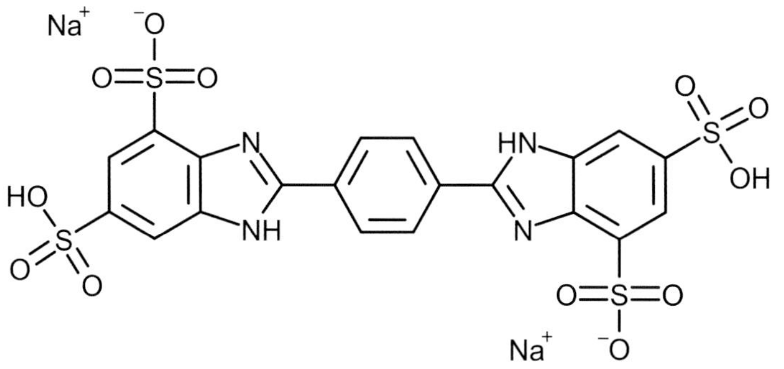

GENERAL

Disodium phenyl dibenzimidazole tetrasulfonate is a relatively new UVA filter with UV absorbance maximum (λ_{max}) at 335 nm (4,12). The literature on adverse reactions to sunscreens has been reviewed in several recent and older publications (5-11,14). A review of photocontact allergy to sunscreens was published in 2010 (13).

CONTACT ALLERGY

Patch testing in groups of patients

In 2008-2011, in 12 European countries, 1031 patients with exposed site dermatitis or a history of a reaction to a sunscreen or topical NSAID were patch- and photopatch tested with disodium phenyl dibenzimidazole tetrasulfonate 10% pet. and there was one (0.1%) positive patch test reaction; its relevance was not specified (2).

Case reports and case series

A patient, who had an immediate contact reaction to a sunscreen product and its ingredient disodium phenyl dibenzimidazole tetrasulfonate, probably also had contact allergy to it. The scratch test showed strong signs of allergic contact dermatitis after 48 hours. A patch test was negative, but had been applied only for 24 hours. In addition, the test substance of 2% in petrolatum may have been inadequate (concentration too low) (1).

Presence in cosmetic products and chemical analyses

In the USA, in April 2017, disodium phenyl dibenzimidazole tetrasulfonate was present in zero of 56,714 cosmetic products of which the composition is known in FDA's Voluntary Cosmetic Registration Program (VCRP) (data obtained from FDA, May 2017). In April 2017, disodium phenyl dibenzimidazole tetrasulfonate was present in zero of 65,52 cosmetic products of which the composition is known in EWG's Skin Deep Cosmetics Database, USA (http://www.ewg.org/skindeep/). It should be realized that sunscreen products containing UV-filters are classified as drugs in the USA, not as cosmetics; the number mentioned here, therefore, is that of cosmetics containing the UV-filter, but it does *not* include their presence in sunscreens. Disodium phenyl dibenzimidazole tetrasulfonate was present in 18 (0.4%) of 4447 cosmetic products collected in Germany, 2006-2009 (3). In a sample of 337 sunscreens marketed in the UK in 2010, disodium phenyl dibenzimidazole tetrasulfonate was present in 3 (0.9%) products (4).

OTHER SIDE EFFECTS

Photosensitivity

Photopatch testing in groups of patients
In 2008-2011, in 12 European countries, 1031 patients with exposed site dermatitis or a history of a reaction to a sunscreen or topical NSAID were patch- and photopatch tested with disodium phenyl dibenzimidazole tetrasulfonate 10% pet. and there were three (0.3%) positive photopatch test reactions. Their relevance was not specified, but of the reactions to all photoallergens together, 44% had current and 11% past relevance (2).

Immediate-type reactions
One patient developed generalized urticaria, swelling of the hands and angioedema a few minutes after the application of a sunscreen containing disodium phenyl dibenzimidazole tetrasulfonate. Subsequently, the patient suffered from vertigo, nausea and dyspnea. A scratch test with the sunscreen product and later with the active ingredient was positive after a few minutes. The scratch test showed signs of allergic contact dermatitis 48 hours later (1).

LITERATURE

1   Lange-Asschenfeldt B, Huegel R, Brasch J. Anaphylactic reaction caused by the UVA absorber disodium phenyl dibenzimidazole tetrasulfonate. Acta Derm Venereol 2005;85:280-281
2   The European Multicentre Photopatch Test Study (EMCPPTS) Taskforce. A European multicentre photopatch test study. Br J Dermatol 2012;166:1002-1009
3   Uter W, Gonçalo M, Yazar K, Kratz E-M, Mildau G, Lidén C. Coupled exposure to ingredients of cosmetic products: III. Ultraviolet filters. Contact Dermatitis 2014;71:162-169
4   Kerr AC. A survey of the availability of sunscreen filters in the U.K. Clin Exp Dermatol 2011;36:541-543
5   Heurung AR, Raju SI, Warshaw EM. Adverse reactions to sunscreen agents: epidemiology, responsible irritants and allergens, clinical characteristics, and management. Dermatitis 2014;25:289-326
6   Heurung AR, Raju SI, Warshaw EM. Contact allergen of the year. Benzophenones. Dermatitis 2014;25:3-10 (contains many mistakes; Erratum in Dermatitis 2014;25:92-95)
7   Avenel-Audran M. Sunscreen products: finding the allergen. Eur J Dermatol 2010;20:161-166
8   Scheuer E, Warshaw E. Sunscreen allergy: a review of epidemiology, clinical characteristics, and responsible allergens. Dermatitis 2006;17:3-11
9   Funk JO, Dromgoole SH, Maibach HI. Sunscreen intolerance: contact sensitization, photocontact sensitization, and irritancy of sunscreen agents. Dermatol Clin 1995;13:473-481
10   Dromgoole SH, Maibach HI. Sunscreening agent intolerance: Contact and photocontact sensitization and contact urticaria. J Am Acad Dermatol 1990;22:1068-1078
11   Shaw T, Simpson B, Wilson B, Oostman H, Rainey D, Storrs F. True photoallergy to sunscreens is rare despite popular belief. Dermatitis 2010;21:185-198
12   Shaath NA. Ultraviolet filters. Photochem Photobiol Sci 2010;9:464-469
13   Shaw T, Simpson B, Wilson B, Oostman H, Rainey D, Storrs F. True photoallergy to sunscreens is rare despite popular belief. Dermatitis 2010;21:185-198
14   Schauder S. Survey of the literature on adverse reactions to preparations containing UV filters (1947-1989) (Literaturübersicht über Unverträglichkeitsreaktionen auf lichtfilterhaltige Produkte von 1947 bis 1989). Z Hautkr 1990;65:982-998 (article in German)

2.163 DISODIUM RICINOLEAMIDO MEA-SULFOSUCCINATE

IDENTIFICATION

Description/definition : Disodium ricinoleamido MEA-sulfosuccinate is a disodium salt of a substituted ethanolamide half ester of sulfosuccinic acid. It conforms to the formula shown below

Chemical class(es) : Sulfosuccinates and sulfosuccinamates

Chemical/IUPAC name : Disodium;4-[2-[[(*E*)-12-hydroxyoctadec-9-enoyl]amino]ethoxy]-4-oxo-3-sulfonatobutanoate

Other names : Butanedioic acid, sulfo-, 1-(2-((12-hydroxy-1-oxo-9-octadecenyl)amino)ethyl) ester, disodium salt; disodium ricinoleyl monoethanolamide sulfosuccinate

CAS registry number (s) : 65277-54-5; 67893-42-9; 60224-42-2; 40754-60-7

EC number(s) : 265-672-1; 267-617-7

Function(s) in cosmetics : EU: cleansing; foam boosting; hydrotrope; skin conditioning; surfactant. USA: surfactants - cleansing agents; surfactants - foam boosters; surfactants - hydrotropes

Patch testing : 1 and 10% water (1); 0.5% and 5% pet. (2)

Molecular formula : $C_{24}H_{41}NNa_2O_9S$

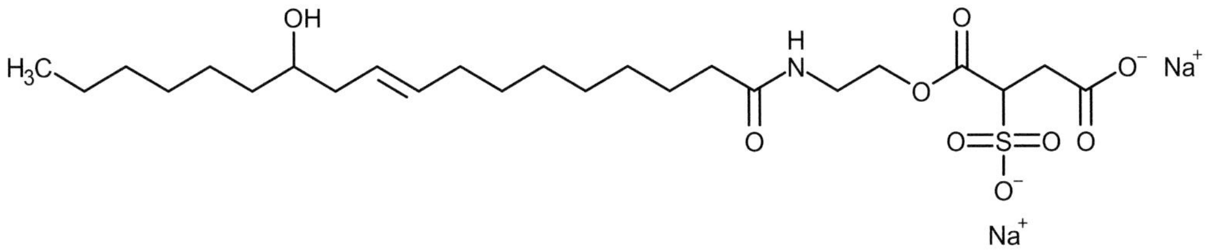

GENERAL

Sulfosuccinates are derived from maleic acid. They are prepared by reacting a hydroxy-containing fatty compound with maleic anhydride to form a mono ester. The ester is then sulfonated by sodium sulfite. The mono-sulfosuccinates are used in personal care products because of their low irritancy (2).

CONTACT ALLERGY

Case reports and case series

A man presented with hand dermatitis of 7 months duration. His hands were frequently exposed to metal dust and grime at work. Consequently, he washed his hands frequently during the day with a hand cleanser. The hand dermatitis improved when he was away from work during holidays. Patch testing showed a positive reaction to the hand cleanser 50% pet. The patient was subsequently patch tested with the constituents of the hand cleanser and reacted to disodium ricinoleamido MEA-sulfosuccinate 0.5% and 5% pet. Twenty controls tested with these materials were negative (2).

A woman developed acute itching of her scalp a few hours after using a new shampoo. Within 2 days, she had an itchy exudative eruption on her forehead, nape of neck and behind the ears, which lasted for two weeks. Patch tests to the European standard series and the constituents of the shampoo gave a positive reaction to disodium ricinoleamido MEA-sulfosuccinate 10% water. Patch testing with this compound in 20 controls was negative. Serial dilution of aqueous disodium ricinoleamido MEA-sulfosuccinate at 0.01%, 0.1% and 1% gave a dose-related response in the patient (1).

Presence in cosmetic products and chemical analyses

In the USA, in April 2017, disodium ricinoleamido MEA-sulfosuccinate was present in 33 of 56,714 cosmetic products of which the composition is known in FDA's Voluntary Cosmetic Registration Program (VCRP) (data obtained from FDA, May 2017). In March 2017, disodium ricinoleamido MEA-sulfosuccinate was present in 22 of 64,983 cosmetic products of which the composition is known in EWG's Skin Deep Cosmetics Database, USA (http://www.ewg.org/skindeep/).

LITERATURE

1   Tan BB, Lear JT, English JSC. Allergic contact dermatitis from disodium ricinoleamido MEA-sulfosuccinate in shampoo. Contact Dermatitis 1996;35:307

2   Reynolds NJ, Peachey RD. Allergic contact dermatitis from a sulfosuccinate derivative in a hand cleanser. Contact Dermatitis 1990;22:59-60

2.164   DISPERSE BLUE 85*

* Not an INCI name

IDENTIFICATION

Description/definition   : Disperse blue 85 is the monoazo color that conforms to the formula shown below
Chemical class(es)   : Color additives
INCI name USA   : Neither in CosIng nor in the Personal Care Products Council Ingredient Database
Chemical/IUPAC name   : 2-[[4-[(2-Chloro-4,6-dinitrophenyl)diazenyl]naphthalen-1-yl]amino]ethanol
Other names   : Disperse blue 85; CI 11370
CAS registry number (s)   : 12222-83-2
Patch testing   : 1% pet. (Chemotechnique)
Molecular formula   : $C_{18}H_{14}ClN_5O_5$

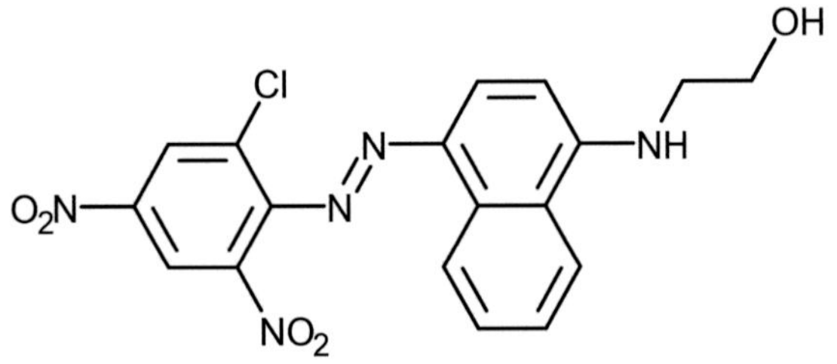

GENERAL

Disperse blue 85 is a monoazo dye, which is used to color polyester, acetate and, sometimes, nylon fibers (4). Textile dye dermatitis, including that caused by disperse blue 85, has been reviewed (6). The literature on non-cosmetic contact allergy to disperse blue 85 in this chapter is only briefly (and incompletely) reviewed.

CONTACT ALLERGY

Case reports and case series

In the period 1996-2013, in a tertiary referral center in Valencia, Spain, 5419 patients were patch tested. Of these, 628 individuals had allergic contact dermatitis to cosmetics. Disperse blue 85 was stated to be the responsible allergen in one case (1). It can be doubted whether disperse blue 85 is used at all in cosmetic products, and, consequently, whether the report from Valencia was correct.

Contact allergy to disperse blue 85 in non-cosmetic products

Disperse blue 85 has been held responsible for (purpuric) allergic contact dermatitis from its presence in clothes (2,3). A woman had a localized eruption on her right leg, which had appeared one month after starting using a rubber brace for a knee injury. The internal surface of the knee brace was covered by a black synthetic textile material. On examination, erythematosquamous patches were observed in a band-like pattern on her right thigh, shin and calf, areas of contact with the fabric of the knee brace. Patch tests gave a positive reaction to disperse blue 85. Replacement of the synthetic black material with white cotton fabric led to disappearance of the skin eruption with no further recurrences. Quite curiously, it was not ascertained that the color was in fact present in the black synthetic textile material of the brace (4). One male patient had purpuric pigmented contact dermatitis from contact allergy to disperse blue 85 in his blue service naval uniform (5).

Presence in cosmetic products and chemical analyses

In May 2017, disperse blue 85 was present in zero of 66,975 cosmetic products of which the composition is known in EWG's Skin Deep Cosmetics Database, USA (http://www.ewg.org/skindeep/). In the USA, in April 2017, disperse blue 85 was present in zero of 56,714 cosmetic products of which the composition is known in FDA's Voluntary Cosmetic Registration Program (VCRP) (data obtained from FDA, May 2017).

LITERATURE

1   Zaragoza-Ninet V, Blasco Encinas R, Vilata-Corell JJ, Pérez-Ferriols A, Sierra-Talamantes C, Esteve-Martínez A, de la Cuadra-Oyanguren J. Allergic contact dermatitis due to cosmetics: A clinical and epidemiological study in a tertiary hospital. Actas Dermosifiliogr 2016;107:329-336

2   Lazarov A, Cordoba M. Purpuric contact dermatitis in patients with allergic reaction to textile dyes and resins. J Eur Acad Dermatol Venereol 2000;14:101-105

3   Lazarov A, Trattner A, David M, Ingber A. Textile dermatitis in Israel: a retrospective study. Am J Contact Derm 2000;11:26-29

4   Lazarov A, Ingber A. Textile dermatitis from disperse blue 85 in a knee brace. Contact Dermatitis 1998;38:357

5   van der Veen JP, Neering H, de Haan P, Bruynzeel DP. Pigmented purpuric clothing dermatitis due to Disperse Blue 85. Contact Dermatitis 1988;19:222-223

6   Hatch KL, Maibach HI. Textile dye dermatitis. J Am Acad Dermatol 1995;32:631-639

2.165   DISPERSE BLUE 106*
Not an INCI name

IDENTIFICATION

Description/definition	: Disperse blue 106 is the monoazo color that conforms to the formula shown below
Chemical class(es)	: Color additives
INCI name USA	: Neither in CosIng nor in the Personal Care Products Council Ingredient Database
Chemical/IUPAC name	: 2-[N-Ethyl-3-methyl-4-[(5-nitro-1,3-thiazol-2-yl)diazenyl]anilino]ethanol
Other names	: Disperse blue 106; CI 111935
CAS registry number (s)	: 12223-01-7
EC number(s)	: 271-183-4
Patch testing	: 1% pet. (Chemotechnique, SmartPracticeCanada, SmartPracticeEurope); also present in the textile dye mix (Chemotechnique, SmartPracticeCanada)
Molecular formula	: $C_{14}H_{17}N_5O_3S$

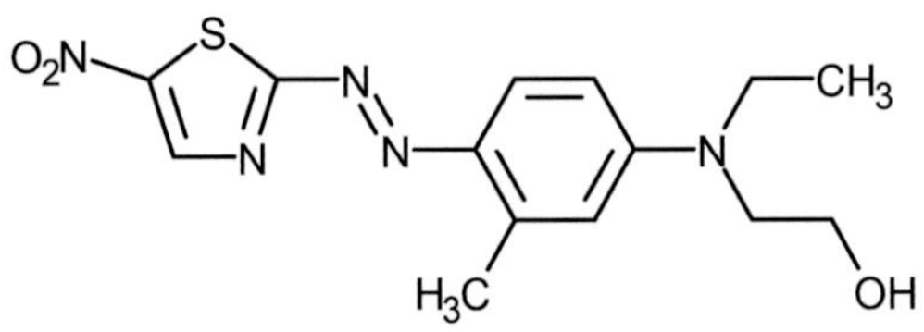

GENERAL

Disperse blue 106 is a well-known cause of allergic contact dermatitis in clothes and other fabrics. Discussing contact allergy and other side effects of this color, which is routinely tested in a textile mix in the European baseline series since 2015 (2), is considered to fall outside the scope of this book. In fact, the presence of the color in hair dyes or other cosmetics has not been ascertained, which includes the case described below (1).

CONTACT ALLERGY

Case reports and case series

A woman had a history of several years of generalized pruritus and intermittent erythematous rashes, primarily on the scalp, face, and neck. These symptoms began when she started to dye her hair blue. Exacerbations would occur soon after repeated dying. She was unable to report or bring in a specific brand of dye, as she had been to multiple hair salons throughout the community and used multiple products, but she confirmed that all dyes were blue. Patch testing only revealed a positive reaction to disperse blue 106, but p-phenylenediamine was negative. The patient was instructed to avoid all products containing blue dye, but she continues to use the same hair products and still suffers from scalp dermatitis. The authors suggest that disperse blue 106 should probably be considered in the setting of blue hair dyes. They offer no proof for that except the circumstantial evidence in this case. In fact, disperse blue 106 was not specifically identified in their search of store-based and salon-based semi-permanent hair dye products, but the products' labels indicated that 'azo' dyes might be present (1).

Cross-reactions, pseudo-cross-reactions and co-reactions

Disperse blue 106 may cross-react with structurally related chemicals, notably those with a para-structure. Cross-reactivity between para-compounds is discussed in Chapter 2.359 p-Phenylenediamine.

Presence in cosmetic products and chemical analyses

In the USA, in April 2017, disperse blue 106 was present in zero of 56,714 cosmetic products of which the composition is known in FDA's Voluntary Cosmetic Registration Program (VCRP) (data obtained from FDA, May 2017). In April 2017, was present in zero of 65,522 cosmetic products of which the composition is known in EWG's Skin Deep Cosmetics Database, USA (http://www.ewg.org/skindeep/).

LITERATURE

1   Soffer GK, Toh J, Clements S, Jariwala S. A case of chronic contact dermatitis resulting from the use of blue hair dye. Contact Dermatitis 2016;75:258-259
2   Isaksson M, Ryberg K, Goossens A, Bruze M. Recommendation to include a textile dye mix in the European baseline series. Contact Dermatitis 2015;73:15-20

2.166   DISPERSE YELLOW 3

IDENTIFICATION

Description/definition	: Disperse yellow 3 is the aromatic diazo compound that comforms to the structural formula shown below
Chemical class(es)	: Diazo compounds; aromatic compounds; amides
INCI name USA	: Not in the Personal Care Products Council Ingredient Database
Chemical/IUPAC name	: *N*-[4-(2-(2-Hydroxy-5-methylphenyl)diazenyl)phenyl]-acetamide
Other names	: CI 11855
CAS registry number (s)	: 2832-40-8
EC number(s)	: 220-600-8
Function(s) in cosmetics	: EU: prohibited since 2004
EU cosmetic restrictions	: Regulated in Annex II/1055 of the Regulation (EC) No. 1223/2009 (prohibited)
Patch testing	: 1.0% pet. (Chemotechnique, SmartPracticeEurope, SmartPracticeCanada); also present in the textile dye mix (Chemotechnique, SmartPracticeCanada)
Molecular formula	: $C_{15}H_{15}N_3O_2$

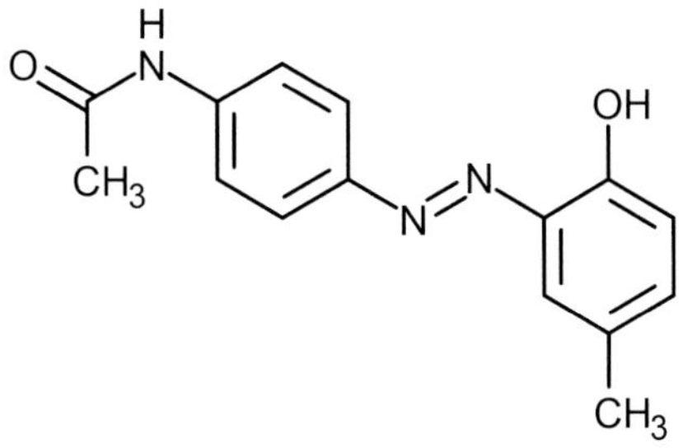

GENERAL

Disperse yellow 3 is a well-known cause of allergic contact dermatitis in clothes and other fabrics (3,4,5). Discussing contact allergy to and other side effects of this color, which is routinely tested in a textile dye mix in the European baseline series since 2015 (1), is considered to fall outside the scope of this book.

CONTACT ALLERGY

Case reports and case series

In a clinic in Oslo, Norway, in the period 1980-1982, patch and photopatch test studies were performed in 23 patients with reactions to sunscreens. The offending allergens could be traced in 18 of the 23 patients. In one patient, there was a positive patch test to disperse yellow 3. As this was listed in a table titled 'Allergy to sunscreen ingredients', it is assumed that disperse yellow was the allergen or one of the allergens in a sunscreen preparation in one individual (2).

Cross-reactions, pseudo-cross-reactions and co-reactions

Disperse yellow 3 may cross-react with structurally related chemicals, notably those with a para-structure. Cross-reactivity between para-compounds is discussed in Chapter 2.350 *p*-Phenylenediamine.

LITERATURE

1   Isaksson M, Ryberg K, Goossens A, Bruze M. Recommendation to include a textile dye mix in the European baseline series. Contact Dermatitis 2015;73:15-20
2   Thune P. Contact and photocontact allergy to sunscreens. Photodermatol 1984;1:5-9
3   Hotta E, Tamagawa-Mineoka R, Masuda K, Katoh N. Pustular allergic contact dermatitis caused by Disperse Yellow 3 in a dark blue dress. Allergol Int 2017 Mar 30. pii: S1323-8930(17)30021-7. doi: 10.1016/j.alit.2017.03.001. (Epub ahead of print)
4   Heratizadeh A, Geier J, Molin S, Werfel T. Contact sensitization in patients with suspected textile allergy. Data of the Information Network of Departments of Dermatology (IVDK) 2007-2014. Contact Dermatitis. 2017 Feb 24. doi: 10.1111/cod.12760. [Epub ahead of print]
5   Lisi P, Stingeni L, Cristaudo A, Foti C, Pigatto P, Gola M, Schena D, Corazza M, Bianchi L. Clinical and epidemiological features of textile contact dermatitis: an Italian multicentre study. Contact Dermatitis 2014;70:344-350

2.167   DISTEARYL PHTHALIC ACID AMIDE

IDENTIFICATION

Description/definition : Distearyl phthalic acid amide is the organic compound that conforms to the formula
                         shown below, where R represents the hydrogenated C16-18 alkyl moiety
Chemical class(es)   : Amides; carboxylic acids
Chemical/IUPAC name   : 2-(Dioctadecylcarbamoyl)benzoic acid
Other names   : Distearyl phthalamic acid; benzoic acid, 2-((dioctadecylamino)carbonyl)-
CAS registry number (s) : 87787-81-3
Function(s) in cosmetics : EU: emollient; skin conditioning. USA: skin conditioning agents - emollient
Patch testing   : 0.1%, 1% and 3% pet. (1)
Molecular formula   : $C_{44}H_{79}NO_3$

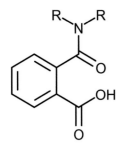

GENERAL

Distearyl phthalic acid amide is an emulsifier and suspending agent for silicones, pyrithione zinc, selenium sulfide, etc. It provides uniform emulsification and suspension of active ingredients, increasing their stability even at high temperatures (1).

CONTACT ALLERGY

Case reports and case series

A woman suffering from seborrheic dermatitis was advised by her doctor to use a particular shampoo. One day after using it, she had intense pruritus of the scalp. Two days later she used it again, and immediately developed erythema on the forehead and around the nose, with mild edema. Over the course of the day the lesions spread to the scalp, face, neck, and chest, with a micropapular rash on the hands and forearms. The pruritus and dermatitis lesions were confined to the areas that came into contact with the shampoo. Subsequently, nodular lesions consistent with enlarged lymph nodes appeared behind the ears and in the cervical region. In the next few days, fine scaling developed in the affected areas, with eyelid edema.

Patch tests to the standard series were negative. An open application test performed with a sample of undiluted shampoo on the volar forearm gave a positive reactions after 2 days, with erythema, edema, and microvesicles. Later, patch tests were carried out with all 14 components of the shampoo, which gave a positive reaction only to distearyl phthalic acid amide 3%. A repeat test was positive. Subsequently, the patient was tested with distearyl phthalic acid amide 0.1% pet. and 1% pet. and had strong reactions to both test substances. Five controls were negative. Finally, a use test with distearyl phthalic acid amide at 3%, 1% and 0.1% pet. was performed. After 2 days, positive reactions were observed, with substantial erythema, edema, and microvesicles to all three concentrations (1).

Presence in cosmetic products and chemical analyses

In the USA, in April 2017, distearyl phthalic acid amide was present in 8 of 56,714 cosmetic products of which the composition is known in FDA's Voluntary Cosmetic Registration Program (VCRP) (data obtained from FDA, May 2017). In March 2017, distearyl phthalic acid amide was present in one of 64,983 cosmetic products of which the composition is known in EWG's Skin Deep Cosmetics Database, USA (http://www.ewg.org/skindeep/).

LITERATURE

1   Carballada F, Núñez R, Martín-Lázaro J, Boquete M. Distearyl phthalic acid amide, a new contact allergen.
     Contact Dermatitis 2014;71:310-312

2.168 DITRIMETHYLOLPROPANE TRIETHYLHEXANOATE

IDENTIFICATION

Description/definition : Ditrimethylolpropane triethylhexanoate is the triester of ditrimethylolpropane and ethylhexanoic acid that conforms to the formula shown below, where RCO- represents the ethylhexanoic acid moiety
Chemical class(es) : Esters
Other names : di-2,2-Dihydroxymethylbutyl ether, triester with 2-ethylhexanoic acid
CAS registry number (s) : 533926-00-0
Function(s) in cosmetics : EU: binding; emollient; skin conditioning . USA: binders; dispersing agents – nonsurfactant; skin-conditioning agents - emollient
Patch testing : pure (1)
Molecular formula : $C_{36}H_{68}O_8$

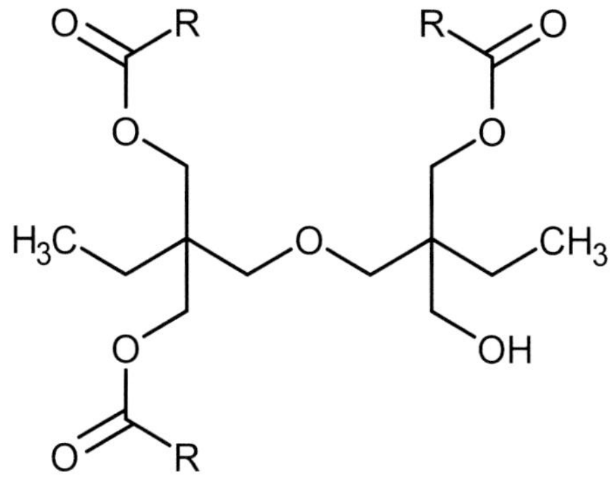

GENERAL

Ditrimethylolpropane triethylhexanoate is a new pigment solvent that has superior pigment dispersibility to conventional solvents such as diisostearyl malate. It is a white or light yellow liquid oil, and is a triester consisting of ditrimethylolpropane and 2-ethylhexanoate. When ditrimethylolpropane triethylhexanoate is used together with wax, the mixture is hard, and this enables the lipstick to have a smoother texture because of the reduction in the volume of wax in the lipstick. Ditrimethylolpropane triethylhexanoate is stable against heat, and mixes well with other oils; it may be used for various products, including lip sticks and skin care products (1).

CONTACT ALLERGY

Case reports and case series
A woman with a history of atopic dermatitis and urticaria presented with cheilitis of several years' duration. She had been treated with topical steroids, and changed her lipstick a year ago, but her cheilitis had not improved. Patch tests were performed with the Japanese standard allergen series as well as samples of her cosmetics. There was a positive reaction to her current lipstick 'as is' only. The patient was subsequently patch tested with the 18 ingredients in the lipstick obtained from the manufacturer and showed a positive reaction to ditrimethylolpropane triethylhexanoate 'as is'. Four controls were negative. Ditrimethylolpropane triethylhexanoate accounted for 15% of the lipstick (1).

Presence in cosmetic products and chemical analyses
In the USA, in April 2017, ditrimethylpropane triethylhexanoate was present in zero of 56,714 cosmetic products of which the composition is known in FDA's Voluntary Cosmetic Registration Program (VCRP) (data obtained from FDA, May 2017). In March 2017, ditrimethylolpropane triethylhexanoate was present in zero of 64,983 cosmetic products of which the composition is known in EWG's Skin Deep Cosmetics Database, USA (http://www.ewg.org/skindeep/).

LITERATURE

1 Miura M, Isami M, Yagami A, Matsunaga K. Allergic contact cheilitis caused by ditrimethylolpropane triethylhexanoate in a lipstick. Contact Dermatitis 2011;64:301-302

2.169   DMDM HYDANTOIN

IDENTIFICATION

Description/definition	: DMDM hydantoin is the organic compound that conforms to the formula shown below
Chemical class(es)	: Amides; heterocyclic compounds
Chemical/IUPAC name	: 1,3-bis(Hydroxymethyl)-5,5-dimethylimidazolidine-2,4-dione
Other names	: 1,3-Dimethylol-5,5-dimethylhydantoin; dimethylol dimethylhydantoin
CAS registry number (s)	: 6440-58-0
EC number(s)	: 229-222-8
CIR review(s)	: J Am Coll Toxicol 1988;7:245-277 (access: www.cir-safety.org/ingredients)
Function(s) in cosmetics	: EU: preservative. USA: preservatives
EU cosmetic restrictions	: Regulated in Annex V/33 of the Regulation (EC) No. 1223/2009
Patch testing	: 1.0% pet. (Chemotechnique, SmartPracticeCanada); 2.0% water (Chemotechnique, SmartPracticeEurope, SmartPracticeCanada); in the NACDG studies, the petrolatum-based patch test material was significantly more sensitive than DMDM hydantoin in an aqueous base (66)
Molecular formula	: $C_7H_{12}N_2O_4$

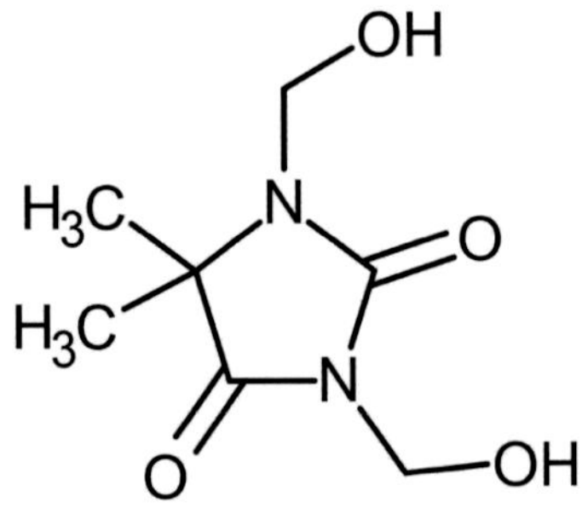

GENERAL

DMDM hydantoin (dimethylol dimethylhydantoin) is a formaldehyde-releasing preservative, which is mainly used in cosmetics (47). However, it may also be used in herbicides, cutting oils, paints, adhesives, copying paper, and inks (79). At recommended use levels, it is active against fungi, yeast, and gram-positive and gram-negative bacteria (33). This material exists as an equilibrium mixture with MDM hydantoin (monomethylol dimethylhydantoin) and DM hydantoin (dimethylhydantoin). The author suspects that contact allergy to DMDM hydantoin is virtually always caused by formaldehyde. The parent molecule DM hydantoin (dimethylhydantoin) has so far never reacted (but neither has it been tested in patients allergic to DMDM hydantoin) (19). Negative reactions to formaldehyde in DMDM-sensitive individuals may conveniently be explained by false-positive reactions to DMDM hydantoin (19) or false-negative reactions to formaldehyde. In all studies, formaldehyde has been tested in a concentration of 1% in water, which we now know to give false-negative results in some 40% of all formaldehyde-allergic individuals (52,53).

The literature on formaldehyde-releasers in cosmetic products including DMDM hydantoin up to 2009-2010 has been reviewed by the author (27,47). The literature on formaldehyde-releasers up to 1990 has been reviewed in refs. 22 and 23. Other useful preservative allergy reviews have appeared in 2014 (79) and 2004 (80).

CONTACT ALLERGY

Patch testing in groups of patients

Results of testing DMDM hydantoin in consecutive patients suspected of contact dermatitis (routine testing) back to 1985 are shown in table 2.169.1. Results of patch testing DMDM hydantoin in groups of *selected* patients (e.g., patients with eyelid dermatitis or individuals suspected of cosmetic allergy) back to 1994 are shown in table 2.169.2.

Patch testing in consecutive patients suspected of contact dermatitis: routine testing

DMDM hydantoin is not routinely tested in Europe, but has been part of the screening series of the North American Contact Dermatitis Group (NACDG) for over 25 years. Their results have been published biannually (table 2.169.1). Since 1992, the preservative has been tested in a concentration of 1% both in petrolatum and in water. The petrolatum-based DMDM hydantoin test material was statistically significantly more sensitive than the same allergen in an aqueous base (66); in the more recent NACDG studies (15,16), the water-based preparation has not been tested anymore. In these NACDG studies, frequencies of sensitization (to the petrolatum-based material) have ranged from 1.0% to 2.8%. Between 1994 and 2008, there was a stable frequency of around 2.5% (11,12,13,24,26,29,30), but in the more recent reports, there was a decline to 1.0%, 1.6% and 1.0% (15,16,67), probably from a decrease of its use in cosmetic products (see 'Presence of DMDM hydantoin in cosmetic products' below). In other USA centers, frequencies ranging from 0.8% to 3.4% positive patch test reactions to DMDM hydantoin have been observed (4,25,28,39). In early studies in The Netherlands and Switzerland, rates were only 1.2% and 1.7%, despite using a higher test concentration of 3% in water (32,33).

In some investigations, no relevance figures were provided. In the NACDG studies, 'definite + probable relevance' has ranged from 15 to 49% (mean 37%, median 39% [excl. the 2013-2014 period]). The implicated products were never mentioned, but contact allergy to DMDM hydantoin is (virtually) always the result of its presence in cosmetic products. The author has found no convincing cases of non-cosmetic allergic contact dermatitis from this preservative, although topical drugs have been suggested to be causative of DMDM hydantoin-induced allergic contact dermatitis in one IVDK study (18).

Table 2.169 1 Patch testing in groups of patients: Routine testing

Years and Country	Test conc. & vehicle	Number of patients tested | positive (%)		Selection of patients (S); Relevance (R); Comments (C)	Ref.
2013-14 USA, Canada	1% pet.	4859	49 (1.0%)	R: definite + probable relevance: 45%	67
2011-12 USA, Canada	1% pet.	4232	67 (1.6%)	R: definite + probable relevance: 49%	15
2009-10 USA, Canada	1% pet.	4304	43 (1.0%)	R: definite + probable relevance: 31%	16
2006-2010 USA	1% pet.	3087	(2.0%)	R: 64%	39
	2% water	3085	(1.4%)	R: 58%	
2007-8 USA, Canada	1% pet.	5082	(2.7%)	R: definite + probable relevance: 39%	12
	1% water	5082	(1.1%)	R: definite + probable relevance: 55%	
2005-6 USA, Canada	1% pet.	4439	(2.6%)	R: definite + probable relevance: 45%	11
	1% water	4433	(1.4%)	R: definite + probable relevance: 42%	
2000-2005 USA	1% pet.	3757	(2.2%)	R: 75%	4
	1% water	3428	(1.3%)	R: 84%	
2003-4 USA, Canada	1% pet.	5140	118 (2.3%)	R: not stated	13
	1% water	5141	70 (1.4%)	R: not stated	
2001-2002 USA	1% pet.	4897	(2.8%)	R: definite + probable relevance: 29%	24
	1% water	4897	(2.2%)	R: definite + probable relevance: 34%	
1998-2000 USA	1% pet.	1321	(0.8%)	R: not stated	25
	1% water	1042	(0.5%)	R: not stated	
1998-00 USA, Canada	1% pet.	5801	(2.0%)	R: definite + probable relevance: 15%	26
	1% water	5767	(1.6%)	R: definite + probable relevance: 20%	
1994-1999 USA		474	(3.4%)	R: not stated	28
1996- 8 USA, Canada	1% pet.	4093	(2.6%)	R: definite, probable and possible relevance: 93%	29
	1% water	4093	(1.9%)	R: definite, probable and possible relevance 82%	
1994-1996 USA	1% pet.	3082	(2.3%)	R: definite + probable relevance: 49%	30
	1% water	3064	(2.1%)	R: definite + probable relevance: 44%	
1992-1994 USA	1% pet.	3485	(1.6%)	R: definite + probable + possible relevance: 56%	31
	1% water	3479	(1.8%)	R: definite + probable + possible relevance: 56%	
1989-90 Switzerland	3% water	2295	(1.7%)	R: not stated	32
1985 Netherlands	3% water	501	(1.2%)	R: not stated	33

Patch testing in groups of selected patients
Data on patch testing with DMDM hydantoin in groups of selected patients back to 1994 are summarized in table 2.169.2. In most studies, a higher test concentration of 2% (either in water or in petrolatum) was used for patch testing. Despite this and despite the selection for possible reactions to cosmetics, frequencies higher than in routine testing have not been observed in non-USA/Canada studies. In one USA study, a 4.1% prevalence was observed in a small group of 342 patients with atopic dermatitis as subgroup of 2453 successive patients suspected of contact dermatitis (54). Relevance data were lacking or unspecified in all but two publication. In one of these, performed by the IVDK, 30% of the reactions were considered to be caused by cosmetics and 22% by topical drugs (18). In the other study, a 2000-2007 USA investigation, all 20 positive patch test reactions were scored as relevant, but this included 'questionable' and 'past' relevance (3).

Case reports and case series
DMDM hydantoin was stated to be the (or an) allergen in 6 patients in a group of 603 individuals suffering from cosmetic dermatitis, seen in the period 2010-2015 in Leuven, Belgium (38). DMDM hydantoin was responsible for 37 out of 959 cases of non-fragrance cosmetic allergy where the causal allergen was identified, Belgium, 2000-2010 (2). In a group of 2193 patients (1582 women, 611 men) with (presumed) cosmetic allergy, 127 reactions (6%) were

caused by DMDM hydantoin (in petrolatum) in a study of the NACDG, 2001-2004, DMDM hydantoin (in petrolatum) ranking 11th in the list of most frequent allergens (5).

Table 2.169.2 Patch testing in groups of patients: Selected patient groups

Years and Country	Test conc. & vehicle	Number of patients tested	positive (%)	Selection of patients (S); Relevance (R); Comments (C)	Ref.
1994-2013 USA		342	14 (4.1%)	S: patients with atopic dermatitis as subgroup of 2453 successive patients suspected of contact dermatitis; R: not stated; C: in the non-atopic group, the frequency was only 1.9%; yet, the frequency was not significantly higher in the atopic dermatitis patients group	54
2007-2012 IVDK	2% pet.	654	1 (0.1%)	S: female hairdressers with current or previous occupational contact dermatitis; R: not stated	69
		1415	3 (0.3%)	S: female patients, clients of hairdressers, in who hair cosmetics were regarded as a cause of dermatitis, and who had never worked as hairdressers; R: not stated	
2010-2011 Korea	2% pet.	584	10 (1.7%)	S: patients suspected of allergic cosmetic dermatitis; R: not stated	37
2006-2011 IVDK	2% water	6931	(0.3%)	S: patients suspected of cosmetic intolerance and tested with a preservative series; R: not stated	68
2006-2010 USA		100	1 (1%)	S: patients with eyelid dermatitis; R: not stated	14
2001-2010 Australia	2% water	4296	113 (2.6%)	S: not stated; R: 46%	46
1994-2010 USA, Canada	1% pet.	432	? (?)	S: hairdressers/cosmetologists; R: in the group of 187 patients who had at least one relevant occupationally related reaction, 8 (4.3%) reacted to DMDM hydantoin	70
2005-2009 Spain	2% water	1163	10 (0.9%)	S: patients allergic to formaldehyde or quaternium-15, or suspicion of cosmetic or industrial contact dermatitis; R: not specified	1
1996-2009 IVDK	2% pet.	78,266	388 (0.5%) [a]	S: not specified; R: not specified	4
2000-2007 USA	1% pet.	937	14 (1.5%)	S: patients tested with a supplemental cosmetic screening series; R: 100% (both test substances); C: weak study: a. high rate of macular erythema and weak reactions; b. relevance figures included 'questionable' and 'past' relevance	3
	2% water	327	6 (1.8%)		
1993-2006 Australia	2% water	3709	(2.1%)	S: not stated; R: 52%	48
2001-2005 USA	2% water	411	(1.2%)	S: not stated; R: 60%	34
2003-2004 USA	1% water	268	5 (1.9%)	S: patients with pure eyelid dermatitis; R: this was the number of relevant reactions	40
1994-2004 USA		46	1 (2.2%)	S: patients with allergic contact dermatitis of the eyelids; R: the reaction was relevant, but the causative product(s) were not mentioned	36
2001-2002 Sweden	2% water	1075	(0.9%)	S: patients referred for routine testing willing to participate in a study on cosmetic use and adverse reactions; R: not stated	8
1997-2000 Israel		244	2 (0.8%)	S: patients suspected of cosmetic dermatitis; R: 64% of all patch test reactions in the cosmetic series was relevant	42
1994-2000 IVDK	2% water	34,321	174 (0.5%)	S: patients tested with a 'topicals' test series; R:current relevance in 56 (32%) patients, mostly from cosmetics and topical drugs; C: 45% co-reactivity with formaldehyde	18
	2% pet.	1808	6 (0.3%)		
1990–1994 IVDK	2% pet.	1374	(1.1%)	S: not specified, selected from 28,349 patients; R: not stated	35

[a] age-standardized and sex-standardized proportions
IVDK: Information Network of Departments of Dermatology, Germany, Austria, Switzerland

In a Finnish occupational contact dermatitis clinic, in a period of 6.5 years, the following cases of occupational allergic contact dermatitis from formaldehyde released by DMDM hydantoin were observed (occupation and causative products mentioned): two hairdressers and many products; a hairdresser and shampoo; a home aid and shampoo; a farmer and shower soap, liquid soap and hand cream; a hairdresser and styling products (45). A woman had allergic contact dermatitis from formaldehyde released by DMDM hydantoin in a moisturizing lotion (50). A mother had hand dermatitis from contact allergy to DMDM hydantoin in the wipes she used for her baby's hygiene (10).

Contact allergy to DMDM hydantoin in non-cosmetic products

In a group of 180 patients with positive patch test reactions to DMDM hydantoin, 56 reactions were thought to be currently relevant. Cosmetics were 'considered to be causal' in 30% and topical drugs in 22%. Four patients had occupational allergic contact dermatitis, but the incriminated products were not mentioned (18).

Cross-reactions, pseudo-cross-reactions and co-reactions

DMDM hydantoin is a formaldehyde-releaser. In the majority of patients reacting to it, contact allergy to the preservative is the result of sensitivity to formaldehyde. In these cases, pseudo-cross-reactions may be observed to formaldehyde and other formaldehyde-releasers including diazolidinyl urea, imidazolidinyl urea, quaternium-15 and - to a lesser degree - 2-bromo-2-nitropropane-1,3-diol (6). The subject of formaldehyde-releasers and pseudo-cross-reactivity is summarized in Chapter 2.188 Formaldehyde and discussed in detail in a review article by the author (47).

Provocation tests

In 4 out of 12 formaldehyde-allergic patients (33%) who performed repeated open application tests with a creamcontaining 1% DMDM hydantoin on the volar aspect of the underarm, dermatitis was observed after 3-6 days. Repeat testing with the cream containing the preservative in a concentration of 0.25% (estimated to contain approximately 200 ppm formaldehyde) was negative in 2 patients, produced only itching but no visible skin changes in one and provoked mild dermatitis in the fourth formaldehyde-sensitive individual (19). However, the test lasted only one week, which we now know to be (far) too short. It has been demonstrated that patients allergic to formaldehyde may react positively later to patch tests with DMDM hydantoin and MDM (monomethylol dimethylhydantoin), but not to the parent molecule DM hydantoin (dimethylhydantoin) (19).

Presence of DMDM hydantoin in cosmetic products

In July 2017, DMDM hydantoin was present in 1378 of 69,545 cosmetic products (1.6%) of which the composition is known in EWG's Skin Deep Cosmetics Database, USA (http://www.ewg.org/skindeep/); six years earlier, the percentage had still been 6.6 (27). In the USA, in April 2017, DMDM hydantoin was present in 2740 of 56,714 cosmetic products of which the composition is known in FDA's Voluntary Cosmetic Registration Program (VCRP) (data obtained from FDA, May 2017). DMDM hydantoin was present in 278 of 4737 (5.9%) commonly used cosmetic products of which the full composition was known in 2016 in The Contact Allergen Management Program (CAMP) database of the American Contact Dermatitis Society (74). DMDM hydantoin was present in 8 (15%) of 54 personal hygiene wet wipes for which ingredient information was obtained online and from retail stores, USA, 2016 (73). DMDM hydantoin was present in 29 (16%) of 178 facial wipes for which ingredient information was obtained online and from retail stores, USA, 2016 (72). In the USA, in 2015-2016, 63 diaper wipes and 41 topical diaper preparations from a large retailer were screened for the presence of potential sensitizers. DMDM hydantoin was found in 5/63 (8%) disposable diaper wipes and in none of 41 topical diaper preparations (78).

In 2014, in Thailand, the labels of 1000 cosmetic products (593 leave-on, 407 rinse-off products) were examined for the presence of preservatives. These were partly purchased in shops and on markets and partly brought in by patients. DMDM hydantoin was present in 54 products (5.4%); in the leave-on products, the percentage was 3.5 and in the rinse-off products 8.1 (76). Of 179 emollients available in Poland in 2014, 10 (5.6%) contained DMDM hydantoin (77). In 2013, 60 cosmetic products manufactured and purchased in Israel (40 stay-on and 20 rinse-off products) were investigated for preservatives. According to the labelling, 18 (30%) cosmetics contained DMDM hydantoin. In the stay-on products (hand and body creams), the percentage was 18, whereas 11 of the 20 shampoos and soaps (55%) were preserved with DMDM hydantoin (49). In 2009, in the USA, the ingredient lists of 796 hair products from one company were screened for the presence of DMDM hydantoin. The chemical was present in 30% of 279 shampoos, in 0% of 231 conditioners, and in 0% of 286 styling products (43). In 2009, in the USA, the ingredient lists of 657 miscellaneous cosmetics from one company were screened for the presence of DMDM hydantoin. DMDM hydantoin was present in 0% of 195 antiperspirants/deodorants, in 0% of 41 powders, in 0% of 167 shaving products, in 2% of 201 sunblocks, and in 28% of 53 wipes (44).

DMDM hydantoin was present in only 0.2% of 4133 stay-on cosmetic products purchased in Germany, 2006-2009 (7). In Germany, in 2006-2009, the labels of 4680 cosmetic products were screened for the presence of preservatives. DMDM hydantoin was present in 1.3% of the products, according to labelling information (71).

The preservative was a component of 17% of 204 cosmetic products (92 shampoos, 61 hair conditioners, 34 liquid soaps, 17 wet tissues) in Sweden, 2008 (9). Also in 2008, 19.5% of 33,212 cosmetics and toiletries registered in the USA Food and Drug Administration (FDA) Voluntary Cosmetic Registration Database contained a formalde-hyde-releaser. They were more frequently used in rinse-off products (27.3%) than in stay-on cosmetics (16.9%). DMDM hydantoin was present in 5.4% of all products; in stay-on cosmetics, the percentage was 3.0, whereas 12.6% of rinse-off products contained the preservative (20). In the same period, of 496 stay-on cosmetic products present in a local drugstore and investigated by checking the ingredient labelling, 18 products (3.6%) proved to contain this preserva-tive. Any formaldehyde-releaser was found in 122 of this group of stay-on products (24.6%) (20). In 1998, 100 moisturizers sold in Sweden were analysed for the presence and amount of preservatives. Thirty-five products contained a formaldehyde-releaser, of which three had DMDM hydantoin as preservative (41). In 1996, in the USA, DMDM hydantoin was present in 5.0% of approximately 20,000 formulae voluntarily registered by cosmetic companies in the FDA Voluntary Cosmetic Registration Database (21).

Amounts of free formaldehyde released by DMDM hydantoin and chemical analyses
DMDM hydantoin is produced by reacting formaldehyde with DM hydantoin (5,5-dimethylhydantoin). Therefore, it is a formaldehyde-releaser. One mole of DMDM hydantoin can release a total of 2 mole of formaldehyde. The composition of DMDM hydantoin as determined by gas chromatography is as follows: 94-98% DMDM hydantoin, and 2-6% decomposition products including free formaldehyde. DMDM hydantoin decomposes to 1-hydroxymethyl-5,5-dimethylhydantoin (1-MDMH) or 3-hydroxymethyl-5,5-dimethylhydantoin (3-MDMH) (both a monomethylol dimethylhydantoin, MDM hydantoin), releasing a molecule of formaldehyde. Next, 1-MDMH or 3-MDMH decomposes to dimethylhydantoin (DM hydantoin), releasing a second molecule of formaldehyde (55). The amounts of free formaldehyde released by DMDM hydantoin in products depend on its concentration, the pH of the product, the temperature (the higher the temperature the more formaldehyde is present in solution after constant time) (51,65), the age of the product (upon storage increased levels of formaldehyde will be released [51]), the level of microbial contamination, and the other constituents of the products preserved with DMDM hydantoin (61,63,64,65). For this preservative, the pH is important: in alkaline environment, more formaldehyde is released (table 2.169.3 [56]).

DMDM hydantoin was said to contain 0.5-2% free formaldehyde and concentrations in cosmetics range from 0.1% to 0.6% (58,59). It has been suggested, that most formulations will, therefore, contain between 20 and 120 ppm free formaldehyde (22,60). However, these estimates may be too low, as a cream preserved with 0.15 wt% DMDM hydantoin contained 0.013 wt% (130 ppm) free formaldehyde (56) and a shampoo preserved with 0.4% DMDM hydantoin had a level of 294 ppm free formaldehyde (62) (table 2.169.3). The presence of protein in shampoo significantly decreased the amount of free formaldehyde compared to the same shampoo without protein (table 2.169.3), indicating that free formaldehyde was complexed by the protein introduced (62). Examples of reports of free formaldehyde concentrations in products containing DMDM hydantoin are shown in table 2.169.3. Results of analysis of free formaldehyde in DMDM hydantoin patch test preparations are presented in Chapter 2.188 Formaldehyde (17).

In recent experiments, DMDM hydantoin in cosmetics released about the same amount of formaldehyde as quaternium-15 and imidazolidinyl urea, less than paraformaldehyde and diazolidinyl urea, but more than methenamine and 2-bromo-2-nitropropane-1,3-diol (51).

Table 2.169.3 Reports of free formaldehyde released from products containing DMDM hydantoin (adapted from [47])

Product	Conc. of DMDM hydantoin		Free formaldehyde (ppm)	Ref.
DMDM hydantoin preservative solution	0.25%	pH 8.5-9	470	56
		pH 6-6.5	270	
		pH 4-4.5	210	
Cream	0.15%		130	56
Preservative buffer solution	0.1%		300	57
Shampoo containing protein	0.1%		36	62
	0.2%		84	
	0.4%		160	
	0.8%		292	
Shampoo *not* containing protein	0.1%		108	62
	0.2%		183	
	0.4%		294	
	0.8%		505	

In 2013, 60 cosmetic products manufactured and purchased in Israel (40 stay-on and 20 rinse-off products) were investigated for the presence of DMDM hydantoin by HPLC. Six of 9 shampoos (67%) contained the preservative in amounts ranging from 730 to 1290 ppm; four of 11 soaps (36%) contained DMDM hydantoin in amounts ranging from 280 to 960 ppm; five of 23 body creams (22%) contained the preservative in amounts ranging from 800 to 1950 ppm and one of 17 hand creams (7%) contained DMDM hydantoin in an amount of 1500 ppm (49).

OTHER SIDE EFFECTS

Photosensitivity
A nurse had occupational photoallergic contact dermatitis from DMDM hydantoin in a soap used at work (75).

LITERATURE
1 Latorre N, Borrego L, Fernández-Redondo V, García-Bravo B, Giménez-Arnau AM, Sánchez J, et al. Patch testing with formaldehyde and formaldehyde-releasers: multicenter study in Spain (2005-2009). Contact Dermatitis 2011;65:286-292

2 Travassos AR, Claes L, Boey L, Drieghe J, Goossens A. Non-fragrance allergens in specific cosmetic products. Contact Dermatitis 2011;65:276-285

3 Wetter DA, Yiannias JA, Prakash AV, Davis MD, Farmer SA, el-Azhary RA, et al. Results of patch testing to personal care product allergens in a standard series and a supplemental cosmetic series: an analysis of 945 patients from the Mayo Clinic Contact Dermatitis Group, 2000-2007. J Am Acad Dermatol 2010;63:789-798

4 Davis MD, Scalf LA, Yiannias JA, Cheng JF, El-Azhary RA, Rohlinger AL, et al. Changing trends and allergens in the patch test standard series. Arch Dermatol 2008;144:67-72

5 Warshaw EM, Buchholz HJ, Belsito DV et al. Allergic patch test reactions associated with cosmetics: Retrospective analysis of cross-sectional data from the North American Contact Dermatitis Group, 2001-2004. J Am Acad Dermatol 2009;60:23-38

6 Schnuch A, Lessmann H, Geier J, Uter W. Contact allergy to preservatives. Analysis of IVDK data 1996-2009. Br J Dermatol 2011;164:1316-1325

7 Mildau G. INCI labelling of fragrances and preservatives on 5451 randomly selected cosmetic products in Germany, 2006 to 2009. Karlsruhe: Chemisches und Veterinär-Untersuchungsamt, 2010

8 Lindberg M, Tammela M, Bostrom A, Fischer T, Inerot A, Sundberg K, et al. Are adverse skin reactions to cosmetics underestimated in the clinical assessment of contact dermatitis? A prospective study among 1075 patients attending Swedish patch test clinics. Acta Derm Venereol 2004;84:291-295

9 Yazar K, Johnsson S, Lind M-L, Boman A, Lidén C. Preservatives and fragrances in selected consumer-available cosmetics and detergents. Contact Dermatitis 2011;64:265-272

10 Fields KS, Nelson T, Powell D. Contact dermatitis caused by baby wipes. J Am Acad Dermatol 2006;54:S230-S232

11 Zug KA, Warshaw EM, Fowler JF Jr, Maibach HI, Belsito DL, Pratt MD, et al. Patch-test results of the North American Contact Dermatitis Group 2005-2006. Dermatitis 2009;20:149-160

12 Fransway AF, Zug KA, Belsito DV, Deleo VA, Fowler JF Jr, Maibach HI, et al. North American Contact Dermatitis Group patch test results for 2007-2008. Dermatitis 2013;24:10-21

13 Warshaw EM, Belsito DV, DeLeo VA, Fowler JF Jr, Maibach HI, Marks JG, et al. North American Contact Dermatitis Group patch-test results, 2003-2004 study period. Dermatitis 2008;19:129-136

14 Wenk KS, Ehrlich AE. Fragrance series testing in eyelid dermatitis. Dermatitis 2012;23:22-26

15 Warshaw EM, Maibach HI, Taylor JS, Sasseville D, DeKoven JG, Zirwas MJ, et al. North American Contact Dermatitis Group patch test results: 2011-2012. Dermatitis 2015;26:49-59

16 Warshaw EM, Belsito DV, Taylor JS, Sasseville D, DeKoven JG, Zirwas MJ, et al. North American Contact Dermatitis Group patch test results: 2009 to 2010. Dermatitis 2013;24:50-59

17 Emeis D, De Groot AC, Brinkmann J. Determination of formaldehyde in formaldehyde-releaser patch test preparations. Contact Dermatitis 2010;63:57-62

18 Uter W, Frosch PJ and (for IVDK Study Group and the German Contact Dermatitis Research Group, DKG). Contact allergy from DMDM hydantoin, 1994–2000. Contact Dermatitis 2002;47:57-58

19 De Groot AC, van Joost T, Bos JD, van der Meeren HLM, Weyland JW. Patch test reactivity to DMDM hydantoins. Contact Dermatitis 1988;18:197-201

20 De Groot AC, Veenstra M. Formaldehyde-releasers in cosmetics in the USA and in Europe. Contact Dermatitis 2010;62:221-224

21 Steinberg D. Frequency of use of preservatives in the United States. Paper given at Preservatech, Paris, 1996. www.creative-developments.co.uk/papers/Preservatives%201999.htm (last accessed 20-3-2009).

22 Fransway AF. The problem of preservation in the 1990s: I. Statement of the problem. Solution(s) of the industry, and the current use of formaldehyde and formaldehyde-releasing biocides. Am J Contact Dermatitis 1991;2:6-23

23 Fransway AF, Schmitz NA. The problem of preservation in the 1990s: II. Formaldehyde and formaldehyde-releasing biocides: incidences of cross-reactivity and the significance of the positive response to formaldehyde. Am J Contact Dermatitis 1991;2:78-88

24 Pratt MD, Belsito DV, DeLeo VA, Fowler JF Jr, Fransway AF, Maibach HI, et al. North American Contact Dermatitis Group patch-test results, 2001–2002 study period. Dermatitis 2004;15:176-183

25 Wetter DA, Davis MDP, Yiannias JA, Cheng JF, Connolly SM, el-Azhary RA, et al. Patch test results from the Mayo Contact Dermatitis Group, 1998–2000. J Am Acad Dermatol 2005;53:416-421

26 Marks JG Jr, Belsito DV, DeLeo VA, Fowler JF Jr, Fransway AF, Maibach HI, et al. North American Contact Dermatitis Group patch-test results, 1998–2000. Am J Contact Dermat 2003;14:59-68

27 De Groot AC, White IR, Flyvholm M-A, Lensen G, Coenraads P-J. Formaldehyde-releasers in cosmetics: relationship to formaldehyde contact allergy. Part 1. Characterization, frequency and relevance of sensitization, and frequency of use in cosmetics. Contact Dermatitis 2010;62:2-17

28 Shaffer MP, Belsito DV. Allergic contact dermatitis from glutaraldehyde in health care workers. Contact Dermatitis 2000;43:150-156

29 Marks JG Jr, Belsito DV, DeLeo VA, Fowler JF Jr, Fransway AF, Maibach HI, et al. North American Contact Dermatitis Group patch test results, 1996–1998. Arch Dermatol 2000;136:272-273

30 Marks JG Jr, Belsito DV, DeLeo VA, Fowler JF Jr, Fransway AF, Maibach HI,et al. North American Contact Dermatitis Group patch test results for the detection of delayed-type hypersensitivity to topical allergens. J Am Acad Dermatol 1998;38:911-918

31 Marks JG, Belsito DV, DeLeo VA, Fowler JF, Fransway AF, Maibach HI,et al. North American Contact Dermatitis Group standard tray patch test results 1992 through 1994. Am J Contact Dermatitis 1995;6:160-165

32 Perrenoud D, Bircher A, Hunziker T, Suter H, Bruckner-Tuderman L, Stäger J, et al. Frequency of sensitization to 13 common preservatives in Switzerland. Contact Dermatitis 1994;30:276-279

33 De Groot AC, Bos JD, Jagtman BA, Bruynzeel DP, van Joost Th, Weyland JW. Contact allergy to preservatives –II. Contact Dermatitis 1986;15:218-222

34 Davis MD, Scalf LA, Yiannias JA, et al. Changing trends and allergens in the patch test standard series. A Mayo Clinic 5-year retrospective review, January 1, 2001, through December 31, 2005. Arch Dermatol 2008;144:67-72

35 Schnuch A, Geier J, Uter W, Frosch PJ. Patch testing with preservatives, antimicrobials and industrial biocides. Results from a multicentre study. Br J Dermatol 1998;138:467-476

36 Amin KA, Belsito DV. The aetiology of eyelid dermatitis: a 10-year retrospective analysis. Contact Dermatitis 2006;55:280-285

37 Lee SS, Hong DK, Jeong NJ, Lee JH, Choi YS, Lee AY, et al. Multicenter study of preservative sensitivity in patients with suspected cosmetic contact dermatitis in Korea. J Dermatol 2012;39:677-681

38 Goossens A. Cosmetic contact allergens. Cosmetics 2016, 3, 5; doi:10.3390/cosmetics3010005

39 Wentworth AB, Yiannias JA, Keeling JH, Hall MR, Camilleri MJ, Drage LA, et al. Trends in patch-test results and allergen changes in the standard series: a Mayo Clinic 5-year retrospective review (January 1, 2006, to December 31, 2010). J Am Acad Dermatol 2014;70:269-275

40 Rietschel RL, Warshaw EM, Sasseville D, Fowler JF Jr, DeLeo VA. Belsito DV, et al. Common contact allergens associated with eyelid dermatitis: data from the North American Contact Dermatitis Group 2003-2004 study period. Dermatitis 2007;18:78-81

41 Gruvberger B, Bruze M, Tammela M. Preservatives in moisturizers on the Swedish market. Acta Derm Venereol 1998;78:52-56

42 Trattner A, Farchi Y, David M. Cosmetics patch tests: first report from Israel. Contact Dermatitis 2002;47:180-181

43 Scheman A, Jacob S, Katta R, Nedorost S, Warshaw E, Zirwas M, et al. Part 2 of a 4 part series. Hair cosmetics: trends and alternatives. Data from the American Contact Alternative Group. J Clin Aesthet Dermatol 2011;4:42-46

44 Scheman A, Jacob S, Katta R, Nedorost S, Warshaw E, Zirwas M, et al. Part 4 of a 4 part series. Miscellaneous products: trends and alternatives in deodorants, antiperspirants, sunblocks, shaving products, powder, and wipes. Data from the American Contact Alternative Group. J Clin Aesthet Dermatol 2011;4:35-39

45 Aalto-Korte K, Kuuliala O, Suuronen K, Alanko K. Occupational contact allergy to formaldehyde and formaldehyde releasers. Contact Dermatitis 2008;59:280-289

46 Toholka R, Wang Y-S, Tate B, Tam M, Cahill J, Palmer A, Nixon R. The first Australian Baseline Series: Recommendations for patch testing in suspected contact dermatitis. Australas J Dermatol 2015;56:107-115

47 De Groot AC, White IR, Flyvholm M-A, Lensen G, Coenraads P-J. Formaldehyde-releasers in cosmetics: relationship to formaldehyde contact allergy. Part 2. Patch test relationship to formaldehyde contact allergy, experimental provocation tests, amount of formaldehyde released and assessment of risk to consumers allergic to formaldehyde. Contact Dermatitis 2010;62:18-31

48 Chow ET, Avolio AM, Lee A, Nixon R. Frequency of positive patch test reactions to preservatives: The Australian experience. Australas J Dermatol 2013;54:31-35

49 Horev L, Isaksson M, Engfeldt M, Persson L, Ingber A, Bruze M. Preservatives in cosmetics in the Israeli market conform well to the EU legislation. J Eur Acad Dermatol Venereol 2015;29:761-766

50 Tanglertsampan C. Allergic contact dermatitis from formaldehyde with initially negative repeated open application test. Contact Dermatitis 2003;48:171-172

51 Lv C, Hou J, Xie W, Cheng H. Investigation on formaldehyde release from preservatives in cosmetics. Int J Cosm Sci 2015;37:474-478

52 Pontén A, Aalto-Korte K, Agner T, Andersen KE, Giménez-Arnau AM, Gonçalo M. Patch testing with 2.0% (0.60 mg/cm^2) formaldehyde instead of 1.0% (0.30 mg/cm^2) detects significantly more contact allergy. Contact Dermatitis 2013;68:50-53

53 Hauksson I, Pontén A, Gruvberger B, Isaksson M, Bruze M. Clinically relevant contact allergy to formaldehyde may be missed by testing with formaldehyde 1.0%. Br J Dermatol 2011;164:568-572

54 Shaughnessy CN, Malajian D, Belsito DV. Cutaneous delayed-type hypersensitivity in patients with atopic dermatitis: reactivity to topical preservatives. J Am Acad Dermatol 2014;70:102-107

55 Asada A, Doi T, Takeda A, Kajimura K. Quantification of 1,3-dimethylol-5,5-dimethylhydantoin and its decomposition products in cosmetics by high-performance liquid chromatography. J Pharm Biomed Anal 2012;67-68:163-168

56 Emeis D, Anker W, Wittern K-P. Quantitative 13C NMR spectroscopic studies on the equilibrium of formaldehyde with its releasing preservatives. Anal Chem 2007;79:2096-2100

57 Kijami K, Takeda M, Okaya Y, et al. A study on release of formaldehyde from its donor-type preservatives. Anal Sci 1991;7(Suppl): 913-916

58 Rosen M. Glydant and MDMH as cosmetic preservative. In: JJ Jabara, Ed. Cosmetic and Drug Preservation. Principles and practice. New York: Marcel Dekker Inc., 1984:165-190

59 Expert Panel of the Cosmetic Ingredient Review. Final report of the safety assessment for DMDM hydantoin. J Am Coll Toxicol 1988;7:245-277

60 Johansen M, Bundgaard H. Kinetics of formaldehyde release from the cosmetic preservative Germall 115. Arch Pharm Chem Sci Ed 1981;9:117-122

61 Geier J, Lessmann H, Schuch A, Fuchs Th. Kontaktallergien durch formaldehydabspaltende Biozide. Allergologie 1997;20:215-224 (article in German)

62 Rosen M, McFarland A. Free formaldehyde in anionic shampoos. J Soc Cosmet Chem 1984;35:157-169

63 Geier J, Lessmann H, Schnuch A, Uter W. Contact sensitizations in metalworkers with occupational dermatitis exposed to water-based metalworking fluids: results of the research project 'FaSt'. Int Arch Occup Environ Health 2004;77:543-551

64 Geier J, Lessmann H, Becker D, et al. Formaldehydabspalter. Dermatol Beruf Umwelt 2008;56:34-36 (article in German)

65 Engelhardt H, Klinkner R. Determination of free formaldehyde in the presence of donators in cosmetics by HPLC and post-column derivation. Chromatographia 1985;20:559-565

66 Rietschel RL, Warshaw EM, Sasseville D, Fowler JF Jr, DeLeo VA, Belsito DV, Taylor JS, et al; North American Contact Dermatitis Group. Sensitivity of petrolatum and aqueous vehicles for detecting allergy to imidazolidinylurea, diazolidinylurea, and DMDM hydantoin: a retrospective analysis from the North American Contact Dermatitis Group. Dermatitis 2007;18:155-162

67 DeKoven JG, Warshaw EM, Belsito DV, Sasseville D, Maibach HI, Taylor JS, et al. North American Contact Dermatitis Group Patch Test Results: 2013-2014. Dermatitis 2017;28:33-46

68 Dinkloh A, Worm M, Geier J, Schnuch A, Wollenberg A. Contact sensitization in patients with suspected cosmetic intolerance: results of the IVDK 2006-2011. J Eur Acad Dermatol Venereol 2015;29:1071-1081

69 Uter W, Gefeller O, John SM, Schnuch A, Geier J. Contact allergy to ingredients of hair cosmetics – a comparison of female hairdressers and clients based on IVDK 2007–2012 data. Contact Dermatitis 2014;71:13-20

70 Warshaw EM, Wang MZ, Mathias CGT, Maibach HI, Belsito DV, Zug KA, et al. Occupational contact dermatitis in hairdressers/cosmetologists; retrospective analysis of North American Contact Dermatitis Group data, 1994 to 2010. Dermatitis 2012;23:258-268

71 Uter W, Yazar K, Kratz EM, Mildau G, Lidén C. Coupled exposure to ingredients of cosmetic products: II. Preservatives. Contact Dermatitis 2014;70:219-226

72 Aschenbeck KA, Warshaw EM. Allergenic ingredients in facial wet wipes. Dermatitis 2017 Mar 23. doi: 10.1097/DER.0000000000000268. [Epub ahead of print]

73 Aschenbeck KA, Warshaw EM. Allergenic ingredients in personal hygiene wet wipes. Dermatitis 2017 Mar 23. doi: 10.1097/DER.0000000000000275. [Epub ahead of print]

74 Beene KM, Scheman A, Severson D, Reeder MJ. Prevalence of preservatives across all product types in the Contact Allergen Management Program. Dermatitis 2017;28:81-87

75 Jensen OC. Recurrent bouts of photodermatitis. J Am Acad Dermatol 1989;21:1036

76 Bunyavaree M, Kasemsarn P, Boonchai W. Cosmetic preservative labelling on the Thai market. Contact Dermatitis 2016;74:217-221

77 Osinka K, Karczmarz A, Krauze A, Feleszko W. Contact allergens in cosmetics used in atopic dermatitis: analysis of product composition. Contact Dermatitis 2016;75:241-243

78 Yu J, Treat J, Chaney K, Brod B. Potential allergens in disposable diaper wipes, topical diaper preparations, and disposable diapers: under-recognized etiology of pediatric perineal dermatitis. Dermatitis 2016;27:110-118

79 Yim E, Baquerizo Nole KL, Tosti A. Contact dermatitis caused by preservatives. Dermatitis 2014;25:215-231

80 Sasseville D. Hypersensitivity to preservatives. Dermatol Ther 2004;17:251-263

2.170 DODECYL GALLATE

IDENTIFICATION

Description/definition : Dodecyl gallate is the ester of gallic acid that conforms to the formula shown below
Chemical class(es) : Esters; phenols
Chemical/IUPAC name : Dodecyl 3,4,5-trihydroxybenzoate
Other names : Lauryl gallate; E312 (in foods)
CAS registry number (s) : 1166-52-5
EC number(s) : 214-620-6
Function(s) in cosmetics : EU: antioxidant. USA: antioxidants
Patch testing : 0.25% pet. (Chemotechnique); 0.3% pet. (SmartPracticeCanada)
Molecular formula : $C_{19}H_{30}O_5$

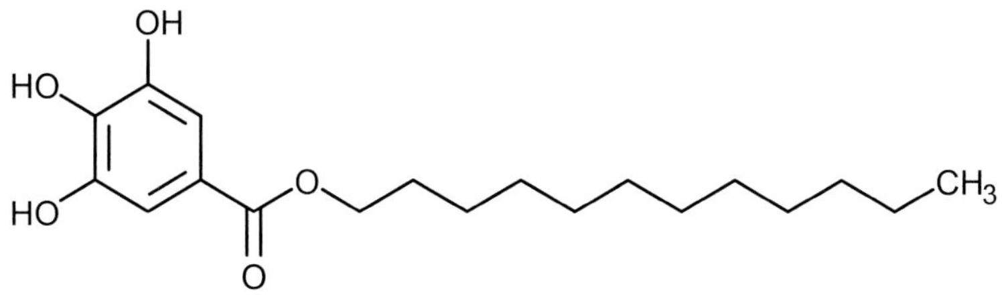

GENERAL

Gallates are antioxidants which, when added in small quantities, retard or prevent oxidation; they have been in use since 1947. The most commonly used gallic acid esters are propyl, octyl (= caprylyl) and dodecyl (= lauryl) gallate, which differ from each other in terms of the length of their side chain. Propyl gallate and other gallates are widely used as antioxidants in the cosmetic industry (creams, lotions, and lipsticks; only propyl gallate), food industry (bakery goods, frying oils, soups, sauces, chewing gum, and potato chips), and in pharmaceutical and industrial products (eardrops, suppositories, and transformer oils) (9,25). Gallates are potential allergens (moderate to strong sensitizers in animal experiments [9]), but relatively few cases of contact dermatitis due to gallates have been reported to date (15). The low rates of sensitization has been explained by oral tolerance (25).

An extensive review of the literature on contact allergy to gallates has been published in 2017 (26).

CONTACT ALLERGY

Patch testing in groups of patients

Results of studies patch testing dodecyl gallate in consecutive patients suspected of contact dermatitis (routine testing) and in groups of selected patients are shown in table 2.170.1. In routine testing, a 1% frequency of sensitization was found in a very small Turkish study (19). In groups of *selected* patients (e.g., patients suspected of allergic cosmetic dermatitis, patients with allergic contact cheilitis, patients with leg ulcers, patients tested with a preservative and cosmetics series), rates of sensitization have ranged from 0.5% to 22%. The 22% rate was found in a small study of 41 patients with allergic contact cheilitis (20). Nearly all of the nine positive patch tests were considered to be relevant, but the causative products were not mentioned (20). A high prevalence (18.9%) was also observed in patients with burning mouth syndrome. A number of these patients improved significantly after avoiding gallates in foods and lipsticks (22).

In most other studies, relevance rates were not mentioned or specified (15,16). In Australia, 240 of 3418 (7.0%) of patients tested with a cosmetics series reacted to dodecyl gallate 0.25% pet. Quite remarkably, only 1% had definite relevance, 6% were scored as 'possibly relevant' (mostly margarines and cosmetics), whereas for 93% of all 240 positive patch tests no relevance could be found (23). In a study from the USA, 91% of 87 positive patch test reactions were scored as relevant, but this included 'questionable' and 'past' relevance (1).

Case reports and case series

Two patients had allergic contact cheilitis from lip preparations used for cosmetic and sunscreening purposes (8). Five patients were sensitized to dodecyl gallate in cosmetic creams (10, data cited in ref. 9).

Table 2.170.1 Patch testing in groups of patients

Years and Country	Test conc. & vehicle	Number of patients tested | positive (%)		Selection of patients (S); Relevance (R); Comments (C)	Ref.
Routine testing					
2005-2006 Turkey		93	1 (1%)	R: the reaction was considered to be relevant	19
Testing in groups of selected patients					
2008-2012 Canada	0.3% pet.	132	25 (18.9%)	S: patients with burning mouth syndrome; R: 74% relevance for all allergens together	22
2011 China	0.25% pet.	201	3 (1.5%)	S: healthy student volunteers 19-30 years; R: not stated	18
2010-2011 Korea	0.25% pet.	584	6 (1.0%)	S: patients suspected of allergic cosmetic dermatitis; R: not stated	14
2001-2011 USA	0.25% pet.	41	9 (22%)	S: patients with allergic contact cheilitis; R: 8/9 relevant	20
2001-2010 Australia	0.25% pet.	3000	220 (7.3%)	S: not stated; R: 11%; overlap with ref. 23	17
1993-2010 Australia	0.25% pet.	3418	240 (7.0%)	S: patients tested with a cosmetic series; R: only 1% was definitely relevant, 6% possible (mostly margarines and cosmetics) and 93% was of unknown relevance; overlap with data from ref. 17	23
2004-2008 France	0.5% pet.	423	7 (1.7%)	S: patients with leg ulcers; R: not stated	13
2000-2007 USA	0.25% pet.	937	87 (9.2%)	S: patients tested with a supplemental cosmetic screening series; R: 91%; C: weak study: a. high rate of macular erythema and weak reactions; b. relevance figures included 'questionable' and 'past' relevance	1
1985-2006 Spain	0.25% pet.	1173	6 (0.5%)	S: patients tested with a preservative and cosmetic series or with a bakery series (n=69); R: of 46 patients reacting to one or more gallates (propyl, octyl, dodecyl), 35 had relevant reactions; 29 were caused by cosmetics, of which 24 were lip products causing allergic contact cheilitis; there were 7 relevant reactions to octyl gallate in bakery products	15
1997-2000 Israel		244	5 (2.0%)	S: patients suspected of cosmetic dermatitis; R: 64% of all patch test reactions in the cosmetic series was relevant	16
1990-1994 Germany	0.3% pet.	3475	20 (0.6%)	S: patients tested with a preservative series; R: not stated	12
<1990 India	0.25% pet.	69	2 (3%)	S: patients, with features suggestive of allergic contact dermatitis and histories of prolonged use of numerous topical preparations, or of exacerbation or spread of dermatitis following the use of such preparations; R: not stated	21

Contact allergy to dodecyl gallate in non-cosmetic products

Five patients had occupational contact dermatitis from dodecyl gallate in margarine (2,3). Another 5 reacted to a mixture of dodecyl-, octyl- and propylgallate, present in a concentration of 2% in margarine (4). A cheese counter assistant had contact allergy to dodecyl gallate; the presence of this antioxidant in the cheese was not verified, but when she started working (again) as cashier, the dermatitis disappeared (6). A boy had recurrent swelling of the lower lip; he was allergic to dodecyl gallate and the symptoms completely disappeared when he had a diet free of dodecyl gallate (7). Four out of 10 workers in a factory producing washing powder became sensitized to the powder's ingredient dodecyl gallate, present in a concentration of 0.05% (11).

One patient allergic to propyl gallate and dodecyl gallate developed angioedema of the lips after eating foods containing gallates (15). A woman presented with a swollen tongue. Patch testing was positive to dodecyl gallate, commonly reported as being present in edible oil and oily foods such as margarine. The patient avoided foods presumed to contain gallates and over a period of 6 weeks there was a substantial improvement in her tongue symptoms (23). A man had contact allergy to dodecyl gallate in a salicylic acid oil preparation resulting in seborrheic-like dermatitis of the scalp and the face (24). A woman had unspecified contact dermatitis from dodecyl gallate in margarine (27). Another female individual had ACD from dodecyl gallate in an unspecified ointment (27).

A female baker had occupational hand dermatitis from dodecyl gallate, added to fresh apples to prevent discolouration (28).

Cross-reactions, pseudo-cross-reactions and co-reactions

Octyl gallate (5). Of 46 patients allergic to gallates, 16 (35%) reacted to more than one gallate (propyl, octyl, dodecyl) (15). In animal experiments, cross-reactions occurred when the difference between the sensitizing compound and the related gallate was 4 or less carbon atoms (9).

Presence in cosmetic products and chemical analyses
In the USA, in April 2017, dodecyl gallate was present in zero of 56,714 cosmetic products of which the composition is known in FDA's Voluntary Cosmetic Registration Program (VCRP) (data obtained from FDA, May 2017). In April 2017, dodecyl gallate was present in zero of 66,648 cosmetic products of which the composition is known in EWG's Skin Deep Cosmetics Database, USA (http://www.ewg.org/skindeep/).

OTHER SIDE EFFECTS

Miscellaneous side effects
Contact allergy to dodecyl gallate in foods has been linked with Melkersson–Rosenthal syndrome (5).

LITERATURE

1   Wetter DA, Yiannias JA, Prakash AV, Davis MD, Farmer SA, el-Azhary RA, et al. Results of patch testing to personal care product allergens in a standard series and a supplemental cosmetic series: an analysis of 945 patients from the Mayo Clinic Contact Dermatitis Group, 2000-2007. J Am Acad Dermatol 2010;63:789-798

2   Brun R. Kontaktekzem auf Laurylgallat und p-Hydroxy-benzoesäureester. Berufsdermatosen 1964;12:281-284

3   Brun R. Eczéma de contact à un antioxydant de la margarine (gallate) et changement de métier. Dermatologica 1970;140:390-394

4   Von Burckhardt W, Fierz U. Antioxydanten in der Margarine als Ursache von Gewerbeekzemen. Dermatologica 1964;129:431-432

5   Wong GA E, Shear NH. Melkersson–Rosenthal syndrome associated with allergic contact dermatitis from octyl and dodecyl gallates. Contact Dermatitis 2003;49:266-267

6   Raccagni AA, Frattagli M, Baldari U, Righini MG. Lauryl gallate hand dermatitis in a cheese counter assistant. Contact Dermatitis 1997;37:182

7   Lewis FM, Shah M, Gawkrodger DJ. Contact sensitivity to food additives can cause oral and perioral symptoms. Contact Dermatitis 1995;33:429-430

8   Serra-Baldrich E, Puig LL, Arnau AG, Camarasa JG. Lipstick allergic contact dermatitis from gallates. Contact Dermatitis 1995;32:359-360

9   Hausen BM, Beyer W. The sensitizing capacity of the antioxidants propyl, octyl, and dodecyl gallate and some related gallic acid esters. Contact Dermatitis 1992;26:253-258

10   Huriez L, Martin P, Venoverschelde M, Mennecier J. L'allergie aux sels d'ammonium quaternaire. Bull Soc Franc Derm 1966;73:260-262 (Article in French)

11   Van der Meeren HLM. Dodecyl gallate, permitted in food, is a strong sensitizer. Contact Dermatitis 1987;16:260-262

12   Schnuch A, Geier J, Uter W, Frosch PJ. Patch testing with preservatives, antimicrobials and industrial biocides. Results from a multicentre study. Br J Dermatol 1998;138:467-476

13   Barbaud A, Collet E, Le Coz CJ, Meaume S, Gillois P. Contact allergy in chronic leg ulcers: results of a multicentre study carried out in 423 patients and proposal for an updated series of patch tests. Contact Dermatitis 2009;60:279-287

14   Lee SS, Hong DK, Jeong NJ, Lee JH, Choi YS, Lee AY, et al. Multicenter study of preservative sensitivity in patients with suspected cosmetic contact dermatitis in Korea. J Dermatol 2012;39:677-681

15   García-Melgares ML, de la Cuadra J, Martín B, Laguna C, Martínez L, Alegre V. Sensitization to gallates: review of 46 cases. Actas Dermosifiliogr 2007;98:688-693

16   Trattner A, Farchi Y, David M. Cosmetics patch tests: first report from Israel. Contact Dermatitis 2002;47:180-181

17   Toholka R, Wang Y-S, Tate B, Tam M, Cahill J, Palmer A, Nixon R. The first Australian Baseline Series: Recommendations for patch testing in suspected contact dermatitis. Australas J Dermatol 2015;56:107-115

18   Zhao J, Li LF. Contact sensitization to cosmetic series of allergens in a general population in Beijing. J Cosmet Dermatol 2014;13:68-71

19   Ada S, Seçkin D. Patch testing in allergic contact dermatitis: is it useful to perform the cosmetic series in addition to the European standard series? J Eur Acad Dermatol Venereol 2010;24:1192-1196

20   O'Gorman SM, Torgerson RR. Contact allergy in cheilitis. Int J Dermatol 2016;55:e386-e391

21   George ND, Srinivas CR, Balachandran C, Shenoi SD. Sensitivity to various ingredients of topical preparations following prolonged use. Contact Dermatitis 1990;23:367-368

22   Lynde CB, Grushka M, Walsh SR. Burning mouth syndrome: patch test results from a large case series. J Cutan Med Surg 2014;18:174-179

23   Gamboni SE, Palmer AM, Nixon RL. Allergic contact stomatitis to dodecyl gallate? A review of the relevance of positive patch test results to gallates. Australas J Dermatol 2013;54:213-217

24   Kuznetsov AV, Erlenkeuser-Uebelhoer I, Thomas P. Contact allergy to propylene glycol and dodecyl gallate mimicking seborrheic dermatitis. Contact Dermatitis 2006;55:307-308

25   Perez A, Basketter DA, White IR, McFadden J. Positive rates to propyl gallate on patch testing: a change in trend. Contact Dermatitis 2008;58:47-48

26   Holcomb ZE, Van Noord MG, Atwater AR. Gallate contact dermatitis: product update and systematic review. Dermatitis 2017;28:115-127

27   Rudzki E, Baranowska A. Reactions to gallic acid esters. Contact Dermatitis 1975;1:393 (article inaccessible, data cited in ref. 26).

28   Lee A, Nixon R. Contact dermatitis from sodium metabisulfite in a baker. Contact Dermatitis 2001;44:127-128

2.171 DROMETRIZOLE

IDENTIFICATION

Description/definition : Drometrizole is the benzotriazole derivative that conforms to the formula shown below
Chemical class(es) : Heterocyclic compounds; phenols
Chemical/IUPAC name : 2-(Benzotriazol-2-yl)-4-methylphenol
Other names : 2-(2-Hydroxy-5-methylphenyl)benzotriazole; Tinuvin® P
CAS registry number (s) : 2440-22-4
EC number(s) : 219-470-5
CIR review(s) : J Am Coll Toxicol 1986;5:455-470; Int J Toxicol 2008;27(Suppl.1):63-75
(access: www.cir-safety.org/ingredients)
Merck Index monograph : 4766
Function(s) in cosmetics : EU: UV-absorber. USA: light stabilizers
Patch testing : 1.0% pet. (Chemotechnique); 5% pet. may be preferable (5)
Molecular formula : $C_{13}H_{11}N_3O$

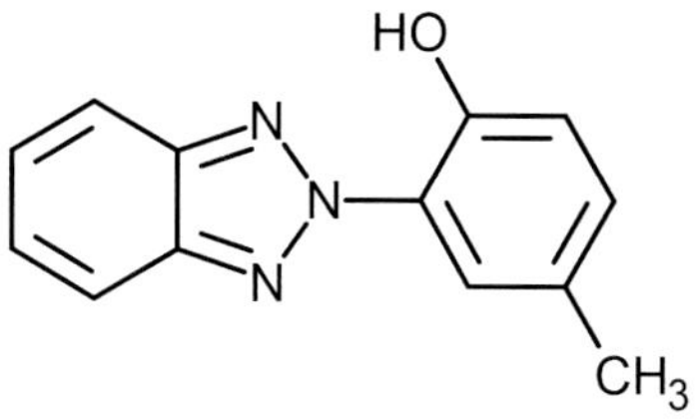

GENERAL

Drometrizole is a UVA/B filter with UV absorbance maxima (λmax,1, λmax,2) at 300 and 340 nm (8,17). It is used in plastic materials of different types, synthetic and natural fibers, cosmetic products, and dental materials (7). The literature on adverse reactions to sunscreens has been reviewed in several recent and older publications (9-14,18).

A review of photocontact allergy to sunscreens was published in 2010 (16).

CONTACT ALLERGY

Case reports and case series

In a group of 75 patients allergic to cosmetic products, seen in a private practice in The Netherlands in the period 1981-1986, one case was caused by drometrizole in a nail lacquer (15, same patient as in ref. 5). A female medical secretary had suffered from swelling of her eyelids and an itching eruption on the face for a week. She strongly suspected allergy to one of her facial cosmetic products. Immediately following the onset of the eruption she had stopped using these cosmetics, but she had continued the use of her nail varnish. On examination, the right upper eyelid was edematous, and showed slight erythema and scaling; on the cheeks a mild papular eruption was noted. After the eruption had subsided, patch tests with the European standard series and her 22 cosmetic products showed a positive reaction to one of the nail varnishes. Later, when tested with its ingredients, there were positive reactions to the color ingredients 'Synthetic Pearl I and II', containing bismuth oxychloride. When, in a third patch test session, the constituents of Synthetic Pearl were tested, the patient proved to be allergic to drometrizole (Tinuvin® P). She had a recurrence once, after using another 'pearlescent' nail varnish (5). Drometrizole in face creams has been reported as the cause of allergic contact dermatitis in 4 women; three of them had become sensitized to the same cosmetic product (6). An unknown number of patients had allergic contact dermatitis from drometrizole in cosmetics (2, cited in ref. 1).

Contact allergy to drometrizole in non-cosmetic products

One patient had ACD from drometrizole in spandex tapes sewn into underwear (1). Another individual reacted to the UV-filter in a watch strap (3). A man presented with a necrolytic migratory erythema. Subsequent investigation revealed a pancreatic tumor with glucagon secretion. The tumor was removed, with parts of the pancreas, the spleen, the left kidney and the mid-colon. A colostomy was performed. The patient started wearing a colostomy device. Nine months later, the patient developed dermatitis around the anus praeter, exactly where the skin was covered by the appliance. Patch tests with the different parts of the device gave positive reactions. Tests with the European standard series and a plastic and glue series showed contact allergy to drometrizole. The manufacturer confirmed that drometrizole was used at concentrations of less than 0.5% in the core of the plastic sheet of the bag. As the core is completely surrounded by a layer without drometrizole, it was concluded that drometrizole had migrated to the outer layer (4).

A woman for 25 years has had dental gold and for many years she has also had various acrylic composite restorative materials. At one point, she noticed gingivitis in her frontal upper jaw, more pronounced close to two teeth, of which one was restored with gold and the other one with a composite filling. The gingiva around these fillings were red, elevated, ulcerated, and bleeding. In her frontal upper gingiva, she also had lichenoid reactions verified by histological examination. Patch tests with an extensive dental screening series revealed positive reactions to drometrizole 1% pet. and gold sodium thiosulfate 0.5% pet. Analysis by HPLC showed the presence of drometrizole in the dental restorative material in an approximate concentration of 0.09% wt./wt. The presence of drometrizole in this material was later confirmed by its manufacturer. The patient's gingivitis healed completely when the gold filling and all composite fillings were replaced by materials not containing gold or drometrizole (7).

Presence in cosmetic products and chemical analyses
In the USA, in April 2017, drometrizole was present in 85 of 56,714 cosmetic products of which the composition is known in FDA's Voluntary Cosmetic Registration Program (VCRP) (data obtained from FDA, May 2017). In April 2017, drometrizole was present in one older product of 65,522 cosmetic products of which the composition is known in EWG's Skin Deep Cosmetics Database, USA (http://www.ewg.org/skindeep/). It should be realized, that sunscreen products containing UV-filters are classified as drugs in the USA, not as cosmetics; the number mentioned here, therefore, is that of cosmetics containing the UV-filter, but it does *not* include their presence in sunscreens. Drometrizole was present in 11% of 329 sunscreen products (incl. 21 lipstick sunscreens) marketed in the UK in 2005 (8).

OTHER SIDE EFFECTS

Other non-eczematous contact reactions
Drometrizole has apparently caused hypo- and hyperpigmentation; details are unknown (2).

LITERATURE
1   Arisu K, Hayakawa R, Ogino Y, Matsunaga K, Kaniwa M-A. Tinuvin® P in a spandex tape as a cause of clothing dermatitis. Contact Dermatitis 1992;26:311-316
2   Hayakawa R, Matsunaga K, Kobayashi M. Leukomelanoderma from Tinuvin® P. Allergy in Practice 1983;21:38-43
3   Nikklasson B, Björkner B. Contact allergy to the UV-absorber Tinuvin P in plastics. Contact Dermatitis 1989;21:330-334
4   Van Hecke E, Vossaert K. Allergic contact dermatitis from an ostomy bag. Contact Dermatitis 1988;18:121-122
5   De Groot AC, Liem DH. Contact allergy to Tinuvin P. Contact Dermatitis 1983;9:324-325
6   Cronin E. Cosmetics. In: Contact Dermatitis. Churchill Livingstone: Edinburgh, 1980:102,155
7   Björkner B, Niklasson B. Contact allergy to the UV absorber Tinuvin P in a dental restorative material. Am J Cont Derm 1997;8:6-7
8   Wahie S, Lloyd JJ, Farr PM. Sunscreen ingredients and labelling: a survey of products available in the U.K. Clin Exp Dermatol 2007;32:359-364
9   Heurung AR, Raju SI, Warshaw EM. Adverse reactions to sunscreen agents: epidemiology, responsible irritants and allergens, clinical characteristics, and management. Dermatitis 2014;25:289-326
10 Heurung AR, Raju SI, Warshaw EM. Contact allergen of the year. Benzophenones. Dermatitis 2014;25:3-10 (contains many mistakes; Erratum in Dermatitis 2014;25:92-95)
11 Avenel-Audran M. Sunscreen products: finding the allergen. Eur J Dermatol 2010;20:161-166
12 Scheuer E, Warshaw E. Sunscreen allergy: a review of epidemiology, clinical characteristics, and responsible allergens. Dermatitis 2006;17:3-11
13 Funk JO, Dromgoole SH, Maibach HI. Sunscreen intolerance: contact sensitization, photocontact sensitization, and irritancy of sunscreen agents. Dermatol Clin 1995;13:473-481
14 Dromgoole SH, Maibach HI. Sunscreening agent intolerance: Contact and photocontact sensitization and contact urticaria. J Am Acad Dermatol 1990;22:1068-1078
15 De Groot AC. Contact allergy to cosmetics: Causative ingredients. Contact Dermatitis 1987;17:26-34
16 Shaw T, Simpson B, Wilson B, Oostman H, Rainey D, Storrs F. True photoallergy to sunscreens is rare despite popular belief. Dermatitis 2010;21:185-198
17 Shaath NA. Ultraviolet filters. Photochem Photobiol Sci 2010;9:464-469
18 Schauder S. Survey of the literature on adverse reactions to preparations containing UV filters (1947-1989) (Literaturübersicht über Unverträglichkeitsreaktionen auf lichtfilterhaltige Produkte von 1947 bis 1989). Z Hautkr 1990;65:982-998 (article in German)

2.172 DROMETRIZOLE TRISILOXANE

IDENTIFICATION

Description/definition : Drometrizole trisiloxane is the heterocyclic compound that conforms to the formula shown below
Chemical class(es) : Heterocyclic compounds; phenols; siloxanes and silanes
Chemical/IUPAC name : Phenol, 2-(2H-benzotriazol-2-yl)-4-methyl-6-(2-methyl-3-(1,3,3,3-tetramethyl-1-(trimethylsilyl)oxy)-disiloxanyl)propyl
CAS registry number (s) : 155633-54-8
Function(s) in cosmetics : EU: UV-absorber; UV-filter. USA: light stabilizers
EU cosmetic restrictions : Regulated in Annex VI/16 of the Regulation (EC) No. 1223/2009
Patch testing : 10.0% pet. (Chemotechnique)
Molecular formula : $C_{24}H_{39}N_3O_3Si_3$

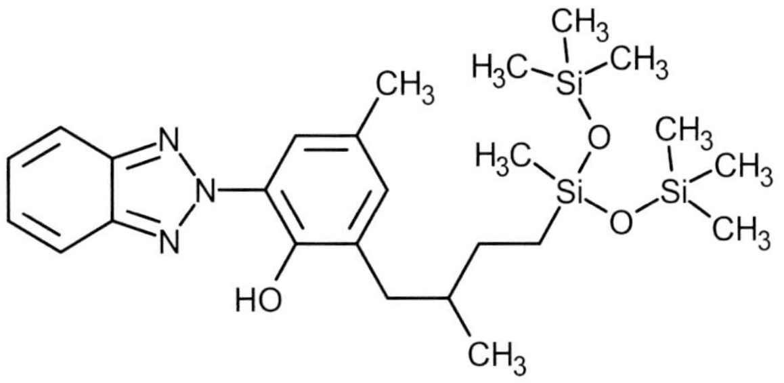

GENERAL

Drometrizole trisiloxane, also known as Mexoryl® XL, is a photostable, oil soluble, chemical light filter, that was developed in 1999. It is a hydroxybenzotriazole. Drometrizole trisiloxane is the first photostable broad-UV filter against UVA and UVB. It consists of two chemical groups: 12-hydroxyphenylbenzotriazole, which absorbs both in the UVA and UVB range, and a siloxane chain, which is liposoluble. Drometrizole trisiloxane has absorbance maxima ($\lambda_{max,1}$, $\lambda_{max,2}$) at 303 and 341 nm (18). It is not used alone in sunscreens because of its limited spectral activity. The UV-filter is therefore combined with other chemical and physical filters to obtain high sun protection factor (SPF) values (6,17). The literature on adverse reactions to sunscreens has been reviewed in several recent and older publications (8-13,15,19).

CONTACT ALLERGY

Case reports and case series

Drometrizole trisiloxane was responsible for 1 out of 959 cases of non-fragrance cosmetic allergy where the causal allergen was identified, Belgium, 2000-2010 (1). One positive patch test reaction to drometrizole trisiloxane in 819 patients was ascribed to cosmetic allergy (2).

A woman had an eczematous rash that started five days after she had returned from a sunny holiday. It had started on her legs and back, and had spread so extensively, that she was hospitalized. Patch tests with an extended standard series, a cosmetic series and a textile series were negative. Two sunscreens were patch and photopatch tested undiluted: there were positive reactions at D4 to both products on non-irradiated and irradiated skin. Their ingredients were patch and photopatch tested, which yielded positive reactions to drometrizole trisiloxane 2.5% alcohol at D4 on both non-irradiated and irradiated skin, consistent with a contact allergic reaction. The UV-filter was present in one sunscreen. Fifteen controls were negative to drometrizole trisiloxane 2.5% alc. (6). In this publication, it was mentioned that 'Allergic reactions to drometrizole trisiloxane are not unknown but are very rare (personal communication from manufacturer)' (6).

Presence in cosmetic products and chemical analyses

In the USA, in April 2017, drometrizole trisiloxane was present in 4 of 56,714 cosmetic products of which the composition is known in FDA's Voluntary Cosmetic Registration Program (VCRP) (data obtained from FDA, May 2017). In April 2017, drometrizole trisiloxane was present in one older product of 65,522 cosmetic products of which the composition is known in EWG's Skin Deep Cosmetics Database, USA (http://www.ewg.org/skindeep/). It should be realized that sunscreen products containing UV-filters are classified as drugs in the USA, not as cosmetics; the number mentioned here, therefore, is that of cosmetics containing the UV-filter, but it does not include their presence in sunscreens.

Drometrizole trisiloxane was present in 6.1% of 4447 cosmetic products collected in Germany, 2006-2009 (5). Drometrizole trisiloxane was present in 12 of 75 (16%) sunscreen creams and lotions from 30 European and US producers purchased in Denmark in 2001 in a concentration range of 0.08-7.4% (7). In a sample of 337 sunscreens marketed in the UK in 2010, drometrizole trisiloxane was present in 13% (16). In 2012, in Switzerland, 116 cosmetics from seven widely used leave-on product categories (19 lip care products, 8 lipsticks, 29 face creams, 11 liquid makeup foundations, 3 aftershaves, 7 hand creams and 39 sunscreens) were investigated to determine the frequency of occurrence and concentrations of 22 organic UV filters in these products. Drometrizole trisiloxane was found in 7% of the products in a concentration range of 0.43-3.06%, mean 0.95% (14).

OTHER SIDE EFFECTS

Photosensitivity

In the period 2008-2011, in 12 European countries, 1031 patients with exposed site dermatitis or history of a reaction to a sunscreen or topical NSAID were photopatch tested with drometrizole trisiloxane 10% pet. and one patient (0.1%) had a positive photopatch test. Its relevance was not stated, but of the reactions to the entire group of photoallergens tested, 44% had current and 11% past relevance (4). In the period 2004-2006, in Italy, 1082 patients with histories and clinical features suggestive of photoallergic contact dermatitis were tested with a commercial sunscreen containing drometrizole trisiloxane and 5 (0.5%) had a positive photopatch test; all reactions were considered relevant. By excluding allergy to the other ingredients of the commercial product, it was assumed that the reaction was caused by drometrizole trisiloxane (3).

LITERATURE

1   Travassos AR, Claes L, Boey L, Drieghe J, Goossens A. Non-fragrance allergens in specific cosmetic products. Contact Dermatitis 2011;65:276-285
2   Kohl L, Blondeel A, Song M. Allergic contact dermatitis from cosmetics: retrospective analysis of 819 patch-tested patients. Dermatology 2002;204:334-337
3   Pigatto PD, Guzzi G, Schena D, Guarrera M, Foti C, Francalanci S, et al. Photopatch tests: an Italian multicentre study from 2004 to 2006. Contact Dermatitis 2008;59:103-108
4   The European Multicentre Photopatch Test Study (EMCPPTS) Taskforce. A European multicentre photopatch test study. Br J Dermatol 2012;166:1002-1009
5   Uter W, Gonçalo M, Yazar K, Kratz E-M, Mildau G, Lidén C. Coupled exposure to ingredients of cosmetic products: III. Ultraviolet filters. Contact Dermatitis 2014;71:162-169
6   Hughes TM, Martin JA, Lewis VJ, Stone NM. Allergic contact dermatitis to drometrizole trisiloxane in a sunscreen with concomitant sensitivities to other sun screens. Contact Dermatitis 2005;52:226-227
7   Rastogi SC. UV filters in sunscreen products – a survey. Contact Dermatitis 2002;46:348-351
8   Heurung AR, Raju SI, Warshaw EM. Adverse reactions to sunscreen agents: epidemiology, responsible irritants and allergens, clinical characteristics, and management. Dermatitis 2014;25:289-326
9   Heurung AR, Raju SI, Warshaw EM. Contact allergen of the year. Benzophenones. Dermatitis 2014;25:3-10 (contains many mistakes; Erratum in Dermatitis 2014;25:92-95)
10   Avenel-Audran M. Sunscreen products: finding the allergen. Eur J Dermatol 2010;20:161-166
11   Scheuer E, Warshaw E. Sunscreen allergy: a review of epidemiology, clinical characteristics, and responsible allergens. Dermatitis 2006;17:3-11
12   Funk JO, Dromgoole SH, Maibach HI. Sunscreen intolerance: contact sensitization, photocontact sensitization, and irritancy of sunscreen agents. Dermatol Clin 1995;13:473-481
13   Dromgoole SH, Maibach HI. Sunscreening agent intolerance: Contact and photocontact sensitization and contact urticaria. J Am Acad Dermatol 1990;22:1068-1078
14   Manová E, von Goetz N, Hauri U, Bogdal C, Hungerbühler K. Organic UV filters in personal care products in Switzerland: A survey of occurrence and concentrations. Int J Hyg Environ Health 2013;216:508-514
15   Shaw T, Simpson B, Wilson B, Oostman H, Rainey D, Storrs F. True photoallergy to sunscreens is rare despite popular belief. Dermatitis 2010;21:185-198
16   Kerr AC. A survey of the availability of sunscreen filters in the U.K. Clin Exp Dermatol 2011;36:541-543
17   Antoniou C, Kosmadaki MG, Stratigos AJ, Katsambas AD. Sunscreens - what's important to know. J Eur Acad Dermatol Venereol 2008;22:1110-1118
18   Shaath NA. Ultraviolet filters. Photochem Photobiol Sci 2010;9:464-469
19   Schauder S. Survey of the literature on adverse reactions to preparations containing UV filters (1947-1989) (Literaturübersicht über Unverträglichkeitsreaktionen auf lichtfilterhaltige Produkte von 1947 bis 1989). Z Hautkr 1990;65:982-998 (article in German)

2.173   EDTA

IDENTIFICATION

Description/definition : EDTA is the substituted diamine that conforms to the formula shown below
Chemical class(es) : Alkyl-substituted amino acids
Chemical/IUPAC name : 2-[2-[bis(Carboxymethyl)amino]ethyl-(carboxymethyl)amino]acetic acid
Other names : Edetic acid; ethylenediaminetetraacetic acid; 1,2-ethanediamine, *N,N,N',N'*-
    tetrakis(carboxymethyl)-
CAS registry number (s) : 60-00-4
EC number(s) : 200-449-4
CIR review(s) : Int J Toxicol 2002;21(Suppl.2):95-142 (access: www.cir-safety.org/ingredients)
Merck Index monograph : 4835
Function(s) in cosmetics : EU: chelating. USA: chelating agents
Patch testing : Disodium EDTA dihydrate 1% pet. (Chemotechnique, SmartPracticeCanada)
Molecular formula : $C_{10}H_{16}N_2O_8$

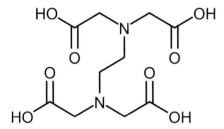

GENERAL

EDTA and its salts are widely used as preservative in ear and nose drops, local anesthetics and ophthalmic solutions. Although EDTA does not possess primary antibacterial properties, in these materials, it enhances the antibacterial actions of benzalkonium chloride and thimerosal in disrupting the lipid/protein complex of micro-organisms' cell walls. EDTA can also be found in certain foodstuffs such as salad oil and wine. It is a sequestering agent based on its ability to bind metallic ions such as nickel, calcium and magnesium, forming insoluble inactive complexes, thus preventing oxidation and discoloration of the aforementioned preparations. Its chelating properties can be further used in the treatment of systemic disease such as urinary calculi, calciferous corneal deposits, hypercalcaemia and lead poisoning (5).

The literature on contact allergy to EDTA from before 1991 has been reviewed (11).

CONTACT ALLERGY

It is very likely that, in the number (if not many or all) of reported cases of contact allergy to EDTA presented here, the products to which patients were allergic did not in fact contain EDTA *per se* (ethylenediaminetetraacetic acid; edetic acid), but one of its salts (disodium, trisodium, tetrasodium, see their respective Chapters).

Patch testing in groups of patients

There are no studies in which consecutive patients suspected of contact dermatitis have been patch tested with EDTA (routine testing). Four early studies in which groups of selected patients have been tested with EDTA are shown in table 2.173.1. In general, low frequencies of sensitization (0.2%-1.9%) were observed. The selection procedures were sometimes not mentioned and relevance was discussed in not a single study (3,4,11,12).

Table 2.173.1 Patch testing in groups of patients: Selected patient groups

Years and Country	Test conc. & vehicle	Number of patients tested	positive (%)	Selection of patients (S); Relevance (R); Comments (C)	Ref.
1984-1991 USA	1% pet.	108	2 (1.9%)	S: patients with stomatological problems; R: not stated	11
1968-1983 Italy	1% pet.	529	2 (0.4%)	S: not stated; R: not stated	12
1981 France	2% pet.	465	1 (0.2%)	S: patients suspected of allergy to cosmetics, drugs, industrial products, or clothes; R: not stated	4
1975-6 USA, Canada	1% pet.	215	(0.9%)	S: not stated; R: not stated	3

Case reports and case series

EDTA was stated to be the (or an) allergen in one patient in a group of 603 individuals suffering from cosmetic dermatitis, seen in the period 2010-2015 in Leuven, Belgium (2).

A woman presented with a 1-year history of dermatitis that began on her upper eyelids and subsequently spread to her face, earlobes, behind her ears, forearms, legs, and right dorsal hand. Patch tests with the NACDG standard series, corticosteroids, cosmetics, preservatives, vehicles, and perfumes and flavorings series, as well as her personal products, gave positive reactions to EDTA disodium dihydrate 1% in petrolatum and to several products containing EDTA, including two hair gels, two facial moisturizers, and a contact lens solution. After avoiding topical products containing EDTA in topical products and in foods, the dermatitis improved significantly (1).

Contact allergy to EDTA in non-cosmetic products

One patient had allergic contact dermatitis of the eyelids from EDTA in a contact lens solution (1). A man had periorbital vesicular dermatitis due to EDTA in an ophthalmic solution, after having been sensitized to another ophthalmic preparation containing disodium EDTA. The authors described two other patients with positive patch test reactions to EDTA, but clinical relevance was unclear (6). A woman with recurrent leg ulcers had mild stasis dermatitis. After applying a clioquinol – corticosteroid paste, a weeping dermatitis developed which spread to her legs, arms and face. Patch tests were positive to the paste and later its ingredients gave positive reactions to sodium EDTA 1% in water and in pet. on two occasions. The manufacturer stated that the product contained EDTA (7).

Cross-reactions, pseudo-cross-reactions and co-reactions

Cross-reactivity to ethylenediamine has been described (6,10), but most authors found no cross-sensitization, despite some structural similarities (1,7,8,9,11).

Presence in cosmetic products and chemical analyses

In May 2016, EDTA was present in 330 of 66,659 cosmetic products of which the composition is known in EWG's Skin Deep Cosmetics Database, USA (http://www.ewg.org/skindeep/). In the USA, in April 2017, EDTA was present in 1213 of 56,714 cosmetic products of which the composition is known in FDA's Voluntary Cosmetic Registration Program (VCRP) (data obtained from FDA, May 2017).

LITERATURE

1   Pruitt C, Warshaw EM. Allergic contact dermatitis from ethylenediaminetetraacetic acid. Dermatitis 2010;21:121-122
2   Goossens A. Cosmetic contact allergens. Cosmetics 2016, 3, 5; doi:10.3390/cosmetics3010005
3   Rudner EJ. North American Group Results. Contact Dermatitis 1977;3:208-209
4   Meynadier JM, Meynadier J, Colmas A, Castelain PY, Ducombs G, Chabeau G, et al. Allergy to preservatives. Ann Dermatol Venereol 1982;109:1017-1023
5   Bhushan M, Beck MH. Allergic contact dermatitis from disodium ethylenediamine tetra-acetic acid (EDTA) in a local anaesthetic. Contact Dermatitis 1998;38:183
6   Raymond JZ, Gross PR. EDTA: preservative dermatitis. Arch Dermatol 1969;100:436-440
7   De Groot AC. Contact allergy to EDTA in a topical corticosteroid preparation. Contact Dermatitis 1986;15:250-252
8   Fisher AA. Does ethylenediamine hydrochloride cross-react with ethylenediamine tetra-acetate? Contact Dermatitis 1975;1:267-268
9   Fisher AA. Cross sensitisation between ethylenediamine and ethylenediamine tetra-acetate. J Am Acad Dermatol 1982;7:808
10 Eriksen KE. Allergy to ethylenediamine. Arch Dermatol 1975;111:791
11 Fransway AF. The problem of preservation in the 1990s. III. Agents with preservative function independent of formaldehyde release. Am J Contact Derm 1991;2:145-174
12 Angelini G, Vena GA, Meneghini CL. Allergic contact dermatitis to some medicaments. Contact Dermatitis 1985;12:263-269

2.174   EQUAE LAC

IDENTIFICATION

Description/definition	: Equae lac is the whole milk from female horses
Chemical class(es)	: Biological products
INCI name USA	: Mare milk
Other names	: Mare's milk
Function(s) in cosmetics	: EU: skin conditioning. USA: skin-conditioning agents - miscellaneous
Diagnostic testing	: RAST, prick tests

GENERAL

Discussion of side effects of equae lac (mare's milk) in this chapter is limited to reactions caused by its presence in cosmetic products.

CONTACT ALLERGY

Case reports and case series

A woman had chronic itchy, vesicular, and erythematous dermatitis on the extensor surfaces of both forearms from contact allergy to mare's milk in soap and shampoo (2). This patient, who also had immediate contact reactions to mare's milk in these cosmetic products, is discussed further in the section 'Immediate contact reactions'.

OTHER SIDE EFFECTS

Immediate-type reactions

A woman had rapidly occurring swelling of the eyelids and itchy wheals on the face a few minutes following the application of a facial cream. Previous intermittent applications for 3 months had been well tolerated. A prick test with the cream 'as is' gave an immediate reaction. Prick tests with 2 of its ingredients were also positive: mare's milk and milk powder (as used in the product and diluted with water), but there was no reaction to cow's milk (not present in the product). Measurement of specific IgE in the patient's serum with RAST gave positive reactions to horse milk (>100 kU/l), α-lactalbumin (77 kU/l), and cow's milk (71 kU/l). However, the patient could drink cow's milk without any adverse reaction. An oral provocation test with mare's milk was not performed. No specific IgE was detected for β-lactoglobulin, casein, horse dander and horse meat (1).

An atopic woman had chronic itchy, vesicular, and erythematous lesions on the extensor surfaces of both forearms for several weeks. She had used mare's milk (MM) based organic soap and shampoo for 3 months and also took dietary supplements based on mare's milk. The cutaneous symptoms were exacerbated immediately after the use of the cosmetics products, and she vomited repeatedly immediately after the first intake of the pills. All symptoms disappeared during a travel but resumed once at home. Skin prick tests (SPTs) were positive for crude mare's milk (8 mm), boiled milk (15 mm), pill powder (10 mm), and shampoo (7 mm), both at immediate and delayed readings (72 h). SPTs were also positive for goat's (4 mm) and sheep's (6 mm) milk, but negative for cow's milk. Specific IGE (RAST) was demonstrated for goat's milk, sheep's milk, mare's milk, and cow's milk and for α-lactalbumin, β-lactoglobulin ad caseins from cow milk. Specific IgE, measured by enzyme-linked immunosorbent assay, was also demonstrated against the patient's shampoo, pill powder, and mare's milk extracts. The cosmetic products and the pills were also analyzed by Western blot, showing that the shampoo and pills contained the same proteins as mare's milk. A lymphoblastic transformation test was positive for the pill powder. These tests showed, according to the authors, immediate and delayed sensitivity to mare's milk and its derivatives (pills and shampoo). After exclusion of all MM-based products, all symptoms disappeared (2).

Presence in cosmetic products and chemical analyses

In the USA, in April 2017, mare milk was present in zero of 56,714 cosmetic products of which the composition is known in FDA's Voluntary Cosmetic Registration Program (VCRP) (data obtained from FDA, May 2017). In April 2017, mare milk was present in zero of 66,485 cosmetic products of which the composition is known in EWG's Skin Deep Cosmetics Database, USA (http://www.ewg.org/skindeep/).

LITERATURE

1   Verhulst L, Kerre S, Goossens A. The unsuspected power of mare's milk. Contact Dermatitis 2016;74:376-377
2   Doyen V. Protein contact dermatitis and food allergy to mare milk. Ann Allergy Asthma Immunol 2013;10:390-391

2.175   ETHOXYDIGLYCOL

IDENTIFICATION

Description/definition	: Ethoxydiglycol is the ether alcohol that conforms to the formula shown below
Chemical class(es)	: Alcohols; ethers
Chemical/IUPAC name	: 2-(2-Ethoxyethoxy)ethanol
Other names	: Ethanol, 2-(2-ethoxyethoxy)-; diethylene glycol monoethyl ether; ethyl carbitol; Carbitol®
CAS registry number (s)	: 111-90-0
EC number(s)	: 203-919-7
CIR review(s)	: J Am Coll Toxicol 1985;4:223-248 (access: www.cir-safety.org/ingredients)
SCCS opinion(s)	: SCCS/1507/13 (2); SCCS/1316/10 (3); SCCP/1200/08 (4); SCCP/1044/06 (5)
Merck Index monograph	: 4404
Function(s) in cosmetics	: EU: humectant; perfuming; solvent. USA: fragrance ingredients; solvents; viscosity decreasing agents
Patch testing	: Concentration unknown (test concentration was as in the cosmetic product), test vehicle unknown (1)
Molecular formula	: $C_6H_{14}O_3$

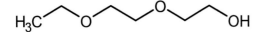

GENERAL

Ethoxydiglycol is used as solvent for cellulose esters in lacquer, thinner formulations, varnishes, enamels, paints, and also in low concentrations in cosmetics (1).

CONTACT ALLERGY

Case reports and case series

A woman was seen with a 14-year history of hand eczema. It worsened when she handled detergents and other cleaning products, and improved when she avoided such products and applied topical corticosteroids and moisturizers. At one point, she developed a new episode of hand dermatitis, which worsened when she began applying a cream containing chitin. Patch tests were carried out to the Portuguese standard series, bakery, cosmetic, preservatives and corticosteroid series, and her own topical products. There was a positive reaction to the cream. The 23 components of the cream were supplied at the same concentrations as in the cream and the patient reacted to ethoxydiglycol (which was termed ethyl diglycol carbitol by the authors) and to chitosan gluconate (1).

Presence in cosmetic products and chemical analyses

In the USA, in April 2017, ethoxydiglycol was present in 741 of 56,714 cosmetic products of which the composition is known in FDA's Voluntary Cosmetic Registration Program (VCRP) (data obtained from FDA, May 2017). In March 2017, ethoxydiglycol was present in 136 of 64,983 cosmetic products of which the composition is known in EWG's Skin Deep Cosmetics Database, USA (http://www.ewg.org/skindeep/).

LITERATURE

1   Pereira F, Pereira C, Lacerda MH. Contact dermatitis due to a cream containing chitin and a Carbitol. Contact Dermatitis 1998;38:290-291
2   SCCS (Scientific Committee on Consumer Safety). Opinion on diethylene glycol monoethyl ether (DEGEE), SCCS/1507/13, 26 February 2013. Available at: http://ec.europa.eu/health/scientific_committees/consumer_safety/docs/sccs_o_119.pdf
3   SCCS (Scientific Committee on Consumer Safety). Opinion on diethylene glycol monoethyl ether (DEGEE), SCCS/1316/10, 21 September 2010. Available at: http://ec.europa.eu/health/scientific_committees/consumer_safety/docs/sccs_o_039.pdf
4   SCCP (Scientific Committee on Consumer Products). Opinion diethyleneglycol monoethylether, SCCP/1200/08, 16 December 2008. Available at: http://ec.europa.eu/health/ph_risk/committees/04_sccp/docs/sccp_o_161.pdf
5   SCCP (Scientific Committee on Consumer Products). Opinion diethyleneglycol monoethylether, SCCP/1044/06, 19 December 2006. Available at: http://ec.europa.eu/health/ph_risk/committees/04_sccp/docs/sccp_o_082.pdf

2.176   ETHYL ACRYLATE

IDENTIFICATION

Description/definition : Ethyl acrylate is the organic compound that conforms to the formula shown below
Chemical class(es) : Esters
Chemical/IUPAC name : Ethyl prop-2-enoate
CAS registry number (s) : 140-88-5
EC number(s) : 205-438-8
SCCS opinion(s) : SCCNFP/0320/00 (18)
Merck Index monograph : 5083
Function(s) in cosmetics : EU: plasticizer; formerly used as fragrance ingredient; USA: plasticizers
EU cosmetic restrictions : Regulated in Annex II/435 of the Regulation (EC) No. 1223/2009 (prohibited when used as a fragrance ingredient)
Patch testing : 0.1% pet. (Chemotechnique, SmartPracticeEurope, SmartPracticeCanada)
Molecular formula : $C_5H_8O_2$

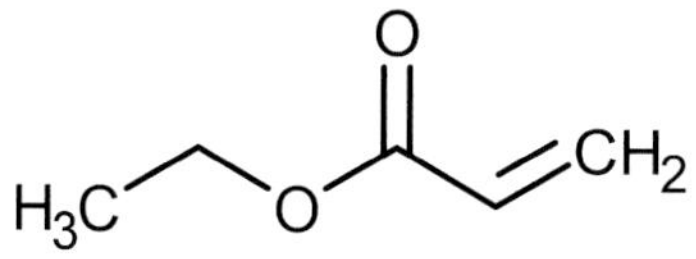

GENERAL

Discussion of contact allergy to (meth)acrylates *from non-cosmetic sources* is considered to fall outside the scope of this book. Therefore, only contact allergy from their presence in cosmetics is presented, which virtually always is from artificial nails. There are many reports of contact allergy to artificial nails, but the specific sensitizers have rarely been identified and – consequently - such publications are not presented in this and other acrylate and methacrylate monographs. Discussion is limited to publications in which the culprit (meth)acrylates have been identified, e.g., from information found in Material Data Safety Sheets, data obtained from the manufacturer or from chemical analyses.

Patients often react to many (meth)acrylates on patch testing. Primary sensitization to methacrylates may result in both methacrylate and acrylate cross-sensitization. Conversely, patients sensitized to acrylates are unlikely to show cross-sensitization to methacrylates (6).

General aspects of acrylates and methacrylates are presented in Chapter 2.219 HEMA (hydroxyethyl methacrylate). A discussion of general aspects of artificial nails, contact allergy to these products, the clinical picture of allergic contact dermatitis and other side effects of sculptured nails can also be found there. A very useful review of contact sensitization to allergens in nail cosmetics, with emphasis on acrylic manicures, was published in 2017 (24).

CONTACT ALLERGY

Patch testing in groups of patients
Results of routine patch testing (testing in consecutive patients suspected of contact dermatitis) back to 1994 are shown in table 2.1761. Results of testing in groups of *selected* patients (e.g., patients with eyelid dermatitis, hairdressers/cosmetologists, female patients with hand eczema, who had contact with artificial nails) back to 2004 are shown in table 2.176.2.

Patch testing in consecutive patients suspected of contact dermatitis: routine testing
As ethyl acrylate is included in the screening tray of the North American Contact Dermatitis Group, there are many data on ethyl acrylate contact allergy available from the USA + Canada, where the NACDG publishes their patch test results biannually. The results are shown in table 2.176.1. Frequencies of sensitization have been fairly constant, ranging from 0.7% to 1.8%. In an early NACDG study, present relevance was indicated to be 71% (13), in their other studies 'definite + probable relevance' ranged from 26% to 52%.

Patch testing in groups of selected patients
Data on patch testing with ethyl acrylate in groups of selected patients back to 2004 are summarized in table 2.176.2. Frequencies of sensitization were usually low, ranging from 0.5% to 3%. In one study, a 15% rate was found, which is entirely due to the selection procedure: female patients with hand eczema, who had contact with artificial nails (1). Relevance was usually high (1,15,20), in two studies only relevant reactions were reported (17,23).

Table 2.176.1 Patch testing in groups of patients: Routine testing

Years and Country	Test conc. & vehicle	Number of patients tested	positive (%)	Selection of patients (S); Relevance (R); Comments (C)	Ref.
2013-14 USA, Canada	0.1% pet.	4859	55 (1.1%)	R: definite + probable relevance: 40%	19
2011-12 USA, Canada	0.1% pet.	4230	39 (0.9%)	R: definite + probable relevance: 26%	7
2009-10 USA, Canada	0.1% pet.	4301	30 (0.7%)	R: definite + probable relevance: 31%	8
2004-2010 USA	0.1% pet.	3087	(1.6%)	R: 42%	16
2007-8 USA, Canada	0.1% pet.	5076	(1.2%)	R: definite + probable relevance: 52%	3
2005-6 USA, Canada	0.1% pet.	4428	(0.9%)	R: definite + probable relevance: 39%	2
2003-4 USA, Canada	0.1% pet.	5141	56 (1.1%)	R: not stated	4
2001-2 USA, Canada	0.1% pet.	4899	(1.3%)	R: definite + probable relevance: 27%	10
1998-2000 USA	0.1% pet.	5802	(1.3%)	R: definite + probable relevance: 31%	11
1998-2000 USA	0.1% pet.	1323	(1.1%)	R: not stated	14
1994-1996 USA	0.1% pet.	3074	(1.8%)	R: definite + probable relevance: 48%	12
1992-1994 USA	0.1% pet.	3470	(0.9%)	R: present relevance: 71%	13

Table 2.176.2 Patch testing in groups of patients: Selected patient groups *

Years and Country	Test conc. & vehicle	Number of patients tested	positive (%)	Selection of patients (S); Relevance (R); Comments (C)	Ref.
2006-2010 USA	0.1% pet.	100	3 (3%)	S: patients with eyelid dermatitis; R: not stated	5
1994-2010 USA, Canada	0.1% pet.	432	? (?)	S: hairdressers/cosmetologists; R: in the group of 187 patients who had at least one relevant occupationally rela- ted reaction, 17 (9.1%) reacted to ethyl acrylate	21
1993-2010 Australia		164	5 (3.0%)	S: hairdressers and apprentice hairdressers presenting at an occupational dermatology clinic; R: 100%	20
2003-2004 USA	0.1% pet.	268	3 (1.1%)	S: patients with pure eyelid dermatitis; R: this was the number of relevant reactions	17
2001-2004 Israel	0.1% pet.	55	8 (15%)	S: female patients with hand eczema, who had contact with artificial nails; R: 100% current relevance	1
1998-04 USA, Canada	1% pet.	1252	6 (0.5%)	S: health care workers; R: only occupation-related (=relevant) reactions were recorded; C: because of this selection, the frequency of sensitization is low; the frequency was not signi- cantly higher than the rate of occupation-related reactions in non-health care workers (0.2%); the causative products were mostly dentistry materials	23
1994-2004 USA		46	1 (2%)	S: patients with allergic contact dermatitis of the eyelids; R: the reaction was relevant, but the culprit product was not mentioned	15

* examples, not a full review

Case reports and case series

A group of 55 female patients presenting with hand eczema and who had contact with artificial nails, were patch tested with a series of acrylates in one center in Israel, 2001-2004. Twenty-one had one or more positive reactions, of who 14 were professional beauticians specializing in nail sculpturing. All reactions, including 8 to ethyl acrylate, were stated to be of current relevance (1). Because of the general lack of information on the composition of artificial nail materials, the fact that the author did no analyses of these products and the frequent occurrence of cross-reactivity among acrylates, one may wonder whether this statement can be accepted as entirely correct.

A woman had, for about 5 years, repeatedly experienced itching erythema at the perionychium of several fingers on which she had placed artificial nails. Marked edema and erythema was noted. The reaction was caused by contact allergy to ethyl acrylate in the acrylic nails (24).

Patch test sensitization

Patch test sensitization has occurred from ethyl acrylate 0.5% pet. and 1% pet. (22).

Presence in cosmetic products and chemical analyses

In the USA, in April 2017, ethyl acrylate was present in zero of 56,714 cosmetic products of which the composition is known in FDA's Voluntary Cosmetic Registration Program (VCRP) (data obtained from FDA, May 2017). In February 2017, ethyl acrylate was present in zero of 64,480 cosmetic products of which the composition is known in EWG's Skin Deep Cosmetics Database, USA (http://www.ewg.org/skindeep/).

LITERATURE

1 Lazarov A. Sensitization to acrylates is a common adverse reaction to artificial fingernails. J Eur Acad Derm Venereol 2007;21:169-174

2 Zug KA, Warshaw EM, Fowler JF Jr, Maibach HI, Belsito DL, Pratt MD, et al. Patch-test results of the North American Contact Dermatitis Group 2005-2006. Dermatitis 2009;20:149-160

3 Fransway AF, Zug KA, Belsito DV, Deleo VA, Fowler JF Jr, Maibach HI, et al. North American Contact Dermatitis Group patch test results for 2007-2008. Dermatitis 2013;24:10-21

4 Warshaw EM, Belsito DV, DeLeo VA, Fowler JF Jr, Maibach HI, Marks JG, et al. North American Contact Dermatitis Group patch-test results, 2003-2004 study period. Dermatitis 2008;19:129-136

5 Wenk KS, Ehrlich AE. Fragrance series testing in eyelid dermatitis. Dermatitis 2012;23:22-26

6 Aalto-Korte K, Henriks-Eckerman M-L, Kuuliala O, Jolanki R. Occupational methacrylate and acrylate allergy – cross-reactions and possible screening allergens. Contact Dermatitis 2010;63:301-312

7 Warshaw EM, Maibach HI, Taylor JS, Sasseville D, DeKoven JG, Zirwas MJ, et al. North American Contact Dermatitis Group patch test results: 2011-2012. Dermatitis 2015;26:49-59

8 Warshaw EM, Belsito DV, Taylor JS, Sasseville D, DeKoven JG, Zirwas MJ, et al. North American Contact Dermatitis Group patch test results: 2009 to 2010. Dermatitis 2013;24:50-59

9 Boehncke WH, Schmitt M, Zollner T M, Hensel O. Nail polish allergy; an important differential diagnosis in contact dermatitis. Dtsch Med Wochenschr 1997;122:849-852

10 Pratt MD, Belsito DV, DeLeo VA, Fowler JF Jr, Fransway AF, Maibach HI, et al. North American Contact Dermatitis Group patch-test results, 2001–2002 study period. Dermatitis 2004;15:176-183

11 Marks JG Jr, Belsito DV, DeLeo VA, Fowler JF Jr, Fransway AF, Maibach HI, et al. North American Contact Dermatitis Group patch-test results, 1998–2000. Am J Contact Dermat 2003;14:59-62

12 Marks JG Jr, Belsito DV, DeLeo VA, Fowler JF Jr, Fransway AF, Maibach HI,et al. North American Contact Dermatitis Group patch test results for the detection of delayed-type hypersensitivity to topical allergens. J Am Acad Dermatol 1998;38:911-918

13 Marks JG, Belsito DV, DeLeo VA, Fowler JF, Fransway AF, Maibach HI,et al. North American Contact Dermatitis Group standard tray patch test results 1992 through 1994. Am J Contact Dermatitis 1995;6:160-165

14 Wetter DA, Davis MDP, Yiannias JA, Cheng JF, Connolly SM, el-Azhary RA, et al. Patch test results from the Mayo Contact Dermatitis Group, 1998–2000. J Am Acad Dermatol 2005;53:416-421

15 Amin KA, Belsito DV. The aetiology of eyelid dermatitis: a 10-year retrospective analysis. Contact Dermatitis 2006;55:280-285

16 Wentworth AB, Yiannias JA, Keeling JH, Hall MR, Camilleri MJ, Drage LA, et al. Trends in patch-test results and allergen changes in the standard series: a Mayo Clinic 5-year retrospective review (January 1, 2006, to December 31, 2010). J Am Acad Dermatol 2014;70:269-275

17 Rietschel RL, Warshaw EM, Sasseville D, Fowler JF Jr, DeLeo VA. Belsito DV, et al. Common contact allergens associated with eyelid dermatitis: data from the North American Contact Dermatitis Group 2003-2004 study period. Dermatitis 2007;18:78-81

18 SCCFNP (Scientific Committee on Cosmetic Products and Non-Food Products Intended for Consumers). Opinion concerning an initial list of perfumery materials which must not form part of fragrances compounds used in cosmetic products 3 May 2000, SCCNFP/0320/00. Available at: http://ec.europa.eu/health/ph_risk/committees/sccp/documents/out116_en.pdf

19 DeKoven JG, Warshaw EM, Belsito DV, Sasseville D, Maibach HI, Taylor JS, et al. North American Contact Dermatitis Group Patch Test Results: 2013-2014. Dermatitis 2017;28:33-46

20 Lyons G, Roberts H, Palmer A, Matheson M, Nixon R. Hairdressers presenting to an occupational dermatology clinic in Melbourne, Australia. Contact Dermatitis 2013;68:300-306

21 Warshaw EM, Wang MZ, Mathias CGT, Maibach HI, Belsito DV, Zug KA, et al. Occupational contact dermatitis in hairdressers/cosmetologists; retrospective analysis of North American Contact Dermatitis Group data, 1994 to 2010. Dermatitis 2012;23:258-268

22 Kanerva L, Estlander T, Jolanki R. Sensitization to patch test acrylates. Contact Dermatitis 1988;18:10-15

23 Warshaw EM, Schram SE, Maibach HI, Belsito DV, Marks JG Jr, Fowler JF Jr, et al. Occupation-related contact dermatitis in North American health care workers referred for patch testing: cross-sectional data, 1998 to 2004. Dermatitis 2008;19:261-274

24 Chou M, Dhingra N, Strugar TL. Contact sensitization to allergens in nail cosmetics. Dermatitis 2017;28:231-240

2.177   3-O-ETHYL ASCORBIC ACID

IDENTIFICATION

Description/definition   : 3-*o*-Ethyl ascorbic acid is the organic compound that conforms to the formula shown below
Chemical class(es)   : Alcohols; ethers; heterocyclic compounds
Chemical/IUPAC name   : (2*R*)-2-[(1*S*)-1,2-Dihydroxyethyl]-3-ethoxy-4-hydroxy-2*H*-furan-5-one
Other names   : Vitamin C ethyl
CAS registry number (s)   : 86404-04-8
EC number(s)   : 617-849-3
Function(s) in cosmetics   : EU: skin conditioning. USA: skin-conditioning agents - miscellaneous
Patch testing   : 0.05%-5% pet. (1); 1% water (2); 10% water (3)
Molecular formula   : $C_8H_{12}O_6$

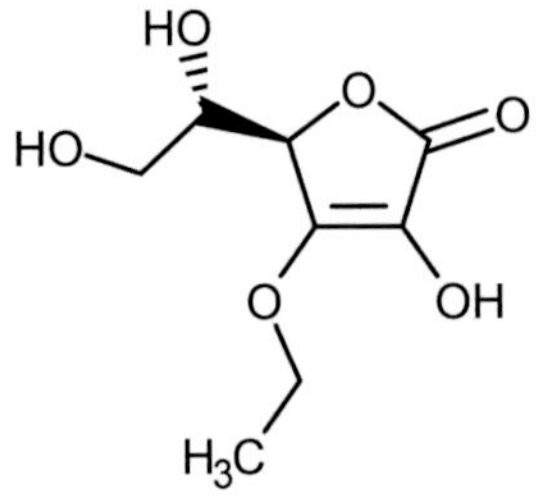

GENERAL

3-*o*-Ethyl ascorbic acid is a vitamin C-derivative which is used in skin-lightening creams. The chemical inhibits production of melanin within the melanocyte via inhibition of tyrosinase activity.

CONTACT ALLERGY

Case reports and case series

A woman presented with a 2-month history of facial dermatitis, with erythema and edema of the eyelids, which spread to the rest of the face. She had started to apply a skin-lightening cream and other cosmetic products to treat pigment macules on her face 3 months before. Patch tests were positive to 2 cosmetic creams. Subsequent patch tests with the ingredients of both creams showed positivity only to their ingredient 3-*o*-ethyl ascorbic acid 10% in water. Twenty controls were negative (3). A Japanese woman presented with an 18-month history of erythema and scales on her face and neck. Patch testing showed a positive reaction to the cosmetic lotion used by the patient. Additional patch testing with the ingredients of the cosmetic produced a positive reaction to 3-*o*-ethyl ascorbic acid 1% in water (2).

A woman had a 6-month history of periocular erythema and swelling. She had applied a skin-lightening lotion to the face every summer for the past 6 years. In the previous summer, an itchy erythematous rash appeared on her face. A patch test with the lotion was positive; a repeated open application test (ROAT) resulted in itchy erythema and papules. Patch testing with the ingredients of the lotion gave a positive patch test reaction to 3-*o*-ethyl ascorbic acid in a dilution series in the concentration range of 0.05% to 5% pet. (1).

Presence in cosmetic products and chemical analyses

In the USA, in April 2017, 3-*o*-ethyl ascorbic acid was present in 50 of 56,714 cosmetic products of which the composition is known in FDA's Voluntary Cosmetic Registration Program (VCRP) (data obtained from FDA, May 2017). In March 2017, 3-*o*-ethyl ascorbic acid (ethyl ascorbic acid) was present in 14 of 64,983 cosmetic products of which the composition is known in EWG's Skin Deep Cosmetics Database, USA (http://www.ewg.org/skindeep/).

LITERATURE

1   Yagami A, Suzuki K, Morita Y, Iwata Y, Sano A, Matsunaga K. Allergic contact dermatitis caused by 3-*o*-ethyl-l-ascorbic acid (vitamin C ethyl). Contact Dermatitis 2014;70:376-377
2   Numata T, Kobayashi Y, Ito T, Harada K, Tsuboi R, Okubo Y. Two cases of allergic contact dermatitis due to skin-whitening cosmetics. Allergology International 2015;64:194-195
3   Victoria-Martínez AM, Mercader-García P. Allergic contact dermatitis due to 3-*o*-ethyl-L-ascorbic acid contained in skin-lightening cosmetics. Dermatitis 2017;28:89

2.178 ETHYL CYANOACRYLATE

IDENTIFICATION

Description/definition	: Ethyl cyanoacrylate is the ester that conforms to the formula shown below
Chemical class(es)	: Esters
Chemical/IUPAC name	: Ethyl 2-cyanoprop-2-enoate
CAS registry number (s)	: 7085-85-0
EC number(s)	: 230-391-5
Merck Index monograph	: 5112
Function(s) in cosmetics	: EU: film forming. USA: not reported
Patch testing	: 10% pet. (Chemotechnique, SmartPracticeCanada)
Molecular formula	: $C_6H_7NO_2$

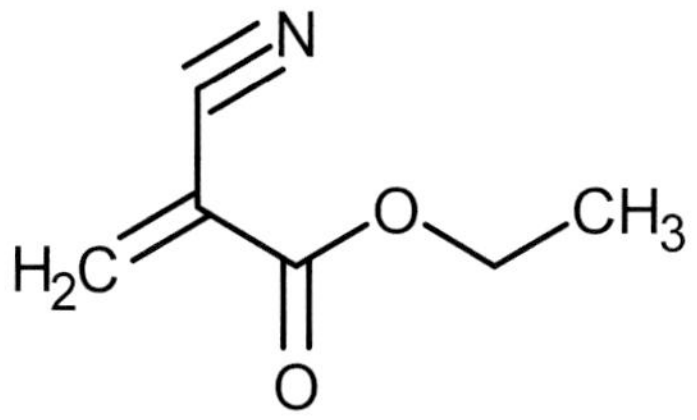

GENERAL

Glues based on cyanoacrylates (ethyl, octyl, butyl) are widely used as contact adhesives for metal, glass, rubber, plastics and textiles, as well as for biological materials, including binding tissues and sealing wounds in surgery and applications in dentistry (5,20). With the growing popularity of temporary beauty enhancements, there is increasing exposure to ethyl cyanoacrylate from its use with artificial nail, hair and eyelash extensions. Although cyanoacrylates are used directly on the skin, contact sensitization and allergic contact dermatitis are infrequent. The rapid polymerization and immediate bonding of the cyanoacrylate to the surface keratin is thought to prevent penetration beyond the stratum corneum, and therefore contact with antigen-presenting cells deeper in the epidermis (5). However, in the last three decades, case reports have indicated that ethyl cyanoacrylate is able to induce contact allergy from its use with artificial nails, and, more recently, with eyelash extensions, both in consumers and in nail and eyelash extension technicians (38).

An important application of ethyl cyanoacrylate is to glue artificial nails to the nail plate; probably all such glues contain ethyl cyanoacrylate (17). Contact allergy to the glue can cause fingertip eczema, dermatitis of the periungual skin, paronychia and dermatitis elsewhere (ectopic dermatitis, probably from hand transfer) (1,3,21). In many cases, there is also nail dystrophy and sometimes onycholysis, paronychia and subungual hyperkeratosis (1,2,4,16). Eyelash extensions have become increasingly popular. The artificial lashes are dipped into glue, and attached by a technician, lash by lash, to the client's natural lashes, which may sensitize both clients (5,10) and cause occupational allergic contact dermatitis in technicians (9).

In the presence of water, the cyanoacrylate polymer slowly deteriorates, forming cyanoacetate derivatives, water, and formaldehyde, which may induce persistence of contact dermatitis (1), notably in patients allergic to formaldehyde (10).

It should be appreciated that, strictly speaking, neither prepared artificial nails and hair extensions, nor the glue containing cyanoacrylate to fixate them, are considered to be cosmetics. Another cause of dermatitis from glue used to fixate plastic nails is p-tert-butylphenolformaldehyde resin and an allergen in plastic nail tricresyl ethyl phthalate (36).

CONTACT ALLERGY

Patch testing in groups of patients

Patch testing ethyl cyanoacrylate in groups of consecutive patients suspected of contact dermatitis (routine testing) has been performed by the members of the North American Contact Dermatitis Group (NACDG) in the periods 2013-2014 (37) and 2011-2012 (11). Frequencies of sensitization were 0.4% (18 of 4859 patients tested) and 0.3% (14 of 4230 patients tested). In the 2011-2012 study, 50% of the reactions were either of 'definite' or 'probable' relevance (11), in the 2013-2014 period the rate was only 28% (37).

One US study has tested ethyl cyanoacrylate 10% pet. in selected patients (they were tested with a supplemental cosmetic screening series). Of 871 patients tested in the period 2000-2007, 10 (1.1%) had a positive reaction. Eight (80%) was considered to be relevant, but this included 'questionable' and 'past' relevance (41).

Case reports and case series

'Cyanoacrylate' was stated to be the (or an) allergen in one patient in a group of 603 individuals suffering from cosmetic dermatitis, seen in the period 2010-2015 in Leuven, Belgium (35).

Artificial nails

Two patients with hand dermatitis who had contact with artificial nails reacted to ethyl cyanoacrylate, which was considered to be of current relevance in both women (13). One patient had allergic contact dermatitis of the fingertips superimposed on atopic dermatitis from ethyl cyanoacrylate in artificial nails glue. The dermatitis was so severe that she had sick leave for several months (14). Three patients were allergic to ethyl cyanoacrylate in artificial nail glue. They all had fingertip dermatitis, two had dermatitis elsewhere on the body, of who one extensive (ectopic dermatitis), one had periungual eczema and paronychia, and two of the women had nail disorders including subungual hyperkeratosis, onycholysis and nail dystrophy (1). One patient developed paronychia, onychia, dystrophy, and discoloration of her fingernails after using ethyl cyanoacrylate 'Krazy Glue' to attach silk nails to her nail plates (16). One individual had nail dystrophy and periungual dermatitis due to artificial nail cyanoacrylate glue sensitivity (2).

One patient had paronychia and onycholysis from contact allergy to ethyl cyanoacrylate in artificial nail glue (4), another one developed paronychia and fingertip dermatitis (40). A nail technician had ACD of her hands and extensive ectopic dermatitis from her work and from gluing nails on herself; when wearing polypropylene gloves and not applying the nails to herself, she could continue her work (21). A manicurist had occupational ACD of the hands from cyanoacrylate glue (22). Three patients, two manicurists and a customer, had ACD from ethyl cyanoacrylate glue. All 3 came into contact with the glue during 'nail wrapping'. In this process, ethyl cyanoacrylate glue is used to adhere glue-impregnated silk or linen to the nail plate which is then filed to shape the nail. This procedure creates fine acrylic-containing dust which may be transferred to other distant cutaneous sites, such as the eyelids (25). One patient had non-occupational ACD from ethyl cyanoacrylate in false nails glue (38).

Eyelash extensions

One patient had repeated episodes of ACD of the eyelids from ethyl cyanoacrylate used for gluing eyelash extensions (5). Another had dermatitis of the eyelids from ethyl cyanoacrylate in the glue for 'false eyelashes'. She also reacted to (meth)acrylates in artificial nails. In addition, this patient was allergic to formaldehyde (10). The latter finding may have contributed to the dermatitis, as cyanoacrylate glues for eyelashes have been shown to contain formaldehyde (8). An eyelash extension technician, who had previously been sensitized occupationally from her work applying artificial nails, developed allergic contact dermatitis of the hands from cyanoacrylate and methyl methacrylate in the glue she used (9). Two patients had non-occupational ACD from ethyl cyanoacrylate present in false eyelashes glue (38).

Contact allergy to ethyl cyanoacrylate in other products

One patient had extensive dermatitis diagnosed as small-plaque parapsoriasis (3). She strengthened her brittle fingernails with tea-bag paper glued onto each nail plate with an ethyl cyanoacrylate adhesive (Krazy Glue). Colored nail polish was then applied over the paper. She proved to be allergic to ethyl cyanoacrylate and after removal of the allergen, all symptoms disappeared (3). In a group of 165 patients with allergic contact dermatitis of the eyelids, seen in Little Rock, USA between 2001 and 2003, 5 cases were caused by contact allergy to (ethyl?) cyanoacrylate (12). One patient had occupational ACD from fixing microchips to plastic phone cards with ethyl cyanoacrylate glue (18). An apprentice cobbler had occupational ACD from the hands, arms and abdomen from ethyl cyanoacrylate in the glues he worked with (20).

A hairstylist had mild fingertip dermatitis but fierce oedematous dermatitis of the eyelids. At work, she attached pieces of false hair to bald scalps with two glues. She reacted to both glues, which consisted for >99% of ethyl cyanoacrylate (23). A boy developed ACD from the ears and the skin behind them from daily applying an (ethyl?) cyanoacrylate glue in an attempt to correct his floppy ears (24). A child with diabetes had ACD from an adhesive on a glucose sensor set. The patient had a positive patch test to ethyl cyanoacrylate. The manufacturer confirmed the present of 'cyanoacrylates' in the adhesive, but it was not stated whether actually it contained the ethyl ester (28). Another patient suffering from diabetes also developed allergic contact dermatitis from ethyl cyanoacrylate in the sensor adhesive used in a continuous glucose monitoring device (42).

Cross-reactions, pseudo-cross-reactions and co-reactions

Not to or from acrylates or methacrylates (14,15,16,17,31,33,34). Octyl cyanoacrylate (30,31).

Presence in cosmetic products and chemical analyses

In May 2017, ethyl cyanoacrylate was present in 23 of 66,659 cosmetic products of which the composition is known in EWG's Skin Deep Cosmetics Database, USA (http://www.ewg.org/skindeep/). In the USA, in April 2017, ethyl cyanoacrylate was present in 14 of 56,714 cosmetic products of which the composition is known in FDA's Voluntary Cosmetic Registration Program (VCRP) (data obtained from FDA, May 2017). Cyanoacrylate glues were found to contain formaldehyde (8, article not read).

OTHER SIDE EFFECTS

Irritant contact dermatitis
An outbreak of irritant facial dermatitis in five patients from a cyanoacrylate glue among a group of electronic assembly workers has been described. It was caused by vaporization of monomer under conditions of low relative humidity. No further outbreak occurred when the humidity of the working environment was raised above 55% (19).

Miscellaneous side effects
Of 107 women who visited ophthalmologic clinics in Japan with complaints of eye symptoms resulting from eyelash extensions between March 2007 and March 2010, 64 had keratoconjunctivitis due to invasion of glue or removing agents, 42 had allergic blepharitis due to glues, three developed conjunctival erosion due to eyelid-fixing tapes, one had allergic blepharitis due to eyelid-fixing tapes, and one individual was noted to have subconjunctival hemorrhage due to compression during removal of extensions. Patch tests to confirm contact allergy were not performed (8).

Nail discoloration
A 45-year-old man had a whitish transverse strip on the left middle finger nail. He first noted the lesion 1 h after a drop of ethyl cyanoacrylate glue had fallen onto this nail, during do it-yourself. He had promptly wiped off the glue with water and then with ether. After the nail had grown out, histopathology (light and electron microscopy) was performed. The authors stated that focal degeneration of the intermediate layer of the nail plate probably occurred by reaction of a-keratin fibrils with products of ethyl cyanoacrylate hydrolysis (27).

Respiratory diseases
Respiratory diseases including rhinitis and asthma from occupational contact to ethyl cyanoacrylate and other cyanoacrylates have been reported (6,7,39); the exact pathomechanism is unclear. Two beauticians developed rhinitis and asthma from ethyl cyanoacrylate glue that they used when applying eyelash extensions (32). Asthma and rhinitis has also been observed in a patient due to a ethyl cyanoacrylate instant glue used in building model airplanes (26). Occupational asthma from cyanoacrylates has been reviewed (29,39).

LITERATURE

1   Guin JD, Baas K, Nelson-Adesokan P. Contact sensitization to cyanoacrylate adhesive as a cause of severe onychodystrophy. Int J Dermatol 1998;37:31-36
2   Shelley ED, Shelley WB. Nail dystrophy and periungual dermatitis due to cyanoacrylate glue sensitivity. J Am Acad Dermatol 1988;19:574-575 (letter)
3   Shelley ED, Shelley WB. Chronic dermatitis simulating small-plaque parapsoriasis due to cyanoacrylate adhesive used on fingernails. JAMA 1984;252:2455-2456
4   Kanerva L, Estlander T. Allergic onycholysis and paronychia caused by cyanoacrylate nail glue, but not by photobonded methacrylate nails. Eur J Dermatol 2000;10:223-225
5   Bhargava K, White JM, White IR. Eyelid allergic contact dermatitis caused by ethyl cyanoacrylate-containing eyelash adhesive. Contact Dermatitis 2012; 67:306-307
6   Quirce S, Baeza M L, Tornero P, Blasco A, Barranco R, Sastre J. Occupational asthma caused by exposure to cyanoacrylate. Allergy 2001;56:446-449
7   Savonius B, Keskinen H, Tuppurainen M, Kanerva L. Occupational respiratory disease caused by acrylates. Clin Exp Allergy 1993;23:416-424
8   Amano Y, Sugimoto Y, Sugita M. Ocular disorders due to eyelash extensions. Cornea 2012: 31: 121–125.
9   Pesonen M, Kuuliala O, Henriks-Eckerman M-L, Aalto-Korte K. Occupational allergic contact dermatitis caused by eyelash extension glues. Contact Dermatitis 2012;67:307-308
10 Shanmugam S, Wilkinson M. Allergic contact dermatitis caused by a cyanoacrylate-containing false eyelash glue. Contact Dermatitis 2012;67:309-310
11 Warshaw EM, Maibach HI, Taylor JS, Sasseville D, DeKoven JG, Zirwas MJ, et al. North American Contact Dermatitis Group patch test results: 2011-2012. Dermatitis 2015;26:49-59
12 Guin JD. Eyelid dermatitis: A report of 215 patients. Contact Dermatitis 2004;50:87-90
13 Lazarov A. Sensitization to acrylates is a common adverse reaction to artificial fingernails. J Eur Acad Derm Venereol 2007;21:169-174
14 Isaksson M, Siemund I, Bruze M. Allergic contact dermatitis from ethylcyanoacrylate in an office worker

with artificial nails led to months of sick leave. Contact Dermatitis 2007;57:346-347

15 Kanerva L. Ethyl cyanoacrylate does not cross-react with methacrylates and acrylates. Am J Contact Dermat 1997;8:54

16 Fisher AA. Allergic reactions to cyanoacrylate 'Krazy glue' nail preparations. Cutis 1987;40:475-479

17 Constandt L, Van Hecke E, Naeyaert J-M, Goossens A. Screening for contact allergy to artificial nails. Contact Dermatitis 2005;52:73-77

18 Conde-Salazar L, Rojo S, Guimaraens D. Occupational allergic contact dermatitis from cyanoacrylate. Am J Contact Derm 1998;9:188-189

19 Calnan CD. Cyanoacrylate dermatitis. Contact Dermatitis 1979;5:165-167

20 Bruze M, Björkner B, Lepoittevin JP. Occupational allergic contact dermatitis from ethyl cyanoacrylate. Contact Dermatitis 1995;32:156-159

21 Fitzgerald DA, Bhaggoe R, English JS. Contact sensitivity to cyanoacrylate nail-adhesive with dermatitis at remote sites. Contact Dermatitis 1995;32:175-176

22 Jacobs MC, Rycroft RJ. Allergic contact dermatitis from cyanoacrylate? Contact Dermatitis 1995;33:71

23 Tomb RR, Lepoittevin JP, Durepaire F, Grosshans E. Ectopic contact dermatitis from ethyl cyanoacrylate instant adhesives. Contact Dermatitis 1993;28:206-208

24 Pigatto PD, Giacchetti A, Altomare GF. Unusual sensitization to cyanoacrylate ester. Contact Dermatitis 1986;14:193-194

25 Belsito DV. Contact dermatitis to ethyl-cyanoacrylate containing glue. Contact Dermatitis 1987;17:234-236

26 Kopp SK, McKay RT, Moiler DR, Cassedy K, Brooks SM. Asthma and rhinitis due to ethyl cyanoacrylate instant glue. Ann Intern Med 1985;102:613-615

27 Ena P, Mazzarello V, Fenu G, Rubino C. Leukonychia from 2-ethyl-cyanoacrylate glue. Contact Dermatitis 2000;42:105-106

28 Schwensen JF, Friis UF, Zachariae C, Johansen JD. Sensitization to cyanoacrylates caused by prolonged exposure to a glucose sensor set in a diabetic child. Contact Dermatitis 2016;74:124-125

29 Andujar R, Cruz M-J, Villar A, Morell F, Muñoz X. High eosinophil levels and poor evolution in occupational asthma due to cyanoacrylate exposure. Am J Ind Med 2011;54:714-718

30 El-Dars LD, Chaudhury W, Hughes TM, Stone NM. Allergic contact dermatitis to Dermabond after orthopaedic joint replacement. Contact Dermatitis 2010;62:315-317

31 Gonzalo-Garijo MA, Perez-Calderon R, Perez-Rangel I, Sánchez-Vega S, Constantino JA, Zambonino MA, et al. Contact dermatitis after orthopaedic surgery. Contact Dermatitis 2009;61:299-300

32 Lindström I, Suojalehto H, Henriks-Eckerman ML, Suuronen K. Occupational asthma and rhinitis caused by cyanoacrylate-based eyelash extension glues. Occup Med (Lond) 2013;63:294-297

33 Kanerva L, Jolanki R, Estlander T. 10 Years of patch testing with the (meth)acrylate series. Contact Dermatitis 1997;37:255-258

34 Sasseville D. Acrylates in contact dermatitis. Dermatitis 2012;23:6-16

35 Goossens A. Cosmetic contact allergens. Cosmetics 2016, 3, 5; doi:10.3390/cosmetics3010005

36 Burrows D, Rycroft RJG. Contact dermatitis from PTBP and tricresyl ethyl phthalate in a plastic resin. Contact Dermatitis 1981;7:336-337

37 DeKoven JG, Warshaw EM, Belsito DV, Sasseville D, Maibach HI, Taylor JS, et al. North American Contact Dermatitis Group Patch Test Results: 2013-2014. Dermatitis 2017;28:33-46

38 Muttardi K, White IR, Banerjee P. The burden of allergic contact dermatitis caused by acrylates. Contact Dermatitis 2016;75:180-184

39 Walters GI, Robertson AS, Moore VC, Burge PS. Occupational asthma caused by acrylic compounds from SHIELD surveillance (1989-2014). Occup Med (Lond) 2017;67:282-289

40 Guin JD, Wilson P. Onycholysis from nail lacquer: a complication of nail enhancement? Am J Cont Derm 1999;10:34-36

41 Wetter DA, Yiannias JA, Prakash AV, Davis MD, Farmer SA, el-Azhary RA, et al. Results of patch testing to personal care product allergens in a standard series and a supplemental cosmetic series: an analysis of 945 patients from the Mayo Clinic Contact Dermatitis Group, 2000-2007. J Am Acad Dermatol 2010;63:789-798

42 Aschenbeck KA, Hylwa SA. A diabetic's allergy: Ethyl cyanoacrylate in glucose sensor adhesive. Dermatitis 2017;28:289-291

2.179 ETHYLHEXYL DIMETHYL PABA

IDENTIFICATION

Description/definition   : Ethylhexyl dimethyl PABA is the ester of 2-ethylhexyl alcohol and dimethyl *p*-aminobenzoic acid, which conforms generally to the formula shown below
Chemical class(es)   : PABA derivatives
Chemical/IUPAC name   : 2-Ethylhexyl 4-(dimethylamino)benzoate
Other names   : Octyl dimethyl PABA; 4-dimethylaminobenzoate of ethyl-2-hexyl; Padimate O; Escalol® 507
CAS registry number (s) : 21245-02-3; 58817-05-3
EC number(s)   : 244-289-3
SCCS opinion(s)   : SCCNFP, 17 February 1999 (43)
Merck Index monograph : 4524 (4-(Dimethylamino)benzoic acid)
Function(s) in cosmetics : EU: UV-absorber; UV-filter. USA: light stabilizers; sunscreen agents
EU cosmetic restrictions : Regulated in Annex VI/21 of the Regulation (EC) No. 1223/2009
Patch testing   : 5.0% pet. (Chemotechnique); 10.0% pet. (Chemotechnique, SmartPracticeCanada); 5.0% alc. (Chemotechnique)
Molecular formula   : $C_{17}H_{27}NO_2$

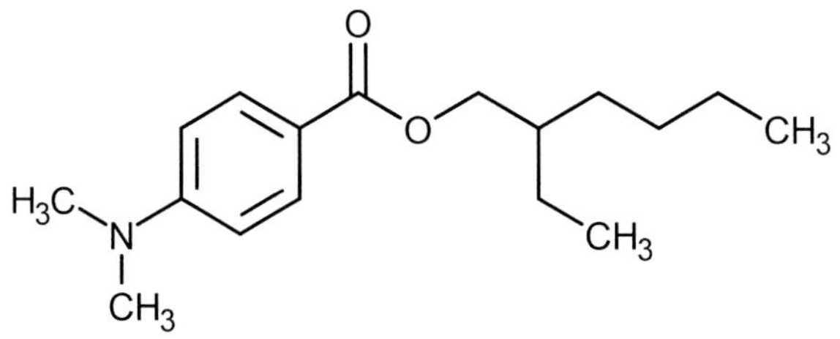

GENERAL

Ethylhexyl dimethyl PABA is a UVB-absorber (35). The literature on adverse reactions to sunscreens has been reviewed in several recent and older publications (11,37-41). A review of photocontact allergy to sunscreens was published in 2010 (47).

CONTACT ALLERGY

Patch testing in groups of patients
There have been no studies in which ethylhexyl dimethyl PABA was patch tested in consecutive patients suspected of contact dermatitis (routine testing). Results of testing in groups of *selected* patients (e.g., patients suspected of photosensitivity, patients with dermatitis affecting mainly light-exposed skin or with a history of a sunscreen skin reaction) back to 1990 are shown in table 2.179.1. Test concentrations used have been 2% pet., 3% pet., 5% pet., 5% alc. and 10% pet., but the higher test concentrations have not clearly resulted in more positive reactions, the mode of selection probably being the more important determinant. In 15 studies testing groups of selected patients, frequencies of sensitization have ranged from 0.1% to 20%. In 12 of the 15 studies, rates were 1.6% or lower. The high frequency of 20% (when tested with 5% alc. versus 15% when tested with 5% pet.) was seen in a study from Canada, which had certain weaknesses (14). In the majority of the investigations, the relevance of the positive patch test reactions to ethylhexyl dimethyl PABA was either not stated or specified for the UV-filter. In 7 studies providing relevance data, the relevance rates ranged from 0% to 100%, but the numbers of positive patients were small (n=1-7) (1,5,7,20,22,32,45).

Case reports and case series
In a group of 46 patients with allergic contact dermatitis of the eyelids seen in Kansas City, USA, between 1994 and 2004, one case (2%) was caused by contact allergy to ethylhexyl dimethyl PABA (source not mentioned) (42). In a group of 819 patients, one reaction to ethylhexyl dimethyl PABA was ascribed to cosmetic allergy (12). In a group of 46 New Zealand farmers with dermatitis, investigated in one center in 1994-1997, one had occupational contact allergy to ethylhexyl dimethyl PABA (36). In the period 1978-1991, there were 2 relevant patch test reactions to ethylhexyl dimethyl PABA in one center in Leuven, Belgium (25). In a 1-year-period (1996-1997), one patient had a positive patch test to ethylhexyl dimethyl PABA in one center in Italy; the reaction was relevant from its presence in sunscreens (29). Of 280 patients tested with sunscreens in London, 1985-1987, one had ACD from ethylhexyl

dimethyl PABA in a sunscreen (30). Ethylhexyl dimethyl PABA was responsible for five out of 399 cases of cosmetic allergy where the causal allergen was identified in a study of the NACDG, USA, 1977-1983 (10).

Table 2.179.1 Patch testing in groups of patients: Selected patient groups

Years and Country	Test conc. & vehicle	Number of patients tested	positive (%)		Selection of patients (S); Relevance (R); Comments (C)	Ref.
2011-2013 Colombia	10% pet.	112	3	(2.6%)	S: dermatitis affecting mainly light-exposed skin, a history of a sunscreen or a topical NSAID skin reaction; R: 100%	45
2001-2010 Canada	5% alc.	160	32	(20%)	S: patients with suspected photosensitivity and patients who developed pruritus or a rash after sunscreen applica- tion; R: not stated; C: very weak study: inadequate reading of test results, erythema only was considered to represent a positive patch test reaction	14
	5% pet.	160	24	(15%)		
2000-2007 USA	5% pet.	870	3	(0.3%)	S: patients tested with a supplemental cosmetic screening series; R: 100%; C: weak study: a. high rate of macular erythema and weak reactions; b. relevance figures included 'questionable' and 'past' relevance	20
2000-2005 USA	5% alc.	178	1	(0.6%)	S: patients photopatch tested for suspected photoderma- titis; R: not relevant	32
	5% pet.	178	2	(1.1%)	S: patients photopatch tested for suspected photoderma- titis; R: 1 reaction was relevant	
2001-2003 Colombia	10% pet.	82	1	(1.2%)	S: patients with a clinical diagnosis of photoallergic contact dermatitis; R: 65% of all reactions in the study were relevant	18
2000-2002 UK, I, NL	10% pet.	1155	7	(0.6%)	S: patients suspected of photosensitivity or reaction to a sunscreen; R: current relevance 2, unknown 4, past relevance 1	1
1993-2000 Australia	2% pet.	149	1	(0.7%)	S: patients suspected of photosensitivity; R: of 17 patient who had contact or photocontact reactions to a panel of 10 sunscreens, 10 were considered to have relevant reactions	27
1996-1998 UK		167	2	(1.2%)	S: patients with suspected photosensitivity; R: 'most cases' in the entire group were relevant	6
1983-1998 UK	2% pet.	2715	3	(0.1%)	S: patients suspected of photosensitivity or with (a history of) dermatitis at exposed sites; R: not stated	17
1981-1996 Germany	10% pet.	316	1	(0.3%)	S: patients suspected of clinical photosensitivity; R: not stated	2
1990-1994 France	2% or 10% pet.	370	2	(0.5%)	S: patients with suspected photodermatitis; R: not specified, 72% of all reactions in the study were considered relevant	8
1986-1993 USA	2% pet. or 5% alc.	138	2	(1.4%)	S: patients suspected of photosensitivity; R: both reactions were relevant	7
1989-1991 UK	2% pet.	99	3	(3%)	S: 45 patients with photosensitivity dermatitis/actinic reticuloid syndrome and 54 with polymorphic light eruption; R: not specified	3
1989-1990 France	2% pet.	54	1	(2%)	S: patients suspected of photosensitivity; R: the reaction was relevant	22
1985-1990 USA	3% pet.	187	3	(1.6%)	S: patients with a history of photosensitivity; R: one reaction of combined contact/photocontact allergy was relevant	5

I: Ireland; NL: Netherlands; UK: United Kingdom

Two patients (9) and another 2 (16,24) had allergic contact dermatitis from ethylhexyl dimethyl PABA in sunscreens (9). Another individual had both allergic and photoallergic contact allergy to ethylhexyl dimethyl PABA in a sunscreen (23). One patient was reported to have allergic contact dermatitis from ethylhexyl dimethyl PABA in a sunscreen; however, it was only *assumed* that ethylhexyl dimethyl PABA was the culprit, it was not tested separately (21). In a group of 73 patients referred to a contact dermatitis clinic in Melbourne, Australia, 1990-1991, who reported a history of reactions to sunscreens, there were 2 positive patch tests to ethylhexyl dimethyl PABA; the relevance of these reactions was not specified (34). In the period 1981-1989, 56 patients (43 women, 13 men) were diagnosed with contact allergy or photocontact allergy to UV-filters in one center in Germany. There was one contact allergic and one photoallergic reactions to ethylhexyl dimethyl PABA. All reactions were relevant and all 46 patients who could be (photo)patch tested with their own sunscreens (and a few of them with other cosmetics) had one or more positive (photo)patch tests to these products (48, overlap with ref.2).

Cross-reactions, pseudo-cross-reactions and co-reactions

Ethylhexyl dimethyl PABA may cross-react with structurally related chemicals, notably those with a para-structure. Cross-reactivity between para-compounds is discussed in Chapter 2.359 *p*-Phenylenediamine. PABA (11,23); isobutyl PABA (4,11); *not* to PABA (7)

Presence in cosmetic products and chemical analyses

In June 2017, ethylhexyl dimethyl PABA was present in 32 of 68,866 cosmetic products of which the composition is known in EWG's Skin Deep Cosmetics Database, USA (http://www.ewg.org/skindeep/). It should be realized that sunscreen products containing UV-filters are classified as drugs in the USA, not as cosmetics; the number mentioned here, therefore, is that of cosmetics containing the UV-filter, but it does *not* include their presence in sunscreens. In the USA, in April 2017, ethylhexyl dimethyl PABA was present in an unknown number of 56,714 cosmetic products of which the composition is known in FDA's Voluntary Cosmetic Registration Program (VCRP) (accidentally no data requested from FDA). In 2012, in Switzerland, 116 cosmetics from seven widely used leave-on product categories (19 lip care products, 8 lipsticks, 29 face creams, 11 liquid makeup foundations, 3 aftershaves, 7 hand creams and 39 sunscreens) were investigated to determine the frequency of occurrence and concentrations of 22 organic UV filters in these products. Ethylhexyl dimethyl PABA was found in 2% of the products in a concentration range of 2.37-6.05%, mean 4.21% (44).

Ethylhexyl dimethyl PABA was present in 12.6% of 4447 cosmetic products collected in Germany, 2006-2009 (15). Ethylhexyl dimethyl PABA was present in 3% of 329 sunscreen products (incl. 21 lipstick sunscreens) marketed in the UK in 2005 (35). Ethylhexyl dimethyl PABA was present in 1 of 75 (1.3%) sunscreen creams and lotions from 30 European and US producers purchased in Denmark in 2001 in a concentration of 2.6% (28).

Minimal amounts of PABA and benzocaine were found as contaminants in most batches of ethylhexyl dimethyl PABA (26).

OTHER SIDE EFFECTS

Photosensitivity

Photopatch testing in groups of patients

Results of photopatch testing ethylhexyl dimethyl PABA in groups of selected patients (e.g., patients suspected of photosensitivity, patients with dermatitis affecting mainly light-exposed skin or with a history of a sunscreen skin reaction) back to 1993 are shown in table 2.179.2. Test concentrations used have been 2% pet., 5% pet., 5% alc. and 10% pet., but the higher test concentrations have not clearly resulted in more positive reactions, the mode of selection probably being the more important determinant. In 12 studies testing groups of selected patients, frequencies of photosensitization have ranged from 0.1% to 8.1%. In 9 of the 12 studies, rates were 1.7% or lower. The high frequency of 8.1% (when tested with 5% alc. versus 7.5% when tested with 5% pet.) was seen in a study from Canada, which had certain weaknesses (14). In the majority of the investigations, the relevance of the positive photopatch test reactions to ethylhexyl dimethyl PABA was either not stated or specified for the UV-filter. In 5 studies providing relevance data, the relevance rates ranged from 67% to 100%, but the numbers of positive patients were small (n=1-3) (1,7,13,32,46).

Case reports

One individual had both allergic and photoallergic contact allergy to ethylhexyl dimethyl PABA in a sunscreen (23). In a group of 11 patients who identified themselves as 'allergic' or 'having a reaction' to sunscreens and who were photopatch tested extensively, one had a positive photopatch test to ethylhexyl dimethyl PABA; the patient had previously used sunscreens containing ethylhexyl dimethyl PABA (31). One case of photoallergic contact dermatitis from ethylhexyl dimethyl PABA in a sunscreen was seen in Singapore, 1992-1996 (33). Another patient was presented as having photoallergic contact dermatitis from a sunscreen product containing ethylhexyl dimethyl PABA. Ethylhexyl dimethyl PABA itself was not tested, but because of positive photopatch tests to the sunscreen product and to isobutyl PABA, the authors concluded that ethylhexyl dimethyl PABA must have been the offending agent (4).

In the period 1981-1989, 56 patients (43 women, 13 men) were diagnosed with contact allergy or photocontact allergy to UV-filters in one center in Germany. There was one contact allergic and one photoallergic reactions to ethylhexyl dimethyl PABA. All reactions were relevant and all 46 patients who could be (photo)patch tested with their own sunscreens (and a few of them with other cosmetics) had one or more positive (photo)patch tests to these products (48, overlap with ref.2).

Table 2.179.2 Photopatch testing in groups of patients

Years and Country	Test conc. & vehicle	Number of patients tested	positive (%)		Selection of patients (S); Relevance (R); Comments (C)	Ref.
2007-2011 Singapore	10% pet.	22	1	(5%)	S: not stated; R: the reaction was relevant	46
2001-2010 Canada	5% alc.	160	13	(8.1%)	S: patients with suspected photosensitivity and patients	14
	5% pet.	160	12	(7.5%)	who developed pruritus or a rash after sunscreen application; R: not stated; C: very weak study: inadequate reading of test results, erythema only was considered to represent a positive patch test reaction	
2004-2006 Italy	10% pet.	1082	1	(0.1%)	S: patients with histories and clinical features suggestive of photoallergic contact dermatitis; R: 100%	13
1993-2006 USA	5% alc.	76	3	(3.9%)	S: not stated; R: 56% of all reactions to sunscreens were considered 'probably relevant'	19
2000-2005 USA	5% alc.	178	3	(1.7%)	S: patients photopatch tested for suspected photodermatitis; R: all 3 reactions were relevant	32
	5% pet.	178	1	(0.6%)	S: patients photopatch tested for suspected photodermatitis; R: not relevant	32
2001-2003 Colombia	10% pet.	82	1	(1.2%)	S: patients with a clinical diagnosis of photoallergic contact dermatitis; R: 65% of all reactions in the study were relevant	18
2000-2002 UK, I, NL	10% pet.	1155	3	(0.3%)	S: patients suspected of photosensitivity or reaction to a sunscreen; R: current relevance 2, unknown 1	1
1996-1998 UK		167	1	(0.6%)	S: patients with suspected photosensitivity; R: 'most cases' in the entire group were relevant	6
1983-1998 UK	2% pet.	2715	5	(0.2%)	S: patients suspected of photosensitivity or with (a history of) dermatitis at exposed sites; R: 37% for all photoallergens together	17
1981-1996 Germany	10% pet.	316	2	(0.6%)	S: patients suspected of clinical photosensitivity; R: not stated	2
1990-1994 France	2% or 10% pet.	370	1	(0.3%)	S: patients with suspected photodermatitis; R: not specified, 72% of all reactions in the study were considered relevant	8
1986-1993 USA	2% pet. or 5% alc.	138	2	(1.4%)	S: patients suspected of photosensitivity; R: both reactions were relevant	7

I: Ireland; NL: Netherlands; UK: United Kingdom

LITERATURE

1   Bryden A, Moseley H, Ibbotson S, Chowdhury MM, Beck MH, Bourke J, et al. Photopatch testing of 1155 patients: results of the U.K. multicentre photopatch test study group. Brit J Dermatol 2006;155:737-747

2   Schauder S, Ippen H. Contact and photocontact sensitivity. Review of a 15-year experience and of the literature to suncreens. Contact Dermatitis 1997;37:221-232

3   Bilsland D, Ferguson J. Contact allergy to sunscreen chemicals in photosensitivity dermatitis/actinic reticuloid syndrome (PD/AR) and polymorphic light eruption. Contact Dermatitis 1993;29:70-73

4   Weller P, Freeman S. Photocontact allergy to octyldimethyl PABA. Austr J Dermatol 1984;25:73-76

5   DeLeo VA, Suarez SM, Maso MJ. Photoallergic contact dermatitis. Results of photopatch testing in New York, 1985 to 1990. Arch Dermatol 1992;128:1513-1518

6   Bell HK, Rhodes LE. Photopatch testing in photosensitive patients. Br J Dermatol 2000;142:589-590

7   Fotiades J, Soter NA, Lim HW. Results of evaluation of 203 patients for photosensitivity in a 7.3 year period. J Am Acad Dermatol 1995;33:597-602

8   Journe F, Marguery M-C, Rakotondrazafy J, El Sayed F, Bazex J. Sunscreen sensitization: a 5-year study. Acta Derm Venereol (Stockh) 1999;79:211-213

9   Thune P. Contact and photocontact allergy to sunscreens. Photodermatol 1984;1:5-9

10   Adams RM, Maibach HI, Clendenning WE, Fisher AA, Jordan WJ, Kanof N, et al. A five-year study of cosmetic reactions. J Am Acad Dermatol 1985;13:1062-1069

11   Dromgoole SH, Maibach HI. Sunscreening agent intolerance: Contact and photocontact sensitization and contact urticaria. J Am Acad Dermatol 1990;22:1068-1078

12   Kohl L, Blondeel A, Song M. Allergic contact dermatitis from cosmetics: retrospective analysis of 819 patch-tested patients. Dermatology 2002;204:334-337

13   Pigatto PD, Guzzi G, Schena D, Guarrera M, Foti C, Francalanci S, et al. Photopatch tests: an Italian multicentre study from 2004 to 2006. Contact Dermatitis 2008;59:103-108

14   Greenspoon J, Ahluwalia R, Juma N, Rosen CF. Allergic and photoallergic contact dermatitis: A 10-year experience. Dermatitis 2013;24:29-32

15 Uter W, Gonçalo M, Yazar K, Kratz E-M, Mildau G, Lidén C. Coupled exposure to ingredients of cosmetic products: III. Ultraviolet filters. Contact Dermatitis 2014;71:162-169

16 Camarasa JG, Serra-Baldrich E. Allergic contact dermatitis to sunscreens. Contact Dermatitis 1986;15:253-254

17 Darvay A, White I, Rycroft R, Jones AB, Hawk JL, McFadden JP. Photoallergic contact dermatitis is uncommon. Br J Dermatol 2001;145:597-601

18 Rodriguez E, Valbuena M, Rey M, Porras de Quintana L. Causal agents of photoallergic contact dermatitis diagnosed in the national institute of dermatology of Columbia. Photoderm Photoimmunol Photomed 2006;22:189-192

19 Victor FC, Cohen DE, Soter NA. A 20-year analysis of previous and emerging allergens that elicit photoallergic contact dermatitis. J Am Acad Dermatol 2010;62:605-610

20 Wetter DA, Yiannias JA, Prakash AV, Davis MD, Farmer SA, el-Azhary RA, et al. Results of patch testing to personal care product allergens in a standard series and a supplemental cosmetic series: an analysis of 945 patients from the Mayo Clinic Contact Dermatitis Group, 2000-2007. J Am Acad Dermatol 2010;63:789-798

21 Thompson G, Maibach H, Epstein J. Allergic contact dermatitis from sunscreen preparations complicating photodermatitis. Arch Dermatol 1977;113:1252-1253

22 Lenique P, Machet L, Vaillant L, Bensaid P, Muller C, Khallouf R, Lorette G. Contact and photocontact allergy to oxybenzone. Contact Dermatitis 1992;26:177-181

23 Crowe MJ, Banks SL, Guin JD. Photoallergic and allergic contact dermatitis to butyl-methoxydibenzoylmethane. Am J Cont Derm 1992;3:33-34

24 Ricci C, Vaccari S, Cavalli M, Vincenzi C. Contact sensitization to sunscreens. Am J Cont Derm 1997;8:165-166

25 Theeuwes M, Degreef H, Dooms-Goossens A. Para-aminobenzoic acid (PABA) and sunscreen allergy. Am J Cont Derm 1992;3:206-207

26 Bruze M, Fregert S, Gruvberger B. Occurrence of *para*-aminobenzoic acid and benzocaine as contaminants in sunscreen agents of para-aminobenzoic acid type. Photodermatology 1984;1:277-285

27 Crouch RB, Foley PA, Baker CS. The results of photopatch testing 172 patients to sunscreening agents at the photobiology clinic, St Vincent's Hospital, Melbourne. Australas J Dermatol 2002;43:74

28 Rastogi SC. UV filters in sunscreen products – a survey. Contact Dermatitis 2002;46:348-351

29 Ricci C, Pazzaglia M, Tosti A. Photocontact dermatitis from UV filters. Contact Dermatitis 1998;38:343-344

30 English JSC, White IR, Cronin K. Sensitivity to sunscreens. Contact Dermatitis 1987;17:159-162

31 Shaw T, Simpson B, Wilson B, Oostman H, Rainey D, Storrs F. True photoallergy to sunscreens is rare despite popular belief. Dermatitis 2010;21:185-198

32 Scalf LA, Davis MDP, Rohlinger AL, Connolly SM. Photopatch testing of 182 patients: A 6-year experience at the Mayo Clinic. Dermatitis 2009;20:44-52

33 Ang P, Ng SK, Goh CL. Sunscreen allergy in Singapore. Am J Cont Derm 1998;9:42-44

34 Nixon RL, Frowen KE, Lewis AE. Skin reactions to sunscreens. Australas J Dermatol 1997;38:S83-S85.

35 Wahie S, Lloyd JJ, Farr PM. Sunscreen ingredients and labelling: a survey of products available in the U.K. Clin Exp Dermatol 2007;32:359-364

36 Rademaker M. Occupational contact dermatitis among New Zealand farmers. Australas J Dermatol 1998;39:164-167

37 Heurung AR, Raju SI, Warshaw EM. Adverse reactions to sunscreen agents: epidemiology, responsible irritants and allergens, clinical characteristics, and management. Dermatitis 2014;25:289-326

38 Heurung AR, Raju SI, Warshaw EM. Contact allergen of the year. Benzophenones. Dermatitis 2014;25:3-10 (contains many mistakes; Erratum in Dermatitis 2014;25:92-95)

39 Avenel-Audran M. Sunscreen products: finding the allergen. Eur J Dermatol 2010;20:161-166

40 Scheuer E, Warshaw E. Sunscreen allergy: a review of epidemiology, clinical characteristics, and responsible allergens. Dermatitis 2006;17:3-11

41 Funk JO, Dromgoole SH, Maibach HI. Sunscreen intolerance: contact sensitization, photocontact sensitization, and irritancy of sunscreen agents. Dermatol Clin 1995;13:473-481

42 Amin KA, Belsito DV. The aetiology of eyelid dermatitis: a 10-year retrospective analysis. Contact Dermatitis 2006;55:280-285

43 SCCNFP (Scientific Committee on Cosmetics and Non Food Products). Opinion concerning 2-Ethylhexyl-4-dimethylaminobenzoate, 17 February 1999. Available at: http://ec.europa.eu/health/scientific_committees/consumer_safety/opinions/sccnfp_opinions_97_04/sccp_out54_en.htm

44 Manová E, von Goetz N, Hauri U, Bogdal C, Hungerbühler K. Organic UV filters in personal care products in Switzerland: A survey of occurrence and concentrations. Int J Hyg Environ Health 2013;216:508-514

45 Valbuena Mesa MC, Hoyos Jiménez EV. Photopatch testing in Bogota (Colombia): 2011–2013. Contact Dermatitis 2016;74:11-17

46 Chuah SY, Leow YH, Goon AT, Theng CT, Chong WS. Photopatch testing in Asians: a 5-year experience in Singapore. Photodermatol Photoimmunol Photomed 2013;29:116-120

47 Shaw T, Simpson B, Wilson B, Oostman H, Rainey D, Storrs F. True photoallergy to sunscreens is rare despite popular belief. Dermatitis 2010;21:185-198

48 Schauder S. Adverse reactions to sunscreening agents in 58 patients (part 3). Z Hautkr 1991;66:294-318 (article in German)

49 Schauder S. Survey of the literature on adverse reactions to preparations containing UV filters (1947-1989) (Literaturübersicht über Unverträglichkeitsreaktionen auf lichtfilterhaltige Produkte von 1947 bis 1989). Z Hautkr 1990;65:982-998 (article in German)

2.180   ETHYLHEXYLGLYCERIN

IDENTIFICATION

Description/definition : Ethylhexylglycerin is the organic compound that conforms to the formula shown below
Chemical class(es) : Alcohols; ethers
Chemical/IUPAC name : 3-(2-Ethylhexoxy)propane-1,2-diol
Other names : Octoxyglycerin
CAS registry number (s) : 70445-33-9
EC number(s) : 408-080-2
CIR review(s) : Int J Toxicol 2013;32(Suppl.3):5-21 (access: www.cir-safety.org/ingredients)
Function(s) in cosmetics : EU: skin conditioning. USA: deodorant agents; skin-conditioning agents - miscellaneous
Patch testing : 5.0% pet. (Chemotechnique, SmartPracticeCanada); sometimes, higher concentrations may be indicated to identify contact allergy to ethylhexylglycerin (14)
Molecular formula : $C_{11}H_{24}O_3$

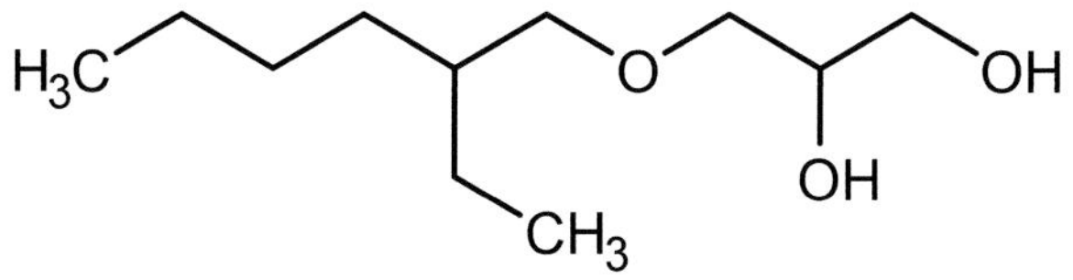

GENERAL

Ethylhexylglycerin is a relatively new and synthetic cosmetic ingredient, manufactured by a German company and marketed under the trade name Sensiva SC®50. It contains >99% pure ethylhexylglycerin, with α-tocopherol (added as an antioxidant to stabilize the formulation) and 2-ethylhexyl glycidyl ether as possible impurities. It has the appearance of a pale to colorless liquid, and is formed by a condensation reaction between 2-ethylhexanol and glycerin, yielding a surfactant with a hydrophilic head (glycerin) and a hydrophobic tail (alkyl group) . It can be found in a wide variety of cosmetics. Concentrations in cosmetics up to 2% and 8% have been reported in both leave-on and rinse-off products, respectively, although much lower concentrations (e.g. <1%) may be in use. Owing to its ability to inhibit the growth of odor-causing bacteria, ethylhexylglycerin may be used as an alternative to parabens, and it may also enhance the efficacy of cosmetic preservatives, such as phenoxyethanol, methylisothiazolinone, methylparaben, and glycols (14).

The NACDG has added ethylhexylglycerin 5% pet. to their screening series in 2013 (7,13).

CONTACT ALLERGY

Patch testing in groups of patients

Results of patch testing ethylhexylglycerin in consecutive patients suspected of contact dermatitis (routine testing) and of testing in groups of selected patients are shown in table 2.180.1. In routine testing, prevalences of positive reactions were very low (2,9). In a group of selected patients, 10 of 557 tested individuals (1.8%) reacted to ethylhexylglycerin 5% and/or 10% pet., but the selection criteria were not described. However, all reactions were definitely relevant and caused by stay-on cosmetic products (14).

Table 2.180.1 Patch testing in groups of patients

Years and Country	Test conc. & vehicle	Number of patients tested | positive (%)		Selection of patients (S); Relevance (R); Comments (C)	Ref.
Routine testing					
2013-14 USA, Canada	5% pet.	4856	12 (0.2%)	R: definite + probable relevance: 42%	9
Denmark 2011-2012	5% pet.	785	1 (0.1)	R: the reaction could be ascribed to a face cream con-taining ethylhexylglycerin	2
Testing in groups of selected patients					
1990-2015 Belgium	5% and/or 10% pet.	557	10 (1.8%)	S: not specified; R: all were definitely relevant and caused by stay-on cosmetic products	14

Case reports and case series

Ethylhexylglycerin was stated to be the (or an) allergen in 4 patients in a group of 603 individuals suffering from cosmetic dermatitis, seen in the period 2010-2015 in Leuven, Belgium (8). Ethylhexylglycerin was responsible for 8 out of 959 cases of non-fragrance cosmetic allergy where the causal allergen was identified, Belgium, 2000-2010 (1). In the period 1990 to 2015, 13 patients with allergic contact dermatitis from ethylhexylglycerin were evaluated at two Belgian University Centers. The patients were patch tested with the European baseline series, a cosmetic series, and, if deemed necessary, additional series. Both the cosmetic products used and their single ingredients were patch tested. All but one of the ethylhexylglycerin-allergic patients were female, with a median age of 43 years. Most often, they had dermatitis on the face, and sometimes on the hands and/or axillae or more generalized. The causative products were leave-on cosmetics, including a high number of facial creams, sun protection creams, and deodorants labeled to be 'hypo-allergenic' and 'preservative-free'. It was concluded that ethylhexylglycerin is a rare, but highly relevant, cosmetic sensitizer, that routine patch testing in a cosmetic series may be considered and that higher test concentrations may be indicated in selected cases (14). The patients presented in this article very likely include those mentioned in refs. 1,3 and 8.

A woman developed a pruritic rash on her hands and forearms, spreading to the trunk while sparing the upper arms, after applying an ointment and a skin aerosol to treat irritant hand eczema caused by intensive gardening. She had positive patch tests to both products and their ingredient ethylhexylglycerin (10). Another woman had a history of childhood eczema, severe hand dermatitis and multiple contact allergies. After a flare of dermatitis on the face, neck, trunk, elbows, and legs, she was patch tested again and now reacted to some additional allergens, ethylhexylglycerin, and a baby lotion containing this substance (11,12). Additional single case reports of contact dermatitis from allergy to ethylhexylglycerin have been reported from its presence in facial cream (2,3), various creams (5), and sunscreen products (4,6,7). All but one were women who had dermatitis of the face from creams or allergic contact dermatitis at the sites of application of sunscreens.

Presence in cosmetic products and chemical analyses

In the USA, in April 2017, ethylhexylglycerin was present in 3160 of 56,714 cosmetic products of which the composition is known in FDA's Voluntary Cosmetic Registration Program (VCRP) (data obtained from FDA, May 2017). In April 2017, ethylhexylglycerin was present in 2050 of 65,52 cosmetic products of which the composition is known in EWG's Skin Deep Cosmetics Database, USA (http://www.ewg.org/skindeep/). In the USA, in 2015-2016, 63 diaper wipes and 41 topical diaper preparations from a large retailer were screened for the presence of potential sensitizers. Ethylhexylglycerin was found in 5/63 (8%) disposable diaper wipes and in 3/41 (7%) topical diaper preparations (15).

LITERATURE

1   Travassos AR, Claes L, Boey L, Drieghe J, Goossens A. Non-fragrance allergens in specific cosmetic products. Contact Dermatitis 2011;65:276-285
2   Andersen KE. Ethylhexylglycerin – a contact allergen in cosmetic products. Dermatitis 2012;23:291
3   Linsen G, Goossens A. Allergic contact dermatitis from ethylhexylglycerin. Contact Dermatitis 2002;47:169
4   Stausbøl-Grøn B, Andersen KE. Allergic contact dermatitis to ethylhexylglycerin in a cream. Contact Dermatitis 2007;57:193-194
5   Mortz CG, Otkjaer A, Andersen KE. Allergic contact dermatitis to ethylhexylglycerin and pentylene glycol. Contact Dermatitis 2009;61:180
6   Dorschner RA, Shaw DW. Allergic contact dermatitis from ethylhexylglycerin. Dermatitis 2012;23:134
7   Sasseville D, Stanciu M. Allergic contact dermatitis from ethylhexylglycerin in sunscreens. Dermatitis 2014;25:42-43
8   Goossens A. Cosmetic contact allergens. Cosmetics 2016, 3, 5; doi:10.3390/cosmetics3010005
9   DeKoven JG, Warshaw EM, Belsito DV, Sasseville D, Maibach HI, Taylor JS, et al. North American Contact Dermatitis Group Patch Test Results: 2013-2014. Dermatitis 2017;28:33-46
10 Harries C, Mühlenbein S, Geier J, Pfützner W. Allergic contact dermatitis caused by ethylhexylglycerin in both an ointment and a skin aerosol. Contact Dermatitis 2016;74:181-182
11 Hagen SL, Warshaw EM. Allergic contact dermatitis from ethylhexylglycerin. Dermatitis 2016;27:e12
12 Hagen SL, Warshaw E. The latest occult "hypoallergenic" allergen: Ethylhexylglycerin. Dermatitis. 2016 Dec 20. doi: 10.1097/DER.0000000000000249. (Epub ahead of print)
13 Schalock PC, Dunnick CA, Nedorost S, Brod B, Warshaw E, Mowad C. American Contact Dermatitis Society Core Allergen Series: 2017 Update. Dermatitis 2017;28:141-143
14 Aerts O, Verhulst L, Goossens A. Ethylhexylglycerin: a low-risk, but highly relevant, sensitizer in 'hypo-allergenic' cosmetics. Contact Dermatitis 2016;74:281-288
15 Yu J, Treat J, Chaney K, Brod B. Potential allergens in disposable diaper wipes, topical diaper preparations, and disposable diapers: under-recognized etiology of pediatric perineal dermatitis. Dermatitis 2016;27:110-118

2.181 ETHYLHEXYL METHOXYCINNAMATE

IDENTIFICATION

Description/definition	: Ethylhexyl methoxycinnamate is the ester of 2-ethylhexyl alcohol and methoxycinnamic acid, which conforms to the formula shown below
Chemical class(es)	: Esthers
Chemical/IUPAC name	: 2-Ethylhexyl (*E*)-3-(4-methoxyphenyl)prop-2-enoate
Other names	: Octyl methoxycinnamate; octinoxate; Parsol® MCX
CAS registry number (s)	: 5466-77-3
EC number(s)	: 226-775-7
Merck Index monograph	: 6769
Function(s) in cosmetics	: EU: UV-absorber; UV-filter. USA: light stabilizers; sunscreen agents
EU cosmetic restrictions	: Regulated in Annex VI/12 of the Regulation (EC) No. 1223/2009
Patch testing	: 7.5% pet. (Chemotechnique); 10.0% pet. (Chemotechnique, SmartPracticeCanada)
Molecular formula	: $C_{18}H_{26}O_3$

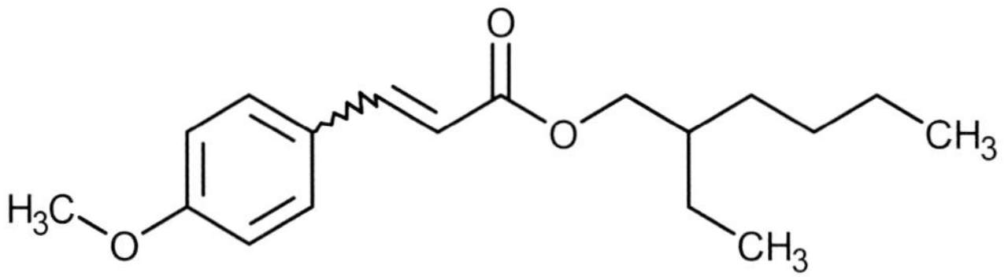

GENERAL

Ethylhexyl methoxycinnamate is a UVB filter with UV absorbance maximum (λ_{max}) at 311nm (56). It has been used in Europe since 1970 (35). It may be combined with bis-ethylhexyloxyphenol methoxyphenyl triazine to improve photostability (59,60). The literature on adverse reactions to sunscreens has been reviewed in several recent and older publications (42-47,62). A review of photocontact allergy to sunscreens was published in 2010 (57).

CONTACT ALLERGY

Patch testing in groups of patients

There are no studies in which ethylhexyl methoxycinnamate was patch tested in consecutive patients suspected of contact dermatitis (routine testing). Results of testing in groups of *selected* patients (e.g., patients suspected of photosensitivity, patients with dermatitis affecting mainly light-exposed skin or with a history of a sunscreen skin reaction) back to 1991 are shown in table 2.181.1. Test concentrations used have been 2% pet. and/or 10% pet., but the higher test concentrations have not clearly resulted in more positive reactions, the mode of selection probably being the more important determinant. In 11 studies testing groups of selected patients, frequencies of sensitization have ranged from 0.1% to 7.5%. In 7 of 11 studies, rates were 1% or lower. The high frequency of 7.5% was seen in a study from Canada, which had certain weaknesses (17). In all but three investigations, the relevance of the positive patch test reactions to ethylhexyl methoxycinnamate was either not stated or specified for the UV-filter. In one study, 3 of 5 positive patch tests (60%) were currently relevant (1); in another one, only 6/41 (15%) reactions were considered to be relevant (52). In a study from the USA, all 7 positive patch test reactions were scored as relevant, but this included 'questionable' and 'past' relevance (13).

Case reports and case series

Ethylhexyl methoxycinnamate was stated to be the (or an) allergen in 2 patients in a group of 603 individuals suffering from cosmetic dermatitis, seen in the period 2010-2015 in Leuven, Belgium (49). In the period 1996-2013, in a tertiary referral center in Valencia, Spain, 5419 patients were patch tested. Of these, 628 individuals had allergic contact dermatitis to cosmetics. Ethylhexyl methoxycinnamate was the responsible allergen in four cases (54, overlap with ref. 50). Ethylhexyl methoxycinnamate was responsible for 3 out of 959 cases of non-fragrance cosmetic allergy where the causal allergen was identified, Belgium, 2000-2010 (12). Seven relevant cases of contact allergy or photocontact allergy to ethylhexyl methoxycinnamate were seen in one center in Australia in an 18-year period up to 2012 (16). In the period 2000-2007, 202 patients with allergic contact dermatitis caused by cosmetics were seen in Valencia, Spain. In this group, three individuals reacted to ethylhexyl methoxycinnamate from its presence in sunscreens (50, overlap with ref. 54).

Table 2.181.1 Patch testing in groups of patients: Selected patient groups

Years and Country	Test conc. & vehicle	Number of patients tested | positive (%)		Selection of patients (S); Relevance (R); Comments (C)	Ref.
2008-2011 12 European countries	10% pet.	1031	2 (0.2%)	S: patients with exposed site dermatitis or history of a reaction to a sunscreen or topical NSAID; R: not specified	18
2001-2010 Canada		160	12 (7.5%)	S: patients with suspected photosensitivity and patients who developed pruritus or a rash after sunscreen application; R: not stated; C: very weak study: inadequate reading of test results, erythema only was considered to represent a positive patch test reaction	17
2001-2010 Australia	10% pet.	2379	41 (1.7%)	S: not stated; R: 15%	52
2000-2007 USA	10% pet.	870	7 (0.8%)	S: patients tested with a supplemental cosmetic screening series; R: 100%; C: weak study: a. high rate of macular erythema and weak reactions; b. relevance figures included 'questionable' and 'past' relevance	13
2000-2005 USA	10% pet.	157	3 (1.9%)	S: patients photopatch tested for suspected photodermatitis; R: one reaction was relevant	32
2000-2002 UK, I, NL	10% pet.	1155	5 (0.4%)	S: patients suspected of photosensitivity or reaction to a sunscreen; R: 3 current relevance, 2 unknown	1
1993-2000 Australia	2% pet.	172	2 (1.2%)	S: patients suspected of photosensitivity; R: of 17 patient who had contact or photocontact reactions to a panel of 10 sunscreens, 10 were considered to have relevant reactions	26
1996-1998 UK		167	1 (0.6%)	S: patients with suspected photosensitivity; R: 'most cases' in the entire group were relevant	5
1983-1998 UK	2% or 10% pet.	2715	4 (0.1%)	S: patients suspected of photosensitivity or with (a history of) dermatitis at exposed sites; R: not stated	2
1981-1996 Germany	2% or 10% pet.	355	3 (0.8%)	S: patients suspected of clinical photosensitivity; R: not stated	3
1989-1991 UK	2% pet.	99	1 (1%)	S: 45 patients with photosensitivity dermatitis/actinic reticuloid syndrome and 54 with polymorphic light eruption; R: not specified	55

I: Ireland; NL: Netherlands; UK: United Kingdom

In a 1-year-period (1996-1997), 1 patient had a positive patch test to ethylhexyl methoxycinnamate in one center in Italy; the reaction was relevant from its presence in sunscreens (29). In a 4-month-period in 1996, 475 patients with contact allergy to 'cosmetic ingredients' were collected in 5 centers in Belgium, UK and Germany. There were 2 reactions to ethylhexyl methoxycinnamate; relevance was not stated (48). One case of ACD from ethylhexyl methoxycinnamate in a moisturizer was seen in Singapore, 1992-1996 (33). In the period 1978-1991, there was one relevant patch test reactions to ethylhexyl methoxycinnamate in a center in Leuven, Belgium (25). A child had allergic contact dermatitis from ethylhexyl methoxycinnamate in 3 sunscreens (4). One positive patch test reaction to ethylhexyl methoxycinnamate was ascribed to cosmetic allergy (14). One individual had ACD from ethylhexyl methoxycinnamate in sunscreen (23). Another patient had photo-aggravated contact allergy to ethylhexyl methoxycinnamate in a sunscreen product (24).

Cross-reactions, pseudo-cross-reactions and co-reactions (including photoreactions)
Isoamyl *p*-methoxycinnamate (3). Other cinnamic acid derivatives, e.g., those found in the fragrance mix I and *Myroxylon pereirae* resin (balsam of Peru) (24). It has been suggested that methoxycinnamates may show cross-reactions to other cinnamates that can be found in perfumes, topical remedies, cosmetics, and food flavoring agents such as cinnamic acid, cinnamal, cinnamon extract and balsam of Peru, and that sensitized patients should be advised to avoid such products (37). However, there were no positive patch or photopatch tests to ethylhexyl methoxycinnamate in 18 patients allergic to cinnamon or cinnamate chemicals such as cinnamal, cinnamic acid, cinnamyl alcohol or balsam of Peru, which contains various cinnamates (38). Photocross-reactivity to and from isoamyl *p*-methoxycinnamate (3, 8 [8 not read]).

Presence in cosmetic products and chemical analyses
In June 2017, ethylhexyl methoxycinnamate was present in 1523 of 68,866 cosmetic products of which the composition is known in EWG's Skin Deep Cosmetics Database, USA (http://www.ewg.org/skindeep/). It should be realized that sunscreen products containing UV-filters are classified as drugs in the USA, not as cosmetics; the number mentioned here, therefore, is that of cosmetics containing the UV-filter, but it does *not* include their presence in sunscreens. In the USA, in April 2017, ethylhexyl methoxycinnamate was present in 5886 of 56,714 cosmetic products of which the composition is known in FDA's Voluntary Cosmetic Registration Program (VCRP)

(data obtained from FDA, May 2017). In 2012, in Switzerland, 116 cosmetics from seven widely used leave-on product categories (19 lip care products, 8 lipsticks, 29 face creams, 11 liquid makeup foundations, 3 aftershaves, 7 hand creams and 39 sunscreens) were investigated to determine the frequency of occurrence and concentrations of 22 organic UV filters in these products. Ethylhexyl methoxycinnamate was found in 51% of the products in a concentration range of 0.11-8.63%, mean 4.0% (51).

In a sample of 337 sunscreens marketed in the UK in 2010, ethylhexyl methoxycinnamate was present in 18% (41). In the USA, sunscreen products were purchased and evaluated in 1997 (n=59), 2003 (n=188) and again in 2009 (n=330). A combination of butyl methoxydibenzoylmethane and ethylhexyl methoxycinnamate was present in 2% of the products in 1997, in 20% in 2003 and in 19% in 2009 (58). Ethylhexyl methoxycinnamate was present in 38.5% of 4447 cosmetic products collected in Germany, 2006-2009 (19). Ethylhexyl methoxycinnamate was present in 54% of 329 sunscreen products (incl. 21 lipstick sunscreens) marketed in the UK in 2005 (36). Ethylhexyl methoxycinnamate was present in 37 of 75 (49%) sunscreen creams and lotions from 30 European and US producers purchased in Denmark in 2001 in a concentration range of 0.01-9.0% (28).

OTHER SIDE EFFECTS

Photosensitivity

Photopatch testing in groups of patients
Results of photopatch testing ethylhexyl methoxycinnamate in groups of selected patients (e.g., patients suspected of photosensitivity, patients with dermatitis affecting mainly light-exposed skin or with a history of a sunscreen skin reaction) back to 1993 are shown in table 2.181.2. Test concentrations used have been 2% pet. and /or 10% pet., but the higher test concentration has not clearly resulted in more positive reactions, the mode of selection probably being the more important determinant. In 17 studies, frequencies of photosensitization have ranged from 0.1% to 10% (table 2.181.2). In 14/17 studies, positive photoreactions scored 2% or lower. The high sensitization rate of 10% was seen in a small group of 82 patients from Colombia with a clinical diagnosis of photoallergic contact dermatitis, in which 8 had a positive photopatch test to ethylhexyl methoxycinnamate; their relevance was not specified for the UV-filter (10). In most studies, relevance was either not mentioned or specified for ethylhexyl methoxycinnamate, but in the studies that provided relevance data, most positive photopatch tests were considered to be relevant (1,15,32).

Table 2.181.2 Photopatch testing in groups of patients

Years and Country	Test conc. & vehicle	Number of patients tested	positive (%)	Selection of patients (S); Relevance (R); Comments (C)	Ref.
2011-2013 Colombia	10% pet.	112	2 (1.8%)	S: dermatitis affecting mainly light-exposed skin, a history of a sunscreen skin or topical NSAID skin reaction; R: 50%	53
2008-2011 12 Euro-pean countries	10% pet.	1031	7 (0.7%)	S: patients with exposed site dermatitis or history of a reaction to a sunscreen or topical NSAID; R: 44% current and 11% past relevance for all photoallergens together	18
2000-2011 UK	10% pet.	157	2 (1.3%)	S: children <18 years suspected of photosensitivity; R: the reactions were caused by sunscreen products	30
2001-2010 Canada		160	5 (3.1%)	S: patients with suspected photosensitivity and patients who developed pruritus or a rash after sunscreen applica-tion; R: not stated; C: very weak study: inadequate reading of test results, erythema only was considered to represent a positive patch test reaction	17
2003-2007 Portugal	10% pet.	83	1 (1.2%)	S: patients with suspected photoaggravated facial dermati-tis or systemic photosensitivity; R: all sunscreen photopatch tests were of current or past relevance	27
2004-2006 Italy	10% pet.	1082	12 (1.1%)	S: patients with histories and clinical features suggestive of photoallergic contact dermatitis; 2/12 were cases of photoaugmented contact allergy; Relevance: 92%	15
2000-2005 USA	10% pet.	157	3 (1.9%)	S: patients photopatch tested for suspected photoderma-titis; R: 2 reactions were relevant	32
2001-2003 Colombia	10% pet.	82	8 (10%)	S: patients with a clinical diagnosis of photoallergic contact dermatitis; R: 65% of all reactions in the study were relevant	10
2000-2002 UK, I, NL	10% pet.	1155	8 (0.7%)	S: patients suspected of photo sensitivity or reaction to a sunscreen; R: 7 current relevance, 1 unknown relevance	1
1993-2000 Australia	2% pet.	172	3 (1.7%)	S: patients suspected of photosensitivity; R: of 17 patient who had contact or photocontact reactions to a panel of 10 sunscreens, 10 were considered to have relevant reactions	26

Table 2.181.2 Photopatch testing in groups of patients (*continued*)

Years and Country	Test conc. & vehicle	Number of patients tested | positive (%)		Selection of patients (S); Relevance (R); Comments (C)	Ref.
1994-1999 NL	10% pet.	55	1 (1.8%)	S: patients suspected of photosensitivity disorders; R: not stated	9
1996-1998 UK		167	5 (3.0%)	S: patients with suspected photosensitivity; R: 'most cases' in the total study group were considered relevant	5
1983-1998 UK	2% or 10% pet.	2715	2 (0.1%)	S: patients suspected of photosensitivity or with (a history of) dermatitis at exposed sites; R: 37% for all photoallergens together	2
1990-1996 Sweden	2% pet.	355	3 (0.8%)	S: patients suspected of photosensitivity; R: not stated	31
1981-1996 Germany	2% or10% pet.	355	4 (1.1%)	S: patients suspected of clinical photosensitivity; R: not stated	3
1990-1994 France	2% or 10% pet.	370	2 (0.5%)	S: patients with suspected photodermatitis; R: not specified, 72% of all reactions in the study were considered relevant	6
1991-1993 Singapore	2% pet.	62	1 (2%)	S: patients with clinical features suggestive of photosensitivity; R: not stated	12

I: Ireland; NL: Netherlands; UK: United Kingdom

Case reports

Several authors have presented single case reports of photoallergic contact dermatitis from ethylhexyl methoxycinnamate in sunscreens (20,33,40). Another patient had photo-aggravated contact allergy to ethylhexyl methoxycinnamate in a sunscreen (24). Seven relevant cases of contact allergy or photocontact allergy to ethylhexyl methoxycinnamate were seen in one center in Australia in an 18-year period up to 2012 (16). A woman had photocontact allergy to ethylhexyl methoxycinnamate in a sunscreen and a milky lotion (21).One patient had photocontact dermatitis from ethylhexyl methoxycinnamate (7, article not read). In the period 1981-1989, 56 patients (43 women, 13 men) were diagnosed with contact allergy or photocontact allergy to UV-filters in one center in Germany. There were 3 photoallergic reactions to ethylhexyl methoxycinnamate. All reactions were relevant and all 46 patients who could be (photo)patch tested with their own sunscreens (and a few of them with other cosmetics) had one or more positive (photo)patch tests to these products (61, overlap with refs. 3 and 8).

Several centers have reported positive photopatch tests to ethylhexyl methoxycinnamate, but without specifying their relevance (22,34,39).

Miscellaneous side effects

Milia developed in one patient after an episode of bullous photoallergic contact dermatitis from sunscreens containing benzophenone-3, butyl methoxydibenzoylmethane and ethylhexyl methoxycinnamate (11).

LITERATURE

1   Bryden A, Moseley H, Ibbotson S, Chowdhury MM, Beck MH, Bourke J, et al. Photopatch testing of 1155 patients: results of the U.K. multicentre photopatch test study group. Brit J Dermatol 2006;155:737-747

2   Darvay A, White I, Rycroft R, Jones AB, Hawk JL, McFadden JP. Photoallergic contact dermatitis is uncommon. Br J Dermatol 2001;145:597-601

3   Schauder S, Ippen H. Contact and photocontact sensitivity. Review of a 15-year experience and of the literature to suncreens. Contact Dermatitis 1997;37:221-232

4   Helsing P, Austad J. Contact dermatitis mimicking photodermatosis in a 1-year-old child. Contact Dermatitis 1991;24:140-141

5   Bell HK, Rhodes LE. Photopatch testing in photosensitive patients. Br J Dermatol 2000;142:589-590

6   Journe F, Marguery M-C, Rakotondrazafy J, El Sayed F, Bazex J. Sunscreen sensitization: a 5-year study. Acta Derm Venereol (Stockh) 1999;79:211-213

7   Itoh M, Kinoshita M, Kurikawa S, et al. A case of photocontact dermatitis due to Parson MCX. Environ Dermatol 1994;1(suppl.1):31 (in Japanese)

8   Schauder S. Kontaktekzem durch Lichtfilterhaltige Lichtschutzmittel und Kosmetika. Aktuelle Dermatologie 1991;17:47-57

9   Bakkum RS, Heule F. Results of photopatch testing in Rotterdam during a 10-year period. Br J Dermatol 2002;146:275-279

10   Rodriguez E, Valbuena M, Rey M, Porras de Quintana L. Causal agents of photoallergic contact dermatitis diagnosed in the national institute of dermatology of Columbia. Photoderm Photoimmunol Photomed 2006;22:189-192

11 Bryden AM, Ferguson J, Ibbotson SH. Milia complicating photocontact allergy to absorbent sunscreen chemicals. Clin Exp Dermatol 2003;28:668-669

12 Travassos AR, Claes L, Boey L, Drieghe J, Goossens A. Non-fragrance allergens in specific cosmetic products. Contact Dermatitis 2011;65:276-285

13 Wetter DA, Yiannias JA, Prakash AV, Davis MD, Farmer SA, el-Azhary RA, et al. Results of patch testing to personal care product allergens in a standard series and a supplemental cosmetic series: an analysis of 945 patients from the Mayo Clinic Contact Dermatitis Group, 2000-2007. J Am Acad Dermatol 2010;63:789-798

14 Kohl L, Blondeel A, Song M. Allergic contact dermatitis from cosmetics: retrospective analysis of 819 patch-tested patients. Dermatology 2002;204:334-337

15 Pigatto PD, Guzzi G, Schena D, Guarrera M, Foti C, Francalanci S, et al. Photopatch tests: an Italian multicentre study from 2004 to 2006. Contact Dermatitis 2008;59:103-108

16 Nixon RL. Contact dermatitis to sunscreens. Dermatitis 2012;23:140-141

17 Greenspoon J, Ahluwalia R, Juma N, Rosen CF. Allergic and photoallergic contact dermatitis: A 10-year experience. Dermatitis 2013;24:29-32

18 The European Multicentre Photopatch Test Study (EMCPPTS) Taskforce. A European multicentre photopatch test study. Br J Dermatol 2012;166:1002-1009

19 Uter W, Gonçalo M, Yazar K, Kratz E-M, Mildau G, Lidén C. Coupled exposure to ingredients of cosmetic products: III. Ultraviolet filters. Contact Dermatitis 2014;71:162-169

20 Perez Ferriols A, Aliaga Boniche A. Photoallergic eczema caused by sunscreens in a 12-year-old girl. Contact Dermatitis 2000;43:229-230

21 Kimura K, Katoh T. Photoallergic contact dermatitis from the sunscreen ethylhexyl-p-methoxycinnamate (Parsol® MCX). Contact Dermatitis 1995;32:304-305

22 Trevisi P, Vincenzi C, Chieregato C, Guerra L, Tosti A. Sunscreen sensitization: a three-year study. Dermatology 1994;189:55-57

23 Gonçalo M, Ruas E, Figueiredo A, Gonçalo S. Contact and photocontact sensitivity to sunscreens. Contact Dermatitis 1995;33:278-280

24 Ricci C, Vaccari S, Cavalli M, Vincenzi C. Contact sensitization to sunscreens. Am J Cont Derm 1997;8:165-166

25 Theeuwes M, Degreef H, Dooms-Goossens A. Para-aminobenzoic acid (PABA) and sunscreen allergy. Am J Cont Derm 1992;3:206-207

26 Crouch RB, Foley PA, Baker CS. The results of photopatch testing 172 patients to sunscreening agents at the photobiology clinic, St Vincent's Hospital, Melbourne. Australas J Dermatol 2002;43:74

27 Cardoso J, Canelas MM, Gonçalo M, Figueiredo A. Photopatch testing with an extended series of photoallergens: a 5-year study. Contact Dermatitis 2009;60:325-329

28 Rastogi SC. UV filters in sunscreen products – a survey. Contact Dermatitis 2002;46:348-351
    29 Ricci C, Pazzaglia M, Tosti A. Photocontact dermatitis from UV filters. Contact Dermatitis 1998;38:343-344

30 Haylett AK, Chiang YZ, Nie Z, Ling TC, Rhodes LE. Sunscreen photopatch testing: a series of 157 children. Br J Dermatol 2014;171:370-375

31 Berne B, Ross AM. 7 years experience of photopatch testing with sunscreen allergens in Sweden. Contact Dermatitis 1998;38:61-64

32 Scalf LA, Davis MDP, Rohlinger AL, Connolly SM. Photopatch testing of 182 patients: A 6-year experience at the Mayo Clinic. Dermatitis 2009;20:44-52

33 Ang P, Ng SK, Goh CL. Sunscreen allergy in Singapore. Am J Cont Derm 1998;9:42-44

34 Nixon RL, Frowen KE, Lewis AE. Skin reactions to sunscreens. Australas J Dermatol 1997;38:S83-S85.

35 Kerr A, Ferguson J. Photoallergic contact dermatitis. Photodermatol Photoimmunol Photomed 2010;26:56-65

36 Wahie S, Lloyd JJ, Farr PM. Sunscreen ingredients and labelling: a survey of products available in the U.K. Clin Exp Dermatol 2007;32:359-364

37 Fisher AA. Sunscreen dermatitis: Part II-The cinnamates. Cutis 1992;50:253-254.

38 Pentinga SE, Kuik DJ, Bruynzeel DP, Rustemeyer T. Do 'cinnamon-sensitive' patients react to cinnamate UV filters? Contact Dermatitis 2009;60:210-213

39 Collaris E, Frank J. Photoallergic contact dermatitis caused by ultraviolet filters in different sunscreens. Int J Dermatol 2008;47:35-37

40 Schmidt T, Ring J, Abeck D. Photoallergic contact dermatitis due to combined UVB (4-methylbenzylidene camphor/octyl methoxycinnamate) and UVA (benzophenone-3/butyl methoxydibenzoylmethane) absorber sensitization. Dermatology 1998;196:354-357

41 Kerr AC. A survey of the availability of sunscreen filters in the U.K. Clin Exp Dermatol 2011;36:541-543

42 Heurung AR, Raju SI, Warshaw EM. Adverse reactions to sunscreen agents: epidemiology, responsible irritants and allergens, clinical characteristics, and management. Dermatitis 2014;25:289-326

43 Heurung AR, Raju SI, Warshaw EM. Contact allergen of the year. Benzophenones. Dermatitis 2014;25:3-10 (contains many mistakes; Erratum in Dermatitis 2014;25:92-95)

44   Avenel-Audran M. Sunscreen products: finding the allergen. Eur J Dermatol 2010;20:161-166

45   Scheuer E, Warshaw E. Sunscreen allergy: a review of epidemiology, clinical characteristics, and responsible allergens. Dermatitis 2006;17:3-11

46   Funk JO, Dromgoole SH, Maibach HI. Sunscreen intolerance: contact sensitization, photocontact sensitization, and irritancy of sunscreen agents. Dermatol Clin 1995;13:473-481

47   Dromgoole SH, Maibach HI. Sunscreening agent intolerance: Contact and photocontact sensitization and contact urticaria. J Am Acad Dermatol 1990;22:1068-1078

48   Goossens A, Beck MH, Haneke E, McFadden JP, Nolting S, Durupt G, Ries G. Adverse cutaneous reactions to cosmetic allergens. Contact Dermatitis 1999;40:112-113

49   Goossens A. Cosmetic contact allergens. Cosmetics 2016, 3, 5; doi:10.3390/cosmetics3010005

50   Laguna C, de la Cuadra J, Martín-González B, Zaragoza V, Martínez-Casimiro L, Alegre V. Allergic contact dermatitis to cosmetics. Actas Dermosifiliogr 2009;100:53-60

51   Manová E, von Goetz N, Hauri U, Bogdal C, Hungerbühler K. Organic UV filters in personal care products in Switzerland: A survey of occurrence and concentrations. Int J Hyg Environ Health 2013;216:508-514

52   Toholka R, Wang Y-S, Tate B, Tam M, Cahill J, Palmer A, Nixon R. The first Australian Baseline Series: Recommendations for patch testing in suspected contact dermatitis. Australas J Dermatol 2015;56:107-115

53   Valbuena Mesa MC, Hoyos Jiménez EV. Photopatch testing in Bogota (Colombia): 2011–2013. Contact Dermatitis 2016;74:11-17

54   Zaragoza-Ninet V, Blasco Encinas R, Vilata-Corell JJ, Pérez-Ferriols A, Sierra-Talamantes C, Esteve-Martínez A, de la Cuadra-Oyanguren J. Allergic contact dermatitis due to cosmetics: A clinical and epidemiological study in a tertiary hospital. Actas Dermosifiliogr 2016;107:329-336

55   Bilsland D, Ferguson J. Contact allergy to sunscreen chemicals in photosensitivity dermatitis/actinic reticuloid syndrome (PD/AR) and polymorphic light eruption. Contact Dermatitis 1993;29:70-73

56   Shaath NA. Ultraviolet filters. Photochem Photobiol Sci 2010;9:464-469

57   Shaw T, Simpson B, Wilson B, Oostman H, Rainey D, Storrs F. True photoallergy to sunscreens is rare despite popular belief. Dermatitis 2010;21:185-198

58   Wang SQ, Tanner PR, Lim HW, Nash JF. The evolution of sunscreen products in the United States- a 12-year cross sectional study. Photochem Photobiol Sci 2013;12:197-202

59   Antoniou C, Kosmadaki MG, Stratigos AJ, Katsambas AD. Sunscreens - what's important to know. J Eur Acad Dermatol Venereol 2008;22:1110-1118

60   Chatelain E, Gabard B. Photostabilization of butyl methoxydibenzoylmethane (avobenzone) and ethylhexyl methoxycinnamate by bis-ethylhexyloxyphenol methoxyphenyl triazine (Tinosorb S), a new UV broadband filter. Photochem Photobiol 2001;74:401-406

61   Schauder S. Adverse reactions to sunscreening agents in 58 patients (part 3). Z Hautkr 1991;66:294-318 (article in German)

62   Schauder S. Survey of the literature on adverse reactions to preparations containing UV filters (1947-1989) (Literaturübersicht über Unverträglichkeitsreaktionen auf lichtfilterhaltige Produkte von 1947 bis 1989). Z Hautkr 1990;65:982-998 (article in German)

2.182   BIS-ETHYLHEXYLOXYPHENOL METHOXYPHENYL TRIAZINE

IDENTIFICATION

Description/definition	: bis-Ethylhexyloxyphenol methoxyphenyl triazine is the heterocyclic compound that conforms to the formula shown below
Chemical class(es)	: Heterocyclic compounds; phenols
Chemical/IUPAC name	: 2,2'-[6-(4-Methoxyphenyl)-1,3,5-triazine-2,4-diyl]bis[5-[(2-ethylhexyl)oxy]-phenol]
Other names	: Bemotrizinol; anisotriazine; Tinosorb® S
CAS registry number (s)	: 187393-00-6
Merck Index monograph	: 2300
Function(s) in cosmetics	: EU: skin conditioning; UV-absorber; UV-filter. USA: hair conditioning agents; sunscreen agents
EU cosmetic restrictions	: Regulated in Annex VI/25 of the Regulation (EC) No. 1223/2009
Patch testing	: 10.0% pet. (Chemotechnique)
Molecular formula	: $C_{38}H_{49}N_3O_5$

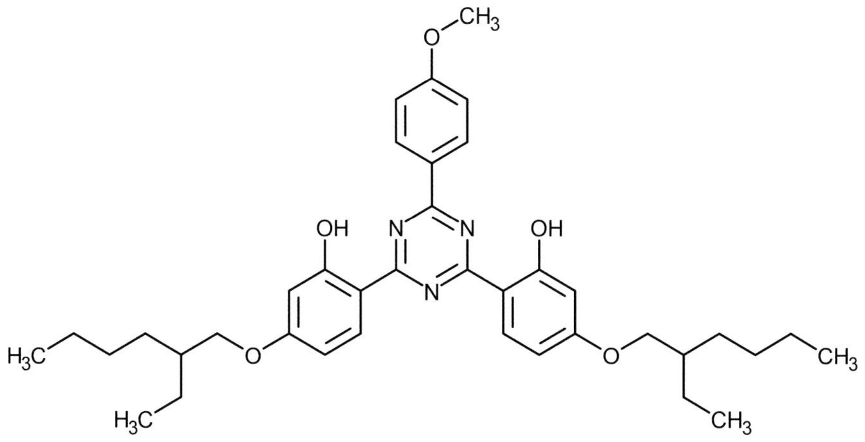

GENERAL

Bis-ethylhexyloxyphenol methoxyphenyl triazine is a UVA/B filter with UV absorbance maxima ($\lambda_{max,1}$, $\lambda_{max,2}$) at 310 and 343 nm (14). It is photostable and can increase the photostability of butyl methoxydibenzoylmethane and ethylhexyl methoxycinnamate (13,16). The literature on adverse reactions to sunscreens has been reviewed in several recent and older publications (5-10,12,17). A review of photocontact allergy to sunscreens was published in 2010 (15).

CONTACT ALLERGY

Patch testing in groups of patients

In the period 2008-2011, in 12 European countries, 1031 patients with exposed site dermatitis or history of a reaction to a sunscreen or topical NSAID were patch and photopatch tested with bis-ethylhexyloxyphenol methoxyphenyl triazine 10% pet. and 1 (0.1%) had a positive patch test. The relevance of this reaction was not specified (1).

Presence in cosmetic products and chemical analyses

In the USA, in April 2017, bis-ethylhexyloxyphenol methoxyphenyl triazine was present in 15 of 56,714 cosmetic products of which the composition is known in FDA's Voluntary Cosmetic Registration Program (VCRP) (data obtained from FDA, May 2017). In April 2017, bis-ethylhexyloxyphenol methoxyphenyl triazine was present in 6 of 65,52 cosmetic products of which the composition is known in EWG's Skin Deep Cosmetics Database, USA (http://www.ewg.org/skindeep/). It should be realized that sunscreen products containing UV-filters are classified as drugs in the USA, not as cosmetics; the number mentioned here, therefore, is that of cosmetics containing the UV-filter, but it does *not* include their presence in sunscreens. In 2012, in Switzerland, 116 cosmetics from seven widely used leave-on product categories (19 lip care products, 8 lipsticks, 29 face creams, 11 liquid makeup foundations, 3 aftershaves, 7 hand creams and 39 sunscreens) were investigated to determine the frequency of occurrence and concentrations of 22 organic UV filters in these products. Bis-ethylhexyloxyphenol methoxyphenyl triazine was found in 34% of the products in a concentration range of 0.41-4.74%, mean 1.73% (11).

In a sample of 337 sunscreens marketed in the UK in 2010, bis-ethylhexyloxyphenol methoxyphenyl triazine was present in 59% (4). Bis-ethylhexyloxyphenol methoxyphenyl triazine was present in 16.4% of 4447 cosmetic products collected in Germany, 2006-2009 (2). Bis-ethylhexyloxyphenol methoxyphenyl triazine was present in 16% of 329 sunscreen products (incl. 21 lipstick sunscreens) marketed in the UK in 2005 (3).

OTHER SIDE EFFECTS

Photosensitivity
In the period 2008-2011, in 12 European countries, 1031 patients with exposed site dermatitis or history of a reaction to a sunscreen or topical NSAID were patch and photopatch tested with bis-ethylhexyloxyphenol methoxyphenyl triazine 10% pet. and 3 (0.3%) had a positive photopatch test. The relevance of these reactions were not specified, but of all photoallergens together, 44% of the positive photopatch tests had current and 11% past relevance (1).

LITERATURE

1 The European Multicentre Photopatch Test Study (EMCPPTS) Taskforce. A European multicentre photopatch test study. Br J Dermatol 2012;166:1002-1009
2 Uter W, Gonçalo M, Yazar K, Kratz E-M, Mildau G, Lidén C. Coupled exposure to ingredients of cosmetic products: III. Ultraviolet filters. Contact Dermatitis 2014;71:162-169
3 Wahie S, Lloyd JJ, Farr PM. Sunscreen ingredients and labelling: a survey of products available in the U.K. Clin Exp Dermatol 2007;32:359-364
4 Kerr AC. A survey of the availability of sunscreen filters in the U.K. Clin Exp Dermatol 2011;36:541-543
5 Heurung AR, Raju SI, Warshaw EM. Adverse reactions to sunscreen agents: epidemiology, responsible irritants and allergens, clinical characteristics, and management. Dermatitis 2014;25:289-326
6 Heurung AR, Raju SI, Warshaw EM. Contact allergen of the year. Benzophenones. Dermatitis 2014;25:3-10 (contains many mistakes; Erratum in Dermatitis 2014;25:92-95)
7 Avenel-Audran M. Sunscreen products: finding the allergen. Eur J Dermatol 2010;20:161-166
8 Scheuer E, Warshaw E. Sunscreen allergy: a review of epidemiology, clinical characteristics, and responsible allergens. Dermatitis 2006;17:3-11
9 Funk JO, Dromgoole SH, Maibach HI. Sunscreen intolerance: contact sensitization, photocontact sensitization, and irritancy of sunscreen agents. Dermatol Clin 1995;13:473-481
10 Dromgoole SH, Maibach HI. Sunscreening agent intolerance: Contact and photocontact sensitization and contact urticaria. J Am Acad Dermatol 1990;22:1068-1078
11 Manová E, von Goetz N, Hauri U, Bogdal C, Hungerbühler K. Organic UV filters in personal care products in Switzerland: A survey of occurrence and concentrations. Int J Hyg Environ Health 2013;216:508-514
12 Shaw T, Simpson B, Wilson B, Oostman H, Rainey D, Storrs F. True photoallergy to sunscreens is rare despite popular belief. Dermatitis 2010;21:185-198
13 Antoniou C, Kosmadaki MG, Stratigos AJ, Katsambas AD. Sunscreens - what's important to know. J Eur Acad Dermatol Venereol 2008;22:1110-1118
14 Shaath NA. Ultraviolet filters. Photochem Photobiol Sci 2010;9:464-469
15 Shaw T, Simpson B, Wilson B, Oostman H, Rainey D, Storrs F. True photoallergy to sunscreens is rare despite popular belief. Dermatitis 2010;21:185-198
16 Chatelain E, Gabard B. Photostabilization of butyl methoxydibenzoylmethane (avobenzone) and ethylhexyl methoxycinnamate by bis-ethylhexyloxyphenol methoxyphenyl triazine (Tinosorb S), a new UV broadband filter. Photochem Photobiol 2001;74:401-406
17 Schauder S. Survey of the literature on adverse reactions to preparations containing UV filters (1947-1989) (Literaturübersicht über Unverträglichkeitsreaktionen auf lichtfilterhaltige Produkte von 1947 bis 1989). Z Hautkr 1990;65:982-998 (article in German)

2.183 ETHYLHEXYL SALICYLATE

IDENTIFICATION

Description/definition	: Ethylhexyl salicylate is the ester of 2-ethylhexyl alcohol and salicylic acid, that conforms to the formula shown below
Chemical class(es)	: Esters; phenols
Chemical/IUPAC name	: 2-Ethylhexyl 2-hydroxybenzoate
Other names	: Octyl salicylate; octisalate
CAS registry number (s)	: 118-60-5
EC number(s)	: 204-263-4
CIR review(s)	: Int J Toxicol 2003;22(Suppl.3):1-108 (access: www.cir-safety.org/ingredients)
SCCS opinion(s)	: SCCNFP, 21 January 1998 (21)
Merck Index monograph	: 8130
Function(s) in cosmetics	: EU: UV-absorber; UV-filter. USA: fragrance ingredients; light stabilizers; sunscreen agents
EU cosmetic restrictions	: Regulated in Annex VI/20 of the Regulation (EC) No. 1223/2009
Patch testing	: 5% pet. (Chemotechnique); 10% pet. (Chemotechnique)
Molecular formula	: $C_{15}H_{22}O_3$

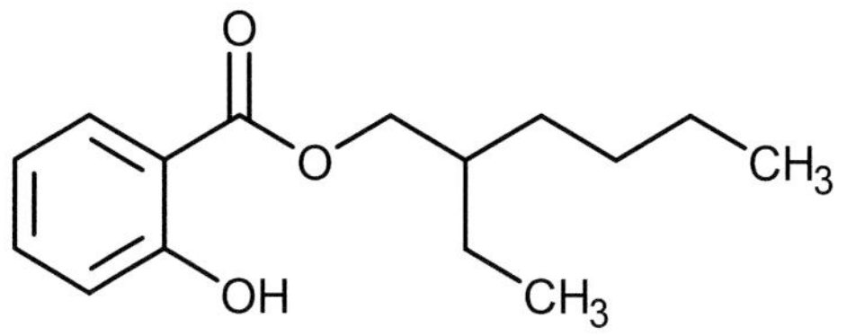

GENERAL

Ethylhexyl salicylate is a UVB filter with UV absorbance maximum (λ_{max}) at 305 nm (28). It has been used in Europe since the 1980s (11). The literature on adverse reactions to sunscreens has been reviewed in several recent and older publications (14-19,29). A review of photocontact allergy to sunscreens was published in 2010 (25). Ethylhexyl salicylate is also used as a fragrance material (27).

CONTACT ALLERGY

Patch testing in groups of patients

There have been no studies in which consecutive patients suspected of contact dermatitis have been patch tested with ethylhexyl salicylate (routine testing). Results of testing ethylhexyl salicylate in groups of *selected* patients (e.g., patients suspected of photosensitivity, patients with dermatitis affecting mainly light-exposed skin or with a history of a sunscreen skin reactions) are shown in table 2.183.1. In five studies, frequencies of sensitization ranged from 0.1% to 5.6%. The study with the 5.6% score had certain weaknesses, however. In two studies mentioning relevance, one of 2 positive patch tests (23) and 2 out of 3 reactions (10) were considered to be relevant, but the culprit products were not mentioned.

Table 2.183.1 Patch testing in groups of patients: Selected patient groups

Years and Country	Test conc. & vehicle	Number of patients tested	positive (%)	Selection of patients (S); Relevance (R); Comments (C)	Ref.
2012-2014 USA		243	3 (1.2%)	S: patients using products containing ethylhexyl salicylate; R: not stated	30
2011-2013 Colombia	5% pet.	112	2 (1.8%)	S: dermatitis affecting mainly light-exposed skin, or a history of a sunscreen or of a topical NSAID skin reaction; R: 50%	23
2008-2011 12 European countries	10% pet.	1031	1 (0.1%)	S: patients with exposed site dermatitis or history of a reaction to a sunscreen or topical NSAID; R: not specified	2
2001-2010 Canada		160	9 (5.6%)	S: patients with suspected photosensitivity and patients who developed pruritus or a rash after sunscreen application; R: not stated; C: very weak study: inadequate reading of test results, erythema only was considered to represent a positive patch test reaction	1
2000-2005 USA	5% pet.	176	3 (1.7%)	S: patients photopatch tested for suspected photodermatitis; R: 2 reactions were relevant	10

Case reports and case series
Ethylhexyl salicylate was stated to be the (or an) allergen in one patient in a group of 603 individuals suffering from cosmetic dermatitis, seen in the period 2010-2015 in Leuven, Belgium (20). In the period 1996-2013, in a tertiary referral center in Valencia, Spain, 5419 patients were patch tested. Of these, 628 individuals had allergic contact dermatitis to cosmetics. Ethylhexyl salicylate was the responsible allergen in one case (24). In a group of 146 patients patch tested for cheilitis in Amersham, UK, between 1982 and 2001, there was one positive patch test reaction to ethylhexyl salicylate considered to be relevant for the lip dermatitis. Over half of the reactions in the entire group were ascribed to lipsticks and lip salves (7). One patient had contact dermatitis from allergy to ethylhexyl salicylate in a cosmetic cream (4). There have also been a few single case reports of allergic contact dermatitis from ethylhexyl salicylate in sunscreen preparations (5,8,26).

Cross-reactions, pseudo-cross-reactions and co-reactions
cis-3-Hexenyl salicylate (6,8). Weak co-reactions to benzyl salicylate and phenazone salicylate (5). Not to homosalate (8). Not to other salicylates (methyl salicylate, phenyl salicylate, benzyl salicylate, sodium salicylate, salicylic acid, acetyl salicylic acid, and salicylaldehyde) (26). Benzyl salicylate (30).

Presence in cosmetic products and chemical analyses
In June 2017, ethylhexyl salicylate was present in 1332 of 68,864 cosmetic products of which the composition is known in EWG's Skin Deep Cosmetics Database, USA (http://www.ewg.org/skindeep/). It should be realized that sunscreen products containing UV-filters are classified as drugs in the USA, not as cosmetics; the number mentioned here, therefore, is that of cosmetics containing the UV-filter, but it does not include their presence in sunscreens. In the USA, in April 2017, ethylhexyl salicylate was present in 3537 of 56,714 cosmetic products of which the composition is known in FDA's Voluntary Cosmetic Registration Program (VCRP) (data obtained from FDA, May 2017). In 2012, in Switzerland, 116 cosmetics from seven widely used leave-on product categories (19 lip care products, 8 lipsticks, 29 face creams, 11 liquid makeup foundations, 3 aftershaves, 7 hand creams and 39 sunscreens) were investigated to determine the frequency of occurrence and concentrations of 22 organic UV filters in these products. Ethylhexyl salicylate was found in 25% of the products in a concentration range of 0.07-5.26%, mean 3.64% (22).

In a sample of 337 sunscreens marketed in the UK in 2010, ethylhexyl salicylate was present in 33% of the products (13). Ethylhexyl salicylate was present in 12.6% of 4447 cosmetic products collected in Germany, 2006-2009 (3). Ethylhexyl salicylate was present in 21% of 329 sunscreen products (incl. 21 lipstick sunscreens) marketed in the UK in 2005 (12). Ethylhexyl salicylate was present in 8 of 75 (11%) sunscreen creams and lotions from 30 European and US producers purchased in Denmark in 2001 in a concentration range of 1.4-4.7% (9).

OTHER SIDE EFFECTS

Photosensitivity
Results of photopatch testing ethylhexyl salicylate in groups of selected patients (e.g., patients suspected of photosensitivity, patients with dermatitis affecting mainly light-exposed skin or with a history of a sunscreen skin reactions) are shown in table 2.183.2. In four studies, frequencies of photosensitization were consistently low and ranged from 0.2% to 1.3%. In the studies were relevance was mentioned, there was one relevant photopatch test only (10).

Table 2.183.2 Photopatch testing in groups of patients

Years and Country	Test conc. & vehicle	Number of patients tested	positive (%)	Selection of patients (S); Relevance (R); Comments (C)	Ref.
2011-2013 Colombia	5% pet.	112	1 (0.9%)	S: dermatitis affecting mainly light-exposed skin, or a history of a sunscreen or a topical NSAID skin reaction; R: not relevant	23
2008-2011 12 European countries	10% pet.	1031	2 (0.2%)	S: patients with exposed site dermatitis or history of a reaction to a sunscreen or topical NSAID; R: 44% current and 11% past relevance for all photoallergens together	2
2001-2010 Canada		160	2 (1.3%)	S: patients with suspected photosensitivity and patients who developed pruritus or a rash after sunscreen application; R: not stated; C: see table 2.183.1 for Comments	1
2000-2005 USA	5% pet.	176	2 (1.1%)	S: patients photopatch tested for suspected photodermatitis; R: one reaction was relevant	10

LITERATURE

1   Greenspoon J, Ahluwalia R, Juma N, Rosen CF. Allergic and photoallergic contact dermatitis: A 10-year experience. Dermatitis 2013;24:29-32

2   The European Multicentre Photopatch Test Study (EMCPPTS) Taskforce. A European multicentre photopatch test study. Br J Dermatol 2012;166:1002-1009

3   Uter W, Gonçalo M, Yazar K, Kratz E-M, Mildau G, Lidén C. Coupled exposure to ingredients of cosmetic products: III. Ultraviolet filters. Contact Dermatitis 2014;71:162-169

4   Singh M, Beck MH. Octyl salicylate: a new contact sensitivity. Contact Dermatitis 2007;56:48

5   Mortz CG, Thormann H, Goossens A, Andersen KE. Contact dermatitis from ethylhexyl salicylate and other salicylates. Dermatitis 2010;21:E7–E10

6   Van Ketel WG. Sensitization to cis-3-hexenyl salicylate. Contact Dermatitis 1983;9:154

7   Strauss RM, Orton DI. Allergic contact cheilitis in the United Kingdom: a retrospective study. Am J Contact Dermat 2003;14:75-77

8   Shaw DW. Allergic contact dermatitis from octisalate and cis-3-hexenyl salicylate. Dermatitis 2006;17:152-155

9   Rastogi SC. UV filters in sunscreen products – a survey. Contact Dermatitis 2002;46:348-351

10 Scalf LA, Davis MDP, Rohlinger AL, Connolly SM. Photopatch testing of 182 patients: A 6-year experience at the Mayo Clinic. Dermatitis 2009;20:44-52

11 Kerr A, Ferguson J. Photoallergic contact dermatitis. Photodermatol Photoimmunol Photomed 2010;26:56-65

12 Wahie S, Lloyd JJ, Farr PM. Sunscreen ingredients and labelling: a survey of products available in the U.K. Clin Exp Dermatol 2007;32:359-364

13 Kerr AC. A survey of the availability of sunscreen filters in the U.K. Clin Exp Dermatol 2011;36:541-543

14 Heurung AR, Raju SI, Warshaw EM. Adverse reactions to sunscreen agents: epidemiology, responsible irritants and allergens, clinical characteristics, and management. Dermatitis 2014;25:289-326

15 Heurung AR, Raju SI, Warshaw EM. Contact allergen of the year. Benzophenones. Dermatitis 2014;25:3-10 (contains many mistakes; Erratum in Dermatitis 2014;25:92-95)

16 Avenel-Audran M. Sunscreen products: finding the allergen. Eur J Dermatol 2010;20:161-166

17 Scheuer E, Warshaw E. Sunscreen allergy: a review of epidemiology, clinical characteristics, and responsible allergens. Dermatitis 2006;17:3-11

18 Funk JO, Dromgoole SH, Maibach HI. Sunscreen intolerance: contact sensitization, photocontact sensitization, and irritancy of sunscreen agents. Dermatol Clin 1995;13:473-481

19 Dromgoole SH, Maibach HI. Sunscreening agent intolerance: Contact and photocontact sensitization and contact urticaria. J Am Acad Dermatol 1990;22:1068-1078

20 Goossens A. Cosmetic contact allergens. Cosmetics 2016, 3, 5; doi:10.3390/cosmetics3010005

21 SCCNFP (Scientific Committee on Cosmetics and Non Food Products). Opinion concerning 2-ethylhexyl salicylate, 21 January 1998. Available at: http://ec.europa.eu/health/scientific_committees/consumer _safety/opinions/sccnfp_opinions_97_04/sccp_out26_en.htm

22 Manová E, von Goetz N, Hauri U, Bogdal C, Hungerbühler K. Organic UV filters in personal care products in Switzerland: A survey of occurrence and concentrations. Int J Hyg Environ Health 2013;216:508-514

23 Valbuena Mesa MC, Hoyos Jiménez EV. Photopatch testing in Bogota (Colombia): 2011–2013. Contact Dermatitis 2016;74:11-17

24 Zaragoza-Ninet V, Blasco Encinas R, Vilata-Corell JJ, Pérez-Ferriols A, Sierra-Talamantes C, Esteve-Martínez A, de la Cuadra-Oyanguren J. Allergic contact dermatitis due to cosmetics: A clinical and epidemiological study in a tertiary hospital. Actas Dermosifiliogr 2016;107:329-336

25 Shaw T, Simpson B, Wilson B, Oostman H, Rainey D, Storrs F. True photoallergy to sunscreens is rare despite popular belief. Dermatitis 2010;21:185-198

26 Miralles JC, Escudero AI, Carbonell A, Martínez A, Fernández E, Cardona P. Allergic contact dermatitis from ethylhexyl salicylate. J Investig Allergol Clin Immunol 2015;25:66-67

27 Lapczynski A, McGinty D, Jones L, Letizia CS, Api AM. Fragrance material review on ethyl hexyl salicylate. Food Chem Toxicol 2007;45 (Suppl. 1):S393-396

28 Shaath NA. Ultraviolet filters. Photochem Photobiol Sci 2010;9:464-469

29 Schauder S. Survey of the literature on adverse reactions to preparations containing UV filters (1947-1989) (Literaturübersicht über Unverträglichkeitsreaktionen auf lichtfilterhaltige Produkte von 1947 bis 1989). Z Hautkr 1990;65:982-998 (article in German)

30 Scheman A, Te R. Contact allergy to salicylates and cross-reactions. Dermatitis 2017;28:291

2.184   ETHYLHEXYL TRIAZONE

IDENTIFICATION

Description/definition   : Ethylhexyl triazone is the heterocyclic organic compound that conforms to the formula
                            shown below
Chemical class(es)   : Heterocyclic compounds
Chemical/IUPAC name   : Benzoic acid, 4,4',4''-(1,3,5-triazine-2,4,6-triyltriimino)tris-,tris(2-ethylhexyl) ester
Other names   : Octyl triazone
CAS registry number (s)   : 88122-99-0
EC number(s)   : 402-070-1
Merck Index monograph   : 5134
Function(s) in cosmetics : EU: UV-absorber; UV-filter. USA: light stabilizers
EU cosmetic restrictions : Regulated in Annex VI/15 of the Regulation (EC) No. 1223/2009
Patch testing   : 10% pet. (Chemotechnique)
Molecular formula   : $C_{48}H_{66}N_6O_6$

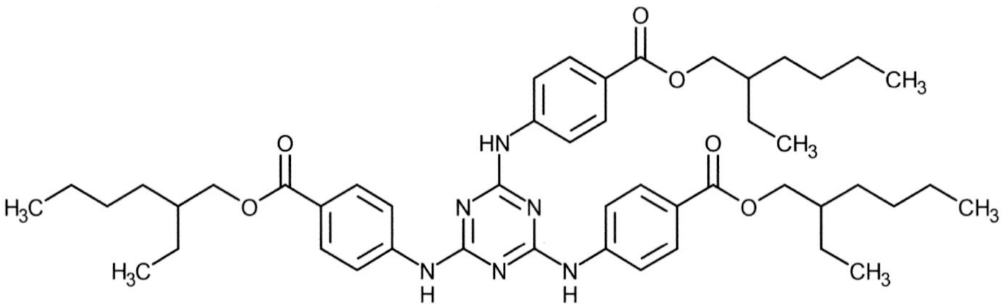

GENERAL

Ethylhexyl triazone is a relatively new UVB filter with UV absorbance maximum (λ_{max}) at 314 nm (17). A concentration of 5% is recommended for a high sun protection factor. Due to its polar nature, it has a good affinity for
skin keratin. Ethylhexyl triazone is completely insoluble in water and stable toward light. Because of its low
penetration into the skin, it is also used in day creams (5). The literature on adverse reactions to sunscreens has been
reviewed in several recent and older publications (9-14,16,18). A review of photocontact allergy to sunscreens was
published in 2010 (16).

CONTACT ALLERGY

Patch testing in groups of patients
In the period 2000-2002, in the UK, Ireland and The Netherlands, 1155 patients suspected of photosensitivity or
reaction to a sunscreen were patch tested with ethylhexyl triazone 10% pet. and 3 (0.3%) had a positive reaction.
The relevance of these reactions was unknown (1).

Presence in cosmetic products and chemical analyses
In the USA, in April 2017, ethylhexyl triazone was present in 10 of 56,714 cosmetic products of which the
composition is known in FDA's Voluntary Cosmetic Registration Program (VCRP) (data obtained from FDA, May
2017). In April 2017, ethylhexyl triazone was present in 2 of 65,52 cosmetic products of which the composition is
known in EWG's Skin Deep Cosmetics Database, USA (http://www.ewg.org/skindeep/). It should be realized that
sunscreen products containing UV-filters are classified as drugs in the USA, not as cosmetics; the number mentioned
here, therefore, is that of cosmetics containing the UV-filter, but it does not include their presence in sunscreens. In
2012, in Switzerland, 116 cosmetics from seven widely used leave-on product categories (19 lip care products, 8
lipsticks, 29 face creams, 11 liquid makeup foundations, 3 aftershaves, 7 hand creams and 39 sunscreens) were
investigated to determine the frequency of occurrence and concentrations of 22 organic UV filters in these products.
Ethylhexyl triazone was found in 13% of the products in a concentration range of 0.39-4.83%, mean 2.24% (15).

In a sample of 337 sunscreens marketed in the UK in 2010, ethylhexyl triazone was present in 16% (8). Ethylhexyl
triazone was present in 13.7% of 4447 cosmetic products collected in Germany, 2006-2009 (4). Ethylhexyl triazone
was present in 15% of 329 sunscreen products (incl. 21 lipstick sunscreens) marketed in the UK in 2005 (7).
Ethylhexyl triazone was present in 3 of 75 (4%) sunscreen creams and lotions from 30 European and US producers
purchased in Denmark in 2001 in a concentration range of 0.9-1.4% (6).

OTHER SIDE EFFECTS

Photosensitivity
Ethylhexyl triazone has been photopatch tested in several studies in groups of selected patients, usually patients suspected of photosensitivity or photoallergic contact dermatitis (1,2,3,5). Their results are shown in table 2.184.1. In all studies, rates of photosensitization were low and only a few photoallergic patients were detected. About half of the reactions were considered to be relevant.

Table 2.184.1 Photopatch testing in groups of patients

Years and Country	Test conc. & vehicle	Number of patients tested	positive (%)	Selection of patients (S); Relevance (R); Comments (C)	Ref.
2008-2011 12 European countries	10% pet.	1031	3 (0.3%)	S: patients with exposed site dermatitis or history of a reaction to a sunscreen or topical NSAID; R: 44% current and 11% past relevance for all photoallergens together	3
2004-2006 Italy	5% pet.	1082	2 (0.2%)	S: patients with histories and clinical features suggestive of photoallergic contact dermatitis; 1/2 were cases of photo-aggravated contact allergy; R: 50%	2
2000-2002; UK, I, NL	10% WSP	1155	2 (0.2%)	S: patients suspected of photosensitivity or reaction to a sunscreen. R: C1, D1; C: also contact allergy	1
2000-2001 UK	5% pet.	120	1 (0.8%)	S: not stated; R: reaction from a sunscreen	5

I: Ireland; NL: Netherlands; UK: United Kingdom; WSP White soft paraffin
Relevance: C: current; D: unknown; O: old/past

Case reports
A woman presented with an erythematous bullous eruption over her hands, arms and lower legs, which she had developed while on a holiday in Spain. She had been using a sunblock SPF 24. She had suffered from a similar, but less severe, rash during a previous holiday. Patch tests to a standard and a face series showed positive reactions to the fragrance mix and *Myroxylon pereirae*, which were not of current relevance, as she did not use fragranced products. The patient was also photopatch tested and reacted to a sunscreen product and to its ingredients butyl methoxydibenzoylmethane and ethylhexyl triazone at the site irradiated with 5 J UVA (5).

LITERATURE
1   Bryden A, Moseley H, Ibbotson S, Chowdhury MM, Beck MH, Bourke J, et al. Photopatch testing of 1155 patients: results of the U.K. multicentre photopatch test study group. Brit J Dermatol 2006;155:737-747
2   Pigatto PD, Guzzi G, Schena D, Guarrera M, Foti C, Francalanci S, et al. Photopatch tests: an Italian multicentre study from 2004 to 2006. Contact Dermatitis 2008;59:103-108
3   The European Multicentre Photopatch Test Study (EMCPPTS) Taskforce. A European multicentre photopatch test study. Br J Dermatol 2012;166:1002-1009
4   Uter W, Gonçalo M, Yazar K, Kratz E-M, Mildau G, Lidén C. Coupled exposure to ingredients of cosmetic products: III. Ultraviolet filters. Contact Dermatitis 2014;71:162-169
5   Sommer S, Wilkinson SM, English JSC, Ferguson J. Photoallergic contact dermatitis from the sunscreen octyl triazone. Contact Dermatitis 2002;46:304-305
6   Rastogi SC. UV filters in sunscreen products – a survey. Contact Dermatitis 2002;46:348-351
7   Wahie S, Lloyd JJ, Farr PM. Sunscreen ingredients and labelling: a survey of products available in the U.K. Clin Exp Dermatol 2007;32:359-364
8   Kerr AC. A survey of the availability of sunscreen filters in the U.K. Clin Exp Dermatol 2011;36:541-543
9   Heurung AR, Raju SI, Warshaw EM. Adverse reactions to sunscreen agents: epidemiology, responsible irritants and allergens, clinical characteristics, and management. Dermatitis 2014;25:289-326
10 Heurung AR, Raju SI, Warshaw EM. Contact allergen of the year. Benzophenones. Dermatitis 2014;25:3-10 (contains many mistakes; Erratum in Dermatitis 2014;25:92-95)
11 Avenel-Audran M. Sunscreen products: finding the allergen. Eur J Dermatol 2010;20:161-166
12 Scheuer E, Warshaw E. Sunscreen allergy: a review of epidemiology, clinical characteristics, and responsible allergens. Dermatitis 2006;17:3-11
13 Funk JO, Dromgoole SH, Maibach HI. Sunscreen intolerance: contact sensitization, photocontact sensitization, and irritancy of sunscreen agents. Dermatol Clin 1995;13:473-481

14 Dromgoole SH, Maibach HI. Sunscreening agent intolerance: Contact and photocontact sensitization and contact urticaria. J Am Acad Dermatol 1990;22:1068-1078

15 Manová E, von Goetz N, Hauri U, Bogdal C, Hungerbühler K. Organic UV filters in personal care products in Switzerland: A survey of occurrence and concentrations. Int J Hyg Environ Health 2013;216:508-514

16 Shaw T, Simpson B, Wilson B, Oostman H, Rainey D, Storrs F. True photoallergy to sunscreens is rare despite popular belief. Dermatitis 2010;21:185-198

17 Shaath NA. Ultraviolet filters. Photochem Photobiol Sci 2010;9:464-469

18 Schauder S. Survey of the literature on adverse reactions to preparations containing UV filters (1947-1989) (Literaturübersicht über Unverträglichkeitsreaktionen auf lichtfilterhaltige Produkte von 1947 bis 1989). Z Hautkr 1990;65:982-998 (article in German)

2.185   ETHYL METHACRYLATE

IDENTIFICATION

Description/definition   : Ethyl methacrylate is the ester of ethyl alcohol and methacrylic acid, which conforms to the formula shown below
Chemical class(es)   : Esters
Chemical/IUPAC name   : Ethyl 2-methylprop-2-enoate
CAS registry number (s)   : 97-63-2
EC number(s)   : 202-597-5
CIR review(s)   : J Am Coll Toxicol 1995;14:452-467; Int J Toxicol 2002;21(Suppl.1):63-79 (access: www.cir-safety.org/ingredients)
Function(s) in cosmetics   : EU: viscosity controlling. USA: artificial nail building
Patch testing   : 2.0% pet. (Chemotechnique, SmartPracticeEurope)
Molecular formula   : $C_6H_{10}O_2$

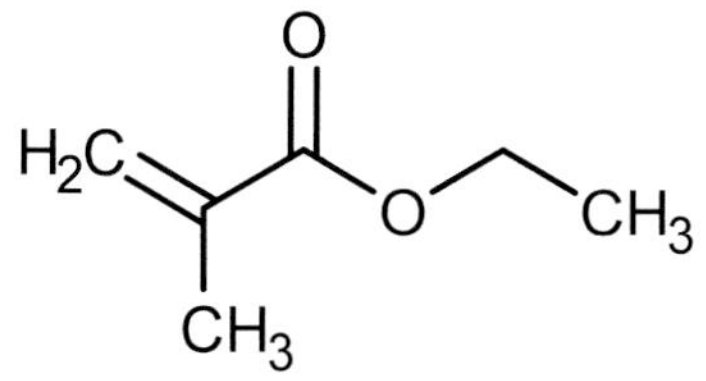

GENERAL

Discussion of contact allergy to (meth)acrylates *from non-cosmetic sources* is considered to fall outside the scope of this book. Therefore, only contact allergy from their presence in cosmetics is presented, which virtually always is from artificial nails. There are many reports of contact allergy to artificial nails, but the specific sensitizers have rarely been identified and – consequently - such publications are not presented in this and other acrylate and methacrylate monographs. Discussion is limited to publications in which the culprit (meth)acrylates have been identified, e.g., from information found in Material Data Safety Sheets, data obtained from the manufacturer or from chemical analyses.

Patients often react to many (meth)acrylates on patch testing. Primary sensitization to methacrylates may result in both methacrylate and acrylate cross-sensitization. Conversely, patients sensitized to acrylates are unlikely to show cross-sensitization to methacrylates (8).

General aspects of acrylates and methacrylates are presented in Chapter 2.219 HEMA (hydroxyethyl methacrylate). A discussion of general aspects of artificial nails, contact allergy to these products, the clinical picture of allergic contact dermatitis and other side effects of sculptured nails can also be found there. A very useful review of contact sensitization to allergens in nail cosmetics, with emphasis on acrylic manicures, was published in 2017 (10).

CONTACT ALLERGY

Patch testing in groups of patients
Studies in which consecutive patients suspected of contact dermatitis have been tested with ethyl methacrylate (routine testing) and studies testing groups of selected patients are planned to be discussed in a future publication.

Case reports and case series
Ethyl methacrylate was responsible for 5 out of 399 cases of cosmetic allergy where the causal allergen was identified in a study of the NACDG, USA, 1977-1983 (1). A group of 55 female patients presenting with hand eczema and who had contact with artificial nails, were patch tested with a series of acrylates in one center in Israel, 2001-2004. Twenty-one had one or more positive reactions, of who 14 were professional beauticians specializing in nail sculpturing. All reactions, including 9 to ethyl methacrylate, were stated to be of current relevance (4). Because of the general lack of information on the composition of artificial nail materials, the fact that the author did no analyses of these products and the frequent occurrence of cross-reactivity among acrylates, one may wonder whether this statement can be accepted as entirely correct.

Three patients had allergic reactions with painful onychia and paronychia to ethyl methacrylate in sculptured nails/nail extenders (7). One patient had paronychia and eyelid dermatitis from contact allergy to ethyl methacrylate in cold-cured artificial nails (2). A cosmetician teaching other cosmeticians how to make artificial nails developed occupational contact dermatitis of the hands and face from contact allergy to ethyl methacrylate in monomer liquid for sculptured nails. GC-MS analysis showed the product to contain 90% ethyl methacrylate (3).

A nail modeler became sensitized and developed allergic contact dermatitis on the left hand from sculpturing the not-yet hardened resin with a file in the right hand; the causative agent was ethyl methacrylate (5). A female manicurist, who also wore artificial nails herself, had severe itchy eczema of the fingers and onycholysis. She reacted to the liquid monomer 1% and 2% pet. The products contained 90% ethyl methacrylate. Ethyl methacrylate itself was not tested, but the patient reacted to hydroxyethyl methacrylate and ethylene glycol dimethacrylate, which makes the causative role of ethyl methacrylate highly likely (9). One individual had widespread dermatitis from ethyl methacrylate in artificial nails (6).

Presence in cosmetic products and chemical analyses
In the USA, in April 2017, ethyl methacrylate was present in 12 of 56,714 cosmetic products of which the composition is known in FDA's Voluntary Cosmetic Registration Program (VCRP) (data obtained from FDA, May 2017). In August 2017, ethyl methacrylate was present in 2 of 70,516 cosmetic products of which the composition is known in EWG's Skin Deep Cosmetics Database, USA (http://www.ewg.org/skindeep/).

LITERATURE
1   Adams RM, Maibach HI, Clendenning WE, Fisher AA, Jordan WJ, Kanof N, et al. A five-year study of cosmetic reactions. J Am Acad Dermatol 1985;13:1062-1069
2   Marks JG, Bishop ME, Willis WF. Allergic contact dermatitis to sculptured nails. Arch Dermatol 1979;115:100
3   Kanerva L, Lauerma A, Estlander T, Alanko K, Henriks-Eckerman ML, Jolanki R. Occupational allergic contact dermatitis caused by photobonded sculptured nails and a review of (meth)acrylates in nail cosmetics. Am J Cont Derm 1996;7:109-115
4   Lazarov A. Sensitization to acrylates is a common adverse reaction to artificial fingernails. J Eur Acad Derm Venereol 2007;21:169-174
5   Schubert HK, Linder K, Prater E. Kontaktallergie im Nagelstudio. Z Haut-und-Geschlechtskrankheiten 1992;67:1067-1069. Data cited in ref. 6
6   Fitzgerald DA, English JSC. Widespread contact dermatitis from sculptured nails. Contact Dermatitis 1994;30:118
7   Fisher AA. Cross reactions between methyl methacrylate monomer and acrylic monomers presently used in acrylic nail preparations. Contact Dermatitis 1980;6:345-347
8   Aalto-Korte K, Henriks-Eckerman M-L, Kuuliala O, Jolanki R. Occupational methacrylate and acrylate allergy – cross-reactions and possible screening allergens. Contact Dermatitis 2010;63:301-312
9   Minamoto K. Allergic contact dermatitis from two-component acrylic resin in a manicurist and a dental hygienist. J Occup Health 2014;56:229-234
10   Chou M, Dhingra N, Strugar TL. Contact sensitization to allergens in nail cosmetics. Dermatitis 2017;28:231-240

2.186   ETHYL METHOXYCINNAMATE

IDENTIFICATION

Description/definition   : Ethyl methoxycinnamate is the organic compound that conforms to the formula shown below
Chemical class(es)   : Esters; ethers
Chemical/IUPAC name   : Ethyl (*E*)-3-(4-methoxyphenyl)prop-2-enoate
CAS registry number (s)   : 1929-30-2
EC number(s)   : 217-679-6
Function(s) in cosmetics : EU: UV-absorber. USA: light stabilizers
Patch testing   : 10% pet.
Molecular formula   : $C_{12}H_{14}O_3$

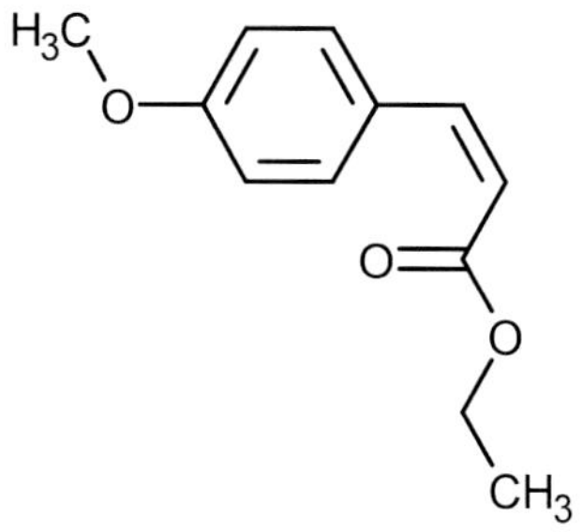

GENERAL

Ethyl methoxycinnamate is a UVB-absorber (2). The literature on adverse reactions to sunscreens has been reviewed in several recent and older publications (3-8,10,11).

CONTACT ALLERGY

Patch testing in groups of patients

In the UK, in the period 1983-1998, 2715 patients suspected of photosensitivity or with (a history of) dermatitis at exposed sites were patch tested with ethyl methoxycinnamate 2% and there were two (<0.1%) reactions. The relevance of these positive patch tests was not mentioned (1).

Case reports and case series

In a 4-month-period in 1996, 475 patients with contact allergy to 'cosmetic ingredients' were collected in 5 centers in Belgium, UK and Germany. There was one reaction to ethyl methoxycinnamate; relevance was not stated (9).

Presence in cosmetic products and chemical analyses

In the USA, in April 2017, ethyl methoxycinnamate was present in zero of 56,714 cosmetic products of which the composition is known in FDA's Voluntary Cosmetic Registration Program (VCRP) (data obtained from FDA, May 2017). In April 2017, ethyl methoxycinnamate was present in zero of 65,522 cosmetic products of which the composition is known in EWG's Skin Deep Cosmetics Database, USA (http://www.ewg.org/skindeep/). It should be realized that sunscreen products containing UV-filters are classified as drugs in the USA, not as cosmetics; the number mentioned here, therefore, is that of cosmetics containing the UV-filter, but it does *not* include their presence in sunscreens. Ethyl methoxycinnamate was present in 10 (3%) of 329 sunscreen products (incl. 21 lipstick sunscreens) marketed in the UK in 2005 (2).

OTHER SIDE EFFECTS

Photosensitivity

In the UK, in the period 1983-1998, 2715 patients suspected of photosensitivity or with (a history of) dermatitis at exposed sites were photopatch tested with ethyl methoxycinnamate 2% and later 10% pet. and there were two (<0.1%) reactions. The relevance of these positive photopatch tests was not specified, but for all tested photocontact allergens together, 37% of positive reactions were considered relevant (1).

LITERATURE

1   Darvay A, White I, Rycroft R, Jones AB, Hawk JL, McFadden JP. Photoallergic contact dermatitis is uncommon. Br J Dermatol 2001;145:597-601

2   Wahie S, Lloyd JJ, Farr PM. Sunscreen ingredients and labelling: a survey of products available in the U.K. Clin Exp Dermatol 2007;32:359-364

3   Heurung AR, Raju SI, Warshaw EM. Adverse reactions to sunscreen agents: epidemiology, responsible irritants and allergens, clinical characteristics, and management. Dermatitis 2014;25:289-326

4   Heurung AR, Raju SI, Warshaw EM. Contact allergen of the year. Benzophenones. Dermatitis 2014;25:3-10 (contains many mistakes; Erratum in Dermatitis 2014;25:92-95)

5   Avenel-Audran M. Sunscreen products: finding the allergen. Eur J Dermatol 2010;20:161-166

6   Scheuer E, Warshaw E. Sunscreen allergy: a review of epidemiology, clinical characteristics, and responsible allergens. Dermatitis 2006;17:3-11

7   Funk JO, Dromgoole SH, Maibach HI. Sunscreen intolerance: contact sensitization, photocontact sensitization, and irritancy of sunscreen agents. Dermatol Clin 1995;13:473-481

8   Dromgoole SH, Maibach HI. Sunscreening agent intolerance: Contact and photocontact sensitization and contact urticaria. J Am Acad Dermatol 1990;22:1068-1078

9   Goossens A, Beck MH, Haneke E, McFadden JP, Nolting S, Durupt G, Ries G. Adverse cutaneous reactions to cosmetic allergens. Contact Dermatitis 1999;40:112-113

10 Shaw T, Simpson B, Wilson B, Oostman H, Rainey D, Storrs F. True photoallergy to sunscreens is rare despite popular belief. Dermatitis 2010;21:185-198

11 Schauder S. Survey of the literature on adverse reactions to preparations containing UV filters (1947-1989) (Literaturübersicht über Unverträglichkeitsreaktionen auf lichtfilterhaltige Produkte von 1947 bis 1989). Z Hautkr 1990;65:982-998 (article in German)

2.187 ETHYLPARABEN

IDENTIFICATION

Description/definition : Ethylparaben is the ester of ethyl alcohol and *p*-hydroxybenzoic acid, which conforms to the formula shown below
Chemical class(es) : Esters; phenols
Chemical/IUPAC name : Ethyl 4-hydroxybenzoate
Other names : Ethyl parahydroxybenzoate
CAS registry number (s) :120-47-8
EC number(s) : 204-399-4
CIR review(s) : J Am Coll Toxicol 1984;3:147-209; Int J Toxicol 2008;27(Suppl.4):1-82 (access: www.cir-safety.org/ingredients)
SCCS opinion(s) : SCCS/1348/10 (5); SCCP/0874/05 (6)
Merck Index monograph : 5160
Function(s) in cosmetics : EU: preservative. USA: fragrance ingredients; preservatives
EU cosmetic restrictions : Regulated in Annex V/12 of the Regulation (EC) No. 1223/2009
Patch testing : 3.0% pet. (Chemotechnique, SmartPracticeEurope, SmartPracticeCanada); also present in the paraben mix (see there)
Molecular formula : $C_9H_{10}O_3$

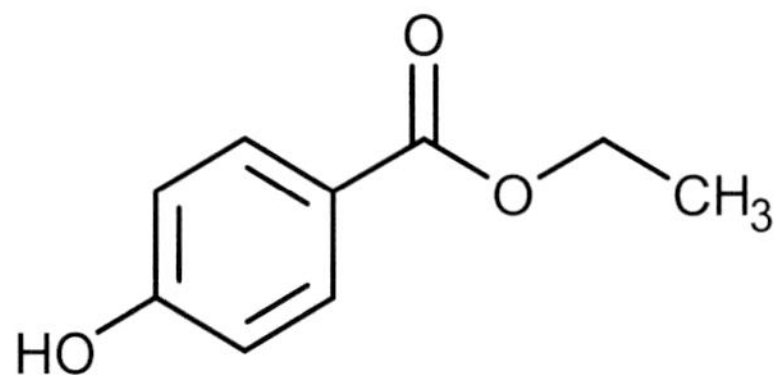

GENERAL

For general information on paraben esters see Chapter 2.333 Paraben mix. The literature on contact allergy to and other information on parabens, in which the ester is not specified ('paraben mix', 'paraben', 'parabens'), is also discussed in that chapter. The literature on contact allergy to ethylparaben and other paraben esters from before 1991 has been reviewed in ref. 7. Other, more recent, useful reviews were published in 2005 (parabens) (15), 2004 (16) and 2014 (21) (parabens and other preservatives). The subject of possible endocrine effects of parabens is discussed in the section 'Systemic side effects' of Chapter 2.333 Paraben mix).

CONTACT ALLERGY

Patch testing in groups of patients

Routine testing

In 1985, in The Netherlands, 627 consecutive patients suspected of contact dermatitis were patch tested with ethylparaben 5% pet. and 2 (0.3%) had a positive patch test reaction. The relevance of these reactions was not stated (2).

Testing in groups of selected patients

Between 1971 and 1986, in Denmark, 60 patients previously reacting to the paraben mix (benzyl-, butyl-, ethyl-, methyl- and propylparaben) were tested with all five components at 5% pet. Forty (67%) reacted to one or more of the paraben-esters, most of who reacted to 2 or more. There were 23 reactions (38%) to ethylparaben. The relevance of these positive patch test reactions was not mentioned (10).

Case reports and case series

A woman reported severe itching and erythema of the face and scalp, with eyelid edema, after using a tar shampoo for the treatment of dandruff. This happened on several occasions, she having initially tolerated the preparation. Patch testing with the European standard series, a facial series, and coal and wood tars gave positive reactions to the paraben mix and balsam of Peru. Further testing with individual components of the paraben mix showed positive results to ethylparaben, propylparaben and butylparaben. The ingredient listing of the shampoo included 'parabens'; no specific data on the esters were provided (20).

Contact allergy to ethylparaben in non-cosmetic products

One patient had allergic contact dermatitis from ethylparaben and other parabens in multiple topical pharmaceutical preparations (8). In Denmark, creams, ointments, and powders containing ethyl paraben 5% have long been popular remedies for athlete's foot since 1935. This explains over half of the 340 cases of paraben sensitivity diagnosed at the Finsen Institute in that country and reported at the beginning of the 1960s (9). The first cases of contact sensitivity to ethylparaben in antifungal preparations were reported in 1940 (14). (Probably) two patients had allergic contact dermatitis from ethylparaben (and presumably also from other parabens) in topical pharmaceuticals (12).

Cross-reactions, pseudo-cross-reactions and co-reactions

Co-reactions with other paraben-esters are seen frequently (7,9,10). As most patients are exposed to more than one paraben, it is difficult to determine whether these co-reactions result from cross-sensitivity or from concomitant sensitization (11). See also this section in Chapter 2.333 Paraben mix.

Presence in cosmetic products and chemical analyses

In the USA, in April 2017, ethylparaben was present in 4595 of 56,714 cosmetic products of which the composition is known in FDA's Voluntary Cosmetic Registration Program (VCRP) (data obtained from FDA, May 2017). In February 2017, ethylparaben was present in 1297 of 64,482 cosmetic products of which the composition is known in EWG's Skin Deep Cosmetics Database, USA (http://www.ewg.org/skindeep/). Ethylparaben was present in 5 (9%) of 54 personal hygiene wet wipes for which ingredient information was obtained online and from retail stores, USA, 2016 (23). Ethylparaben was present in 6 (3%) of 178 facial wipes for which ingredient information was obtained online and from retail stores, USA, 2016 (22). Of 179 emollients available in Poland in 2014, 26 (15%) contained ethylparaben (18).

In Germany, in 2006-2009, the labels of 4680 cosmetic products were screened for the presence of preservatives. Ethylparaben was present in 19.9% of the products, according to labeling information (19). Ethylparaben was present in 22% of 204 cosmetic products (92 shampoos, 61 hair conditioners, 34 liquid soaps, 17 wet tissues) in Sweden, 2008 (1). Ethylparaben was present in 59 of 1774 (3.3%) cosmetics and toiletries in 2002 resp. in 58 of 1170 (5.0%) such products in 2005, filed in the Danish Product Register Database (PROBAS) (3). In a group of 67 samples of skin creams, randomly selected from retail outlets in Denmark in 1999, 29 (43%) contained ethylparaben in a concentration range of 0.003% to 0.100% (4).

In the beginning of the 1990s, 215 cosmetic products, 158 leave-on cosmetics and 57 rinse-off cosmetics, from 79 cosmetic-producing companies, collected in Denmark, were analysed for paraben content with high performance liquid chromatography (HPLC) (17).Of all the products investigated, 93% were found to contain paraben(s). Paraben was detected in 77% of the rinse-off products and in 99% of the leave-on products. Total paraben content in the paraben-positive cosmetics was 0.01%-0.59%, except in one sun-lotion that contained 0.87% parabens. Rinse-off cosmetics contained 0.01-0.50% parabens and the paraben content in leave-on products was 0.01-0.59%. Ethylparaben was present in 32% of the paraben-positive products in a concentration range of 0.01% to 0.19% (w/w) (17).

OTHER SIDE EFFECTS

Immediate-type reactions

A man had contact urticaria from moisturizing preparations and other common skin products containing parabens. An open test with ethylparaben was positive. A Prausnitz-Küstner test was also positive, indicating that this was an immunologic immediate contact reaction to ethylparaben (13).

LITERATURE

1   Yazar K, Johnsson S, Lind M-L, Boman A, Lidén C. Preservatives and fragrances in selected consumer-available cosmetics and detergents. Contact Dermatitis 2011;64:265-272
2   De Groot AC, Weyland JW, Bos JD, Jagtman BA. Contact allergy to preservatives (I). Contact Dermatitis 1986;14:120-122
3   Flyvholm, MA. Preservatives in registered chemical products. Contact Dermatitis 2005;53:27-32
4   Rastogi SC. Analytical control of preservative labelling on skin creams. Contact Dermatitis 2000;43:339-343
5   SCCS (Scientific Committee on Consumer Safety). Opinion on parabens, 14 December 2010, revision of 22 March 2011, SCCS/1348/10. Available at:
    http://ec.europa.eu/health/scientific_committees/consumer_safety/docs/sccs_o_041.pdf

6   SCCP (Scientific Committee on Consumer Products). Extended Opinion on Parabens, underarm cosmetics and breast cancer, 28 January 2005, SCCP/0874/05. Available at: http://ec.europa.eu/health/archive/ph_risk/committees/04_sccp/docs/sccp_o_00d.pdf

7   Fransway AF. The problem of preservation in the 1990s: III. Agents with preservative function independent of formaldehyde release. Am J Cont Derm 1991;2:145-174

8   Schorr WP, Mohajerin AH. Paraben sensitivity. Arch Dermatol 1966;93:721-723

9   Hjorth N, Trolle-Lassen C. Skin reactions to ointment bases. Trans St John Hosp Derm Soc 1963;49:127-140

10   Menné T, Hjorth N. Routine patch testing with paraben esters. Contact Dermatitis 1988;19:189-191

11   Hansen J, Møllgaard B, Avnstorp C, Menné T. Paraben contact allergy: Patch testing and in vitro absorption/metabolism. Am J Cont Derm 1993;4:78-86

12   Schorr WF. Paraben allergy. A cause of intractable dermatitis. JAMA 1968;204:859-862

13   Henry JC, Tchen EH, Becker LE. Contact urticaria to parabens. Arch Dermatol 1979;115:1231-1232

14   Bonnevie P. Overfolmsomhed for aetylparauxybenzoat (Mycocten). Nord med 1940;6:684-686

15   Cashman AL, Warshaw EM. Parabens: A review of epidemiology, structure, allergenicity, and hormonal properties. Dermatitis 2005;16:57-66

16   Sasseville D. Hypersensitivity to preservatives. Dermatol Ther 2004;17:251-263

17   Rastogi SC, Schouten A, de Kruijf N, Weijland JW. Contents of methyl-, ethyl-, propyl-, butyl- and benzylparaben in cosmetic products. Contact Dermatitis 1995;32:28-30

18   Osinka K, Karczmarz A, Krauze A, Feleszko W. Contact allergens in cosmetics used in atopic dermatitis: analysis of product composition. Contact Dermatitis 2016;75:241-243

19   Uter W, Yazar K, Kratz EM, Mildau G, Lidén C. Coupled exposure to ingredients of cosmetic products: II. Preservatives. Contact Dermatitis 2014;70:219-226

20   Cooper SM, Shaw S. Allergic contact dermatitis from parabens in a tar shampoo. Contact Dermatitis 1998;39:140

21   Yim E, Baquerizo Nole KL, Tosti A. Contact dermatitis caused by preservatives. Dermatitis 2014;25:215-231

22   Aschenbeck KA, Warshaw EM. Allergenic ingredients in facial wet wipes. Dermatitis 2017 Mar 23. doi: 10.1097/DER.0000000000000268. [Epub ahead of print]

23   Aschenbeck KA, Warshaw EM. Allergenic ingredients in personal hygiene wet wipes. Dermatitis 2017 Mar 23. doi: 10.1097/DER.0000000000000275. [Epub ahead of print]

2.188   FORMALDEHYDE

IDENTIFICATION

Description/definition	: Formaldehyde is a volatile aldehyde that conforms to the formula shown below
Chemical class(es)	: Aldehydes
Chemical/IUPAC name	: Formaldehyde
Other names	: Methanal; methyl aldehyde; methylene oxide; oxomethane; oxymethylene
CAS registry number (s)	: 50-00-0
EC number(s)	: 200-001-8
CIR review(s)	: J Am Coll Toxicol 1984;3:157-184; Int J Toxicol 2013;32(Suppl.4):5-32 (access: www.cir-safety.org/ingredients)
SCCS opinion(s)	: SCCS/1538/14 (133); SCCNFP/587/02 (134)
Merck Index monograph	: 5533
Function(s) in cosmetics	: EU: preservative. USA: cosmetic biocides; denaturants; preservatives
EU cosmetic restrictions	: Regulated in Annexes III/13 and V/5 of the Regulation (EC) No. 1223/2009
Patch testing	: 1.0% water (Chemotechnique, SmartPracticeEurope, SmartPracticeCanada); 2.0% water (Chemotechnique, SmartPracticeCanada); 1.0% pet. (Chemotechnique); the test concentration of formaldehyde in the European Baseline Series was increased from 1% to 2% (in water) in 2013 (28) as, with this higher concentration, far more patients allergic to formaldehyde are identified (15,16,28,32,33,81)
Molecular formula	: CH_2O

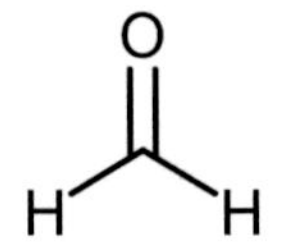

GENERAL

Formaldehyde (methanal) is a colorless gas with a characteristic pungent odor. Formalin is a 37%-40% aqueous solution of formaldehyde, to which 10-15% methyl alcohol has been added to inhibit polymerization. This simple aldehyde is ubiquitous in the environment, and is generated in and released from the smoke of burning wood, coal, charcoal, tobacco, natural gas, and kerosene. Formaldehyde also occurs naturally in certain foods such as coffee, dried bean curd, cod fish, caviar, maple syrup, shiitake mushrooms, and smoked ham. It is an irritant as well as an allergen and a potential respiratory carcinogen. It can be formed by breaking, conversion and oxidization of ingested aspartame (an artificial sweetener) and possibly cause migraines in formaldehyde-allergic individuals (55).

Formaldehyde can be used as a disinfectant as it kills most bacteria and fungi. It was first commercially used in embalming fluid and as a preservative for laboratory specimens. Later it was used to make plywood and asphalt shingles. It is also added in bonded leather, waterproof glues, fertilizers, and photographic developer. Exposure to formaldehyde is difficult to estimate because the chemical – besides being used as such – is incorporated into a large variety of products and reactants in many chemical processes, including formaldehyde-releasers, polymerized plastics, metalworking fluids, medicaments, fabrics, cosmetics and detergents (49). Examples of products that may contain formaldehyde are shown in table 2.188.1.

In finished products, there may be several sources of formaldehyde, some of which are 'hidden' or 'occult' (49,198), including formaldehyde added as an active ingredient for preservation; formaldehyde released from formaldehyde-releasers (usually preservatives); formaldehyde which is used for the preservation of raw materials used to prepare the product; formaldehyde in formaldehyde-based raw materials used to prepare the product; formaldehyde used to sterilize vessels for the storage of raw materials or products; formaldehyde released by package materials such as formaldehyde resins coating cosmetic and pharmaceutical tubes; formaldehyde formed *in situ* by degradation of some non-formaldehyde-containing components of the product, e.g., ethoxylated alcohols (173) and other surfactants (49).

Scope of this chapter and reviews

In this chapter, only dermatological side effects of formaldehyde are presented. Discussion of systemic side effects (e.g., carcinogenicity [217]), asthma from inhalation and other non-dermatological adverse reactions is considered to fall outside the scope of this book. The literature on contact allergy to formaldehyde and formaldehyde-releasers up to 2009-2010 has been reviewed by the author in refs. 31,34,37,38, 49,50 and 52. Literature before 1991 has been discussed in refs. 39 and 40. When important literature references appear to be missing in this chapter, they are discussed in these review articles and are not presented here again or their data are cited in this chapter with these reviews as reference.

Table 2.188.1 Examples of products that may contain formaldehyde (adapted from ref. 49)*

adhesives (glues, pastes, cements)	impregnating agents
agricultural chemicals (seed disinfectants)	latex rubber
antifreeze agents	metalworking fluids (31,34)
asphalt shingles	mildew preventatives (fruits, vegetables)
binders (polymers)	paint removers
castings (154)	paper and paper industry (175, 184)
cellulose esters	phenolic resins in adhesives and footwear
chipboard	photocopier toner (172)
cleaning products (191)	surface active agents
clothing and textiles (crease-resistant) (38,52)	tanning agents
coloring agents	tissue fixatives (181)
construction materials	vaccines (192,193)
corrosion inhibitors	urea plastics in adhesives and footwear
cosmetics (50)	dental preparations (162,163)
photographic paper and solutions	deodorizers
plywood	disinfectants
polishes and finishes	dry cleaning materials
printing inks (186)	embalming fluids (202)
reusable protective gloves (159)	fabric softeners (189)
starch (spray and powdered) (180)	filling agents (stopping, putty, etc.)
moistened baby toilet tissue (174)	flame retardant
orthopedic casts (154)	flooring materials
paints, lacquers, coatings (147)	footwear (resins and plastics)
leather (179)	formaldehyde resins (melamine-, urea-, etc.)
medications: wart remedies	fumigants
laboratory chemicals	glues
hydrocarbons (e.g., oil)	hardeners

* some uses mentioned here, found in literature, may have been abandoned

CONTACT ALLERGY

Into the 1980s, prevalence rates of sensitization to formaldehyde in consecutive patients suspected of contact dermatitis (routine testing) were high in the USA, Canada, many European countries (56,57) and Japan (58). Formaldehyde in clothes was an important source of sensitization (122,155,156,157,158) as was its use as an antiperspirant (121,122,123). In Japan, the high frequency of 18% in 1977 dropped to 2.8% a couple of years later. This fall reflected its Government's regulations which restricted the levels of formaldehyde allowed in underclothes (58). Formaldehyde *per se* was previously used as a preservative in cosmetics, as a disinfectant, as an antiperspirant and in textile finish resins releasing large amounts of formaldehyde, resulting in high sensitization rates (59). However, its use in cosmetics has largely been abandoned and replaced with formaldehyde-releasers due to allegations of carcinogenicity. As a disinfectant it was partly replaced by other compounds like glutaraldehyde and glyoxal. Also, low formaldehyde textile resins were introduced. Thus, since the 1980s, there has been a decline in the frequency of sensitization in most countries.

Nevertheless, currently, formaldehyde still is a common cause of contact allergy. The frequency of sensitization to formaldehyde remains at a stable level of around 2-2.5% in most (European) countries in the general patch test population (148). In the USA, however, rates of 8-9% were rule rather than exception up to 2008, after which the frequencies started to decrease to levels of 6-7% (table 2.188.3). Still, these are probably underestimations. Recently, the patch test concentration was raised from 1% to 2% in water; with this concentration, more patients allergic to formaldehyde are identified (15,16,28,32,33,81).

Often, the products causing formaldehyde sensitization or elicitation of allergic contact dermatitis are not preserved with formaldehyde itself, but with agents that release formaldehyde under usage conditions, the so-called formaldehyde-releasers (or formaldehyde donors). These are shown in the section 'Cross-, pseudo-cross- and co-reactions' below.

Currently, most reactions to formaldehyde, especially in women, who are affected 1.2-1.5 times more frequently than men, are believed to result from contact with cosmetics and household products (40,60,82) in which formaldehyde-releasers are frequently used. They often have hand eczema with or without facial dermatitis

(62,63,80). This is explained by the hands being exposed to household cleansing agents such as washing-up liquids (187), where formaldehyde is often found in combination with detergents that impair barrier function and increase penetration (63). Facial dermatitis results from the use of cosmetics. Sensitization to formaldehyde may also be caused by occupational exposure, especially in metalworkers and the medical professions (39,40,61,62,64,212).

The prognosis of dermatitis caused by formaldehyde is not very good (62,63,65,187). As formaldehyde is so widely distributed in the environment, it is difficult to avoid. Also, cosmetic products not labeled to contain formaldehyde or a formaldehyde-releaser, may actually prove to contain those when analysed (139). In one study of 11 patients with hand dermatitis and contact allergy to formaldehyde, all had used one or more products containing formaldehyde or formaldehyde-releasers (187). Even when the patients try to, most will still suffer from exacerbations of dermatitis (62,63,65), though fewer in number than in those not paying attention to their allergy (65).

Patch testing in the general population and in subgroups

There are several investigations in some European countries in which random samples of the population of certain age groups have been patch tested with formaldehyde (table 2.188.2). The highest prevalence was found in Norway in 2005: 0.9%, in women 1.0% and in men 0.7% (111). In two Danish studies (110,112), lower frequencies were found. However, in these investigations, the patch tests were read only at day 2, which may have resulted in underestimation of the actual rate of sensitization.

Results of testing formaldehyde in subgroups of the population are shown in table 2.188.2. In Denmark, of 1146 8th grade schoolchildren investigated in 1995-1996, none reacted to formaldehyde (114,116). When 442 of them were reinvestigated 15 years later, 0.7% (women 0.7%, men 0.6%) had become sensitized to formaldehyde (109). Similar frequencies were observed in Thailand (113) and Germany (115,117), albeit in other populations.

Table 2.188.2   Contact allergy in the general population and in subgroups

Year and country	Selection and number tested	Prevalence of contact allergy			Comments	Ref.
		Total	Women	Men		
General population						
2008-11 five European countries	general population, random sample, 18-74 years, n=3119	0.4%	0.5%	0.2%		108
2008 Denmark	general population, random sample, 15-41 years, n=469		1.1%	0%	patch tests were read on day 2 only	112
2006 Denmark	general population, random sample, 18-69 years, n=3460	0.2%	0.3%	0.1%	patch tests were read on day 2 only	110
2005 Norway	general population, random sample, 18-69 years, n=1236	0.9%	1.0%	0.7%		111
Subgroups						
2010 Denmark	unselected population of 8th grade schoolchildren in Denmark, 15 years later; n=442	0.7%	0.7%	0.6%	follow-up study	109
2005-2006 Thailand	adult volunteers recruited by advertising, 18-55 years, n=2545	0.7%	0.7%	0.8%	patch tests were read on day 2 only	113
1997-1998 Germany	adults 28-78 year, with a large percentage (>50%) of atopic individuals, n=1141	0.6%	0.3%	0.8%		115, 117
1995-1996 Denmark	8th grade school children, 12-16 years, n=1146	0%	0%	0%		114, 116

Estimates of the 10-year prevalence of contact allergy to formaldehyde in the general population of Denmark based on the CE-DUR method ranged from 0.50% to 0.68% (106). In a similar study from Germany, the estimated prevalence in the general population in the period 1992-2000 ranged from 0.3% to 0.7% (107).

Patch testing in groups of patients

Results of patch testing formaldehyde in consecutive patients suspected of contact dermatitis (routine testing) back to 2000 are shown in table 2.188.3. Results of testing in groups of *selected* patients (e.g., nurses with occupational contact dermatitis, individuals with eyelid dermatitis, children with dermatitis, hairdressers, painters, patients with allergic contact cheilitis or ACD of the face) back to 1994 are shown in table 2.188.4.

Patch testing in consecutive patients suspected of contact dermatitis: routine testing

As formaldehyde is included in the European Baseline Series, the screening tray of the North American Contact Dermatitis Group (NACDG) and most other national series routinely tested in consecutive patients suspected of contact dermatitis, there are many data on formaldehyde contact allergy available, notably from European countries and from the USA + Canada, where the NACDG publishes their patch test results biannually.

Table 2.188.3 Patch testing in groups of patients: Routine testing

Years and Country	Test conc. & vehicle	Number of patients tested	positive (%)	Selection of patients (S); Relevance (R); Comments (C)	Ref.
2013-14 USA, Canada	2% water	4858	339 (7.0%)	R: definite + probable relevance: 22%	223
	1% water	4858	274 (5.6%)	R: definite + probable relevance: 18%	
2013-2014 12 European countries, 46 departments [b]	1% water	19,829	(1.5%)	R: not stated; C: results of 6 occupational dermatology clinics and one pediatric clinic not included in these figures; range of positive reactions: 0%-3.5% (1% test substance), 0%-2.6% (2% test substance)	231
	2% water	9972	(1.8%)		
2011-12 USA, Canada	1% water	4237	278 (6.6%)	R: definite + probable relevance: 22%	29
2009-2012, 12 European countries [b]	1% water	48,676	(0.7%) [a]	R: not stated; C: range per country 1.2-5.0%	230
	2% water	12,195	(1.0%) [a]	R: not stated; C: range per country 1.0-3.4%	
1996-2012 Italy	1% water	23,774	(3.3%)	R: not stated; C: the face was affected statistically more frequent than in patients not allergic to formaldehyde	80
2011 Sweden	2% water	2122	72 (3.4%)	R: not stated; C: range per center: 0-9.7%	140
	1% water	2122	40 (1.9%)	R: not stated; C: range per center: 0.6-4.1%	
2009-10 USA, Canada	1% water	4305	250 (5.8%)	R: definite + probable relevance: 27%	30
2009-2010 10 European countries + USA	2% water	3591	122 (3.4%)	R: not stated; C: prevalences ranged from 1.3% to 11.9%; irritant reactions ranged from 0% to 21%	15
	1% water	3591	66 (1.8%)	R: not stated; C: prevalences ranged from 0.7% to 8.5%; irritant reactions ranged from 0% to 8%	
2006-2010 USA	1% water	3093	(7.8%)	R: 64%	95
2001-2010 Australia	1% water	5144	279 (5.4%)	R: 43%	219
2009 Sweden	1% water	3112	(2.5%)	R: not stated	91
2005-2009 Spain	1% water	7838	135 (1.7%)	R: not specified	4
1996-2009 IVDK	1% water	121,558	1908 (1.5%) [a]	R: not stated	9
2007-2008 11 European countries [b]	1% water	25,181	417 (1.7%) [a]	R: not stated; C: prevalences ranged from 0.7% (Switzerland) to 5.9% (Finland, high %, data from an occupational clinic)	1
2007-8 USA, Canada	1% water	5081	(7.7%)	R: definite + probable relevance: 38%	17
1985-2008 Denmark	1% water	18,179	555 (3.1%)	R: not stated; C: range per 3 year periods: 2.2-4.4%	150
2005-6 USA, Canada	1% water	4445	(9.0%)	R: definite + probable relevance: 36%	13
2005-2006 10 European countries [b]	1% water	18,503	450 (2.4%)	R: not stated; C: prevalences were 1.8% in Central Europe, 2.0% in West, 3.7% in Northeast and 4.2% in South Europe	151
1993-2006 Australia	1% water	6845	(4.6%)	R: 42%	206
2000-2005 USA	1% water	3836	(9.0%)	R: 76%	7
2004-2005 UK	1% water	6958	(1.9%)	R: not stated	84
1985-2005 Denmark	1% water	14,980	(2.9%)	R: not stated	43
2004, 11 European countries [b]	1% water	9956	203 (2.0%) [a]	R: not stated; C: range positives per center: 0.0%-5.1%	10
2003-4 USA, Canada	1% water	5142	447 (8.7%)	R: not stated	18
2001-2004 IVDK	1% water	31,045	(1.7%)	R: not stated	42
1998-2004 Israel	1% water	2156	(1.8%)	R: not stated	41
1992-2004 Turkey	1% water	1038	13 (1.3%)	R: not stated; C: prevalence in women 1.1%, in men 1.5%	88
2002-2003 Europe [b]	1% water	9213	(2.0%)	R: not stated; C: 17 centers in 9 European countries	45
2001-02 USA, Canada	1% water	4909	(8.4%)	R: definite + probable relevance: 15%	46
2000-2002 Finland	1% water	11,798	(2.5%)	R: not stated	54
1999-2001 Sweden	1% water	3790	(2.6%)	R: not stated; C: prevalence in women 2.3%, in men 1.7% (standardized prevalences)	85
1997-2001 Czech Rep.	1% water	12,058	501 (4.2%)	R: not stated; C: prevalence in men 3.1%, in women 4.7%	89
1998-2000 USA	1% water	1321	(7.9%)	R: not stated	86
1996-2000 Europe	1% water	26,210	(2.3%)	R: not stated; C: prevalence in women 2.4%, in men 2.0%; C: ten centers, seven countries, EECDRG study	90

[a] age-standardized and sex-standardized proportions
[b] study of the ESSCA (European Surveillance System on Contact Allergies)
EECDRG: European Environmental and Contact Dermatitis Research Group
IVDK: Information Network of Departments of Dermatology, Germany, Austria, Switzerland

In European countries, since 2000, frequencies of positive patch test reactions to formaldehyde have ranged from 1.0% to 4.2%; most were in the 1.7%-2.5% range. In the USA + Canada, however, NACDG prevalences were 7.7% to 9.0% up to 2008, after which a small decline to 5.8% in 2009-2010, 6.6% in 2011-2012 and 5.6% in 2013-2014 was observed (29,30,223). The causes of the large discrepancy between European countries and the USA + Canada are as yet unknown.

It should be realized, that these percentages may still be an underestimation. In all but five recent studies (15,140,223,230,231), patients have been patch tested with formaldehyde 1% in water. In the investigations in which patients have been tested both with 1% and 2% formaldehyde, the rates of sensitization were always higher and in some nearly doubled with the higher test concentration: 3.5% versus 1.9% (140) and 3.4% versus 1.8% (15). Indeed, the test concentration of formaldehyde in the European Baseline Series was increased from 1% to 2% (in water) in 2013 (28) as, with this higher concentration, far more patients allergic to formaldehyde are identified (15,16,28,32,33,81).

Relevance data are largely lacking: in most studies, they are not mentioned at all. In the NACDG studies, 'definite' + 'probable' relevance has ranged from 15% to 38% (13,17,29,30,46,223). In 2 other USA studies, 64% (95) and 76% (7) of the positive patch tests were considered to be relevant and in a 1993-2006 Australian study, the percentage was 42 (206). Details on the incriminated products were never provided.

Patch testing in groups of selected patients
Results of testing in groups of selected patients (e.g., nurses with occupational contact dermatitis, individuals with eyelid dermatitis, children with dermatitis, hairdressers, painters, patients with allergic contact cheilitis or ACD of the face) back to 1994 are shown in table 2.188.4. Frequencies observed in USA studies were generally not higher than in routine testing. In a small study in 57 patients with facial allergic contact dermatitis, 6 (11%) had contact allergy to formaldehyde (97). This can readily be explained by the fact that the group had been selected on the basis of proven allergic contact dermatitis and that formaldehyde (mostly from formaldehyde-releasers) is an important contact allergen in cosmetics. In European studies, rates of 3-5% were observed in patients with occupational contact dermatitis (146) including painters, who had significantly more often contact allergy than non-painter controls (147).

In 13/25 studies, no relevance data were provided. In the studies that did address the relevance issue, relevance percentages were usually high, up to 100% (in some studies only relevant reactions were presented). However, causative products were mentioned in one study only: sterilizing solutions (non-skin), cosmetics, chemical products and medical devices (220).

Table 2.188.4 Patch testing in groups of patients: Selected patient groups

Years and Country	Test conc. & vehicle	Number of patients		Selection of patients (S); Relevance (R); Comments (C)	Ref.
		tested	positive (%)		
2013-2015 USA		1109	64 (5.8%)	S: children 0-18 years suspected of contact dermatitis; R: 77%	232
2003-2014 IVDK	1% water	5202	(1.0%)	S: patients with stasis dermatitis / chronic leg ulcers; R: not stated; C: percentage of reactions not significantly higher than in a control group of routine testing	235
2011-2013 Sweden		2224	5 (0.2%)	S: adolescents aged 15.8-18.9 years; R: not stated; C: the patch test reactions were read only at D2, which means that the actual frequency may have been higher	145
1996-2013 Netherlands	1% water	1000	6 (0.6%)	S: children aged 0-17 years; R: not stated	234
2003-2012 IVDK		2047	48 (2.3%)	S: nurses with occupational contact dermatitis; R: not stated	20
2002-2011 Denmark		399	6 (1.5%)	S: hairdressers with contact dermatitis; R: not stated	226
2006-2010 USA	1% water	100	6 (6%)	S: patients with eyelid dermatitis; R: not stated	19
2002-2010 11 European countries [a]	1% water	9986	(3.0%)	S: patients with occupational contact dermatitis; R: not stated; C: the adjusted prevalence ratio versus patients with no occupational contact dermatitis was 1.75	146
2001-2010 Denmark	1% water	219	11 (5.0%)	S: painters; R: not stated; C: significantly higher frequency than in non-painter controls (19/1095, 1.7%)	147
2000-2010 IVDK		4383	50 (1.1%)	S: patients with periorbital dermatitis; R: not stated	47
1994-2010 USA, Canada	1% water	432	? (?)	S: hairdressers / cosmetologists; R: in the group of 184 patients who had at least one relevant occupationally related reaction, 27 (14.7%) reacted to formaldehyde	227
1994-2004 USA	1% water	46	3 (6.5%)	S: patients with allergic contact dermatitis of the eyelids; R: these were relevant reactions, but the causative products were not mentioned	92
2001-04 USA, Canada	1% water	60	2 (3.3%)	S: patients with allergic contact cheilitis; R: these reactions were relevant, but the causative products were not mentioned	96
1998-04 USA, Canada	1% water	1254	10 (0.8%)	S: health care workers; R: only occupation-related (=relevant)	220

Table 2.188.4 Patch testing in groups of patients: Selected patient groups (*continued*)

Years and Country	Test conc. & vehicle	Number of patients tested	positive (%)	Selection of patients (S); Relevance (R); Comments (C)	Ref.
				reactions were recorded; C: in the light of this selection, the frequency of sensitization is low; the frequency was not significantly higher than the rate of occupation-related reactions in non-health care workers (0.7%); the causative products were sterilizing solutions (non-skin), cosmetics, chemical products and medical devices	
1995-2004 UK	1% water	500	3 (0.6%)	S: children 0-16 years referred for patch testing; R: all 3 reactions were relevant	233
2001-2 USA, Canada	1% water	2193	167 (7.6%)	S: patients with (presumed) cosmetic allergy; R: not stated	8
1995-1999 IVDK	1% water	972	(1.3%)	S: patients with allergic periorbital contact dermatitis; R: not stated	128
1994-1998 UK	1% water	232	3 (1.3%)	S: patients with eyelid dermatitis; R: all were currently relevant, but the causative products were not mentioned	93
1995-1997 USA		57	6 (11%)	S: patients with facial allergic contact dermatitis; R: only relevant reactions were mentioned, causative products were not mentioned	97
1990-1994 IVDK		587	16 (2.7%)	S: patients with periorbital eczema; R: not stated	228

[a] study of the ESSCA (European Surveillance System on Contact Allergies)
IVDK: Information Network of Departments of Dermatology, Germany, Austria, Switzerland

Case reports and case series

Case series

Formaldehyde was stated to be the (or an) allergen in 26 patients in a group of 603 individuals suffering from cosmetic dermatitis, seen in the period 2010-2015 in Leuven, Belgium (94). In the period 1996-2013, in a tertiary referral center in Valencia, Spain, 5419 patients were patch tested. Of these, 628 individuals had allergic contact dermatitis to cosmetics. Formaldehyde was the responsible allergen in twelve cases (224, overlap with ref. 135). Formaldehyde was responsible for 74 out of 959 cases of non-fragrance cosmetic allergy where the causal allergen was identified, Belgium, 2000-2010 (5). In the period 2000-2007, 202 patients with allergic contact dermatitis caused by cosmetics were seen in Valencia, Spain. In this group, six individuals reacted to formaldehyde from its presence in nail hardener (n=1), in gel/soap (n=2), in toothpaste (n=1), and in shampoo (n=2) (135, overlap with ref. 224). Sixty-six formaldehyde-allergic subjects reacted to cosmetic skin-care products containing formaldehyde-releasers, but none reacted to 'rinse-off' cosmetics (152, article not read).

In 3 clinics in Belgium, in the period 1978-1985, 279 patients with allergic contact dermatitis exclusively caused by cosmetics were seen. In this group, there were 18 reactions to formaldehyde. It was implied that this was the cause of the allergic reaction (215). Formaldehyde was responsible for 16 out of 399 cases of cosmetic allergy where the causal allergen was identified in a study of the NACDG, USA, 1977-1983 (6). In a group of 119 patients with allergic contact dermatitis from cosmetics, investigated in The Netherlands in 1986-1987, one case was caused by formaldehyde in a nail hardener (118,119). In a group of 75 patients allergic to cosmetic products, seen in a private practice in The Netherlands in the period 1981-1986, one case was caused by formaldehyde in a shampoo (120).

Case reports

One individual developed generalized dermatitis from contact allergy to formaldehyde in a liquid soap (12). Another patient had severe allergic contact dermatitis from formaldehyde in a hair-straightening product, which contained 2.8% formaldehyde (21). Two patients had relevant positive patch test reactions to moisturizers and one of them to a sun protection lotion. They were both allergic to formaldehyde and the presence of formaldehyde in the cosmetics was demonstrated by chemical analysis (131). Another woman had relevant positive patch test reactions to rouge and to its ingredient formaldehyde (131). One individual had dermatitis of the hands from contact allergy to formaldehyde present in a moistened baby toilet tissue (174). Three patients had dermatitis of the scalp from contact allergy to formaldehyde present in their shampoos (190). An unknown number of people reacted to formaldehyde in shampoo (221). A hairdresser who was allergic to formaldehyde developed exacerbations of dermatitis each time she worked with shampoos containing formaldehyde (222).

Nine patients had allergic contact dermatitis from baby towelettes. They all had hand dermatitis, one also perianal eczema. Five individuals used the towelettes for their childrens' hygiene, two were occupationally exposed (a nurse and a machine repairman working in the factory where the towelettes were produced), the others used them on their person. In this group of nine, 7 reacted to formaldehyde. Six of these 7 co-reacted to quaternium-15. It was suggested that preservatives are the main allergens (sometimes combined with fragrances) in these products, but the composition of the culprit towelettes was not provided. However, it is likely that, if formaldehyde was indeed the or an allergen, it was released from quaternium-15 present in the product as preservative (there were no reactions to other formaldehyde-releasers) (195). A plate maker had occupational ACD from formaldehyde present in a hand-washing agent (64). One patient had stomatitis and cheilitis due to allergy to formaldehyde present in mouthwash (201).

Nail lacquers

Three women reacted to formaldehyde used as solvent in nail lacquers (126). Two patients had relevant positive patch test reactions to nail polishes and to their ingredient formaldehyde, the presence of which was demonstrated by chemical analysis (131). In a group of 157 patients with allergic contact dermatitis from nail lacquer, seen in one clinic in Brazil in the period 1996-2006, 141 (90%) had positive patch test results only to tosylamide/formaldehyde resin (TFR), 9 (6%) had positive results to formaldehyde and TFR and 1 patient (1%) had positive results to formaldehyde and the nail varnish. All results were considered relevant. However, it was not verified that the nail lacquers contained free formaldehyde (194). *Comments.* Indeed, as tosylamide/ formaldehyde resin is based on tosylamide (synonym: toluenesulfonamide) and formaldehyde, free formaldehyde is said to be present in the majority of nail lacquers, with concentrations varying from 0.02% to 0.5% (reference lost in writing). Despite this, the allergen in nail lacquers appears to be the resin itself and people do not become sensitized to formaldehyde from the use of these nail cosmetics. The amount of free formaldehyde in finished, dried nail lacquer is believed to be nil and nail lacquers do not seem to cause dermatitis in patients already allergic to formaldehyde (49). Indeed, it was recently shown that tosylamide/formaldehyde resin is very stable and hardly releases any formaldehyde from several matrices (216).

Toothpastes

One patient developed stinging and tenderness of the gums with erythema and swelling together with moderate cheilitis from a 'sensitive teeth formula' toothpaste containing 1.3% formalin (formaldehyde solution). She had previously been sensitized to formaldehyde while working as a jeweler's assistant with formaldehyde containing polishes (48). One individual had swelling of the upper lip and later of the eyelids plus ulceration of the inner part of the lip and gingiva from contact allergy to formaldehyde in a toothpaste. He had applied this product for 30 minutes undiluted; the toothpaste contained 1.3% formalin (formaldehyde solution). The medical authorities received >100 reports of adverse reactions to this toothpaste (98).

A patient was described in a US journal with the title 'Eczematous contact dermatitis of the palm due to toothpaste (99). The allergen was cited as formaldehyde in ref. 100. However, the authors of ref. 101 mentioned that it was a toothpaste 'that contained compound G-4' (which is dichlorophene) and Cronin in her book states that 'patch testing with the toothpaste was positive' (102). In 1933, three patients with reactions of the oral mucosa and the adjacent skin were reported, in who the condition was due to a toothpaste, which contained a solution of formaldehyde. One case was thought to be a 'true idiosyncrasy', in the two others the author considered the condition to be due to an allergy, which was later exacerbated by the use of a mouthwash (103, data cited in refs. 104 and 105).

A woman who was contact allergic to formaldehyde developed pharyngitis and dysphonia from a toothpaste containing formaldehyde. Oral intake of a capsule containing formaldehyde resulted after a few hours in headache, pharyngitis, dysphonia, and colitis-like pain. Later, a provocation test with the capsule was again positive (211).

Antiperspirants (not used anymore)

One patient had axillary dermatitis from formaldehyde sensitivity in a deodorant (121). Four (122) and 10 (123) such patients were reported in a period when formaldehyde solutions were often used as antiperspirant.

Nail hardeners

Nail hardeners, which were widely used in the 1960s in the USA, were essentially solutions of formaldehyde in concentrations ranging from 4% to 40% (11). Reactions to these products are well recognized (11,23, 136,137,142). The nail changes reported were onycholysis, bluish discoloration of the nail plate, splinter hemorrhages of the nail bed, subungual hyperkeratosis, severe throbbing pain in the fingers and dryness of the skin. Nail shedding was uncommon (79). Resolving hemorrhages produced reddish-rust or yellow discoloration of the nail. Discontinuation of the nail hardener resulted in complete resolution. Pterygium inversum has been observed (44), as has ectopic contact dermatitis of the face, even associated with hemorrhages of the lips in nail biters (87). Airborne contact dermatitis of the face was also seen (137). The reactions of the nail apparatus were usually attributed to the formaldehyde content of the nail hardeners. While positive patch tests to formaldehyde have been elicited in some patients (11,124,125), other workers have suggested that it was an irritant rather than an allergic contact reaction.

Some brands of nail hardeners used in the 1960s containing formaldehyde caused so many cases of nail damage, that they were recalled by the FDA. Nail hardeners containing formaldehyde have not been available anymore in the

USA since 1969 (79), but imported products still caused onycholysis in a patient in 1981 (79). In the EU, however, a maximum of 2.2% free formaldehyde is allowed in nail hardeners. In 2016, two patients were reported who had vesicular and pustular dermatitis and psoriasis-like nail changes from contact allergy to formaldehyde present in a nail hardener (144).

Contact allergy to formaldehyde in non-cosmetic products
Full discussion of contact allergy to formaldehyde in non-cosmetic products is considered to fall outside the scope of this book. The author has previously published extensive (review) articles on contact allergy to (formaldehyde in) textile finishes (38,51,52,53), metalworking fluids (31,34) and to other formaldehyde-releasers (31,34). Only a few selected cases of contact allergy to formaldehyde in non-cosmetic products are presented here.

Non-occupational allergic contact dermatitis from formaldehyde in non-cosmetic products
One patient had allergic contact dermatitis from hidden (non-labeled) formaldehyde in skin disinfecting swabs (22). There have been several case reports of patients allergic to formaldehyde, who may have developed eyelid dermatitis from the ingestion of aspartame, an artificial sweetener in foods, drinks and chewing gums; formaldehyde is a metabolic product produced in the liver from aspartame (24,25,26,27). Three patients had allergic contact dermatitis of the lower legs due to exposure to orthopedic casts. In each instance, the causative agent was considered to be free formaldehyde derived from the melamine formaldehyde resin incorporated into the casts. All patients had positive patch tests to formaldehyde, and free formaldehyde was demonstrated in the cast material (154). A woman had dermatitis confined to the sides of the neck, the axillae, elbow flexures, and breast area corresponding to her brassiere. A patch test to formaldehyde was positive. Analysis by the chromotropic acid method of the patient's clothes including brassiere and underwear showed the presence of formaldehyde. Subsequent analysis of the fabric softener used by the patient was positive for formaldehyde. The manufacturer stated that it contained 0.7% formaldehyde as a preservative (189).

A woman developed allergic contact cheilitis from kissing the corps of her diseased boyfriend, which was preserved with formaldehyde, at the funeral (202). One patient had systemic allergic contact dermatitis from an influenza vaccination containing formaldehyde (204). In a similar case, a woman had exacerbation of previous hand dermatitis on two occasions and generalized pruritus one day after the third hepatitis B vaccination, which contained formaldehyde (192). A woman had allergic contact dermatitis of the opposing surfaces of the second and third fingers of both hands from formaldehyde released by smoking a particular brand of cigarettes (205).

Occupational allergic contact dermatitis from formaldehyde in non-cosmetic products
One patient had airborne allergic contact dermatitis from formaldehyde released from quaternium-15 in a photocopier toner (172). In a magazine seller, occupational allergic contact dermatitis of the hands was ascribed to formaldehyde in newspaper; however, the incriminated paper was not analyzed for the presence of formaldehyde (175). A woman had vesicular hand dermatitis from contact allergy to formaldehyde present in jeans and other textiles that she had contact with during her work in a clothing store (183). A bank clerk had occupational ACD of the hands ascribed to formaldehyde in bank notes he had to count manually (184). A woman working in a laboratory had ACD of the right hand, neck and perioral region from formaldehyde released by methylol urea present in a laboratory diluent (185).

A printer reacted to formaldehyde present in a barrier cream. He had also contact with formaldehyde released by glycol diacetal present in a fountain solution (186). Occupational exposure to a photographic product containing 35-40% formaldehyde was the probable source of sensitization in one patient with hand dermatitis (187). A formaldehyde-allergic gardener had occupational ACD from a pesticide containing a polymerization product of formaldehyde and free formaldehyde (64). A woman repairing sand cores had occupational allergic contact dermatitis from formaldehyde present in both the repairing material and the sand cores (213).

Cross-reactions, pseudo-cross-reactions and co-reactions
Patient allergic to formaldehyde may also have positive patch test reactions (co-reactions) to formaldehyde-releasers (formaldehyde donors), chemicals that, under certain circumstances, release formaldehyde (236,243). The positive patch test reaction to the formaldehyde-releaser then mostly is the result of an allergic reaction to the formaldehyde present in the patch test material (pseudo-cross-reactivity). The frequency of co-reactivity depends *inter alia* on the amount of formaldehyde that is released by the donor. In the case of formaldehyde-releasers used as preservatives in cosmetics, the highest co-reactivity rates are seen with quaternium-15 and DMDM hydantoin, the lowest with 2-bromo-2-nitropropane-1,3-diol and imidazolidinyl urea (37). Alternatively, the formaldehyde-releasers may also show positive patch test reactions *without* formaldehyde contact allergy. However, if there are reactions to 3 or more releasers, this is nearly always due to pseudo-cross-reactivity to formaldehyde (82).

Contact allergies to formaldehyde and methylchloroisothiazolinone/methylisothiazolinone (MCI) and/or methylisothiazolinone are significantly associated, as well as contact allergies to these preservatives and fragrance allergy. This results from concomitant or successive sensitization to these chemicals in the same or different products rather than from cross-reactivity (203). The association between MCI/MI and formaldehyde has been observed in two UK studies also (199,243).

Pseudo-cross-reactions in patients allergic to formaldehyde

Patients allergic to formaldehyde may show positive patch test reactions to one or more formaldehyde-releasers from the presence of formaldehyde in the patch test materials. Formaldehyde-releasers used in cosmetics, that have caused contact allergy / allergic contact dermatitis, are shown in table 2.188.5 (37,49,50), those used in finishes in clothes in table 2.188.6 (38,49,52), formaldehyde-releasers used as preservatives in metalworking fluids are summarized in table 2.188.7 (31,34,49) as are miscellaneous formaldehyde-releasers (31,34). For other formaldehyde-releasers which have not caused contact allergy / allergic contact dermatitis thus far and chemicals synthesized from formaldehyde that may still contain residues of free formaldehyde (e.g. melamine/formaldehyde and urea-formaldehyde resins) see ref. 49.

More detailed data on the relationship between formaldehyde allergy and reactions to formaldehyde-releasers used in metalworking fluids, in clothes (durable press chemical finishes) and miscellaneous releasers are considered to fall outside the scope of this chapter and can be found in the relevant review articles written by the author (31,34, 38,52). The relationship of formaldehyde allergy to formaldehyde releasing preservatives used in cosmetics has been discussed in refs. 37 and 50. A summary is shown in table 2.188.8, including data from (some) studies that were published after the reviews appeared; see also refs. 236 and 243.

Table 2.188.5 Formaldehyde-releasing chemicals in cosmetics (adapted from ref. 49)

Name	CAS number	Synonyms
Benzylhemiformal	14548-60-8	Phenylmethoxymethanol; (benzyloxy)methanol
5-Bromo-5-nitro-1,3-di-oxane	30007-47-7	Bromonitrodioxane
2-Bromo-2-nitropropane-1,3-diol	52-51-7	Bromonitropropanediol; bronopol
Diazolidinyl urea	78491-02-8	N,N'-Bis(hydroxymethyl)urea; 1-[1,3-bis(hydroxymethyl)-2,5-dioxoimidazolidin-4-yl]-1,3-bis(hydroxymethyl)urea
DMDM hydantoin	6440-58-0	Dimethyloldimethylhydantoin; DMDMH; 1,3-dimethylol-5,5-dimethylhydantoin; 1,3-bis(hydroxymethyl)-5,5-dimethyl-imidazolidine-2,4-dione
Imidazolidinyl urea	39236-46-9	Imidurea; bis(methylolhydantoinurea)methane; 3-[3-(hydroxyl-methyl)-2,5-dioxo-imidazolidin-4-yl]-1-[[[3-(hydroxymethyl)-2,5-dioxo-imidazolidin-4-yl]carbamoylamino]methyl]urea
Methenamine	100-97-0	Aminoform; formamine; hexamine; hexamethylene tetramine; methenamide; 1,3,5,7-tetraazatricyclo(3.3.1.1.13,7)decane
Paraformaldehyde	30525-89-4	Paraform; poly(oxymethylene)
Quaternium-15	4080-31-3	N-(3-Chloroallyl)hexaminium chloride; chloroallylhexaminium chloride; 1-(3-chloroallyl)-3,5,7-triaza-1-azonia-adamantane chloride; hexamethylene tetramine chloroallyl chloride
Sodium hydroxymethyl-glycinate	70161-44-3	Glycine, N-(hydroxymethyl)-, sodium salt (1:1); N-hydroxymethyl-glycine (mono)sodium salt; sodium N-(hydroxymethyl)glycinate

Table 2.188.6 Formaldehyde-releasing chemicals in textile finishes (adapted from ref. 49)

Name	CAS number	Synonyms
Dihydroxydimethylolethyl-eneurea, methylated	68411-81-4	4,5-Dihydroxy-1,3-bis(hydroxymethyl)imidazolidin-2-one, methyl-ated; dimethylolglyoxalurea, methylated
1,3-Dimethyl-4,5-dihydroxy-ethyleneurea	3923-79-3	4,5-Dihydroxy-1,3-dimethylimidazolidin-2-one
Dimethylol dihydroxyethy-eneurea	1854-26-8	4,5-Dihydroxy-1,3-bis(hydroxymethyl)imidazolidin-2-one; 1,3-bis(hydroxymethyl)-4,5-dihydroxy-2-imidazolidinone
Dimethylolethyleneurea	136-84-5	1,3-Bis(hydroxymethyl)imidazolidin-2-one
Dimethylolpropyleneurea	3270-74-4	1,3-Bis(hydroxymethyl)-1,3-diazinan-2-one; DMPU; tetrahydro-1,3-bis(hydroxymethyl)-1H-pyrimidin-2-one
Tetramethylol acetylene-diurea	5395-50-6	Tetrakis(hydroxymethyl)glycoluril; tetramethylolglycoluril

Table 2.188.7 Formaldehyde-releasing chemicals in metalworking fluids and miscellaneous (adapted from ref. 49)

Name	CAS number	Synonyms
Preservatives used in metalworking fluids		
Bioban® CS-1135	81099-36-7	Mixture of 4,4-dimethyloxazolidine and 3,4,4-trimethyloxazolidine; the INCI name for 4,4-dimethyloxazolidine is dimethyl oxazolidine.
Bioban® CS-1246	7747-35-5	1-Aza-5-ethyl-3,7-dioxabicyclo(3.3.0)octane; 5-ethyl-1-aza-3,7-dioxabicyclo(3.3.0)octane; 7-ethylbicyclooxazolidine; 7a-ethyldihydro-1H,3H,5H-oxazolo(3,4-c)oxazole
Bioban® P-1487	37304-88-4	Morpholine, 4,4'-(2-ethyl-2-nitro-1,3-propanediyl)bis-, mixture with 4-(2-nitrobutyl)morpholine; mixture of 4-(2-nitrobutyl)morpholine and 4,4'-(2-ethyl-nitrotrimethylene)dimorpholine
1,6-Dihydroxy-2,5-dioxahexane	3586-55-8	Dimethylol glycol (INCI); 2,5-dioxahexane-1,6-diol; [1,2-ethanediyl bis(oxy)]bismethanol; (ethylenedioxy)dimethanol; ethyleneglycoldiformal; 2-(hydroxymethoxy)ethoxymethanol
Forcide® 78 I	77044-78-1	2-Hydroxymethylaminoethanol-tri-N-ethylhydroxy-2-aminomethylene; 3-[bis(2-hydroxyethyl)amino]-2-[(2-hydroxyethyl) (hydroxymethyl)amino]-2-propen-1-ol
Forcide® 78 II	4719-04-4 7779-27-3	[Tris(N-hydroxyethyl)hexahydrotriazine], mixture with hexahydro-1,3,5-triethyl-1,3,5-triazine); hexahydro-1,3,5- triethyl-s-triazine; triethyltrimethylenetriamine
N,N'-Methylenebis(5-methyloxazolidine)	66204-44-2	3,3'-Methylenebis(5-methyloxazolidine)
4,4'-Methylenedimorpholine	5625-90-1	Bismorpholinomethane; dimorpholinomethane; 4,4'-methylenebis-morpholine; N,N'-methylenebismorpholine
Propyleneglycol hemiformal		
Tris(N-hydroxyethyl)hexahydrotriazine	4719-04-4	Triazinetriethanol; hexahydro-1,3,5-tris(hydroxyethyl)triazine; 1,3,5-triazine-1,3,5(2H,4H,6H)triethanol; trihydroxyethylhexahydro s-triazine; 1,3,5-trihydroxyethylhexahydrotriazine; Grotan® BK
Tris(hydroxymethyl)nitromethane	126-11-4	2-(Hydroxymethyl)-2-nitro-1,3-propanediol; nitromethylidynetrimethanol; trimethylolnitromethane; tris nitro
Miscellaneous formaldehyde-releasers		
MDM hydantoin	116-25-6	1-Hydroxymethyl-5,5-dimethylhydantoin; 1-hydroxymethyl-5,5-dimethyl-2,4-imidazolidinedione; MDMH; methylol dimethyl hydantoin; monomethylol dimethyl hydantoin
N-Methylolchloracetamide	832-19-1	Chloracetamide-N-methylol; 2-chloro-N-(hydroxymethyl)acetamide
Preventol® D2	2749-70-4	Bis(benzyloxy)methane; 1,1'-(methylenebis(oxymethylene)) bisbenzene; phenylmethoxymethoxybenzylbenzene

Pseudo-cross-reactions in patients allergic to formaldehyde to formaldehyde-releasers used as preservatives in cosmetic products

A summary of the relationship between formaldehyde and formaldehyde-releasers used as preservatives in cosmetics is shown in table 2.188.8. The data are based on 12 studies reviewed in ref. 37 (including ref. 199, which at that time had only been presented in a Society Meeting) and more recent investigations (4,82,153). Co-reactivity (which is in fact pseudo-cross-reactivity) to formaldehyde-releasers is lowest for 2-bromo-2-nitropropanediol, followed by imidazolidinyl urea. Diazolidinyl urea and DMDM hydantoin have an intermediate position (co-reactivity max. 20-30%) and quaternium-15 most frequently co-reacts to formaldehyde. This means that only in a limited number of patients who are allergic to formaldehyde, the amount of free formaldehyde in the patch test preparation is high enough to induce a positive patch test reaction (218). Indeed, 2-bromo-2-nitropropane-1,3-diol and imidazolidinyl urea release (far) less formaldehyde than quaternium-15, with diazolidinyl urea and DMDM hydantoin in intermediate positions (37). It is likely that co-reactions will be observed especially in patients who have a strong sensitivity, as shown by strongly positive patch test reactions to formaldehyde. Indeed, this has been demonstrated in female patients for formaldehyde and quaternium-15 (153).

Pseudo-cross-reactions in patients allergic to formaldehyde-releasers to formaldehyde

Conversely, many patients reacting to a formaldehyde-releaser co-react (pseudo-cross-react) to formaldehyde. Some examples and the frequencies with which formaldehyde co-reacts are shown in table 2.188.9. Low rates are found for 2-bromo-2-nitropropane-1,3-diol, which means that a positive patch test to this chemical is infrequently caused by formaldehyde. Reactions to the other 4 releasers, however, appear to be caused in 50-60% of the cases by

Table 2.188.8 Co-reactivity to formaldehyde-releasers in patients allergic to formaldehyde (4,37,82,153,199)

Formaldehyde-releaser	Percentage positive [a]	Median % [a]
2-Bromo-2-nitropropane-1,3-diol	1-10	4
Diazolidinyl urea	4-30	16
DMDM hydantoin	4-19	19
Imidazolidinyl urea	4-23	9
Quaternium-15	21-73	30

[a] based on the studies mentioned in the title of the table plus 12 studies reviewed in ref. 37

formaldehyde sensitivity. In fact, rates may even be higher, as in these studies formaldehyde was patch tested at 1% in water (currently 2% in water), which means that false-negative reactions to formaldehyde may have occurred in a number of cases. Why there is so much variation in the percentages of co-reactivity to formaldehyde in individual studies (e.g., range diazolidinyl urea 12-81%, imidazolidinyl urea 11-63%, quaternium-15 27-83%) currently remains unexplained.

Patients often react to more than one releaser (82). Whereas cross-reactions between imidazolidinyl urea and diazolidinyl urea (independent of formaldehyde sensitivity) are well known, reactions to 2 or more chemically unrelated releasers almost always indicate the patient to be allergic to formaldehyde.

Table 2.188.9 Co-reactivity to formaldehyde in patients reacting to formaldehyde-releasers (4,37,82,140,153)

Formaldehyde-releaser	Percentage positive to formaldehyde (range) [b]	Mean % [a]	Median %
2-Bromo-2-nitropropane-1,3-diol	2–50 [c]	15	18
Diazolidinyl urea	12–81	59	43
DMDM hydantoin	37–83	57	64
Imidazolidinyl urea	11–65	49	34
Quaternium-15	27–83	55	55

[a] the mean is based on all studies reviewed in ref. 37 plus data from ref. 82, adjusted for sample size
[b] based on all studies mentioned in the title of the table plus 12 studies reviewed in ref. 37 (including ref. 199, which at that time had only been presented in a Society Meeting)
[c] the high prevalence of 50% was 1 patient in a group of 2 patients reacting to 2-bromo-2-nitropropane-1,3-diol

Should patients allergic to formaldehyde avoid contact with all products containing a formaldehyde-releaser?
Whether it is necessary for patients allergic to formaldehyde to avoid all formaldehyde-releasing preservatives is largely unknown. Some authors have suggested that it is sufficient to avoid only those formaldehyde-releasers that, in addition to formaldehyde, also elicit a positive patch test reaction (196). Others, however, think that it is prudent for formaldehyde-sensitive subjects to recommend avoidance of products containing *any* releaser (82,187,197,198). When used on normal skin, levels of 130 ppm in stay-on products may be safe for most formaldehyde-sensitive patients (200). However, the application of creams containing amounts of free formaldehyde as low as 2.5-10.0 ppm has been shown under experimental conditions to be able to aggravate existing dermatitis in some formaldehyde-sensitive individuals (141). The literature on the amounts of formaldehyde released by various preservatives used in cosmetics has been summarized in ref. 37.

Whether products containing a formaldehyde-releaser will elicit ACD in formaldehyde-sensitive individuals will not only depend on the amount of free formaldehyde, but also on the nature of the product (stay-on versus rinse-off), the site of contact (thick versus thin skin), the frequency and duration of contact and the skin status (healthy versus diseased skin). Thus, for specific products and individuals, it is usually impossible to predict whether they can be safely used by patients allergic to formaldehyde. Thus, the general rule of avoiding all formaldehyde-releasers with the possible exception of 2-bromo-2-nitropropane-1,3-diol has some merit (37). Products that are really important for individual patients can be used in a trial under normal use circumstances; alternatively, a ROAT test (twice daily application to the forearm for 2-4 weeks) can be performed (with stay-on products).

Provocation tests
Data on provocation tests with formaldehyde and products containing formaldehyde up to 2010 are summarized in ref. 37. In an early study, 11 formaldehyde-sensitive subjects pump-sprayed a 12% methanol-in-water solution (0.7 gm of solution) containing 29 ppm formaldehyde into one axilla twice a day for two weeks. Minimal dermatitis appeared in 2 subjects (14). In Denmark, in 1997, twenty patients allergic to formaldehyde performed a ROAT with a

leave-on cosmetic product containing on average 300 ppm formaldehyde for one week. No definite positive reactions were observed. It was concluded that allergic reactions are unlikely to happen with the type of product used or that the exposure time was too short (which we now know is definitely the case, sometimes reactions appear after more than 2-3 weeks only) (176). In a 2005 Danish experimental use test exposure study with a cream preserved with diazolidinyl urea in patients allergic to formaldehyde, it was demonstrated that the amount of formaldehyde that does *not* elicit dermatitis in formaldehyde-sensitive subjects applied to normal skin should be between 130 and 370 ppm (200).

In a Swedish study published in 2010, 18 patients with positive patch test reactions to formaldehyde 2.0% but negative to 1.0%, and a control group of 19 patients with dermatitis but without allergy to formaldehyde and formaldehyde-releasers, performed ROATs with a moisturizer containing 2000 ppm formaldehyde, the maximum concentration permitted in leave-on cosmetics according to EU regulations. The same moisturizer without formaldehyde served as a control. In the control group there were no allergic reactions to either of the moisturizers. Nine of 17 formaldehyde-allergic patients (53%) reacted with an allergic response to the moisturizer containing formaldehyde. No positive reactions were observed to the moisturizer without formaldehyde (16).

In another Swedish study, performed in 2015, fifteen formaldehyde-allergic patients and a control group of 12 individuals without contact allergy to formaldehyde and formaldehyde-releasers, performed repeated open application tests (ROATs) during 4 weeks with four different moisturizers. These products were preserved with DMDM hydantoin in concentrations of 0.6%, 0.33%, 0.06% and 0% w/w, corresponding to >40, 20-40, 2.5-10 and 0 ppm free formaldehyde as determined by the chromotropic acid (CA) spot test. The ROAT was performed on areas of experimentally induced sodium lauryl sulfate dermatitis. Nine of the 15 formaldehyde-allergic individuals had reappearance or worsening of dermatitis on the areas that were treated with moisturizers containing formaldehyde, of who 9 reacted to the >40 ppm moisturizer, 6 to the moisturizer containing 20-40 ppm and 2 to the 2.5-10 ppm containing moisturizer. No such reactions were observed in the control group or for the moisturizers without formaldehyde in the formaldehyde-allergic individuals. It was concluded that low concentrations of formaldehyde often found in skin care products by the CA method are sufficient to worsen an existing dermatitis in formaldehyde-allergic individuals (141).

Patch test studies with dilution series
In Denmark, in 1997, the eliciting threshold concentration of formaldehyde in formaldehyde-sensitive individuals in the occluded patch test was investigated. Twenty formaldehyde-sensitive patients were patch tested with formaldehyde solutions with concentrations of formaldehyde ranging from 25 to 10,000 ppm. Ten of the 20 patients only reacted to 10,000 ppm (1%) formaldehyde, 9 to 5,000 ppm, 3 to 1,000 ppm, two to 500 ppm and 1 patient reacted to 250 ppm formaldehyde. It was concluded that the threshold concentration for occluded patch test to formaldehyde in formaldehyde-sensitive patients is 250 ppm (176).

Presence of formaldehyde in cosmetic products and chemical analysis
Data on chemical analyses of the amount of formaldehyde released by formaldehyde-releasers and products containing them up to 2010 are summarized in ref. 37 and presented in the chapters of the individual formaldehyde-releasers. Data on the frequency of use of formaldehyde *per se* and formaldehyde-releasers in cosmetics are discussed in ref. 50.

In the USA, in April 2017, formaldehyde was present in 39 of 56,714 cosmetic products of which the composition is known in FDA's Voluntary Cosmetic Registration Program (VCRP) (data obtained from FDA, May 2017). In August 2017, formaldehyde was present in 14 of over 70,693 cosmetic products of which the composition is known in EWG's Skin Deep Cosmetics Database, USA (http://www.ewg.org/skindeep/). In a group of sixty different Israeli brand cosmetics, including shampoos, liquid soaps, body creams and hand creams purchased in 2014, formaldehyde was present in 38 (63%) products in concentrations ranging from 4 to 429 ppm (36).

In Sweden, in 2012-2013, 245 cosmetics from 10 formaldehyde-allergic and 30 non-allergic patients (controls) matched for age and sex were investigated with the chromotropic acid spot test, which is a semi-quantitative method measuring the release of formaldehyde. Formaldehyde was found in 58 of 245 (23.7%) products. Twenty-six of 126 (20.6%) leave-on products released formaldehyde, and 17 of 26 (65.4%) of these were not declared to contain formaldehyde or formaldehyde-releasers. Among the rinse-off products, there were 32 of 119 (26.8%) formaldehyde-releasing products, and nine of 32 (28.0%) of these were not labeled as containing formaldehyde or formaldehyde-releasers. Five of 10 formaldehyde-allergic patients brought leave-on products with ≥40 ppm formaldehyde, as compared with 4 of 30 in the control group (significant difference). It was concluded that patients allergic to formaldehyde were more exposed to it in cosmetic products and that cosmetic products used by formaldehyde-allergic patients that are not declared to contain formaldehyde or formaldehyde-releasing preservatives, should be analyzed for its presence (139).

Some hair treatment products sold in the EU between 2008 and 2014 were found to contain high concentrations (0.3%-25%) of formaldehyde, exceeding the maximum allowed limit (0.02%) (132). In 2012, 7 hair straighteners

('Brazilian keratin treatment') purchased on-line in South Africa, were analysed for their content of free formaldehyde. One contained 0.17% formaldehyde. In the other 6, concentrations ranged from 0.96% to 1.4%, which is 5-7 times higher than the maximum concentration allowed in the EU, and that recommended as maximum level by the Cosmetic Ingredient Review (CIR) in the USA. Five of these 6 brands were labeled as formaldehyde-free (74). In a similar study in 2012, 7 of 10 hair straightening products used in Germany contained high amount of formaldehyde (0.42-5.83%) with an average concentration of 1.46% (75). Professional hair smoothing treatments, even those labeled 'formaldehyde-free', have the potential to produce airborne formaldehyde concentrations that meet or exceed current occupational exposure limits (76).

In Germany, in 2006-2009, the labels of 4680 cosmetic products were screened for the presence of preservatives. Formaldehyde was present in zero of the products, according to labelling information (229). In Sweden, of 204 cosmetic products purchased in 2008, 29% contained a formaldehyde-releaser according to the labelling, but none contained formaldehyde as labeled ingredient. Of 97 washing-up liquids and multipurpose cleaners on the market in Sweden, none contained formaldehyde as registered ingredient, but 11% contained a formaldehyde-releaser (73). In 2008, 0.3% of 33,212 cosmetics and toiletries (stay-on products 0.2%, rinse-off products 0.7%) registered in the USA Food and Drug Administration (FDA) Voluntary Cosmetic Registration Database contained formaldehyde solution (formalin) (83). In the same period, in the Netherlands, of 496 stay-on cosmetic products present in a local drugstore and investigated by checking the ingredient labelling, zero products proved to contain this preservative. Any formaldehyde-releaser was found in 122 of this group of stay-on products (24.6%) (83).

In Denmark, between 2000 and 2008, 5437 products of 314 patients allergic to formaldehyde (range per patient: 1-64 products) were tested for the presence of formaldehyde. In 75% of the patients, at least one product tested positive for formaldehyde. Seven hundred and fifty different products proved to contain formaldehyde; 78% were cosmetics, 16% household products, 3.9% occupational products and 2.4% were categorized as 'other' (82).

In 2003, formaldehyde *per se* as a preservative was present in only 118 products registered with the FDA. It was not stated what the total number of cosmetic products registered at the FDA was in 2003 (72) (probably between 20,000 and 30,000). Formaldehyde was present in 31 of 1774 (1.7%) cosmetics and toiletries in 2002 and in 17 of 1170 (1.5%) such products in 2005 in the files of the Danish Product Register Database (PROBAS) (127). In 2000, in Denmark, preservatives were analysed in 67 skin creams to verify the data on the product labels. Thirty-four (51%) contained formaldehyde, either from formaldehyde-releasers or from its presence *per se* (69). In 1998, 100 moisturizers sold in Sweden were analyzed for the presence and amount of preservatives. Thirty-five products contained a formaldehyde-releaser. Ten products contained more than 200 ppm formaldehyde, and in 9 of these a formaldehyde-releaser was present. The concentrations of the releasers did not exceed the EU permitted maximum in any product (70). In 1998, in Switzerland, 10 brands of moistened baby toilet tissues were investigated for the presence of formaldehyde. All brands proved to contain formaldehyde, concentrations ranging from 18 to 209 ppm (174).

In 1997, in Finland, 20 brands and 42 samples of nail polishes were analysed. All the polishes contained allergenic tosylamide/formaldehyde resin (TFR) in concentrations ranging from 0.08 to 11.0%. The concentration of total formaldehyde varied from 0.02% to 0.5%. The more TFR a nail polish contained, the higher its formaldehyde content was. It was concluded that probably not only TFR-allergic but also formaldehyde-allergic persons may develop dermatitis from many of the nail polishes studied (77) (which is currently considered to be unlikely). In the USA, formaldehyde *per se* as a preservative was present in <1% of approximately 20,000 formulae registered with the FDA in 1996 (71). Eight of 20 mascaras purchased in Finland in 1996 contained free formaldehyde in concentrations ranging from 0.03% to 0.007%; according to the authors, these concentrations are potentially high enough to cause allergic contact dermatitis in patients with strong contact allergy to formaldehyde (78).

A 1993 study of washing and cleaning agents showed that formaldehyde-releasing compounds were among the most commonly registered preservatives in such products (66). In 1992, 161 rinse-off products and 124 leave-on products produced in various European countries and the USA were investigated in Denmark for the presence of formaldehyde. Thirty per cent proved to contain (free and bound) formaldehyde (67). In the same year, in Switzerland, 34 cosmetic products were investigated of which nineteen (56%) were found to contain free formaldehyde (68).

Analysis of formaldehyde in formaldehyde and formaldehyde-releaser patch test materials
Analyses of commercial patch test preparations of formaldehyde and formaldehyde-releasers with the ^{13}C NMR spectroscopic method have shown no free formaldehyde in petrolatum-based preparations of benzylhemiformal, diazolidinyl urea or quaternium-15 (detection limit: 0.01% w/w) (35). However these preparations, when brought in contact with water for a 30 hour period, all delivered free formaldehyde by hydrolysis in concentrations between 0.013% w/w (130 ppm) and the detection limit of 0.01% w/w (100 ppm). The content of free formaldehyde in commercial aqueous test materials are shown in table 2.188.10. In all nine commercial aqueous patch test

substances, free formaldehyde was demonstrated with concentrations ranging from 0.03% to 0.37%. In the two commercial 1% formaldehyde solutions, actual concentrations were 0.99% and 1.2% (35).

Table 2.188.10 Free formaldehyde in commercial aqueous patch test preparations (35)

Test material	Test concentration and vehicle	Provider [a]	Formaldehyde content %w/w	ppm
Diazolidinyl urea	1% water	Brial	0.20	2000
Dimethylol dihydroxyethyleneurea	4.5% water	Brial	0.054	540
Dimethylol dihydroxyethyleneurea (Fixapret CPN®)	4.5% water	Chemotechnique	0.16	1600
Dimethylol dihydroxyethyleneurea, modified (Fixapret ECO®)	5% water	Chemotechnique	0.083	830
DMDM hydantoin	2% water	Brial	0.29	2900
DMDM hydantoin	2% water	Chemotechnique	0.15	1500
DMDM hydantoin	1% water	Brial	0.11	1100
Formaldehyde	1% water	Brial	1.20	12,000
Formaldehyde	1% water	Chemotechnique	0.99	9900
Imidazolidinyl urea	2% water	Brial	0.046	460
Tris(N-hydroxyethyl)hexahydrotriazine	1% water	Chemotechnique	0.03	300

[a] Brial: www.smartpracticeeurope.com (formerly www.brial.com); Chemotechnique: www.chemotechnique.se

Aqueous test solutions were in this study also prepared by a supplier of test materials of those releasers that were commercially provided in petrolatum. The results of analyses for free formaldehyde are shown in table 2.188.11. The range of free formaldehyde was 0.019% (190 ppm) to 0.37% (3700 ppm). Free formaldehyde was not detected in the 2-bromo-2-nitropropane-1,3-diol, methenamine and tris(hydroxymethyl)nitromethane solutions (detection limit: 0.01%, 100 ppm) (35).

Table 2.188.11 Free formaldehyde in aqueous solutions prepared by a provider of patch test materials (35) [a]

Test material	Test concentration and vehicle	Formaldehyde content %w/w	ppm
Benzylhemiformal	1% water	0.37	3700
Bioban® CS 1135	1% water	0.10	1000
Bioban® CS 1246	1% water	0.06	600
2-Bromo-2-nitropropane-1,3-diol	0.5% water	nd (<0.01%)	<100
Diazolidinyl urea	2% water	0.29	2900
Imidazolidinyl urea	2% water	0.054	540
Methenamine	1% water	nd (<0.01%)	<100
N,N-methylenebis(5-methyloxazolidine)	1% water	0.15	1500
Quaternium-15	1% water	0.11	1100
Quaternium-15	2% water	0.21	2100
Tris(N-hydroxyethyl)hexahydrotriazine	1% water	0.019	190
Tris(hydroxymethyl)nitromethane (tris nitro)	1% water	nd (<0.01%)	<100

[a] all provided by Brial: www.smartpracticeeurope.com (formerly www.brial.com)
nd: not detected (lower than the detection limit of 0.01%, 100 ppm)

OTHER SIDE EFFECTS

Irritant contact dermatitis
Formaldehyde vapors can be an irritant to mucous membranes, especially for atopic persons (237). Formaldehyde in nail hardeners formerly caused irritant contact dermatitis of the skin of the fingers (see the section 'Other non-eczematous contact reactions' below).

Short-term exposure to formaldehyde causes skin barrier dysfunction in both healthy children and children with atopic dermatitis (AD), and this effect is more prominent in children with AD (242).

Photosensitivity

Photopatch testing in groups of patients
In two studies, groups of selected patients (patients suspected of photodermatoses, patients with a history of photosensitivity) have been photopatch tested with formaldehyde 1% (table 2.188.12). In a Chinese study, an amazing 4.7% of the patients had positive reactions. However, the relevance of these reactions was not mentioned and neither were causative products (225). In a small US study from 1985-1990, there were 3 positive photopatch tests in a group of 83 patients (3.6%) with a history of photosensitivity. No relevance was found and the authors suggested that these reactions had been phototoxic rather than photoallergic (3).

Table 2.188.12 Photopatch testing in groups of patients

Years and Country	Test conc. & vehicle	Number of patients tested | positive (%)		Selection of patients (S); Relevance (R); Comments (C)	Ref.
2005-2014 China	1% water	6113	287 (4.7%)	S: patients suspected of photodermatoses; R: not stated	225
1985-1990 USA	1% water	83	3 (3.6%)	S: patients with a history of photosensitivity; R: not relevant; C: the authors suggested the reactions to be phototoxic	3

Case reports and series
A patient had immediate-type photosensitivity on exposed skin; he had a similar immediate reaction to light-exposed formaldehyde. The relationship between the two events, the mechanism (phototoxic, photoallergic) and causative products were all unknown (2).

Immediate-type reactions
Of 50 individuals who had open tests with formaldehyde 2% in water on the forearm, 10 showed local macular erythema after 45 minutes, termed 'contact urticaria' by the authors (129). In a group of 664 patch tested patients, there were 4 (0.6%) immediate contact reactions to formaldehyde as shown by 'well distinguished erythema' after 30 minutes (130).

A 20-year-old woman who was subjected to hemodialysis for the past 4 years had allergic contact dermatitis from formaldehyde. She was dialyzed with a dialyzer sterilized with formaldehyde and developed within minutes a severe anaphylactic shock requiring resuscitation. Prick tests performed with 0.1% and 1% formaldehyde were positive, whereas they were negative in control subjects. RAST to formaldehyde was strongly positive. A patch test with formaldehyde 1% in water was also strongly positive and induced an anaphylactic shock 26 hours after the skin application of the patch test material. It was concluded that the patients suffered from a combined type IV contact allergy an immediate-type allergy to formaldehyde mediated by IgE (143).

A man developed facial and lip edema, generalized pruritus and generalized urticaria with central chest ache, 30 minutes after topical application of a disinfectant combined with a 10% formaldehyde solution to his right hand; there was no reaction on the hand itself. A skin prick test was positive and serum formaldehyde-specific IgE was strongly positive (160).

There are many reports of immediate reactions to formaldehyde present in dental compounds, notably root canal disinfectants, symptoms ranging from urticaria to anaphylaxis (161-171,207-210). Most patients had positive prick tests, and often IgE antibodies to formaldehyde were demonstrated. In about half of the cases, there was also a positive patch test to formaldehyde, indicating combined type I and type IV allergy. The literature on this subject up to 2002 has been reviewed in refs. 162 and 209. A 'half delayed hypersensitivity reaction' to formaldehyde included in a root canal sealer has also been reported. This reaction was loco-regional and 'late'. It was suggested that the reaction was probably caused by overflowing of formaldehyde as demonstrated by radiography (214).

One patient had an urticarial reaction to a patch test with formaldehyde 1% in water. Soon thereafter, respiratory symptoms developed with a strong decline in pulmonary function test results. The patient had a prior history of anaphylaxis to formaldehyde vapor inhalation. *In vitro* tests were not performed (source unknown, cited in ref. 138). In a woman with recurrent urticaria, rhinitis and occasional bronchospasm, an open test on the back with formaldehyde 1% in water (to which she had previously had a ?+ patch test reaction), provoked wheals at 30 minutes on the face, neck, trunk and forearm, together with shivering, oculorhinitis, eyelid edema and bronchospasm. Three hours after the test application, a large wheal appeared at the formaldehyde site. One month later, open tests with the formaldehyde-releasers quaternium-15, 2-bromo-2-nitropropane-1,3-diol and imidazolidinyl urea were all strongly positive. The source of formaldehyde contact was not mentioned (177).

In older literature, formaldehyde was cited to cause occupational urticaria in 'Phenolic and amino resin workers, fumigators and laboratory workers (178). Single case reports have described contact urticaria from formaldehyde present in leather (179), spray starch (180), and solutions of formaldehyde used in a pathology department for tissue fixation (181). A histology technician in a dermatopathology laboratory suffered from sneezing and an itchy rash on her arms, legs, and nose occurring within 30 minutes of working under a ventilation hood processing formalin-fixed specimens. Symptoms resolved 15 minutes after moving away from the hood. A skin prick test with formalin was positive (237). A female dermatologist developed flares of asthma when exposed to formalin (40% formaldehyde) in the grossing room. Prick testing with 1% formaldehyde was then performed. Immediately, she experienced a large wheal of one centimeter, generalized pruritus, paleness, and a severe asthma flare (237).

A peculiar type of contact urticaria has been described, in which application of formaldehyde solution on normal skin had to be repeated twice daily for some days, before an immediate reaction with a sharply demarcated burning erythema would develop 5 to 10 minutes after application of the formaldehyde solution and disappearing after 30 minutes. This was called 'Multiple application delayed onset contact urticaria' (182). A similar reaction was observed in 3 of 14 healthy volunteers, two of who also showed urtication. The relevance of the reactions, both in patients and volunteers, remained obscure, as was the pathomechanism responsible (182).

A woman developed bronchospasm and laryngospasm due to accidental inhalation of formaldehyde vapor. A similar episode occurred shortly afterwards, when the patient happened to enter a room soon after it had been disinfected. Later, a 1% formaldehyde in water patch test was applied to the forearm on healthy skin. After 15 min, a whealing reaction at the site of the patch test was evident and later an erythema of 7 centimeter diameter appeared. Simultaneously, the patient reported a sense of retrosternal constriction and dry cough. Twenty minutes later, tests showed strongly reduced pulmonary function (188).

Asthma

Formaldehyde is listed as a cause of occupational asthma in 'Asthma in the Workplace' (240), but in the United Kingdom Health and Safety Executive's publication 'Asthmagen? ', it was *not* considered to be a respiratory sensitizer (241). Because of this discrepancy, in a review article, formaldehyde was labeled as a 'potential' cause of occupational asthma (239). Three cases of occupational asthma have been observed in an occupational medicine clinic in Finland in the period 1991-2011 (238). Asthmatic reactions from formaldehyde are also mentioned in three patients in the section 'Immediate-type reactions' above (177,188,237). More extensive discussion of this subject is considered to fall outside the scope of this book.

Other non-eczematous contact reactions

Nail hardeners, which were widely used in the 1960s in the USA, were essentially solutions of formaldehyde in concentrations ranging from 4% to 40% (11). Reactions to these products are well recognized (11,23, 136,137,142). The nail changes reported were onycholysis, bluish discoloration of the nail plate, splinter hemorrhages of the nail bed, subungual hyperkeratosis, severe throbbing pain in the fingers and dryness of the skin. Nail shedding was uncommon (79). Resolving hemorrhages produced reddish-rust or yellow discoloration of the nail. Discontinuation of the nail hardener resulted in complete resolution. Pterygium inversum has been observed (44).

The reactions of the nail apparatus were usually attributed to the formaldehyde content of the nail hardeners. While positive patch tests to formaldehyde have been elicited in some patients (11,124,125), other investigators have suggested that it was an irritant rather than an allergic contact reaction. Some brands of nail hardeners used in the 1960s containing formaldehyde caused so many cases of nail damage, that they were recalled by the FDA. Such nail hardeners containing formaldehyde have not been available anymore in the USA since 1969 (79), but imported products still caused onycholysis in a patient in 1981 (79).

OTHER INFORMATION

Lonicera Japonica extract leached formaldehyde from its plastic container (149).

LITERATURE

1 Uter W, Aberer W, Armario-Hita JC, , Fernandez-Vozmediano JM, Ayala F, Balato A, et al. Current patch test results with the European baseline series and extensions to it from the 'European Surveillance System on Contact Allergy' network, 2007-2008. Contact Dermatitis 2012;67:9-19
2 Shelley WB. Immediate sunburn-like reaction in a patient with formaldehyde photosensitivity. Arch Dermatol 1982;118:117-118
3 DeLeo VA, Suarez SM, Maso MJ. Photoallergic contact dermatitis. Results of photopatch testing in New York, 1985 to 1990. Arch Dermatol 1992;128:1513-1518
4 Latorre N, Borrego L, Fernández-Redondo V, García-Bravo B, Giménez-Arnau AM, Sánchez J, et al. Patch testing with formaldehyde and formaldehyde-releasers: multicenter study in Spain (2005-2009). Contact Dermatitis 2011;65:286-292
5 Travassos AR, Claes L, Boey L, Drieghe J, Goossens A. Non-fragrance allergens in specific cosmetic products. Contact Dermatitis 2011;65:276-285

6   Adams RM, Maibach HI, Clendenning WE, Fisher AA, Jordan WJ, Kanof N, et al. A five-year study of cosmetic reactions. J Am Acad Dermatol 1985;13:1062-1069

7   Davis MD, Scalf LA, Yiannias JA, Cheng JF, El-Azhary RA, Rohlinger AL, et al. Changing trends and allergens in the patch test standard series. Arch Dermatol 2008;144:67-72

8   Warshaw EM, Buchholz HJ, Belsito DV et al. Allergic patch test reactions associated with cosmetics: Retrospective analysis of cross-sectional data from the North American Contact Dermatitis Group, 2001-2004. J Am Acad Dermatol 2009;60:23-38

9   Schnuch A, Lessmann H, Geier J, Uter W. Contact allergy to preservatives. Analysis of IVDK data 1996-2009. Br J Dermatol 2011;164:1316-1325

10 ESSCA Writing Group. The European Surveillance System of Contact Allergies (ESSCA): results of patch testing the standard series, 2004. J Eur Acad Dermatol Venereol 2008;22:174-181

11 Lazar P. Reactions to nail hardeners. Arch Dermatol 1966;94:446-448

12 Zemtsov A, Taylor JS, Evey P, et al. Allergic contact dermatitis from formaldehyde in a liquid soap. Clev Clin J Med 1990;57:301-303

13 Zug KA, Warshaw EM, Fowler JF Jr, Maibach HI, Belsito DL, Pratt MD, et al. Patch-test results of the North American Contact Dermatitis Group 2005-2006. Dermatitis 2009;20:149-160

14 Jordan WP, Sherman WT, King SE. Threshold responses in formaldehyde-sensitive subjects. J Am Acad Dermatol 1979;1:44-48

15 Pontén A, Aalto-Korte K, Agner T, Andersen KE, Giménez-Arnau AM, Gonçalo M. Patch testing with 2.0% (0.60 mg/cm^2) formaldehyde instead of 1.0% (0.30 mg/cm^2) detects significantly more contact allergy. Contact Dermatitis 2013;68:50-53

16 Hauksson I, Pontén A, Gruvberger B, Isaksson M, Bruze M. Clinically relevant contact allergy to formaldehyde may be missed by testing with formaldehyde 1.0%. Br J Dermatol 2011;164:568-572

17 Fransway AF, Zug KA, Belsito DV, Deleo VA, Fowler JF Jr, Maibach HI, et al. North American Contact Dermatitis Group patch test results for 2007-2008. Dermatitis 2013;24:10-21

18 Warshaw EM, Belsito DV, DeLeo VA, Fowler JF Jr, Maibach HI, Marks JG, et al. North American Contact Dermatitis Group patch-test results, 2003-2004 study period. Dermatitis 2008;19:129-136

19 Wenk KS, Ehrlich AE. Fragrance series testing in eyelid dermatitis. Dermatitis 2012;23:22-26

20 Molin S, Bauer A, Schnuch A, Geier J. Occupational contact allergy in nurses: results from the Information Network of Departments of Dermatology 2003–2012. Contact Dermatitis 2015;72:164-171

21 Van Lerberghe, L. and Baeck, M. A case of acute contact dermatitis induced by formaldehyde in hair-straightening products. Contact Dermatitis 2014;70:384-386

22 Friis UF, Dahlin J, Bruze M, Menné, T, Johansen JD. Hidden exposure to formaldehyde in a swab caused allergic contact dermatitis. Contact Dermatitis 2014;70:258-260.

23 March CH. Allergic contact dermatitis to a new formula to strengthen nails, Arch Derm 1966;93:720

24 Hill AM, Belsito DV. Systemic contact dermatitis of the eyelids caused by formaldehyde derived from aspartame? Contact Dermatitis 2003;49:258-259

25 Veien NK, Lomholt HB. Systemic allergic dermatitis presumably caused by formaldehyde derived from aspartame. Contact Dermatitis 2012;67:315-316

26 Castanedo-Tardan MP, González ME, Connelly EA, Giordano K, Jacob SE. Systemitized contact dermatitis and montelukast in an atopic boy. Pediatr Dermatol 2009;26:739-743

27 Matiz C, Jacob SE. Systemic contact dermatitis in children: how an avoidance diet can make a difference. Pediatr Dermatol 2011;28:368-374

28 Pontén A, Goossens A, Bruze M. Recommendation to include formaldehyde 2.0% aqua in the European baseline patch test series. Contact Dermatitis 2013;69:372-374

29 Warshaw EM, Maibach HI, Taylor JS, Sasseville D, DeKoven JG, Zirwas MJ, et al. North American Contact Dermatitis Group patch test results: 2011-2012. Dermatitis 2015;26:49-59

30 Warshaw EM, Belsito DV, Taylor JS, Sasseville D, DeKoven JG, Zirwas MJ, et al. North American Contact Dermatitis Group patch test results: 2009 to 2010. Dermatitis 2013;24:50-59

31 De Groot A, Geier J, Flyvholm M-A, Lensen G, Coenraads P-J. Formaldehyde-releasers: relationship to formaldehyde contact allergy. Metalworking fluids and remainder. Part 1. Contact Dermatitis 2010;63:117-128

32 Hauksson I, Pontén A, Gruvberger B, Isaksson M, Bruze M. Routine diagnostic patch-testing with formaldehyde 2.0% (0.6 mg/cm2) may be an advantage compared to 1.0%. Acta Derm Venereol 2010;90:480-484

33 De Groot AC. Contact allergy to formaldehyde (Invited Commentary). Br J Dermatol 2011;164:463

34 De Groot A, Geier J, Flyvholm M-A, Lensen G, Coenraads P-J. Formaldehyde-releasers: Relationship to formaldehyde contact allergy, Part 2: Metalworking fluids and remainder. Contact Dermatitis 2010;63:129-139

35 Emeis D, De Groot AC, Brinkmann J. Determination of formaldehyde in formaldehyde-releaser patch test preparations. Contact Dermatitis 2010;63:57-62

36 Horev L, Isaksson M, Engfeldt M, Persson L, Ingber A, Bruze M. Preservatives in cosmetics in the Israeli market conform well to the EU legislation. JEADV 2015;29:761-766

37 De Groot AC, White IR, Flyvholm M-A, Lensen G, Coenraads P-J. Formaldehyde-releasers in cosmetics: relationship to formaldehyde contact allergy. Part 2. Patch test relationship to formaldehyde contact allergy, experimental provocation tests, amount of formaldehyde released and assessment of risk to consumers allergic to formaldehyde. Contact Dermatitis 2010;62:18-31

38 De Groot AC, Le Coz C, Lensen G, Flyvholm M-A, Maibach H, Coenraads P-J. Formaldehyde-releasers: relationship to formaldehyde contact allergy. Formaldehyde-releasers in clothes: durable press chemical finishes. Part 1. Contact Dermatitis 2010;62:259-271

39 Fransway AF. The problem of preservation in the 1990s: I. Statement of the problem. Solution(s) of the industry, and the current use of formaldehyde and formaldehyde-releasing biocides. Am J Contact Dermat 1991;2:6-23

40 Fransway AF, Schmitz NA. The problem of preservation in the 1990s: II. Formaldehyde and formaldehyde-releasing biocides: incidences of cross-reactivity and the significance of the positive response to formaldehyde. Am J Contact Dermatitis 1991;2:78-88

41 Lazarov A. European Standard Series patch test results from a contact dermatitis clinic in Israel during the 7-year period from 1998 to 2004. Contact Dermatitis 2006;55:73-76

42 Worm M, Brasch J, Geier J, Uter W, Schnuch A. Epikutantestung mit der DKG-Standardreihe 2001-2004. Hautarzt 2005;56:1114-1124

43 Carlsen BC, Menné T, Johansen JD. 20 Years of standard patch testing in an eczema population with focus on patients with multiple contact allergies. Contact Dermatitis 2007;57:76-83

44 Daly BM, Johnson M. Pterygium inversum inguis due to nail fortifier. Contact Dermatitis 1986;15:256-257

45 Uter W, Hegewald J, Aberer W et al. The European standard series in 9 European countries, 2002/2003 – First results of the European Surveillance System on Contact Allergies. Contact Dermatitis 2005;53:136-145

46 Pratt MD, Belsito DV, DeLeo VA, Fowler JF Jr, Fransway AF, Maibach HI, et al. North American Contact Dermatitis Group patch-test results, 2001-2002 study period. Dermatitis 2004;15:176-183

47 Landeck L, John SM, Geier J. Periorbital dermatitis in 4779 patients – patch test results during a 10-year period. Contact Dermatitis 2014;70:205-212

48 Ormerod, AD, Main RA. Sensitisation to "sensitive teeth" toothpaste. Contact Dermatitis 1985;13:192-193

49 De Groot AC, Flyvholm M-A, Lensen G, Menné T, Coenraads P-J. Formaldehyde-releasers: relationship to formaldehyde contact allergy. Contact allergy to formaldehyde and inventory of formaldehyde-releasers. Contact Dermatitis 2009;61:63-85

50 De Groot AC, White IR, Flyvholm M-A, Lensen G, Coenraads P-J. Formaldehyde-releasers: relationship to formaldehyde contact allergy. II. Formaldehyde-releasers used in cosmetics. Part 1. Characterization, frequency and relevance of sensitization, and frequency of use in cosmetics. Contact Dermatitis 2010;62:2-17

51 De Groot AC, Maibach HI. Does allergic contact dermatitis from formaldehyde in clothes treated with durable-press chemical finishes exist in the USA? Contact Dermatitis 2010;62:127-136

52 De Groot AC, Le Coz CJ, Lensen GJ, Flyvholm M-A, Maibach HI, Coenraads P-J. Formaldehyde-releasers: relationship to formaldehyde contact allergy. Part 2. Formaldehyde-releasers in clothes: durable press chemical finishes. Contact Dermatitis 2010;63:1-9

53 De Groot AC, Maibach HI. Allergic contact dermatitis caused by durable-press finishes does exist in the USA. [Reply to Letter to the Editor]. Contact Dermatitis 2010;63:234-235

54 Hasan T, Rantanen T, Alanko K, Harvima RJ, Jolanki R, Kalimo K, et al. Patch test reactions to cosmetic allergens in 1995-1997 and 2000-2002 in Finland – a multicentre study. Contact Dermatitis 2005;53:40-45

55 Jacob SE, Stechschulte S. Formaldehyde, aspartame, and migraines : a possible connection. Dermatitis 2008;19:E10-11

56 Gollhausen R, Enders F, Przybilla B, Burg G, Ring J. Trends in allergic contact sensitization. Contact Dermatitis 1988;18:147-154

57 Vestey JP, Gawdrodger DJ, Wong W-K, Buxton PK. An analysis of 501 consecutive contact clinic consultations. Contact Dermatitis 1986;15:119-125

58 Sugai T, Yamamoto S. Decrease in the incidence of contact sensitivity to formaldehyde. Contact Dermatitis 1980;6:154

59 Epstein E, Maibach HI. Formaldehyde allergy. Incidence and patch test problems. Arch Dermatol 1966;94:186-190

60 Flyvholm MA, Menné T. Allergic contact dermatitis from formaldehyde. A case study focusing on sources of formaldehyde exposure. Contact Dermatitis 1992;27:27-36

61 Schnuch A, Geier J, Uter W, Frosch PJ. Patch testing with preservatives, antimicrobials and industrial biocides. Results from a multicentre study. Br J Dermatol 1998;138:467-476

62 Cronin E. Formaldehyde is a significant allergen in women with hand eczema. Contact Dermatitis 1991;25:276-282

63   Agner T, Flyvholm M-A, Menné T. Formaldehyde allergy : A follow-up study. Am J Contact Dermatitis 1999;10:12-17

64   Aalto-Korte K, Kuuliala O, Suuronen K, Alanko K. Occupational contact allergy to formaldehyde and formaldehyde releasers. Contact Dermatitis 2008;59:280-289

65   Kang KM, Corey G, Storrs FJ. Follow-up study of patients allergic to formaldehyde and formaldehyde releasers: retention of information, compliance, course, and persistence of allergy. Am J Contact Dermatitis 1995;6:209-215

66   Flyvholm M-A. Contact allergens in registered cleaning agents for industrial and household use. Br J Ind Med 1993;50:1043-1050

67   Rastogi SC. A survey of formaldehyde in shampoos and skin creams on the Danish market. Contact Dermatitis 1992;27:235-240

68   Gryllaki-Berger M, Mugny Ch, Perrenoud D, Pannatier A, Frenk E. A comparative study of formaldehyde detection using chromotropic acid, acetylacetone and HPLC in cosmetics and household products. Contact Dermatitis 1992;26:149-154

69   Rastogi SC. Analytical control of preservative labelling on skin creams. Contact Dermatitis 2000;43:339-343

70   Gruvberger B, Bruze M, Tammela M. Preservatives in moisturizers in the Swedish market. Acta Derm Venereol (Stockh) 1998;78:52-56

71   Steinberg D. Frequency of use of preservatives in the United States. Paper given at Preservatech, Paris, 1996. www.creative-developments.co.uk/papers/Preservatives%201999.htm (last accessed 14 January 2009)

72   Sasseville D. Hypersensitivity to preservatives. Dermatologic Therapy 2004;17:251-263

73   Yazar K, Johnsson S, Lind ML, Boman A, Lidén C. Preservatives and fragrances in selected consumer-available cosmetics and detergents. Contact Dermatitis 2011;64:265-272

74   Maneli MH, Smith P, Khumalo NP. Elevated formaldehyde concentration in 'Brazilian keratin type' hair-straightening products: a cross-sectional study. J Am Acad Dermatol 2014;70:276-280

75   Monakhova YB, Kuballa T, Mildau G, Kratz E, Keck-Wilhelm A, Tschiersch C, et al. Formaldehyde in hair straightening products: rapid H NMR determination and risk assessment. Int J Cosmet Sci 2013;35:201-206

76   Pierce JS, Abelmann A, Spicer LJ, Adams RE, Glynn ME, Neier K, et al. Characterization of formaldehyde exposure resulting from the use of four professional hair straightening products. J Occup Environ Hyg 2011;8:686-699

77   Sainio E-L, Engström K, Henriks-Eckerman M-L, Kanerva L. Allergenic ingredients in nail polishes. Contact Dermatitis 1997;37:155-162

78   Sainio EL, Henriks-Eckerman M-L, Kanerva L. Colophony, formaldehyde and mercury in mascaras. Contact Dermatitis 1996;34:364-365

79   Mitchell JC. Non-inflammatory onycholysis from formaldehyde-containing nail hardener. Contact Dermatitis 1981;7:173

80   Prodi A, Rui F, Belloni Fortina A, Corradin MT, Larese Filon F. Sensitization to formaldehyde in northeastern Italy, 1996 to 2012. Dermatitis 2016;27:21-25

81   Pontén A, Bruze M. Contact allergen of the year. Formaldehyde. Dermatitis 2015;26:3-6

82   Lundov MD, Johansen JD, Carlsen BC, Engkilde K, Menné T, Thyssen JP. Formaldehyde exposure and patterns of concomitant contact allergy to formaldehyde and formaldehyde-releasers. Contact Dermatitis 2010;63:31-36

83   De Groot AC, Veenstra M. Formaldehyde-releasers in cosmetics in the USA and in Europe. Contact Dermatitis 2010;62:221-224

84   Jong CT, Statham BN, Green CM, King CM, Gawkrodger DJ, Sansom JE, et al. Contact sensitivity to preservatives in the UK 2004–2005: results of a multicenter study. Contact Dermatitis 2007;57:165-168

85   Lindberg M, Edman B, Fischer T, Stenberg B. Time trends in Swedish patch test data from 1992 to 2000. A multi-centre study based on age- and sex-adjusted results of the Swedish standard series. Contact Dermatitis 2007;56:205-210

86   Wetter DA, Davis MDP, Yiannias JA, Cheng JF, Connolly SM, el-Azhary RA, et al. Patch test results from the Mayo Contact Dermatitis Group, 1998–2000. J Am Acad Dermatol 2005;53:416-421

87   Hüldin DH. Hemorrhages of the lips secondary to nail hardeners. Cutis 1968;4:708

88   Akyol A, Boyvat A, Peksari Y, Gurgey E. Contact sensitivity to standard series allergens in 1038 patients with contact dermatitis in Turkey. Contact Dermatitis 2005;52:333-337

89   Machovcova A, Dastychova E, Kostalova D, et al. Common contact sensitizers in the Czech Republic. Patch test results in 12,058 patients with suspected contact dermatitis. Contact Dermatitis 2005;53:162-166

90   Bruynzeel DP, Diepgen TL, Andersen KE, Brandão FM, Bruze M, Frosch PJ, et al (EECDRG). Monitoring the European Standard Series in 10 centres 1996–2000. Contact Dermatitis 2005;53:146-152

91   Fall S, Bruze M, Isaksson M, Lidén C, Matura M, Stenberg B, Lindberg M. Contact allergy trends in Sweden – a retrospective comparison of patch test data from 1992, 2000, and 2009. Contact Dermatitis 2015;72:297-304

92   Amin KA, Belsito DV. The aetiology of eyelid dermatitis: a 10-year retrospective analysis. Contact Dermatitis 2006;55:280-285

93 Cooper SM, Shaw S. Eyelid dermatitis: an evaluation of 232 patch test patients over 5 years. Contact Dermatitis 2000: 42;291-293

94 Goossens A. Cosmetic contact allergens. Cosmetics 2016, 3, 5; doi:10.3390/cosmetics3010005

95 Wentworth AB, Yiannias JA, Keeling JH, Hall MR, Camilleri MJ, Drage LA, et al. Trends in patch-test results and allergen changes in the standard series: a Mayo Clinic 5-year retrospective review (January 1, 2006, to December 31, 2010). J Am Acad Dermatol 2014;70:269-275

96 Zug KA, Kornik R, Belsito DV, DeLeo VA, Fowler JF Jr, Maibach HI, et al. Patch-testing North American lip dermatitis patients: Data from the North American Contact Dermatitis Group, 2001 to 2004. Dermatitis 2008;19:202-208

97 Katz AS, Sherertz EF. Facial dermatitis: Patch test results and final diagnoses. Am J Cont Dermat 1999;10:153-156

98 Duffin P, Cowan GC. An allergic reaction to toothpaste. J Irish Dent Assoc 1985;31:11-12.

99 Löwenthal K. Eczematous contact dermatitis of the palm due to toothpaste. New York State J Med 1952;53:1437-1438 (data cited in refs. 11,12 and 13)

100 De Groot AC, Weyland JW, Nater JP. Unwanted effects of cosmetics and drugs used in dermatology. 3rd edition. Amsterdam: Elsevier Science BV, 1994:187-189

101 Fisher AA, Tobin I. Sensitivity to compound G-4 ('Dichlorophene') in dentifrices. JAMA 1953;151:998-999.

102 Cronin E. Contact Dermatitis. Edinburgh London new York: Churchill Livingstone; 1980: 678.

103 Weinberger W. Ein Fall von akutem Ekzem infolge Formalin Idiosynkrasie. Ztschr f Stomatol 1933;31:1077-1081 (data cited in refs. 104 and 105) (article in German).

104 Beinhauer LG. Cheilitis and dermatitis from toothpaste. Arch Dermatol 1940;41:892-894.

105 Sainio E-L, Kanerva L. Contact allergens in toothpastes and a review of their hypersensitivity. Contact Dermatitis 1995;33:100-105

106 Thyssen JP, Uter W, Schnuch A, Linneberg A, Johansen JD. 10-year prevalence of contact allergy in the general population in Denmark estimated through the CE-DUR method. Contact Dermatitis 2007;57:265-272

107 Schnuch A, Uter W, Geier J, Gefeller O (for the IVDK study group). Epidemiology of contact allergy: an estimation of morbidity employing the clinical epidemiology and drug-utilization research (CE-DUR) approach. Contact Dermatitis 2002;47:32-39

108 Diepgen TL, Ofenloch RF, Bruze M, Bertuccio P, Cazzaniga S, Coenraads P-J, et al. Prevalence of contact allergy in the general population in different European regions. Br J Dermatol 2016;174:319-329

109 Mortz CG, Bindslev-Jensen C, Andersen KE. Prevalence, incidence rates and persistence of contact allergy and allergic contact dermatitis in The Odense Adolescence Cohort Study: a 15-year follow-up. Brit J Dermatol 2013;168:318-325

110 Thyssen JP, Linneberg A, Menné T, Nielsen NH, Johansen JD. Contact allergy to allergens of the TRUE-test (panels 1 and 2) has decreased modestly in the general population. Br J Dermatol 2009;161:1124-1129

111 Dotterud LK, Smith-Sivertsen T. Allergic contact sensitization in the general adult population: a population-based study from Northern Norway. Contact Dermatitis 2007;56:10-15

112 Nielsen NH, Linneberg A, Menné T, Madsen F, Frølund L, Dirksen A, et al. Allergic contact sensitization in an adult Danish population: two cross-sectional surveys eight years apart (the Copenhagen Allergy Study). Acta Derm Venereol 2001;81:31-34

113 White JML, Gilmour NJ, Jeffries D, Duangdeeden I, Kullavanijaya P, Basketter DA, et al. A general population from Thailand: incidence of common allergens with emphasis on para-phenylenediamine. Clin Exp Allergy 2007;37:1848-1853

114 Mortz CG, Lauritsen JM, Bindslev-Jensen C, Andersen KE. Contact allergy and allergic contact dermatitis in adolescents: prevalence measures and associations. Acta Derm Venereol 2002;82:352-358

115 Schäfer T, Böhler E, Ruhdorfer S, Weigl L, Wessner D, Filipiak B, et al. Epidemiology of contact allergy in adults. Allergy 2001;56:1192-1196

116 Mortz CG, Lauritsen JM, Bindslev-Jensen C, Andersen KE. Prevalence of atopic dermatitis, asthma, allergic rhinitis, and hand and contact dermatitis in adolescents. The Odense Adolescence Cohort Study on Atopic Diseases and Dermatitis. Br J Dermatol 2001;144:523-532

117 Uter W, Ludwig A, Balda BR, Schnuch A, Pfahlberg A, Schäfer T, Wichmann HE, Ring J. The prevalence of contact allergy differed between population-based data and clinic–based data. J Clin Epidemiol 2004;57:627-632

118 De Groot AC, Bruynzeel DP, Bos JD, van der Meeren HL, van Joost T, Jagtman BA, Weyland JW. The allergens in cosmetics. Arch Dermatol 1988;124:1525-1529

119 De Groot AC. Adverse reactions to cosmetics. PhD Thesis, University of Groningen, The Netherlands: 1988, chapter 3.4, pp.105-113

120 De Groot AC. Contact allergy to cosmetics: Causative ingredients. Contact Dermatitis 1987;17:26-34

121 Cronin E. Contact Dermatitis. Edinburgh: Churchill Livingstone, 1980:109

122 Marcussen PV. Contact dermatitis due to formaldehyde in textiles 1934-1958. Acta Derm Venereol 1959;39:348-356

123 Eberhartinger Ch, Ebner H. Beitrag zur Kenntnis der Formalin-Kontakt-Allergie. Berufsdermatosen 1964;12:301-316

124 Fisher AA. Case presentations from the patch test clinic. American Academy of Dermatology, San Francisco, December 5, 1978. Cutis 1979;23:743,746,753,847,852,855,863,871

125 Rice EG. Allergic reactions to nail hardeners. Cutis 1968;4:971-972

126 Cronin E. Contact Dermatitis. Edinburgh: Churchill Livingstone, 1980:155

127 Flyvholm, MA. Preservatives in registered chemical products. Contact Dermatitis 2005;53:27-32

128 Herbst RA, Uter W, Pirker C, Geier J, Frosch PJ. Allergic and non-allergic periorbital dermatitis: patch test results of the Information Network of the Departments of Dermatology during a 5-year period. Contact Dermatitis 2004;51:13-19

129 Emmons WW, Marks JG. Immediate and delayed reactions to cosmetic ingredients. Contact Dermatitis 1985;13:258-265

130 Katsarou A, Armenaka M, Ale I, Koufou V, Kalogeromitros, D. Frequency of immediate reactions to the European standard series. Contact Dermatitis 1999;41:276-279

131 Held E, Johansen JD, Agner T, Menné T. Contact allergy to cosmetics: testing with patients' own products. Contact Dermatitis 1999;40:310-315

132 Neza E, Centini M. Microbiologically contaminated and over-preserved cosmetic products according Rapex 2008–2014. Cosmetics 2016, 3, 3; doi:10.3390/cosmetics3010003

133 SCCS (Scientific Committee on Consumer Safety). Opinion on the safety of the use of formaldehyde in nail hardeners, SCCS/1538/14, 7 November 2014. Available at: http://ec.europa.eu/health/scientific_committees/consumer_safety/docs/sccs_o_164.pdf

134 SCCNFP (Scientific Committee on Cosmetics and Non Food Products). Opinion concerning a clarification on the formaldehyde and para-formaldehyde entry in Directive 76/768/EEC on cosmetic products, 17 December 2002, SCCNFP/587/02. Available at: http://ec.europa.eu/health/archive/ph_risk/committees/sccp/documents/out187_en.pdf

135 Laguna C, de la Cuadra J, Martín-González B, Zaragoza V, Martínez-Casimiro L, Alegre V. Allergic contact dermatitis to cosmetics. Actas Dermosifiliogr 2009;100:53-60

136 Jawny L, Spada FJ. Contact dermatitis to a new nail hardener. Arch Derm 1967;95:199

137 Baran R. Nail cosmetics: allergies and irritations. Am J Clin Dermatol 2002;3:547-555

138 Skinner SL, Fowler JF Jr. Contact anaphylaxis: a review. Am J Cont Derm 1995;6:133-142

139 Hauksson I, Pontén A, Isaksson M, Hamada H, Engfeldt M, Bruze M. Formaldehyde in cosmetics in patch tested dermatitis patients with and without contact allergy to formaldehyde. Contact Dermatitis 2016;74:145-151

140 Isaksson M, Bråred-Christensson J, Engfeldt M, Lindberg M, Matura M, Möller H, et al. Swedish Contact Dermatitis Research Group. Patch testing with formaldehyde 2.0% in parallel with 1.0% by the Swedish contact dermatitis research group. Acta Derm Venereol 2014;94:408-410

141 Hauksson I, Pontén A, Gruvberger B, Isaksson M, Engfeldt M, Bruze M. Skincare products containing low concentrations of formaldehyde detected by the chromotropic acid method cannot be safely used in formaldehyde-allergic patients. Br J Dermatol 2016;174:371-379

142 Rosenzweig R, Scher R. Nail cosmetics: adverse reactions. Am J Contact Dermatitis 1993;4:71-77

143 Maurice F, Rivory JP, Larsson PH, Johansson SG, Bousquet J. Anaphylactic shock caused by formaldehyde in a patient undergoing long-term hemodialysis. J All Clin Immunol 1986;77:594-597

144 Mestach L, Goossens A. Allergic contact dermatitis and nail damage mimicking psoriasis caused by nail hardeners. Contact Dermatitis 2016;74:112-114

145 Lagrelius M, Wahlgren C-F, Matura M, Kull I, Lidén C. High prevalence of contact allergy in adolescence: results from the population-based BAMSE birth cohort. Contact Dermatitis 2016;74:44-51

146 Pesonen M, Jolanki R, Larese Filon F, Wilkinson M, Kręcisz B, Kieć-Świerczyńska M, et al. Patch test results of the European baseline series among patients with occupational contact dermatitis across Europe – analyses of the European Surveillance System on Contact Allergy network, 2002–2010. Contact Dermatitis 2015;72:154-163

147 Mose AP, Lundov MD, Zachariae C, Menné T, Veien NK, Laurberg G, Kaaber K, et al. Occupational contact dermatitis in painters – an analysis of patch test data from the Danish Contact Dermatitis Group. Contact Dermatitis 2012;67:293-297

148 Svedman C, Andersen KE, Brandão FM, Bruynzeel DP, Diepgen TL, et al. Follow-up of the monitored levels of preservative sensitivity in Europe. Overview of the years 2001–2008. Contact Dermatitis 2012;67:312-314

149 Gallo R, Paolino S, Salis A, Cinotti E, Parodi A. Positive patch test reaction to Lonicera japonica extract in a patient sensitized to formaldehyde. Contact Dermatitis 2012;66:47-49

150 Thyssen JP, Engkilde K, Lundov MD, Carlsen BC, Menné T, Johansen JD. Temporal trends of preservative allergy in Denmark (1985–2008). Contact Dermatitis 2010;62:102-108

151 Uter W, Rämsch C, Aberer W, Ayala F, Balato A, Beliauskiene A, et al. The European baseline series in 10 European Countries, 2005/2006 – Results of the European Surveillance System on Contact Allergies (ESSCA). Contact Dermatitis 2009;61:31-38

152 Richter G. Allergologic aspects of skin-cleansing products. Wien Med Wochenschr (Suppl) 1990;108/90:10-12

153 De Groot AC, Blok J, Coenraads P-J. Relationship between formaldehyde and quaternium-15 contact allergy. Influence of strength of patch test reactions. Contact Dermatitis 2010;63:187-191

154 Logan WA, Perry HD. Cast dermatitis due to formaldehyde sensitivity. Arch Dermatol 1972;106:717-721

155 O'Quinn SE, Kennedy CB. Contact dermatitis due to formaldehyde in clothing textiles. JAMA 1965;194:593-596

156 Cronin E. Formalin textile dermatitis. Br J Dermatol 1963;75:267-273

157 Berrens L, Young E, Jansen LH. Free formaldehyde in textiles in relation to formalin contact sensitivity. Br J Dermatol 1964;76:110-115

158 Fisher AA, Kanof NB, Biondi EM. Free formaldehyde in textiles and paper: Clinical significance. Arch Dermatol 1962;86:753-756

159 Pontén A. Formaldehyde in reusable protective gloves. Contact Dermatitis 2006;54:268-271

160 Lim SW, Smith W, Gillis D, Kette F. IgE-mediated allergy to formaldehyde from topical application. Contact Dermatitis 2006;54:230

161 Haikel Y, Braun JJ, Zana H, Boukari A, de Blay F, Pauli G. Anaphylactic shock during endodontic treatment due to allergy to formaldehyde in a root canal sealant. J Endod 2000;26:529-531

162 Kunisada M, Adachi A, Asano H, Horikawa T. Anaphylaxis due to formaldehyde released from root-canal disinfectant. Contact Dermatitis 2002;47:215-218

163 Tas E, Pletscher M, Bircher AJ. IgE-mediated urticaria from formaldehyde in a dental root canal compound. J Investig Allergol Clin Immunol 2002;12:130-133

164 Al-Nashi YG, Al-Rubayi A. A case of sensitivity to tricresol formalin. Br Dent J 1977;142:52

165 Forman GH, Ord RA. Allergic endodontic angio-oedema in response to periapical endomethasone. Br Dent J 1986;160:348-350

166 Ito M, Sai M, Handa Y, et al. Allergic reaction to formaldehyde contained in formocresol. J Dent Med 1988;28:897-904 (article in Japanese, data cited in ref. 162)

167 Ebner H, Kraft D. Formaldehyde-induced anaphylaxis after dental treatment? Contact Dermatitis 1991;24:307-309

168 Fehr B, Huwyler T, Wuthrich B. Formaldehyde and paraformaldehyde allergy. Schweiz Monatsschr Zahnnmed 1992;102:94-96 (article in German)

169 Wantke F, Hemmer W, Haglmuller T, Gotz M, Jarish R. Anaphylaxis after dental treatment with a formaldehyde containing tooth-filling material. Allergy 1995;50:274-276

170 Sayed F, Seite-Bellezza D, Sans B, Bayle-Lebey P, Maguery MC, Bazex J. Contact urticaria from formaldehyde in a root canal dental paste. Contact Dermatitis 1995;33:353

171 Sayama S, Tanabe H, Kizaki J. A case of anaphylactic shock caused by dental paste for root canal. Jpn J Clin Dermatol 1996;50:1067-1069 (article in Japanese, data cited in ref. 162)

172 Zina AM, Fanan E, Bundino S. Allergic contact dermatitis from formaldehyde and quaternium-15 in photocopier toner. Contact Dermatitis 2000;43:241

173 Bergh M, Magnusson K, Nilsson JLG, Karlberg A-T. Formation of formaldehyde and peroxides by air oxidation of high purity polyoxyethylene surfactants. Contact Dermatitis 1998;39:14-20

174 Piletta-Zanin P-A, Pasche-Koo F, Auderset PC, Huggengerger D, Saurat JH, Hauser C. Detection of formaldehyde in moistened baby toilet tissues. Contact Dermatitis 1998;38:46-47

175 Sanchez I, Rodriguez F, Quiñones D, Garcia-Abujeta JL, Fernandez L, Martin-Gil D. Occupational dermatitis due to formaldehyde in newspaper. Contact Dermatitis 1997;37:131-132

176 Flyvholm M-A, Hall BM, Agner T, Tiedemann E, Greenhill P, Vanderveken W, Freeberg FE, Menné T. Threshold for occluded formaldehyde patch test in formaldehyde-sensitive patients. Contact Dermatitis 1997;36:26-33

177 Torresani C, Periti I, Beski L. Contact urticaria syndrome from formaldehyde with multiple physical urticarias. Contact Dermatitis 1996;35:174-175

178 Key MM. Some unusual allergic reactions in industry. Arch Dermatol 1961;83:3-6

179 Helander I. Contact urticaria from leather containing formaldehyde. Arch Dermatol 1977;113:1443

180 McDaniel WR, Marks MJG. Contact urticaria due to sensitivity to spray starch. Arch Dermatol 1979;115:628

181 Lindskov R. Contact urticaria from formaldehyde. Contact Dermatitis 1982;8:333-334

182 Andersen KE, Maibach HI. Multiple application delayed onset contact urticaria: possible relation to certain unusual formalin and textile reactions? Contact Dermatitis 1984;10:227-234

183 Bracamonte BG, Ortiz de Frutos FJ, Diez LI. Occupational allergic contact dermatitis due to formaldehyde and textile finish resins. Contact Dermatitis 1995;33:139-140

184 Koch P. Occupational contact dermatitis from colophony and formaldehyde in banknote paper. Contact Dermatitis 1995;32:371-372

185 Van Hecke E, Suys E. Where next to look for formaldehyde? Contact Dermatitis 1994;31:268

186 Reid CM, Rycroft RJG. Allergic contact dermatitis from sources of MCI/MI biocide and formaldehyde in a printer. Contact Dermatitis 1993;28:252-253

187 Flyholm M-A, Menné T. Allergic contact dermatitis from formaldehyde. Contact Dermatitis 1992;27:27-36

188 Orlandini A, Viotti G, Magno L. Anaphylactoid reaction induced by patch testing with formaldehyde in an asthmatic. Contact Dermatitis 1988;19:383-384

189 Kofohd ML. Contact dermatitis to formaldehyde in fabric softeners. Contact Dermatitis 1984;11:254

190 Bruynzeel DP, van Ketel WG, de Haan P. Formaldehyde contact sensitivity and the use of shampoos. Contact Dermatitis 1984;10:179-180

191 Lembo G, Balato N, Cusano F. Unusual formaldehyde dermatitis. Contact Dermatitis 1982;8:272

192 Ring J. Exacerbation of eczema by formalin-containing hepatitis B vaccine in formaldehyde-allergic patient. Lancet 1986;2:522-523

193 Leventhal JS, Berger EM, Brauer JA, Cohen DE. Hypersensitivity reactions to vaccine constituents: a case series and review of the literature. Dermatitis 2012;23:102-109

194 Lazzarini R, Duarte I, de Farias DC, Santos CA, Tsai AI. Frequency and main sites of allergic contact dermatitis caused by nail varnish. Dermatitis 2008;19:319-322

195 Guin JD, Kincannon J, Church FL. Baby-wipe dermatitis: preservative-induced hand eczema in parents and persons using moist towelettes. Am J Cont Derm 2001;12:189-192

196 Herbert C, Rietschel RL. Formaldehyde and formaldehyde releasers: How much avoidance of cross-reacting agents is required? Contact Dermatitis 2004;50:371-373

197 Scheman A, Jacob S, Zirwas M, Warshaw E, Nedorost S, Katta R, et al. Contact allergy: Alternatives for the 2007 North American Contact Dermatitis Group (NACDG) standard screening tray. Dis Mon 2008;54:7-156

198 Flyvholm M-A. Formaldehyde exposure at the workplace and in the environment. Allergologie 1997;20:225-231

199 Statham BN, Smith EV, Bodger OG, Green CM, King CM, Ormerod AD, et al. Concomitant contact allergy to methylchloroisothiazolinone/ methylisothiazolinone and formaldehyde-releasing preservatives. Contact Dermatitis 2010;62:56-57

200 Zachariae C, Hall B, Cottin M, Cupperman S, Andersen KE, Menné T. Experimental elicitation of contact allergy from a diazolidinyl urea-preserved cream in relation to anatomical region, exposure time and concentration. Contact Dermatitis 2005;53:268-277

201 Fisher AA. Cited in ref. 39

202 Saad A, Bogorodskaya M, Harwell C, Tcheurekdjian H, Hostoffer R. Contact dermatitis to formaldehyde from kissing a corpse? Dermatitis 2016;27:231-232

203 Pontén A, Bruze M, Engfeldt M, Hauksson I, Isaksson M. Concomitant contact allergies to formaldehyde, methylchloroisothiazolinone/methylisothiazolinone, methylisothiazolinone, and fragrance mixes I and II. Contact Dermatitis 2016;75:285-289

204 Kuritzky LA, Pratt M. Systemic allergic contact dermatitis after formaldehyde-containing influenza vaccination. J Cutan Med Surg 2015;19:504-506

205 Carew B, Muir J. Patch testing for allergic contact dermatitis to cigarettes: Smoked/unsmoked components and formaldehyde factors. Australas J Dermatol 2014;55:225-226

206 Chow ET, Avolio AM, Lee A, Nixon R. Frequency of positive patch test reactions to preservatives: The Australian experience. Australas J Dermatol 2013;54:31-35

207 Kijima A, Nishino H, Umeda J, Kataoka Y. Type 1 allergy to formaldehyde in root canal sealant after dental treatment: two case reports and review of the literature. Arerugi 2007;56:1397-1402 (article in Japanese)

208 Nabeshima Y, Tanaka T, Hide M. Anaphylaxis after dental treatment with a formaldehyde-containing tooth-filling material. Acta Derm Venereol 2004;84:497-498

209 Braun JJ, Zana H, Purohit A, Valfrey J, Scherer P, Haïkel Y, de Blay F, Pauli G. Anaphylactic reactions to formaldehyde in root canal sealant after endodontic treatment: four cases of anaphylactic shock and three of generalized urticaria. Allergy 2003;58:1210-1215

210 Braun JJ, Valfrey J, Scherer P, Zana H, Haikel Y, Pauli G. IgE allergy due to formaldehyde paste during endodontic treatment. A propos of 4 cases: 2 with anaphylactic shock and 2 with generalized urticaria. Rev Stomatol Chir Maxillofac 2000;101:169-174 (article in French)

211 Charpin D, Dutau H, Falzon S. Hypersensitivity to formaldehyde. Allergy 2000;55:986-987

212 Kieć-Swierczyńska M, Krecisz B, Krysiak B, Kuchowicz E, Rydzyński K. Occupational allergy to aldehydes in health care workers. Clinical observations. Experiments. Int J Occup Med Environ Health 1998;11:349-358

213 Dahlquist I. Contact allergy to colophony and formaldehyde from sand cores. Contact Dermatitis 1981;7:167-168

214 Drouet M, Le Sellin J, Bonneau JC, Sabbah A. Allergy to root canal sealant. Allerg Immunol (Paris) 1986;18:41-43 (article in French)

215 Dooms-Goossens A, de Boulle K, Dooms M, Degreef H. Imidazolidinyl urea dermatitis. Contact Dermatitis 1986;14:322-324

216 Lv C, Hou J, Xie W, Cheng H. Investigation on formaldehyde release from preservatives in cosmetics. Int J Cosm Sci 2015;37:474-478

217 Kim KH, Jahan SA, Lee JT. Exposure to formaldehyde and its potential human health hazards. J Environ Sci Health C Environ Carcinog Ecotoxicol Rev 2011;29:277-299

218 Rietschel RL, Warshaw EM, Sasseville D, Fowler JF Jr, DeLeo VA, Belsito DV, Taylor JS, et al; North American Contact Dermatitis Group. Sensitivity of petrolatum and aqueous vehicles for detecting allergy to imidazolidinylurea, diazolidinylurea, and DMDM hydantoin: a retrospective analysis from the North American Contact Dermatitis Group. Dermatitis 2007;18:155-162

219 Toholka R, Wang Y-S, Tate B, Tam M, Cahill J, Palmer A, Nixon R. The first Australian Baseline Series: Recommendations for patch testing in suspected contact dermatitis. Australas J Dermatol 2015;56:107-115

220 Warshaw EM, Schram SE, Maibach HI, Belsito DV, Marks JG Jr, Fowler JF Jr, et al. Occupation-related contact dermatitis in North American health care workers referred for patch testing: cross-sectional data, 1998 to 2004. Dermatitis 2008;19:261-274

221 Bork K, Heise D, Rosinus A. Formaldehyde in Haarschampoos. Dermatosen 1979;27:10-12

222 Wilkinson DS, Budden MG, Hambly EM. A 10-year review of an industrial dermatitis clinic. Contact Dermatitis 1980;6:11-17

223 DeKoven JG, Warshaw EM, Belsito DV, Sasseville D, Maibach HI, Taylor JS, et al. North American Contact Dermatitis Group Patch Test Results: 2013-2014. Dermatitis 2017;28:33-46

224 Zaragoza-Ninet V, Blasco Encinas R, Vilata-Corell JJ, Pérez-Ferriols A, Sierra-Talamantes C, Esteve-Martínez A, de la Cuadra-Oyanguren J. Allergic contact dermatitis due to cosmetics: A clinical and epidemiological study in a tertiary hospital. Actas Dermosifiliogr 2016;107:329-336

225 Hu Y, Wang D, Shen Y, Tang H. Photopatch testing in Chinese patients over 10 years. Dermatitis 2016;27:137-142

226 Schwensen JF, Johansen JD, Veien NK, Funding AT, Avnstorp C, Østerballe M, et al. Occupational contact dermatitis in hairdressers: an analysis of patch test data from the Danish Contact Dermatitis Group, 2002–2011. Contact Dermatitis 2014;70:233-237

227 Warshaw EM, Wang MZ, Mathias CGT, Maibach HI, Belsito DV, Zug KA, et al. Occupational contact dermatitis in hairdressers/cosmetologists; retrospective analysis of North American Contact Dermatitis Group data, 1994 to 2010. Dermatitis 2012;23:258-268

228 Ockenfels H, Seemann U, Goos M. Contact allergy in patients with periorbital eczema: an analysis of allergens. Dermatology 1997;195:119-124

229 Uter W, Yazar K, Kratz EM, Mildau G, Lidén C. Coupled exposure to ingredients of cosmetic products: II. Preservatives. Contact Dermatitis 2014;70:219-226

230 Giménez-Arnau AM, Deza G, Bauer A, Johnston GA, Mahler V, Schuttelaar ML, et al. Contact allergy to preservatives: ESSCA* results with the baseline series, 2009-2012. J Eur Acad Dermatol Venereol 2017;31:664-671

231 Uter W, Amario-Hita JC, Balato A, Ballmer-Weber B, Bauer A, Belloni Fortina A, et al. European Surveillance System on Contact Allergies (ESSCA): results with the European baseline series, 2013/14. J Eur Acad Dermatol Venereol 2017 Jun 19. doi: 10.1111/jdv.14423. [Epub ahead of print]

232 Goldenberg A, Mousdicas N, Silverberg N, Powell D, Pelletier JL, Silverberg JI, et al. Pediatric Contact Dermatitis Registry inaugural case data. Dermatitis 2016;27:293-302

233 Clayton TH, Wilkinson SM, Rawcliffe C, Pollock B, Clark SM. Allergic contact dermatitis in children: should pattern of dermatitis determine referral? A retrospective study of 500 children tested between 1995 and 2004 in one U.K. centre. Br J Dermatol 2006;154:114-117

234 Lubbes S, Rustemeyer T, Sillevis Smitt JH, Schuttelaar ML, Middelkamp-Hup MA. Contact sensitization in Dutch children and adolescents with and without atopic dermatitis - a retrospective analysis. Contact Dermatitis 2017;76:151-159

235 Erfurt-Berge C, Geier J, Mahler V. The current spectrum of contact sensitization in patients with chronic leg ulcers or stasis dermatitis - new data from the Information Network of Departments of Dermatology (IVDK). Contact Dermatitis 2017;77:151-158

236 Scheman A, Hipolito R, Severson D, Youkhanis N. Allergy cross-reactions: retrospective clinical data and review of the literature. Dermatitis 2017;28:128-140

237 Dean AM , Secrest AM, Powell DL. Contact urticaria from occupational exposure to formaldehyde. Dermatitis 2016;27:232

238 Helaskoski E, Suolajehto H, Kuuliala O, Aalto-Korte K. Prick testing with chemicals in the diagnosis of occupational contact urticaria and respiratory diseases. Contact Dermatitis 2014;72:20-32

239 Arrandale VH, Liss GM, Tarlo SM, Pratt MD, Sasseville D, Kudla I, Holness DL. Occupational contact allergens: are they also associated with occupational asthma? Am J Ind Med 2012;55:353-360

240 Bernstein IL, Chan-Yeung M, Malo JL, Bernstein DI, Eds. Asthma in the Workplace, 3rd Edn. New York: Taylor & Francis, 2006

241 UK Health and Safety Executive. 2001. Asthmagen? critical assessment of the evidence for agents implicated in occupational asthma. Available at: http://www.hse.gov.uk/asthma/asthmagen.pdf

242 Kim J, Han Y, Ahn JH, Kim SW, Lee SI, Lee KH, Ahn K. Airborne formaldehyde causes skin barrier dysfunction in atopic dermatitis. Br J Dermatol 2016;175:357-363

243 Lynch MD, White JM, McFadden JP, Wang Y, White IR, Banerjee P. A dynamic landscape of allergen associations in delayed-type cutaneous hypersensitivity. Br J Dermatol 2017;176:184-196

2.189   FRUCTOOLIGOSACCHARIDES

IDENTIFICATION

Description/definition   : Fructooligosaccharides are oligosaccharides produced either enzymatically from sugar beets, chemically from the degradation of inulin or transfructosylation processes, and consist chiefly of kestose, nystose, fructosylnystose, bifurcose, inulobiose, inulotriose and inulotetrose
Chemical class(es)   : Carbohydrates
CAS registry number (s) : **308066-66-2**
Function(s) in cosmetics : EU: humectant; skin conditioning. USA: skin-conditioning agents - humectant
Patch testing   : 10% water (1)

GENERAL

Fructooligosaccharides are used as humectants and skin conditioning agents in cosmetic products, but also as artificial sweeteners in food (1).

CONTACT ALLERGY

Case reports and case series

A 6-year-old child had a curettage procedure for mollusca contagiosa, and a skin cream was prescribed for after-care. He then developed acute dermatitis on his arms and trunk at the sites of application of the cream. The patient was patch tested with the European baseline series and his own skin cream, which yielded a positive reaction to the cream. A repeated open application test (ROAT) with this cream gave a positive reaction after 3 days. Further patch testing was performed with all ingredients of the product. These ingredients were also tested open. The parents removed the patches at D2, and a reading was performed on D3. There was a strongly positive reaction to fructo-oligosaccharide 10% water in the occlusive patch test. The reaction in the open test with fructooligosaccharide 10% water was also positive. Thirty control tests were negative. After the patient avoided any skin product containing fructooligosaccharides, the dermatitis cleared (1).

Presence in cosmetic products and chemical analyses

In the USA, in April 2017, fructooligosaccharides was present in 12 of 56,714 cosmetic products of which the composition is known in FDA's Voluntary Cosmetic Registration Program (VCRP) (data obtained from FDA, May 2017). In August 2017, fructooligosaccharides was present in 2 of 70.516 cosmetic products of which the composition is known in EWG's Skin Deep Cosmetics Database, USA (http://www.ewg.org/skindeep/).

LITERATURE

1   Vigan M. A case of allergic contact dermatitis caused by fructo oligosaccharide. Contact Dermatitis 2012;66:111-112

2.190   GLUCOSAMINE HCl

IDENTIFICATION

Description/definition	: Glucosamine HCl is the amine salt that conforms to the formula shown below
Chemical class(es)	: Amines; carbohydrates
Chemical/IUPAC name	: (3R,4R,5S,6R)-3-Amino-6-(hydroxymethyl)oxane-2,4,5-triol;hydrochloride
Other names	: Glucosamine chlorhydrate; glucosamine hydrochloride; chitosamine hydrochloride; 2-amino-2-deoxy-D-glucopyranose hydrochloride; chondrosamine hydrochloride
CAS registry number (s)	: 66-84-2
EC number(s)	: 200-638-1
Function(s) in cosmetics	: EU: antistatic; hair conditioning. USA: pH adjusters
Patch testing	: Concentration unknown (tested as in the cosmetic product), test vehicle unknown (1)
Molecular formula	: $C_6H_{14}ClNO_5$

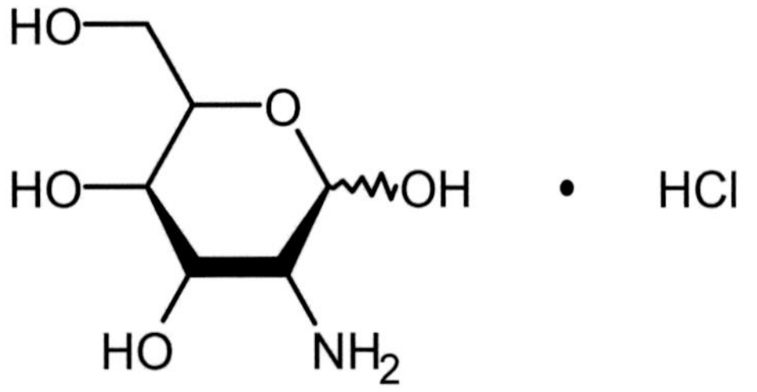

CONTACT ALLERGY

Case reports and case series
A woman was seen with a 14-year history of hand eczema. It worsened when she handled detergents and other cleaning products, and improved when she avoided such products and applied topical corticosteroids and moisturizers. At one point, she developed a new episode of hand dermatitis, which worsened when she began applying a cream containing chitin. Patch tests were carried out to the Portuguese standard series, bakery, cosmetic, preservatives and corticosteroid series, and her own topical products. There was a positive reaction to the cream. The 23 components of the cream were supplied at the same concentrations as in the cream and the patient reacted to glucosamine hydrochloride and chitosan gluconate. Eight controls were negative (1).

Presence in cosmetic products and chemical analyses
In the USA, in April 2017, glucosamine HCl was present in 122 of 56,714 cosmetic products of which the composition is known in FDA's Voluntary Cosmetic Registration Program (VCRP) (data obtained from FDA, May 2017). In August 2017, glucosamine HCl was present in 52 of 70,516 cosmetic products of which the composition is known in EWG's Skin Deep Cosmetics Database, USA (http://www.ewg.org/skindeep/).

LITERATURE
1   Pereira F, Pereira C, Lacerda MH. Contact dermatitis due to a cream containing chitin and a Carbitol. Contact Dermatitis 1998;38:290-291

2.191 GLUTARALDEHYDE

IDENTIFICATION

Description/definition : Glutaraldehyde is the dialdehyde that conforms to the formula shown below
Chemical class(es) : Aldehydes
INCI name USA : Glutaral
Chemical/IUPAC name : 1,5-Pentanedial
Other names : Glutardialdehyde
CAS registry number (s) : 111-30-8
EC number(s) : 203-856-5
CIR review(s) : J Am Coll Toxicol 1996;15:98-139 (access: www.cir-safety.org/ingredients)
Merck Index monograph : 5778
Function(s) in cosmetics : EU: preservative. USA: cosmetic biocides; fragrance ingredients; preservatives
EU cosmetic restrictions : Regulated in Annex V/48 of the Regulation (EC) No. 1223/2009
Patch testing : 0.5% pet. (Chemotechnique); 0.2% pet. (Chemotechnique); 0.3% pet. (SmartPracticeEurope, SmartPracticeCanada); 1% pet. (SmartPracticeCanada)
Molecular formula : $C_5H_8O_2$

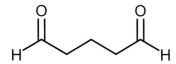

GENERAL

Glutaraldehyde is a dialdehyde with various properties. When in alkaline solution, it is an effective sterilizing chemical with bactericidal, fungicidal, virucidal, and sporicidal properties widely used in health care settings for cold sterilization of surgical instruments and surface disinfection. It has also been used in tissue fixation for histopathology and electron microscopy, embalming, in allergy vaccines, in the treatment of hyperhidrosis, onychomycosis and warts (44), as a tanning agent for leather, in wall-paper and photographic film and for friction blister prophylaxis in soldiers, athletes, and ballet dancers (23,25,29,30,34). In solution, glutaraldehyde is colorless and smells like apples (25).

Glutaraldehyde is an extremely rare sensitizer in cosmetics (only one case report) and is hardly, if at all, used in these products. It is, however, a well-known cause of allergic contact dermatitis in health care personnel (11,15,16, 19,21,23,24,28,29,32,37,38,40,42,47,49,51,57), notably in dentistry, and to a lesser degree in cleaning and maintenance staff in health care institutions (16,24,33,36) from the use of sterilizing solutions and disinfectants. Glutaraldehyde can also cause irritation of the skin and the upper and lower airways (59). It produces a yellow-brown skin discoloration and imparts an odor to the skin it contacts (23).

It has been shown that commercial glutaraldehyde 1% test substances may actually contain 25-50% of this amount, which may result in false-negative reactions (50). Conversely, glutaraldehyde 1% pet. may also induce irritant, false-positive reactions (35).Commercial test preparations may contain 5% sorbitan sesquioleate for dispersion of glutaraldehyde. Positive reactions can, consequently, also be caused by the emulsifier, which may falsely be attributed to glutaraldehyde contact allergy if sorbitan sesquioleate is not tested concurrently.

CONTACT ALLERGY

Patch testing in groups of patients

Results of testing glutaraldehyde in consecutive patients suspected of contact dermatitis (routine testing) back to 1998 are shown in table 2.191.1. Results of testing in groups of *selected* patients (e.g., health care workers, funeral service workers) back to 1989 are shown in table 2.191.2.

Patch testing in consecutive patients suspected of contact dermatitis: routine testing

Results of routine testing with glutaraldehyde are shown in table 2.191.1. Glutaraldehyde has been in the screening series of the North American Contact Dermatitis Group (NACDG) for over 2 decades, and all available investigations are from the NACDG (which publishes their results biannually) or other US centers. In ten studies, frequencies of sensitization have ranged from 0.8% to 4.8%, but in 8/10, rates were 1.5% or lower. Rates have been consistently low since 2006 (0.8%-1.5%) with very low relevance scores (9% -22% 'definite' or 'probable' relevance (2,3,6,7,9). Probably as a result, in 2017, glutaraldehyde was removed from the American Contact Dermatitis Society Core Allergen Series (48).

Table 2.191.1 Patch testing in groups of patients: Routine testing

Years and Country	Test conc. & vehicle	Number of patients tested | positive (%)		Selection of patients (S); Relevance (R); Comments (C)	Ref.
2013-14 USA, Canada	1% water	4858	41 (0.8%)	R: definite + probable relevance: 12%	9
2011-12 USA, Canada	1% pet.	4213	64 (1.5%)	R: definite + probable relevance: 17%	6
2009-10 USA, Canada	1% pet.	4293	39 (0.9%)	R: definite + probable relevance: 15%	7
2007-8 USA, Canada	1% pet.	5072	(1.1%)	R: definite + probable relevance: 9%	3
2005-6 USA, Canada	1% pet.	4413	(1.3%)	R: definite + probable relevance: 22%	2
2000-2005 USA	1% pet.	743	(4.8%)	R: 36%	1
2000-2005 USA	0.2% pet.	3831	(0.8%)	R: 52%	1
2003-4 USA, Canada	1% pet.	5135	61 (1.2%)	R: not stated	4
2001-2 USA, Canada	1% pet.	4878	(1.4%)	R: definite + probable relevance: 40%	53
1998-00 USA, Canada	1% pet.	5802	(1.9%)	R: definite + probable relevance: 23%	54
1996-8 USA, Canada	1% pet.	4094	(2.6%)	R: definite + probable + possible relevance: 48%	55

Patch testing in groups of selected patients

Results of testing in groups of selected patients back to 1989 are shown in table 2.191.2. In 10 investigations (7 in health care workers, one in hairdressers/cosmetologists, one in funeral service men, one unspecified), frequencies of sensitization have ranged from 3.6% to 13.2%. Relevance was (very) high from selection, but the causative products were mentioned in one study only: 'mostly sterilizing solutions and disinfectants' (11). In several studies, the rates of sensitization to glutaraldehyde were significantly higher than in control groups of individuals not working in health care (11,49,51,57). In groups of randomly selected dental hygienists / dental assistants and in funeral service workers, 10.9% and 10% were found to have positive patch tests to glutaraldehyde, but only a few of these individuals had active dermatitis (31,57).

Table 2.191.2 Patch testing in groups of patients: Selected patient groups

Years and Country	Test conc. & vehicle	Number of patients tested | positive (%)		Selection of patients (S); Relevance (R); Comments (C)	Ref.
1994-2014 USA		165	6 (3.6%)	S: health care workers; R: all had occupational relevance; C: in a large control group there were no positive reactions to glutaraldehyde	49
2003-2012 IVDK		1796	68 (3.8%)	S: nurses with occupational contact dermatitis; R: not stated	5
1994-2010 USA, Canada	0.5% pet	?	? (?)	S: hairdressers/cosmetologists; R: in the group of 15 patients who had at least one relevant occupationally related reaction, one (6.7%) reacted to glutaraldehyde	10
1994-2006 USA	1% pet.	53	7 (13.2%)	S: health care workers with allergic contact dermatitis; R: 100%, only relevant reactions were presented; C: in a control group of non- health care workers, the frequency was only 0.9%; in a subgroup of health care workers with *occupational* allergic contact dermatitis, 7 (23%) were caused by glutaraldehyde	51
1998-04 USA, Canada	1% pet.	1249	62 (5.0%)	S: health care workers; R: only occupation-related (= relevant) reactions were recorded; C: the frequency was significantly higher than the rate of occupation-related reactions in non-health care workers (0.1%); the causative products were mostly sterilizing solutions and disinfectants	11
<2003 USA	1% pet.	101	11 (10.9%)	S: randomly selected dental hygienists and dental assistants; R: in 6 patients with active dermatitis, 2 reacted to glutaraldehyde; C: there were also 4 ?+ reactions; the frequency of sensitization was significantly higher than in a control group	57
1998-2000 USA	1% pet.	1040	(5.5%)	S: not stated; R: not stated	52
1994-1998 Italy	0.5% water	72	5 (7%)	S: health care personnel with occupational allergic contact dermatitis; R: 100%	58
<1998 Poland		280	33 (12.4%)	S: health care workers with dermatitis; R: no data available (article not read); C: nurses, physicians and dental assistants were most frequently affected (cited in ref. 42)	32
<1989 Canada	1% water	84	8 (10%)	S: funeral service workers; R: not stated; C: only one Individual had active dermatitis	31

IVDK: Information Network of Departments of Dermatology, Germany, Austria, Switzerland

Case reports and case series

A young woman was seen with a seven-month history of acute and chronic eczematous changes of the scalp with secondary infection and alopecia. The patient had been treated with both systemic corticosteroids and antibiotics. Despite these measures, her dermatitis continued to flare, with accompanying significant hair loss. The patient related the onset of her scalp problem to the use of a new hair conditioner. Physical examination showed large subacute, oozing eczematous plaques of the posterior and parietal areas of the scalp with large areas of hair loss. Left posterior auricular and cervical adenopathy were present. Wood's lamp examination and potassium hydroxide scrapings of the scalp areas were negative. No facial eczema or nail changes were present. A scalp biopsy specimen showed alopecia and subacute spongiform dermatitis, suggestive of hypersensitivity dermatitis.

The patient was instructed to stop the use of all hair preparations and two weeks later, her scalp dermatitis showed a 90% improvement. She was later patch tested with a screening series, a cosmetic series, her hair spray (as is), her conditioner diluted 1:5 aqueous, and glutaraldehyde 2% water (a labeled ingredient of the conditioner). At D3, there was a positive patch test reaction to glutaraldehyde, but not to the diluted conditioner. Additional patches with 1%, 0.5%, 0.1%, and 0.05% glutaraldehyde were applied the same day and all but the 0.05% concentration showed positive reactions at D3. The manufacturer of the cosmetic product stated that the concentration of glutaraldehyde as a preservative in the preparation was less than 1%. The patient performed a provocative use test with the conditioner, applying it twice daily to her forearm. After three days, she reported redness and itching at the site. After avoidance of products containing glutaraldehyde, the dermatitis disappeared and the patient's hair has fully regrown (8).

Contact allergy to glutaraldehyde in non-cosmetic products

In the period 1994-1999, in one center in the USA, 55 health care workers were patch tested with glutaraldehyde 0.2%, 0.5% and/or 1% pet. and 9 (18%) had a positive patch test. All had hand dermatitis and all reactions were relevant. The group consisted of 4 dental hygienists, 2 nurses, one optical goods worker, one health technician and one dental assistant. In a control group of 417 patients with dermatitis not involved in health care, only 1.9% had a positive reaction, of which none was relevant (42). In the period 1981-1987, in an occupational and environmental health clinic in Canada, 13 health care workers were seen with occupational contact dermatitis, mainly of the hands, from glutaraldehyde allergy. The group consisted of 5 dental assistants, 3 endoscopy nurses, 2 central supply nurses, one veterinarian, one respiratory technician and a funeral service worker (29).

Case reports: health care workers

There have been several case reports and small case series of occupational allergic contact dermatitis from gluta-raldehyde in health care workers: three dental assistants (23), one dental assistant (21), a dental nurse (38), one more dental nurse (41), two theater nurses (15), two nurses (28), one nurse (16), two hospital workers disinfecting endoscopes (43), a renal dialysis unit assistant (19) and one woman sterilizing endoscopy material and a nurse (24). A hospital maintenance employee developed an airborne contact dermatitis from contact allergy to glutaraldehyde from cleaning respiratory therapy equipment (36). An unknown number of cases of allergic contact dermatitis from glutaraldehyde in health personnel, including radiologists and X-ray technicians, have been observed (37, details unknown, article not read).

Case reports: other professions and non-occupational sensitization

Two farmers had occupational allergic hand dermatitis from glutaraldehyde in disinfectants (12). Two hairdressers developed occupational allergic contact dermatitis from glutaraldehyde present in a product to disinfect scissors, combs and hairbrushes (13). Three cleaning ladies in a hospital (24), another cleaning lady (16) and a cleaner in a vascular radiology department (33) all had occupational allergic contact dermatitis of the hands from glutaraldehyde. One patient had allergic contact dermatitis of the feet from glutaraldehyde used to treat hyperhidrosis (23). A man developed paronychial dermatitis of the fingernails from treatment of onychomycosis with 10% buffered glutaral-dehyde solution (23). Another individual had dermatitis from contact allergy to glutaraldehyde present in a topical medicament to treat his warts (44). Of 8 individuals experimentally treated with 5% glutaraldehyde solution for its anhidrotic effects, one became sensitized to glutaraldehyde; 2 of 6 other individuals treated with 10% glutaralde-hyde also became sensitized to it (22). Other case reports of allergic contact dermatitis from glutaraldehyde have been presented in refs. 17,18, and 20.

Cross-reactions, pseudo-cross-reactions and co-reactions

Twenty subjects allergic to glutaraldehyde were patch tested with formaldehyde 2% water and none reacted, indicating a lack of cross-sensitivity from glutaraldehyde to formaldehyde (14). Co-reactions to formaldehyde have been observed and are probably the result of concomitant or independent sensitization rather than cross-reactivity (19,24,29). Some authors considered some degree of cross-reactivity possible (42), although they did not find indications for it in a later study (57). Glyoxal (38,39,56); phthalic dicarboxaldehyde (47).

Provocation tests

In six patients previously sensitized to glutaraldehyde by a modified Draize test, ROATs with 25% glutaraldehyde solution on the soles were negative, but ROATs in the antecubital fossa with 2.5% solution were strongly positive after 2 days already (26). Open patch testing with 550 ppm of glutaraldehyde and wearing softened T-shirts (0.4 ppm of glutaraldehyde in the rinse water) next to the skin has been found to be below the threshold level for elicitation of contact dermatitis in individuals sensitized to glutaraldehyde by a modified Draize test (27).

Presence in cosmetic products and chemical analyses

In June 2017, glutaraldehyde (glutaral) was present in four of 69,543 cosmetic products of which the composition is known in EWG's Skin Deep Cosmetics Database, USA (http://www.ewg.org/skindeep/). In the USA, in April 2017, glutaraldehyde was present in 14 of 56,714 cosmetic products of which the composition is known in FDA's Voluntary Cosmetic Registration Program (VCRP) (data obtained from FDA, May 2017).

OTHER SIDE EFFECTS

Irritant contact dermatitis

Glutaraldehyde can cause irritation of the skin (23).

Other non-eczematous contact reactions

Health care workers are at risk for the development of irritant-induced or sensitizer-induced occupational asthma when exposed to glutaraldehyde (45,59,60). Glutaraldehyde produces a yellow-brown discoloration and imparts an odor to the skin it contacts (23).

LITERATURE

1   Davis MD, Scalf LA, Yiannias JA, Cheng JF, El-Azhary RA, Rohlinger AL, et al. Changing trends and allergens in the patch test standard series. Arch Dermatol 2008;144:67-72
2   Zug KA, Warshaw EM, Fowler JF Jr, Maibach HI, Belsito DL, Pratt MD, et al. Patch-test results of the North American Contact Dermatitis Group 2005-2006. Dermatitis 2009;20:149-160
3   Fransway AF, Zug KA, Belsito DV, Deleo VA, Fowler JF Jr, Maibach HI, et al. North American Contact Dermatitis Group patch test results for 2007-2008. Dermatitis 2013;24:10-21
4   Warshaw EM, Belsito DV, DeLeo VA, Fowler JF Jr, Maibach HI, Marks JG, et al. North American Contact Dermatitis Group patch-test results, 2003-2004 study period. Dermatitis 2008;19:129-136
5   Molin S, Bauer A, Schnuch A, Geier J. Occupational contact allergy in nurses: results from the Information Network of Departments of Dermatology 2003–2012. Contact Dermatitis 2015;72:164-171
6   Warshaw EM, Maibach HI, Taylor JS, Sasseville D, DeKoven JG, Zirwas MJ, et al. North American Contact Dermatitis Group patch test results: 2011-2012. Dermatitis 2015;26:49-59
7   Warshaw EM, Belsito DV, Taylor JS, Sasseville D, DeKoven JG, Zirwas MJ, et al. North American Contact Dermatitis Group patch test results: 2009 to 2010. Dermatitis 2013;24:50-59
8   Jaworsky C, Taylor JS, Evey P, Handel D. Allergic contact dermatitis to glutaraldehyde in a hair conditioner. Cleveland Clin J Med 1987;54:443-444
9   DeKoven JG, Warshaw EM, Belsito DV, Sasseville D, Maibach HI, Taylor JS, et al. North American Contact Dermatitis Group Patch Test Results: 2013-2014. Dermatitis 2017;28:33-46
10   Warshaw EM, Wang MZ, Mathias CGT, Maibach HI, Belsito DV, Zug KA, et al. Occupational contact dermatitis in hairdressers/cosmetologists; retrospective analysis of North American Contact Dermatitis Group data, 1994 to 2010. Dermatitis 2012;23:258-268
11   Warshaw EM, Schram SE, Maibach HI, Belsito DV, Marks JG Jr, Fowler JF Jr, et al. Occupation-related contact dermatitis in North American health care workers referred for patch testing: cross-sectional data, 1998 to 2004. Dermatitis 2008;19:261-274
12   Kieć-Świerczyńska M, Krecisz B, Pałczyński C, Walusiak J, Wittczak T, Ruta U. Allergic contact dermatitis from disinfectants in farmers. Contact Dermatitis 2001;45:168-169
13   Kieć-Świerczyńska M, Krecisz B. Occupational allergic contact dermatitis in hairdressers due to glutaraldehyde. Contact Dermatitis 2001;44:185-186
14   Maibach H. Glutaraldehyde: cross-reactions to formaldehyde? Contact Dermatitis 1975;1:326-327
15   Sanderson K, Cronin E. Glutaraldehyde and contact dermatitis. Br Med J 1968;3(5621):802
16   Hansen KS. Glutaraldehyde occupational dermatitis. Contact Dermatitis 1983;9:81-82
17   Cronin E. Sensitivity to glutaraldehyde. Contact Dermatitis Newsletter 1968;3:40
18   Harman RRM, O'Crady KI. Contact dermatitis due to sensitivity to Cidex (activated glutaraldehyde). Contact Dermatitis Newsletter 1972: 11:279-280

19 Neering H, van Ketel WG. Glutaraldehyde and formaldehyde allergy. Contact Dermatitis Newsletter 1974;16:518

20 Skog E. Sensitivity to glutaraldehyde. Contact Dermatitis Newsletter 1968;4:79

21 Lyon TC. Allergic contact dermatitis due to Cidex. Oral Surgery 1971;32:895-898

22 Gordon BI, Maibach HI. Eccrine anhidrosis due to glutaraldehyde, formaldehyde, and iontophoresis. J Invest Dermatol 1969;53:436-439

23 Jordan WP, Dahl MV, Albert HL. Contact dermatitis from glutaraldehyde. Arch Dermatol 1972;105:94-95

24 Gonçalo S, Brandão FM, Pecegueiro M, Moreno JA, Sousa I. Occupational contact dermatitis to glutaraldehyde. Contact Dermatitis 1984;10:183-184

25 Juhlin L, Hansson H. Topical glutaraldehyde for plantar hyperhidrosis. Arch Dermatol 1968;97:327-330

26 Maibach HI, Prystowsky SD. Glutaraldehyde (pentanedial) allergic contact dermatitis. Arch Dermatol 1977;113:170-171

27 Weaver JE, Maibach HI. Dose-response relationships in allergic contact dermatitis. Glutaraldehyde-containing liquid fabric softener. Contact Dermatitis 1977;3:65-68

28 Bardazzi F, Melino M, Alagna G, Veronisi S. Glutaraldehyde dermatitis in nurses. Contact Dermatitis 1986;14:319-320

29 Nethercott JR, Holness DL, Page E. Occupational contact dermatitis due to glutaraldehyde in health care workers. Contact Dermatitis 1988;18:193-196

30 Cronin E. Contact Dermatitis. Edinburgh: Churchill Livingstone, 1980:796

31 Holness DL, Nethercott JR. Health status of funeral service workers exposed to formaldehyde. Arch Environ Health 1989;44:222-228

32 Kieć-Swierczyńska M1, Krecisz B, Krysiak B, Kuchowicz E, Rydzyński K. Allergy to aldehydes in health care workers. Clinical observations. Experiments. Int Occup Med Environ Health 1998;11:349-358

33 Di Prima T, de Pasquale R, Nigro M. Contact dermatitis from glutaraldehyde. Contact Dermatitis 1988;19:219-220

34 Comaish S. Glutaraldehyde lowers skin friction and enhances skin resistance to acute friction injury. Acta Dermato-Venereologica 1973;53:455-460

35 Hansen EM, Menné T. Glutaraldehyde: patch test, vehicle and concentration. Contact Dermatitis 1990;23:369-370

36 Fowler JF. Allergic contact dermatitis from glutaraldehyde exposure. J Soc Occup Med 1989;31:852-853

37 Fisher AA. Reactions to glutaraldehyde with particular reference to radiologists and X-ray technicians. Cutis 1981;28:113-122

38 Kanerva L, Miettinen P, Alanko K, Estlander T, Jolanki R. Occupational allergic contact dermatitis from glyoxal, glutaraldehyde and neomycin sulfate in a dental nurse. Contact Dermatitis 2000; 42:116-117

39 Elsner P, Pevny I, Burg G. Occupational contact dermatitis due to glyoxal in healthcare workers. Am J Cont Derm 1990;1:250-253

40 Schnuch A, Uter W, Geier J, Frosch P J, Rustemeyer T. Contact allergies in healthcare workers. Results from the IVDK. Acta Dermato-venereologica 1998;78:358-363

41 Cusano F, Luciano S. Contact allergy to benzalkonium chloride and glutaraldehyde in a dental nurse. Contact Dermatitis 1993;28:127

42 Shaffer MP, Belsito DV. Allergic contact dermatitis from glutaraldehyde in health-care workers. Contact Dermatitis 2000;43:150-156

43 Fisher AA. Allergic contact dermatitis of the hands from Sporicidin (glutaraldehyde-phenate) used to disinfect endoscopes. Cutis 1990;45:227-228

44 Martin L, Guennoc B, Machet L, Dupin M. Non-occupational contact allergy to glutaraldehyde. Contact Dermatitis 1997;37:137

45 Arrandale VH, Liss GM, Tarlo SM, Pratt MD, Sasseville D, Kudla I, Holness DL. Occupational contact allergens: are they also associated with occupational asthma? Am J Ind Med 2012;55:353-360

46 Zemtsov A. Evaluation of antigenic determinant in glutaraldehyde contact dermatitis by patch testing with chemically related substances. Am J Cont Derm 1992;3:138-141

47 Geier J, Schnuch A. Glutaraldehyd – Berufsspektrum eines Allergens. Dermatosen 1995;43:30-31

48 Schalock PC, Dunnick CA, Nedorost S, Brod B, Warshaw E, Mowad C. American Contact Dermatitis Society Core Allergen Series: 2017 update. Dermatitis 2017;28:141-143

49 Kadivar S, Belsito DV. Occupational dermatitis in health care workers evaluated for suspected allergic contact dermatitis. Dermatitis 2015;26:177-183

50 Siegel PD, Fowler JF, Law BF, Warshaw EM, Taylor JS. Concentrations and stability of methyl methacrylate, glutaraldehyde, formaldehyde and nickel sulfate in commercial patch test allergen preparations. Contact Dermatitis 2014;70:309-315

51 Suneja T, Belsito DV. Occupational dermatoses in health care workers evaluated for suspected allergic contact dermatitis. Contact Dermatitis 2008;58:285-290

52 Wetter DA, Davis MD, Yiannias JA, Cheng JF, Connolly SM, el-Azhary RA, et al. Patch test results from the Mayo Clinic Contact Dermatitis Group, 1998-2000. J Am Acad Dermatol 2005;53:416-421

53 Pratt MD, Belsito DV, DeLeo VA, Fowler JF Jr, Fransway AF, Maibach HI, et al. North American Contact Dermatitis Group patch-test results, 2001–2002 study period. Dermatitis 2004;15:176-183

54 Marks JG Jr, Belsito DV, DeLeo VA, Fowler JF Jr, Fransway AF, Maibach HI, et al. North American Contact Dermatitis Group patch-test results, 1998–2000. Am J Contact Dermat 2003;14:59-62

55 Marks JG Jr, Belsito DV, DeLeo VA, Fowler JF Jr, Fransway AF, Maibach HI, et al. North American Contact Dermatitis Group patch test results, 1996–1998. Arch Dermatol 2000;136:272-274

56 Aalto-Korte K, Mäkelä EA, Huttunen M, Suuronen K, Jolanki R. Occupational contact allergy to glyoxal. Contact Dermatitis 2005;52:276-281

57 Ravis SM, Shaffer MP, Shaffer CL, Dehkharghani S, Belsito DV. Glutaraldehyde-induced and formaldehyde-induced allergic contact dermatitis among dental hygienists and assistants. J Am Dent Assoc 2003;134:1072-1078

58 Nettis E, Colanardi MC, Soccio AL, Ferrannini A, Tursi A. Occupational irritant and allergic contact dermatitis among healthcare workers. Contact Dermatitis 2002;46:101-107

59 Copeland S, Nugent K. Persistent and unusual respiratory findings after prolonged glutaraldehyde exposure. Int J Occup Environ Med 2015;6:177-183

60 Walters GI, Moore VC, McGrath EE, Burge PS, Henneberger PK. Agents and trends in health care workers' occupational asthma. Occup Med (Lond) 2013;63:513-516

2.192 GLYCERIN

IDENTIFICATION

Description/definition	: Glycerin is the polyhydric alcohol that conforms generally to the formula shown below
Chemical class(es)	: Polyols
Chemical/IUPAC name	: Propane-1,2,3-triol
Other names	: Glycerol; 1,2,3-trihydroxypropane
CAS registry number (s)	: 56-81-5
EC number(s)	: 200-289-5
Merck Index monograph	: 5790
CIR review(s)	: Final report, December 2014 (access: www.cir-safety.org/ingredients)
Function(s) in cosmetics	: EU: denaturant; humectant; perfuming; solvent. USA: denaturants; fragrance ingredients; hair conditioning agents; humectants; oral care agents; oral health care drugs; skin protectants; skin-conditioning agents - humectants; viscosity decreasing agents
Patch testing	: 1% water (3); 1%-5%-10% water (5); 50% in water is not irritant (4)
Molecular formula	: $C_3H_8O_3$

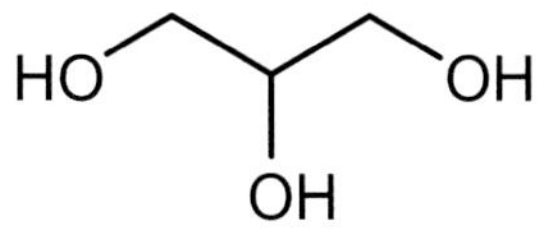

GENERAL

Glycerin is a humectant found in cosmetic preparations. It is a very rare cause of allergic contact dermatitis. Glycerin has largely been replaced in cosmetic products by propylene glycol, which is known to have a greater solubility and is less expensive (2).

CONTACT ALLERGY

Patch testing in groups of patients

In Finland, before 1979, 'thousands' of consecutive patients with suspected contact dermatitis were patch tested (routine testing) with glycerin 50% in water and there were two positive reactions. Both patients had widespread dermatitis from a cream containing 10% glycerin; an oral challenge test with glycerin in one patient was positive (4). Also in Finland, before 1976, 420 consecutive patients were patch tested with glycerin 50% in water and there was one positive reaction. The patient was on the staff of the allergy laboratory of the dermatological clinic in Helsinki and had hand dermatitis caused by applying a mixture of glycerin (1 part) and 70 % ethanol (9 parts) on the hands after washing them with soap and water (5).

Case reports and case series

A woman had suffered from patchy dermatitis of the eyelids, face, neck, scalp and axillae for 7 months. Patch tests with the European standard series, bases, cosmetics and hairdressers series and her own cosmetic products gave a positive reaction to a moisturizing cream. Later, ingredient patch testing revealed contact allergy to glycerin, tested 1% in water. Avoidance of this allergen resulted in healing of the patient's dermatitis (3). A patient, known to be allergic to Arnica, was patch tested with various cosmetic preparations containing Arnica extract. She reacted to three of these products, but was also allergic to glycerin (and various other ingredients) present in one or more of these Arnica-containing preparations (2).

A female patient had suffered from a pruritic and erythematopapular eruption on her face for 6 months. These symptoms were somewhat improved by treatment with topical corticosteroids. Patch tests with the standard series of the Japanese Contact Dermatitis Society and the patient's cosmetics gave positive reactions to a cosmetic lotion, tested as is and a cleansing foam, tested 1% in water. When tested with the ingredients, the patient reacted to glycerin (1% water) and 1,3-butylene glycol (1% water), which were present in both cosmetic products. Control testing in 30 patients with atopic dermatitis was negative. Subsequent avoidance of daily use of products containing these chemicals resulted in a significant improvement in symptoms within two weeks (1).

A woman with a long history of atopic dermatitis presented with an acute deterioration of her skin condition. She had hand eczema for many years, but recently developed a more widespread pattern of dermatitis that began on the face. Patch tests with the European standard series, medicament, plant and textile series and with her own cosmetic products gave a positive reaction to an 'itch relief' cosmetic cream. Later, she was tested with the individual constituents and the original product, and now reacted to the product, the ingredient polidocanol and to the water phase of the product, consisting of 85% glycerin with trometamol and benzoyl peroxide. The patch test with benzoyl peroxide was negative. As the patient declined further patch testing to constituents of the water phase, it remained uncertain whether glycerin or trometamol was the (other) allergenic culprit in the cream (7). Two patients had widespread dermatitis from a cream containing 10% glycerin (4). A housewife had hand dermatitis from glycerin in a hand lotion (6).

Contact allergy to glycerin in non-cosmetic products

One laboratory worker had occupational allergic contact dermatitis of the hands from glycerin in a mixture of glycerin and ethanol, which was applied to the hands after washing them with soap and water (5). Glycerin has been implicated in allergic contact dermatitis from transdermal therapeutic systems (8, data cited in ref. 9).

Cross-reactions, pseudo-cross-reactions and co-reactions

Although glycerin and 1,3-butylene glycol, to which a female patient had positive patch tests, were both present in 2 cosmetic products that had caused allergic contact dermatitis, the authors suggested that co-reactivity may have been indicative of cross-sensitivity (1).

Presence in cosmetic products and chemical analyses

In the USA, in April 2017, glycerin was present in 20627 of 56,714 cosmetic products of which the composition is known in FDA's Voluntary Cosmetic Registration Program (VCRP) (data obtained from FDA, May 2017). In April 2017, glycerin was present in 9617 of 65,522 cosmetic products of which the composition is known in EWG's Skin Deep Cosmetics Database, USA (http://www.ewg.org/skindeep/). Glycerin was present in 114 (64%) of 178 facial wipes for which ingredient information was obtained online and from retail stores, USA, 2016 (10). Glycerin was present in 32 (59%) of 54 personal hygiene wet wipes for which ingredient information was obtained online and from retail stores, USA, 2016 (11).

OTHER SIDE EFFECTS

Provocation tests

In one patient allergic to glycerin, an oral challenge test was performed with 5 ml of glycerin. An exanthema appeared within 2 hours and disappeared on the following day (4).

LITERATURE

1 T amagawa-Mineoka R, Katoh N, Kishimoto S. Allergic contact dermatitis due to 1,3-butylene glycol and glycerol. Contact Dermatitis 2007;56:297-298
2 Paulsen E, Christensen LP, Andersen KA. Cosmetics and herbal remedies with Compositae plant extracts – are they tolerated by Compositae-allergic patients? Contact Dermatitis 2008;58:15-23
3 Preston PW, Finch TM. Allergic contact dermatitis from glycerin in a moisturizing cream. Contact Dermatitis 2003;49:221-222
4 Hannuksela M. Allergic and toxic reactions caused by cream bases in dermatological patients. Int J Cosmet Sci 1979;1:257-263
5 Hannuksela M, Förström L. Contact hypersensitivity to glycerol. Contact Dermatitis 1976;2:291
6 Thyresson N, Lodin A, Nilzen A. Eczema of the hands due to triethanolamine in cosmetic handlotions for housewives. Acta Derm Venereol 1956;36:355-359
7 Fairhurst D, Wilkinson M. Independent sensitization to polidocanol and trometamol or glycerol within same product. Contact Dermatitis 2007;56:179
8 Kounis NG, Zavras GM, Papadaki PJ, Soufras GD, Poulos EA, Goudevenos J, et al. Allergic reactions to local glyceryl trinitrate administration. Br J Clin Pract 1996;50:437-439
9 Musel AL, Warshaw EM. Cutaneous reactions to transdermal therapeutic systems. Dermatitis 2006:17:109-122
10 Aschenbeck KA, Warshaw EM. Allergenic ingredients in facial wet wipes. Dermatitis 2017 Mar 23. doi: 10.1097/DER.0000000000000268. [Epub ahead of print]
11 Aschenbeck KA, Warshaw EM. Allergenic ingredients in personal hygiene wet wipes. Dermatitis 2017 Mar 23. doi: 10.1097/DER.0000000000000275. [Epub ahead of print]

2.193 GLYCERYL ABIETATE

IDENTIFICATION

Description/definition : Glyceryl abietate is the monoester of glycerin and abietic acid, which conforms to the formula shown below

Chemical class(es) : Glyceryl esters and derivatives

Chemical/IUPAC name : 2,3-Dihydroxypropyl (1S,4aR,4bS)-1,4a-dimethyl-7-propan-2-yl-2,3,4,4b,5,6,10,10a-octahydrophenanthrene-1-carboxylate

Other names : Abietic acid glycerol ester

CAS registry number (s) : 1337-89-9

Function(s) in cosmetics : EU: emollient. USA: skin-conditioning agents - emollient; viscosity increasing agents – nonaqueous

Patch testing : 20% pet. (1)

Molecular formula : $C_{23}H_{36}O_4$

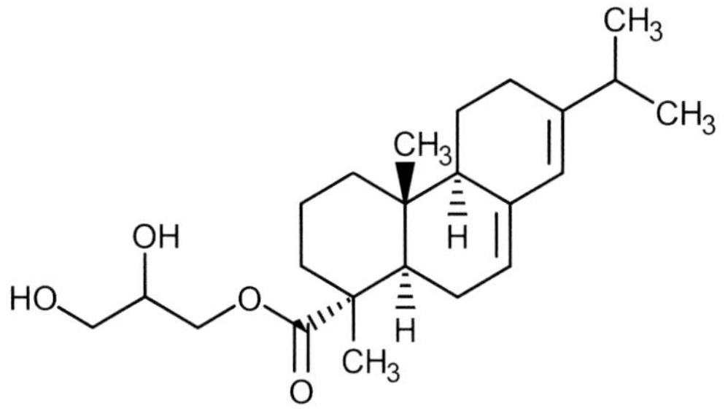

CONTACT ALLERGY

Case reports and case series

A woman, with no history of atopy, developed eczematous cheilitis after continuous use of a lipstick. Patch tests with the European standard series gave a positive reaction to fragrance mix. A patch test with the lipstick as is was also positive. Further tests with the individual components of the lipstick showed positive reactions to glyceryl abietate and glyceryl hydrogenated rosinate, both at 20% pet. The dermatitis resolved after topical corticosteroid treatment and stopping the use of the lipstick. Glyceryl abietate is the main constituent of glyceryl hydrogenated rosinate and, according to the authors, also the main allergen (1).

Contact allergy to glyceryl abietate in non-cosmetic products

A woman, with no history of atopy, presented with eczema of the lower limbs after use of cold hair-removal strips once a month for the previous 3 months. Patch tests with the European standard series showed reactions to fragrance mix and *Myroxylon pereirae* (balsam of Peru), and a test with a piece of the hair-removal strip was also positive. Further tests with the individual components of the strips gave a positive reaction to glyceryl hydrogenated rosinate. A positive reaction was also obtained to glyceryl abietate 20% pet. The dermatitis resolved completely after 10 days treatment with topical corticosteroids and suspension of use of the depilatory strips, and no recurrence was observed during a 6-month follow-up. Glyceryl abietate is the main constituent in glyceryl hydrogenated rosinate and, according to the authors, also the main allergen (1).

Cross-reactions, pseudo-cross-reactions and co-reactions

Glyceryl hydrogenated rosinate (1); not to (unmodified) colophonium.

Presence in cosmetic products and chemical analyses

In the USA, in April 2017, glyceryl abietate was present in 14 of 56,714 cosmetic products of which the composition is known in FDA's Voluntary Cosmetic Registration Program (VCRP) (data obtained from FDA, May 2017). In August 2017, glyceryl abietate was present in one of 70,516 cosmetic products of which the composition is known in EWG's Skin Deep Cosmetics Database, USA (http://www.ewg.org/skindeep/).

LITERATURE

1   Bonamonte D, Foti, C, Angelini G. Contact allergy to ester gums in cosmetics. Contact Dermatitis 2001;45:110-111

2.194 GLYCERYL CAPRYLATE

IDENTIFICATION

Description/definition	: Glyceryl caprylate is the monoester of glycerin and caprylic acid, which conforms to the formula shown below
Chemical class(es)	: Glyceryl esters and derivatives
Chemical/IUPAC name	: 2,3-Dihydroxypropyl octanoate
Other names	: Glyceryl monocaprylate; octanoic acid, monoester with glycerol; monocaprylin
CAS registry number (s)	: 26402-26-6
EC number(s)	: 247-668-1
CIR review(s)	: Final report, May 2000; Int J Toxicol 2004;23(Suppl.2):55-94; Final report, December 2015 (access: www.cir-safety.org/ingredients)
Function(s) in cosmetics	: EU: emollient; emulsifying. USA: skin-conditioning agents - emollient; surfactants – emulsifying agents
Patch testing	: 1-5% pet. (1)
Molecular formula	: $C_{11}H_{22}O_4$

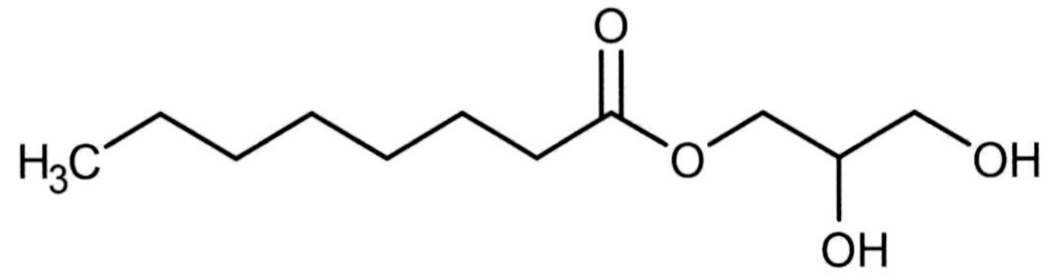

CONTACT ALLERGY

Case reports and case series

A woman presented with a history of facial eczema for several years. The lesions had occurred after application of a skin care cream. After remission of the skin lesions, patch tests were performed with the German baseline series, external products series, preservatives series, fragrances series, and several of the patient's own suspected cosmetics. After 3 days, there were many positive reactions, including to the face cream. Subsequently, a repeated open application test (ROAT) was performed with the cosmetic product, and the patient showed a distinct reaction with erythema and vesicles already one day after the first application. Patch testing with the ingredients of the face cream yielded a positive reaction to glyceryl caprylate 5% pet. To rule out an irritant reaction to glyceryl caprylate, further patch testing with lower concentrations was conducted. After 72 hr, reactions were observed to glyceryl caprylate 0.1% pet. and 1% pet. None of 3 healthy control persons reacted to glyceryl caprylate 5% pet. Upon avoiding contact with cosmetics containing this compound, the patient remained symptom-free (1).

The commercial product glyceryl caprylate used in the cream was composed of 90% glyceryl monocaprylate, 6% glyceryl dicaprylate, 4% free glycerol, and <0.1% glyceryl tricaprylate. As the authors saw a distinct reaction even to very low concentrations of glyceryl caprylate in this patient (0.1%), they considered contact allergy to the diester or the triester contained in the formulation unlikely (1).

Presence in cosmetic products and chemical analyses

In the USA, in April 2017, glyceryl caprylate was present in 448 of 56,714 cosmetic products of which the composition is known in FDA's Voluntary Cosmetic Registration Program (VCRP) (data obtained from FDA, May 2017). In March 2017, glyceryl caprylate was present in 485 of 64,983 cosmetic products of which the composition is known in EWG's Skin Deep Cosmetics Database, USA (http://www.ewg.org/skindeep/).

LITERATURE

1   Herbert VG, Spiro JM, Reich K, Steinkraus V, Karimi J, Martin V, Breuer K. Glyceryl (mono)caprylate – a new contact allergen. Contact Dermatitis 2013;69:383-385

2.195 GLYCERYL DIISOSTEARATE

IDENTIFICATION

Description/definition : Glyceryl diisostearate is the diester of glycerin and isostearic acid, that conforms generally to the formula shown below
Chemical class(es) : Glyceryl esters and derivatives
Chemical/IUPAC name : [3-Hydroxy-2-(16-methylheptadecanoyloxy)propyl] 16-methylheptadecanoate
Other names : di(Isooctadecanoic) acid, diester with glycerol
CAS registry number (s) : 68958-48-5
EC number(s) : 273-368-5
CIR review(s) : Final report, June 2002; Int J Toxicol 2007;26(Suppl.3):1-30 (access: www.cir-safety.org/ingredients)
Function(s) in cosmetics : EU: emollient; emulsifying; opacifying. USA: skin-conditioning agents - emollient
Patch testing : 35% pet. (1); 1.77% pet. (2)
Molecular formula : $C_{39}H_{76}O_5$

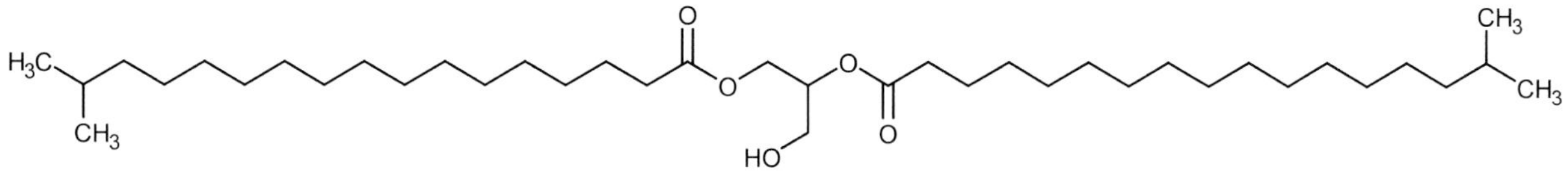

CONTACT ALLERGY

Case reports and case series

A female patient had allergic contact cheilitis from 2 lipsticks. She was patch test positive to the lipsticks, to glyceryl diisostearate in both lipsticks and to diisostearyl malate in one. Glyceryl diisostearate from the manufacturer was investigated by gas chromatography and proved to have the following composition: glyceryl diisostearate 66%, glyceryl triisostearate 29%, glyceryl (mono)isostearate 0.43%, isostearic acid 0.21% and unknown 4%. The commercial diisostearyl malate was also analyzed and proved to contain diisostearyl malate 93.3%, isostearyl alcohol 3.91% and unknown 2.79%. Next, the patient was patch tested with all chemicals including purified glyceryl diisostearate and diisostearyl malate. The patient now reacted to all chemicals except isostearic acid. However, the purified glyceryl diisostearate and isosteary malate only had weak positive reactions when tested undiluted, whereas glyceryl (mono)isostearate 0.01% pet. and isostearyl alcohol 0.25% pet. showed strong patch test reactions. It was concluded that these impurities were the most important sensitizers in the lipstick(s) (1).

Another woman presented with itchy facial erythema. Patch testing showed a positive reaction to a foundation cream. Further patch testing with its individual ingredients gave a positive reaction to glyceryl diisostearate 1.77% pet. Her face cleared in a few days with withdrawal of the foundation and application of a mild topical corticosteroid (2).

Cross-reactions, pseudo-cross-reactions and co-reactions
For co-reactivities see under Case reports and case series.

Presence in cosmetic products and chemical analyses
In the USA, in April 2017, glyceryl diisostearate was present in 165 of 56,714 cosmetic products of which the composition is known in FDA's Voluntary Cosmetic Registration Program (VCRP) (data obtained from FDA, May 2017). In March 2017, glyceryl diisostearate was present in one older product of 64,983 cosmetic products of which the composition is known in EWG's Skin Deep Cosmetics Database, USA (http://www.ewg.org/skindeep/).

LITERATURE
1 Hayakawa R, Matsunaga K, Suzuki M, Arima Y, Ohkido Y. Lipstick dermatitis due to C18 aliphatic compounds. Contact Dermatitis 1987;16:215-219
2 Tanaka M, Shimizu S, Miyakawa S. Contact dermatitis from glyceryl di-isostearate. Contact Dermatitis 1993;29:41-42

2.196   GLYCERYL HYDROGENATED ROSINATE

IDENTIFICATION

Description/definition	: Glyceryl hydrogenated rosinate is the monoester of glycerin and hydrogenated mixed long chain acids derived from colophonium (rosin)
Chemical class(es)	: Glyceryl esters and derivatives
CAS registry number (s)	: 65997-13-9
EC number(s)	: 266-042-9
CIR review(s)	: Final report, May 2000; Int J Toxicol 2004;23(Suppl.2):55-94; Final report, December 2015 (access: www.cir-safety.org/ingredients)
Function(s) in cosmetics	: EU: film forming. USA: skin-conditioning agents - emollient; surfactants – emulsifying agents
Patch testing	: 20% pet. (1)

GENERAL

Glyceryl hydrogenated rosinate may be confused with glyceryl rosinate, both of which are called ester gums, but which are different products.

Case reports and case series

A woman, with no history of atopy, developed eczematous cheilitis after continuous use of a lipstick. Patch tests with the European standard series gave a positive reaction to fragrance mix. A patch test with the lipstick as is was also positive. Further tests with the individual components of the lipstick showed positive reactions to glyceryl hydrogenated rosinate and glyceryl abietate, both at 20% pet. The dermatitis resolved after topical corticosteroid treatment and stopping the use of the lipstick. Glyceryl abietate is the main constituent of glyceryl hydrogenated rosinate and, according to the authors, also the main allergen in glyceryl hydrogenated rosinate (1).

Contact allergy to glyceryl hydrogenated rosinate in non-cosmetic products

A woman, with no history of atopy, presented with eczema of the lower limbs after use of cold hair-removal strips once a month for the previous 3 months. Patch tests with the European standard series showed reactions to fragrance mix and *Myroxylon pereirae* (balsam of Peru), and a test with a piece of the hair-removal strip was also positive. Further tests with the individual components of the strips gave a positive reaction to glyceryl hydrogenated rosinate. A positive reaction was also obtained to glyceryl abietate 20% pet. The dermatitis resolved completely after 10 days treatment with topical corticosteroids and suspension of use of the depilatory strips, and no recurrence was observed during a 6-month follow-up. Glyceryl abietate is the main constituent in glyceryl hydrogenated rosinate and, according to the authors, also the main allergen in glyceryl hydrogenated rosinate (1).

Another woman was seen with a severe bullous eruption, that was located on the dorsal region of the right wrist and hand. It followed repeated applications of a medicated patch containing ketoprofen, which was prescribed to relieve the symptoms of a tendinitis. The clinical signs were restricted to the site of application of the patch. After healing, patch tests showed positive reactions to the patch itself and to its component glyceryl hydrogenated rosinate (20% pet.). Five healthy subjects patch tested as controls showed no reactions (2).

Cross-reactions, pseudo-cross-reactions and co-reactions

Glyceryl abietate (1). Not to (unmodified) colophonium.

Presence in cosmetic products and chemical analyses

In the USA, in April 2017, glyceryl hydrogenated rosinate was present in 34 of 56,714 cosmetic products of which the composition is known in FDA's Voluntary Cosmetic Registration Program (VCRP) (data obtained from FDA, May 2017). In March 2017, glyceryl hydrogenated rosinate was present in 4 products of 64,983 cosmetic products of which the composition is known in EWG's Skin Deep Cosmetics Database, USA (http://www.ewg.org/skindeep/).

LITERATURE

1   Bonamonte D, Foti C, Angelini G. Contact allergy to ester gums in cosmetics. Contact Dermatitis 2001;45:110-111
2   Foti C, Bonamonte D, Conserva A, Casulli C, Angelini G. Allergic contact dermatitis to glyceryl-hydrogenated rosinate in a topical plaster. Contact Dermatitis 2006;55:120-121

2.197   GLYCERYL ISOSTEARATE

IDENTIFICATION

Description/definition	: Glyceryl isostearate is the monoester of glycerin and isostearic acid, which conforms generally to the formula shown below
Chemical class(es)	: Glyceryl esters and derivatives
Chemical/IUPAC name	: 1,3-Dihydroxypropan-2-yl 16-methylheptadecanoate
Other names	: Isooctadecanoic acid, monoester with glycerol
CAS registry number (s)	: 66085-00-5; 32057-14-0
EC number(s)	: 266-124-4
CIR review(s)	: Final report, May 2000; Int J Toxicol 2004;23(Suppl.2):55-94; Final report, December 2015 (access: www.cir-safety.org/ingredients)
Function(s) in cosmetics	: EU: emollient; emulsifying. USA: skin-conditioning agents – emollient; surfactants – emulsifying agents
Patch testing	: 1% pet. (2)
Molecular formula	: $C_{21}H_{42}O_4$

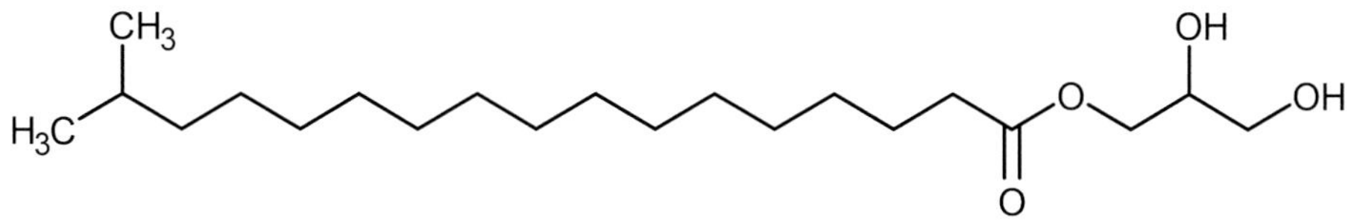

CONTACT ALLERGY

Case reports and case series

A woman presented with a several year history of persistent itchy and scaly erythema on the lips, which appeared after using five different lipsticks. Patch tests to these lipsticks and the ingredients of two of them showed positive reactions to all lipsticks, glyceryl isostearate 1% pet. and several other components. The patient stopped using these lipsticks and has remained symptom-free (2). Two similar cases were reported from Japan (1,3).

Another female patient had allergic contact cheilitis from 2 lipsticks. She was patch test positive to the lipsticks, glyceryl diisostearate in both lipsticks and to diisostearyl malate in one. Glyceryl diisostearate from the manufacturer was investigated by gas chromatography and proved to have the following composition: glyceryl diisostearate 66%,glyceryl triisostearate 29%, glyceryl (mono)isostearate 0.43%, isostearic acid 0.21% and unknown 4%. The commercial diisostearyl malate was also analyzed and proved to contain diisostearyl malate 93.3%, isostearyl alcohol 3.91% and unknown 2.79%. Next, the patient was patch tested with all chemicals including purified glyceryl diisostearate and diisostearyl malate. The patient now reacted to all chemicals except isostearic acid. However, the purified glyceryl diisostearate and isosteary malate only had weak positive reactions when tested undiluted, whereas glyceryl (mono)isostearate 0.01% pet. and isostearyl alcohol 0.25% pet. showed strong patch test reactions. It was concluded that these impurities were the most important sensitizers in the lipstick(s) (4).

Cross-reactions, pseudo-cross-reactions and co-reactions

Diisostearyl malate (2). See for other co-reactions under Case reports and case series. (ref. 4).

Presence in cosmetic products and chemical analyses

In the USA, in April 2017, glyceryl isostearate was present in 103 of 56,714 cosmetic products of which the composition is known in FDA's Voluntary Cosmetic Registration Program (VCRP) (data obtained from FDA, May 2017). In March2017, glyceryl isostearate was present in zero of 64,655 cosmetic products of which the composition is known in EWG's Skin Deep Cosmetics Database, USA (http://www.ewg.org/skindeep/).

LITERATURE

1   Tanaka B, Inaba Y, NakagawaM, Suzuki K, Matsunaga K. A case of contact cheilitis due to glyceryl isostearate. J Environ Dermatol Cutan Allergol 2009;3:163-169 (in Japanese)
2   Inui S, Azukizawa H, Katayama I. Recurrent contact cheilitis because of glyceryl isostearate, diisostearyl maleate, oleyl alcohol, and Lithol Rubine BCA in lipsticks. Contact Dermatitis 2009;60:231-232
3   Tanabe N, Ito Y, Miura H, Nose T, Nakatani S, Kozuka T, Inoue C. Contact cheilitis due to glyceryl isostearate: a case study. Environ Dermatol 1999: 6: 171–179 (in Japanese).
4   Hayakawa R, Matsunaga K, Suzuki M, Arima Y, Ohkido Y. Lipstick dermatitis due to C18 aliphatic compounds. Contact Dermatitis 1987;16:215-219

2.198 GLYCERYL ISOSTEARATE/MYRISTATE

IDENTIFICATION

Description/definition	: Glyceryl isostearate/myristate is the monoester of glycerin esterified with a blend of isostearic and myristic acids
Chemical class(es)	: Glyceryl esters and derivatives
Other names	: Isooctadecanoic acid, monoester with 1,2,3-propanetriol monotetradecanoate; glyceryl monoisostearate monomyristate
CAS registry number (s)	: 126539-55-7
CIR review(s)	: Final report, May 2000; Int J Toxicol 2004;23(Suppl.2):55-94; Int J Toxicol 2010;29 (Suppl.3):162-186 (access: www.cir-safety.org/ingredients)
Function(s) in cosmetics	: EU: emollient; emulsifying; skin conditioning; surfactant. USA: skin-conditioning agents – emollient; surfactants – emulsifying agents
Patch testing	: 7% pet. (1).

CONTACT ALLERGY

Case reports and case series

After starting to use three kinds of lipsticks from unknown Japanese manufacturers, a woman had developed pruritic erythema on her lips within a few days. A positive patch test reaction was seen to one of the lipsticks, tested as is, at D3. The patient was then patch tested with 32 ingredients of this lipstick at appropriate dilutions. Only glyceryl isostearate/myristate 7% pet. was positive at D3, but negative to 1% and 0.1% pet. Patch tests with the 7% pet. glyceryl isostearate/myristate test preparation in 6 control subjects showed no reactions at D2 or D3 (1).

Presence in cosmetic products and chemical analyses

In the USA, in April 2017, glyceryl isostearate/myristate was present in zero of 56,714 cosmetic products of which the composition is known in FDA's Voluntary Cosmetic Registration Program (VCRP) (data obtained from FDA, May 2017). In March 2017, glyceryl isostearate/myristate was present in zero of 64,983 cosmetic products of which the composition is known in EWG's Skin Deep Cosmetics Database, USA (http://www.ewg.org/skindeep/).

LITERATURE

1   Asai M, Kawada A, Aragane Y, Tezuka T. Allergic contact cheilitis due to glyceryl monoisostearate monomyristate in a lipstick. Contact Dermatitis 2001;45:173

2.199 GLYCERYL PABA

IDENTIFICATION

Description/definition : Glyceryl PABA is the ester of glycerin and *p*-aminobenzoic acid, which conforms to the formula shown below
Chemical class(es) : Glyceryl esters and derivatives; PABA derivatives
Chemical/IUPAC name : 2,3-Dihydroxypropyl 4-aminobenzoate
Other names : Lisadimate; 1-(4-aminobenzoate)-1,2,3-propanetriol; glyceryl paraaminobenzoate; 1,2,3-propanetriol 1-(4-aminobenzoate)
CAS registry number (s) : 136-44-7
EC number(s) : 205-244-3
Merck Index monograph : 5793
Function(s) in cosmetics : EU: formerly used as UV-absorber; delisted in 1986. USA: light stabilizers; sunscreen agents
EU cosmetic restrictions : Regulated in Annex II/167 of the Regulation (EC) No. 1223/2009 (prohibited)
Patch testing : Glyceryl PABA 5% pet.; benzocaine (ethyl aminobenzoate(5% pet.
Molecular formula : $C_{10}H_{13}NO_4$

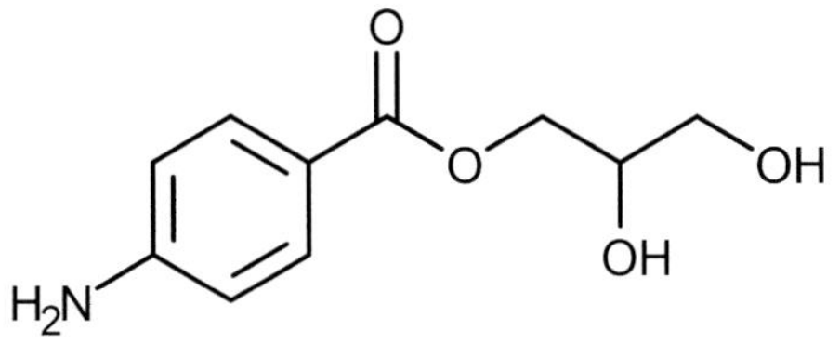

GENERAL

Glyceryl PABA is a UVB filter with UV absorbance maximum (λ_{max}) at 297 nm (22). Sensitization to glyceryl PABA was first reported in 1948/1949 (2,5). Soon thereafter and later additional reports of contact allergy, of photocontact allergy and of photoaggravated contact allergy appeared (1,3,6,7,8,9,12). Many patients with glyceryl PABA sensitization showed strong co-reactions to benzocaine (2,5,6,7,8), thereby suggesting that the sensitization may be due to the presence of impurities, notably benzocaine, in the glyceryl PABA product (7). Indeed, benzocaine was found in many commercial sources of glyceryl PABA and sunscreens containing glyceryl PABA in concentrations ranging from 1 to 18% (11). This finding has been confirmed since then repeatedly (9,10,13,14). It was subsequently shown that over half of the patients known to be allergic to benzocaine had positive patch test reactions to a glyceryl PABA sample containing 0.3% of benzocaine as impurity, none reacting to a sunscreen containing 0.001% benzocaine (10). Conversely, no allergic responses were observed when patients (photo)allergic to commercial glyceryl PABA were (photo)patch tested with glyceryl PABA that had been purified and did not contain benzocaine (12,14). Thus, many of the (early) reports of contact allergy to glyceryl PABA may have falsely implicated glyceryl PABA as the sensitizer. Nevertheless, true allergy to the PABA derivative also seems to exist, as two cases of allergic or photo-allergic reactions to glyceryl PABA in which there was no reaction to benzocaine have been reported (15).

The literature on adverse reactions to sunscreens has been reviewed in several recent and older publications (16-21,25). A review of photocontact allergy to sunscreens was published in 2010 (23). Glyceryl PABA is not used anymore in cosmetic and sunscreen products.

CONTACT ALLERGY

Case reports and case series

Glyceryl PABA was responsible for 5 out of 399 cases of cosmetic allergy where the causal allergen was identified in a study of the NACDG, USA, 1977-1983 (4). The first patient with contact allergy to glyceryl PABA was reported in 1948/1949; the reaction was interpreted as cross-reaction to previous benzocaine and sulfonamide sensitization (2,5). Two patients had allergic contact dermatitis from glyceryl PABA in sunscreens (6,15). Two single cases of combined contact allergy and photocontact allergy to glyceryl PABA in a sunscreen have been reported (1,8). Four patients reacted to glyceryl PABA in sunscreen preparations; all also had strongly positive patch test reactions to benzocaine (7).

Cross-reactions, pseudo-cross-reactions and co-reactions
Aniline (6,7); benzocaine (2,6,7,8); butyl aminobenzoate (2,6); PABA (2,6,7,24); p-phenylenediamine (2,6,7); picric acid (2); procaine (2,7); saccharin (2); sulfadiazine (2); sulfaguanidine (2); sulfanilamide (2). Most patients reacting to commercial glyceryl PABA were not allergic to the purified sunscreen itself (12,14), but to benzocaine contained in it as impurity (7). Indeed, >50% of benzocaine-sensitive individuals reacted to glyceryl PABA containing 0.3% benzocaine (10). There is *no* cross-sensitivity to pentyl (amyl) dimethyl PABA and octyl dimethyl PABA (7), as these do not contain benzocaine (13).

Presence in cosmetic products and chemical analyses
In June 2017, glyceryl PABA was present in zero of 68,866 cosmetic products of which the composition is known in EWG's Skin Deep Cosmetics Database, USA (http://www.ewg.org/skindeep/). In the USA, in April 2017, glyceryl PABA was present in zero of 56,714 cosmetic products of which the composition is known in FDA's Voluntary Cosmetic Registration Program (VCRP) (data obtained from FDA, May 2017). PABA and benzocaine were demonstrated in all batches of commercial glyceryl PABA in concentrations of >0.1% (13).

OTHER SIDE EFFECTS

Photosensitivity
One patient had combined contact allergy and photocontact allergy to glyceryl PABA in a sunscreen (1). Another individual had combined contact and photocontact allergy to glyceryl PABA and to benzocaine (8). Two patients with photoallergic contact dermatitis from glyceryl PABA in sunscreen products have been reported (3,15). One individual with contact dermatitis from a sunscreen preparation containing glyceryl PABA had photocontact allergy to commercial glyceryl PABA (containing 20% benzocaine) and benzocaine; the patient did *not* react to purified (benzocaine-free) glyceryl PABA (12).

LITERATURE

1   Goldman GC, Epstein E. Contact photosensitivity dermatitis from sun protective agent. Arch Derm 1969;100:447-449
2   Meltzer L, Baer RL. Sensitization to monoglycerol para-aminobenzoate. J Invest Dermatol 1949;12:31-39
3   Satulsky EM. Photosensitization induced by monoglycerol paraaminobenzoate; a case report. AMA Arch Derm Syphilol 1950;62:711-713
4   Adams RM, Maibach HI, Clendenning WE, Fisher AA, Jordan WJ, Kanof N, et al. A five-year study of cosmetic reactions. J Am Acad Dermatol 1985;13:1062-1069
5   Baer RL, Meltzer L. Sensitization to monoglyceryl *para*-aminobenzoate. J Invest Dermatol 1948;11:5
6   Curtis GH, Crawford PF. Cutaneous sensitivity to monoglycerol paraminobenzoate. Cleveland Clinical Quarterly 1951;18:35-41
7   Fisher AA. Sunscreen dermatitis due to glyceryl PABA: significance of cross-reactions to this PABA ester. Cutis 1976;18:495-500
8   Caro I. Contact allergy/photoallergy to glyceryl PABA and benzocaine. Contact Dermatitis 1978;4:381-382
9   Fisher AA. Dermatitis due to benzocaine present in sunscreens containing glyceryl PABA (Escalol 106). Contact Dermatitis 1977;3:170-171
10   Hjorth N, Wilkinson D, Magnusson B, Bandmann HJ, Maibach H. Glyceryl-*p*-aminobenzoate patch testing in benzocaine-sensitive subjects. Contact Dermatitis 1978;4:46-48
11   Fisher AA. The presence of benzocaine in sunscreens containing glyceryl PABA (Escalol 106). Arch Dermatol 1977;113:1299-1300
12   Kaidbey KH, Allen H. Photocontact dermatitis to benzocaine. Arch Dermatol 1981;117:77-79
13   Bruze M, Fregert S, Gruvberger B. Occurrence of *para*aminobenzoic acid and benzocaine as contaminants in sunscreen agents of *para*-aminobenzoic acid type. Photodermatology 1984;1:277-285
14   Bruze M, Gruvberger B, Thune P. Contact and photocontact allergy to glyceryl *para*-aminobenzoate. Photodermatology 1988;5:162-165
15   Thune P. Contact and photocontact allergy to sunscreens. Photodermatology 1984;1:5-9
16   Heurung AR, Raju SI, Warshaw EM. Adverse reactions to sunscreen agents: epidemiology, responsible irritants and allergens, clinical characteristics, and management. Dermatitis 2014;25:289-326
17   Heurung AR, Raju SI, Warshaw EM. Contact allergen of the year. Benzophenones. Dermatitis 2014;25:3-10 (contains many mistakes; Erratum in Dermatitis 2014;25:92-95)
18   Avenel-Audran M. Sunscreen products: finding the allergen. Eur J Dermatol 2010;20:161-166
19   Scheuer E, Warshaw E. Sunscreen allergy: a review of epidemiology, clinical characteristics, and responsible allergens. Dermatitis 2006;17:3-11

20 Fink JO, Dromgoole SH, Maibach HI. Sunscreen intolerance: contact sensitization, photocontact sensitization, and irritancy of sunscreen agents. Dermatol Clin 1995;13:473-481

21 Dromgoole SH, Maibach HI. Sunscreening agent intolerance: Contact and photocontact sensitization and contact urticaria. J Am Acad Dermatol 1990;22:1068-1078

22 Shaath NA. Ultraviolet filters. Photochem Photobiol Sci 2010;9:464-469

23 Shaw T, Simpson B, Wilson B, Oostman H, Rainey D, Storrs F. True photoallergy to sunscreens is rare despite popular belief. Dermatitis 2010;21:185-198

24 Mathias CGT, Maibach HI, Epstein J. Allergic contact photo-dermatitis to paraaminobenzoic acid. Arch Dermatol 1978;114:1665-1666

25 Schauder S. Survey of the literature on adverse reactions to preparations containing UV filters (1947-1989) (Literaturübersicht über Unverträglichkeitsreaktionen auf lichtfilterhaltige Produkte von 1947 bis 1989). Z Hautkr 1990;65:982-998 (article in German)

2.200   GLYCERYL RICINOLEATE

IDENTIFICATION

Description/definition	: Glyceryl ricinoleate is the monoester of glycerin and ricinoleic acid, which conforms generally to the formula shown below
Chemical class(es)	: Glyceryl esters and derivatives
Chemical/IUPAC name	: 2,3-Dihydroxypropyl (Z,12R)-12-hydroxyoctadec-9-enoate
Other names	: (R)-12-Hydroxyoleic acid, monoester with glycerol
CAS registry number (s)	: 1323-38-2; 141-08-2; 5086-52-2
EC number(s)	: 215-353-8; 205-455-0
CIR review(s)	: J Am Coll Toxicol 1988;7:721-739; Int J Toxicol 2007;26(Suppl.3):31-77; Final report, December 2015 (access: www.cir-safety.org/ingredients)
Function(s) in cosmetics	: EU: emollient. USA: skin-conditioning agents – emollient; surfactants – emulsifying agents
Patch testing	: 20%-30% pet. (1)
Molecular formula	: $C_{21}H_{40}O_5$

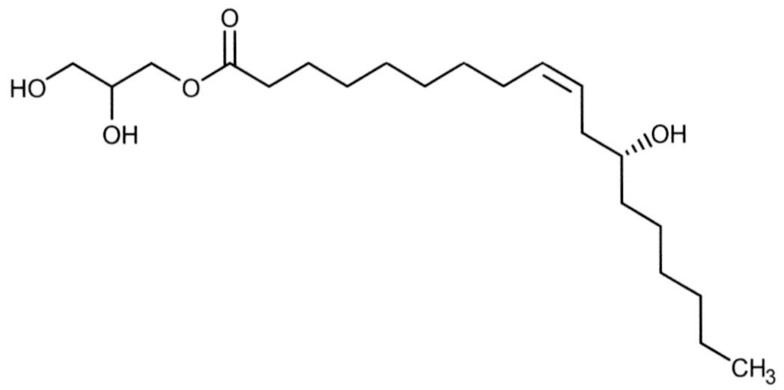

CONTACT ALLERGY

Case reports and case series

A woman developed a pruritic erythema in both axillae after the use of a new deodorant, which was caused by contact allergy to zinc ricinoleate in the deodorant. One week later, she developed an acute contact dermatitis of the lips after using a previously-tolerated perfumed lipstick. When patch tested, she reacted to the lipstick. The manufacturer of the lipstick provided 12 materials for patch testing, of which only 1 mixture was strongly positive. The breakdown testing of this mixture of 10 substances revealed only a positive reaction to 20% and 30% glyceryl ricinoleate (1).

In a group of 46 patients with allergic contact dermatitis of the eyelids seen in Kansas City, USA, between 1994 and 2004, one case was caused by contact allergy to glyceryl ricinoleate; however, the source product of sensitization was not mentioned (3).

Cross-reactions, pseudo-cross-reactions and co-reactions

Zinc ricinoleate, sulfated castor oil (1). Hydrogenated castor oil, sulfated castor oil, zinc ricinoleate, PEG-400 ricinoleate (INCI name: PEG-8 ricinoleate) and sodium sulforicinate (2).

Presence in cosmetic products and chemical analyses

In the USA, in April 2017, glyceryl ricinoleate was present in 45 of 56,714 cosmetic products of which the composition is known in FDA's Voluntary Cosmetic Registration Program (VCRP) (data obtained from FDA, May 2017). In March 2017, glyceryl ricinoleate was present in 8 of 64,983 cosmetic products of which the composition is known in EWG's Skin Deep Cosmetics Database, USA (http://www.ewg.org/skindeep/).

LITERATURE

1   Magerl A, Heiss R, Frosch PJ. Allergic contact dermatitis from zinc ricinoleate in a deodorant and glyceryl ricinoleate in a lipstick. Contact Dermatitis 2001;44:119-121
2   Dooms-Goossens A, Dupré K, Borghijs A, Swinnen C, Dooms M, Degreef H. Zinc ricinoleate: sensitizer in deodorants. Contact Dermatitis 1987;16:292-294
3   Amin KA, Belsito DV. The aetiology of eyelid dermatitis: a 10-year retrospective analysis. Contact Dermatitis 2006;55:280-285

2.201 GLYCERYL ROSINATE

IDENTIFICATION

Description/definition	: Glyceryl rosinate is the monoester of glycerin and mixed long chain acids derived from rosin (colophony, colophonium)
Chemical class(es)	: Glyceryl esters and derivatives
Other names	: Resin acids and rosin acids, esters with glycerol; glycerol ester of rosin
CAS registry number (s)	: 8050-31-5
EC number(s)	: 232-482-5
CIR review(s)	: Final report, May 2000; Int J Toxicol 2004;23(Suppl.2):55-94; Final report, December 2015 (access: www.cir-safety.org/ingredients)
Function(s) in cosmetics	: EU: film forming; perfuming. USA: fragrance ingredients; skin-conditioning agents - emollient; surfactants – emulsifying agents
Patch testing	: 20% pet. (3,4,5)

GENERAL

Glyceryl rosinate should not be confused with glyceryl *hydrogenated* rosinate (CAS 65997-13-9), both of which are often called ester gum or ester gum resin, but which are different products.

CONTACT ALLERGY

Testing in groups of patients
In the period 1982-2000, in Amersham, UK, 1270 patients with leg ulcers were patch tested to colophonium 20% pet. and to 'ester gum resin' 25% pet., made by the hospital's pharmacy. 106 patients were patch test positive to either gum resin or colophonium. 75 (71%) reacted to ester gum resin and 64 (60%) to colophonium. 33 (31%) patients were positive to both ester gum resin and colophonium. 42 (40%) were positive to ester gum resin alone and 31 (29%) patients were positive to colophonium alone. It was concluded that if testing with ester gum resin had not been performed, 42 patients (40%) with leg ulcers with a relevant contact allergy would have been missed (although it seems unlikely that the reaction to ester gum resin was relevant 100% of the patients reacting to it but not to colophonium). It was recommended that all leg ulcer patients should be tested to both colophonium and ester gum resin (14). Unfortunately, it is uncertain whether this ester gum resin was glyceryl rosinate or glyceryl hydrogenated rosinate.

Case reports and case series
Glyceryl rosinate was stated to be the (or an) allergen in one patient in a group of 603 individuals suffering from cosmetic dermatitis, seen in the period 2010-2015 in Leuven, Belgium (13). Glyceryl rosinate was responsible for 1 out of 959 cases of non-fragrance cosmetic allergy where the causal allergen was identified, Belgium, 2000-2010 (1). Glyceryl rosinate was the allergen or one of the allergens in a depilatory wax in 5 patients with allergic contact dermatitis from the wax (4,5).

A woman had had hay fever and dry lips for many years. She developed pruritic papules, swelling and pigmentation on and around her lips after applying several brands of lipsticks. Patch tests with 2 lipsticks were positive. Later, when tested with the ingredients of one of these, the patient reacted to glyceryl rosinate 2% and 30% pet., to colophonium 20% pet. and to pentaerythrityl rosinate 2% pet. (7). An unknown number of patients had allergic contact cheilitis from glyceryl rosinate in lipsticks (8,9,10); apparently there is a tendency towards pigmented cosmetic dermatitis (10).

Contact allergy to glyceryl rosinate in non-cosmetic products
A woman reacted to a hydrocolloid dressing and glyceryl rosinate. This reaction was probably a cross-reaction to pentaerythrityl rosinate, which was present in the hydrocolloid dressing (3). An unknown number of patients had allergic contact dermatitis from glyceryl rosinate in 'hypoallergenic' adhesive tape (6). A man was hospitalized with an 18-month history of stasis ulcers of his left leg. These had been treated with paste bandages supported by supporting bandages. During his admission, another brand of bandages was applied for support, after which the leg again became eczematous. Patch tests with the European standard series and a leg ulcer series gave positive reactions to BHT and ester gum resin (deodorized glycerol ester of colophony, glyceryl rosinate). There were no reactions to paste bandages, but one support bandage, which contained glyceryl rosinate, was positive. After discontinuing bandages containing glyceryl rosinate, the eczema improvement considerably (12).

Cross-reactions, pseudo-cross-reactions and co-reactions
Patients may or may not cross-react to the standard (unmodified) colophonium (4,5,7,14). Pentaerythrityl rosinate (3,7,11). Triethylene glycol hydrogenated rosinate (4,5)

Presence in cosmetic products and chemical analyses
In the USA, in April 2017, glyceryl rosinate was present in 98 of 56,714 cosmetic products of which the composition is known in FDA's Voluntary Cosmetic Registration Program (VCRP) (data obtained from FDA, May 2017). In April 2017, glyceryl rosinate was present in 27 of 65,522 cosmetic products of which the composition is known in EWG's Skin Deep Cosmetics Database, USA (http://www.ewg.org/skindeep/).

Miscellaneous side effects
Two patients had pigmented contact cheilitis from glyceryl rosinate ('ester gum') in lipsticks (2,7).

LITERATURE

1   Travassos AR, Claes L, Boey L, Drieghe J, Goossens A. Non-fragrance allergens in specific cosmetic products. Contact Dermatitis 2011;65:276-285
2   Tamaki S, Matunaka M, Imoto Y. Pigmented lip dermatitis caused by ester gum. Environ Dermatol 1996;3:348-351 (in Japanese)
3   Pereira TM, Flour M, Goossens A. Allergic contact dermatitis from modified colophonium in wound dressings. Contact Dermatitis 2007;56:5-9
4   Goossens A, Armingaud P, Avenel-Audran M et al. An epidemic of allergic contact dermatitis due to epilating products. Contact Dermatitis 2002;46:67-70
5   Goossens A. An epidemic of allergic contact dermatitis due to epilating products. Contact Dermatitis 2001;45:360
6   Umebayashi Y. Allergic contact dermatitis from ester gums in so-called hypoallergenic adhesive tapes. Environ Dermatol 1998;5:233-238 (in Japanese)
7   Inoue A, Shoji A, Aso S. Allergic lipstick cheilitis due to ester gum and ricinoleic acid. Contact Dermatitis 1998;39:39
8   Ogino Y, Hosokawa K, Suzuki M, Matsunaga K, Hirose O, Arima Y, Hayakawa R. Allergic contact dermatitis due to ester gum in a lipstick. Skin Research 1989:31 (Suppl.6):180-184 (in Japanese)
9   Nishioka K, Murata M, Ishikawa T. 3 cases of lipstick dermatitis. Environ Dermatol 1995;2:119-124 (in Japanese)
10 Research Group of Japanese Society for Contact Dermatitis. Ester gum, its optimum patch test concentration and cross reactions with related agents, and the trend of pigmented contact dermatitis (facial melanosis). Skin Research 1991;33 (suppl.11):177-182 (in Japanese)
11 Mallon E, Powell SM. Allergic contact dermatitis from Granuflex hydrocolloid dressing. Contact Dermatitis 1994;30:110-111
12 Dissanayake M, Powell SM. Allergic contact dermatitis from BHT in leg ulcer patients. Contact Dermatitis 1989;21:195-196
13 Goossens A. Cosmetic contact allergens. Cosmetics 2016, 3, 5; doi:10.3390/cosmetics3010005
14 Salim A, Shaw S. Recommendation to include ester gum resin when patch testing patients with leg ulcers. Contact Dermatitis 2001;44:34

2.202 GLYCERYL STEARATE

IDENTIFICATION

Description/definition	: Glyceryl stearate is the monoester of glycerin and stearic acid, that conforms generally to the formula shown below
Chemical class(es)	: Glyceryl esters and derivatives
Chemical/IUPAC name	: 2,3-Dihydroxypropyl octadecanoate
Other names	: Glyceryl monostearate
CAS registry number (s)	: 31566-31-1; 123-94-4; 11099-07-3; 85666-92-8
EC number(s)	: 250-705-4; 204-664-4; 234-325-6
CIR review(s)	: J Am Coll Toxicol 1982;1:169-192; Final report, December 2015 (access: www.cir-safety.org/ingredients)
Merck Index monograph	: 5794
Function(s) in cosmetics	: EU: emollient; emulsifying. USA: fragrance ingredients; skin-conditioning agents – emollient; surfactants – emulsifying agents
Patch testing	: 20% pet. (4)
Molecular formula	: $C_{21}H_{42}O_4$

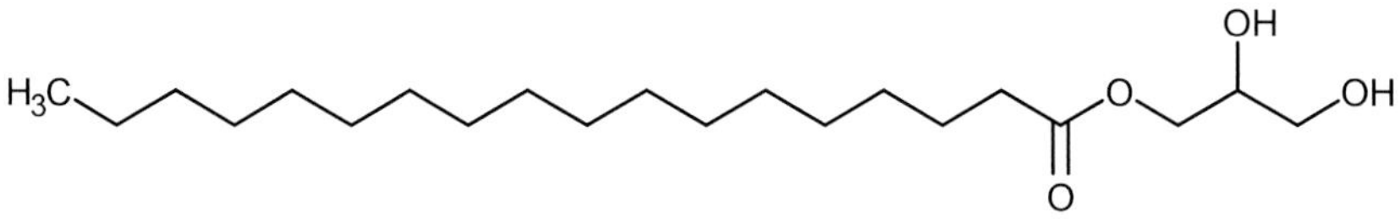

CONTACT ALLERGY

Case reports and case series
One patient reacted to the combination of glyceryl stearate 4.9% with polyoxyethylene (23) lauryl ether (laureth-23) present in a cosmetic cream; one year later, however, the reaction could not be reproduced (2). Three patients had contact allergy to glyceryl stearate present in a moisturizing cream (3). A female nurse had ACD from glyceryl stearate in a body lotion; she reacted to the lotion and to its ingredient glyceryl stearate 20% pet. Twenty controls were negative (4). Another individual had ACD from glyceryl stearate in a deodorant cream (5). Apparent worsening of actinic reticuloid was caused by contact allergy to glyceryl stearate in a sunscreen preparation (6).

Cross-reactions, pseudo-cross-reactions and co-reactions
Possibly cross-reactivity from hydroxystearic acid (1).

Presence in cosmetic products and chemical analyses
In the USA, in April 2017, glyceryl stearate was present in 6175 of 56,714 cosmetic products of which the composition is known in FDA's Voluntary Cosmetic Registration Program (VCRP) (data obtained from FDA, May 2017). In March 2017, glyceryl stearate was present in 2892 of 64,983 cosmetic products of which the composition is known in EWG's Skin Deep Cosmetics Database, USA (http://www.ewg.org/skindeep/).

Glyceryl stearate was present in 56 (32%) of 178 facial wipes for which ingredient information was obtained online and from retail stores, USA, 2016 (7). In 1984, glyceryl stearate was present in 1531 of approximately 19,000 cosmetic formulas on file with the FDA, USA (4).

LITERATURE
1   Kimura M, Kawada A, Ogino M, Murayama Y. Simultaneous contact sensitivity to hydroxystearic acid and C18-36 acid triglyceride in lip glosses. Contact Dermatitis 2002;47:115
2   Wantke F, Hemmer W, Gotz M, Jarisch R. Contact dermatitis from jojoba oil and myristyl lactate/maleated soybean oil. Contact Dermatitis 1996;34:71-72
3   Batten, TL, Wakeel RA, Douglas WS, Evans C, White MI, Moody R, Ormerod AD. Contact dermatitis from the old formula E45 cream. Contact Dermatitis 1994;30:159-161
4   De Groot AC, van der Meeren HLM, Weyland JW. Cosmetic allergy from stearic acid and glyceryl stearate. Contact Dermatitis 1988;19:77-78
5   Schwartzberg S. Allergic eczematous contact dermatitis caused by sensitization to glyceryl monostearate. Ann Allergy 1961;19: 402-403

6   Millard LG, Barrett PL. Contact allergy from Mexenone masquerading as an exacerbation of light sensitivity. Contact Dermatitis 1980;6:222-223

7   Aschenbeck KA, Warshaw EM. Allergenic ingredients in facial wet wipes. Dermatitis 2017 Mar 23. doi: 10.1097/DER.0000000000000268. [Epub ahead of print]

2.203   GLYCERYL THIOGLYCOLATE

IDENTIFICATION

Description/definition : Glyceryl thioglycolate is the monoester of glycerin and thioglycolic acid, which generally conforms to the formula shown below
Chemical class(es) : Glyceryl esters and derivatives; thio compounds
Chemical/IUPAC name : 2,3-Dihydroxypropyl 2-sulfanylacetate
Other names : Glyceryl monothioglycolate; mercaptoacetic acid, monoester with propane-1,2,3-triol
CAS registry number (s) : 30618-84-9
EC number(s) : 250-264-8
CIR review(s) : J Am Coll Toxicol 1991;10:135-192; Int J Toxicol 2009;28(Suppl.1):68-133 (access: www.cir-safety.org/ingredients)
SCCS opinion(s) : SCCS/1520/13 (31)
Function(s) in cosmetics : EU: hair waving or straightening. USA: hair waving / straightening agents
EU cosmetic restrictions : Regulated in Annex III/2b of the Regulation (EC) No. 1223/2009
Patch testing : 1.0% pet. (Chemotechnique, SmartPracticeEurope, SmartPracticeCanada)
Molecular formula : $C_5H_{10}O_4S$

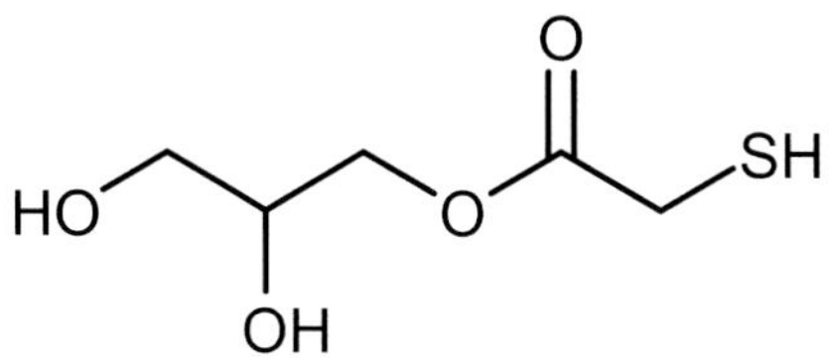

GENERAL

Permanent waves create a long-lasting curl in hair by a two-step process that involves reducing disulfide bonds in keratin and then reforming them once the hair has been wound into the desired shape. Glyceryl thioglycolate (GTG) is the reducing agent used in many 'acid permanent waves' or 'hot permanent waves'. It was introduced in the 1970s by the cosmetics industry in its search for a product that would be less damaging to hair during the waving process than the previously used ammonium thioglycolate in 'cold permanent waving'. Ammonium thioglycolate was a known irritant, but it rarely sensitized. From an allergological point of view, this replacement was an unlucky choice. Permanent waving with glyceryl thioglycolate soon was found to sensitize consumers, causing allergic contact dermatitis of the scalp, neck, ears and sometimes the forehead and − far more often − hairdressers, causing hand dermatitis, especially of the fingers (fingertips, dorsal skin of the fingers) (40). As an allergen, GTG was especially problematic since it may remain on hair for several weeks up to three months and, consequently, sensitized patients often had long-lasting dermatitis of the scalp (5,49). Of course, this also implies that cutting the hair of clients who have had a perm weeks to 3 months before may be an allergological threat to sensitized hairdressers. Another problem for hairdressers was that rubber gloves may not be protective during the permanent wave procedure, as glyceryl thioglycolate can penetrate certain rubber gloves (40).

In Germany, some years after the introduction of glyceryl thioglycolate onto the German market, an epidemic of contact allergy in hairdressers was observed. Clients were also found to be sensitized, although not as frequently (41). A similarly high prevalence was observed in a Dutch specialized clinic, where nearly 60% of 103 hairdressers were contact allergic to glyceryl thioglycolate (39). In the mid-1990s, GTG was voluntarily withdrawn from the German market by its main producers. Subsequently, in December 1997, a 'technical rule for hazardous substances 540' was set in force in Germany, calling for the substitution of GTG with other, less allergenic agents (largely eliminating GTG) (12). Within a few years, the success of this intervention was confirmed: the proportion of hairdressers reacting positively to glyceryl thioglycolate dropped from initially 45% in 1992 to less than 20% in 1997 and 1998 (43). In following years, the decline continued, reaching 0% prevalence in 2004-2005 in the youngest age group, who had presumably not been exposed to GTG any more (12). However, after 2007, some re-emergence of glyceryl thioglycolate sensitization in Germany was noted, but in 2012, none of 82 patch tested hairdressers reacted to GTG in a study performed by the IVDK (35).

CONTACT ALLERGY

Patch testing in groups of patients
Results of routine patch testing (testing in consecutive patients suspected of contact dermatitis) with glyceryl thioglycolate back to 1994 are shown in table 2.203.1. Results of testing in groups of *selected* patients (e.g.,

hairdressers with contact dermatitis, clients of hairdressers suspected of reactions to hair cosmetics, patients with eyelid dermatitis) back to 1990 are shown in table 2.203.2.

Patch testing in consecutive patients suspected of contact dermatitis: routine testing

Glyceryl thioglycolate has been part of the North American Contact Dermatitis Group (NACDG) screening series since the beginning of the 1990s and all data of routine patch testing relate to studies from the USA and Canada, notably those performed by the members of the NACDG (table 2.203.1). With one exception (5% in 1994-1996 [18]), the frequency of sensitization between 1992 and 2008 has been fairly constant, mostly between 1.5% and 2%. In the NACDG studies, 'definite + probable' relevance scores ranged from 11 to 39%. In their 2009-2010 study period, the NACDG found a low prevalence of sensitization to GTG of 0.6% with only 26% 'definite + probable' relevance (14); subsequently, glyceryl thioglycolate was removed from the NACDG routine series.

Table 2.203.1 Patch testing in groups of patients: Routine testing

Years and Country	Test conc. & vehicle	Number of patients tested	positive (%)	Selection of patients (S); Relevance (R); Comments (C)	Ref.
2009-10 USA, Canada	1% pet.	4291	26 (0.6%)	R: definite + probable relevance: 26%	14
2006-2010 USA	1% pet.	3073	(1.9%)	R: 28%	25
2007-8 USA, Canada	1% pet.	5073	(1.8%)	R: definite + probable relevance: 11%	8
2005-6 USA, Canada	1% pet.	4422	(1.6%)	R: definite + probable relevance: 18%	7
2000-2005 USA	1% pet.	3842	(1.5%)	R: 61%	3
2003-4 USA, Canada	1% pet.	5134	58 (1.1%)	R: not stated	9
2001-2 USA, Canada	1% pet.	4897	(1.9%)	R: definite + probable relevance: 33%	15
1998-2000 USA, Can.	1% pet.	5800	(2.0%)	R: definite + probable relevance: 28%	16
1998-2000 USA	1% pet.	1318	(1.5%)	R: not stated	20
1996-98 USA, Canada	1% pet.	4094	(1.9%)	R: definite + probable + possible relevance: 39%	17
1994-1996 USA	1% pet.	3075	(5.0%)	R: definite + probable relevance: 36%	18
1992-1994 USA	1% pet.	3463	(2.1%)	R: current relevance: 55%	19

Patch testing in groups of selected patients

Data on patch testing with glyceryl thioglycolate in groups of selected patients back to 1994 are summarized in table 2.203.2. Most studies investigated hairdressers. The frequency of sensitization in these groups has ranged from 1.0% to 57%. These large discrepancies may partly be explained by selection procedures. The extremely high frequency of 57% in a 1989-1992 study from The Netherlands, for example, was performed in a clinic that specialized in occupational contact dermatitis in hairdressers (39). Other factors may include the extent of use of permanent waves in certain countries and regions (fashion), the extent of the use of glyceryl thioglycolate in these permanent waves and its concentration, and preventive measures (or lack of them). In many studies, GTG was an important allergen, having sensitized over 10% of the investigated hairdressers (6,27,28,30,33,36,39). Quite remarkably, relevance data were provided only in 2 studies from specialized occupational clinics (89% [39] and 96% [33]), and from a study from the USA (89% [2]), but the latter percentage included 'questionable' and 'past' relevance. In groups of patients suspected to react to hair cosmetics, patients with eyelid dermatitis or individuals with scalp dermatitis, frequencies of sensitization were only 1.1% to 3.3% (table 2.203.2). Generally speaking, the problem of GTG sensitization has diminished considerably in the past 10-15 years, at least in some countries (12,14,35,36,43), which reflects the replacement of glyceryl thioglycolate in permanent wave with other, less sensitizing, chemicals.

Table 2.203.2 Patch testing in groups of patients: Selected patient groups

Years and Country	Test conc. & vehicle	Number of patients tested	positive (%)	Selection of patients (S); Relevance (R); Comments (C)	Ref.
2007-2012 IVDK	1% pet.	701	31 (4.7%)	S: female hairdressers with current or previous occupational contact dermatitis; R: not stated	35
		1691	19 (1.1%)	S: female patients, clients of hairdressers, in who hair cosmetics were regarded as a cause of dermatitis, and who had never worked as hairdressers; R: not stated	
2002-2011 Denmark		384	4 (1.0%)	S: hairdressers with contact dermatitis; R: not stated	34
2006-2010 USA	1% pet.	100	2 (2%)	S: patients with eyelid dermatitis; R: not stated	13
2001-2010 Australia	1% pet.	270	22 (8.1%)	S: not stated; R: 55%	32
1994-2010 USA, Canada	1% pet.	432	? (?)	S: hairdressers/cosmetologists; R: in the group of 187 patients who had at least one relevant occupationally related reaction, 101 (54%) reacted to glyceryl thioglycolate	10
1993-2010 Australia		164	26 (16%)	S: hairdressers and apprentice hairdressers presenting at an occupational dermatology clinic; R: 96%	33

Table 2.203.2 Patch testing in groups of patients: Selected patient groups (*continued*)

Years and Country	Test conc. & vehicle	Number of patients tested	positive (%)	Selection of patients (S); Relevance (R); Comments (C)	Ref.
2000-2007 USA	1% pet.	942	26 (2.8%)	S: patients tested with a supplemental cosmetic screening series; R: 89%; C: weak study: a. high rate of macular erythema and weak reactions; b. relevance figures included 'questionable' and 'past' relevance	2
1980-2007 UK	1% pet.	538	115 (21.4%)	S: hairdressers tested with a hairdressers series; R: not specified; C: decrease in sensitization rates in later years	36
2003-2006 IVDK	1% pet.	429	(9.8%)	S: female hairdressers with suspected occupational contact dermatitis; R: not stated	11
		614	(1.6%)	S: women with suspected reactions to hair cosmetics; R: not stated	
1999-2004 UK		550	46 (8.4%)	S: patients tested with the hairdressing series; R: only reactions that were of current or past relevance were collected	37
1994-2003 Spain		300	(4.0%)	S: hairdressers suspected of occupational contact dermatitis; R: not specified	26
1993-2003 IVDK	1% pet.	627	21 (3.3%)	S: patients with scalp dermatitis; R: not stated	22
2000-2002 Finland		461	(1.1%)	S: patients tested with a hairdressing series; R: not stated	21
1995-2002 IVDK		884	(18.1%)	S: female hairdressers with present or past occupational contact dermatitis; R: not specified	27
		1217	(1.7%)	S: clients of hairdressers suspected to react to hairdressing cosmetics or hair care products; R: not specified	27
1990-1999 Italy	1% pet.	209	25 (11.9%)	S: hairdressers with contact dermatitis; R: not specified	6
1995-1996 Finland		358	(3.1%)	S: patients tested with a hairdressing series; R: not stated	21
1985-1994 Greece	2.5% pet.	106	6 (5.6%)	S: hairdressers with contact dermatitis; R: not specified	38
1980-1993 Spain	1% pet.	111	3 (2.7%)	S: hairdressers; R: not specified	29
1989-1992 The Netherlands	1% pet.	103	59 (57%)	S: hairdressers seen in a specialized clinic for hairdressers; R: not specified for glyceryl thioglycolate, but 92 of the patients (89%) had occupational allergic contact dermatitis	39
1988-1991, 8 European countries		809	161 (18.7%)	S: hairdressers with hand dermatitis; R: not stated	28
1985-1990 Italy	1% pet.	302	34 (11.3%)	S: hairdressers with contact dermatitis; R: not specified	30

Case reports and case series

Case series

Glyceryl thioglycolate (GTG) was stated to be the (or an) allergen in one patient in a group of 603 individuals suffering from cosmetic dermatitis, seen in the period 2010-2015 in Leuven, Belgium (24). In 1582 female patients with (presumed) cosmetic allergy, 83 reactions (5.3%) were caused by glyceryl thioglycolate in a study of the NACDG, 2001-2004, GTG being the 9th most frequent allergen (4). In a 4-month-period in 1996, 475 patients with contact allergy to 'cosmetic ingredients' were collected in 5 centers in Belgium, UK and Germany. There were 9 reactions to glyceryl thioglycolate; relevance was not stated (23). In the period 1980 to 1983, 8 hairdressers and 4 clients with allergic contact dermatitis from glyceryl thioglycolate in permanent wave products were seen at the University Clinic in Portland, Oregon, USA. The hairdressers had dermatitis of the fingers (fingertips, dorsal aspects of the fingers), the clients dermatitis of the scalp, neck, ears or forehead. The authors mention another 29 hairdressers and 7 clients with ACD from GTG thioglycolate investigated by colleagues in the USA and Canada, to who they had given their patch test material (which was not commercially available at that time) (40).

Glyceryl thioglycolate was responsible for 25 out of 399 cases (6.3%) of cosmetic allergy where the causal allergen was identified in a study of the NACDG, USA, 1977-1983 (1). In a hospital in Vancouver, Canada, 5 of 7 hairdressers patch tested in a 4-month period in 1981 with glyceryl thioglycolate 2.5% pet. had positive reactions. They all had hand dermatitis which was ascribed to GTG in acid permanent. The fingertips of the (left) hand of the operator, where the curls are held, were usually the first to be affected. It should be realized that the test concentration of 2.5% used may cause some irritant reactions (46). An unknown number of clients of hairdressers with allergic contact dermatitis from glyceryl thioglycolate in permanent wave were reported from Germany (42).

Case reports

A hairdresser had occupational allergic contact dermatitis combined with an immediate contact reaction to glyceryl thioglycolate; the latter was discovered during patch testing (44). Three clients of hairdressers had ACD from glyceryl thioglycolate in permanent wave on the scalp (and face in one) (47). Three hairdressers developed ACD of the hands from GTG in permanent wave (47). A hair dresser had occupational ACD of the hands from glyceryl thioglycolate in permanent wave. She reacted to GTG and to hair that had been treated with permanent wave immediately before and several weeks before (49).

Cross-reactions, pseudo-cross-reactions and co-reactions
Ammonium thioglycolate (5,40,47); diglyceryl thioglycolate (unknown chemical) (48); diglyceryl dithioglycolate (unknown chemical) (5).

Presence in cosmetic products and chemical analyses
In the USA, in April 2017, glyceryl thioglycolate was present in 3 of 56,714 cosmetic products of which the composition is known in FDA's Voluntary Cosmetic Registration Program (VCRP) (data obtained from FDA, May 2017). In August 2017, glyceryl thioglycolate was present in zero of 70.516 cosmetic products of which the composition is known in EWG's Skin Deep Cosmetics Database, USA (http://www.ewg.org/skindeep/).

OTHER SIDE EFFECTS

Immediate-type reactions
Patch testing was performed in a hairdresser with hand dermatitis. After several hours, she developed an erythematous streak at the site of the glyceryl thioglycolate patch test on the right side of her back that spread to the right elbow. She noted that this streak disappeared after several hours. At the day 4 reading, she had a positive reaction to glyceryl thioglycolate. The same day, GTG was applied open on her left hand above the areas of dermatitis, and urticarial lesions developed at that site within 10 minutes (44).

Other non-eczematous contact reactions
A woman was seen for evaluation of chronic idiopathic urticaria. She had worked as a hairdresser for 9 years. The hives appeared 3 years earlier, a few days after a permanent wave solution container accidentally ruptured spraying her face, chest, and arms with an 80% aqueous solution of glyceryl thioglycolate. Emergency care for chemical burns, severe conjunctivitis, and corneal abrasions resulted in healing, but four days later generalized hives appeared. These persisted daily, except when she was away from work. Economic pressures forced her to continue to work while control of the hives was achieved with daily antihistamines and courses of systemic corticosteroid therapy. The relentless severity of the hives and associated arthralgia's finally led the patient to stop work after 2 years. A definitive demonstration of the specific cause of her chronic urticaria was achieved by scratch tests with GTG. She had positive urticarial responses (wheal 10 mm) to 1:12,500 saline dilutions of glyceryl thioglycolate. Saline controls were negative. Patch tests to 1% GTG in petrolatum were repeatedly negative. The authors hypothesized that the urticaria was related to inhalation of glyceryl thioglycolate, rather than being caused by skin contact (45).

LITERATURE
1   Adams RM, Maibach HI, Clendenning WE, Fisher AA, Jordan WJ, Kanof N, et al. A five-year study of cosmetic reactions. J Am Acad Dermatol 1985;13:1062-1069
2   Wetter DA, Yiannias JA, Prakash AV, Davis MD, Farmer SA, el-Azhary RA, et al. Results of patch testing to personal care product allergens in a standard series and a supplemental cosmetic series: an analysis of 945 patients from the Mayo Clinic Contact Dermatitis Group, 2000-2007. J Am Acad Dermatol 2010;63:789-798
3   Davis MD, Scalf LA, Yiannias JA, Cheng JF, El-Azhary RA, Rohlinger AL, et al. Changing trends and allergens in the patch test standard series. Arch Dermatol 2008;144:67-72
4   Warshaw EM, Buchholz HJ, Belsito DV et al. Allergic patch test reactions associated with cosmetics: Retrospective analysis of cross-sectional data from the North American Contact Dermatitis Group, 2001-2004. J Am Acad Dermatol 2009;60:23-38
5   Morrison LH, Storrs FJ. Persistence of an allergen in hair after glyceryl monothioglycolate-containing permanent wave solutions. J Am Acad Dermatol 1988;19:52-59
6   Iorizzo M, Parente G, Vincenzi C, Pazzaglia M, Tosti A. Allergic contact dermatitis in hairdressers; frequency and source of sensitization. Eur J Dermatol 2002;12:179-182
7   Zug KA, Warshaw EM, Fowler JF Jr, Maibach HI, Belsito DL, Pratt MD, et al. Patch-test results of the North American Contact Dermatitis Group 2005-2006. Dermatitis 2009;20:149-160
8   Fransway AF, Zug KA, Belsito DV, Deleo VA, Fowler JF Jr, Maibach HI, et al. North American Contact Dermatitis Group patch test results for 2007-2008. Dermatitis 2013;24:10-21
9   Warshaw EM, Belsito DV, DeLeo VA, Fowler JF Jr, Maibach HI, Marks JG, et al. North American Contact Dermatitis Group patch-test results, 2003-2004 study period. Dermatitis 2008;19:129-136

10   Warshaw EM, Wang MZ, Mathias CGT, Maibach HI, Belsito DV, Zug KA, et al. Occupational contact dermatitis in hairdressers/cosmetologists; retrospective analysis of North American Contact Dermatitis Group data, 1994 to 2010. Dermatitis 2012;23:258-268

11   Uter W, Lessmann H, Geier J, Schnuch A. Contact allergy to hairdressing allergens in female hairdressers and clients – current data from the IVDK, 2003-2006. J Dtsch Dermatol Ges 2007;5:993-1001

12   Uter W, Geier J, Lessmann H, Schnuch A. Is contact allergy to glyceryl monothioglycolate still a problem in Germany? Contact Dermatitis 2006;55:54-56

13   Wenk KS, Ehrlich AE. Fragrance series testing in eyelid dermatitis. Dermatitis 2012;23:22-26

14   Warshaw EM, Belsito DV, Taylor JS, Sasseville D, DeKoven JG, Zirwas MJ, et al. North American Contact Dermatitis Group patch test results: 2009 to 2010. Dermatitis 2013;24:50-59

15   Pratt MD, Belsito DV, DeLeo VA, Fowler JF Jr, Fransway AF, Maibach HI, et al. North American Contact Dermatitis Group patch-test results, 2001–2002 study period. Dermatitis 2004;15:176-183

16   Marks JG Jr, Belsito DV, DeLeo VA, Fowler JF Jr, Fransway AF, Maibach HI, et al. North American Contact Dermatitis Group patch-test results, 1998–2000. Am J Contact Dermat 2003;14:59-62

17   Marks JG Jr, Belsito DV, DeLeo VA, Fowler JF Jr, Fransway AF, Maibach HI, et al. North American Contact Dermatitis Group patch test results, 1996–1998. Arch Dermatol 2000;136:272-273

18   Marks JG Jr, Belsito DV, DeLeo VA, Fowler JF Jr, Fransway AF, Maibach HI,et al. North American Contact Dermatitis Group patch test results for the detection of delayed-type hypersensitivity to topical allergens. J Am Acad Dermatol 1998;38:911-918

19   Marks JG, Belsito DV, DeLeo VA, Fowler JF, Fransway AF, Maibach HI,et al. North American Contact Dermatitis Group standard tray patch test results 1992 through 1994. Am J Contact Dermatitis 1995;6:160-165

20   Wetter DA, Davis MDP, Yiannias JA, Cheng JF, Connolly SM, el-Azhary RA, et al. Patch test results from the Mayo Contact Dermatitis Group, 1998–2000. J Am Acad Dermatol 2005;53:416-421

21   Hasan T, Rantanen T, Alanko K, Harvima RJ, Jolanki R, Kalimo K, et al. Patch test reactions to cosmetic allergens in 1995–1997 and 2000–2002 in Finland –a multicentre study. Contact Dermatitis 2005;53:40-45

22   Hillen U, Grabbe S, Uter W. Patch test results in patients with scalp dermatitis: analysis of data of the Information Network of Departments of Dermatology. Contact Dermatitis 2007;56:87-93

23   Goossens A, Beck MH, Haneke E, McFadden JP, Nolting S, Durupt G, Ries G. Adverse cutaneous reactions to cosmetic allergens. Contact Dermatitis 1999;40:112-113

24   Goossens A. Cosmetic contact allergens. Cosmetics 2016, 3, 5; doi:10.3390/cosmetics3010005

25   Wentworth AB, Yiannias JA, Keeling JH, Hall MR, Camilleri MJ, Drage LA, et al. Trends in patch-test results and allergen changes in the standard series: a Mayo Clinic 5-year retrospective review (January 1, 2006, to December 31, 2010). J Am Acad Dermatol 2014;70:269-275

26   Valks R, Conde-Salazar L, Malfeito J, Ledo S. Contact dermatitis in hairdressers, 10 years later: patch-test results in 300 hairdressers (1994 to 2003) and comparison with previous study. Dermatitis 2005;16:28-31

27   Uter W, Lessmann H, Geier J, Schnuch A. Contact allergy to ingredients of hair cosmetics in female hairdressers and clients: an 8-year analysis of IVDK data. Contact Dermatitis 2003;49:236-240

28   Frosch PJ, Burrows D, Camarasa JG, Dooms-Goossens A, Ducombs G, Lahti A, et al. Allergic reactions to a hairdressers' series: results from 9 European centres. Contact Dermatitis 1993;28:180-183

29   Conde-Salazar L, Baz M, Guimaraens D, Cannavo A. Contact dermatitis in hairdressers: patch test results in 379 hairdressers (1980-1993). Am J Cont Dermat 1995;6:19-23

30   Guerra L, Tosti A, Bardazzi F, Pigatto P, Lisi P, Santucci B, et al. Contact dermatitis in hairdressers: the Italian experience. Contact Dermatitis 1992;26:101-107

31   SCCS (Scientific Committee on Consumer Safety). Opinion on thioglycolic acid and its salts (TGA), 11 November 2013, SCCS/1520/13. Available at: http://ec.europa.eu/health/scientific_committees/consumer_safety/docs/sccs_o_141.pdf

32   Toholka R, Wang Y-S, Tate B, Tam M, Cahill J, Palmer A, Nixon R. The first Australian Baseline Series: Recommendations for patch testing in suspected contact dermatitis. Australas J Dermatol 2015;56:107-115

33   Lyons G, Roberts H, Palmer A, Matheson M, Nixon R. Hairdressers presenting to an occupational dermatology clinic in Melbourne, Australia. Contact Dermatitis 2013;68:300-306

34   Schwensen JF, Johansen JD, Veien NK, Funding AT, Avnstorp C, Østerballe M, et al. Occupational contact dermatitis in hairdressers: an analysis of patch test data from the Danish Contact Dermatitis Group, 2002–2011. Contact Dermatitis 2014;70:233-237

35   Uter W, Gefeller O, John SM, Schnuch A, Geier J. Contact allergy to ingredients of hair cosmetics – a comparison of female hairdressers and clients based on IVDK 2007–2012 data. Contact Dermatitis 2014;71:13-20

36   O'Connell RL, White IR, McFadden JP, White JML. Hairdressers with dermatitis should always be patch tested regardless of atopy status. Contact Dermatitis 2010;62:177-181

37   Katugampola RP, Statham BN, English JSC, Wilkinson MM, Foulds IS, Green CM, Ormerod AD, et al. A multicentre review of the hairdressing allergens tested in the UK. Contact Dermatitis 2005;53:130-132

38 Katsarou A, Koufou B, Takou K, Kalogeromitros D, Papanayiotou G, Vareltzidis A. Patch test results in hairdressers with contact dermatitis in Greece (1985-1994). Contact Dermatitis 1995;33:347-348

39 Van der Walle HB, Brunsveld VM. Dermatitis in hairdressers (I): the experience of the past 4 years. Contact Dermatitis 1994;4:217-221

40 Storrs F. Permanent wave contact dermatitis: contact allergy to glyceryl monothioglycolate. J Am Acad Dermatol 1984;11:74-85

41 Peters K-P, Frosch PJ, Uter W, et al. Typ IV-Allergien auf Friseurberufsstoffe. Ergebnisse einer multizentrischen Studie in acht Kliniken der Deutschen Kontaktallergiegruppe und des 'Informationsverbundes Dermatologischer Kliniken' in Deutschland. Derm Beruf Umwelt 1994;42:50-57

42 Schnuch A, Geier J. Glycerylmonothioglykolat-Sensibilisierung bei Friseurkunden. Dermatol Beruf Umwelt 1995;43:29 (article in German)

43 Uter W, Geier J, Schnuch A for the IVDK Study Group. Downward trend of sensitization to glyceryl monothioglycolate in Germany. Dermatology 2000;200:132-133

44 Engasser P. Type I and Type IV immune responses to glyceryl thioglycolate. Contact Dermatitis 2000;42:298

45 Shelley WB, Shelley ED, Talanin NY. Urticaria due to occupational exposure to glyceryl monothioglycolate permanent wave solution. Acta Dermato-venereologica 1998;78:471-472

46 Warshawshki L, Mitchell JC, Storrs FJ. Allergic contact dermatitis from glyceryl monothioglycolate in hairdressers. Contact Dermatitis 1982;7:351-352

47 Tosti A, Melino M, Bardazzi F. Contact dermatitis due to glyceryl monothioglycolate. Contact Dermatitis 1988;19:71-72

48 Landers MC, Law S, Storrs FJ. Permanent-wave dermatitis: contact allergy to cysteamine hydrochloride. Am J Contact Dermat 2003;14:157-160

49 Reygagne A, Garnier R, Efthymiou ML, Gervais P. Glycerol monothioglycolate eczema in a hairdresser. Persistence of the allergen in the hair several weeks after the application of a permanent. J Toxicol Clin Exp 1991;11:183-187 (Article in French)

2.204   GLYCIDYL METHACRYLATE*

Not an INCI name

IDENTIFICATION

Description/definition : Glycidyl methacrylate is the 2,3 epoxypropyl ester of methacrylic acid, which conforms to the formula shown below
Chemical class(es) : Esters
INCI name USA : Neither in CosIng nor in the Personal Care Products Council Ingredient Database
Chemical/IUPAC name : Oxiran-2-ylmethyl 2-methylprop-2-enoate
Other names : 2,3-Epoxypropyl methacrylate; 2-((methacryloxy)methyl)oxirane
CAS registry number (s) : 106-91-2
EC number(s) : 203-441-9
Patch testing : 2% pet.
Molecular formula : $C_7H_{10}O_3$

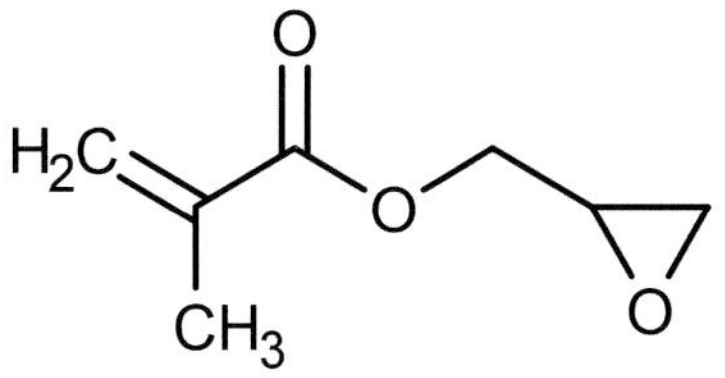

GENERAL

Discussion of contact allergy to (meth)acrylates *from non-cosmetic sources* is considered to fall outside the scope of this book. Therefore, only contact allergy from their presence in cosmetics is presented, which virtually always is from artificial nails. There are many reports of contact allergy to artificial nails, but the specific sensitizers have rarely been identified and – consequently - such publications are not presented in this and other acrylate and methacrylate monographs. Discussion is limited to publications in which the culprit (meth)acrylates have been identified, e.g., from information found in Material Data Safety Sheets, data obtained from the manufacturer or from chemical analyses.

Patients often react to many (meth)acrylates on patch testing. Primary sensitization to methacrylates may result in both methacrylate and acrylate cross-sensitization. Conversely, patients sensitized to acrylates are unlikely to show cross-sensitization to methacrylates (9).

General aspects of acrylates and methacrylates are presented in Chapter 2.219 HEMA (hydroxyethyl methacrylate). A discussion of general aspects of artificial nails, contact allergy to these products, the clinical picture of allergic contact dermatitis and other side effects of sculptured nails can also be found there. A very useful review of contact sensitization to allergens in nail cosmetics, with emphasis on acrylic manicures, was published in 2017 (2).

CONTACT ALLERGY

Case reports and case series

In the period 1996-2013, in a tertiary referral center in Valencia, Spain, 5419 patients were patch tested. Of these, 628 individuals had allergic contact dermatitis to cosmetics. Glycidyl methacrylate was the responsible allergen in one case (1).

Presence in cosmetic products and chemical analyses

In May 2017, glycidyl methacrylate was present in zero of 66,975 cosmetic products of which the composition is known in EWG's Skin Deep Cosmetics Database, USA (http://www.ewg.org/skindeep/). In the USA, in April 2017, glycidyl methacrylate was present in zero of 56,714 cosmetic products of which the composition is known in FDA's Voluntary Cosmetic Registration Program (VCRP) (data obtained from FDA, May 2017).

LITERATURE

1   Zaragoza-Ninet V, Blasco Encinas R, Vilata-Corell JJ, Pérez-Ferriols A, Sierra-Talamantes C, Esteve-Martínez A, de la Cuadra-Oyanguren J. Allergic contact dermatitis due to cosmetics: A clinical and epidemiological study in a tertiary hospital. Actas Dermosifiliogr 2016;107:329-336
2   Chou M, Dhingra N, Strugar TL. Contact sensitization to allergens in nail cosmetics. Dermatitis 2017;28:231-240

2.205   GLYCINE SOJA SEED EXTRACT

IDENTIFICATION

Description/definition	: Glycine soja seed extract is an extract of the soybean, *Glycine soja*, Leguminosae
Chemical class(es)	: Botanical products and botanical derivatives
INCI name USA	: Glycine soja (soybean) seed extract
Other names	: Soybean extract; soybean seed extract
Merck Index monograph	: 10126 (soybean)
Function(s) in cosmetics	: EU: skin conditioning. USA: skin-conditioning agents - miscellaneous
Patch testing	: Extract 10% and 20% dilutions (1)

According to the Personal Care Products Council Ingredient Database, the accepted scientific name for *Glycine soja* is *Glycine max*. However, in the U.S. National Plant Germplasm System, *Glycine soja* is an accepted name and *Glycine max.* ssp. *soja* a synonym (https://npgsweb.ars-grin.gov/gringlobal/search.aspx?).

GENERAL

Soybean is used extensively as an inexpensive filler in many food products. Its nutty flavour improves taste, its high protein content increases nutritional value, and it serves to prolong shelf life. Indirect exposure to soy, because of its many commercial uses, including cosmetics, is almost inevitable (1).

CONTACT ALLERGY

Case reports and case series
A woman presented with a 5-month history of reacting to a facial cosmetic cream. Within a few hours after application, she would develop erythema and, by the next day, swelling of the face. She was patch tested to the standard, preservative, perfume and flavors, vehicle/emulsifier, cosmetic and facial series, and the facial cream tested as is. She was positive on day 4 to the cosmetic product. Later, the patient was patch tested to the components of the cosmetic cream. She was once again positive to the cream, and also to its components soybean extract and ceramide 3 together (2% pet.), but not to ceramide 3 alone (5% pet.). Subsequently, soybean extract dilutions (20%, 10% and 1%) were all positive. They were also applied to the forearm and read at 30 minutes, when there was slight erythema with the 20% dilution; there was subsequently a palpable erythema at the 20% and 10% dilution sites when read at 3 days. Despite the rapid reaction at 30 minutes to the highest concentration of soybean extract, the patient had eaten soybean previously without adverse reactions, and an allergen-specific IgE test to soybean was negative.

Presence in cosmetic products and chemical analyses
In March 2017, glycine soja seed extract was present in 130 of 64,983 cosmetic products of which the composition is known in EWG's Skin Deep Cosmetics Database, USA (http://www.ewg.org/skindeep/). *Glycine soja* (soybean) was present in 11 (6%) of 178 facial wipes for which ingredient information was obtained online and from retail stores, USA, 2016 (2).

OTHER SIDE EFFECTS

Immediate contact reactions
A patient with cosmetic contact dermatitis from glycine soja seed extract in a cosmetic cream possibly also had a (weak) immediate-type allergy to the extract (1).

LITERATURE

1   Shaffrali FCG, Gawkrodger DJ. Contact dermatitis from soybean extract in a cosmetic cream. Contact Dermatitis 2001;44:51-52
2   Aschenbeck KA, Warshaw EM. Allergenic ingredients in facial wet wipes. Dermatitis 2017 Mar 23. doi: 10.1097/DER.0000000000000268. [Epub ahead of print]

2.206   GLYCOL HEMA-METHACRYLATE

IDENTIFICATION

Description/definition	: Glycol HEMA-methacrylate is the organic compound that conforms to the formula shown below
Chemical class(es)	: Esters
INCI name USA	: Glycol dimethacrylate
Chemical/IUPAC name	: 2-(2-Methylprop-2-enoyloxy)ethyl 2-methylprop-2-enoate
Other names	: Ethylene dimethacrylate; ethylene glycol dimethacrylate
CAS registry number (s)	: 97-90-5
EC number(s)	: 202-617-2
CIR review(s)	: Int J Toxicol 2005;24(Suppl.5):53-100 (access: www.cir-safety.org/ingredients)
Function(s) in cosmetics	: EU: film forming. USA: artificial nail builders
Patch testing	: 2.0% pet. (Chemotechnique, SmartPracticeEurope, SmartPracticeCanada)
Molecular formula	: $C_{10}H_{14}O_4$

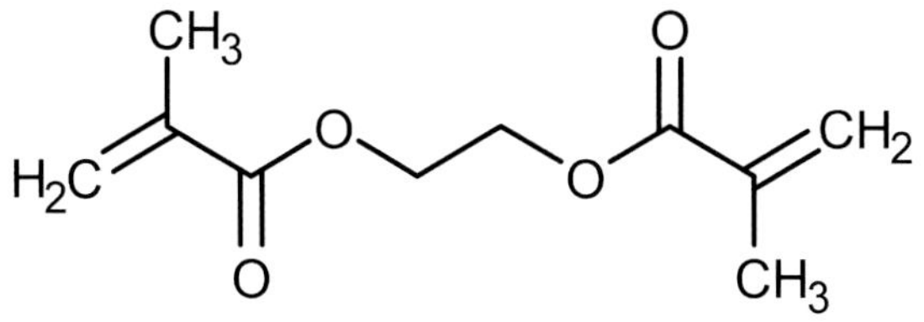

GENERAL

Discussion of contact allergy to (meth)acrylates *from non-cosmetic sources* is considered to fall outside the scope of this book. Therefore, only contact allergy from their presence in cosmetics is presented, which virtually always is from artificial nails. There are many reports of contact allergy to artificial nails, but the specific sensitizers have rarely been identified and – consequently - such publications are not presented in this and other acrylate and methacrylate monographs. Discussion is limited to publications in which the culprit (meth)acrylates have been identified, e.g., from information found in Material Data Safety Sheets, data obtained from the manufacturer or from chemical analyses.

Patients often react to many (meth)acrylates on patch testing. Primary sensitization to methacrylates may result in both methacrylate and acrylate cross-sensitization. Conversely, patients sensitized to acrylates are unlikely to show cross-sensitization to methacrylates (5).

General aspects of acrylates and methacrylates are presented in Chapter 2.219 HEMA (hydroxyethyl methacrylate). A discussion of general aspects of artificial nails, contact allergy to these products, the clinical picture of allergic contact dermatitis and other side effects of sculptured nails can also be found there. A very useful review of contact sensitization to allergens in nail cosmetics, with emphasis on acrylic manicures, was published in 2017 (11).

CONTACT ALLERGY

Patch testing in groups of patients
Studies in which consecutive patients suspected of contact dermatitis have been tested with glycol HEMA-methacrylate (routine testing) and studies testing groups of selected patients are planned to be discussed in a future publication.

Case reports and case series
Glycol HEMA-methacrylate was stated to be the (or an) allergen in 11 patients in a group of 603 individuals suffering from cosmetic dermatitis, seen in the period 2010-2015 in Leuven, Belgium (6). In the period 1996-2013, in a tertiary referral center in Valencia, Spain, 5419 patients were patch tested. Of these, 628 individuals had allergic contact dermatitis to cosmetics. Glycol HEMA-methacrylate was the responsible allergen in 24 cases (8). Glycol HEMA-methacrylate was responsible for 5 out of 959 cases of non-fragrance cosmetic allergy where the causal allergen was identified, Belgium, 2000-2010 (1). In the period 2000-2007, 202 patients with allergic contact dermatitis caused by cosmetics were seen in the same clinic in Valencia, Spain (overlap with ref. 8). In this group, there were 10 beauticians with occupational allergic contact dermatitis of the hands, who reacted to multiple (meth)acrylates from their presence in artificial nail materials. Of these ten individuals, seven reacted to glycol HEMA-methacrylate, which

reactions were apparently relevant (although it can be doubted that the presence of these specific chemicals in the products could always be verified) (7).

A group of 55 female patients presenting with hand eczema and who had contact with artificial nails, were patch tested with a series of acrylates in one center in Israel, 2001-2004. Twenty-one had one or more positive reactions, of who 14 were professional beauticians specializing in nail sculpturing. All reactions, including 13 to glycol HEMA-methacrylate, were stated to be of current relevance (3). Because of the general lack of information on the composition of artificial nail materials, the fact that the author did no analyses of these products and the frequent occurrence of cross-reactivity among acrylates, one may wonder whether this statement can be accepted as entirely correct.

One patient had allergic contact paronychia from glycol HEMA-methacrylate in sculptured nails (2). A manicurist had occupational, partly airborne, allergic contact dermatitis from glycol HEMA-methacrylate in a nail strengthener and a UV-cured nail gel (in the discussion it was stated, contrary to the case description, that the product used did *not* this particular methacrylate (4).

Patch test sensitization
Two patients became sensitized from patch tests with glycol HEMA-methacrylate 2% pet. (9,10).

Presence in cosmetic products and chemical analyses
In August 2017, glycol-HEMA methacrylate was present in zero of 70,589 cosmetic products of which the composition is known in EWG's Skin Deep Cosmetics Database, USA (http://www.ewg.org/skindeep/). In the USA, in April 2017, glycol HEMA-methacrylate was present in zero of 56,714 cosmetic products of which the composition is known in FDA's Voluntary Cosmetic Registration Program (VCRP) (data obtained from FDA, May 2017).

LITERATURE
1   Travassos AR, Claes L, Boey L, Drieghe J, Goossens A. Non-fragrance allergens in specific cosmetic products. Contact Dermatitis 2011;65:276-285
2   Fisher AA. Cross reactions between methyl methacrylate monomer and acrylic monomers presently used in acrylic nail preparations. Contact Dermatitis 1980;6:345-347
3   Lazarov A. Sensitization to acrylates is a common adverse reaction to artificial fingernails. J Eur Acad Derm Venereol 2007;21:169-174
4   Erdmann SM, Sachs B, Merk HF. Adverse reactions to sculptured nails. Allergy 2001;56:581-582
5   Aalto-Korte K, Henriks-Eckerman M-L, Kuuliala O, Jolanki R. Occupational methacrylate and acrylate allergy – cross-reactions and possible screening allergens. Contact Dermatitis 2010;63:301-312
6   Goossens A. Cosmetic contact allergens. Cosmetics 2016, 3, 5; doi:10.3390/cosmetics3010005
7   Laguna C, de la Cuadra J, Martín-González B, Zaragoza V, Martínez-Casimiro L, Alegre V. Allergic contact dermatitis to cosmetics. Actas Dermosifiliogr 2009;100:53-60
8   Zaragoza-Ninet V, Blasco Encinas R, Vilata-Corell JJ, Pérez-Ferriols A, Sierra-Talamantes C, Esteve-Martínez A, de la Cuadra-Oyanguren J. Allergic contact dermatitis due to cosmetics: A clinical and epidemiological study in a tertiary hospital. Actas Dermosifiliogr 2016;107:329-336
9   Malanin K. Active sensitization to camphoroquinone and double active sensitization to acrylics with long-lasting patch test reactions. Contact Dermatitis 1993;29:284-285
10 Kanerva L, Estlander T, Jolanki R. Active sensitization caused by 2-hydroxyethyl methacrylate, 2-hydroxypropyl methacrylate, ethyleneglycol dimethacrylate and N,N-dimethylaminoethyl methacrylate. J Eur Acad Derm Venereol 1992;1:165-169
11 Chou M, Dhingra N, Strugar TL. Contact sensitization to allergens in nail cosmetics. Dermatitis 2017;28:231-240

2.207 GLYCYRRHETINIC ACID

IDENTIFICATION

Description/definition	: Glycyrrhetinic acid is an organic compound derived from glycyrrhizic acid or shredded licorice roots, which conforms to the formula shown below
Chemical class(es)	: Sterols
Chemical/IUPAC name	: (2S,4aS,6aR,6aS,6bR,8aR,10S,12aS,14bR)-10-Hydroxy-2,4a,6a,6b,9,9,12a-hepta-methyl-13-oxo-3,4,5,6,6a,7,8,8a,10,11,12,14b-dodecahydro-1H-picene-2-carboxylic acid
Other names	: Enoxolone; glycyrrhetic acid; olean-12-en-29-oic acid, 3-hydroxy-11-oxo-, (3β,20β)-; uralenic acid; glycyrrhetin
CAS registry number (s)	: 471-53-4
EC number(s)	: 207-444-6
CIR review(s)	: Int J Toxicol 2007;26(Suppl.2):79-112 (access: www.cir-safety.org/ingredients)
Merck Index monograph	: 4914
Function(s) in cosmetics	: EU: skin conditioning. USA: skin-conditioning agents - miscellaneous
Patch testing	: 10% pet. (3,4); 1% pet. (5); 20% pet. (6); 0.02% - 0.2% aqua/alc. (may in some cases be too low [1])
Molecular formula	: $C_{30}H_{46}O_4$

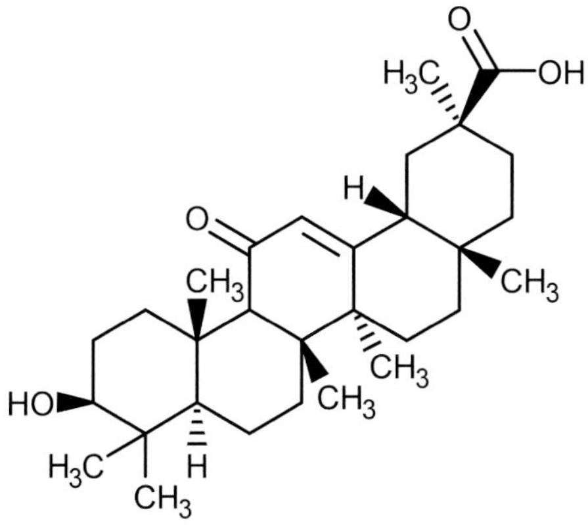

GENERAL

Glycyrrhetinic acid is a pentacyclic triterpene derived from the hydrolysis of glycyrrhizic acid (glycyrrhizin), one of the main components of licorice root, or *Glycyrrhiza glabra*. Because of its steroid-like chemical structure, it possesses anti-inflammatory activity, as well as antibacterial, antiviral and antifungal activities. It is used for its anti-inflammatory and antipruritic effects in the treatment of atopic dermatitis (2).

CONTACT ALLERGY

Case reports and case series

A woman with a past history of eczematous lesions at sites of contact with costume jewellery and adhesive dressings had repeated episodes of contact dermatitis that occurred over a period of 3 years. The lesions involved the lips, the axillae, and the face. The patient implicated two lip balms, a deodorant, and a post-sun moisturizing cream. She was first patch tested with the North American Contact Dermatitis Group baseline series and the four suspected cosmetics and had positive reactions to colophonium, nickel sulfate and each of her four cosmetics. The manufacturers of the cosmetics provided their separate ingredients, and in a second session of patch testing, positive reactions were seen to glycyrrhetinic acid 0.02% and 0.2% alcohol/water, present in a deodorant and an after-sun product. The allergen in the other cosmetics was Ricinus communis (castor) seed oil (1).

Contact allergy to glycyrrhetinic acid in non-cosmetic products

Three patients had allergic contact dermatitis from enoxolone (glycyrrhetinic acid) present in topical pharmaceutical products (3,4,5). A woman developed facial angioedema 12 hours after taking 2 tablets containing tyrothricin, enoxolone, sulfaguanidine and benzocaine. Worsening symptoms required emergency treatment with systemic corticosteroids. Examination revealed severe swelling of the lips and the left side of her face (the side on which the tablets had been left to dissolve), accompanied by inflammation of the oral mucosa. Patch testing was first performed with a sample of the tablet, as is, and the European standard series. The patient reacted to the tablet and the caine mix. Oral administration of tyrothricin and sulfaguanidine gave no reaction. No oral challenge with benzocaine was carried out. Ten hours after taking 10 mg of enoxolone, the patient complained of discomfort in the mouth. Erythema and edema on the left side of the oral mucosa were detected a few hours later. She was then patch tested with enoxolone, which gave a minimal erythema at 10% pet. but a positive patch test reaction at 20% pet. Ten healthy controls tested with enoxolone 10% and 20% pet. were negative (6).

Presence in cosmetic products and chemical analyses

In the USA, in April 2017, glycyrrhetinic acid was present in 137 of 56,714 cosmetic products of which the composition is known in FDA's Voluntary Cosmetic Registration Program (VCRP) (data obtained from FDA, May 2017). In March 2017, glycyrrhetinic acid was present in 27 of 64,983 cosmetic products of which the composition is known in EWG's Skin Deep Cosmetics Database, USA (http://www.ewg.org/skindeep/).

LITERATURE

1 Sasseville D, Desjardins M, Almutawa F. Allergic contact dermatitis caused by glycyrrhetinic acid and castor oil. Contact Dermatitis 2011;64:168-169
2 Veraldi S, De Micheli P, Schianchi R, Lunardon L. Treatment of pruritus in mild-to-moderate atopic dermatitis with a topical non-steroidal agent. J Drugs Dermatol 2009;8:537-359
3 Fernàndez JC, Gamboa P, Jáuregui I, González G, Antépara I. Concomitant sensitization to enoxolone and mafenide in a topical medicament. Contact Dermatitis 1992;27:262
4 Tanaka S, Otsuki T, Matsumoto Y, Hayakawa R, Sugiura M. Allergic contact dermatitis from enoxolone. Contact Dermatitis 2001;44:192
5 Oiso N, Ota T, Yoshinaga E, Endo H, Kawara S, Kawada A. Allergic contact dermatitis mimicking atopic dermatitis due to enoxolone in a topical medicament. Contact Dermatitis 2006;54:351
6 Villas-Martinez F, Joral Badas A, Garmendia Goitia JF, Aguirre I. Sensitization to oral enoxolone. Contact Dermatitis 1994;30:124

2.208 GLYCYRRHIZA GLABRA (LICORICE) ROOT EXTRACT

IDENTIFICATION

Description/definition	: Glycyrrhiza glabra root extract is an extract of the roots of the licorice, *Glycyrrhiza glabra* L., Leguminosae
Chemical class(es)	: Botanical products and botanical derivatives
INCI name USA	: Glycyrrhiza glabra (licorice) root extract
Other names	: Licorice extract
CAS registry number (s)	: 84775-66-6
EC number(s)	: 283-895-2
Merck Index monograph	: 5810 (Glycyrrhiza)
Function(s) in cosmetics	: EU: bleaching; emollient; perfuming; skin conditioning; smoothing; soothing. USA: antioxidants; skin bleaching agents; skin-conditioning agents - humectant; skin-conditioning agents - miscellaneous
Patch testing	: 1% water (3); 0.5%-5% pet. (2); the highest concentration is not irritant (2); 1% pet. (4); licorice flavonoid 2% pet. (6)

GENERAL

Liquorice (Glycyrrhiza genus) roots have been used as a raw plant material for medicinal purposes since ancient times. Today, it is widely used in modern folk medicine alone and also in many multicomponent preparations with a variety of claimed biological activities including those of wound healing, antiseptic, and anti-allergic (5). Oil-soluble licorice extracts are widely used in skin-lightening cosmetics in Japan. They are ethanolic extracts from *Glycyrrhiza glabra* L. and contain flavonoid compounds including glabridin (considered the main active agent), glabrene, glabrone, and glabrol. None of these ethanolic extracts contain glycyrrhizic acid (glycyrrhizin), which is a *water*-soluble licorice extract used in medicaments (2,4) (see Chapter 2.210 Glycyrrhizic acid).

CONTACT ALLERGY

Case reports and case series

A woman had allergic contact dermatitis of the face from oil-soluble licorice extract in facial cream, foundation and essence (2). One patient had ACD from licorice extract used as skin whitening agent in a cosmetic; the allergen was glabridin (1). One individual had allergic contact dermatitis from licorice root extract in a cosmetic 'recovery' cream (4).

Another patient had cosmetic dermatitis with itching facial erythema from 2 whitening creams; the causative ingredient was a mixture of licorice flavonoids, in which glabridin and licoflavone A were detected (6). One individual had ACD from Glycyrrhiza glabra (licorice) root extract present in a skin-whitening cream (3).

Presence in cosmetic products and chemical analyses

In the USA, in April 2017, Glycyrrhiza glabra (licorice) root extract was present in 669 of 56,714 cosmetic products of which the composition is known in FDA's Voluntary Cosmetic Registration Program (VCRP) (data obtained from FDA, May 2017). In March 2017, Glycyrrhiza glabra root extract was present in 417 of 64,983 cosmetic products of which the composition is known in EWG's Skin Deep Cosmetics Database, USA (http://www.ewg.org/skindeep/).

OTHER SIDE EFFECTS

Other non-eczematous contact reactions

A woman developed patchy depigmentation induced by the use of a skin-lightening cream containing kojic dipalmitate, Glycyrrhiza glabra (liquorice) root extract and Mitracarpus scaber (button grass) plant extract (7).

LITERATURE

1   Matsunaga K, Fujisawa Y. Two cases with allergic contact dermatitis due to whitening agents. Aesthet Dermatol 1995;5:81-86 (in Japanese) (data cited in ref. 2)
2   Nishioka K, Seguchi T. Contact allergy due to oil-soluble licorice extracts in cosmetic products. Contact Dermatitis 1999;40:56
3   Numata T, Kobayashi Y, Ito T, Harada K, Tsuboi R, Okubo Y. Two cases of allergic contact dermatitis due to skin-whitening cosmetics. Allergology International 2015;64:194-195

4   O'Connell RL, White IR, White JML, McFadden JP. Liquorice extract in a cosmetic product causing contact allergy. Contact Dermatitis 2008;59:52

5   Obolentseva GV, Litvinenko VI, Ammosov AS, Popova TP, Sampiev AM. Pharmacological and therapeutic properties of liquorice preparations (a review). Pharm Chem J 1999;33:427-434

6   Kanoh H, Banno Y, Nakamura M, Seishima M. Contact allergy to liquorice flavonoids: analysis with liquid chromatography–mass spectrometry. Contact Dermatitis 2016;74:191-192

7   Madhogaria S, Ahmed I. Leucoderma after use of a skin-lightening cream containing kojic dipalmitate, liquorice root extract and Mitracarpus scaber extract. Clin Exp Dermatol 2010;35:e103-105

2.209   GLYCYRRHIZA INFLATA ROOT EXTRACT

IDENTIFICATION

Description/definition : Glycyrrhiza inflata root extract is an extract of the roots of *Glycyrrhiza inflata*,
                         Leguminosae
Chemical class(es)   : Botanical products and botanical derivatives
Function(s) in cosmetics : EU: skin conditioning. USA: Skin-conditioning agents - miscellaneous
Patch testing   : 1% pet.

GENERAL

Glycyrrhiza inflata is one of the (at least) 30 species of the genus *Glycyrrhiza*, to which also the species *Glycyrrhiza glabra* and *Glycyrrhiza uralensis* belong. From their roots, called liquorice, extracts are obtained (liquorice extracts). Oil-soluble (ethanolic) extracts mainly contain flavonoids (e.g., glabridin), whereas water-soluble (dry) extracts typically contain saponins such as glycyrrhizin, a mixture of potassium and calcium salts of 18β-glycyrrhizic acid (glycyrrhizate), which may be hydrolysed to form 18β-glycyrrhetinic acid (syn. glycyrrhizinate; enoxolone) (see Chapter 2.210 Glycyrrhizic acid [= glycyrrhizin], Chapter 2.208 Glycyrrhiza glabra (liquorice) root extract and Chapter 2.207 Glycyrrhetinic acid [= enoxolone]) (1).

   Applications of liquorice extracts include use as flavoring agents in pharmaceuticals, tobacco, beer, candy, food supplements, and herbal teas. These extracts are popular in Chinese and modern folk medicine (e.g. as an expectorant, to relieve throat irritation, for peptic ulcers, and for digestive problems). Furthermore, oil-soluble liquorice extracts inhibit tyrosinase activity *in vitro* and promote depigmentation, making them popular ingredients in skin-lightening cosmetics in Asia (1). Glycyrrhiza inflata root extract can be present as a skin conditioning agent in sunscreens and in cosmetics marketed for use in individuals with acne, or with 'sensitive' and rosacea-prone skin (1).

CONTACT ALLERGY

Case reports and case series
Two men had dermatitis of the beard area. When tested with their cosmetics, they both reacted to a shaving cream. Subsequent patch testing with the ingredients of these cosmetics gave positive reactions to Glycyrrhiza inflata root extract 1% pet. and 1% alc. Twenty controls were negative to the test material 1% pet. After avoiding the product, liquorice-containing products and (in one) products containing his other allergens, the dermatitis healed and has not recurred since (1).

Cross-reactions, pseudo-cross-reactions and co-reactions
Not to dipotassium glycyrrhizate 1% pet. (1)

Presence in cosmetic products and chemical analyses
In July 2017, Glycyrrhiza inflata root extract was present in 11 of 69,548 cosmetic products of which the composition is known in EWG's Skin Deep Cosmetics Database, USA (http://www.ewg.org/skindeep/).

LITERATURE

1 Wuyts L, van Hoof T, Lambert J, Aerts O. Allergic contact dermatitis caused by aftershave creams containing *Glycyrrhiza inflata*. Contact Dermatitis 2017;77:49-51

2.210　GLYCYRRHIZIC ACID

IDENTIFICATION

Description/definition	: Glycyrrhizic acid is a natural material extracted from *Glycyrrhiza glabra*, which conforms generally to the formula shown below
Chemical class(es)	: Carbohydrates; sterols
Chemical/IUPAC name	: (2*S*,3*S*,4*S*,5*R*,6*R*)-6-[(2*S*,3*R*,4*S*,5*S*,6*S*)-2-[[(3*S*,4a*R*,6a*R*,6b*S*,8a*S*,11*S*,12a*R*, 14a*R*,14b*S*)-11-carboxy-4,4,6a,6b,8a,11,14b-heptamethyl-14-oxo-2,3,4a,5,6, 7,8,9,10,12,12a,14a-dodecahydro-1*H*-picen-3-yl]oxy]-6-carboxy-4,5-dihydroxy- oxan-3-yl]oxy-3,4,5-trihydroxyoxane-2-carboxylic acid
Other names	: Glycyrrhizin; glycyrrhizinic acid
CAS registry number (s)	: 1405-86-3
EC number(s)	: 215-785-7
CIR review(s)	: Int J Toxicol 2007;26(Suppl.2):79-112 (access: www.cir-safety.org/ingredients)
Merck Index monograph	: 5811
Function(s) in cosmetics	: EU: humectant; skin conditioning. USA: flavoring agents; fragrance ingredients; skin-conditioning agents - miscellaneous
Patch testing	: 0.3% water (1)
Molecular formula	: $C_{42}H_{62}O_{16}$

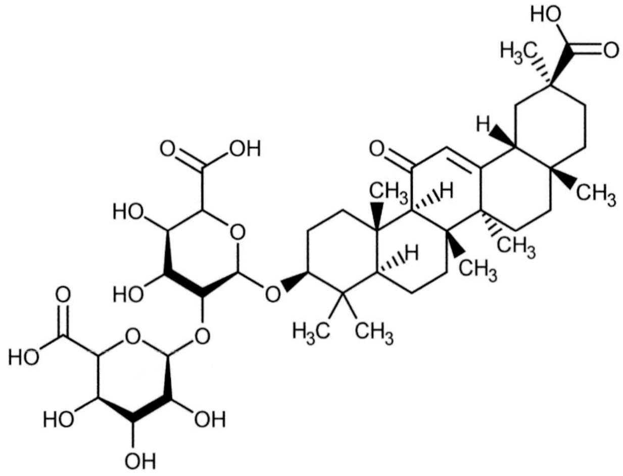

CONTACT ALLERGY

Case reports and case series

A woman had long-term androgenetic alopecia, which she started treating with topical daily application of 5% minoxidil. On the 5th day, erythema and micropapules, with burning and itching, appeared locally leading to cessation of the treatment. After a month of oral antihistamine and topical corticosteroid therapy, with complete resolution of the previous signs of local irritation, alternative treatment was started with topical application of another hair restorer, mainly consisting of *Ruscus auleatus*, glycyrrhizic acid and *Serenoa serrulata*. Two weeks later, she again noticed erythematous papules, scaling and itching on her scalp, which once more led to therapeutic withdrawal. Patch testing with the Portuguese standard series, 5% minoxidil (in the commercial form used by the patient) and the hair restorer was performed and only the hair restorer gave a positive patch test.

The manufacturer then supplied the 10 components (coded) of the hair restorer and when patch tested with them, the patient showed a positive reaction to glycyrrhizic acid 0.3% in water. Twenty controls were negative (1). Another patient from Japan in an early publication had an (unspecified) hypersensitivity reaction to glycyrrhizic acid (2, data cited in ref. 3).

Presence in cosmetic products and chemical analyses

In the USA, in April 2017, glycyrrhizic acid was present in 4 of 56,714 cosmetic products of which the composition is known in FDA's Voluntary Cosmetic Registration Program (VCRP) (data obtained from FDA, May 2017). In March 2017, glycyrrhizic acid was present in 7 of 64,983 cosmetic products of which the composition is known in EWG's Skin Deep Cosmetics Database, USA (http://www.ewg.org/skindeep/).

LITERATURE

1 Cabrita SF, Silva R, Correia MP. Allergic contact dermatitis due to glycyrrhizic acid as an ingredient of a hair restorer. Contact Dermatitis 2003;49:46
2 Kuriyama Y, Takano T, Okada F, Nukada T. Hypersensitivity to glycyrrhizin. A case report. Med J Osaka Univ 1975; 26:75-78 (data cited in ref. 3)
3 Wuyts L, van Hoof T, Lambert J, Aerts O. Allergic contact dermatitis caused by aftershave creams containing *Glycyrrhiza inflata*. Contact Dermatitis 2017;77:49-51

2.211 GUAIAZULENE

IDENTIFICATION

Description/definition	: Guaiazulene is the color additive that conforms to the formula shown below
Chemical class(es)	: Color additives; hydrocarbons
Chemical/IUPAC name	: 1,4-Dimethyl-7-propan-2-ylazulene
Other names	: 1,4-Dimethyl-7-(1-methylethyl)azulene
CAS registry number (s)	: 489-84-9
EC number(s)	: 207-701-2
Merck Index monograph	: 5860
Function(s) in cosmetics	: EU: antimicrobial; perfuming. USA: colorants; fragrance ingredients
Patch testing	: 1% pet.
Molecular formula	: $C_{15}H_{18}$

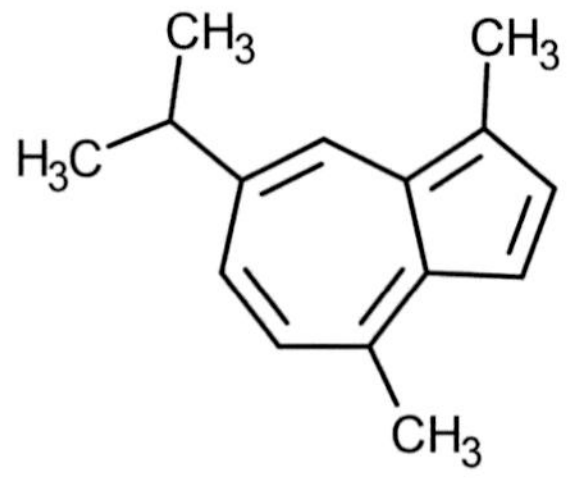

CONTACT ALLERGY

Case reports and case series

Five patient with contact cheilitis were reported from Italy. All had used the same toothpaste for some years and complained of discomfort of the lips with scaling, cracking and dryness of vermillion and surrounding skin; occasionally, they showed more evident changes often with erythema and exudation. Two patients complained of subjective symptoms indicative of stomatitis, such as loss of taste, a burning sensation or soreness. Patch tests with the European standard series, the dental screening test series and the individual components of the toothpaste showed sensitivity to only one substance, guaiazulene. To confirm that the reaction to guaiazulene was of an allergic nature, further studies were carried out. Patch tests with guaiazulene 1% pet. on 50 controls were negative. Histopathology of patch test lesions in 2 patients showed spongiosis and deep mononuclear infiltration, indicative of allergic contact dermatitis. Finally, a use test with the toothpaste in 3 patients gave a positive reaction. i.e., it reproduced the symptoms. The clinical history of the individual patients combined with the results of allergological and histological investigations, and prompt improvement in clinical manifestations on withdrawal of the toothpaste in all 5 patients, pointed – according to the authors – to contact allergy as the most likely pathogenetic mechanism (2).

One positive patch test reaction to guaiazulene was ascribed to cosmetic allergy (1). One patient had contact cheilitis from guaiazulene used as a counterirritant in lipsticks (3). Five other individuals had allergic contact cheilitis from guaiazulene in mouthwashes (4).

Presence in cosmetic products and chemical analyses

In the USA, in April 2017, guaiazulene was present in 40 of 56,714 cosmetic products of which the composition is known in FDA's Voluntary Cosmetic Registration Program (VCRP) (data obtained from FDA, May 2017). In March 2017, guaiazulene was present in 4 of 65,326 cosmetic products of which the composition is known in EWG's Skin Deep Cosmetics Database, USA (http://www.ewg.org/skindeep/).

LITERATURE

1   Kohl L, Blondeel A, Song M. Allergic contact dermatitis from cosmetics: retrospective analysis of 819 patch-tested patients. Dermatology 2002;204:334-337
2   Angelini G, Vena GA. Allergic contact cheilitis to guaiazulene. Contact Dermatitis 1984;10:311
3   Cronin E. Contact dermatitis from cosmetics. J Soc Cosm Chem 1967; 18:681-691
4   Angelini G, Vena GA, Giglio G, Fiordalisi F, Meneghini CL. Contact dermatitis due to cosmetics. J Appl Cosmetol 1985;3:223-236

2.212 GUANINE

IDENTIFICATION

Description/definition : Guanine is a natural purine that conforms to the formula shown below
Chemical class(es) : Color additives; heterocyclic compounds
Chemical/IUPAC name : 2-Amino-3,7-dihydropurin-6-one
Other names : CI 75170; 2-amino-6-hydroxypurine; pearl essence
CAS registry number (s) : 73-40-5
EC number(s) : 200-799-8
Merck Index monograph : 5869
Function(s) in cosmetics : EU: opacifying. USA: colorants; opacifying agents
EU cosmetic restrictions : Regulated in Annex IV/113 of the Regulation (EC) No. 1223/2009
Patch testing : Powdered guanine pure (1)
Molecular formula : $C_5H_5N_5O$

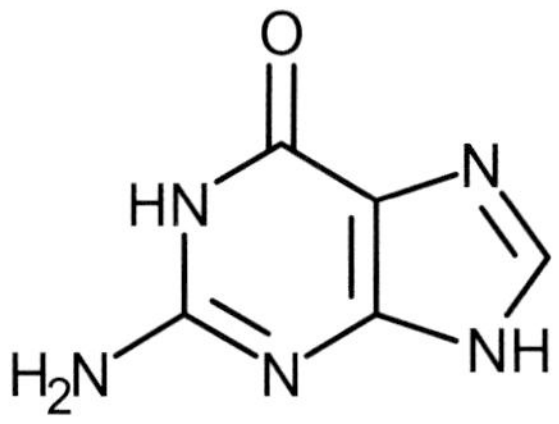

CONTACT ALLERGY

Case reports and case series

In a one-year-period, in the USA, in 1958, four patients were seen with a patchy eczematous contact-type dermatitis of the eyelids, face, chin, and neck. Patch tests with their ordinary nail lacquers were negative, but positive results were obtained with pearly or frosted nail lacquer. Testing with the various ingredients of these products, including the solvent, plasticizer, resin, and pigment, were negative, but patch tests to the pearly material were positive. The pearly material was made from the fish scales of sardines and consisted chiefly of guanine. Patch tests with pure powdered guanine and powdered defatted sardine fish scales were positive in all 4 patients and negative in 20 controls. All patients were able to use ordinary nail lacquer not containing the guanine without cutaneous reaction. Patch tests with olive-oil extracts of skinless and boneless sardines and with the sardine meat were negative. All of the patients had eaten sardines, with and without the skin and scales, with no obvious reaction. None of them had handled the sardine scales or sardine skins previously (1).

Cross-reactions, pseudo-cross-reactions and co-reactions

Not to adenine, uric acid, caffeine, theobromine, or adenylic acid (1).

Presence in cosmetic products and chemical analyses

In the USA, in April 2017, guanine was present in 88 of 56,714 cosmetic products of which the composition is known in FDA's Voluntary Cosmetic Registration Program (VCRP) (data obtained from FDA, May 2017). In March 2017, guanine was present in 83 of 65,326 cosmetic products of which the composition is known in EWG's Skin Deep Cosmetics Database, USA (http://www.ewg.org/skindeep/).

LITERATURE

1   Stritzler C. Dermatitis of the face caused by guanine in pearly nail lacquer. Arch Dermatol 1958;78:252-253

2.213　GUAR HYDROXYPROPYLTRIMONIUM CHLORIDE

IDENTIFICATION

Description/definition	: Guar hydroxypropyltrimonium chloride is a quaternary ammonium derivative of hydroxypropyl guar
Chemical class(es)	: Gums, hydrophilic colloids and derivatives; quaternary ammonium compounds
Other names	: Guar gum, 2-hydroxy-3-(trimethylammonio)propyl ether, chloride
CAS registry number (s)	: 65497-29-2
Merck Index monograph	: 5877 (Guar gum)
CIR review(s)	: Int J Toxicol 2015;34(Suppl.1):35-65 (access: www.cir-safety.org/ingredients)
Function(s) in cosmetics	: EU: antistatic; film forming; skin conditioning; viscosity controlling. USA: antistatic agents; hair conditioning agents; skin-conditioning agents – miscellaneous; viscosity increasing agents – aqueous
Patch testing	: No data available

CONTACT ALLERGY

Case reports and case series

Two positive patch test reactions to guar hydroxypropyltrimonium chloride were ascribed to cosmetic allergy; clinical details were not provided and the causative products not mentioned (1).

Presence in cosmetic products and chemical analyses

In the USA, in April 2017, guar hydroxypropyltrimonium chloride was present in 1550 of 56,714 cosmetic products of which the composition is known in FDA's Voluntary Cosmetic Registration Program (VCRP) (data obtained from FDA, May 2017). In March 2017, guar hydroxypropyltrimonium chloride was present in 901 of 65,326 cosmetic products of which the composition is known in EWG's Skin Deep Cosmetics Database, USA (http://www.ewg.org/skindeep/).

LITERATURE

1　Kohl L, Blondeel A, Song M. Allergic contact dermatitis from cosmetics: retrospective analysis of 819 patch-tested patients. Dermatology 2002;204:334-337

2.214   HAMAMELIS VIRGINIANA (WITCH HAZEL) BARK/LEAF/TWIG EXTRACT

IDENTIFICATION

Description/definition   : Hamamelis virginiana bark/leaf/twig extract is the extract of the bark, leaves and twigs of the witch hazel, *Hamamelis virginiana* L., Hamamelidaceae
Chemical class(es)   : Botanical products and botanical derivatives
INCI name USA   : Hamamelis virginiana (witch hazel) bark/leaf/twig extract
Other names   : Witch hazel extract
CAS registry number (s)   : 84696-19-5
EC number(s)   : 283-637-9
Merck Index monograph   : 5909 (Hamamelis)
Function(s) in cosmetics   : EU: skin conditioning. USA: cosmetic astringents; skin-conditioning agents – miscellaneous
Patch testing   : 10% alc., 50% alc. and pure (distillate) (1)

GENERAL

Hamamelis virginiana (witch hazel) is a shrub or small tree from the Hamamelidaceae family of plants. Witch hazel extract is attributed astringent, antiseptic, anti-inflammatory, local styptic, and vasoconstrictive properties. It has been used topically for inflammation of the skin and mucous membranes, and today it appears in cosmetic products as well as oral medicine for chronic venous insufficiency (2).

CONTACT ALLERGY

Case reports and case series

A woman started to use a new eye gel, after which edema developed around the eyes within 1 week. She stopped using the eye gel, but instead started to use alternative remedies. Over the following days, edema spread to the rest of the face and neck and became eczema. She was treated systemically with corticosteroids and told not to use any cosmetics or alternative remedies. The dermatitis disappeared and did not relapse. Patch tests were performed with an extended European standard series, preservative and topical medicament series. She was further patch tested with her cosmetics and, later, with selected ingredients of her eye gel provided by the manufacturer. The patient had positive patch tests to the eye gel and to its ingredient Hamamelis virginiana distillate when tested pure, 50% in alcohol and 10% alc. (1). The exact nature of the distillate is unknown. It may have been the Hamamelis virginiana bark/leaf/twig extract, but also bark/leaf extract, bark/twig extract, leaf extract, flower water, leaf water or Hamamelis virginiana water (all CAS nr. 84696-19-5, EC nr. 283-637-9).

Contact allergy to Hamamelis virginiana extract in non-cosmetic products

Of 1032 consecutive patients patch tested with Hamamelis ointment (containing 25% Hamamelis extract) in The Netherlands, 4 had a positive reaction. Two also reacted to lanolin, which was a major constituent of the ointment. In these two and the other two patient, no patch testing with the separate ingredients of the ointment (including the Hamamelis extract) was performed (8).

Presence in cosmetic products and chemical analyses

In the USA, in April 2017, Hamamelis virginiana (witch hazel) bark/leaf/twig extract was present in 129 of 56,714 cosmetic products of which the composition is known in FDA's Voluntary Cosmetic Registration Program (VCRP) (data obtained from FDA, May 2017). In march 2017, Hamamelis virginiana (witch hazel) was present in 169 (extract) and 77 (distillate) of 65,326 cosmetic products of which the composition is known in EWG's Skin Deep Cosmetics Database, USA (http://www.ewg.org/skindeep/). *Hamamelis virginiana* (witch hazel) was present in 19 (11%) of 178 facial wipes for which ingredient information was obtained online and from retail stores, USA, 2016 (4). Of 19,000 cosmetic formulations on file at the Food and Drug Administration in 1978, 147 products contained witch hazel as extract, distillate or as such (1).

LITERATURE

1   Granlund H. Contact allergy to witch hazel. Contact Dermatitis 1994;31:195
2   Paulsen E, Christensen LP, Andersen KA. Cosmetics and herbal remedies with Compositae plant extracts – are they tolerated by Compositae-allergic patients? Contact Dermatitis 2008;58:15-23
3   Bruynzeel DP, van Ketel WG, Young E, van Joost Th, Smeenk G. Contact sensitization by alternative topical medicaments containing plant extracts. Contact Dermatitis 1992;27:278-279
4   Aschenbeck KA, Warshaw EM. Allergenic ingredients in facial wet wipes. Dermatitis 2017 Mar 23. doi: 10.1097/DER.0000000000000268. [Epub ahead of print]

2.215 HC BLUE NO. 7

This chemical has two entries (INCI names) in CosIng: HC Blue no. 7 and 6-Methoxy-2-methylamino-3-aminopyridine HCl.

IDENTIFICATION

Description/definition	: 6-Methoxy-2-methylamino-3-aminopyridine HCl / HC Blue no. 7 is the hair color that conforms to the formula shown below
Chemical class(es)	: Color additives - hair
INCI name USA	: 6-Methoxy-2-methylamino-3-aminopyridine HCl
Chemical/IUPAC name	: 6-Methoxy-*N*2-methylpyridine-2,3-diamine;dihydrochloride
Other names	: 3-Amino-2-methylamino-6-methoxypyridine dihydrochloride; 6-methoxy-2-methylamino-3-aminopyridine HCl
CAS registry number (s)	: 83732-72-3; 90817-34-8
EC number(s)	: 280-622-9
SCCS opinion(s)	: SCCNFP/0643/03 (2)
Function(s) in cosmetics	: EU: hair dyeing. USA: hair colorants
EU cosmetic restrictions	: Regulated in Annex III/203 of the Regulation (EC) No. 1223/2009
Patch testing	: 1% pet. (1); the test concentration may induce slight irritation in 10% of the tested individuals (1)
Molecular formula	: $C_7H_{13}Cl_2N_3O$

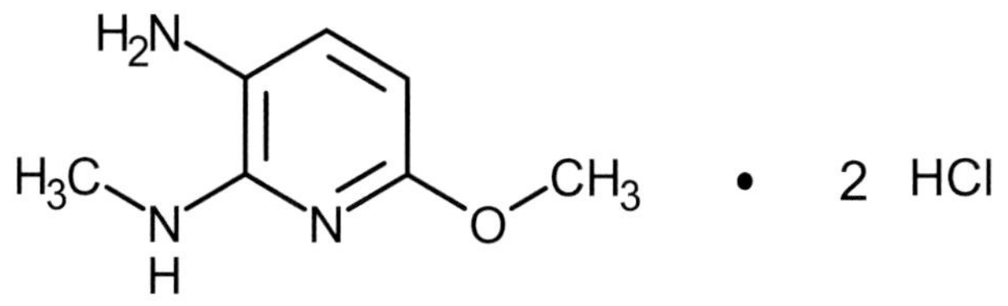

CONTACT ALLERGY

Case reports and case series

A woman had colored her hair with oxidative hair dyes five times a year for more than 15 years. Three days after she last used a hair dye, she developed severe edema around her eyes and exudation from the scalp and ears. She required hospital treatment. Patch testing with the European baseline series produced no reactions. Later, additional testing with individual ingredients in the hair dye product she had last used was undertaken. In the process of patch testing, there was a flare-up reaction with redness and itching on the ears and on the back. The only positive reaction was to HC blue no. 7 (1% pet.). The test material was tested on 54 consecutive eczema patients, which resulted in 49 negative reactions and 5 irritant reactions (1).

Cross-reactions, pseudo-cross-reactions and co-reactions

Not to *p*-phenylenediamine or other hair dyes (1).

Presence in cosmetic products and chemical analyses

In the USA, in April 2017, 6-methoxy-2-methylamino-3-aminopyridine HCl was present in 3 of 56,714 cosmetic products of which the composition is known in FDA's Voluntary Cosmetic Registration Program (VCRP) (data obtained from FDA, May 2017). In March 2017, 6-methoxy-2-methylamino-3-aminopyridine HCl was present in zero of 65,326 cosmetic products of which the composition is known in EWG's Skin Deep Cosmetics Database, USA (http://www.ewg.org/skindeep/).

In southern Germany, in 2013-2014, the labels of 924 permanent oxidative hair dyes were checked for the presence of hair dye components. The 924 products analyzed revealed a total of 58 different hair dye components. HC blue No.7 was present in 1 (0.1%) of the 924 products (3).

LITERATURE

1   Søsted H, Nielsen NH, Menné, T. Allergic contact dermatitis to the hair dye 6-methoxy-2-methylamino-3-aminopyridine HCl (INCI HC Blue no. 7) without cross-sensitivity to PPD. Contact Dermatitis 2009;60:236-237

2   SCCNFP (Scientific Committee on Cosmetics and Non Food Products). Opinion concerning HC Blue no.7, 18 March 2003, SCCNFP/0643/03. Available at: http://ec.europa.eu/health/archive/ph_risk/committees/sccp/documents/out_192.pdf

3   Kirchlecher S, Hübner A, Uter W. Survey of sensitizing constituents of oxidative hair dyes (retail and professional products) in Germany. J Dtsch Dermatol Ges 2016;14:707-715

2.216   HC RED NO. 7

IDENTIFICATION

Description/definition	: HC red no. 7 is the substituted aniline derivative that corresponds to the structure shown below
Chemical class(es)	: Color additives – hair; aromatic organic compound; amino-nitro compounds
Chemical/IUPAC name	: 2-(4-Amino-3-nitroanilino)ethanol
Other names	: Amino-2-nitro-4-(β-hydroxyethyl)aminobenzene; 2-nitro-4-(β-hydroxyethylamino)-aniline; 1-hydroxyethylamino-3-nitro-4-aminobenzene (wrong name, used in ref. 1)
CAS registry number(s)	: 24905-87-1
EC number(s)	: 246-521-9
CIR review(s)	: Int J Toxicol 2008;27(Suppl.1):45-54 (access: www.cir-safety.org/ingredients)
SCCS opinion(s)	: SCCS/1229/09 (2); SCCNFP/0678/03 (3)
Function(s) in cosmetics	: EU: hair dyeing; USA: hair colorants
EU cosmetic restrictions	: Regulated in Annex III/I/266 of the Regulation (EC) No. 2012/21/EU
Patch testing	: 1 pet. (1)
Molecular formula	: $C_8H_{11}N_3O_3$

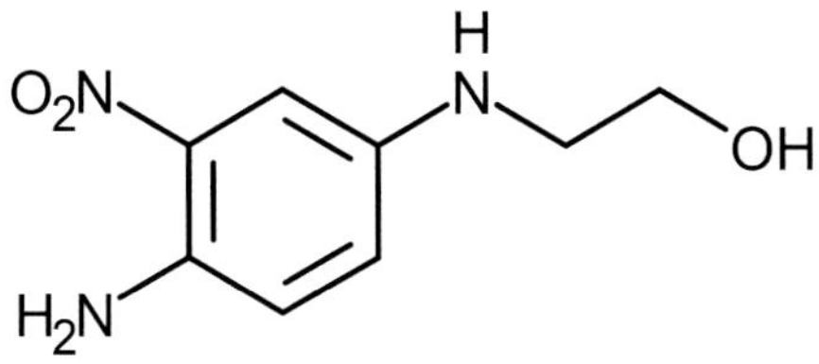

CONTACT ALLERGY

Case reports

A woman, with no family or personal history of atopy, presented with a very itchy polymorphic dermatitis of 2 months duration. Large erythematous, edematous, slightly scaly patches were present on the upper trunk, sides of the neck and fronts of the wrists, with several excoriated or psoriasiform papules. These favoured the abdomen and lower limbs and varied in size from pin-point to 1 centimeter or more across. The eruption had started on the ears and sides of the neck 2 days after the use of a semi-permanent hair preparation containing 3 nitro dyes. The dermatitis cleared with antihistamines and systemic steroid therapy in 4 weeks. Patch tests with the GIRDCA standard series were negative, while the patient's hair dye (as is) gave a strongly positive reaction. Further patch testing was carried out with the 3 nitro dyes, and she reacted to all three including 2-(4-amino-3-nitroanilino)ethanol (HC red no. 7) 1% pet., which chemical was termed incorrectly 1-hydroxyethylamino-3-nitro-4-aminobenzene by the authors. Testing with the 3 nitro dyes in 10 controls showed no reactions (1).

Cross-reactions, pseudo-cross-reactions and co-reactions

Not to p-phenylenediamine (1). Concomitant sensitization or cross-reactivity to o-nitro-p-phenylenediamine, 1-hydroxy-3-nitro-4-aminobenzene (4-amino-3-nitrophenol) and 3-nitro-p-hydroxyethylaminophenol (incorrectly termed N-(β-hydroxyethyl)-2-nitro-4-hydroxyaminobenzene) (1).

Presence in cosmetic products and chemical analyses

In the USA, in April 2017, HC red #7 was present in 3 of 56,714 cosmetic products of which the composition is known in FDA's Voluntary Cosmetic Registration Program (VCRP) (data obtained from FDA, May 2017). In March 2017, HC red no. 7 was present in zero of 65,326 cosmetic products of which the composition is known in EWG's Skin Deep Cosmetics Database, USA (http://www.ewg.org/skindeep/).

LITERATURE

1   Perno P, Lisi P. Psoriasis-like contact dermatitis from a hair nitro dye. Contact Dermatitis 1990;23:123-124
2   SCCS (Scientific Committee on Consumer Safety). Opinion on HC red no.7, SCCS/1229/09, 8 December 2009. Available at: https://ec.europa.eu/health/scientific_committees/consumer_safety/docs/sccs_o_007.pdf
3   SCCFNP (Scientific Committee on Cosmetic Products and Non-Food Products Intended for Consumers). Opinion on HC red no. 7, SCCNFP/0678/03, 24-25 June 2003. Available at: https://ec.europa.eu/health/archive/ph_risk/committees/sccp/documents/out209_en.pdf

2.217   HC YELLOW NO. 7

IDENTIFICATION

Description/definition   : HC Yellow no. 7 is the hair color that conforms to the formula shown below
Chemical class(es)   : Color additives - hair
Chemical/IUPAC name   : 2-[4-[(4-Aminophenyl)diazenyl]-N-(2-hydroxyethyl)-3-methylanilino]ethanol
Other names   : 1-(4-Aminophenylazo)-2-methyl-4-bis(β-hydroxyethyl)aminobenzene
CAS registry number (s)   : 104226-21-3
EC number(s)   : 146-420-6
SCCS opinion(s)   : SCCNFP/0675/03 (1); SCCS/1292/10 (2)
Function(s) in cosmetics : EU: hair dyeing. USA: hair colorants
EU cosmetic restrictions : Regulated in Annex III/260 of the Regulation (EC) No. 1223/2009 and in Annex III/I/272
                            of Directive 2012/21/EU
Patch testing   : 1% and 10% pet. (3)
Molecular formula   : $C_{17}H_{22}N_4O_2$

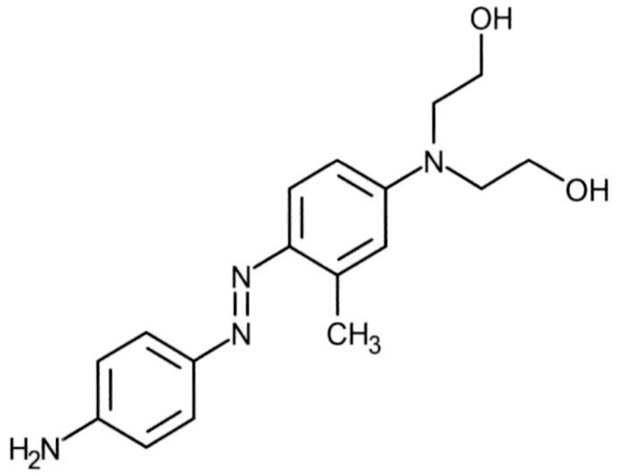

GENERAL

HC yellow no. 7 is used in semi-permanent and temporary non-oxidative hair dyeing products.

CONTACT ALLERGY

Case reports and case series

A woman known to be allergic to permanent hair colors developed itchy, erythematous, edematous, scaly plaques located on the neck 2 days after the 2nd application of a violet semi-permanent hair dye. Multiple lesions on the eyelids, behind the ears, neck and upper extremities developed over a short period of time. The lesions subsided in 2 weeks with frequent shampooing and oral corticosteroids (3). Upon patch testing, she reacted to p-phenylenediamine, the caine mix, the black rubber mix, multiple para-dyes from the hairdressers' series and to HC yellow 7 1% and 10% pet., present in the violet semi-permanent hair dye. Twenty-five controls patch tested with HC Yellow 7 10% pet. were negative at D2 and D4 (3).

Cross-reactions, pseudo-cross-reactions and co-reactions

Possibly cross-reactivity from p-phenylenediamine or other para-dyes(3). Cross-reactivity between para-compounds is discussed in Chapter 2.359 p-Phenylenediamine.

Presence in cosmetic products and chemical analyses

In the USA, in April 2017, HC yellow no. 7 was present in zero of 56,714 cosmetic products of which the composition is known in FDA's Voluntary Cosmetic Registration Program (VCRP) (data obtained from FDA, May 2017). In March 2017, HC yellow no.7 was present in 2 older products of 65,351 cosmetic products of which the composition is known in EWG's Skin Deep Cosmetics Database, USA (http://www.ewg.org/skindeep/).

LITERATURE

1   SCCFNP (Scientific Committee on Cosmetic Products and Non-Food Products Intended for Consumers). Opinion concerning HC yellow no. 7, 24-25 June 2003, SCCNFP/0675/03. Available at: http://ec.europa.eu/health/ph_risk/committees/sccp/documents/out216_en.pdf

2   SCCS (Scientific Committee on Consumer Safety). Opinion on HC yellow no. 7, SCCS/1292/10, 21 September 2010. Available at: https://ec.europa.eu/health/scientific_committees/consumer_safety/docs/sccs_o_032.pdf

3   Sánchez-Pérez J, Río IGD, Ruiz SA, Diez AG. Allergic contact dermatitis from direct dyes for hair colouration in hairdressers' clients. Contact Dermatitis 2004;50:261-262

2.218   HELICHRYSUM ITALICUM FLOWER EXTRACT

IDENTIFICATION

Description/definition   : Helichrysum italicum flower extract is an extract obtained from the flowers of the
                              curryplant, *Helichrysum italicum*, Compositae
Chemical class(es)   : Botanical products and botanical derivatives
INCI name USA   : Helichrysum italicum extract; the CAS number 90045-56-0 of the INCI EU refers to
                              Helichrysum angustifolium flower extract in the INCI USA
CAS registry number (s)   : 90045-56-0
EC number(s)   : 289-918-2
Function(s) in cosmetics   : EU: perfuming. USA: skin-conditioning agents - miscellaneous
Patch testing   : 3% pet., both the hydrophilic and lipophilic fraction (1)

GENERAL

Helichrysum italicum is a plant commonly found in dry, sandy and stony areas of Mediterranean regions, and belongs to the Compositae (formerly Asteraceae) family. This plant is attributed anti-inflammatory, anti-allergic, antioxidant and antimicrobial activities (1). The current state of knowledge of the pharmacological activities of *Helichrysum italicum*, as well as its traditional uses, toxicity, drug interactions and safety has been reviewed in 2014 (2).

CONTACT ALLERGY

Case reports and case series

A non-atopic woman presented with eczematous lesions on her legs, trunk, and upper limbs. One month before the development of the eczema, she had been applying an emollient cream to her legs based on natural ingredients to treat a moderate dryness of the skin. She was treated with topical corticosteroids and instructed to avoid further contact with the suspected topical product. Three months after the complete resolution of the lesions, she was patch tested with the Italian Society of Allergological, Occupational and Environmental Dermatology (SIDAPA) standard baseline series, a 'natural ingredients' series and with the emollient cream 'as is'. Readings showed positive reactions to Myroxylon pereirae and to the cream 'as is'. Subsequently, patch tests were performed with the ingredients of the cream, provided by the manufacturer, which yielded positive reactions at both D2 and D4, for the hydrophilic fraction and the lipophilic fraction of flowering tops of *Helichrysum* at 3% pet. Ten healthy volunteers were patch tested with both substances, with negative results (1).

Cross-reactions, pseudo-cross-reactions and co-reactions

Not to the sesquiterpene lactone mix (alantolactone, dehydrocostus lactone, costunolide) (1).

Presence in cosmetic products and chemical analyses

In the USA, in April 2017, Helichrysum Italicum extract was present in 63 of 56,714 cosmetic products of which the composition is known in FDA's Voluntary Cosmetic Registration Program (VCRP) (data obtained from FDA, May 2017). In March 2017, Helichrysum italicum flower extract was present in 2 of 65,351 cosmetic products of which the composition is known in EWG's Skin Deep Cosmetics Database, USA (http://www.ewg.org/skindeep/).

LITERATURE

1   Foti C, Guida S, Antelmi A, Romita P, Corazza M. Allergic contact dermatitis caused by *Helichrysum italicum* contained in an emollient cream. Contact Dermatitis 2013;69:62-63
2   Antunes Viegas D, Palmeira-de-Oliveira A, Salgueiro L, Martinez-de-Oliveira J, Palmeira-de-Oliveira R. *Helichrysum italicum*: from traditional use to scientific data. J Ethnopharmacol 2014;151:54-65

2.219   HEMA

IDENTIFICATION

Description/definition   : HEMA is the organic compound that conforms to the formula shown below
Chemical class(es)   : Esters
Chemical/IUPAC name   : 2-Hydroxyethyl 2-methylprop-2-enoate
Other names   : 2-Hydroxyethyl methacrylate; glycol methacrylate
CAS registry number (s)   : 868-77-9
EC number(s)   : 212-782-2
CIR review(s)   : Int J Toxicol 2005;24(Suppl.5):53-100 (access: www.cir-safety.org/ingredients)
Function(s) in cosmetics : EU: film forming. USA: artificial nail builders
Patch testing   : 2% pet. (Chemotechnique, SmartPracticeCanada); 1% pet. (SmartPracticeEurope,
                            SmartPracticeCanada)
Molecular formula   : $C_6H_{10}O_3$

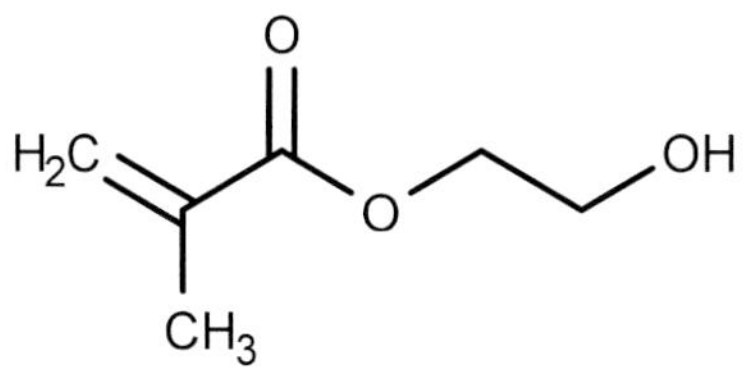

GENERAL

Acrylates and methacrylates are the salts, esters and conjugate bases of acrylic acid and methacrylic acid, respectively. Acrylic (acrylate) plastics (plastics based on polymers of (meth)acrylates) are used in a very wide range of applications. Examples include artificial nail preparations, dental materials, anaerobic sealants, bone cement, dentures, hearing aids, noise protectors, pressure-sensitive adhesives, spectacle frames, UV-curable inks and coatings, water-based acrylic latex paints, and in the caulking of building materials (1,2).

Contact allergy to acrylates and methacrylates is well known, the methacrylates being the more frequent causes of allergic contact dermatitis. The sensitizers are the monomers. Cured end products usually do not sensitize or cause symptoms in previously sensitized patients, as they do not contain enough reactive monomers. The greatest risk of sensitization is when there is skin contact with uncured acrylate material containing monomers, which is most likely to happen with inks, coatings, paints, varnishes, adhesives, within dentistry and when doing artificial nails. Risk occupations include dentists, dental nurses, dental technicians, nail technicians, printers, painters, and workers in paint factories (1,2,17).

Patients often react to many (meth)acrylates on patch testing. Primary sensitization to methacrylates may result in both methacrylate and acrylate cross-sensitization. Conversely, patients sensitized to acrylates are unlikely to show cross-sensitization to methacrylates (3). Acrylates are usually tested at 0.1% in petrolatum, methacrylates can be patch tested at 2% in petrolatum (1,2).

Discussion of contact allergy to (meth)acrylates from non-cosmetic sources is considered to fall outside the scope of this book. Therefore, only contact allergy from their presence in cosmetics is presented, which virtually always is from artificial nails and – more recently – form UV-cured nail polishes. A very useful review of contact sensitization to allergens in nail cosmetics, with emphasis on acrylic manicures, was published in 2017 (85).

Artificial nails

Artificial nails are nowadays among the main causes of (meth)acrylate contact allergy in developed countries (4,5,6,77). There are various types of artificial nails: preformed plastic nail tips (press-on nails), 'silk nails' and sculptured nails, which include so-called chemically cured 'acrylic nails' or photo-bonded 'gel nails' (7). Only the sculptured nails are considered to be cosmetics in the EU. Nail tips and silk nails are usually glued using cyanoacrylate products. In the 'acrylic nail' method, liquid monomer and powdered polymer are mixed and painted onto the nail and extension template. The liquid monomer is typically composed of ethyl methacrylate or another monomethacrylate, and the polymer powder usually contains polymethyl or polyethyl methacrylate. The liquid monomer is highly sensitizing, but the powdered (non-sensitizing) polymer may also contain traces of monomers (2,7).

In light-cured sculptured 'gel nails', the resins are serially applied in many layers, first a primer and then the acrylic nail resin, after which the layer is cured in a 'photobonding box' and the procedure is repeated. The primer often is methacrylic acid or 2-hydroxyethyl methacrylate (HEMA). The resin part is typically based on epoxyacrylates or acrylated urethane as matrix monomers in combination with cross-linking acrylate or methacrylate monomers (7).

Generally speaking, there is insufficient knowledge of the exact composition of nail acrylics. This is the main reason that, although many reports of contact allergy to artificial nails (e.g., 4,5,6,7,8,9,10,11,12,22,38,39,40,41,47,48,51,52, 62,65,68,80,81,82,83) have been published after the first cases were described in 1956 and 1957 (55,56,66), the specific sensitizer(s) have rarely been identified *and such publications are not discussed in the monographs in this book*. Few authors have analyzed sculptured nail materials to identify the culprit acrylates (30,54).

Both nail technicians (e.g., beauticians, who often wear sculptured nails themselves) and their customers are at risk of becoming sensitized to acrylates. In the last two decades, ACD caused by (meth)acrylates has become a significant and increasing problem in both consumers using acrylate nails and those working with them (4,5,6,77). In a recent UK study, for example, 94% of cases of occupational sensitization to (meth)acrylates was seen in 'beauticians', whereas 81% of the non-occupational cases were deemed to be related to nail products containing acrylates (4). In other studies also, the majority or a large portion of relevant reactions were attributed to artificial nails (6,12,45,49) and nail artists comprised 80% of all occupational cases in one study (6). In some investigations, however (especially older ones), dental workers were more (or most) frequently implicated in (meth)acrylate occupational allergic contact dermatitis (3,50).

Symptoms of allergic reactions include dermatitis of the hands, especially the fingertips ('pulpitis') and the perionychial skin, the face (including eyelids [52], neck and lips), paronychia, nail disorders including dystrophy (13,65) and onycholysis (which may also be seen in patients wearing acrylic nails who are not allergic [58,59,60]), and deformation or hyperkeratosis of the nail bed (2,65). Extensive or generalized dermatitis is seen occasionally (14) and airborne contact dermatitis often plays a role, especially in occupational cases (8,15,40,81,82). Prolonged (72) and even permanent loss of nails (16,63) has been described and painful paresthesia (which may also develop without acrylate sensitization) may be very bothersome (8,16,17,18,19) and even permanent (20,63). The (meth)acrylates may also induce occupational asthma and rhinitis or worsen existing airway problems (5,6,15,21,22,64,81). Infections with bacteria and fungi (notably *Candida* species) are far from rare (83) and transmission of infection has been reported (23,57), including dangerous transmissions by health personnel (24,25). Rare (possible) complications are Raynaud's phenomenon (26) and pterygium inversum unguis (27).

In some cases, patients sensitized to (meth)acrylates from artificial nails may subsequently experience problems with other acrylate products such as dentures, temporary crowns or other dental materials causing either occupational allergic contact dermatitis or stomatitis (42,43,44). In addition, sensitization to acrylates used in acrylic nail products may place patients at risk for aseptic loosening of joints following orthopedic prostheses that require bone cement (46).

Nail sculptors working in nail salons had significantly more often throat irritation than matched controls. Also, nose and skin irritation, drowsiness, dizzy spells and trembling of the hands were reported consistently more often by sculptors than the control group, but the differences were not statistically significant (61).

Nail polish

Recently, a new type of acrylate-based nail cosmetic has been introduced. Nail polishes containing UV-curing methacrylates have been presented as an alternative to common nail polishes. These products are marketed as more durable and long-lasting than conventional nail polishes. The methacrylate-containing nail polishes are applied directly to the nail plate in several layers, with a brush. Between the applications, each layer is cured with UV light (70). Recently, several patients who had allergic reactions to acrylates in nail polish have been described (29,67,69,70). The reactions occurred more frequently in manicurists than in clients, and usually cause dermatitis of the fingers. Other symptoms have included spreading dermatitis, paresthesia, cheilitis and lip edema, and severe psoriasis-like onychodystrophy with onycholysis and subungual hyperkeratosis (67).

At first, these types of nail polish were only offered by professional nail technicians in beauty salons, but, recently, different kits for home use have appeared on the market (70). A starter kit typically contains transparent base and top coats, a light-emitting diode (LED) lamp emitting UV light, and, sometimes, some colored coats (70). During 2014, 65 reports concerning undesirable effects from the use of UV-curing nail polish of the same brand were received by the Swedish Medical Products Agency (70). The most commonly reported problem was eczema starting around the nails, combined with itching and pain in the fingers. Several customers also reported onycholysis, lesions under the nail plate, or paronychia. Permanent nail damage with thin, brittle nails was also described. In some cases, eczema on other parts of the body, for example on the lips, on the throat, and around the eyes, were reported, indicating that the nail polish had not been completely cured by the provided UV LED lamp. Eight consumers were patch tested in Sweden with the products and their components (70). All tested patients except 1 had contact allergy to one or several of the acrylate or methacrylate ingredients of the nail polish.

CONTACT ALLERGY

Patch testing in groups of patients

Results of routine patch testing with HEMA (testing in consecutive patients suspected of contact dermatitis) back to 2007 are shown in table 2.219.1. Results of testing in groups of *selected* patients (e.g., hairdressers, hairdressers and cosmetologists, patients with a history of acrylate exposure) back to 1994 are also shown in table 2.219.1 (selected studies, not a full literature review).

As HEMA has been included in the screening tray of the North American Contact Dermatitis Group (NACDG) since 2007, there are some data on HEMA contact allergy available, notably from the USA + Canada, where the NACDG publishes their patch test results biannually. In the period 2007-2014, the prevalence of sensitization to HEMA in North America has been fairly constant between 2.0% and 2.6%. Relevance rates were low, ranging from 29% to 44% for 'definite + probable' relevance. Previously, low sensitization frequencies were observed in routine testing in Sweden (0.9%) and Singapore (0.3%) (84).

In groups of *selected* patients, high rates of positive patch test reactions to HEMA were observed in hairdressers and apprentice hairdressers (4.9%, all reactions were relevant) (78), patients with a history of acrylate exposure (10.5%) (35) and in an Australian study (9.5%), which did not state the mode of selecting the patients (74).

Table 2.219.1 Patch testing in groups of patients

Years and Country	Test conc. & vehicle	Number of patients tested	positive (%)	Selection of patients (S); Relevance (R); Comments (C)	Ref.
Routine testing					
2013-14 USA, Canada	2% pet.	4859	128 (2.6%)	R: definite + probable relevance: 29%	75
2011-12 USA, Canada	2% pet.	4230	83 (2.0%)	R: definite + probable relevance: 34%	36
2009-10 USA, Canada	2% pet.	4301	86 (2.0%)	R: definite + probable relevance: 30%	37
2007-8 USA, Canada	2% pet.	5065	(2.4%)	R: definite + probable relevance: 44%	34
2005-2007 Sweden	2% pet.	1609	15 (0.9%)	R: not specified	84
2005-2007 Singapore	2% pet.	1181	3 (0.3%)	R: not specified	84
Testing in groups of selected patients *					
2001-2010 Australia	2% pet.	504	48 (9.5%)	S: not stated; R: 65%	74
1994-2010 USA, Canada	2% pet.	?	? (?)	S: hairdressers/cosmetologists; R: in the group of 57 patients who had at least one relevant occupationally related reaction, 15 (26%) reacted to HEMA	79
1993-2010 Australia		164	8 (4.9%)	S: hairdressers and apprentice hairdressers presenting at an occupational dermatology clinic; R: 100%	78
1991-1994 Finland	2% pet.	124	13 (10.5%)	S: patients with a history of acrylate exposure; R: not stated	35

* selected studies, not a full literature review

Case reports and case series

Case series

HEMA was stated to be the (or an) allergen in 13 patients in a group of 603 individuals suffering from cosmetic dermatitis, seen in the period 2010-2015 in Leuven, Belgium (71). In the period 1996-2013, in a tertiary referral center in Valencia, Spain, 5419 patients were patch tested. Of these, 628 individuals had allergic contact dermatitis to cosmetics. HEMA was the responsible allergen in 28 cases (76). HEMA was responsible for 7 out of 959 cases of non-fragrance cosmetic allergy where the causal allergen was identified, Belgium, 2000-2010 (31). In the period 2000-2007, 202 patients with allergic contact dermatitis caused by cosmetics were seen in Valencia, Spain, in the same clinic as ref. 76 (overlap between the data in these two studies). In this group, there were 10 beauticians with occupational allergic contact dermatitis of the hands, who reacted to multiple (meth)acrylates from their presence in artificial nail materials. Of these ten individuals, seven reacted to HEMA, which reactions were apparently relevant (although it can be doubted that the presence of these specific chemicals in the products could always be verified) (73).

A group of 55 female patients presenting with hand eczema and who had contact with artificial nails, were patch tested with a series of acrylates in one center in Israel, 2001-2004. Twenty-one had one or more positive reactions, of who 14 were professional beauticians specializing in nail sculpturing. All reactions, including 17 to HEMA, were stated to be of current relevance (33). Because of the general lack of information on the composition of artificial nail materials, the fact that the author did no analyses of these products and the frequent occurrence of cross-reactivity among acrylates, one may wonder whether this statement can be accepted as entirely correct.

Six women who had experienced adverse reactions from an UV-cured nail polish had positive patch tests to its ingredient HEMA (70).

Case reports
A manicurist had occupational allergic contact dermatitis from HEMA present in several artificial nail materials she used. The presence of HEMA was not indicated on the labels, but by gas chromatography–mass spectrometry (GC-MS), the methacrylate was detected in the products used by the patients in concentrations ranging from 0.012% to 9.1% (30). One patient had allergic contact dermatitis from HEMA in a nail hardener and a nail gel for making artificial nails (32). A manicurist had occupational, partly airborne, allergic contact dermatitis from HEMA in a nail strengthener and a UV-cured nail gel (32).

Cross-reactions, pseudo-cross-reactions and co-reactions
Patients often react to many (meth)acrylates on patch testing. Primary sensitization to methacrylates may result in both methacrylate and acrylate cross-sensitization. Conversely, patients sensitized to acrylates are unlikely to show cross-sensitization to methacrylates (3). No cross-reactions to ethyl cyanoacrylate (53, see also Chapter 2.178 Ethyl cyanoacrylate).

Presence in cosmetic products and chemical analyses
In August 2017, HEMA was present in 64 of 70,589 cosmetic products of which the composition is known in EWG's Skin Deep Cosmetics Database, USA (http://www.ewg.org/skindeep/). In the USA, in April 2017, hydroxyethyl methacrylate was present in 43 of 56,714 cosmetic products of which the composition is known in FDA's Voluntary Cosmetic Registration Program (VCRP) (data obtained from FDA, May 2017).

Other information
Of patients allergic to (meth)acrylates, some 80-90% have positive patch test reactions to HEMA, which therefore is a suitable screening agent for allergy to artificial nails and other (meth)acrylate products (4,6).

LITERATURE
1   Björkner B, Frick-Engfeldt M, Pontén A, Zimerson E. Plastic materials. In: Johansen JD, Frosch PJ, Lepoittevin J-P, eds. Contact Dermatitis, 5th Edition. Heidelberg Dordrecht London New York: Springer-Verlag 2011, chapter 37:696-728

2   Aalto-Korte K. Acrylic resins. In: Rustemeyer T, Elsner P, John SM, Maibach HI, eds. Kanerva's occupational dermatology, 2nd Edition. Heidelberg New York Dordrecht London: Springer-Verlag, 2012, Chapter 50:543-558

3   Aalto-Korte K, Henriks-Eckerman M-L, Kuuliala O, Jolanki R. Occupational methacrylate and acrylate allergy – cross-reactions and possible screening allergens. Contact Dermatitis 2010;63:301-312

4   Montgomery R, Stocks SJ, Wilkinson SM. Contact allergy resulting from the use of acrylate nails is increasing in both users and those who are occupationally exposed. Contact Dermatitis 2016;74:120-122

5   Kwok C, Money A, Carder M, Turner S, Agius R, Orton D, et al. Cases of occupational dermatitis and asthma in beauticians that were reported to The Health and Occupation Research (THOR) network from 1996 to 2011. Clin Exp Dermatol 2014;39:590-595

6   Ramos L, Cabral R, Gonçalo M. Allergic contact dermatitis caused by acrylates and methacrylates – a 7-year study. Contact Dermatitis 2014;71:102-107

7   Constandt L, van Hecke E, Naeyaert J-M, Goossens A. Screening for contact allergy to artificial nails. Contact Dermatitis 2005;52:73-77

8   Freeman S, Lee M-S, Gudmundsen K. Adverse contact reactions to sculptured acrylic nails: 4 case reports and a literature review. Contact Dermatitis 1995;33:381-385

9   Cravo M, Cardoso JC, Gonçalo M, Figueiredo A. Allergic contact dermatitis from photobonded acrylic gel nails: a review of four cases. Contact Dermatitis 2008;59:250-251

10 Roche E, Cuadra J, Alegre V. Sensitization to acrylates by artificial acrylic nails: review of 15 cases. Actas Dermosifiliogr 2008;99:788-794

11 Hemmer W, Focke M, Wantke F, Götz M, Jarisch R. Allergic contact dermatitis to artificial fingernails prepared from UV light-cured acrylates. J Am Acad Dermatol 1996;35:377-380

12 Koppula S, Fellman J, Storrs F. Screening allergens for acrylate dermatitis associated with artificial nails. Am J Contact Dermatitis 1995;6:78-85

13 Cruz MJ, Baudrier T, Cunha AP, Ferreira O, Azevedo F. Severe onychodystrophy caused by allergic contact dermatitis to acrylates in artificial nails. Cutan Ocul Toxicol 2011;30:323-324

14 Fitzgerald DA, English JSC. Widespread contact dermatitis from sculptured nails. Contact Dermatitis 1994;30:118

15 Vaccaro M, Guarneri F, Barbuzza O, Cannavò SP. Airborne contact dermatitis and asthma in a nail art operator. Int J Occup Med Environ Health 2014;27:137-140

16 Fisher AA. Permanent loss of fingernails due to allergic reaction to an acrylic nail preparation: a sixteen year follow-up study. Cutis 1989;43:404-406

17 Sasseville D. Acrylates in contact dermatitis. Dermatitis 2012;23:6-16

18 Slodownik D, Williams JD, Tate BJ. Prolonged paresthesia due to sculptured acrylic nails. Contact Dermatitis 2007;56:298-299

19 Fisher AA. Adverse nail reactions and paresthesia from 'photobonded acrylate 'sculptured' nails'. Cutis 1990;45:293-294

20 Baran RL, Schibli H. Permanent paresthesia to sculptured nails - a distressing problem. Dermatol Clin 1990;8:1-6

21 Sauni R, Kauppi P, Alanko K, Henriks-Eckerman ML, Tuppurainen M, Hannu T. Occupational asthma caused by sculptured nails containing methacrylates. Am J Ind Med 2008;51:968-974 (Probably the same patient as presented in ref. 64)

22 Torres MC, Linares T, Hernandez MD. Acrylates induced rhinitis and contact dermatitis. Contact Dermatitis 2005;53:114

23 Senay H. Acrylic nails and transmission of infection. Can J Infect Control 1991;6:52

24 Gupta A, Della-Latta P, Todd B, San Gabriel P, Haas J, Wu F, Rubenstein D, Saiman L. Outbreak of extended-spectrum beta-lactamase-producing *Klebsiella pneumoniae* in a neonatal intensive care unit linked to artificial nails. Infect Control Hosp Epidemiol 2004;25:210-215

25 Gordin FM, Schultz ME, Huber R, Zubairi S, Stock F, Kariyil J. A cluster of hemodialysis-related bacteremia linked to artificial fingernails. Infect Control Hosp Epidemiol 2007;28:743-744

26 Barnett JM, Scher RK. Nail cosmetics. Int J Dermatol 1992;31:675-681

27 Paley K, English JC 3rd, Zirwas MJ. Pterygium inversum unguis secondary to acrylate allergy. J Am Acad Dermatol 2008;58(Suppl.2):S53-S54

28 Sainio E-L, Engström K, Henriks-Eckerman M-L, Kanerva L. Allergenic ingredients in nail polishes. Contact Dermatitis 1997;37:155-162

29 Le Q, Cahill J, Palmer-Le A, Nixon R. The rising trend in allergic contact dermatitis to acrylic nail products. Australas J Dermatol 2015;56:221-223

30 Andersen SL, Rastogi SC, Andersen KE. Occupational allergic contact dermatitis to hydroxyethyl methacrylate (2-HEMA) in a manicurist. Contact Dermatitis 2009;61:48-50

31 Travassos AR, Claes L, Boey L, Drieghe J, Goossens A. Non-fragrance allergens in specific cosmetic products. Contact Dermatitis 2011;65:276-285

32 Erdmann SM, Sachs B, Merk HF. Adverse reactions to sculptured nails. Allergy 2001;56:581-582

33 Lazarov A. Sensitization to acrylates is a common adverse reaction to artificial fingernails. J Eur Acad Derm Venereol 2007;21:169-174

34 Fransway AF, Zug KA, Belsito DV, Deleo VA, Fowler JF Jr, Maibach HI, et al. North American Contact Dermatitis Group patch test results for 2007-2008. Dermatitis 2013;24:10-21

35 Kanerva L, Estlander T, Jolanki R, Tarvainen KL. Statistics on allergic patch test reactions caused by acrylate compounds, including data on ethyl methacrylate. Am J Cont Derm 1995;6:75-77

36 Warshaw EM, Maibach HI, Taylor JS, Sasseville D, DeKoven JG, Zirwas MJ, et al. North American Contact Dermatitis Group patch test results: 2011-2012. Dermatitis 2015;26:49-59

37 Warshaw EM, Belsito DV, Taylor JS, Sasseville D, DeKoven JG, Zirwas MJ, et al. North American Contact Dermatitis Group patch test results: 2009 to 2010. Dermatitis 2013;24:50-59

38 Uter W, Geier J. Contact allergy to acrylates and methacrylates in consumers and nail artists – data of the Information Network of Departments of Dermatology, 2004–2013. Contact Dermatitis 2015;72:224-228

39 Patruno C, Ayala F, Napolitano M, Bianca D, Balato N. Occupational allergic contact dermatitis to acrylic fingernails in beauticians. Occup Environ Med 2012;69:772

40 Maio P, Carvalho R, Amaro C, Santos R, Cardoso J. Allergic contact dermatitis from sculptured acrylic nails: special presentation with a possible airborne pattern. Dermatol Online J 2012;8:13 (Letter)

41 Mowad C, Ferringer T. Allergic contact dermatitis from acrylates in artificial nails. Dermatitis 2004;15:51-53

42 Goulding JMR, Finch TM. Acrylates tooth and nail: coexistent allergic contact dermatitis caused by acrylates present in desensitizing dental swabs and artificial fingernails. Contact Dermatitis 2011;65:47-48

43 Macedo NA, Carmona C, Piñeyro I. Contact dermatitis from acrylic nails. Contact Dermatitis 1995;32:362

44 Jung P, Jarisch R, Hemmer W. Hypersensitivity from dental acrylates in a patient previously sensitized to artificial nails. Contact Dermatitis 2005;53:119-120

45 Drucker AM, Pratt MD. Acrylate contact allergy: patient characteristics and evaluation of screening allergens. Dermatitis 2011;22:98-101

46 Haughton AM, Belsito DV. Acrylate allergy induced by acrylic nails resulting in prosthesis failure. J Am Acad Dermatol 2008;59 (Suppl.5):S123-S124

47 Goon T-JA, Bruze M, Zimerson E, Goh C-L, Isaksson M. Contact allergy to acrylates/methacrylates in the acrylate and nail acrylics series in southern Sweden: simultaneous positive patch test reaction patterns and possible screening allergens. Contact Dermatitis 2007;57:21-27

48 Perale L, De Marchi S, Cecchin E, Sechi LA. Methacrylates allergy in a professional beautician. Contact Dermatitis 2005;53:181-182

49   Sood A, Taylor JS. Acrylic reactions: a review of 56 cases. Contact Dermatitis 2003;48:346-347

50   Geukens S, Goossens A. Occupational contact allergy to (meth)acrylates. Contact Dermatitis 2001;44:153-159

51   Tucker SC, Beck MH. A 15-year study of patch testing to (meth)acrylates. Contact Dermatitis 1999;40:278-279

52   Guin JD. Eyelid dermatitis from methacrylates used for nail enhancement. Contact Dermatitis 1998;39:312-313

53   Kanerva L, Jolanki R, Estlander T. 10 Years of patch testing with the (meth)acrylate series. Contact Dermatitis 1997;37:255-258

54   Kanerva L, Lauerma A, Estlander T, Alanko K, Henriks-Eckerman ML, Jolanki R. Occupational allergic contact dermatitis caused by photobonded sculptured nails and a review of (meth) acrylates in nail cosmetics. Am J Contact Dermatitis 1996;7:109-115

55   Canizares O. Contact dermatitis due to the acrylic materials used in artificial nails. Arch Dermatol 1956;74:141-143

56   Lane C W, Kost L B. Sensitivity to artificial nails. Arch Dermatol 1956;74:671-672

57   Parker AV, Cohen EJ, Arentsen JJ. Pseudomonas corneal ulcers after artificial fingernail injuries. Am J Ophthalmol 1989;107:548-549

58   Bentley-Phillips B. Dystrophies due to nail cosmetics. S Afr Med J 1970;14:1293-1295

59   Frumess GM, Lewis HM, Henschel EJ. Disturbance of nails and nail beds produced by artificial fingernails. JAMA 1952;149:828-829

60   Goodwin P. Onycholysis due to acrylic nail applications. Clin Exp Dermatol 1976;1:191-192

61   Hiipakka D, Samimi B. Exposure of acrylic fingernail sculptors to organic vapors and methacrylate dusts. Am Ind Hyg Assoc J 1987;48:230-237

62   Condé-Salazar L, Guimaraens D, Romero LV, González MA, Alomar A. Occupational allergic contact dermatitis to artificial nails. Contact Dermatitis 1986;15:242

63   Fisher AA. Permanent loss of fingernails from sensitization and reaction to acrylic in a preparation designed to make artificial fingernails. J Dermatol Surg Oncol 1980;6:70-71

64   Hannu T, Tuppurainen M, Kauppi P, Alanko K, Henriks-Eckerman ML, Sauni R. [Occupational asthma in a structure nail maker]. Duodecim 2009;125:1209-1213 (article in Finnish). Probably the same patient as presented in ref. 21)

65   Cruz MJ, Baudrier T, Cunha AP, Ferreira O, Azevedo F. Severe onychodystrophy caused by allergic contact dermatitis to acrylates in artificial nails. Cutan Ocul Toxicol 2011;30:323-324

66   Fisher AA, Franks A, Glick H. Allergic sensitization of the skin and nails to acrylic plastic nails. J Allergy 1957;28:84-88

67   Mattos Simoes Mendonca M, LaSenna C, Tosti A. Severe onychodystrophy due to allergic contact dermatitis from acrylic nails. Skin Appendage Disord 2015;1:91-94

68   Vazquez-Osorio I, Espasandin-Arias M, Garcia-Gavin J, Fernandez-Redondo V. Allergic contact dermatitis due to acrylates in acrylic gel nails: a report of 3 cases. Actas Dermosifiliogr 2014;105:430-432

69   Scheers C, André J, Negulescu M, Blondeel A, Kolivras A. Recurrent cheilitis and lip oedema caused by (meth)acrylates present in ultraviolet-curable nail lacquer. Contact Dermatitis 2015;72:341-342

70   Dahlin J, Berne B, Dunér K, Hosseiny S, Matura M, Nyman G, et al. Several cases of undesirable effects caused by methacrylate ultraviolet-curing nail polish for non-professional use. Contact Dermatitis 2016;75:151-156

71   Goossens A. Cosmetic contact allergens. Cosmetics 2016, 3, 5; doi:10.3390/cosmetics3010005

72   Halgmüller T, Hemmer W, Kusak I, et al. Loss of fingernails due to persisting allergic contact dermatitis in an artificial nail designer [abstract]. J Allergy Clin Immunol 1995;95:250

73   Laguna C, de la Cuadra J, Martín-González B, Zaragoza V, Martínez-Casimiro L, Alegre V. Allergic contact dermatitis to cosmetics. Actas Dermosifiliogr 2009;100:53-60

74   Toholka R, Wang Y-S, Tate B, Tam M, Cahill J, Palmer A, Nixon R. The first Australian Baseline Series: Recommendations for patch testing in suspected contact dermatitis. Australas J Dermatol 2015;56:107-115

75   DeKoven JG, Warshaw EM, Belsito DV, Sasseville D, Maibach HI, Taylor JS, et al. North American Contact Dermatitis Group Patch Test Results: 2013-2014. Dermatitis 2017;28:33-46

76   Zaragoza-Ninet V, Blasco Encinas R, Vilata-Corell JJ, Pérez-Ferriols A, Sierra-Talamantes C, Esteve-Martínez A, de la Cuadra-Oyanguren J. Allergic contact dermatitis due to cosmetics: A clinical and epidemiological study in a tertiary hospital. Actas Dermosifiliogr 2016;107:329-336

77   Spencer A, Gazzani P, Thompson DA. Acrylate and methacrylate contact allergy and allergic contact disease: a 13-year review. Contact Dermatitis 2016;75:157-164

78   Lyons G, Roberts H, Palmer A, Matheson M, Nixon R. Hairdressers presenting to an occupational dermatology clinic in Melbourne, Australia. Contact Dermatitis 2013;68:300-306

79   Warshaw EM, Wang MZ, Mathias CGT, Maibach HI, Belsito DV, Zug KA, et al. Occupational contact dermatitis in hairdressers/cosmetologists; retrospective analysis of North American Contact Dermatitis Group data, 1994 to 2010. Dermatitis 2012;23:258-268

80 Kiec-Swierczynska M, Krecisz B, Chomiczewska-Skora D. Occupational contact dermatitis to acrylates in a manicurist. Occup Med (Lond) 2013;63:380-382

81 Vaccaro M, Guarneri F, Barbuzza O, Cannavò SP. Airborne contact dermatitis and asthma in a nail art operator. Int J Occup Med Environ Health 2014;27:137-140

82 Maio P, Carvalho R, Amaro C, Santos R, Cardoso J. Allergic contact dermatitis from sculptured acrylic nails: special presentation with an airborne pattern. Dermatol Reports 2012;4:e6

83 Alcántara-Nicolás FA, Pastor-Nieto MA, Sánchez-Herreros C, Pérez-Mesonero R, Melgar-Molero V, Ballano A, De-Eusebio E. Allergic contact dermatitis from acrylic nails in a flamenco guitarist. Occup Med (Lond) 2016;66:751-753

84 Goon AT, Bruze M, Zimerson E, Goh CL, Soo-Quee Koh D, Isaksson M. Screening for acrylate/methacrylate allergy in the baseline series: our experience in Sweden and Singapore. Contact Dermatitis 2008;59:307-313

85 Chou M, Dhingra N, Strugar TL. Contact sensitization to allergens in nail cosmetics. Dermatitis 2017;28:231-240

2.220 HENNA, BLACK

INTRODUCTION

Although black henna is not a cosmetic ingredient, it is discussed here because the material is used mainly for cosmetic purposes and it contains *p*-phenylenediamine (PPD), one of the major cosmetic allergens. As there is a full review of black henna up to 2013 available from the author (69), the publications on adverse effects are summarized here rather than being discussed in detail; also, the format is somewhat different from the other chapters in this book.

This chapter is largely based on the previous review of the subject by the author (69); selected more recent literature has been added. Cases of allergic reactions from hair dyes caused by previous sensitization to PPD in black henna tattoos published between 2002 and 2014 have been reviewed in 2016 (86), and clinical manifestations of allergic reactions to black henna tattoos in 2017 (91). Although the subject is well known by now, new cases of allergic reactions to black henna tattoos (72,73,75,97,98,99,103) or reactions to hair products in patients previously sensitized by PPD in black henna tattoos (85,93) are still being published, usually because of specific features.

PPD in applications other than black henna, notably in hair dyes, is discussed in Chapter 2.359 *p*-Phenylenediamine.

GENERAL

Black henna is red henna (see Chapter 2.221 Henna (red)), to which *p*-phenylenediamine (PPD) has been added. Natural black henna does not exist. In fact, some black 'henna' preparations do not contain any lawsone, the active ingredient of red henna, ergo no henna at all (1,2). Since around 1997, black henna has been used for the so-called temporary black henna tattoos. These are usually applied to young people and children by street artisan tattoo artists with mobile studios in sunny holiday resort and in attraction parks, at festivals and fairs. PPD is added to henna to accelerate the dying and drying process (to only 30 minutes), to strengthen and darken the color, enhance the design pattern of the tattoo and make it last longer. The henna materials are perceived (and propagated) as 'natural' and (therefor) safe, but adverse effects prove to be frequent. The side effects of red henna and black henna have been fully reviewed in 2013 (69).

CONTACT ALLERGY

Black henna tattoos have caused many allergic reactions, virtually always to PPD, which is an extreme sensitizer (40); this dye has been demonstrated in black henna inks in concentrations of >10% up to 64% (table 2.220.2). These high concentrations of sensitizing materials, the long duration of skin contact, the lack of a neutralizing (oxidizing) agent, (possibly) the presence of oils or solvents in black henna, occlusion during drying, and re-exposure to the allergen from retouching the tattoo after 4-14 days, all increase the risk of skin sensitization.

Most patients with an allergic reaction become sensitized to PPD in the tattoo itself (3-6,8-10,12-19,21). Incubation periods are usually between 8-14 days, but in many instances of active sensitization, short incubation periods of 4 to 7 days have been observed, especially in children. Allergic contact dermatitis to henna tattoos may also develop in patients who are already sensitized to PPD, usually from previous black henna tattooing (24,28,29) or from hair dying (22,23,31); some have previous sensitizations to PPD-related chemicals such as azo dyes in clothes (33), benzocaine (4,30) or sulfonamides (30), and now react to PPD in the tattoo. In these patients, the tattoo reactions develop within 1-2 days.

Clinical picture of allergic contact dermatitis from black henna tattoos

Most patients (about 80%) have the typical clinical picture of acute allergic contact dermatitis with erythema, edema, papules, and vesicles; bullae are often observed (27,104). Though fierce, in most cases the dermatitis is limited to the site of the tattoo and usually in a geometric pattern strictly mirroring the tattoo; however, spreading of the dermatitis and even generalization may occur. Sometimes, there is secondary involvement of non-tattooed adjacent, touching areas of skin or juxtaposed skin in contact with the primary lesion, which has been termed 'sign of the kiss' or 'kissing lesions' (71,74). Lichenoid contact dermatitis is fairly frequent. There are several case reports of (sometimes generalized) erythema multiforme-like contact dermatitis (75,83,88) and single instances of urticaria and angioedema complicating contact allergy (26) (though there were 12 cases of 'urticaria' reported to the FDA [78]) and of pustular allergic contact dermatitis (21). It not infrequently takes several weeks before the eruption subsides even under topical (and sometimes also oral) corticosteroid therapy. Post-inflammatory hypopigmentation (75,89,103) (especially in children) and hyperpigmentation is very frequent and often lasts for more than 6 months. Scarring has been observed (albeit sometimes unconvincingly presented as scars) in a number of patients (11,34). Infections including cellulitis may complicate allergic contact dermatitis (72,78).

Patients sensitized from PPD in henna tattoos may have serious allergic reactions when later dying their hair or eyebrows/lashes (19,35,39,79) with a permanent or semi-permanent dye (5,9,10,13,35,36,37,38,81), sometimes in religious or cultural ceremonies (85). In rare cases, the reaction may be life-threatening from respiratory distress as a result of edematous swelling (38). Children often have very serious reactions to hair dyes after being sensitized from black henna tattoo and frequently need to be admitted to the hospital (37,86). Sometimes, individuals sensitized from a temporary tattoo develop contact dermatitis from being touched by relatives whose hands have been painted with black henna for religious ceremonies (76).

Some sensitized individuals will later developed allergic contact dermatitis from clothes from the presence therein of textile dyes structurally related to PPD (e.g., disperse dyes, table 2.220.1) (86,87). Others have later developed occupational allergic contact dermatitis from black rubber (100) or 4-methylaminophenol sulfate in photo-developing solutions (77) as a result of cross-reactivity to PPD.

The clinical manifestations of allergic reactions to black henna tattoos have been reviewed (91).

Other henna products containing PPD

There are several cases of allergic reactions to black henna used as dye for the eyebrows and –lashes (49) and as hair dye (7,9,50,82). A 57-year-old man developed a painful, blistering skin reaction on his forearm within hours of application of a henna dye he was planning to use to dye his hair as a sort of patch test (51).

Henna 'stone' is a lesser-known commercially available material used to obtain black henna paste (94,96). In some countries, including Turkey, local herb sellers sell it as 'natural stone', a so-called natural source for black henna. However, these stones may contain >80% PPD (95). The stone has to be crushed into powder first, and then mixed with water, hydrogen peroxide and, sometimes, natural henna to obtain black henna paste for the purpose of hair dying or, mainly, temporary tattooing. A girl developed an airborne allergic contact dermatitis one day after crushing a henna stone outdoors on a windy day. She had previously been sensitized from a black henna tattoo (94).

Frequency of allergic reactions to black henna tattoos

In the English literature, up to 2012, over 185 patients sensitized by tattoos have been reported. Seventy cases were reported to the FDA in the period 2002-2014 (78). There have been large case series, some of which were collected in a short period of time (6,17). Not infrequently, siblings were reported to have developed allergic reactions from a tattoo that had been applied at the same time (80). Forty published patients had allergic contact dermatitis to tattoos from existing sensitization, mostly from previous tattoo applications. In addition, reports of over 30 people with (often fierce) reactions to other PPD-containing products, notably hair dyes, were found in the English literature up to 2012. In studies where patients were routinely tested with PPD, of those with a positive patch test reaction, 4.8% (52), 21% (53), resp. 9.1% (54) were (probably) sensitized to PPD from previous tattoos. In 34 Spanish children allergic to PPD, sensitization was caused by a black henna tattoo in 50% (70). At least 6% of the population in Denmark and the UK have ever had a black henna tattoo, with percentages of 30 or over in young females, and their popularity still increases (55,56,57,58). Of those who have a tattoo, an estimated 2.5% will have become sensitized to PPD (55,56,69).

Published data on allergic reactions to tattoos and their sequelae is without any doubt only the tip of the iceberg. Many cases of *de novo* tattoo sensitization may go unnoticed, when later no (or not yet) re-exposure to tattoos, hair dyes or other products containing PPD or cross-reacting substances, sufficient to cause allergic contact dermatitis, takes place. Only a fraction of the people with a tattoo reaction will be referred to the dermatologist. Even of patients who experience (severe) allergic reactions to hair dye, only 10% to 30% will be seen by a doctor and even fewer by a dermatologist (48,59). Thus, taken all data together, it seems safe to assume that allergic reactions to black henna tattoos are a frequent event.

A full review of contact allergy to black henna, including specifics on case series and case reports, up to 2012 has been published in 2013 by the author (69).

Cross-reactions, pseudo-cross-reactions and co-reactions

Primary sensitization to PPD from black henna tattoos frequently leads to cross-reactions with a number of structurally related compounds, notably to other hair dyes, azo dyes used in textiles, rubber chemicals (*N*-isopropyl-*N*'-phenyl-*p*-phenylenediamine, black rubber mix) and benzocaine (table 1). More information on cross-reactions from PPD 9from any source) can be found in Chapter 2.359 *p*-Phenylenediamine.

Table 2.220.1 Cross-reactions in patients sensitized to PPD by black henna tattoos [a] (69)

Cross-reacting compound	Synonyms	CAS	References
Acid yellow 36	metanil yellow; CI 13065	587-98-4	10
p-Aminoazobenzene	aniline yellow; CI 11000	60-09-3	18,19,22,37
4-Amino-*m*-cresol	4-hydroxy-*o*-toluidine	2835-99-6	37
m-Aminophenol	1-amino-3-hydroxybenzene; 3-aminophenol; CI 76545	591-27-5	10,20,35,37,38
p-Aminophenol	1-amino-4-hydroxybenzene;	123-30-8	10,19,20,22,28,35,36,38

Table 2.220.1 Cross-reactions in patients sensitized to PPD by black henna tattoos [a] (69) (*continued*)

Cross-reacting compound	Synonyms	CAS	References
	4-aminophenol; CI 76550		
Aniline	aminobenzene; CI 76000	62-53-3	
Benzocaine	ethyl p-aminobenzoate	**94-09-7**	5,10,20,29,35,37
Bismarck brown R	basic brown 4; CI 21010	8005-78-5	10,18
Black rubber mix			13,21,28
Butacaine	3-dibutylaminopropyl PABA	149-16-6	28
Butanilicaine	2-butylamino-6'-chloro-o-ace-totoluidine	3785-21-5	28
Butyl PABA	butamben; butoform	94-25-7	28
2,4-Diaminoazobenzene	solvent orange 3; CI 11270:1	495-54-5	13
4,4'-Diaminodiphenylmethane	4,4'-methylenedianiline	101-77-9	15,19,28
Direct orange 34	CI 40215	1325-54-8	16
Disperse blue 106	CI 111935	68516-81-4	28
Disperse blue 124		15141-18-1	8,28
Disperse blue 106/124 mix			10,16
Disperse blue 135	unknown chemical		28
Disperse orange 1	CI 11080	2581-69-3	13,16,28,35
Disperse orange 3	CI 11005	730-40-5	10,13,15,18,19,22,28,35,37
Disperse red 1	CI 11110; CI solvent red 14	2872-52-8	13,17,28
Disperse red 17	CI 11210	3179-89-3	13,35
Disperse yellow 3	CI 11855	2832-40-8	8,10,13,14,16,19,28,35
Disperse yellow 9	CI 10375	6373-73-5	35
Hydroquinone	1,4-dihydroxybenzene	123-31-9	10,14,35,37
N-Isopropyl-N'-phenyl-p-phenylene-diamine	4-(isopropylamino)diphenyl-amine	101-72-4	5,10,16,19,20,28,37,39
4-Methylaminophenol sulfate	Metol	55-55-0	77
o-Nitro-p-phenylenediamine	4-amino-2-nitroaniline; CI 76070	5307-14-2	20,22,36
N-Phenyl-p-phenylenediamine	p-aminodiphenylamine	101-54-2	
Procainamide	p-aminobenzoic diethylamino-ethylamide	51-06-09	28
Procaine	2-diethylaminoethyl p-amino-benzoate	59-46-1	28
Pyrogallol	1,2,3-benzenetriol; CI 76515	87-66-1	10,37
Sodium sulfadimidine	sodium sulfamethazine	1981-58-4	28
Sodium sulfamerazine		127-58-2	28
Sulfaguanidine		57-67-0	28
Sulfanilamide	p-aminobenzenesulfonamide	63-74-1	28
Toluene-2,5-diamine	p-toluenediamine; CI 76042	95-70-5	10,15,19,20,22,28,35,36,37
Toluene-2,5-diamine sulfate	p-toluenediamine sulfate; CI 76043	615-50-9	16

[a] Some reactions may have been co-reactions instead of cross-reactions proper; not in all cases was sensitization to PPD proven to be the result of exposition to black henna tattoos

Patch test sensitization
It is strongly recommended *not* to patch test patients with black henna inks, as the high concentrations of PPD may actively sensitize the – not yet allergic – patient and extremely strong patch test reactions may be seen in patients already sensitized to PPD (69).

Analysis of allergen in products
Results of studies identifying and quantifying PPD in black henna preparations are shown in table 2.220.2.

OTHER SIDE EFFECTS

Irritant contact dermatitis
A 'second degree chemical burn' developed in a black henna tattoo, where the skin had started blistering a few hours after application; patch tests were not performed (62). A rare case of irritant dermatitis to an unknown ingredient in a black henna tattoo with consecutive hypopigmentation has been reported. Sensitization to PPD and other para-compounds was excluded by patch test evaluation (84).

Table 2.220.2 Identification and quantification of PPD in black henna preparations

Year	Country	Analytical method	Source of henna samples and color	Nr.	Nr. containing PPD	Conc. PPD (% w/w)	Ref.	
2013	Turkey	HPLC	commercial, black	25	25 (100%)	3.37 − 51.6	92	
2011	USA	GC/MS	not stated (market survey)	10	4 (40%)	4.28 − 27.24	43	
2011	Spain	HPCL	from patients, black	3	3 (100%)	1.17 − 64		1
			commercial, black	2	2 (100%)	2.09 − 12.78		
			commercial, not black	9	0 (0%)			
2010	United Arab Emirates	HPLC	henna salons, black	11	11 (100%)	0.38 - 29.5 (>6 in 6)	42	
			henna salons, red	14	5 (36%)	0.005 − 0.23		
2008	Turkey	IOEGC-MS	cosmetic shops	35	30 (86%)	0.25 − 7.04	44	
2006	Korea	HPLC	tattoo shops, color?	15	3 (20%)	0.25 − 2.35	45	
2005	Spain	HPLC	patient (who was also tattoo artist), (dark brown)	1	1 (100%)	23.5	41	
2002	USA	HPLC	from patient, black	1	1 (100%)	15.7	32	
			commercial samples (color not mentioned)	3	0 (0%)			
2002	Denmark	HPLC	from patient, color?	1	1 (100%)	0.43	46	
2002	Taiwan	MS	commercial black henna	1	1 (100%)	not determined	6	
			natural henna powder	1	0 (0%)			
2001	Germany					on average 6% PPD in henna preparations (cited in ref. 10)		

GC/MS: Gas Chromatography – Mass Spectrometry; HPLC: High Performance Liquid Chromatography; IOEGC-MS: Ion-pair Extraction and Gas Chromatography – Mass Spectrometry; MS: Mass Spectrometry

Immediate-type reactions

One patient had rapidly progressive dyspnea a few minutes after skin application of black henna dye, requiring prompt admission to a hospital emergency department (8).

Other non-eczematous contact reactions

There have been some reports of the appearance of localized hypertrichosis in a black henna tattoo with or without allergic reactions to the tattoo. In all these cases, the hypertrichosis occurred surprisingly rapidly, between 5 and 20 days, when the tattoo was fading away, was asymptomatic, and resolved spontaneously within 3-5 months (47,73,98).

One case of cutaneous mercury deposition after the application of henna dye containing red pigment with a painful cutaneous granuloma and abscess in a 13-year-old has been presented; the subcutaneous tissue with the mercury materials had to be removed surgically (60). In an 8-year-old girl from India, depigmented spots at the tattoo site were seen 3 days after its application (61). In exceptional cases, contact allergy to PPD in a henna tattoo may have provoked Sweet syndrome (25) or eosinophilic cellulitis (Wells' syndrome) (90).

Systemic side effects

The mixing of henna with PPD has been practiced since several decades in certain African countries, notably the Sudan (63). Many cases of toxicity from the black powder for body paining, some fatal, were noted in Sudan in the early 1980s (64). Initial symptoms are massive edema of the face, lips, glottis, pharynx, neck and bronchi, occurring within hours of application of the dye-mix to the skin and sometimes requiring emergency tracheostomy for respiratory obstruction. The symptoms may then progress on the second day to anuria and acute renal failure (64). Such cases are still being reported, also from other countries like Turkey (101).

Ingestion of the mix or PPD alone or material from 'henna stones' (102), either accidental (in children), deliberate (suicidal) or homicidal leads to similar clinical presentations with additionally rhabdomyolysis. Many patients die within 24 hours (65,66).

Pulmonary edema was thought to have been caused by painting the feet with a henna mixture probably containing PPD in one patient (67). Cutaneous vasculitis and crescentic, rapidly progressive glomerulonephritis has been ascribed to the chronic use of henna mixed with PPD for dying of the hair (68).

Poisoning from ingestion of PPD is described in more detail in Chapter 2.359 *p*-Phenylenediamine.

LITERATURE

1   Almeida PJ, Borrego L, Pulido-Melián, González-Díaz O. Quantification of p-phenylenediamine and 2-hydroxy-1,4-naphthoquinone in henna tattoos. Contact Dermatitis 2011;66:33-37

2   El-Shaer NS, Badr JM, Aboul-Ela MA, Gohar YM. Determination of lawsone in henna powders by high performance thin layer chromatography. J Sep Sci 2007;30:3311-3315

3   Kazandjieva J, Grozdev I, Tsankov N. Temporary henna tattoos. Clin Dermatol 2007;25:383-387

4   Wolf R, Wolf D, Matz H, Orion E. Cutaneous reactions to temporary tattoos. Dermatol Online J 2003;9:3

5   Jung P, Sesztak-Greinecker G, Wantke F, Götz M, Jarisch R, Hemmer W. The extent of black henna tattoo's complications are not restricted to PPD-sensitization. Contact Dermatitis 2006;55:57

6   Chung WH, Chang YC, Yang LJ, Hung SI, Wong WR, Lin JY, Chan HL. Clinicopathologic features of skin reactions to temporary tattoos and analysis of possible causes. Arch Dermatol 2002;138:88-92

7   Öztaş MO, Önder M, Öztaş P, Atahan Ç. Contact allergy to henna. J Eur Acad Dermatol Venereol 2001;15: 91-92

8   Ventura MT, Di Leo E, Buquicchio R, Foti C, Arsieni A. Is black henna responsible for asthma and cross reactivity with latex? J Eur Acad Dermatol Venereol 2007;21:714-715

9   Onder M. Temporary holiday "tattoos" may cause lifelong allergic contact dermatitis when henna is mixed with PPD. J Cosmet Dermatol 2003;2:126-130

10   Spornraft-Ragaller P, Kämmerer E, Gillitzer C, Schmitt J. Severe allergic reactions to para-phenylenediamine in children and adolescents: should the patch test concentration of PPD be changed? J Dtsch Dermatol Ges 2012;10:258-263

11   Gunasti S, Aksungur VL. Severe inflammatory and keloidal, allergic reaction due to para-phenylenediamine in temporary tattoos. Indian J Dermatol Venereol Leprol 2010;76:165-167

12   Neri I, Giacomini F, Raone B, Patrizi A. Generalized erythema multiforme after localized allergic dermatitis from dark henna tattoo. Pediatr Dermatol 2009;26:496

13   Gonzalo-Garijo MA, Fernandéz-Duràn DA, Pérez-Calderòn R, Sánchez-Carvajal J. Allergic contact dermatitis due to a temporary henna tattoo, a hair dye and a marker pen. J Investig Allergol Clin Immunol 2008;18:226-227

14   Tan E, Garioch J. Black henna tattoos: coexisting rubber and para-phenylenediamine allergy? Clin Exp Dermatol 2007;32:782-783

15   Valsecchi R, Leghissa P, Di Landro A, Bartolozzi F, Riva M, Bancone C. Persistent leukoderma after henna tattoo. Contact Dermatitis 2007;56:108-109

16   Matulich J, Sullivan J. A temporary henna tattoo causing hair and clothing dye allergy. Contact Dermatitis 2005;53:33-36

17   Sachdev M. Allergic hypersensitivity reactions to temporary henna tattoo: a newer emerging form of beauty contact dermatitis. J Am Acad Dermatol 2005;52(3 Suppl.1):76

18   Boschnakow A, Treudler R, Lieps D, Steinhoff M, Orfanos CE. Temporary tattooing with henna induces contact allergy to textile dyes. J Dtsch Dermatol Ges 2003;1:962-964

19   Schultz E, Mahler V. Prolonged lichenoid reaction and cross-sensitivity to para-substituted amino-compounds due to temporary henna tattoo. Int J Dermatol 2002;41:301-303

20   Marcoux D, Couture-Trudel PM, Riboulet-Delmas G, Sasseville D. Sensitization to para-phenylenediamine from a streetside temporary tattoo. Pediatr Dermatol 2002;19:498-502

21   Mohamed M, Nixon R. Severe allergic contact dermatitis induced by paraphenylenediamine in paint-on temporary 'tattoos'. Australas J Dermatol 2000;41:168-171

22   Le Coz CJ, Lefebvre C, Keller F, Grosshans E. Allergic contact dermatitis caused by skin painting (pseudotattooing) with black henna, a mixture of henna and p-phenylenediamine and its derivatives. Arch Dermatol 2000;136:1515-1517

23   Tosti A, Pazzaglia M, Corazza M, Virgili A. Allergic contact dermatitis caused by mehindi. Contact Dermatitis 2000;42:356

24   Turan H, Okur M, Kaya E, Gun E, Aliagaoglu C. Allergic contact dermatitis to para-phenylenediamine in a tattoo: a case report. Cutan Ocul Toxicol 2013;32:185-187

25   Rosmaninho A, Machado S, Amorim S, Lobo I, Selores M. Henna tattoo and Sweet's syndrome: a possible relation. Eur J Dermatol 2009;19:642

26   Gulen F, Zeyrek D, Altinoz S, Peker E, Demir E, Tanac R. Urticaria and angioneurotic edema due to the temporary henna tattoo. Minerva Pediatr 2006;58:583-585

27   Jung P, Sesztak-Greinecker G, Wantke F, Götz M, Jarisch R, Hemmer W. A painful experience: black henna tattoo causing severe, bullous contact dermatitis. Contact Dermatitis 2006;54:219-220

28   Van den Keybus C, Morren MA, Goossens A. Walking difficulties due to an allergic reaction to a temporary tattoo. Contact Dermatitis 2005;53:180-181

29   Lim SP, Prais L, Foulds IS. Henna tattoos for children: a potential source of para-phenylenediamine and thiuram sensitization. Br J Dermatol 2004;151:1271

30   Arroyo M. Black henna tattoo reaction in a person with sulfonamide and benzocaine drug allergies. J Am Acad Dermatol 2003;48:301-302

31   Van Zuuren EJ, Lavrijsen AP. Allergische reacties en hypopigmentaties na tijdelijke hennatatoeages. Ned Tijdschr Geneeskd 2002;46:1332-1335

32 Brancaccio RR, Brown LH, Chang YT, Fogelman JP, Mafong EA, Cohen DE. Identification and quantification of para-phenylenediamine in a temporary black henna tattoo. Am J Contact Dermat 2002;13:15-18

33 Simpson-Dent SL, Hunt SH, Davison SC, Wakelin SH. Tattoo dermatitis from primary sensitization to clothing dyes. Contact Dermatitis 2001;45:248

34 Lewin PK. Temporary henna tattoo with permanent scarification. CMAJ 1999;160:310

35 Kind F, Scherer K, Bircher AJ. Contact dermatitis to para-phenylenediamine in hair dye following sensitization to black henna tattoos – an ongoing problem. J Dtsch Dermatol Ges 2012;10:572-577

36 Redlick F, DeKoven J. Allergic contact dermatitis to paraphenylenediamine in hair dye after sensitization from black henna tattoos: a report of 6 cases. CMAJ 2007;176:445-446

37 Søsted H, Johansen JD, Andersen KE, Menné T. Severe allergic hair dye reactions in 8 children. Contact Dermatitis 2006;54:87-91

38 Jasim ZF, Darling JR, Handley JM. Severe allergic contact dermatitis to paraphenylene diamine in hair dye following sensitization to black henna tattoos. Contact Dermatitis 2005;52:116-117

39 Bhat J, Smith AG. Xanthelasma palpebrarum following allergic contact dermatitis for para-phenylenediamine In a black eyelash tinting product. Contact Dermatitis 2003;49:311

40 Kligman A. The identification of contact allergens by human assay. J Invest Dermatol 1966;47:393-402

41 Borrego L, Hernandez-Machin B, Gonzalez O, Hernández B. Sensitization to para-phenylenediamine in a streetside temporary tattoo artisan. Contact Dermatitis 2005;52:288-289

42 Al-Suwaidi A, Ahmed H. Determination of para-phenylenediamine (PPD) in henna in the United Arab Emirates. Int J Environ Res Public Health 2010;7:1681-1693

43 Wang PG, Krynitsky AJ. Rapid determination of *para*-phenylenediamine by gas chromatography – mass spectrometry with selected ion monitoring in henna-containing cosmetic products. J Chromatograph B 2011;879:1795-1801

44 Akyüz M, Ata Ş. Determination of aromatic amines in hair dye and henna samples by ion-pair extraction and gas chromatography–mass spectrometry. J Pharm Biomed Anal 2008;47:68-80

45 Kang IJ, Lee MH. Quantification of para-phenylenediamine and heavy metals in henna dye. Contact Dermatitis 2006;55:26-29

46 Avnstorp C, Rastogi SC, Menné T. Acute fingertip dermatitis from temporary tattoo and quantitative chemical analysis of the product. Contact Dermatitis 2002;47:119-120

47 Durmazlar SP, Tatlican S, Eskioglu F. Localized hypertrichosis due to temporary henna tattoos: report of three cases. J Dermatolog Treat 2009;20:371-373

48 Søsted H, Hesse U, Menné T, Andersen KE, Johansen JD. Contact dermatitis to hair dyes in an adult Danish population—an interview based study. Br J Dermatol 2005;153:132-135

49 Pas-Wyroślak A, Wiszniewska M, Krecisz B, Swierczyńska-Machura D, Pałczyński C, Walusiak-Skorupa J. Contact blepharoconjunctivitis due to black henna – a case report. Int J Occup Med Environ Health 2012;25:196-199

50 Broides A, Sofer S, Lazar I. Contact dermatitis with severe scalp swelling and upper airway compromise due to black henna hair dye. Pediatr Emerg Care 2011;27:745-746

51 De Souza B, Russell P, Moir G. Henna skin reaction. Plast Reconstr Surg 2003;111:2487-2488

52 Thyssen JP, Andersen KE, Bruze M, Diepgen T, Giménez-Arnau AM, Gonçalo M, et al. p-Phenylenediamine sensitization is more prevalent in central and southern Europe patch test centres than in Scandinavian: results from a multicentre study. Contact Dermatitis 2009;60:314-319

53 Almeida PJ, Borrego L, Limiñana JM. Age-related sensitization to p-phenylenediamine. Contact Dermatitis 2011;64:172-174

54 Patel S, Basketter DA, Jefferies D, White IR, Rycroft RJ, McFadden JP, et al. Patch test frequency to p-phenylenediamine: follow up over the last 6 years. Contact Dermatitis 2007;56:35-37

55 Bregnhøj A, Søsted H, Menné T, Johansen JD. Exposures and reactions to allergens among hairdressing apprentices and matched controls. Contact Dermatitis 2011;64:85-89

56 Hansen HS, Johansen JD, Thyssen JP Linneberg A, Søsted H. Personal use of hair dyes and temporary black tattoos in Copenhagen hairdressers. Ann Occup Hyg 2010;54:453-458

57 Orton D. A UK study on the use and reported adverse reactions to hair dyes. Contact Dermatitis 2008;58 (suppl. 1):27-28

58 Mortz CG, Bindslev-Jensen C, Andersen KE. Prevalence, incidence rates and persistence of contact allergy and allergic contact dermatitis in The Odense Adolescence Cohort Study: a 15-year follow up. Br J Dermatol 2013;168:318-325

59 Søsted H, Agner T, Andersen KE, Menné T. 55 cases of allergic reactions to hair dye: a descriptive, consumer complaint-based study. Contact Dermatitis 2002;47:299-303

60 Mouzopoulos G, Tsouparopoulos V, Stamatakos M, Mihelarakis I, Pasparakis D, Agapitos E. Cutaneous mercury deposits after henna dye application in the arm. Br J Dermatol 2007;157:394-395

61 Mendiratta V. Acquired leucoderma after henna tattoo in an Indian girl. J Eur Acad Dermatol Venereol 2009;23:582-583

62 Hardwicke J, Azad S. temporary henna tattooing in siblings – An unusual chemical burn. Burns 2006;32:1064-1065

63 De Groot AC, Weyland JW, Nater JP. Unwanted Effects of Cosmetics and Drugs Used in Dermatology, 3rd Ed. Amsterdam: Elsevier, 1994:240-241

64 D'Arcy PF. Fatalities with the use of henna dye. Pharmacy Int 1982;3:217-218

65 Sir Hashim M, Hamza YO, Yahia B, Khogali FM, Sulieman GI. Poisoning from henna dyes and para-phenylenediamine mixtures in children in Khartoum. Ann Trop Paediatr 1992;12:3-6

66 Shalaby SA, Elmasry MK, Abd-Elrahman AE, Abd-Elkarim MA, Abd-Elhaleem ZA. Clinical profile of acute paraphenylenediamine intoxication in Egypt. Toxicol Ind Health 2010;26:81-87

67 Abdulla K, Davidson N. A woman who collapsed after painting her soles. Lancet 1996;348:658

68 Brown JH, McGeown MG, Conway B, Hill CM. Chronic renal failure associated with topical application of paraphenylenediamine. Br Med J 1987;294:155

69 De Groot AC. Side-effects of henna and semi-permanent 'black henna' tattoos: a full review. Contact Dermatitis 2013;69:1-25

70 Ortiz Salvador JM, Esteve Martínez A, Subiabre Ferrer D, Victoria Martínez AM, de la Cuadra Oyanguren J, Zaragoza Ninet V. Para-phenylenediamine allergic contact dermatitis due to henna tattoos in a child and adolescent population. An Pediatr (Barc) 2017;86:122-126 (article in Spanish)

71 Özkaya E. Sign of the kiss allergic dermatitis from black henna and from adhesive tape. Dermatitis 2016;27:143-144

72 Rogers C, King D, Chadha L, Kothandapani JS. 'Black Henna Tattoo': art or allergen? BMJ Case Rep 2016; doi: 10.1136/bcr-2015-212232

73 El Habr C, Mégarbané H. Temporary henna tattoos and hypertrichosis: a case report and review of the literature. J Dermatol Case Rep 2015;9:36-38

74 Foss-Skiftesvik MH, Johansen JD, Thyssen JP. 'Sign of the kiss' from black henna tattoos. Contact Dermatitis 2015;73:370-371

75 Levancini CF, Sancho MI, Serrano VE, Torres EB. Erythema multiforme-like secondary to paraphenylenediamine due to henna tattoo plus residual hypopigmentation. Indian J Dermatol 2015;60:322

76 Goldenberg A, Matiz C, Eichenfield LF. Religious allergic contact dermatitis. Pediatr Dermatol 2015;32:e191-192

77 Chen T, Pratt MD. Photo developer allergic contact dermatitis in a photographer following paraphenylenediamine sensitization from a temporary henna tattoo. J Cutan Med Surg 2015;19:73-76

78 Goldenberg A, Jacob SE. Paraphenylenediamine in black henna temporary tattoos: 12-year Food and Drug Administration data on incidence, symptoms, and outcomes. J Am Acad Dermatol 2015;72:724-726

79 Vogel TA, Coenraads PJ, Schuttelaar ML. Allergic contact dermatitis presenting as severe and persistent blepharoconjunctivitis and centrofacial oedema after dyeing of eyelashes. Contact Dermatitis 2014;71:304-306

80 Hjuler KF, Otkjær A. Allergic contact dermatitis caused by temporary black henna tattoos in two siblings. Ugeskr Laeger 2014;9;176(12). pii: V02130117 (article in Danish)

81 Haluk Akar H, Adatepe S, Tahan F, Solmaz I. Hair dyes and temporary tattoos are a real hazard for adolescents? Eur Ann Allergy Clin Immunol 2014;46:35-37

82 Gokalp H, Kaya K. Angioedema-like allergic contact dermatitis related to black henna. Dermatol Online J. 2014 Feb 18;20(2). pii: doj_21549.

83 Barrientos N, Abajo P, de Vega MM, Dominguez J. Erythema multiforme-like eruption following allergic contact dermatitis in response to para-phenylenediamine in a temporary henna tattoo. Int J Dermatol 2014;53:e348-350

84 Kind F, Hofmeier KS, Bircher AJ. Irritant contact dermatitis from a black henna tattoo without sensitization to para-phenylendiamine. Pediatrics 2013;131:e1974-1976

85 Glatstein MM, Rimon A, Danino D, Scolnik D. Severe allergic contact dermatitis from temporary "black henna" coloring of the hair during religious cultural celebrations: three different cases, same history. Am J Ther 2016;23:e292-294

86 Moro PA, Morina M, Milani F, Pandolfi M, Guerriero F, Bernardo L. Sensitization and clinically relevant allergy to hair dyes and clothes from black henna tattoos: Do people know the risk? An uncommon serious case and a review of the literature. Cosmetics 2016, 3, 23; doi:10.3390/cosmetics3030023

87 Saunders H, O'Brien T, Nixon R. Textile dye allergic contact dermatitis following paraphenylenediamine sensitization from a temporary tattoo. Australas J Dermatol 2004;45:229-231

88 Sarre M-E, Avenel-Audran M, Guerin-Moreau M. Erythema multiforme and allergic contact dermatitis to para-phenylenediamine in a henna tattoo. Contact Dermatitis 2016;75(Suppl.1):74

89 Panfili E, Esposito S, Di Cara G. Temporary black henna tattoos and sensitization to para-phenylenediamine (PPD): Two paediatric case reports and a review of the literature. Int J Environ Res Public Health 2017 Apr 14;14(4). pii: E421. doi: 10.3390/ijerph14040421

90 Nacaroglu HT, Celegen M, Karkıner CS, Günay I, Diniz G, Can D. Eosinophilic cellulitis (Wells' syndrome) caused by a temporary henna tattoo. Postepy Dermatol Allergol 2014;31:322–324

91 Calogiuri G, Di Leo E, Butani L, Pizzimenti S, Incorvaia C, Macchia L, Nettis E. Hypersensitivity reactions due to black henna tattoos and their components: are the clinical pictures related to the immune pathomechanism? Clin Mol Allergy 2017 Apr 10;15:8. doi: 10.1186/s12948-017-0063-6. eCollection 2017

92 Aktas Sukuroglu A, Battal D, Burgaz S. Monitoring of Lawsone, *p*-phenylenediamine and heavy metals in commercial temporary black henna tattoos sold in Turkey. Contact Dermatitis. 2017;76:89-95

93 Işik S, Caglayan-Sözmen S, Anal Ö, Karaman Ö, Uzuner N. Severe neck and face edema in an adolescent-delayed hypersensitivity reaction to hair dye. Pediatr Emerg Care 2017;33:422-423

94 Özkaya E, Topkarci Z. Airborne allergic contact dermatitis caused by a henna stone. Contact Dermatitis 2016;75:191-192

95 Özkaya E, Yazganoglu K D, Arda A, Topkarci Z, Erçag E. The 'henna stone' myth. Indian J Dermatol Venereol Leprol 2013;79:254-256

96 Ozkaya E, Yazganoğlu KD. Henna stone: a lesser-known solid material from which to obtain black henna paste. Contact Dermatitis 2013;69:386

97 Amode R, Sin C, Ante Flor C, Sigal ML, Mahé E. Bullous contact allergy induced by temporary black henna tattoo. Arch Pediatr 2013;20:1258-1259 (article in French)

98 Akpolat ND, Aras A. Local hypertrichosis: A rare complication of a temporary henna tattoo. Turk J Pediatr 2016;58:413-414

99 Choovichian V, Chatapat L, Piyaphanee W.A bubble turtle: Bullous contact dermatitis after a black henna tattoo in a backpacker in Thailand. J Travel Med 2015;22:287-288

100 Hald M, Menné T, Johansen JD, Zachariae C. Severe occupational contact dermatitis caused by black rubber as a consequence of *p*-phenylenediamine allergy resulting from a temporary henna tattoo. Contact Dermatitis 2013;68:377-379

101 Şık G, Çıtak A. Fatal paraphenylenediamine poisoning due to black henna. Turk J Pediatr 2016;58:301-304

102 Naqvi R, Akhtar F, Farooq U, Ashraf S, Rizvi SA. From diamonds to black stone; myth to reality: Acute kidney injury with paraphenylene diamine poisoning. Nephrology (Carlton) 2015;20:887-891

103 Akelma AZ, Cizmeci MN, Sarifakioglu E, Mete E. A child with allergic contact dermatitis due to para-phenylenediamine. J Allergy Clin Immunol Pract 2013;1:399-400

2.221   HENNA

IDENTIFICATION

Description/definition	: Henna is the natural material derived from the dried powdered leaves of *Lawsonia inermis*
Chemical class(es)	: Color additives - hair
Other names	: 2-Hydroxy-1,4-naphthoquinone; Lawsonia inermis extract
CAS registry number (s)	: 84988-66-9; 83-72-7
EC number(s)	: 284-854-1; 201-496-3
Merck Index monograph	: 5956 (Henna)
SCCS opinion(s)	: SCCNFP/0505/01 (30); SCCP/0943/05 (31)
Merck Index monograph	: 4651
Function(s) in cosmetics	: EU: bulking; hair dyeing; skin conditioning. USA: colorants; hair colorants
Patch testing	: Henna powder 10% pet., preferably also lawsone 5% pet. (15)

CAS no. 84988-66-9 and EINECS no. 284-854-1 correspond to extracts and their physically modified derivatives from *Lawsonia inermis*, Lythraceae. Henna with CAS no. 83-72-7 and EINECS no. 201-496-3 correspond to lawsone (2-hydroxy-1,4-naphthoquinone), the main active ingredient present at 1-2% in the dried leaves of the plant (see Chapter 2.277 Lawsone).

GENERAL

Henna is the dried and powdered leaf of the dwarf evergreen shrub *Lawsonia inermis*, a member of the loosestrife family, Lythraceae. The henna plant thrives in arid climates. Saudi Arabia, Iran, Sri Lanka, India, Egypt and the Sudan are its major producers. When applied to the skin, hair or nails, the pigment lawsone (2-hydroxy-1,4-naphthoquinone; CI 75480; CI Natural Orange 6; see Chapter 2.277 Lawsone), which is present in a concentration of 1-2% in henna leaves and natural henna preparations, interacts with the keratin therein to give them a reddish-brown ('rust-red') color; therefor, a frequently used synonym is red henna. Henna has been used as a dye for the skin, hair and nails for over four thousand years and as an expression of body art (mehndi), especially in Islamic and Hindu cultures in the Arab, African and Indian world. At events such as wedding parties, public celebrations and religious ceremonies, henna is applied to the skin of the hands and feet. In India, in particular, the use of henna to create complex pictures on the skin is an ancient art to decorate the body, especially for weddings. These mehndi tattoos are used as a reminder of happiness and as a form of blessing for the wearer (33).

To create the henna tattoo, a paste is made by adding water or oil to henna powder or to ground fresh henna leaves. Essential oils (e.g. Citrus limon peel oil [lemon oil], Eucalyptus globulus leaf oil [eucalyptus oil], Eugenia caryophyllus bud oil [clove oil], or 'Mahalabiya oil', a mixture of various acidic oils), dried powder of indigo plant leafs, mustard oil, lemon juice, beet root juice, nut shell, sugar, tannin concentrates obtained from brewing tea leaves, instant coffee powder, charcoal powder, turpentine, *p*-phenylenediamine (especially in African countries) and even animal urine or other (often secret) ingredients may be added to enhance the darkening effect. This paste is applied to the skin and allowed to remain there for a minimum of 30 minutes to 2-6 hours as the plant's dye penetrates the skin; the longer the exposure, the darker the color will be. The dried paste is then removed to reveal an orange stain, which will darken over the next 2-4 days. A temporary henna tattoo should last approximately 2-6 weeks, until the outer layer of the skin exfoliates.

In Arab countries, henna is also used for (many) medicinal purposes. In the industrial sector the powder is used above all by Muslims and Orthodox Jews to tinge silk, wool, and cotton fabrics. In India, surgeons sometimes use henna as a durable preoperative skin marker (33).

The ethnobotanical, phytochemical and pharmacological aspects of *Lawsonia inermis* L. (henna) have been reviewed in 2014 (42).

CONTACT ALLERGY

A full review of the side effects of red henna, black henna (the combination of red henna and *p*-phenylenediamine) and lawsone (the active ingredient in henna) was published in 2013 (33). See also Chapter 2.220 Henna, black and Chapter 2.277 Lawsone.

Case reports and case series

Nearly 20 case reports of contact allergic reactions to henna (and/or lawsone) have been published (12-29,40,41) (table 2.221.1). It is used extensively (it has been estimated, for example, that at least half the population of India has been exposed to henna at some time in life), so it can be assumed that its sensitizing potential must be negligible

(26). Most patients have been tested only with, and had positive patch tests to, henna preparations as used. It is usually assumed that the allergen in henna is lawsone, but this compound has been tested in a few reports only (14,15,23,25). Thus, in most cases, the actual allergen remains unknown, and some cases of contact allergy may have been caused by other ingredients of the plant or substances later added, for example essential oils (27). Indeed, in three cases the allergen in the henna preparation could be identified as Mahalabiya oil (27). It should also be realized that, whereas contact allergy to red henna or lawsone in some reports was indeed very likely (15,22,23,26 [though the relevance of the positive patch test reaction to lawsone in ref. 23 was unknown]), most cases lacked repeat testing, adequate controls and exclusion of the possibility that the used henna preparations were adulterated with *p*-phenylenediamine (thus creating black henna) (28,41). As a consequence, in only a few patients was contact allergy to red henna proven beyond doubt.

Table 2.221.1 Case reports of contact allergy to / allergic contact dermatitis from henna

Year and Country	Used henna material	Patch test results (positives)	Ref.
2016 Australia	Two henna products mixed with teas	Both products 0.01% water, teas 5% water, PPD (previous reactions to hair dye)	41
2016 Israel	Traditional henna paste	No patch tests performed	40
2011 Tunisia	Powdered dry leaves mixed with water (paste)	Dried leaves of henna 10% pet.	29
2009 Turkey	Henna mixed with vinegar	Product, natural henna 1% saline	12
2009 Tunisia	Henna paste used as hair dye	Henna powder 10% pet.	13
2006 Austria	Black henna tattoo	PPD, lawsone 10% pet.	14
2003 Spain	Henna hair dye	Henna powder 10% pet., lawsone 5% pet.; twenty controls were negative	15
2002 Taiwan	Black henna tattoo	PPD, natural henna powder pure, 10% and 20% water	16, 17
2001 Turkey	Black henna tattoo	PPD, natural henna	18
2001 Turkey	Commercial henna preparation used as hair dye	PPD, commercial henna, natural henna	19
2000 Italy	Tribal tattoo (probably black henna)	PPD, ground dry henna leaves in pet.	20
2000 USA	Black henna tattoo	PPD, unrelated henna powder 10% pet., negative to pure henna 1% water	28
1999 United Arab Emirates	Henna used for dying of the hands	Henna ground leaves in pet.	27
1997 Switzerland	Henna used to dye nails	Henna product 2% water	21
1997 Spain	Henna aqueous paste applied to the hair	Henna powder 10% pet.; 10 controls negative	22
1992 Austria	No henna preparation used, source unknown	Lawsone 5% pet. on two occasions	23
1988 India	Aqueous paste of ground fresh henna leaves	Product, commercial henna	24
1986 India	Commercial henna powder, paste made from fresh henna leaves	Both products and lawsone	25
1980 India	Aqueous paste of henna on hands and feet	Product and aqueous extract	26

PPD *p*-Phenylenediamine

Presence in cosmetic products and chemical analyses

In May 2017, henna was present in 33 (henna) and 105 (henna extract) of 66,659 cosmetic products of which the composition is known in EWG's Skin Deep Cosmetics Database, USA (http://www.ewg.org/skindeep/). In the USA, in April 2017, henna was present in 21 of 56,714 cosmetic products of which the composition is known in FDA's Voluntary Cosmetic Registration Program (VCRP) (data obtained from FDA, May 2017).

OTHER SIDE EFFECTS

Immediate-type reactions

Immediate-type allergy to henna has been reported several times. It is an occupational hazard for hairdressers in the form of (presumably) IgE-mediated reactions with symptoms such as sneezing, conjunctivitis, running nose, dry cough, dyspnea, swelling of the face or (generalized) urticaria (1,2,3,4,5,6). The main event of sensitization is inhalation of henna powder dispersed in the air, but application of pure henna dough on one patient's hand was accompanied by the immediate onset of generalized cutaneous pruritus, rhinitis, conjunctivitis and decreased expiratory airflow (7). The diagnosis is made by prick testing with henna solutions; in one study, inhalation tests provoked an asthmatic attack (6). The allergen in henna is unknown. In the two studies where prick tests were performed with lawsone, they were negative (2,5). Henna-specific IgE has been demonstrated in one study only (2).

Some other cases of possible type-I reactions with positive prick tests to henna have been reported (8,9). Angio-edema of the face within hours of dying hair with henna was suggested to be a type-I allergy to henna, but was more likely a type-IV allergy to *p*-phenylenediamine or henna (10).

A review of contact urticaria caused by ingredients of cosmetics has been provided in ref. 32, a review of cosmetic (and industrial) dyes causing immediate contact reactions in ref. 34.

Systemic side effects
In children with glucose-6-phosphate dehydrogenase deficiency, the application of henna may cause life-threatening hemolysis (35,36,37,38,39). The active dye ingredient in henna, lawsone (2-hydroxy-1,4-naphthoquinone) has been implicated as the cause of henna-induced hemolytic anemia because of its structural similarity to other ortho-substituted 1,4-naphthoquinones, such as menadione, which are known to induce oxidative injury in red blood cells (35). Signs and symptoms may include pallor, lethargy, vomiting, jaundice, anemia, tachycardia, poor peripheral perfusion, shock and even death. See also Chapter 2.227 Lawsone for this subject.

Miscellaneous side effects
Extravagant floral henna tattoo patterns on both forearms and hands has caused problems with peripheral venous cannulation (11). Dark skin pigmentation caused by henna dye may interfere with pulse oximeter readings and make them unreliable (43).

LITERATURE
1   Bolhaar STHP, Mulder M, van Ginkel CJW. IgE-mediated allergy to henna. Allergy 2001;56:248
2   Majoie IML, Bruynzeel DP. Occupational immediate-type hypersensitivity to henna in a hairdresser. Am J Contact Dermatitis 1996;7:38-40
3   Starr JC, Yuringer J, Brasher GW. Immediate type I asthmatic response to henna following occupational exposure in hairdresser. Ann Allergy 1982;48:98-99
4   Cronin E. Immediate-type hypersensitivity to henna. Contact Dermatitis 1979;5:198-199
5   Frosch PJ, Hausen BM. Allergische Reaktionen vom Soforttyp auf dem Haarfärbemittel Henna. Allergologie 1986;8:351-353
6   Pepys J, Hutchcroft BJ, Breslin AB. Asthma due to inhaled chemical agents - persulphate salts and henna in hairdressers. Clin Allergy 1976;6:399-404
7   Ben M'Rad S, Merai S, Grairi H, Yaalaoui S, Tritar F, Djenayah F. Allergie immédiate au henné pur. Rev Fr Allergol Immunol Clin 2004;44:159-160
8   Nikkels A, Henry F, Pierard G. Allergic reactions to decorative skin paintings. J Eur Acad Dermatol Venereol 2000;15:140-142
9   Ventura MT, Di Leo E, Buquicchio R, Foti C, Arsieni A. Is black henna responsible for asthma and cross reactivity with latex? J Eur Acad Dermatol Venereol 2007;21:714-715
10 Onder M. Temporary holiday "tattoos" may cause lifelong allergic contact dermatitis when henna is mixed with PPD. J Cosmet Dermatol 2003;2:126-130
11 Dutta A, Malhotra S. Henna tattoo: an unusual peripheral venous access difficulty. J Anesth 2010;24:321-322
12 Polat M, Dikilitaş M, Õztaş P, Alli N. Allergic contact dermatitis to pure henna. Dermatology Online J 2009;15(1):15
13 Belhadjali H, Ghannouchi N, Amri Ch, Youssef M, Amri M, Zili J. Contact dermatitis to henna used as a hair dye. Contact Dermatitis 2008;58:182
14 Jung P, Sesztak-Greinecker G, Wantke F, Götz M, Jarisch R, Hemmer W. The extent of black henna tattoo's complications are not restricted to PPD-sensitization. Contact Dermatitis 2006;55:57
15 Perez RG, Gonzalez R, Gonzalez M, Soloeta R. Palpebral eczema due to contact allergy to henna used as a hair dye. Contact Dermatitis 2003;48:238
16 Chung WH, Chang YC, Yang LJ, Hung SI, Wong WR, Lin JY, et al. Clinicopathologic features of skin reactions to temporary tattoos and analysis of possible causes. Arch Dermatol 2002;138:88-92
17 Chung WH, Wang CM, Hong HS. Allergic contact dermatitis to temporary tattoos with positive para-phenylenediamine reactions: report of four cases. Int J Dermatol 2001;40:754-756
18 Önder M, Atahan CA, Öztaş P, Öztaş MO. Temporary henna tattoo reactions in children. Int J Dermatol 2001;40:577-579
19 Öztaş MO, Önder M, Öztaş P, Atahan Ç. Contact allergy to henna. J Eur Acad Dermatol Venereol 2001;15:91-92
20 Rubegni P, Fimiani M, de Aloe G, Andreassi L. Lichenoid reaction to temporary tattoo. Contact Dermatitis 2000;42:117-118
21 Etienne A, Piletta P, Hauser C, Pasche-Koo F. Ectopic contact dermatitis from henna. Contact Dermatitis 1997;37:183
22 García Ortiz JC, Terron M, Bellido J. Contact allergy to henna. Int Arch Allergy Immunol 1997;114:298-299
23 Wantke F, Götz M, Jarisch R. Contact dermatitis due to henna, solvent red 1 and solvent red 3. A case report. Contact Dermatitis 1992;27:346-347
24 Nigam PK, Saxena AK. Allergic contact dermatitis from henna. Contact Dermatitis 1988;18:55-56

25 Gupta BN, Mathur AK, Agarwal C, Singh A. Contact sensitivity to henna. Contact Dermatitis 1986;15:303-304

26 Pasricha JS, Gupta R, Panjwani S. Contact dermatitis to henna (Lawsonia). Contact Dermatitis 1980;6:288-289

27 Lestringant GG, Bener A, Frossard PM. Cutaneous reactions to henna and associated additives. Br J Dermatol 1999;141:598-600

28 Sidbury R, Storrs FJ. Pruritic eruption at the site of a temporary tattoo. Am J Contact Dermat 2000;11:182-183

29 Belhadjali H, Akkar H, Youssef M, Mohamed M, Zili J. Bullous allergic contact dermatitis to pure henna in a 3-year-old girl. Pediatr Dermatol 2011;28:580-581

30 SCCNFP (Scientific Committee on Cosmetics and Non Food Products). Opinion concerning *Lawsonia inermis*, Henna, 17 September 2002, SCCNFP/0505/01. Available at: http://ec.europa.eu/health/archive/ph_risk/committees/sccp/documents/out178_en.pdf

31 SCCP (Scientific Committee on Consumer Products). Opinion on *Lawsonia inermis* (Henna), 13 December 2005, SCCP/0943/05. Available at: http://ec.europa.eu/health/ph_risk/committees/04_sccp/docs/sccp_o_034.pdf

32 Verhulst L, Goossens A. Cosmetic components causing contact urticaria: a review and update. Contact Dermatitis 2016;75:333-344

33 De Groot AC. Side-effects of henna and semi-permanent 'black henna' tattoos: a full review. Contact Dermatitis 2013;69:1-25

34 Davari P, Maibach H I. Contact urticaria to cosmetic and industrial dyes. Clin Exp Dermatol 2011;36:1-5

35 Kheir A, Gaber I, Gafer S, Ahmed W. Life-threatening haemolysis induced by henna in a Sudanese child with glucose-6-phosphate dehydrogenase deficiency. East Mediterr Health J 2017;23:28-30

36 Raupp P, Hassan JA, Varughese M, Kristiansson B. Henna causes life threatening haemolysis in glucose-6-phosphate dehydrogenase deficiency. Arch Dis Child 2001;85:411-412

37 Zinkham WH, Oski FA. Henna: a potential cause of oxidative hemolysis and neonatal hyperbilirubinemia. Pediatrics 1996;97:707-709

38 Soker M, Devecioglu C, Haspolat K, Kikicl B, Dogru O. Henna induced acute hemolysis in a G6PD-deficient patient: a case report. Int Pediatr 2000;15:114-116

39 Devecioğlu C, Katar S, Doğru O, Taş MA. Henna-induced haemolytic anemia and acute renal failure. Turk J Pediatr 2001;43:65-66

40 Treister-Goltzman Y, Egbaria E, Peleg R. An allergic reaction to henna used in a traditional painting ceremony. Am J Trop Med Hyg 2016;94:941

41 Swan BC, Tam MM, Higgins CL, Nixon RL. Allergic contact dermatitis to substitute hair dyes in a patient allergic to para-phenylenediamine: Pure henna, black tea and indigo powder. Australas J Dermatol 2016;57:219-221

42 Badoni Semwal R, Semwal DK, Combrinck S, Cartwright-Jones C, Viljoen A. *Lawsonia inermis* L. (henna): ethnobotanical, phytochemical and pharmacological aspects. J Ethnopharmacol 2014;155):80-103

43 Bensghir M, Houba A, El Hila J, Ahtil R, Azendour H, Kamili ND. Henna dye: A cause of erroneous pulse oximetry readings. Saudi J Anaesth 2013;7:474-475

2.222 HESPERIDIN METHYL CHALCONE

IDENTIFICATION

Description/definition : Hesperidin methyl chalcone is the organic compound that conforms to the formula shown below
Chemical class(es) : Flavonoids
Chemical/IUPAC name : 3-(3-Hydroxy-4-methoxyphenyl)-1-[2-hydroxy-6-methoxy-4-[3,4,5-trihydroxy-6-[(3,4,5-trihydroxy-6-methyloxan-2-yl)oxymethyl]oxan-2-yl]oxyphenyl]prop-2-en-1-one
CAS registry number (s) : 24292-52-2
EC number(s) : 246-128-2
Function(s) in cosmetics : EU: antioxidant. USA: antioxidants
Patch testing : 1% and 3% in water (1)
Molecular formula : $C_{29}H_{36}O_{15}$

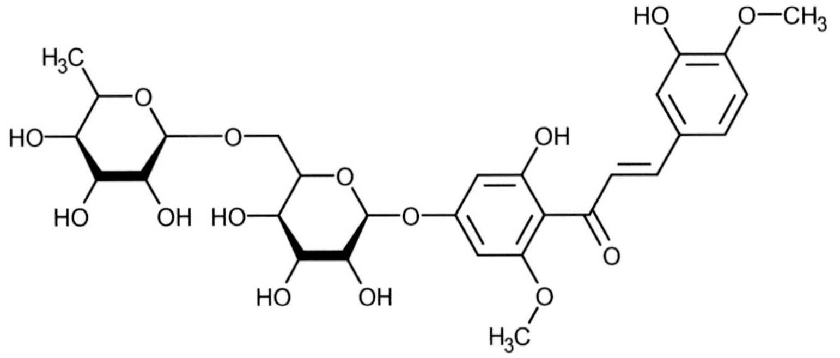

GENERAL

Hesperidin methyl chalcone is a derivative of hesperidin, a plant chemical classified as a bioflavonoid that is found primarily in citrus fruits and is also used in alternative medicine (1). In a combination preparation with Ruscus aculeatus extract and ascorbic acid (vitamin C) it is considered effective in the treatment of chronic venous disease (2).

CONTACT ALLERGY

Case reports and case series

A woman with no known allergies developed, over the course of a year, recurrent dermatitis on the face and neck, which was regarded as seborrheic dermatitis and treated with mild topical corticosteroids. However, because of suspected allergic contact dermatitis, patch tests were performed with the baseline series supplemented with her topical products, tested 'as is'. The only positive reactions were caused by her facial cosmetic products: an eye cream and two other creams including an 'anti-rougeur' cream. Subsequent confirmatory patch tests with the products reproduced positive reactions. The product manufacturers supplied product ingredients for further patch testing. There was only a doubtful (?+) reaction to hesperidin methyl chalcone, an ingredient of the anti-rougeur cream, at 0.2% water on D3 and D7. A repeated open application test with the 0.2% solution (the concentration used in the product) resulted in a mildly positive reaction on the marked area on the volar aspect on the forearm at D14, with erythematous papules covering >25% of the test area. Later, the patient was tested with the chemical 1% and 3% in water and there were strongly positive reactions to both concentrations. Thirteen controls were negative to hesperidin methyl chalcone 3% in water (1).

Presence in cosmetic products and chemical analyses

In the USA, in April 2017, hesperidin methyl chalcone was present in 77 of 56,714 cosmetic products of which the composition is known in FDA's Voluntary Cosmetic Registration Program (VCRP) (data obtained from FDA, May 2017). In March 2017, hesperidin methyl chalcone was present in 24 of 65,351 cosmetic products of which the composition is known in EWG's Skin Deep Cosmetics Database, USA (http://www.ewg.org/skindeep/).

LITERATURE

1 Andersen KE. Hesperidin methyl chalcone – a new cosmetic contact allergen. Contact Dermatitis 2015;72:402-404
2 Jawien A, Bouskela E, Allaert FA, Nicolaïdes AN. The place of Ruscus extract, hesperidin methyl chalcone, and vitamin C in the management of chronic venous disease. Int Angiol 2017;36:31-41

2.223 HEXACHLOROPHENE

IDENTIFICATION

Description/definition : Hexachlorophene is the halogenated phenolic compound that conforms to the formula shown below

Chemical class(es) : Halogen compounds; phenols

Chemical/IUPAC name : 3,4,6-Trichloro-2-[(2,3,5-trichloro-6-hydroxyphenyl)methyl]phenol

CAS registry number (s) : 70-30-4

EC number(s) : 200-733-8

Merck Index monograph : 5986

Function(s) in cosmetics : EU: formerly used as preservative; prohibited since 1990. USA: cosmetic biocides; deodorant agents; pesticides

EU cosmetic restrictions : Regulated in Annex II/371 of the Regulation (EC) No. 1223/2009 (prohibited)

Patch testing : 1.0% pet. (Chemotechnique, SmartPracticeEurope, SmartPracticeCanada)

Molecular formula : $C_{13}H_6Cl_6O_2$

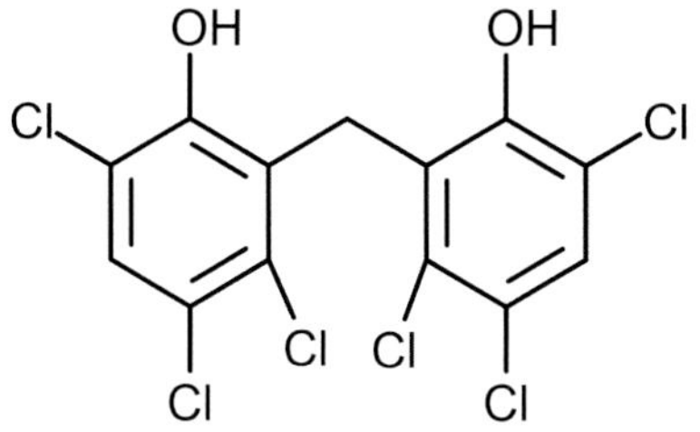

GENERAL

Hexachlorophene is a halogenated phenolic antimicrobial active against *Staphylococcus aureus* and several gram-negative species, but not against *Pseudomonas aeruginosa*, *Candida albicans* or molds. It is an excellent disinfectant, which was since the 1950s for many years used (often at 3% concentration) in hospital nurseries for reducing the incidence of staphylococcal infections in newborns and to combat furunculosis and folliculitis. Whole-body bathing of newborns with 3% solutions of hexachlorophene became standard pediatric practice during the sixties in the USA (44). In addition, hexachlorophene has been an ingredient of many medical preparations, cosmetics and other consumer goods. If hexachlorophene is applied in high concentrations or at frequent intervals to the intact skin, excoriation will result. Hexachlorophene readily penetrates excoriated or otherwise damaged skin, but absorption of this antiseptic through intact skin has also been demonstrated.

Hexachlorophene has been verified as being neurotoxic. Multiple infant deaths in Europe and the USA have been attributed to its topical use (see below the section 'Systemic side effects'). Because of its neurotoxicity, hexachlorophene is used less frequently today (37), but it is still available as skin cleanser and disinfectant. In cosmetics, it is prohibited in the EU. In the USA, because of its toxic effect and ability to penetrate human skin, hexachlorophene may be used only when no other preservative has been shown to be as effective. The concentration of hexachlorophene in a cosmetic may not exceed 0.1 percent, and it may not be used in cosmetics that are applied to mucous membranes, such as the lips (21 CFR 250.250). However, it appears that it is not used in cosmetics at all in the USA (see below, section 'Presence in cosmetic products and chemical analyses').

Hexachlorophene is an infrequent cause of allergic or photoallergic contact dermatitis. Most positive patch tests or photopatch tests seem to be the result of (photo)cross-reactivity to primary bithionol or halogenated salicylanilides (photo)contact allergy.

A general introduction to the halogenated salicylanilides and halogenated phenols can be found in Chapter 2.450. Tetrachlorosalicylanilide. In assessing the data from early studies, and notably in the distinction between contact allergy and photocontact allergy, it should be realized that, in those days, experience with photopatch tests was limited and such tests may not always have been reliable.

CONTACT ALLERGY

Patch testing in groups of patients

Results of patch testing hexachlorophene in consecutive patients suspected of contact dermatitis (routine testing) and of testing groups of *selected* patients (mostly patients with suspected photosensitivity) are shown in table 2.223.1. In three studies performing routine testing with hexachlorophene, rates of sensitization have ranged from 0.3% to 2.2%. In two studies (10,11), the relevance of the observed positive patch tests was not mentioned. In the third, 20 of 45 reactions (44%) were scored as relevant (4), which is surprisingly high considering the very limited use of hexachlorophene in (topical) products; the incriminated products were not mentioned.

In groups of selected patients, rates of sensitization in five studies ranged from 0.4% to 8.1%, but the study with the highest frequency of sensitization had certain weaknesses and relevance was not mentioned (5). In one USA study, 134 of 3743 patients (3.6%) (selection procedure unknown) were patch test positive to hexachlorophene, but the vast majority of reactions were assessed as irritant, non-relevant in nature (37).

Table 2.223.1 Patch testing in groups of patients

Years and Country	Test conc. & vehicle	Number of patients tested	positive (%)	Selection of patients (S); Relevance (R); Comments (C)	Ref.
Routine testing					
2000-2005 USA	1% pet.	3432	45 (1.3%)	R: 20/45 (44%) relevant	4
1998-2000 USA	1% pet.	713	(2.2%)	R: not stated	10
1972-1974 Finland	1% pet.	1796	6 (0.3%)	R: not stated	11
Testing in groups of selected patients					
2001-2010 Canada		160	13 (8.1%)	S: patients with suspected photosensitivity and patients who developed pruritus or a rash after sunscreen application; R: not stated; C: weak study: inadequate reading of test results, erythema only was considered to represent a positive patch test reaction	5
2000-2005 USA	1% pet.	177	3 (1.7%)	S: patients photopatch tested for suspected photodermatitis; R: 1 reaction was relevant	14
1990-1994 France	1% pet.	370	3 (0.8%)	S: patients with suspected photodermatitis; R: not specified; 72% of all reactions in the study were considered relevant	2
1984-1991 USA	1% pet.	3743	134 (3.6%)	S: not specified; R: the vast majority of reactions have been been assessed as irritant, non-relevant in nature	37
1980-1981 4 Scandi-navian countries	1% pet.	745	3 (0.4%)	S: patients suspected of sun-related skin disease; R: not stated	19

Case reports and case series
One patient had axillary dermatitis from contact allergy to hexachlorophene in a deodorant (13). Three patients suspected of photosensitivity, who had not only dermatitis at the sun-exposed areas, but also rather extensive involvement of the covered areas of the trunk, used hexachlorophene-containing soaps, shampoo or shaving preparation and were contact allergic to hexachlorophene (and bithionol). All cleared of their dermatitis when the use of hexachlorophene-containing products was discontinued (25).

Contact allergy to hexachlorophene in non-cosmetic products
A girl had allergic contact dermatitis from hexachlorophene in an antiseptic cream and later from a 'chap lotion' containing hexachlorophene (24). A patient was treated for infected lichen simplex of the leg with a sulfonated bitumen paste containing hexachlorophene. This cured the infection but produced a secondary dermatitis. A patch test to hexachlorophene was positive. The patient remembered intolerance to a soap containing hexachlorophene 4 years earlier (36). Three nurses had occupational allergic contact dermatitis from hexachlorophene in a cream containing 3% of the antimicrobial (38). A woman was sensitized to hexachlorophene in an antiseptic cream and a 'first-aid cream' (13).

Cross-reactions, pseudo-cross-reactions and co-reactions (including photo-reactions)

(Photo)cross-reactions to hexachlorophene
Primary tribromosalicylanilide photosensitization in 15% of cases leads to hexachlorophene photo-cross-reactivity (21). Most cases of photocontact allergy to hexachlorophene result from photocross-sensitivity to primary photosensitization to halogenated salicylanilides, bithionol and other related compounds (3,25,28,29,30,34). Patients photosensitive to bithionol can show a plain contact allergic cross-reaction to hexachlorophene (28,34), but usually not a photocross-reaction (34).

In a group of 35 patients photoallergic to ketoprofen from Sweden, simultaneous photoallergy to hexachlorophene was seen in 6%, to fenticlor (see Chapter 2.457 2,2'-Thiobis(4-chlorophenol)) in 74%, to tetrachlorosalicylanilide in 40%, to triclosan in 9% and to bithionol and tribromosalicylanilide 6% of the patients. No explanation for these co-reactivities was offered (32).

Presence in cosmetic products and chemical analyses

In the USA, in April 2017, hexachlorophene was present in zero of 56,714 cosmetic products of which the composition is known in FDA's Voluntary Cosmetic Registration Program (VCRP) (data obtained from FDA, May 2017). In January 2017, hexachlorophene was present in zero of 64,655 cosmetic products of which the composition is known in EWG's Skin Deep Cosmetics Database, USA (http://www.ewg.org/skindeep/).

OTHER SIDE EFFECTS

Irritant contact dermatitis

Hexachlorophene added to a bath caused irritant contact dermatitis of the scrotum in 2 patients (6,7). Ten more patients were described who experienced an acute episode of primary irritant contact dermatitis due to the use of the antiseptic hexachlorophene. In nine instances, the dermatitis was confined to the scrotum. In the tenth patient, a child, the buttocks were involved. In all cases but one, the dermatitis was associated with the addition of a proprietary hexachlorophene concentrate to a daily bath. In one instance, dermatitis was produced by the direct application of an undiluted hexachlorophene skin cleanser to the scrotal skin. The scrotal dermatitis due to hexachlorophene-medicated baths seemed to be due to the peculiar properties of the hexachlorophene-water-detergent system. Under certain circumstances, a hexachlorophene precipitate was formed which sank to the bottom of the bath and adhered to the scrotal skin and caused irritant dermatitis (39).

Photosensitivity

Photopatch testing in groups of patients

Results of photopatch testing with hexachlorophene in groups of selected patients (e.g., patients suspected of photosensitivity, dermatitis affecting mainly light-exposed skin, patients with histories or clinical pictures suggestive of allergic contact photodermatitis) are shown in table 2.223.2. In 13 studies, rates of photosensitization have ranged from 0.2% to 17%, but were 3.1% or less in 11 of the thirteen investigations (table 2.223.2). The highest frequencies of positive photopatch tests (17% and 6%) were found in two older very small studies of 18 patients with

Table 2.223.2 Photopatch testing in groups of patients

Years and Country	Test conc. & vehicle	Number of patients tested	positive (%)		Selection of patients (S); Relevance (R); Comments (C)	Ref.
2001-2010 Canada		160	5	(3.1%)	S: patients with suspected photosensitivity and patients who developed pruritus or a rash after sunscreen application; R: not stated; C: weak study: inadequate reading of test results, erythema only was considered to represent a positive patch test reaction	5
1992-2006 Greece	1% pet.	207	16	(0.5%)	S: patients suspected of photosensitivity; R: not stated	20
2004-2005 Spain	1% pet.	224	1	(0.7%)	S: not stated; R: not relevant	15
2000-2005 USA	1% pet.	177	3	(1.7%)	S: patients photopatch tested for suspected photodermatitis; R: 2 reactions were relevant	14
1990-1994 France	1% pet.	370	7	(1.9%)	S: patients with suspected photodermatitis; R: not specified, 72% of all reactions in the study were considered relevant	2
1985-1994 Italy		1050	3	(0.3%)	S: patients with histories or clinical pictures suggestive of allergic contact photodermatitis; R: 78% for all photo-allergens together	8
1991-1993 Singapore	1% pet.	62	1	(2%)	S: patients with clinical features suggestive of photosensitivity; R: not stated	16
1985-1990 USA	1% pet.	176	2	(1.2%)	S: patients with a history of photosensitivity; R: not relevant	1
1980-85 Ger, Au, Swi	2% pet.	1129	2	(0.2%)	S: patients suspected of photoallergy, polymorphic light eruption, phototoxicity and skin problems with photo-distribution; R: not stated	9
1980-1985 USA	1% pet.	70	4	(6%)	S: not stated; R: not stated	17
<1984 Norway	1% pet.	18	3	(17%)	S: patients with persistent light reactions; R: not stated	18
1980-1981 4 Scandinavian countries	1% pet.	745	4	(0.5%)	S: patients suspected of sun-related skin disease; R: not stated	19
1967-1975 USA		360	11	(3.1%)	S: patients with a history suggestive of a photosensitivity problem or an eruption involving sun-exposed areas; R: not stated	31

Au: Austria; Ger: Germany; NL: Netherlands; Swi: Switzerland persistent light reactions (18) and in 70 patients in a 1980-1985 USA study, in which neither the mode of selection nor the relevance of the 4 positive photopatch test reactions were mentioned. In fact, in 10 of the 13 studies, relevance was either not mentioned or not specified for hexachlorophene. In the three that did address the issue, 0/1 (15), 2/3 (14), and 0/2 (1) reactions were scored as relevant. Causative products were not mentioned in the one study with 2 relevant photopatch tests (14).

Case reports and series

Of 19 patients with the clinical picture of soap photocontact dermatitis (mostly sharply demarcated erythematous and lichenoid eruption limited to sun-exposed areas of the body, such as the face, neck, hands, and forearms), 16 photo-reacted to tetrachlorosalicylanilide, 4 to bithionol, 3 to hexachlorophene and each one to tribromosalicylanilide and triclocarban. Most patients had a definite history of exposure to a soap containing the offending sensitizing agent (22). In a period of 1.5 year (1966-1967), in a university center in San Francisco, USA, 26 patients suspected of photosensitivity were investigated with photopatch tests with halogenated salicylanilides and related compounds. Tetrachlorosalicylanilide was the most frequent photosensitizer (21/22 tested), followed by bithionol (10/26), tribromosalicylanilide (9/22), hexachlorophene (n=4), triclocarban (n=3) and dichlorophene (n=3). Six patients became persistent light reactors. The relevance of the reactions was not specified. In fact, the authors stated that it was generally impossible to determine which was the original photosensitizer and which positive photopatch tests were the result of photocross-sensitivity (23).

One patient had photoallergic contact dermatitis from hexachlorophene in soap (27). In a young woman, Unna boots were applied for 3 consecutive weeks for erythema nodosum. When she removed the dressings and went into the sun, an acute sunburn-like reaction developed on both legs. Because hexachlorophene was one of the ingredients of the boot, the patient was patch and photopatch tested with hexachlorophene. She had a positive reaction only at the photopatch test site (33). A nurse developed occupational photocontact allergy to hexachlorophene in scrubbing solutions resulting in persistent light reaction (3).

Systemic side effects

The literature on systemic side effects from topical application of hexachlorophene is only briefly and incompletely presented here.

Hexachlorophene has convincingly been shown to be neurotoxic and the drug is absorbed from both damaged and intact skin (52), posing a threat especially to babies and infants. In 1972, in France, accidentally 6.3% of hexachlorophene was added to batches of talcum powder (47,49). Two hundred and four babies fell ill and 36 died from respiratory arrest. Symptoms of intoxication included a severe rash in the diaper area, gastroenteritis, pronounced hyperexcitability and lethargy. In addition, several babies showed hyperestesia, hypertonicity, opisthotonus, pyramidal tract signs, clonic movement of the extremities and papilledema. High blood levels of hexachlorophene were demonstrated. The distribution of symptoms and signs in 224 hexachlorophene poisoning episodes among 204 children is shown in table 2.223.3 (47).

Table 2.223.3 Symptoms and signs of 224 hexachlorophene poisoning episodes among 204 children (47)

Symptoms and signs	Number in episodes and percentage (n=224)		Symptoms and signs	Number in episodes and percentage (n=224)	
Neurological features			**Systemic and skin features**		
Drowsiness	83	(37%)	Erythema of buttocks	209	(93%)
Irritability	75	(33%)	Other cutaneous signs	38	(17%)
Coma	55	(25%)	Fever	99	(44%)
Seizures	39	(17%)	Vomiting	77	(34%)
Babinski sign	24	(11%)	Refusal of food	75	(33%)
Decerebration	22	(10%)	Diarrhea	65	(29%)
Weakness or paralysis	17	(8%)			
Opisthotonus	9	(4%)			

This report was followed by animal experiments with hexachlorophene, confirming a relationship between the drug and morphological and functional disturbances of the nervous system. Consequently, the FDA in 1972 banned all non-prescription use of hexachlorophene. Although several studies confirmed the assumption that hexachlorophene does indeed have a high neurotoxic potential, it must be added that symptoms of neurotoxicity have been observed only after dermal application of large burned (48,51) or otherwise damaged skin areas (51), after the use of high doses on intact skin (47,49) or when used on premature babies (42,43). Hexachlorophene neurotoxicity leads to cerebral edema, exclusively affecting the white matter of the brain and spinal cord, producing a spongiform encephalopathy which transforms the matter into a network of cystic spaces lined by fragments of myelin. There is a degeneration of myelin, nerve cells are unaffected. This process has been shown to be potentially reversible. The clinical symptoms of hexachlorophene neurotoxicity include nausea, vomiting, spasms, coma and finally apnea and death (46).

Hexachlorophene toxicity appears to be a problem of the past. One of the last reported cases of systemic toxicity of hexachlorophene from percutaneous absorption in a child with burns dates back 30 years (26). Shortly before that, a number of children had still been observed with serious poisoning from talcum powder accidentally containing 6.3% hexachlorophene characterized by caustic diaper area dermatitis and encephalopathy (40,41). Useful reviews of hexachlorophene toxicity have been provided in refs. 45, 46 and 50.

Miscellaneous side effects

A children's nurse developed occupational asthma from hexachlorophene powder used as a disinfectant in the hospital (35).

LITERATURE

1 DeLeo VA, Suarez SM, Maso MJ. Photoallergic contact dermatitis. Results of photopatch testing in New York, 1985 to 1990. Arch Dermatol 1992;128:1513-1518

2 Journe F, Marguery M-C, Rakotondrazafy J, El Sayed F, Bazex J. Sunscreen sensitization: a 5-year study. Acta Derm Venereol (Stockh) 1999;79:211-213

3 Kalb RE. Persistent light reaction to hexachlorophene. J Am Acad Dermatol 1991;24:333-334

4 Davis MD, Scalf LA, Yiannias JA, Cheng JF, El-Azhary RA, Rohlinger AL, et al. Changing trends and allergens in the patch test standard series. Arch Dermatol 2008;144:67-72

5 Greenspoon J, Ahluwalia R, Juma N, Rosen CF. Allergic and photoallergic contact dermatitis: A 10-year experience. Dermatitis 2013;24:29-32

6 Wilkinson DS. Hexachlorophene bath hazard. Contact Dermatitis 1978;4:172

7 Baker H, Lloyd MI. Scrotal dermatitis due to hexachlorophene baths. Br J Dermatol 1967;79:727-728

8 Pigatto PD, Legori A, Bigardi AS, Guarrera M, Tosti A, Santucci B, et al. Gruppo Italiano recerca dermatiti da contatto ed ambientali Italian multicenter study of allergic contact photodermatitis: epidemiological aspects. Am J Contact Dermatitis 1996;17:158-163

9 Hölzle E, Neumann N, Hausen B, Przybilla B, Schauder S, Hönigsmann H, et al. Photopatch testing: the 5-year experience of the German, Austrian and Swiss Photopatch Test Group. J Am Acad Dermatol 1991;25:59-68

10 Wetter DA, Davis MDP, Yiannias JA, Cheng JF, Connolly SM, el-Azhary RA, et al. Patch test results from the Mayo Contact Dermatitis Group, 1998–2000. J Am Acad Dermatol 2005;53:416-421

11 Hannuksela M, Kousa M, Pirilä V. Allergy to ingredients of vehicles. Contact Dermatitis 1976;2:105-110

12 Editorial. Hexachlorophene today. Lancet 1982;1:87-88

13 Epstein E. Dichlorophene allergy. Ann Allergy 1966;24:437-439

14 Scalf LA, Davis MDP, Rohlinger AL, Connolly SM. Photopatch testing of 182 patients: A 6-year experience at the Mayo Clinic. Dermatitis 2009;20:44-52

15 De La Cuadra-Oyanguren J, Perez-Ferriols A, Lecha-Carrelero M, et al. Results and assessment of photopatch testing in Spain: towards a new standard set of photoallergens. Actas DermoSifiliograficas 2007;98:96-101

16 Leow YH, Wong WK, Ng SK, Goh CL. 2 years experience of photopatch testing in Singapore. Contact Dermatitis 1994;31:181-182

17 Menz J, Muller SA, Connolly SM. Photopatch testing: a 6-year experience. J Am Acad Dermatol 1988;18:1044-1047

18 Thune P, Eeg-Larsen T. Contact and photocontact allergy in persistent light reactivity. Contact Dermatitis 1984;11:98-107

19 Wennersten G, Thune P, Brodthagen H, Jansen C, Rystedt I, Crames M, et al. The Scandinavian multicenter photopatch study. Contact Dermatitis 1984;10:305-309

20 Katsarou A, Makris M, Zarafonitis G, Lagogianni E, Gregoriou S, Kalogeromitros D. Photoallergic contact dermatitis: the 15-year experience of a tertiary referral center in a sunny Mediterranean city. Int J Immunopathol Pharmacol 2008;21:725-727

21 Osmundsen PE. Contact photodermatitis due to tribromsalicylanilide. Br J Dermatol 1968;80:228-234

22 Freeman RG, Knox JM. The action spectrum of photocontact dermatitis caused by halogenated salicylanilide and related compounds. Arch Dermatol 1968;97:130-136

23 Epstein JH, Wuepper KD, Maibach HI. Photocontact dermatitis to halogenated salicylanilides and related compounds: A clinical and histologic review of 26 patients. Arch Dermatol 1968;97:236-244

24 Gaul LE. Sensitivity to bithionol. Arch Dermatol 1960;81:600

25 O'Quinn S, Kennedy D, Isbell K. Contact photodermatitis due to bithionol and related compounds. JAMA 1967;199:89-92

26 Marquardt ED. Hexachlorophene toxicity in a pediatric burn patient. Drug Intell Clin Pharm 1986;20:624

27 Burry JN, Donald GF. Photo-contact dermatitis from soap. Br J Dermatol 1968;80:711-718

28 Baughman RD. Contact photodermatitis from bithionol. II. Cross-sensitivities to hexachlorophene and salicylanilides. Arch Dermatol 1964;90:153-157

29 Wilkinson DS. Patch test reactions to certain halogenated salicylanilides. Br J Dermatol 1962;74:302-306

30 Crow KD, Wilkinson DS, Osmundsen PE. A review of photoreactions to halogenated salicylanilides. Br J Dermatol 1969;81:180-185

31 Smith SZ, Epstein JH. Photocontact dermatitis to halogenated salicylanilides and related compounds. Our experience between 1967 and 1975. Arch Dermatol 1977;113:1372-1374

32 Hindsén M, Zimerson E, Bruze M. Photoallergic contact dermatitis from ketoprofen in southern Sweden. Contact Dermatitis 2006;54:150-157

33 Praditsuwan P, Taylor JS, Roenigk HH Jr. Allergy to Unna boots in four patients. J Am Acad Dermatol 1995;33(5 Pt.2):906-908

34 Harber LC, Targovnik SE, Baer RL. Studies on contact photosensitivity to hexachlorophene and trichlorocarbanilide in guinea pigs and man. J Invest Dermatol 1968; 51:373-377

35 Nagy L, Orosz M. Occupational asthma due to hexachlorophene. Thorax 1984;39:630-631

36 Epstein S. Hexachlorophene (G-11) in the treatment of eczematous dermatoses. AMA Arch Derm 1955;71:692-695

37 Fransway AF. The problem of preservation in the 1990s. III. Agents with preservative function independent of formaldehyde release. Am J Contact Derm 1991;2:145-174

38 Kanan WJ. Contact dermatitis in Kuwait. J Kuwait Med Ass 1969;3:129

39 Baker H, Ive FA, Lloyd MJ. Primary irritant dermatitis of the scrotum due to hexachlorophene. Arch Dermatol 1969;99:693

40 Larrègue M, Bressieux JM, Laidet B, Titi A. Caustic diaper dermatitis and toxic encephalopathy following the application of talc contaminated by hexachlorophene. Ann Pediatr (Paris) 1986;33:587-592 (article in French)

41 Larrègue M, Laidet B, Ramdene P, Djeridi A. Caustic diaper dermatitis and encephalitis secondary to the application of talcum contaminated with hexachlorophene. Ann Dermatol Venereol 1984;111:789-797 (article in French)

42 Shuman RM, Leech RW, Alvord EC. Neurotoxicity of hexachlorophene in humans. II. A clinicopathological study of 46 premature infants. Arch Neurol 1975;32:320-325

43 Anderson JM, Cockburn F, Forfar JO, Harkness RA, Kelly RW, Kilshaw B. Neonatal spongioform myelinopathy after restricted application of hexachlorophene skin disinfectant. J Clin Pathol 1981;34:25-29

44 Hopkins J. Hexachlorophene: more bad news than good. Food Cosmet Toxicol. 1979;17:410-412

45 Bressler R, Walson PD, Fulginitti VA. Hexachlorophene in the newborn nursery. A risk-benefit analysis and review. Clin Pediatr (Phila) 1977;16:342-351

46 De Groot AC, Weyland JW, Nater JP. Unwanted effects of cosmetics and drugs used in dermatology, 3rd Edition. Amsterdam – London – New York – Tokyo: Elsevier, 1994: 241-242

47 Martin-Bouyer G, Toga M, Lebreton R, Stolley PD, Lockhart J. Outbreak of accidental hexachlorophene poisoning in France. The Lancet 1982;319(8264):91-95

48 Chilcote R, Curley A, Loughlin HH, Jupin JA. Hexachlorophene storage in a burn patient associated with encephalopathy. Pediatrics 1977;59:457-459

49 Jacquelin C, Colomb D. Erythème fessier et coma. Diagnostic étiologique tardif. A propos d'une trentaine de cas d'intoxication par de l'hexachlorophène surdosé dans un talc a usage infantile. Rev d'EEG et de Neurophysiologie Clinique de langue Française 1972;2:414-417

50 Kimbrough RD. Review of the toxicity of hexachlorophene, including its neurotoxicity. J Clin Pharmacol 1973;13:439-444

51 Mullick FG. Hexachlorophene toxicity. Human experience at the Armed Forces Institute of Pathology. Pediatrics 1973;51:395-399

52 Curley A, Kimbrough RD, Hawk RE, Nathenson G, Finberg L. Dermal absorption of hexochlorophane in infants. Lancet 1971;2(7719):296-297

2.224 HEXAMIDINE

IDENTIFICATION

Description/definition : Hexamidine is the organic compound that conforms to the formula shown below
Chemical class(es) : Amines; ethers
Chemical/IUPAC name : 4-[6-(4-Carbamimidoylphenoxy)hexoxy]benzenecarboximidamide
Other names : Benzenecarboximidamide, 4,4'-(1,6-hexanediylbis(oxy))bis-
CAS registry number (s) : 3811-75-4
CIR review(s) : Int J Toxicol 2007;26(Suppl.3):79-88 (access: www.cir-safety.org/ingredients)
SCCS opinion(s) : SCCNFP/0514/01 (3)
Merck Index monograph : 6000
Function(s) in cosmetics : EU: preservative. USA: cosmetic biocides; preservatives
EU cosmetic restrictions : Regulated in Annex V/47 of the Regulation (EC) No. 1223/2009
Patch testing : 0.15% water (2); 0.1% pet. (4)
Molecular formula : $C_{20}H_{26}N_4O_2$

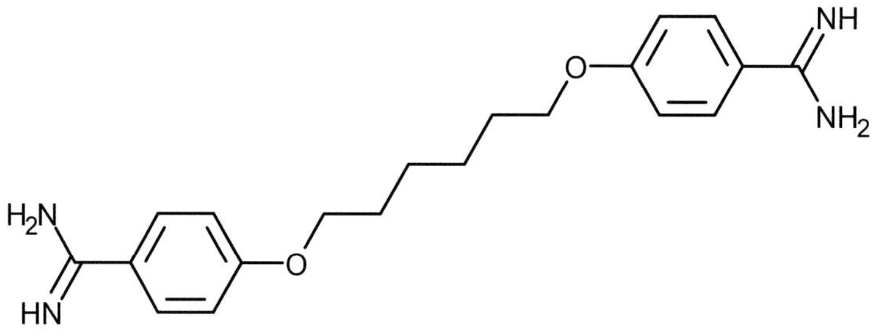

GENERAL

It is not always clear in literature (or data are unknown) whether 'hexamidine' means indeed hexamidine, or its salt hexamidine diisethionate. Hexamidine diisethionate is present in the (especially in France) widely used antiseptic preparation Hexomedine ®. It cannot be excluded and is probably likely, that some of the data below refer to the diisethionate salt rather than to hexamidine itself. See also Chapter 2.225 Hexamidine diisethionate.

CONTACT ALLERGY

Patch testing in groups of patients
In the period 2004-2008, in France, 423 patients with leg ulcers were patch tested with hexamidine 0.15% water and 5 (1.2%) had a positive reaction. The relevance of these reactions was not mentioned (2). In 1981, in France, 465 patients suspected of allergy to cosmetics, drugs, industrial products or clothes were tested with hexamidine and 1 (0.2%) reacted positively; its relevance was not mentioned (4).

Case reports and case series
Four positive patch test reactions to hexamidine were ascribed to cosmetic allergy (1). In a 2-year retrospective study, the members of the French Dermato-Allergology Vigilance network Revidal together found 20 cases of contact allergy to 'hexamidine', possibly hexamidine diisethionate. Most were therapy-related, i.e. from its presence in antiseptics, but one case of sensitization was caused by an - unspecified – cosmetic product (5).

Contact allergy to hexamidine in non-cosmetic products
In a 2-year retrospective study, the members of the French Dermato-Allergology Vigilance network Revidal together found 20 cases of contact allergy to 'hexamidine', probably hexamidine diisethionate. Most were therapy-related, i.e. from its presence in antiseptics (5).

Presence in cosmetic products and chemical analyses
In the USA, in April 2017, hexamidine was present in zero of 56,714 cosmetic products of which the composition is known in FDA's Voluntary Cosmetic Registration Program (VCRP) (data obtained from FDA, May 2017). In March 2017, hexamidine was present in zero of 65,351 cosmetic products of which the composition is known in EWG's Skin Deep Cosmetics Database, USA (http://www.ewg.org/skindeep/).

LITERATURE

1   Kohl L, Blondeel A, Song M. Allergic contact dermatitis from cosmetics: retrospective analysis of 819 patch-tested patients. Dermatology 2002;204:334-337

2   Barbaud A, Collet E, Le Coz CJ, Meaume S, Gillois P. Contact allergy in chronic leg ulcers: results of a multicentre study carried out in 423 patients and proposal for an updated series of patch tests. Contact Dermatitis 2009;60:279-287

3   SCCNFP (Scientific Committee on Cosmetics and Non Food Products). Opinion concerning hexamidine and its salts, including di-diisethionate and di(*p*-hydroxybenzoate), 27 February 2002, SCCNFP/0514/01. Available at: http://ec.europa.eu/health/archive/ph_risk/committees/sccp/documents/out161_en.pdf

4   Meynadier JM, Meynadier J, Colmas A, Castelain PY, Ducombs G, Chabeau G, et al. Allergy to preservatives. Ann Dermatol Venereol 1982;109:1017-1023

5   Barbaud A, Vigan M, Delrous JL, et al. Contact allergy to antiseptics: 75 cases analyzed by the dermato-allergovigilance network (Revidal). Ann Dermatol Venereol 2005;132:962-965

2.225   HEXAMIDINE DIISETHIONATE

IDENTIFICATION

Description/definition   : Hexamidine diisethionate is the organic salt that conforms to the formula shown below
Chemical class(es)   : Amines; isethionates
Chemical/IUPAC name   : 2-Hydroxyethanesulphonic acid, compound with 4,4'-[hexane-1,6-diylbis(oxy)]bis-
                                        [benzenecarboxamidine] (2:1)
Other names   : Hexamidine isethionate
CAS registry number (s)   : 659-40-5
EC number(s)   : 211-533-5
CIR review(s)   : Int J Toxicol 2007;26(Suppl.3):79-88 (access: www.cir-safety.org/ingredients)
SCCS opinion(s)   : SCCNFP/0514/01 (7)
Merck Index monograph : 6000 (Hexamidine)
Function(s) in cosmetics : EU: antifoaming; emollient; preservative; skin conditioning. USA: antidandruff agents;
                                        cosmetic biocides; preservatives
EU cosmetic restrictions : Regulated in Annex V/47 of the Regulation (EC) No. 1223/2009
Patch testing   : 0.15% hydro-alcoholic solution (1)
Molecular formula   : $C_{24}H_{38}N_4O_{10}S_2$

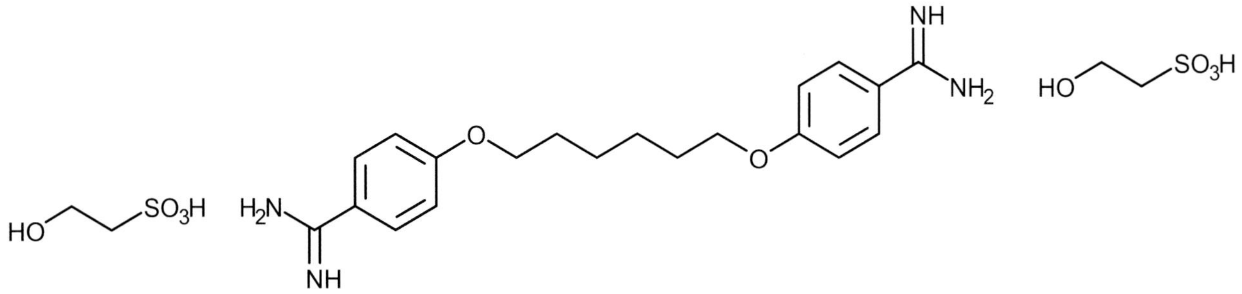

CONTACT ALLERGY

Testing in groups of patients

Between 1997 and 2007, in France, 641 children with atopic dermatitis were patch tested with Hexomedine ® lotion, containing 1% hexamidine diisethionate, and 3 (0.5%) had a positive patch test reaction. There was no current relevance, but two of the three children had used Hexomedine in the past (8).

Case reports and case series

The day after the first application of a cosmetic hair lotion, an 8-year-old girl developed a severely itchy papular eruption on the forehead and scalp, accompanied by edema of the face, particularly the eyelids. It was the only product used on the scalp. Six months previously, the girl had developed papulovesicular lesions in the groin, becoming generalized while treated with an antifungal cream. Upon patch testing with the European standard series and the products used, the patient reacted to ethylenediamine (present in the antifungal cream), the cream itself and the hair lotion tested 'as is'. The manufacturer of the hair lotion provided 8 hydro-ethanolic solutions of its ingredients (concentration unknown). These were negative on patch testing. On further inquiry, the preservative phase (present at 0.3% in the formulation) consisted of 3 compounds: disodium edetate, methylparaben and hexamidine diisethionate. Only the last tested positively at 0.15%. The girl had previously become sensitized to hexamidine isethionate from treating her groin with an antiseptic containing the chemical (1).

In a 2-year retrospective study, the members of the French Dermato-Allergology Vigilance network Revidal together found 20 cases of contact allergy to 'hexamidine', probably hexamidine diisethionate. Most were therapy-related, i.e. from its presence in antiseptics, but one case of sensitization was related to an - unspecified – cosmetic product (9).

Contact allergy to hexamidine diisethionate in non-cosmetic products

One patient reacted to hexamidine diisethionate in an antiseptic (2). One case of contact allergy to hexamidine diisethionate, product unknown (3). Eight patients with positive patch test reactions to hexamidine in the commercial antiseptic Hexomedine® have been reported (4). 147 cases of allergic contact dermatitis from hexamidine diisethionate were reported in early French literature (5,6, data cited in ref. 4). In a 2-year retrospective study, the members of the French Dermato-Allergology Vigilance network Revidal together found 20 cases of contact allergy to 'hexamidine', probably hexamidine diisethionate. Most were therapy-related, i.e. from its presence in antiseptics (9). A boy with atopic dermatitis had ACD from hexamidine diisethionate in a topical antimycotic-corticosteroid pharmaceutical product (10). One case of 'systemic allergy' from topical hexamidine has been reported from Australia; details are unknown (12).

Presence in cosmetic products and chemical analyses
In the USA, in April 2017, hexamidine diisethionate was present in 56 of 56,714 cosmetic products of which the composition is known in FDA's Voluntary Cosmetic Registration Program (VCRP) (data obtained from FDA, May 2017). In March 2017, hexamidine diisethionate was present in 8 of 65,351 cosmetic products of which the composition is known in EWG's Skin Deep Cosmetics Database, USA (http://www.ewg.org/skindeep/).

OTHER SIDE EFFECTS

Photosensitivity
One patient had photoallergic contact dermatitis from hexamidine diisethionate in an antiseptic preparation (11).

LITERATURE

1   Dooms-Goossens A, Vandaele M, Bedert R, Marien K. Hexamidine isethionate: a sensitizer in topical pharmaceutical products and cosmetics. Contact Dermatitis 1989;21:270
2   Van Ketel WG. Allergic contact eczema by Hexomedine®. Contact Dermatitis 1975;1:332
3   Gougerot H, Tabernat J, Mlle. Raufast & Gascoin. Eczema généralisé par sensibilisation à l' hexomedine. Bulletin de la Societé Française de Dermatologie et Syphiligraphie 1950;57:271 (cited in ref. 2)
4   Robin J. Contact dermatitis to hexamidine. Contact Dermatitis 1978;4:375-376
5   Sidi E, Bourgeois-Spinasse J, Arouète, J. Quelques causes d'eczema d'origine medicamenteuses. Revue Francaise d'Allergie 1969;9:179-182 (data cited in ref. 4)
6   Sidi E, Bourgeois-Spinasse J, Arouète, J. Gazette des hôpitaux, 20 Decembre 1968: 1143-1144 (data cited in ref. 4)
7   SCCNFP (Scientific Committee on Cosmetics and Non Food Products). Opinion concerning hexamidine and its salts, including di-isethionate and di(p-hydroxybenzoate), 27 February 2002, SCCNFP/0514/01. Available at: http://ec.europa.eu/health/archive/ph_risk/committees/sccp/documents/out161_en.pdf
8   Mailhol C, Lauwers-Cances V, Rancé F, Paul C, Giordano-Labadie F. Prevalence and risk factors for allergic contact dermatitis to topical treatment in atopic dermatitis: a study in 641 children. Allergy 2009;64:801-806
9   Barbaud A, Vigan M, Delrous JL, Assier H, Avenel-Audran M, Collet E, et al Membres du Groupe du REVIDAL. Contact allergy to antiseptics: 75 cases analyzed by the dermato-allergovigilance network (Revidal). Ann Dermatol Venereol 2005;132(12 Part 1):962-965
10   Brand CU, Ballmer-Weber BK. Contact sensitivity to 5 different ingredients of a topical medicament (Imacort cream). Contact Dermatitis 1995;33:137
11   Boulitrop-Morvan C, Collet E, Dalac S, Bailly N, Jeanmougin M, Lambert D. Photoallergy to hexamidine. Photodermatol Photoimmunol Photomed 1993;9:154-155
12   Mullins RJ. Systemic allergy to topical hexamidine. Med J Aust 2006;185:177

2.226   1,6-HEXANEDIOL DIACRYLATE*

* Not an INCI name

IDENTIFICATION

Description/definition	: 1,6-Hexanediol diacrylate is the organic compound that conforms to the formula shown below
Chemical class(es)	: Esters
INCI name USA	: Neither in CosIng nor in the Personal Care Products Council Ingredient Database
Chemical/IUPAC name	: 6-Prop-2-enoyloxyhexyl prop-2-enoate
Other names	: Hexamethylene diacrylate
CAS registry number (s)	: 13048-33-4
EC number(s)	: 235-921-9
Patch testing	: 0.1% pet. (Chemotechnique)
Molecular formula	: $C_{12}H_{18}O_4$

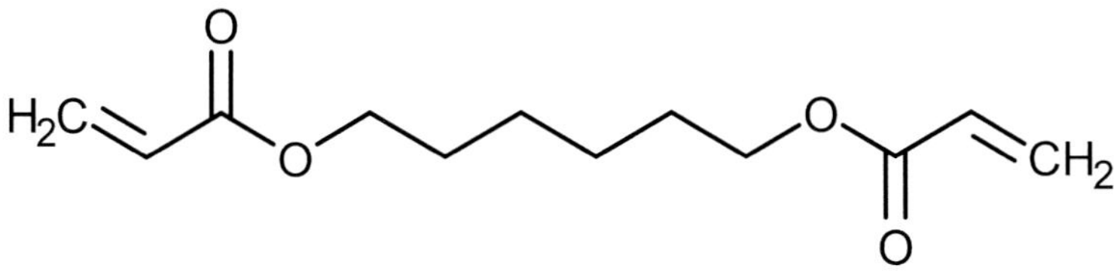

GENERAL

Discussion of contact allergy to (meth)acrylates *from non-cosmetic sources* is considered to fall outside the scope of this book. Therefore, only contact allergy from their presence in cosmetics is presented, which virtually always is from artificial nails. There are many reports of contact allergy to artificial nails, but the specific sensitizers have rarely been identified and – consequently - such publications are not presented in this and other acrylate and methacrylate monographs. Discussion is limited to publications in which the culprit (meth)acrylates have been identified, e.g., from information found in Material Data Safety Sheets, data obtained from the manufacturer or from chemical analyses.

Patients often react to many (meth)acrylates on patch testing. Primary sensitization to methacrylates may result in both methacrylate and acrylate cross-sensitization. Conversely, patients sensitized to acrylates are unlikely to show cross-sensitization to methacrylates (2).

General aspects of acrylates and methacrylates are presented in Chapter 2.219 HEMA (hydroxyethyl methacrylate). A discussion of general aspects of artificial nails, contact allergy to these products, the clinical picture of allergic contact dermatitis and other side effects of sculptured nails can also be found there. A very useful review of contact sensitization to allergens in nail cosmetics, with emphasis on acrylic manicures, was published in 2017 (7).

CONTACT ALLERGY

Patch testing in groups of patients

Studies in which consecutive patients suspected of contact dermatitis have been tested with 1,6-hexanediol diacrylate (routine testing) and studies testing groups of selected patients are planned to be discussed in a future publication.

Case reports and case series

Hexanediol diacrylate was stated to be the (or an) allergen in one patient in a group of 603 individuals suffering from cosmetic dermatitis, seen in the period 2010-2015 in Leuven, Belgium (3). In the period 1996-2013, in a tertiary referral center in Valencia, Spain, 5419 patients were patch tested. Of these, 628 individuals had allergic contact dermatitis to cosmetics. 1,6-Hexanediol diacrylate was the responsible allergen in four cases (4).

A group of 55 female patients presenting with hand eczema, who had contact with artificial nails, were patch tested with a series of acrylates in one center in Israel, 2001-2004. Twenty-one had one or more positive reactions, of who 14 were professional beauticians specializing in nail sculpturing. All reactions, including two to 1,6-hexanediol diacrylate, were stated to be of current relevance (1). Because of the general lack of information on the composition of artificial nail materials, the fact that the author did no analyses of these products and the frequent occurrence of cross-reactivity among acrylates, one may wonder whether this statement can be accepted as entirely correct, especially since primary sensitization to 1,6-hexanediol diacrylate is seen mainly in patients who are (accidentally) exposed to high concentrations of the material (5,6).

Presence in cosmetic products and chemical analyses

In August 2017, 1,6-hexanediol diacrylate was present in zero of 70,647 cosmetic products of which the composition is known in EWG's Skin Deep Cosmetics Database, USA (http://www.ewg.org/skindeep/). In the USA, in April 2017, 1,6-hexanediol diacrylate was present in zero of 56,714 cosmetic products of which the composition is known in FDA's Voluntary Cosmetic Registration Program (VCRP) (data obtained from FDA, May 2017).

LITERATURE

1   Lazarov A. Sensitization to acrylates is a common adverse reaction to artificial fingernails. J Eur Acad Derm Venereol 2007;21:169-174

2   Aalto-Korte K, Henriks-Eckerman M-L, Kuuliala O, Jolanki R. Occupational methacrylate and acrylate allergy – cross-reactions and possible screening allergens. Contact Dermatitis 2010;63:301-312

3   Goossens A. Cosmetic contact allergens. Cosmetics 2016, 3, 5; doi:10.3390/cosmetics3010005

4   Zaragoza-Ninet V, Blasco Encinas R, Vilata-Corell JJ, Pérez-Ferriols A, Sierra-Talamantes C, Esteve-Martínez A, de la Cuadra-Oyanguren J. Allergic contact dermatitis due to cosmetics: A clinical and epidemiological study in a tertiary hospital. Actas Dermosifiliogr 2016;107:329-336

5   Botella-Estrada R, Mora E, de la Cuadra J. Hexanediol diacrylate sensitization after accidental occupational exposure. Contact Dermatitis 1992;26:50-51

6   Vogel TA, Christoffers WA, Engfeldt M, Bruze M, Coenraads PJ, Schuttelaar ML. Severe bullous allergic contact dermatitis caused by glycidyl methacrylate and other acrylates. Contact Dermatitis 2014;71:247-249

7   Chou M, Dhingra N, Strugar TL. Contact sensitization to allergens in nail cosmetics. Dermatitis 2017;28:231-240

2.227   HEXYLDECANOIC ACID

IDENTIFICATION

Description/definition   : Hexyldecanoic acid is the organic compound that conforms to the formula shown below
Chemical class(es)   : Carboxylic acids
Chemical/IUPAC name   : 2-Hexyldecanoic acid
Other names   : Decanoic acid, 2-hexyl-;isopalmitate
CAS registry number (s)   : 25354-97-6
EC number(s)   : 246-886-9
Merck Index monograph   : 6015
Function(s) in cosmetics : EU: cleansing; emulsifying; surfactant. USA: surfactants – cleansing agents
Patch testing   : 10% pet. (1)
Molecular formula   : $C_{16}H_{32}O_2$

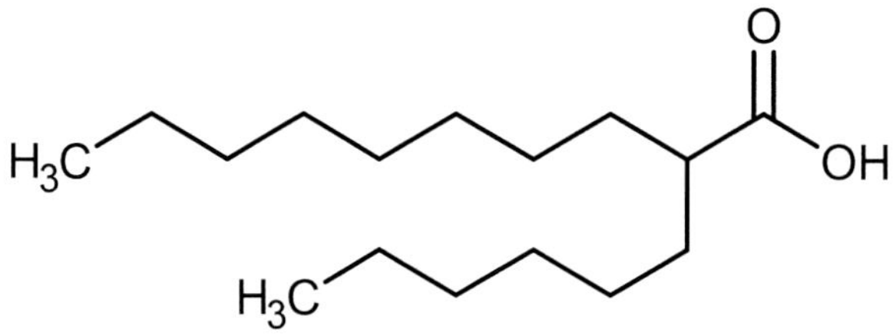

CONTACT ALLERGY

Case reports and case series

A 17-year-old girl was seen with pruritic edematous erythema on her lips. After starting to use 2 kinds of lipstick, from Japanese manufacturers, she had developed this condition within a few days. A patch test to one of the lipsticks was positive. Subsequently, the patient was patch tested with 30 ingredients of this lipstick in appropriate dilutions. Only diglyceryl 2-hexyldecanoic/sebacic acid oligomer 10% pet. was positive at D2 and D3. The lipstick contained 23.5% of this chemical. The patient was then patch tested with 2-hexyldecanoic acid (isopalmitate) 0.1%, 1% and 10% pet., diglycerol 0.1%, 1%, and 10% pet., and sebacic acid 0.1%, 1% and 10% pet. Only 2-hexyldecanoic acid 10% pet. gave a positive reaction at D3. Six controls were negative (1).

Presence in cosmetic products and chemical analyses

In the USA, in April 2017, hexyldecanoic acid was present in zero of 56,714 cosmetic products of which the composition is known in FDA's Voluntary Cosmetic Registration Program (VCRP) (data obtained from FDA, May 2017). In March 2017, hexyldecanoic acid was present in zero of 65,351 cosmetic products of which the composition is known in EWG's Skin Deep Cosmetics Database, USA (http://www.ewg.org/skindeep/).

LITERATURE

1   Kimura M, Kawada A. Contact dermatitis due to 2-hexyldecanoic acid (isopalmitate) in a lipstick. Contact Dermatitis 1999;41:99-100

2.228   HEXYLENE GLYCOL

IDENTIFICATION

Description/definition   : Hexylene glycol is the aliphatic alcohol that conforms to the formula shown below
Chemical class(es)   : Alcohols
Chemical/IUPAC name   : 2-Methylpentane-2,4-diol
Other names   : 2,4-Dihydroxy-2-methylpentane; 2-methyl-2,4-pentanediol
CAS registry number (s)   : 107-41-5
EC number(s)   : 203-489-0
CIR review(s)   : J Am Coll Toxicol 1985;4:223-248 (access: www.cir-safety.org/ingredients)
Merck Index monograph : 6016
Function(s) in cosmetics : EU: emulsifying; perfuming; skin conditioning; solvent; surfactant. USA: fragrance
                            ingredients; solvents; viscosity decreasing agents
Patch testing   : 10% water (SmartPracticeCanada); concentrations of 20% and higher in water cause
                            irritant reactions (2,3)
Molecular formula   : $C_6H_{14}O_2$

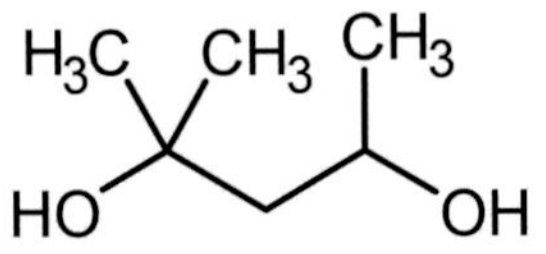

GENERAL

Hexylene glycol is mainly used as a defoaming agent, coupling agent and emulsifier. It may be found in hydraulic brake fluids, printing inks, textile dyes, fuels, lubricants, cosmetics, and topical pharmaceuticals, notably corticosteroid creams and ointments (2).

CONTACT ALLERGY

Patch testing in groups of patients

Routine testing

In the period 1989-1990, in Finland, 1701 consecutive patients suspected of contact dermatitis were tested with hexylene glycol 30% water (routine testing). There were four positive reactions; their relevancy was not mentioned. There were also nearly 9% irritant reactions, indicating this concentration is too high (3). Previously, the same investigators had already demonstrated that occluded patch tests with 50% hexylene glycol and 30% hexylene glycol in water have a high rate of irritant reactions. In a group of 823 consecutive patients suspected of contact dermatitis, one patient may have been truly allergic to hexylene glycol and propylene glycol based on positive patch tests and positive ROATs. Unfortunately, the relevance of the reactions was not commented upon (2).

Testing in groups of selected patients

A group of 230 patients with possible occupational dermatitis from working in the metallurgic industry was patch tested with hexylene glycol 10% in water and 9 (3.9%) had a positive patch test reaction; their relevance was not mentioned (6).

Case reports and case series

Seven positive patch test reactions to hexylene glycol were ascribed to cosmetic allergy (1).

Cross-reactions, pseudo-cross-reactions and co-reactions

Propylene glycol (2); possibly to and/or from propylene glycol and butylene glycol (3).

Presence in cosmetic products and chemical analyses

In the USA, in April 2017, hexylene glycol was present in 2124 of 56,714 cosmetic products of which the composition is known in FDA's Voluntary Cosmetic Registration Program (VCRP) (data obtained from FDA, May 2017). In April 2017, hexylene glycol was present in 710 of 66,223 cosmetic products of which the composition is known in EWG's Skin Deep Cosmetics Database, USA (http://www.ewg.org/skindeep/). Hexylene glycol was present in 26 (15%) of 178 facial wipes for which ingredient information was obtained online and from retail stores, USA, 2016 (7).

OTHER SIDE EFFECTS

Immediate-type reactions

A non-atopic man consulted his general practitioner for burning and dry skin on his back. He was prescribed a topical corticosteroid cream. When the patient applied the cream on his back for the first time, after a few minutes he felt a burning sensation, followed by angioedema of the tongue and eyelids and dyspnea after 45 minutes. At the emergency department of the hospital an urticarial skin reaction was recorded. One month later, an open provocation test with the cream and an ointment of the same brand and type was performed in both cubital folds, resulting in an urticarial rash appearing on both sides after 20 minutes. Skin prick tests with a topical corticosteroid patch series were negative. Skin prick tests were performed with the chemicals which were common to the cream and the ointment. Positive tests were obtained to 1% and 10% hexylene glycol in water in a prick and a rub tests and to the corticosteroid cream, which contained hexylene glycol. Five controls were negative to hexylene glycol. A shampoo containing hexylene glycol showed an urticarial skin reaction 20 minutes after open application. The patient then remembered having reacted in the past to a shampoo with a burning sensation on the head, but he could not remember the brand name. After avoidance of hexylene glycol-containing topical agents and shampoos, the patient has had no skin reactions anymore (5).

Miscellaneous side effects

In (somewhat) older literature, hexylene glycol has been suspected of being comedogenic, based on the rabbit ear assay (4).

LITERATURE

1   Kohl L, Blondeel A, Song M. Allergic contact dermatitis from cosmetics: retrospective analysis of 819 patch-tested patients. Dermatology 2002;204:334-337
2   Kinnunen T, Hannuksela M. Skin reactions to hexylene glycol. Contact Dermatitis 1989;21:154-158
3   Fan W, Kinnunen T, Niinimäki A, Hannuksela M. Skin reactions to glycols used in dermatological and cosmetic vehicles. Am J Cont Dermatit 1991;2:181-183
4   De Groot AC, Weyland JW, Nater JP. Unwanted effects of cosmetics and drugs used in dermatology, 3rd Edition. Amsterdam – London – New York – Tokyo: Elsevier, 1994: Chapter 9, pp. 171-173
5   Spoerl D, Scherer K, Bircher AJ. Contact urticaria with systemic symptoms due to hexylene glycol in a topical corticosteroid: Case report and review of hypersensitivity to glycols. Dermatology 2010;220:238-242
6   Alomar A, Conde-Salazar L, Romaguera C. Occupational dermatoses from cutting oils. Contact Dermatitis 1985;12:129-138
7   Aschenbeck KA, Warshaw EM. Allergenic ingredients in facial wet wipes. Dermatitis 2017 Mar 23. doi: 10.1097/DER.0000000000000268. [Epub ahead of print]

2.229   HEXYLRESORCINOL

IDENTIFICATION

Description/definition	: Hexylresorcinol is the organic compound that conforms to the formula shown below
Chemical class(es)	: Phenols
Chemical/IUPAC name	: 4-Hexylbenzene-1,3-diol
CAS registry number (s)	: 136-77-6
EC number(s)	: 205-257-4
Merck Index monograph	: 6018
Function(s) in cosmetics	: EU: antimicrobial. USA: antimicrobial agents; antioxidants; cosmetic biocides; oral health care drugs
Patch testing	: 0.25% pet. (SmartPracticeEurope, SmartPracticeCanada)
Molecular formula	: $C_{12}H_{18}O_2$

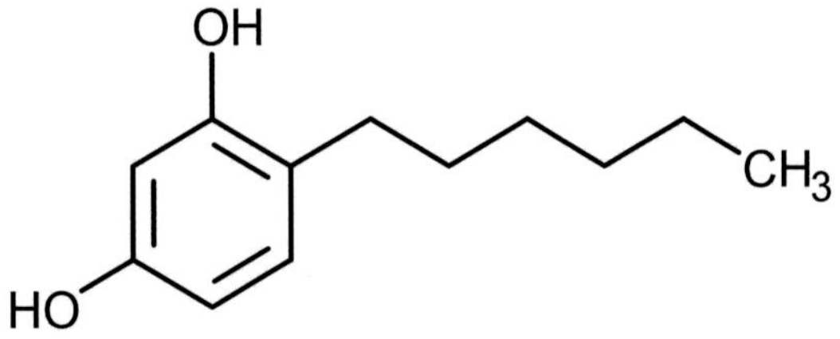

CONTACT ALLERGY

Patch testing in groups of patients

Hexylresorcinol has been patch tested in groups of consecutive patients suspected of contact dermatitis (routine testing) in 3 studies (2,4,5) and in groups of selected patients in two investigations (1,8). Their results are shown in table 2.229.1. In routine testing, rates of sensitization have ranged from 1.8% to 3.3%. Relevance rates have ranged from 19% to 23%, but in none of the studies were responsible products specified (2,4,5). In groups of *selected* patients (patients tested with a cosmetic series, patients with chronic cheilitis) frequencies of sensitization were 1% (8) and 3.0% (1). The latter study, however, had certain weaknesses and the 82% relevance rate included 'questionable' and 'past' relevance (1).

Table 2.229.1 Patch testing in groups of patients

Years and Country	Test conc. & vehicle	Number of patients tested | positive (%)		Selection of patients (S); Relevance (R); Comments (C)	Ref.
Routine testing					
2006-2010 USA	0.25% pet.	3085	(2.0%)	R: 23%	5
2000-2005 USA	0.25% pet.	3835	(3.3%)	R: 19%, not further specified	2
1998–2000 USA	0.25% pet.	711	(1.8%)	R: not stated	4
Testing in groups of selected patients					
2000-2007 USA	0.25% pet.	935	28 (3.0%)	S: patients tested with a supplemental cosmetic screening series; R: 82%; C: weak study: a. high rate of macular erythema and weak reactions; b. relevance figures included 'questionable' and 'past' relevance	1
2001-2006 Italy		129	1 (1%)	S: patients with chronic cheilitis; R: 1 reaction was relevant	8

Case reports and case series

In the USA in 1931, 2 physicians in a period of 2 months saw 6 patients who reacted to toothpaste ST37, a toothpaste containing hexylresorcinol (6). They all had active cheilitis with swelling of the lips and perioral eczema, which started within 4-14 days after first using the toothpaste. The dermatitis in all six patients healed after stopping its use and recurred in one patient who used it later once more. Five of the patients were patch tested (application to the volar aspect of the underarm) with the toothpaste as is and pure hexylresorcinol. The toothpaste was positive in all five (in a crescendo manner), hexylresorcinol reacted (in a crescendo manner) in three patients. An unknown number of controls patients had no reaction to the toothpaste and hexylresorcinol solution was used in full strength on many patients in their daily practice for over a year without producing any instances of dermatitis (6).

Comments: The short period of time before the eruption started may indicate presensitization, irritation or hexylresorcinol being a very strong allergen. Against the latter pleads that only 3/5 patients reacted to a patch test with pure hexylresorcinol. However, the reactions were crescendo and controls were negative, which is in favor of contact allergy (10).

Contact allergy to hexylresorcinol in non-cosmetic products
A female technician in a tobacco factory laboratory had been working for about two weeks exclusively on the estimation of acrolein in a standard test, involving a chemical reaction with 25% hexylresorcinol in alcohol. Great care was taken in handling the hexylresorcinol because it was known to be a strong skin irritant; a non-touch technique was used but gloves were worn when there was possible contact. The patient developed contact dermatitis on the backs and sides of the fingers and fronts of the wrists. Patch tests with the chemicals involved in the standard test were positive to hexylresorcinol 0.1% pet. at D2 and D3 only. A repeat test reproduced the reaction and twenty controls were negative (3).

Cross-reactions, pseudo-cross-reactions and co-reactions
Not to resorcinol (3). Not from resorcinol allergy (9).

Presence in cosmetic products and chemical analyses
In the USA, in April 2017, hexylresorcinol was present in 19 of 56,714 cosmetic products of which the composition is known in FDA's Voluntary Cosmetic Registration Program (VCRP) (data obtained from FDA, May 2017). In April 2017, hexylresorcinol was present in 20 of 66,223 cosmetic products of which the composition is known in EWG's Skin Deep Cosmetics Database, USA (http://www.ewg.org/skindeep/). In 2015, 338 sunscreen, 'anti-ageing' and skin-lightening cosmetic products of 15 brands available in Spain were assessed in order to determine the presence of resorcinol derivatives with skin-lightening properties (phenylethyl resorcinol, hexylresorcinol, and butylresorcinol). Hexylresorcinol was present in 4 (1.2%) of these cosmetics (7).

LITERATURE
1   Wetter DA, Yiannias JA, Prakash AV, Davis MD, Farmer SA, el-Azhary RA, et al. Results of patch testing to personal care product allergens in a standard series and a supplemental cosmetic series: an analysis of 945 patients from the Mayo Clinic Contact Dermatitis Group, 2000-2007. J Am Acad Dermatol 2010;63:789-798
2   Davis MD, Scalf LA, Yiannias JA, Cheng JF, El-Azhary RA, Rohlinger AL, et al. Changing trends and allergens in the patch test standard series. Arch Dermatol 2008;144:67-72
3   Burrows D, Irvine J. Contact dermatitis to hexylresorcinol. Contact Dermatitis 1982;8:71
4   Wetter DA, Davis MDP, Yiannias JA, Cheng JF, Connolly SM, el-Azhary RA, et al. Patch test results from the Mayo Contact Dermatitis Group, 1998–2000. J Am Acad Dermatol 2005;53:416-421
5   Wentworth AB, Yiannias JA, Keeling JH, Hall MR, Camilleri MJ, Drage LA, et al. Trends in patch-test results and allergen changes in the standard series: a Mayo Clinic 5-year retrospective review (January 1, 2006, to December 31, 2010). J Am Acad Dermatol 2014;70:269-275
6   Templeton HJ, Lunsford CJ. Cheilitis and stomatitis from ST 37 toothpaste. Arch Derm Syph 1932;25:439-443
7   Pastor-Nieto M-A, Sánchez-Pedreño P, Martínez-Menchón T, Melgar-Molero V, Alcántara-Nicolás F, de la Cruz-Murie P. Allergic contact dermatitis caused by phenylethyl resorcinol, a skin-lightening agent contained in a sunscreen. Contact Dermatitis 2016;75:250-253
8   Schena D, Fantuzzi F, Girolomoni G. Contact allergy in chronic eczematous lip dermatitis. Eur J Dermatol 2008;18:688-692
9   Barbaud A, Reichert-Penetrat S, Trechot P, Granel F, Schmutz JL. Sensitization to resorcinol in a prescription verrucide preparation: unusual systemic clinical features and prevalence. Ann Dermatol Venereol 2001;128:615-618 (Article in French]
10 De Groot AC. Contact allergy to (ingredients of) toothpastes. Dermatitis 2017;28:95-114

2.230 HINOKITIOL

IDENTIFICATION

Description/definition	: Hinokitiol is the organic compound that conforms generally to the formula shown below
Chemical class(es)	: Alcohols; ketones
Chemical/IUPAC name	: 2-Hydroxy-4-isopropyl-2,4,6-cyclohepta-2,4,6-trien-1-one
Other names	: ß-Thujaplicin
CAS registry number (s)	: 499-44-5; 38094-79-0
EC number(s)	: 207-880-7
Merck Index monograph	: 10814
Function(s) in cosmetics	: EU: antistatic; hair conditioning. USA: fragrance ingredients; hair conditioning agents
Patch testing	: 0.1% alc. (1); 10% pet. (1); the latter concentration may induce irritant responses
Molecular formula	: $C_{10}H_{12}O_2$

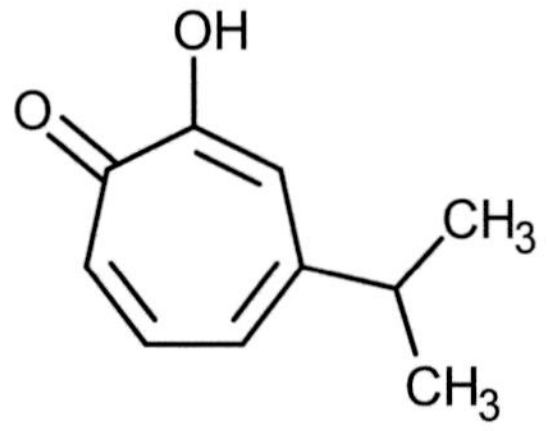

GENERAL

Hinokitiol is a component of the essential oils isolated from Cupressaceae. It was first extracted from 'Taiwan white cedar' (*Chamaecyparis taiwanensis*) in 1936. The name hinokitiol is derived from Hinoki, the Japanese name for white cedar. It has shown antibacterial activity against various bacteria and fungi and has been used as a therapeutic agent against periodontal disease, oral *Candida* infections and oral malodor (2). In cosmetics, it is sometimes used as hair conditioning agent and antistatic and, especially in Japan, as hair growth stimulant (1).

CONTACT ALLERGY

Case reports

A man developed an erythematous eruption over the scalp, face, nape and back of the hands after using a hair liquid. The eruption cleared within a month with treatment with topical corticosteroids and oral antihistamine. Later, he had a relapse after using the same hair liquid. The patient showed erythematous papules and desquamation over the scalp, forehead, nose, perioral region, ears, nape and back of the hands and fingers, simulating a photosensitive dermatitis. Patch tests with the ingredients of the hair liquid were positive to hinokitiol 0.01% and 0.1% alcohol and to hinokitiol 10% pet. on two occasions. Twenty-five controls were tested with hinokitiol 1% and 10% in petrolatum and 5 (20%) showed slight erythema to the 10% test preparation. These individuals were subsequently tested with hinokitiol 0.1% alc. (which gave a strong reaction in the patient), but now, no positive reactions were observed, indicating that this test concentration / vehicle is slightly irritant (1).

Presence in cosmetic products and chemical analyses

In the USA, in April 2017, hinokitiol was present in 8 of 56,714 cosmetic products of which the composition is known in FDA's Voluntary Cosmetic Registration Program (VCRP) (data obtained from FDA, May 2017). In March 2017, hinokitiol was present in 8 of 65,351 cosmetic products of which the composition is known in EWG's Skin Deep Cosmetics Database, USA (http://www.ewg.org/skindeep/).

LITERATURE

1 Fujita M, Aoki T. Allergic contact dermatitis to pyridoxine ester and hinokitiol. Contact Dermatitis 1983;9:61-65
2 Iha K, Suzuki N, Yoneda M, Takeshita T, Hirofuji T. Effect of mouth cleaning with hinokitiol-containing gel on oral malodor: a randomized, open-label pilot study. Oral Surg Oral Med Oral Pathol Oral Radiol 2013;116:433-439

2.231 HOMOSALATE

IDENTIFICATION

Description/definition	: Homosalate is the substituted phenolic compound that conforms to the formula shown below
Chemical class(es)	: Esters; phenols
Chemical/IUPAC name	: Benzoic acid, 2-hydroxy-, 3,3,5-trimethylcyclohexyl ester
Other names	: Homomenthyl salicylate
CAS registry number (s)	: 118-56-9
EC number(s)	: 204-260-8
SCCS opinion(s)	: SCCP/1086/07 (17)
Merck Index monograph	: 6047
Function(s) in cosmetics	: EU: skin conditioning; UV-absorber; UV-filter. USA: fragrance ingredients; light stabilizers; sunscreen ingredients
EU cosmetic restrictions	: Regulated in Annex VI/3 of the Regulation (EC) No. 1223/2009
Patch testing	: 5.0% pet. (Chemotechnique); 10.0% pet. (Chemotechnique)
Molecular formula	: $C_{16}H_{22}O_3$

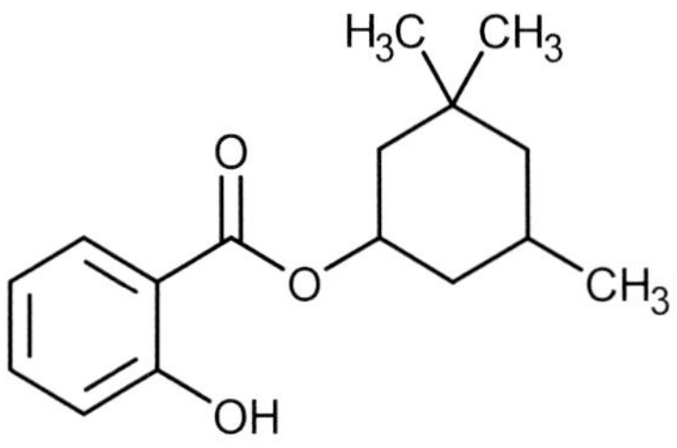

GENERAL

Homosalate is a UVB filter with UV absorbance maximum (λ_{max}) at 306 nm, which has been used in Europe since the 1970s (8,20). The literature on adverse reactions to sunscreens has been reviewed in several recent and older publications (11-16,21). A review of photocontact allergy to sunscreens was published in 2010 (19).

CONTACT ALLERGY

Patch testing in groups of patients

There are no studies in which homosalate has been tested in consecutive patients suspected of contact dermatitis (routine testing). Results of testing in groups of *selected* patients (patients with suspected photosensitivity and patients who developed pruritus or a rash after sunscreen application, patients with suspected photodermatitis) are shown in table 2.231.1. In one study, a frequency of sensitization of 0.6% was found (7), in another investigation the rate was 4.4% (3). However, this study had certain weaknesses and the relevance of the 7 positive patch test reactions to homosalate was not mentioned (3).

Table 2.231.1 Patch testing in groups of patients

Years and Country	Test conc. & vehicle	Number of patients tested | positive (%)		Selection of patients (S); Relevance (R); Comments (C)	Ref.
2001-2010 Canada		160	7 (4.4%)	S: patients with suspected photosensitivity and patients who developed pruritus or a rash after sunscreen applica-tion; R: not stated; C: very weak study: inadequate reading of test results, erythema only was considered to represent a positive patch test reaction	3
2000-2005 USA	5% pet.	178	1 (0.6%)	S: patients photopatch tested for suspected photoderma-titis; R: not relevant	7

Case reports and case series

Two patients had contact allergy with a follicular eruption from homosalate in sunscreens, of which one was 'consort' contact dermatitis (a woman had allergic contact dermatitis from the sunscreen used by her partner). The positive patch tests also had a follicular aspect (2).

Presence in cosmetic products and chemical analyses

In June 2017, homosalate was present in 834 of 64,655 cosmetic products of which the composition is known in EWG's Skin Deep Cosmetics Database, USA (http://www.ewg.org/skindeep/).It should be realized that sunscreen products containing UV-filters are classified as drugs in the USA, not as cosmetics; the number mentioned here, therefore, is that of cosmetics containing the UV-filter, but it does *not* include their presence in sunscreens. In the USA, in April 2017, homosalate was present in 65 of 56,714 cosmetic products of which the composition is known in FDA's Voluntary Cosmetic Registration Program (VCRP) (data obtained from FDA, May 2017).

In 2012, in Switzerland, 116 cosmetics from seven widely used leave-on product categories (19 lip care products, 8 lipsticks, 29 face creams, 11 liquid makeup foundations, 3 aftershaves, 7 hand creams and 39 sunscreens) were investigated to determine the frequency of occurrence and concentrations of 22 organic UV filters in these products. Homosalate was found in 4% of the products in a concentration range of 1.91-9.12%, mean 4.10% (18).

In a sample of 337 sunscreens marketed in the UK in 2010, homosalate was present in 16% (10). Homosalate was present in 0.4% of 4447 cosmetic products collected in Germany, 2006-2009 (5). Homosalate was present in 2% of 329 sunscreen products (incl. 21 lipstick sunscreens) marketed in the UK in 2005 (9). Homosalate was present in 3 of 75 (4%) sunscreen creams and lotions from 30 European and US producers purchased in Denmark in 2001 in a concentration range of 3.7-6.1% (6).

OTHER SIDE EFFECTS

Photosensitivity

Photopatch testing in groups of patients

Results of photopatch testing homosalate in groups of selected patients (e.g., patients suspected of photosensitivity, patients with dermatitis affecting mainly light-exposed skin or with a history of a sunscreen skin reaction) are shown in table 2.231.2. In three studies, the frequency of photosensitization ranged from 0.1% to 1.9%. The highest concentration was seen in a study that had certain weaknesses and the relevance of the positive photopatch tests was not mentioned (3).

Table 2.231.2 Photopatch testing in groups of patients

Years and Country	Test conc. & vehicle	Number of patients tested	positive (%)	Selection of patients (S); Relevance (R); Comments (C)	Ref.
2008-2011 12 Euro-pean countries	10% pet.	1031	1 (0.1%)	S: patients with exposed site dermatitis or history of a reaction to a sunscreen or topical NSAID; R: 44% current and 11% past relevance for all photoallergens together	4
2001-2010 Canada		160	3 (1.9%)	S: patients with suspected photosensitivity and patients who developed pruritus or a rash after sunscreen applica-tion; R: not stated; C: very weak study: inadequate reading of test results, erythema only was considered to represent a positive patch test reaction	3
2000-2005 USA	5% pet.	178	1 (0.6%)	S: patients photopatch tested for suspected photoderma-titis; R: not relevant	7

Case reports and case series

There are no well-documented case reports of photoallergic contact dermatitis from homosalate. In a group of 70 patients photopatch tested between 1980-1985 at the Mayo Clinic, USA, two had positive photopatch tests to homosalate, but relevance was not mentioned (1).

LITERATURE

1   Menz J, Muller SA, Connnolly SM. Photopatch testing: A six year experience. J Am Acad Dermatol 1988;18:1044-1047
2   Rietschel RL, Lewis CW Contact dermatitis to homomenthyl salicylate. Arch Dermatol 1978;114:442-443
3   Greenspoon J, Ahluwalia R, Juma N, Rosen CF. Allergic and photoallergic contact dermatitis: A 10-year experience. Dermatitis 2013;24:29-32
4   The European Multicentre Photopatch Test Study (EMCPPTS) Taskforce. A European multicentre photopatch test study. Br J Dermatol 2012;166:1002-1009
5   Uter W, Gonçalo M, Yazar K, Kratz E-M, Mildau G, Lidén C. Coupled exposure to ingredients of cosmetic products: III. Ultraviolet filters. Contact Dermatitis 2014;71:162-169
6   Rastogi SC. UV filters in sunscreen products – a survey. Contact Dermatitis 2002;46:348-351

7 Scalf LA, Davis MDP, Rohlinger AL, Connolly SM. Photopatch testing of 182 patients: A 6-year experience at the Mayo Clinic. Dermatitis 2009;20:44-52

8 Kerr A, Ferguson J. Photoallergic contact dermatitis. Photodermatol Photoimmunol Photomed 2010;26:56-65

9 Wahie S, Lloyd JJ, Farr PM. Sunscreen ingredients and labelling: a survey of products available in the U.K. Clin Exp Dermatol 2007;32:359-364

10 Kerr AC. A survey of the availability of sunscreen filters in the U.K. Clin Exp Dermatol 2011;36:541-543

11 Heurung AR, Raju SI, Warshaw EM. Adverse reactions to sunscreen agents: epidemiology, responsible irritants and allergens, clinical characteristics, and management. Dermatitis 2014;25:289-326

12 Heurung AR, Raju SI, Warshaw EM. Contact allergen of the year. Benzophenones. Dermatitis 2014;25:3-10 (contains many mistakes; Erratum in Dermatitis 2014;25:92-95)

13 Avenel-Audran M. Sunscreen products: finding the allergen. Eur J Dermatol 2010;20:161-166

14 Scheuer E, Warshaw E. Sunscreen allergy: a review of epidemiology, clinical characteristics, and responsible allergens. Dermatitis 2006;17:3-11

15 Funk JO, Dromgoole SH, Maibach HI. Sunscreen intolerance: contact sensitization, photocontact sensitization, and irritancy of sunscreen agents. Dermatol Clin 1995;13:473-481

16 Dromgoole SH, Maibach HI. Sunscreening agent intolerance: Contact and photocontact sensitization and contact urticaria. J Am Acad Dermatol 1990;22:1068-1078

17 SCCP (Scientific Committee on Consumer Products). Opinion on homosalate, 21 March 2007, SCCP/1086/07. Available at: http://ec.europa.eu/health/archive/ph_risk/committees/04_sccp/docs/sccp_o_097.pdf

18 Manová E, von Goetz N, Hauri U, Bogdal C, Hungerbühler K. Organic UV filters in personal care products in Switzerland: A survey of occurrence and concentrations. Int J Hyg Environ Health 2013;216:508-514

19 Shaw T, Simpson B, Wilson B, Oostman H, Rainey D, Storrs F. True photoallergy to sunscreens is rare despite popular belief. Dermatitis 2010;21:185-198

20 Shaath NA. Ultraviolet filters. Photochem Photobiol Sci 2010;9:464-469

21 Schauder S. Survey of the literature on adverse reactions to preparations containing UV filters (1947-1989) (Literaturübersicht über Unverträglichkeitsreaktionen auf lichtfilterhaltige Produkte von 1947 bis 1989). Z Hautkr 1990;65:982-998 (article in German)

2.232   HYDROABIETYL ALCOHOL

IDENTIFICATION

Description/definition	: Hydroabietyl alcohol is an organic alcohol derived from colophonium
Chemical clas(ses)	: Alcohols
Chemical/IUPAC name	: (1,4a-Dimethyl-7-propan-2-yl-2,3,4,4b,5,6,7,9,10,10a-decahydrophenanthren-1-yl) methanol
Other names	: Dihydroabietyl alcohol; Abitol®
CAS registry number (s)	: 26266-77-3; 13393-93-6
EC number(s)	: 247-574-0; 236-476-3
SCCS opinion(s)	: SCCNFP/0320/00 (11)
Function(s) in cosmetics	: EU: formerly used for bulking; prohibited, delisted in 2004. USA: binders; viscosity increasing agents -nonaqueous
EU cosmetic restrictions	: Regulated in Annex II/440 of the Regulation (EC) No. 1223/2009 (prohibited)
Patch testing	: 1% pet. (4); 10% pet. (3)
Patch testing	: 10% pet. (Chemotechnique, SmartPracticeEurope, SmartPracticeCanada); about 3.5% irritant reactions have been observed (17)
Molecular formula	: $C_{20}H_{34}O$

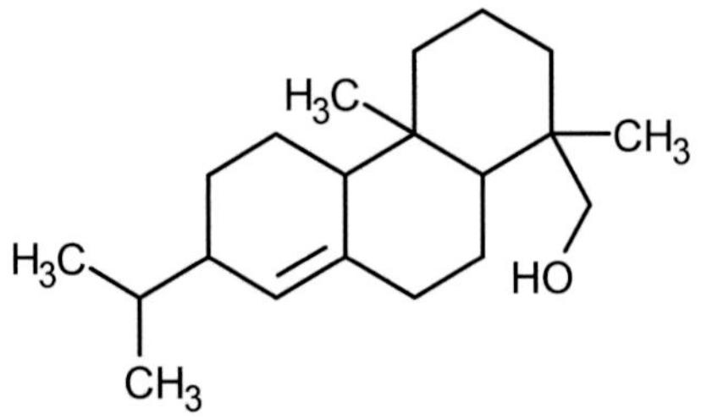

GENERAL

Hydroabietyl alcohol is produced from rosin acids (mainly abietic acid), also called resin acids, that have been hydrogenated to reduce their unsaturation. It contains about 15% non-alcoholic material. The alcoholic part consists of about 45% tetrahydroabietyl alcohol (completely saturated), 40% dihydroabietyl alcohol and 15% dehydroabietyl alcohol (4,5). Apparently, these substances can be separated only with great difficulty and always occur together in hydroabietyl alcohol. Hydroabietyl alcohol is a colorless, tacky, viscous liquid. It has found wide application with natural rubber, synthetic rubber, nitrocellulose, and other polymers as a plasticizer and tackifier for emulsion, solvents, and hot-melt adhesives (3). It is also used as a pigment-grinding medium in plastics, lacquers, and other surface-coating compositions, inks, adhesives, and similar compositions. In addition, it finds application as an intermediate for further chemical processing (4). In cosmetics, hydroabietyl alcohol may be used as binder and viscosity increasing agent, albeit it is prohibited in the EU for cosmetic usage.

CONTACT ALLERGY

Patch testing in groups of patients

Results of studies patch testing hydroabietyl alcohol in consecutive patients suspected of contact dermatitis (routine testing) and in groups of selected patients are shown in table 2.232.1. In routine testing, frequencies of sensitization were 1.3% in Sweden (14) and a very high 6.8% in China, 2003-2005 (8). In neither study were relevance data were provided (8,14).

   In five studies in which groups of *selected* patients have been tested (healthy student volunteers, patients suspected of cosmetic/fragrance allergy), rates of positive patch tests ranged from 0.5% (1/201) in healthy student volunteers (13) to 5.3% in patients suspected of cosmetic and/or fragrance dermatitis and/or reacting to markers of fragrance allergy (19). The test concentration (40%) in this study was unusually high. Relevance rates for hydroabietyl alcohol ranged from 0% (relevance not found [19]) to 86% (1), but in the latter study, relevance figures included 'questionable' and 'past' relevance (1). Causative products were not mentioned.

Case reports and case series

A woman had redness, swelling, and itching around the eyes and cheeks for 2 weeks. Patch tests gave positive reactions to nickel sulfate, colophonium, abietic acid 5% pet. and her mascara, tested as is. Later, when tested with the ingredients of this cosmetic product, the patient reacted to hydroabietyl alcohol 1% pet. The reaction to nickel was also relevant. In order to mask the eczematous lesions around her eyes, the patient wore glasses with metal frames that, according to the dimethylglyoxime test, contained a large amount of nickel (4). Four more women seen in one hospital in London had allergic contact dermatitis from hydroabietyl alcohol in mascaras (9).

Prophetic patch testing with an eyeliner sensitized 3 participants to hydroabietyl alcohol (3). The same procedure was used with another cosmetic containing hydroabietyl alcohol (no specifics given), and now 11 individuals out of 200 subjects became allergic to hydroabietyl alcohol (3). A woman had allergic contact cheilitis. She had positive patch tests to many allergens which were relevant, including hydroabietyl alcohol 10% pet. This was deemed relevant, as the patient used a lip balm containing colophonium, and hydroabietyl alcohol was said to be a sensitizer in colophonium. However, colophonium itself was negative and hydroabietyl alcohol, although a known sensitizer, is a derivative of colophonium and not an important sensitizer in unmodified colophonium (15).

Table 2.232.1 Patch testing in groups of patients

Years and Country	Test conc. & vehicle	Number of patients tested | positive (%)		Selection of patients (S); Relevance (R); Comments (C)	Ref.
Routine testing					
2003-2005 China		599	41 (6.8%)	R: not stated; C: the frequency was 11.8% in patients with cosmetic allergy versus 5.9% in patients not allergic to cosmetics / cosmetic ingredients	8
1983-1985 Sweden	10% pet.	1641	21 (1.3%)	R: not stated	14
Testing in groups of selected patients					
2011 China	10% pet.	201	1 (0.5%)	S: healthy student volunteers 19-30 years; R: not stated	13
2001-2010 Australia	10% pet.	2801	139 (5.0%)	S: not stated; R: 25%	12
2000-2007 USA	10% pet.	943	21 (2.2%)	S: patients tested with a supplemental cosmetic screening series; R: 86%; C: weak study: a. high rate of macular erythema and weak reactions; b. relevance figures included 'questionable' and 'past' relevance	1
1997-2000 Israel		244	3 (1.2%)	S: patients suspected of cosmetic dermatitis; R: 64% of all patch test reactions in the cosmetic series was relevant	10
<1983 Netherlands	40% pet.	182	10 (5.3%)	S: patients suspected of cosmetic and/or fragrance dermatitis and/or reacting to markers of fragrance allergy; R; not found	19

Contact allergy to hydroabietyl alcohol in non-cosmetic products

A woman developed skin lesions on her right thigh a day after liposuction. A blue permanent marker had been used to outline the area at each liposuction. Pruritic, erythematous and infiltrated plaques, with vesicles and papular spread, developed on these lines within a few days. The components of the marker included colophonium, colorants and organic solvents. Patch tests with the permanent marker, in three different colors (blue, red and black), the European standard series, plastics and glues, acrylate and colorants series gave a positive reaction to hydroabietyl alcohol in the plastics and glues series and to the three marker pens, but colophonium was negative. It was implied that hydroabietyl alcohol was the allergen in the marker, though this was probably not confirmed by the manufacturer (2).

A similar case was reported in 2010. This patient reacted to the same marker, to colophonium and to hydroabietyl alcohol. The presence of colophonium was confirmed, but that of hydroabietyl probably not. Nevertheless, the authors stated that 'The relevance to abitol is also present as abitol is used in inks and as an adhesive in the permanent marker' (7). In another case report of ACD to a marker pen containing colophonium, the patient also reacted to colophonium and to hydroabietyl alcohol, but these authors did not specifically ascribe the reaction to hydroabietyl alcohol (20). A young woman had allergic contact dermatitis from hydroabietyl alcohol in an adhesive used for patch testing. She did not react to colophonium or other colophonium derivatives (6).

Cross-reactions, pseudo-cross-reactions and co-reactions

Not to colophonium (6), abietic acid or methyl abietate (4); colophonium (14,16,20); *Myroxylon pereirae* resin (14,16); fragrance mix I (14); *p-tert*-butylphenolformaldehyde resin (14,16); resol resin PFR-2 (14); abietic acid (4,20). Of 75 patients allergic to colophonium and patch tested with hydroabietyl alcohol 10%, 21 (28%) reacted to hydroabietyl alcohol (18).

Presence in cosmetic products and chemical analyses

In May 2017, hydroabietyl alcohol was present in 3 of 66,658 cosmetic products of which the composition is known in EWG's Skin Deep Cosmetics Database, USA (http://www.ewg.org/skindeep/). In the USA, in April 2017, hydroabietyl alcohol was present in 1 of 56,714 cosmetic products of which the composition is known in FDA's Voluntary Cosmetic Registration Program (VCRP) (data obtained from FDA, May 2017).

LITERATURE

1 Wetter DA, Yiannias JA, Prakash AV, Davis MD, Farmer SA, el-Azhary RA, et al. Results of patch testing to personal care product allergens in a standard series and a supplemental cosmetic series: an analysis of 945 patients from the Mayo Clinic Contact Dermatitis Group, 2000-2007. J Am Acad Dermatol 2010;63:789-798

2 Martin-Garcia C, Conde Salazar L, Gonzalez-Mendioca R, Hinojosa M, Sanchez-Cano H. Contact dermatitis due to Edding 3000. Allergy 2004;59:235-236

3 Rapaport MJ. Sensitization to Abitol. Contact Dermatitis 1980;6:137-138

4 Dooms-Goossens,A, Degreef H, Luytens E. Dihydroabietyl alcohol (Abitol®) A sensitizer in mascara. Contact Dermatitis 1979;5:350-353

5 Downs AMR, Sansom JE. Colophony allergy: a review. Contact Dermatitis 1999;41:305-310

6 Cronin E, Calnan CD. Allergy to hydroabietic alcohol in adhesive tape. Contact Dermatitis 1978;4:57

7 Romaguera C, Vilaplana J, Grimalt R. Allergic contact dermatitis from a permanent marker. Dermatitis 2010;21:60-61

8 Li L-F, Liu G, Wang J. Patch test in Chinese patients with cosmetic allergic contact dermatitis to common cosmetic allergens from a European cosmetic series. Contact Dermatitis 2007;57:50-54

9 Cronin E. Contact Dermatitis. Edinburgh: Churchill Livingstone, 1980:111

10 Trattner A, Farchi Y, David M. Cosmetics patch tests: first report from Israel. Contact Dermatitis 2002;47:180-181

11 SCCFNP (Scientific Committee on Cosmetic Products and Non-Food Products Intended for Consumers). Opinion concerning An initial list of perfumery materials which must not form part of fragrances compounds used in cosmetic products, SCCNFP/0320/00. Available at: http://ec.europa.eu/health/ph_risk/committees/sccp/documents/out116_en.pdf

12 Toholka R, Wang Y-S, Tate B, Tam M, Cahill J, Palmer A, Nixon R. The first Australian Baseline Series: Recommendations for patch testing in suspected contact dermatitis. Australas J Dermatol 2015;56:107-115

13 Zhao J, Li LF. Contact sensitization to cosmetic series of allergens in a general population in Beijing. J Cosmet Dermatol 2014;13:68-71

14 Bruze M. Simultaneous reactions to phenol-formaldehyde resins colophony/hydroabietyl alcohol and balsam of Peru/perfume mixture. Contact Dermatitis 1986;14:119-120

15 Fraser K, Pratt M. Polysensitization in recurrent lip dermatitis. J Cutan Med Surg 2015;19:77-80

16 Khanna M, Qasem K, Sasseville D. Allergic contact dermatitis to tea tree oil with erythema multiforme-like id reaction. Am J Contact Dermat 2000;11:238-242

17 Kanerva L, Jolanki R, Alanko K, Estlander T. Patch-test reactions to plastic and glue allergens. Acta Derm Venereol 1999;79:296-300

18 Hausen BM, Mohnert J. Contact allergy due to colophony. (V). Patch test results with different types of colophony and modified-colophony products. Contact Dermatitis 1989;20:295-301

19 Malten KE, van Ketel WG, Nater JP, Liem DH. Reactions in selected patients to 22 fragrance materials. Contact Dermatitis 1984;11:1-10

20 Fresquet E, Guillot B, Raison-Peyron N. Allergic contact dermatitis to rosin after a single accidental permanent marker skin contact. Contact Dermatitis 2006;55:58-59

2.233 HYDROGENATED CASTOR OIL

IDENTIFICATION

Description/definition   : Hydrogenated castor oil is the end product of controlled hydrogenation of Ricinus communis (castor) seed oil
Chemical class(es)   : Fats and oils
CAS registry number (s)   : 8001-78-3
EC number(s)   : 232-292-2
CIR review(s)   : Int J Toxicol 2007;26(Suppl.3):31-77 (access: www.cir-safety.org/ingredients)
Function(s) in cosmetics : EU: emollient; emulsifying; skin conditioning; surfactant; viscosity controlling. USA: skin-conditioning agents – occlusive; viscosity increasing agents - nonaqueous
Patch testing   : pure (2)

CONTACT ALLERGY

Patch testing in groups of patients
In the period 2000-2007, in the USA, 870 patients suspected of cosmetic dermatitis (they were tested with a supplemental cosmetic screening series) were patch tested with hydrogenated castor oil 5% pet. and there were 4 (0.5%) positive reactions. All four were considered to be relevant. However, the implicated products were not mentioned, relevance figures included 'questionable' and 'past' relevance and there were certain weaknesses in this study (1).

Case reports and case series
A man presented with axillary dermatitis following use of an antiperspirant stick. Patch testing to a standard series including hydrogenated castor oil 30% pet., which was listed as one of the constituents, was negative. The material had previously been obtained from another manufacturer for investigation of another case. However, the patient *did* react positively to the antiperspirant applied 'as is'. Constituents of the antiperspirant were then obtained from the manufacturer, and the patient now reacted at D2 and D4 to hydrogenated castor oil 100%. Patch testing with the pharmaceutical grade hydrogenated castor oil 'as is' in 10 controls was negative (2).

A man experienced severe allergic contact dermatitis from hydrogenated castor oil in an underarm deodorant. He also had a positive patch test reaction to 12-hydroxystearic acid, which is the principal fatty acid in hydrogenated castor oil (4).

Contact allergy to hydrogenated castor oil in non-cosmetic products
A woman had edema of the labia, widespread irregular abdominal dermatitis in the right iliac fossa and numerous generalized small wheals from contact allergy to hydrogenated castor oil present in a lubricant, which she used for insertion of a medicated pessary for the treatment of vulvovaginitis (5).

Cross-reactions, pseudo-cross-reactions and co-reactions
Castor oil, sulfated castor oil, glyceryl ricinoleate, PEG-400 ricinoleate (INCI name: PEG-8 ricinoleate), zinc ricinoleate and sodium sulforicinate (3). Pseuro-cross-reaction to 12-hydroxystearic acid, the main fatty acid in hydrogenated castor oil (4).

Presence in cosmetic products and chemical analyses
In the USA, in April 2017, hydrogenated castor oil was present in 649 of 56,714 cosmetic products of which the composition is known in FDA's Voluntary Cosmetic Registration Program (VCRP) (data obtained from FDA, May 2017). In March 2017, hydrogenated castor oil was present in 456 of 65,351 cosmetic products of which the composition is known in EWG's Skin Deep Cosmetics Database, USA (http://www.ewg.org/skindeep/).

LITERATURE
1   Wetter DA, Yiannias JA, Prakash AV, Davis MD, Farmer SA, el-Azhary RA, et al. Results of patch testing to personal care product allergens in a standard series and a supplemental cosmetic series: an analysis of 945 patients from the Mayo Clinic Contact Dermatitis Group, 2000-2007. J Am Acad Dermatol 2010;63:789-798
2   Taghipour K, Tatnall F, Orton D. Allergic axillary dermatitis due to hydrogenated castor oil in a deodorant. Contact Dermatitis 2008;58:168-169

3   Dooms-Goossens A, Dupré K, Borghijs A, Swinnen C, Dooms M, Degreef H. Zinc ricinoleate: sensitizer in deodorants. Contact Dermatitis 1987;16:292-294

4   Shaw DW. Allergic contact dermatitis from 12-hydroxystearic acid and hydrogenated castor oil. Dermatitis 2009;20:E16-20

5   Di Berardino L, Della Torre F. Side effects to castor oil. Allergy 2003;58:826

2.234 HYDROGEN PEROXIDE

IDENTIFICATION

Description/definition	: Hydrogen peroxide is the inorganic oxide that conforms to the formula shown below
Chemical class(es)	: Inorganics
CAS registry number (s)	: 7722-84-1
EC number(s)	: 231-765-0
SCCS opinion(s)	: SCCS/1553/15 (5); SCCP/1129/07 (6); SCCP/0844/04 (7); SCCNFP/0752/03 (8) SCCNFP/0602/02 (9); SCCNFP, 23 June 1999 (10)
Merck Index monograph	: 6105
Function(s) in cosmetics	: EU: antimicrobial; oxidising. USA: antimicrobial agents; cosmetic biocides; oral care agents; oral health care drugs; oxidizing agents
EU cosmetic restrictions	: Regulated in Annex III/12 of the Regulation (EC) No. 1223/2009
Patch testing	: 3.0% water (Chemotechnique)
Molecular formula	: H_2O_2

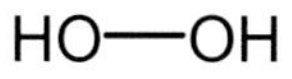

HO—OH

GENERAL

Hydrogen peroxide is a well-known oxidizing agent, widely used as a topical antiseptic. It is used in hairdressing as part of permanent dyes (in 3% and 5% aqueous solution), in color-removing preparations and as a neutralizing agent in permanent waving (1).

CONTACT ALLERGY

Patch testing in groups of patients

Hydrogen peroxide has not been patch tested in consecutive patients suspected of contact dermatitis (routine testing), but selected patients groups have been tested with it in a few studies. The results of these studies are shown in table 2.234.1. In patients tested with a hairdressing series or (apprentice) hairdressers presenting at an occupational dermatology clinic, 0%-2.4% had positive reactions to hydrogen peroxide. Relevance rates, where stated, have ranged from 25% to 100% (1 and 2 patients only), but culprit products were not mentioned (4,11).

Table 2.234.1 Patch testing in groups of patients: Selected patient groups

Years and Country	Test conc. & vehicle	Number of patients tested | positive (%)		Selection of patients (S); Relevance (R); Comments (C)	Ref.
1993-2010 Australia		164	4 (2.4%)	S: hairdressers and apprentice hairdressers presenting at an occupational dermatology clinic; R: 25%	11
2000-2008 USA	3% water	210	(1%)	S: patients tested with a hairdresser's series; R: 100%	4
2000-2002 Finland		473	(0.4%)	S: patients tested with a hairdressing series; R: not stated	3
1995-1996 Finland		145	(0.0%)	S: patients tested with a hairdressing series; R: not stated	3

From 1974 to 1997, at the Section of Dermatology, Finnish Institute of Occupational Health, Helsinki, Finland, over 150 hairdressers have been patch tested with hydrogen peroxide 3% in water; not a single positive patch test reaction was observed, making the authors conclude that hydrogen peroxide must be a rare sensitizer (15,16,17).

Case reports and case series

A hairdresser had an intensely itchy papular rash that had started on her hands and had progressively spread to involve the whole body. When patch tested, she reacted to hydrogen peroxide 3% water and *p*-aminophenol. The authors did not mention what the causative product containing hydrogen peroxide was (1). Another woman had dyed her hair herself at home every 1 or 2 months for the last 6 years. She used a dying cream mixed with aqueous solutions of hydrogen peroxide. Patch tests were positive to hydrogen peroxide 3% water. However, she also had very strong reactions to multiple other (probably relevant) allergens, so irritant patch test reactions caused by the excited skin syndrome can certainly not be excluded (1). An unknown number of patients had occupational allergic contact dermatitis from hydrogen peroxide, probably in hairdresser(s) from cosmetic products (2). A woman had ACD from *p*-phenylenediamine and hydrogen peroxide used for hair dying (18).

Presence in cosmetic products and chemical analyses
In the USA, in April 2017, hydrogen peroxide was present in 403 of 56,714 cosmetic products of which the composition is known in FDA's Voluntary Cosmetic Registration Program (VCRP) (data obtained from FDA, May 2017). In April 2017, hydrogen peroxide was present in 182 of 66,223 cosmetic products of which the composition is known in EWG's Skin Deep Cosmetics Database, USA (http://www.ewg.org/skindeep/).

OTHER SIDE EFFECTS

Irritant contact dermatitis
A young girl suffered a very severe injury to her scalp with necrosis as a result of highlighting her hair. The toxic injury resulted in a scarring alopecia, which could only be treated by plastic reconstructive surgery. The cause for this injury was suggested to have been a higher than usual concentration of hydrogen peroxide used for highlighting the hair (12). The literature on severe acute irritant dermatitis ('burn') of the scalp caused by hair highlighting (from any cause) has been reviewed in 2010 (13).

LITERATURE

1   Aguire A, Zabala R, de Galdeano CS, Landa N, Díaz-Pérez JL. Positive patch tests to hydrogen peroxide in 2 cases. Contact Dermatitis 1994;30:113
2   Gonzalez M, Aguirre A, Oleaga JM, Sanz de Galdeano C. Diaz Perez JL. Dermatitis de contacto en profesionales de peluqueria. Revision de la casuistica de los anos 1990-91 en el Hospital de Cruces. Actas Dermo-Sifiliograficas 1992;83:565-569 (article in Spanish)
3   Hasan T, Rantanen T, Alanko K, Harvima RJ, Jolanki R, Kalimo K, et al. Patch test reactions to cosmetic allergens in 1995–1997 and 2000–2002 in Finland –a multicentre study. Contact Dermatitis 2005;53:40-45
4   Wang MZ, Farmer SA, Richardson DM, Davis MDP. Patch-testing with hairdressing chemicals. Dermatitis 2011;22:16-26
5   SCCS (Scientific Committee on Consumer Safety). Addendum to the scientific Opinion on the safety of oxidative hair dye substances and hydrogen peroxide in products to colour eyelashes, 25 March 2015, SCCS/1553/15. Available at: http://ec.europa.eu/health/scientific_committees/consumer_safety/docs/sccs_o_173.pdf
6   SCCP (Scientific Committee on Consumer Products). Opinion on Hydrogen peroxide, in its free form or when released, in oral hygiene products and tooth whitening products, 18 December 2007, SCCP/1129/07. Available at: http://ec.europa.eu/health/archive/ph_risk/committees/04_sccp/docs/sccp_o_122.pdf
7   SCCP (Scientific Committee on Consumer Products). Opinion on Hydrogen Peroxide in tooth whitening products, 15 March 2005, SCCP/0844/04. Available at: http://ec.europa.eu/health/archive/ph_risk/committees/04_sccp/docs/sccp_o_022.pdf
8   SCCNFP (Scientific Committee on Cosmetics and Non Food Products). Clarification concerning its opinions of the use of hydrogen peroxide in tooth whitening products adopted by the SCCNFP during the 25th Plenary meeting of 20 October 2003, SCCNFP/0752/03. Available at: http://ec.europa.eu/health/archive/ph_risk/committees/04_sccp/docs/sccnfp_o_001.pdf
9   SCCNFP (Scientific Committee on Cosmetics and Non Food Products). Opinion concerning hydrogen (carbamide, zinc) peroxide in tooth bleaching / whitening products, 17 September 2002, SCCNFP/0602/02. Available at: http://ec.europa.eu/health/archive/ph_risk/committees/sccp/documents/out180_en.pdf
10 SCCNFP (Scientific Committee on Cosmetics and Non Food Products). Opinion concerning hydrogen peroxide and hydrogen peroxide releasing substances used in oral care products, 23 June 1999. Available at: http://ec.eu ropa.eu/health/scientific_committees/consumer_safety/opinions/sccnfp_opinions_97_04/sccp_out83_en.htm
11 Lyons G, Roberts H, Palmer A, Matheson M, Nixon R. Hairdressers presenting to an occupational dermatology clinic in Melbourne, Australia. Contact Dermatitis 2013;68:300-306
12 Schröder CM, Höller Obrigkeit D, Merk HF, Abuzahra F. Necrotizing toxic contact dermatitis of the scalp from hydrogen peroxide. Hautarzt 2008;59:148-150 (Article in German)
13 Chan HP, Maibach HI. Hair highlights and severe acute irritant dermatitis ("burn") of the scalp. Cutan Ocul Toxicol 2010;29:229-233
14 Kanerva L, Jolanki R, Riihimäki V, Kalimo K. Patch test reactions and occupational dermatoses caused by hydrogen peroxide. Contact Dermatitis 1998;39:146
15 Leino T, Estlander T, Kanerva L. Occupational allergic dermatoses in hairdressers. Contact Dermatitis 1998;38:166–167

16 Leino T, Tammilehto L, Hytönen M, Sala E, Paakkulainen H, Kanerva L. Occupational and respiratory diseases among hairdressers. Scand J Work Environ Health 1998;24:398-406

17 Kanerva L, Jolanki R, Riihimäki V, Kalimo K. Patch test reactions and occupational dermatoses caused by hydrogen peroxide. Contact Dermatitis 1998;39:146

18 Swan BC, Tam MM, Higgins CL, Nixon RL. Allergic contact dermatitis to substitute hair dyes in a patient allergic to para-phenylenediamine: Pure henna, black tea and indigo powder. Australas J Dermatol 2016;57:219-221

2.235   HYDROLYZED COLLAGEN

IDENTIFICATION

Description/definition	: Hydrolyzed collagen is the hydrolysate of animal or fish collagen derived by acid, enzyme or other method of hydrolysis. It is characterized by a significant level of amino acids, peptides, and proteins including hydroxyproline. It may contain impurities consisting chiefly of carbohydrates and lipids along with smaller quantities of miscellaneous organic substances of biological origin
Chemical class(es)	: Protein derivatives
Other names	: Collagen hydrolysate; hydrolyzed animal protein
CAS registry number (s)	: 92113-31-0; 73049-73-7
EC number(s)	: 295-635-5
CIR review(s)	: J Am Coll Toxicol 1985;4:199-221; Int J Toxicol 2006;25(Suppl.2):1-89 (access: www.cir-safety.org/ingredients)
Function(s) in cosmetics	: EU: antistatic; emollient; film forming; hair conditioning; humectant; skin conditioning. USA: hair conditioning agents; nail conditioning agents; skin-conditioning agents – miscellaneous
Patch testing	: 5%-50% water (3)

CONTACT ALLERGY

Patch testing in groups of patients

In the UK, in 1999, 4 different samples of commercially-used hydrolyzed proteins (5% aq.) from bovine collagen, elastin and keratins were patch tested in 500 consecutive patients suspected of contact dermatitis, but there were no positive reactions (5).

Case reports and case series

Hydrolyzed animal protein (former name for hydrolyzed collagen) was responsible for 1 out of 399 cases of cosmetic allergy where the causal allergen was identified in a study of the NACDG, USA, 1977-1983 (1).

Presence in cosmetic products and chemical analyses

In the USA, in April 2017, hydrolyzed collagen was present in 551 of 56,714 cosmetic products of which the composition is known in FDA's Voluntary Cosmetic Registration Program (VCRP) (data obtained from FDA, May 2017). In March 2017, hydrolyzed collagen was present in 136 of 65,351 cosmetic products of which the composition is known in EWG's Skin Deep Cosmetics Database, USA (http://www.ewg.org/skindeep/).

OTHER SIDE EFFECTS

Immediate-type reactions

A patient with atopic dermatitis experienced episodes of anaphylaxis with development of lip swelling, itching of eyes, throat and genitalia, and airway constriction within minutes after ingestion of dietary supplement or gummy candy, both of which contained hydrolyzed fish collagen. The patient had started applying a moisturizer containing fish atelocollagen on her face 15 months before the first episode of anaphylaxis. The authors speculated that long-term application of the moisturizer on impaired skin surface induced epicutaneous sensitization of fish collagen. The patient had positive skin prick tests to the dietary supplement, hydrolyzed fish collagen, the moisturizer and its ingredient fish atelocollagen (4).

A woman with no history of atopy had her hair dyed. After dye application, her hair was rinsed and a conditioner applied. Two minutes later, confluent urticarial plaques appeared on her scalp, face, neck, and breasts. The cutaneous symptoms were accompanied by conjunctivitis, a serous rhinitis, dyspnea, wheezing, and a dry cough. After immediate admission to the hospital, she received intravenous prednisolone, subcutaneous adrenaline, and oral terfenadine, which resulted in the disappearance of the cutaneous and respiratory symptoms. The hair conditioner was suspected because the patient recalled having had 'eye swelling' and 'face redness' on a previous use of the same product. She was prick tested with the suspected conditioner diluted at 1/16 and 1/8. The prick reactions were strongly positive after 20 minutes but negative at 48 hours; the open patch tests for the same concentrations were negative. Eight control prick tests with the conditioner were all negative. Prick test results with the components of the hair conditioner were negative except for a strong reaction with 'hydrolyzed proteins', which contained a quaternary ammonium compound, stearyl trimethylammonium chloride, and hydrolyzed bovine collagen. These ingredients could not be tested separately due to lack of cooperation of the patient (6).

Two patients with contact urticaria from hydroxypropyltrimonium hydrolyzed collagen in hair conditioners had positive prick tests to hydrolyzed collagen (Nutrilan® H) 1% water (2).

LITERATURE

1   Adams RM, Maibach HI, Clendenning WE, Fisher AA, Jordan WJ, Kanof N, et al. A five-year study of cosmetic reactions. J Am Acad Dermatol 1985;13:1062-1069
2   Niinimäki A, Niinimäki M, Mäkinen-Kiljunen S, Hannuksela M. Contact urticaria from protein hydrolysates in hair conditioners. Allergy 1998;53:1078-1082
3   De Groot AC. Patch Testing, 3rd Edition. Wapserveen, The Netherlands: acdegroot publishing, 2008 (ISBN 978-90-813233-1-4)
4   Fujimoto W, Fukuda M, Yokooji T, Yamamoto T, Tanaka A, Matsuo H. Anaphylaxis provoked by ingestion of hydrolyzed fish collagen probably induced by epicutaneous sensitization. Allergol Int 2016;65:474-476
5   McFadden JP, Rycroft RJ, White IR, Wakelin SH, Basketter DA. Hydrolyzed protein shampoo additives are not a common contact allergen. Contact Dermatitis 2000;43:243
6   Pasche-Koo F, Claeys M, Hauser C. Contact urticaria with systemic symptoms caused by bovine collagen in a hair conditioner. Am J Contact Dermat 1996;7:56-57

2.236   HYDROLYZED WHEAT PROTEIN

IDENTIFICATION

Description/definition   : Hydrolyzed wheat protein is the hydrolyzate of wheat protein derived by acid, enzyme or other method of hydrolysis. It is composed primarily of amino acids, peptides, and proteins. It may contain impurities consisting chiefly of carbohydrates and lipids along with smaller quantities of miscellaneous organic substances of biological origin
Chemical class(es)   : Protein derivatives
Other names   : Protein hydrolyzates, wheat germ
CAS registry number (s)   : 94350-06-8; 222400-28-4; 70084-87-6
EC number(s)   : 305-225-0
CIR review(s)   : Final report, June 2014 (access: www.cir-safety.org/ingredients)
SCCS opinion(s)   : SCCS/1534/14, revision of 22 October 2014 (17,23)
Function(s) in cosmetics : EU: antistatic; hair conditioning; skin conditioning. USA: film formers; hair conditioning agents; skin-conditioning agents - miscellaneous
Patch testing   : 10% water (6); 50% water is not irritant (10)

GENERAL

Wheat (*Triticum* species) is a kind of grass in the Poaceae (Gramineae) family, which is used throughout the world and which is of the staple foods. Various forms of wheat-derived materials may be used in cosmetics, such as wheat protein, wheat germ, wheat germ protein, wheat germ oil, wheat bran, wheat starch, wheat gluten, and wheat kernel. Proteins from wheat are processed through hydrolysis, and the product can preserve and improve skin moisture. Hydrolyzed wheat protein (HWP), which is an amber liquid at room temperature, is added to skin care and hair care products such as moisturizers, soaps, bath gels, and hair conditioners, to many other cosmetics and to detergents because of their surfactant, film-forming, foaming, hydrating and softening properties (15,24).

Contact allergy to 'hydrolyzed wheat protein' in cosmetics is extremely rare, only four cases of cosmetic allergic contact dermatitis have been described (6,10,34) (plus two reacting to palmitoyl hydrolyzed wheat protein [32,33], see Chapter 2.330 Palmitoyl hydrolyzed wheat protein).

Immediate contact reactions, however, have been reported frequently, notably from Japan. In fact, from 2009 on, >2000 Japanese citizens developed contact urticaria and immediate-type systemic reactions, including anaphylaxis and anaphylactic shock, which could be attributed to the use of a particular brand of facial soap containing a specific type of hydrolyzed wheat protein called Glupearl 19S, which was identified as the cause. The 'epidemic' has been incidental and was restricted to Japan; currently, it appears to be under control (20,25).

Several authorities, including the European Commission, took note of this issue, resulting in an opinion on the safety of HWP by the Scientific Committee on Consumer Safety SCCS (SCCS/1534/14) (17,23). It was the opinion of the SCCS that, 'in view of the numbers of reported cases of immediate-type contact urticarial and systemic allergic reactions, the overall risk of sensitization to HWP appears to be low, with the exception of the 'epidemic' in Japan associated with one particular HWP product used in some brands of soap'. However, scientific concerns with regard to the use of HWP in cosmetic products included that (i) there is evidence that sensitisation to HWP is via exposure to cosmetics, not via food and (ii) there are indications that the risk of sensitisation is higher when HWP's of higher molecular weight are used on the skin, in particular as an ingredient of products that have strong surfactant properties such as soaps and liquid soaps. The SCCS considered the use of hydrolyzed wheat proteins safe for consumers in cosmetic products, provided that the maximum molecular weight average of the peptides in hydrolyzates is 3.5 kDa (17,23).

A review of contact urticaria caused by ingredients of cosmetics has been provided in ref. 40.

CONTACT ALLERGY

Case reports and case series

A woman described intense burning over her face, neck, and scalp several hours after applying a new moisturizing cosmetic cream. She developed a florid, itchy rash over her face and neck, which lasted several weeks, settling with the use of topical steroids. Patch testing to the standard, cosmetic, hairdressing, and facial series and her own products gave a positive reaction to the suspected moisturizing cream. When tested with its ingredients, the patient now reacted to hydrolyzed wheat protein 50% water. Twenty controls tested with this material were negative. Testing for immediate-type reactions was negative (10).

Another woman had erythematous, edematous lesions on the eyelids, face and neck for 2 months. The cutaneous lesions improved within 2 weeks of discontinuation of a moisturizing cream she used and treatment with topical corticosteroids. Patch tests with the GEIDC standard and cosmetics series, her own cosmetic cream, and its components gave positive reactions to the cream and one of its ingredients, hydrolyzed wheat protein, tested 10% water (34 controls were negative).Testing for immediate-type reactions was negative (6). Two women from Portugal had allergic contact dermatitis of the face from a cream containing HWP. The patch test to the cream was positive in both, to HWP doubtful positive (test concentration/vehicle not mentioned). However, a ROAT with the hydrolyzed wheat protein material was positive in both patients (34). Another patient, who had contact urticaria from HWP in a cream, had a negative open test, a positive prick test and also a positive patch test to HWP 1% water; however, he only had contact urticaria, not allergic contact dermatitis (37).

Presence in cosmetic products and chemical analyses
In July 2017, hydrolyzed wheat protein was present in 627 of 69,577 cosmetic products of which the composition is known in EWG's Skin Deep Cosmetics Database, USA (http://www.ewg.org/skindeep/). In the USA, in April 2017, hydrolyzed wheat protein was present in 1156 of 56,714 cosmetic products of which the composition is known in FDA's Voluntary Cosmetic Registration Program (VCRP) (data obtained from FDA, May 2017).

OTHER SIDE EFFECTS

Immediate-type reactions
There have been some reports of immediate-type reactions from hydrolyzed wheat protein in cosmetic products observed in Europe, notably in France. These are summarized in table 2.236.1.

Table 2.236.1 Reports of immediate-type reactions to hydrolyzed wheat protein in cosmetics from Europe (adapted from [20])

Year and country	No. of pat.	Cosmetic products	Symptoms after applying cosmetics	Symptoms after eating wheat-containing food	Ref.
2016 Belgium	1	anti-ageing solution	occupational contact urticaria	not mentioned	40
2013 France	1	moisturizing cream	contact urticaria	none	9
2013 Finland	2	hair conditioner spray	occupational rhinitis, asthma, CU	EIA (1 patient), exercise-induced food allergy	39
2012 Spain	1	cosmetic face cream	contact urticaria	none	37
2012 France	2	cosmetics	contact urticaria	generalized urticaria in one patient	18
2010 France	2	'skin tensing' cosmetic, facial cream	contact urticaria	none	31
2006 France	9	creams, shower gel, hair conditioner	contact urticaria	generalized urticaria (n=3), anaphylaxis (n=2), EIA (n=1)	3,5
2006 France	3	shower gel, shampoo, mascara	generalized erythema, contact eczema, facial angioedema with GU	exercise-induced anaphylaxis (n=1)	16
2002 France	1	eyelid cream, moisturizer	contact urticaria	generalized urticaria	4
2000 Finland	1	body cream	contact urticaria	not mentioned	7

CU Contact urticaria; EIA Exercise-induced anaphylaxis; GU Generalized urticaria

An epidemic in Japan
In sharp contrast to the paucity of European cases of immediate contact reactions to HWP (and none from elsewhere in English literature) are reports from Japan. In 2009, 5 Japanese patients were described with wheat-dependent exercise-induced anaphylaxis after using a facial soap containing 0.3% hydrolyzed wheat protein (11). Since then, thousands of users of this facial soap, which contained a specific type of hydrolyzed wheat protein called Glupearl 19S (GP19S) have developed *de novo* immediate-type wheat allergy. The facial soap concerned was called Cha no Shizuku ('Drop of Tea'). In some 70% of the patients, application of the soap caused contact urticaria. About 30% of the sensitized individuals, however, were asymptomatic when they used the soap itself, and symptoms only developed after ingestion of food that contained wheat, usually traditional wheat products such as bread and pasta (20,25).

In a nationwide survey in Japan, on the basis of strict diagnostic criteria, 2111 (2025 females, 86 males; age, 1-93 years; average age, 45.8 years) patients with immediate wheat allergy from sensitization to HWP Glupearl 19S were identified. The age group with the largest share consisted of those in their 40s. The symptoms typically appeared 1 year after starting use of the soap. Most patients used the soap only for their faces, but some used it on other body parts as well. No patients had shown apparent wheat allergy before using this soap. Symptoms of immediate-type allergy to HWP Glupearl 19S included itching, eyelid edema, nasal discharge, and/or wheals within several to 30 min after using Cha-no-Shizuku soap or other products containing hydrolyzed wheat. Most also would develop general symptoms, such as itching, wheals, eyelid edema, nasal discharge, dyspnea, nausea, vomiting, abdominal pain, diarrhea, and decreased blood pressure, within 4 hours after eating wheat products. Anaphylactic shock occurred in about 25% of the patients, often after exercise (exercise-induced anaphylaxis). The exercise-induced anaphylaxis in many ways resembled conventional wheat-dependent exercise-induced anaphylaxis (19), but these conditions differ in terms of the presence of specific IgE antibodies against GP19S in the patients sensitized by the soap (25).

The distribution of skin symptoms *during or after using soap* observed in immediate-type wheat allergy caused by Glupearl 19S in 899 patients were swelling of eyelids (40%), urticaria, itching, and erythema (31%), and no skin symptoms in 27% of the cases (20). Conjunctivitis from HWP in the soap has also been reported (27). Symptoms in this group of 899 patients *after eating wheat products* were swelling of eyelids (77%), urticaria (60%), dyspnea (43%), erythema (38%), itching (31%), anaphylactic shock (25%), diarrhea (16%), nausea (14%), nasal discharge (13%), vomiting (11%), and nasal congestion (11%) (20).

The diagnosis was confirmed with one or more positive laboratory tests: 1. skin prick tests using solutions of the soap, wheat flour, hydrolyzed gluten solutions, and/or ≤0.1% Glupearl 19S solution; 2. immunoassays, such as dot blot, ELISA, and/or western blot to identify specific IgE antibodies to Glupearl 19S in the serum/plasma; 3. basophil activation test using Glupearl 19S (20). Discontinuing the use of this soap was shown to reduce the levels of GP19S-specific IgE antibodies and alleviate symptoms (25,38). Reactions could be prevented by stopping the use of the soap and avoid ingestion of natural wheat products. Five years after cessation of HWP-soap usage, about 50% of the patients were in remission, meaning that they were free of symptoms for more than 3 months without any dietary and physical restriction (21). In May 2011, the company discontinued sales of the soap containing Glupearl 19S and voluntarily began to recall about 46 million cakes of HWP-containing soap (27). Since then, the number of reported patients has gradually decreased and the 'epidemic' now appears to be under control (20).

Various case series with individuals sensitized to HWP Glupearl 19S in facial soap and having immediate-type reactions from the soap and/or food containing wheat have been presented: 41 patients (14), 36 patients (26,35), 18 patients (41), 12 patients (30), 7 patients (8), 3 patients (13) and 2 allergic individuals (5). Single cases have been presented in refs. 27,29,36 and 38. In a woman sensitized to HWP in soap and suffering from chronic headaches and sleepiness, these symptoms completely disappeared after avoiding eating wheat (28).

Immediate-type reactions to wheat in cosmetics other than hydrolyzed wheat protein
Two children with atopic dermatitis had an 'immediate rash' from wheat starch in a cosmetic bath product. Prick tests to wheat flour were positive (22). A woman with exercise-induced anaphylaxis to wheat developed generalized erythema from a cosmetic shower gel containing *Triticum vulgare*. A prick test to wheat flour was positive (22). A woman known to be allergic to wheat flour had 'contact eczema' from a shampoo containing wheat proteins. Prick tests to wheat flour and shampoo were positive (22). A woman known to be allergic to wheat flour developed facial angioedema and generalized urticaria after the application of a mascara containing wheat proteins; prick tests to wheat flour and to the mascara were positive (22).

LITERATURE
1   Chinuki Y, Kaneko S, Sakieda K, Murata S, Yoshida Y, Morita E. A case of wheat-dependent exercise-induced anaphylaxis sensitized with hydrolysed wheat protein in a soap. Contact Dermatitis 2011;65:55-57
2   Fukutomi Y, Itagaki Y, Taniguchi M, Saito A, Yasueda H, Nakazawa T, et al. Rhinoconjunctival sensitization to hydrolyzed wheat protein in facial soap can induce wheat-dependent exercise-induced anaphylaxis. J Allergy Clin Immunol 2011;127:531-533
3   Laurière M, Pecquet C, Bouchez-Mahiout I, Snégaroff J, Bayrou O, Raison-Peyron N, et al. Hydrolysed wheat proteins present in cosmetics can induce immediate hypersensitivities. Contact Dermatitis 2006;54:283-289
4   Pecquet C, Laurière M, Huet S, Leynadier F. Is the application of cosmetics containing protein-derived products safe? Contact Dermatitis 2002;46:123
5   Pecquet C, Bayrou O, Vigan M, Raison N, Laurière M. Hydrolysed wheat protein: a new allergen in cosmetics and food. Contact Dermatitis 2004;50:182-183 (Abstract P14)
6   Sanchez-Perez J, Sanz T, Garcia-Diez A. Allergic contact dermatitis from hydrolyzed wheat protein in cosmetic cream. Contact Dermatitis 2000;42:360
7   Varjonen E, Petman L, Makinen-Kiljunen S. Immediate contact allergy from hydrolyzed wheat in a cosmetic cream. Allergy 2000;55:294-296
8   Chinuki Y, Takahashi H, Dekio I, Kaneko S, Tokuda R, Nagao M, et al. Higher allergenicity of high molecular weight hydrolysed wheat protein in cosmetics for percutaneous sensitization. Contact Dermatitis 2013;68:86-93
9   Leheron C, Bourrier T, Albertini M, Giovannini-Chami L. Immediate contact urticaria caused by hydrolysed wheat proteins in a child via maternal skin contact sensitization. Contact Dermatitis 2013;68:379-380
10 Hann S, Hughes M, Stone N. Allergic contact dermatitis to hydrolyzed wheat protein in a cosmetic cream. Contact Dermatitis 2007;56:119-120
11 Fukutomi Y, Taniguchi M, Takino S, Tanimoto H, Sekiya K, Saito M, et al. Jpn J Allergol 2009;58:1325 (article in Japanese, data cited in ref. 20)

12 Livideanu C, Giordano-Labadie F, Paul C. Contact dermatitis to hydrolyzed wheat protein. Contact Dermatitis 2007;57:283-284

13 Chinuki Y, Sakieda K, Kaneko S, et al. Three cases of wheat-dependent exercise-induced anaphalaxis possibly sensitized by hydrolyzed wheat protein in soap. Japan J Dermatol 2010;120:2421-2425

14 Ota R, Yagami A, Sano A, Nakamura M, Matsunaga K. Immediate hypersensitivity to hydrolyzed wheat proteins in a soap. Contact Dermatitis 2012;66 (Suppl. 2):34

15 Pootongkam S, Nedorost S. Oat and wheat as contact allergens in personal care products. Dermatitis 2013;24:291-295

16 Codreanu F, Morisset M, Cordebar V, Kanny G, Moneret-Vautrin DA. Risk of allergy to food proteins in topical medicinal agents and cosmetics. Eur Ann Allergy Clin Immunol 2006;38:126-130

17 SCCS (Scientific Committee on Consumer Safety). Opinion on the safety of hydrolysed wheat proteins in cosmetic products, submission I, 18 June 2014, SCCS/1534/14, revision of 22 October 2014. Available at: http://ec.europa.eu/health/scientific_committees/consumer_safety/docs/sccs_o_160.pdf

18 Olaiwan A, Pecquet C, Mathelier-Fusade P, Frances C. Contact urticaria induced by hydrolyzed wheat proteins in cosmetics. Ann Dermatol Venereol 2010;137:281-284

19 Scherf KA, Brockow K, Biedermann T, Koehler P, Wieser H. Wheat-dependent exercise-induced anaphylaxis. Clin Exp Allergy 2016;46:10-20

20 Yagami A, Aihara M, Ikezawa Z, Hide M, Kishikawa R, Morita E, et al. Outbreak of immediate-type hydrolyzed wheat protein allergy due to a facial soap in Japan. J Allergy Clin Immunol 2017 May 16. pii: S0091-6749(17)30574-2. doi: 10.1016/j.jaci.2017.03.019. [Epub ahead of print]

21 Hiragun M, Ishii K, Yanase Y, Hiragun T, Hide M. Remission rate of patients with wheat allergy sensitized to hydrolyzed wheat protein in facial soap. Allergol Int 2016;65:109-111

22 Literature reference lost during writing

23 Scientific Committee SCCS, Coenraads PJ. Revision of the opinion on hydrolysed wheat proteins - Sensitisation only. Regul Toxicol Pharmacol 2015;73:668

24 Coenraads P.-J. Sensitization potential of hydrolysed wheat proteins. Contact Dermatitis 2016;74:321-322

25 Nakamura M, Yagami A, Hara K, Sano-Nagai A, Kobayashi T, Matsunaga K. Evaluation of the cross-reactivity of antigens in Glupearl 19S and other hydrolysed wheat proteins in cosmetics. Contact Dermatitis 2016;74:346-352

26 Hiragun M, Ishii K, Hiragun T, Shindo H, Hihara S, Matsuo H, et al. The sensitivity and clinical course of patients with wheat-dependent exercise-induced anaphylaxis sensitized to hydrolyzed wheat protein in facial soap – secondary publication. Allergol Int 2013;62:351-358

27 Mimura T, Noma H, Yamagami S. Conjunctival sensitization to hydrolyzed wheat protein in facial soap. J Investig Allergol Clin Immunol 2014;24:140-141

28 Iseki C, Kawanami T, Tsunoda T, Chinuki Y, Kato T. Chronic headaches and sleepiness caused by facial soap (containing hydrolyzed wheat proteins)-induced wheat allergy. Intern Med 2014;53:151-154

29 Iga N, Tanizaki H, Endo Y, Egawa G, Fujisawa A, Tanioka M, et al. Hydrolyzed wheat protein-containing facial soap-induced wheat-dependent exercise-induced anaphylaxis in a patient without filaggrin mutations. J Dermatol 2013;40:494-495

30 Sugiyama A, Kishikawa R, Nishie H, Takeuchi S, Shimoda T, Iwanaga T, Nishima S, Furue M. Wheat anaphylaxis or wheat-dependent exercise-induced anaphylaxis caused by use of a soap product which contains hydrolyzed wheat proteins. -a report of 12 cases. Arerugi 2011;60:1532-1542 (article in Japanese)

31 Bouchez-Mahiout I, Pecquet C, Kerre S, Snegaroff J, Raison-Peyron N, Lauriere M. High molecular weight entities in industrial wheat protein hydrolysates are immunoreactive with IgE from allergic patients. J Agric Food Chem 2010;58:4207-4215

32 Livideanu C, Giordano-Labadie F, Paul C. Contact dermatitis to hydrolyzed wheat protein. Contact Dermatitis 2007;57:283-284

33 Mailhol C, Lauwers-Cances V, Rancé F, Paul C, Giordano-Labadie F. Prevalence and risk factors for allergic contact dermatitis to topical treatment in atopic dermatitis: a study in 641 children. Allergy 2009;64:801-806

34 Bordalo O. Allergic contact dermatitis from hydrolyzed wheat protein. Contact Dermatitis 2004;50:183-184

35 Hirugan M, Ishii K, Hiragun T, Shindo H, Mihara S, Matsuo H, Hide M. The sensitivity and clinical course of patients with wheat-dependent exercise-induced anaphylaxis sensitized to hydrolyzed wheat protein in facial soap. Arerugi 2011;60:1630-1640 (article in Japanese)

36 Chinuki Y, Morita E. Wheat-dependent exercise-induced anaphylaxis sensitized with hydrolyzed wheat protein in soap. Allergol Int 2012;61:529-537

37 Barrientos N, Vazquez S, Dominguez JD. Contact urticaria induced by hydrolyzed wheat protein in cosmetic cream. Actas Dermosifiliogr 2012;103:750-752

38 Ishii K, Hiragun M, Matsuo H, Hiragun T, Hide M. Remission of wheat-dependent exercise-induced anaphylaxis after the cessation of hydrolysed wheat-containing soap usage. Acta Derm Venereol 2012;92:490-491

39   Airaksinen L, Pallasaho P, Voutilainen R, Pesonen M. Occupational rhinitis, asthma, and contact urticaria caused by hydrolyzed wheat protein in hairdressers. Ann Allergy Asthma Immunol 2013;111:577-579

40   Verhulst L, Goossens A. Cosmetic components causing contact urticaria: a review and update. Contact Dermatitis 2016;75:333-344

41   Kobayashi T, Ito T, Kawakami H, Fuzishiro K, Hirano H, Okubo Y, Tsuboi R. Eighteen cases of wheat allergy and wheat-dependent exercise-induced urticarial/anaphylaxis sensitized by hydrolyzed wheat protein in soap. Int J Dermatol 2015;54:e302-e305

2.237 HYDROPHILIZED CERAMIDE*
Not an INCI name

IDENTIFICATION

Description/definition : Unknown chemical substance
INCI name USA : Neither in CosIng nor in the Personal Care Products Council Ingredient Database
Patch testing : 0.5% pet. (1)

CONTACT ALLERGY

Case reports and case series

A woman complained of itchy redness on her face. She had used three types of moisturizing creams on the same site for 10 days, but the eruption had become worse. Clinical examination showed edematous erythema on her cheeks and neck. A corticosteroid ointment was applied for 5 days and the lesions disappeared. Each medicament and cosmetic that the patient had used was patch tested (as is). She responded positively only to a 'sebum control emulsion'. This cosmetic was manufactured in Japan and contained 0.5% hydrophilized ceramide (modified synthetic ceramide). Next, the patient was patch tested with the ingredients of the emulsion and she reacted only to hydrophilized ceramide 0.25% and 0.5% pet. Patch testing with 0.5% hydrophilized ceramide in pet. in 5 controls was negative (1).

The authors state that this hydrophilized ceramide resembles type 2 ceramide and is chemically synthesized. The material contains some impurities besides the main structure (not further specified, neither the impurities nor the main structure) (1).

Cross-reactions, pseudo-cross-reactions and co-reactions

Not to 'lipophilic ceramide A' 0.5% pet. and 'lipophilic ceramide B' 0.5% pet. (1).

Presence in cosmetic products and chemical analyses

In the USA, in April 2017, hydrophilized ceramide was present in zero of 56,714 cosmetic products of which the composition is known in FDA's Voluntary Cosmetic Registration Program (VCRP) (data obtained from FDA, May 2017). In February 2017, hydrophilized ceramide was present in zero of 64,480 cosmetic products of which the composition is known in EWG's Skin Deep Cosmetics Database, USA (http://www.ewg.org/skindeep/).

LITERATURE

1 Yajima, J. Allergic contact dermatitis due to hydrophilized ceramide. Contact Dermatitis 2002;47:245

2.238 HYDROQUINONE

IDENTIFICATION

Description/definition	: Hydroquinone is the aromatic organic compound that conforms to the formula shown below
Chemical class(es)	: Color additives- hair; phenols
Chemical/IUPAC name	: Benzene-1,4-diol
Other names	: 1,4-Dihydroxybenzene; *p*-hydroxyphenol
CAS registry number (s)	: 123-31-9
EC number(s)	: 204-617-8
CIR review(s)	: J Am Coll Toxicol 1986;5:123-165; J Am Coll Toxicol 1994;3:167-230; Int J Toxicol 2010; 29(Suppl.4):274-287; Final report, December 2014 (access: www.cir-safety.org/ingredients)
SCCS opinion(s)	: SCCNFP/0486/01 (27)
Merck Index monograph	: 6115
Function(s) in cosmetics	: EU: stabilizing. USA: antioxidants; fragrance ingredients; hair colorants; reducing agents; skin bleaching agents
EU cosmetic restrictions	: Regulated in Annex II/1339 of the Regulation (EC) No. 344/2013 (prohibited), with the exception of entry 14 in Annex III (allowed in artificial nails)
Patch testing	: 1.0% pet. (Chemotechnique, SmartPracticeEurope, SmartPracticeCanada); this test concentration may cause irritant reactions (78)
Molecular formula	: $C_6H_6O_2$

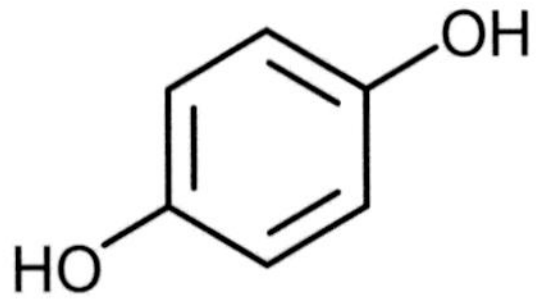

GENERAL

Hydroquinone is a phenolic compound chemically known as 1,4-dihydroxybenzene. It is widely used in industry as reducing agent, photographic developer, stabilizer in paints, varnishes, motor fuels and oils, as antioxidant for fats, and as an antioxidant and stabilizer for certain materials that polymerize in the presence of oxidizing agents. Acrylic monomers, for example, are often stored for several years and hydroquinone prevents their spontaneous polymerization, precipitated by heat, light or traces of oxygen. Hydroquinone may also be present in resins, plastics, cosmetics, medicaments, and as feed additive for cattle (4,5,63). Finally, hydroquinone is present in cigarette smoke, some herbal remedies and in common foods such as cranberries, blueberries, tea, coffee, red wine, rice, and onions. The largest amounts of hydroquinone or arbutin (which is hydrolyzed in the stomach into hydroquinone) are found in wheat and wheat bread, wheat germ and pears (63). Of most interest to dermatologists, hydroquinone is also a depigmenting agent, well-known in clinical treatment of cutaneous hyperpigmentation disorders such as melasma, in a concentration of 2-4%. The chemical was first noted to be a bleaching agent 1936. It inhibits the enzymatic oxidation of tyrosine and phenol oxidases. It inhibits melanin production by inhibiting the sulfhydryl groups and it acts as a substrate for tyrosinase. Hydroquinone covalently binds to histidine and interacts with copper at the active site of tyrosinase. It also inhibits RNA and DNA synthesis and may alter melanosome formation, thus selectively damaging melanocytes. These activities do not 'bleach the skin' but gradually suppress melanin pigment production (33,35,48).

Since 2001, hydroquinone has been banned from cosmetic products (except in artificial nail systems for professional use) in the European Union due to concerns about potential carcinogenicity, but illegal whitening products containing hydroquinone can be found in so-called ethnic shops in some European countries (61). In the USA, in 2006, the Food and Drug Administration (FDA) released a statement proposing a ban on all over-the-counter hydroquinone products, also based on (rodent) studies, which suggested that oral hydroquinone may be a carcinogen. However, there have been no reports of skin cancers or internal malignancies associated with topical hydroquinone use and Regulatory Agencies have concluded that there are insufficient data to classify hydroquinone as a carcinogen (63). To date, a final ruling by the FDA is still pending, and it has been argued that the proposed ban is unnecessarily extreme (39). The Cosmetic ingredient Review in 2010 advised that 'hydroquinone is safe at concentrations of 1% in hair dyes and is safe for use in nail adhesives. Hydroquinone should not be used in other leave-on cosmetics' (71).

Potential side effects of hydroquinone are shown in table 2.238.1. The subject has been extensively discussed in several review articles (33,39,48,49,50,53,63). As the literature on side effects of hydroquinone is vast, this chapter cannot provide a full review of the subject.

Table 2.238.1 Potential side effects of hydroquinone / hydroquinone-containing topical products

Dermatitis
Irritation / irritant contact dermatitis
Contact allergy / allergic contact dermatitis

Pigmentary disorders
Hypopigmentation
Depigmentation (chemical leukoderma)
Hyperpigmentation (post-inflammatory)
Exogenous ochronosis
Discoloration of the nails

Miscellaneous
Pigmentation of the eye and permanent corneal damage
Fish-odor syndrome

CONTACT ALLERGY

Patch testing in groups of patients

There are no studies in which hydroquinone has been tested in consecutive patients suspected of contact dermatitis (routine testing). Results of patch testing hydroquinone in groups of *selected* patients (e.g., hairdressers, patients tested with a hairdressing series, patients with intolerance to endoprostheses [as acrylate bone cement may contain hydroquinone]) are shown in table 2.238.2. In 13 investigations, frequencies of sensitization have ranged from 0.2% to 13%, but most scored below 2%. The highest frequency of 13% was found in a very small study from India in 69 patients with features suggestive of allergic contact dermatitis and histories of prolonged use of numerous topical preparations, or of exacerbation or spread of dermatitis following the use of such products, where 8 patients (13%) had a positive patch test to hydroquinone 1% pet.; the relevance of these reactions was not mentioned (32). In two studies performed by the IVDK, low rates of 0.3% and 0.9% were observed in female hairdressers with current or previous occupational contact dermatitis (3,29). Surprisingly, the frequencies of sensitization were far higher (5.4% and 6.3%) in clients of hairdressers, in who hair cosmetics were regarded as a cause of dermatitis; in these studies also, relevance was not mentioned (3,29). In fact, the issue of relevance was addressed in 2 studies only (25,31). In one, 2 of 4 reactions were considered to be relevant (25), in the other, only relevant reactions (n=7) were collected (31). Culprit products were not mentioned.

Table 2.238.2 Patch testing in groups of patients: Selected patient groups

Years and Country	Test conc. & vehicle	Number of patients tested	positive (%)	Selection of patients (S); Relevance (R); Comments (C)	Ref.
2007-2012 IVDK	1% pet.	709	3 (0.3%)	S: female hairdressers with current or previous occupational contact dermatitis; R: not stated	29
		1703	71 (6.3%)	S: female patients, clients of hairdressers, in who hair cosmetics were regarded as a cause of dermatitis, and who had never worked as hairdressers; R: not stated	
2002-2011 Denmark		284	4 (1.4%)	S: hairdressers with contact dermatitis; R: not stated	28
2005-2010 Germany		66	3 (4.5%)	S: patients with complications from knee or hip arthroplasty; R: not stated	76
2000-2008 USA	1% pet.	209	(1.9%)	S: patients tested with a hairdresser's series; R: 50%	25
<2008 Germany		113	3 (2.7%)	S: patients with intolerance to endoprostheses; R: not stated	75
1997-2007 UK	1% pet.	80	1 (1.3%)	S; patients suspected of hair dye allergy; R: not stated	1
1980-2007 UK	1% pet.	538	1 (0.2%)	S: hairdressers tested with a hairdressers series; R: not specified	30
2003-2006 IVDK	1% pet.	431	(0.9%)	S: female hairdressers with suspected occupational contact dermatitis; R: not stated	3
	1% pet.	612	(5.4%)	S: women with suspected reactions to hair cosmetics; R: not stated	
1999-2004 UK		518	7 (1.4%)	S: patients tested with the hairdressing series; R: only reactions that were of current or past relevance were	31

Years and Country	Test conc. & vehicle	Number of patients tested	positive (%)		Selection of patients (S); Relevance (R); Comments (C)	Ref.
					collected	
2000-2002 Finland		894		(0.3%)	S: patients tested with a hairdressing series; R: not stated	22
1995-2002 IVDK		884		(0.7%)	S: female hairdressers with present or past occupational contact dermatitis; R: not specified	26
		1217		(1.5%)	S: clients of hairdressers suspected to react to hairdressing cosmetics or hair care products; R: not specified	
1995-1996 Finland		438		(0.5%)	S: patients tested with a hairdressing series; R: not stated	22
<1990 India	1% pet.	69	8	(13%)	S: patients with features suggestive of allergic contact dermatitis and histories of prolonged use of numerous topical preparations, or of exacerbation or spread of derma-titis following the use of such preparations; R: not stated	32

IVDK: Information Network of Departments of Dermatology, Germany, Austria, Switzerland

Case reports and case series
Hydroquinone was stated to be the (or an) allergen in 4 patients in a group of 603 individuals suffering from cosmetic dermatitis, seen in the period 2010-2015 in Leuven, Belgium (24). Six positive patch test reactions to hydroquinone were ascribed to cosmetic allergy (2). In a 4-month-period in 1996, 475 patients with contact allergy to 'cosmetic ingredients' were collected in 5 centers in Belgium, UK and Germany. There was one reaction to hydroquinone; relevance was not stated (23). Of 56 patients treated with 2% or 5% hydroquinone cream (exact composition not mentioned), one (using the 5% cream) developed local reactions suggestive of sensitization. This patient was patch tested with both the 2% and the 5% cream. After 48 hours, the patch tests were positive and a generalized eczematous eruption had appeared, but hydroquinone itself was not tested (43). Of 39 patients treated for a variety of pigmentary disorders with 5% hydroquinone ointment (exact composition not mentioned), 2 developed local reactions suggestive of sensitization. Both later reacted to the patch test with the ointment, but hydroquinone itself was not tested separately (42).

A patient became allergic to hydroquinone from a bleaching cream; she also had post-inflammatory hyperpig-mentation, incorrectly called 'exogenous ochronosis' by the authors (4). Another patient also had allergic contact dermatitis from hydroquinone in a skin-lightening cream (19). A woman developed allergic contact dermatitis from hydroquinone present at a 5% concentration in a cream used to prevent post-inflammatory hyperpigmentation after a glycolic acid peel (59). Another woman had allergic contact dermatitis of the face from hydroquinone in a bleaching cream with reticulate post-inflammatory hyperpigmentation (18).

Contact allergy to hydroquinone in non-cosmetic products
One patient had cheilitis and stomatitis from contact allergy to hydroquinone in acrylic dentures (5). One or more similar patients had already been identified in 1958 (6). Hydroquinone has sensitized one or more individuals from its presence in cattle food (46, cited in ref. 47).

Cross-reactions, pseudo-cross-reactions and co-reactions
Pyrocatechol (15); resorcinol (16,17,77); monobenzone (monobenzyl ether of hydroquinone) (55). Hydroquinone may cross-react with structurally related chemicals, notably those with a para-structure. Cross-reactivity between para-compounds is discussed in Chapter 2.359 *p*-Phenylenediamine.

Presence in cosmetic products and chemical analyses
In July 2017, hydroquinone was present in 17 of 69,543 cosmetic products of which the composition is known in EWG's Skin Deep Cosmetics Database, USA (http://www.ewg.org/skindeep/). In the USA, in April 2017, hydroqui-none was present in 25 of 56,714 cosmetic products of which the composition is known in FDA's Voluntary Cosmetic Registration Program (VCRP) (data obtained from FDA, May 2017).

OTHER SIDE EFFECTS

Irritant contact dermatitis
Hypopigmenting creams containing hydroquinone (sometimes in combination with tretinoin) are well known to cause irritation / irritant contact dermatitis with erythema, burning, pruritus, mild edema and scaling (33,35). This is the most common adverse reaction from hydroquinone that can start within days of beginning treatment. It has been reported to occur in 0%-70% of patients on hydroquinone monotherapy and 10%-100% of individuals using combination therapy with hydroquinone (notably with tretinoin) (63). Irritant dermatitis occurs more frequently with

higher concentrations (4%,5%) than with the 2% hydroquinone-containing products (43). As these products are most often used by people with pigmented skin, this irritation or irritant contact dermatitis may result in post-inflammatory hyperpigmentation (4 [incorrectly called exogenous ochronosis],10,33,34,56).

Other non-eczematous contact reactions

While hydroquinone is used to treat hyperpigmentation, it can cause several pigmentary disturbances itself: hypopigmentation, depigmentation (chemical leukoderma), hyperpigmentation, combined de-/hypo- and hyperpigmentation and ochronosis (33).

Hypopigmentation and depigmentation

It is not unusual that some degree of hypopigmentation develops around the areas of hyperpigmentation treated with hydroquinone ('halo-effect') or within the lesions (10); this usually resolves after treatment is interrupted (34,35,41). However, in a concentration of 2% or higher, it can very occasionally cause depigmentation (chemical leukoderma), which may be very long-lasting or even permanent (7,8,9,79). Usually, the shape of the leukoderma is irregular and has been described as 'confetti-like' (10). Sometimes the terms vitiligo (20) or vitiligo-like leukoderma (21) have been used to describe this adverse reaction to hydroquinone.

Four women developed disfiguring depigmentation from creams containing 2% hydroquinone (7,8). One patient developed leukoderma from the use of a bleaching cream containing 2% hydroquinone (60). Three women had leukoderma from topical products containing hydroquinone. Two had used monobenzone before and the 3rd used a hydroquinone hydro-alcoholic solution which also contained tretinoin (9).

Non-cosmetic products

Vitiligo of the hands and underarms developed in an individual servicing automatic self-photography machines, where he had contact with a black and white process containing 7% hydroquinone; the causal relationship was not established (20). Vitiligo-like leukoderma appeared on the hands in a photographic worker who had regular contact with a black and white developer containing 0.06% hydroquinone (21). An X-ray laboratory worker may have developed occupational leukoderma from hydroquinone in a developer for X-ray films (80).

Hyperpigmentation

Hyperpigmentation from hydroquinone is usually post-inflammatory, resulting from irritant contact dermatitis (33,34,56) or allergic contact dermatitis (4,18).

Combined hypo- and hyperpigmentation

Two patients developed a combination of hypopigmentation and hyperpigmentation from the use of hypopigmenting creams, one containing 4% hydroquinone + 0.05% tretinoin and the other 2% hydroquinone as active ingredient(s) (33). A man had combined (post-inflammatory) hyperpigmentation and confetti-like hypopigmentation from hydroquinone bleaching cream (10).

Exogenous ochronosis

Exogenous ochronosis is another type of hyperpigmentation from hydroquinone (4,11,12,13,14,66,83,84). Prolonged application and sun stimulation may cause melanocytes to pass down to the papillary dermis and be taken up by fibroblasts and lead to altered elastic fiber production and excretion of abnormal materials into the new fiber bundles, causing the histological yellow-brown banana-shaped fibers typical for exogenous ochronosis (48). Clinically, the pigmented exogenous ochronotic lesions are most marked on sun-exposed areas of the body, face, upper chest and upper back. The lesions include erythema and mild pigmentation of the face and neck, they may progress to hyperpigmentation with 'caviar-like' papules, and papulonodules may appear with or without surrounding inflammation (48). Exogenous ochronosis can be staged by severity from I to III. Stage I consists of erythema and mild pigmentation of the face and neck; stage II is a progression to hyperpigmentation, black colloid milia, and atrophy with the appearance of 'caviar-like' papules; and stage III includes papulonodules with or without surrounding inflammation (84).

Exogenous ochronosis is typically associated with frequent use of very high concentrations of hydroquinone on a long-term basis, although the reaction can still occur with short-term use of 1 to 2% hydroquinone (38,39). It is most commonly reported in darkly pigmented people in South Africa, where the prevalence of exogenous ochronosis is high. In the United States, a low number of hydroquinone-induced exogenous ochronosis cases have been reported (35,39,66). In fact, the incidence of this adverse reaction is actually very low when topical hydroquinone is used under medical supervision. In a comprehensive search of case reports of exogenous ochronosis from 1966 to 2007, a total of 789 cases were reported: 756 from Africa (where combinations with resorcinol and the use of hydro-alcoholic solutions may increase the risk of this side effect developing [38,54]), 22 from the USA, 8 from Europe, 2 from Puerto Rico and one from India (39). However, there has been a recent rise in the illicit use of products containing high concentrations of hydroquinone available in ethnic stores in the United States (40). It has been concluded that it is excessive and unsupervised use, rather than hydroquinone itself, that is dangerous (48). In some patients with systemic sarcoidosis, cutaneous sarcoidal granulomas have developed on a background of exogenous ochronosis caused by hydroquinone skin lightening products (73,74).

The literature on exogenous ochronosis from hydroquinone from 1966 to 2007 has been presented in ref. 39. Case reports / case series from a later date can be found in refs. 51,52,70,73,82, and 85-95. A useful review of the diagnosis, epidemiology, causes, and treatments of exogenous ochronosis was published in 2015 (84).

Discoloration of the nails
Temporary discoloration of the fingernails was observed in 3/56 individuals treated with 2% or 5% hydroquinone cream (43). Two patients had brown discoloration of the nails from hydroquinone creams. On stopping the skin-lightening creams, the discoloration completely disappeared after one moth in one patient and after 2 months in the other. Hydroquinone is readily oxidized to quinone, a yellow compound, and quinone subsequently undergoes oxidation to hydroxyquinone. This chemical is unstable and polymerizes to products which are dark brown (57). 'Several' patients developed a diffuse orange-brown pigmentation of the fingernails after chronic usage of a bleaching cream containing 1% hydroquinone. The color was irreversible, but it could be prevented in those patients who are using it on the face by a thorough washing of the fingers after usage and a careful avoidance of contamination of the nails. The discoloration was, according to the manufacturer, due to oxidation of hydroquinone; the same color could be seen on the surface of the cream if it was exposed to air for a long time (58). Other cases of nail staining from hydroquinone preparations have been reported in refs. 67,68, and 69.

Systemic side effects
There is a large body of evidence that shows that dermal application of hydroquinone is not associated with significant negative systemic health effects (54). Peripheral neuropathy has been linked to hydroquinone in bleaching creams (62).

Miscellaneous side effects
Ocular complications of hydroquinone are virtually unique to individuals working in industrial occupations who are exposed to atmospheric hydroquinone (65). Complications include conjunctival and corneal staining. Corneal staining has been associated with alterations in visual acuity and a small number of cases of permanent corneal damage (44,63, 64,65). Depending on the length of exposure, workers exposed to atmospheric hydroquinone may also show a reddish discoloration of the hair and exposed skin, especially of the skin on the palms and soles (45). In a 2015 study, exogenous ochronosis lesions of the eyelid, ocular ochronosis and cataract were ascribed to depigmenting treatments with hydroquinone (96).

Hydroquinone may cause a fish odor by reducing the ability to oxidize trimethylamine in chronic bleachers, or precipitate the odor in predisposed subjects who are heterozygotes of the condition of 'fish odor syndrome' (49). The development of squamous cell carcinoma has (unconvincingly) been linked to the use of hydroquinone in bleaching creams (72). According to some investigators, occupational exposure to hydroquinone and its derivatives may induce respiratory impairment, perhaps by an immunological mechanism (81).

LITERATURE
1　Basketter DA, English J. Cross-reactions among hair dye allergens. Cut Ocular Toxicol 2009;28:104-106
2　Kohl L, Blondeel A, Song M. Allergic contact dermatitis from cosmetics: retrospective analysis of 819 patch-tested patients. Dermatology 2002;204:334-337
3　Uter W, Lessmann H, Geier J, Schnuch A. Contact allergy to hairdressing allergens in female hairdressers and clients – current data from the IVDK, 2003-2006. J Dtsch Dermatol Ges 2007;5:993-1001
4　Camarasa JG, Serra-Baldrich E. Exogenous ochronosis with allergic contact dermatitis from hydroquinone. Contact Dermatitis 1994;31:57-58
5　Torres V, Cristina Mano-Azul A, Correia T, Pinto Soares A. Allergic contact cheilitis and stomatitis from hydroquinone in an acrylic dental prosthesis. Contact Dermatitis 1993;29:102-103
6　Magnusson B. Excerpta Medica. III Internal Congress Allergol 1958;131 (cited in ref. 5)
7　Fisher AA. Can bleaching creams contain 2% hydroquinone produce leukoderma? J Am Acad Dermatol 1982;7:134-135
8　Fisher AA. Leukoderma from bleaching creams containing 2% hydroquinone. Contact Dermatitis 1982;8:272-273
9　Romaguera C, Grimalt F. Leukoderma from hydroquinone. Contact Dermatitis 1985;12:183
10　Markey AC, Black AK, Rycroft RJG. Confetti-like depigmentation from hydroquinone. Contact Dermatitis 1989;20:148-149
11　Findlay GH. Ochronosis following skin bleaching with hydroquinone. J Am Acad Dermatol 1982;6:1092-1093
12　Houshaw RA, Zimmerman KG, Menter A. Ochronosislike pigmentation from hydroquinone bleaching creams in

American Blacks. Arch Dermatol 1985;121:105-108

13   Findlay GH, Morrison JGL, Simson IW. Exogenous ochronosis and pigmented colloid milium from hydroquinone bleaching creams. Br J Dermatol 1975;93:613-622

14   Tidman MJ, Horton JJ, Macdonald DM. Hydroquinone-induced ochronosis - light and electron-microscopic features. Clin Exp Dermatol1986;11:224-228

15   Andersen KE, Carisen L. Pyrocatechol contact allergy from a permanent cream dye for eyelashes and eyebrows. Contact Dermatitis 1988;18:306-307

16   Caron GA, Calnan CD. Studies in contact dermatitis. XIV. Resorcin. Trans St John's Hosp Dermatol Soc 1962;48:149-156 (data cited in ref. 15)

17   Keil H. Group reactions in contact dermatitis due to resorcinol. Arch Dermatol 1962;86:212-216 (data cited in ref. 15)

18   Tatebayashi M, Oiso N, Wada T, Suzuki K, Matsunaga K, Kawada A. Possible allergic contact dermatitis with reticulate postinflammatory pigmentation caused by hydroquinone. J Dermatol 2014;41:669-670

19   Romaguera C, Grimalt F. Dermatitis from PABA and hydroquinone. Contact Dermatitis 1983;9:226

20   Kersey P, Stevenson CJ. Vitiligo and occupational exposure to hydroquinone from servicing self-photographing machines. Contact Dermatitis 1981;7:285-287

21   Frenk E, Loi-Zedda, P. Occupational depigmentation due to a hydroquinone-containing photographic developer. Contact Dermatitis 1980;6:238-239

22   Hasan T, Rantanen T, Alanko K, Harvima RJ, Jolanki R, Kalimo K, et al. Patch test reactions to cosmetic allergens in 1995–1997 and 2000–2002 in Finland –a multicentre study. Contact Dermatitis 2005;53:40-45

23   Goossens A, Beck MH, Haneke E, McFadden JP, Nolting S, Durupt G, Ries G. Adverse cutaneous reactions to cosmetic allergens. Contact Dermatitis 1999;40:112-113

24   Goossens A. Cosmetic contact allergens. Cosmetics 2016, 3, 5; doi:10.3390/cosmetics3010005

25   Wang MZ, Farmer SA, Richardson DM, Davis MDP. Patch-testing with hairdressing chemicals. Dermatitis 2011;22:16-26

26   Uter W, Lessmann H, Geier J, Schnuch A. Contact allergy to ingredients of hair cosmetics in female hairdressers and clients: an 8-year analysis of IVDK data. Contact Dermatitis 2003;49:236-240

27   SCCNFP (Scientific Committee on Cosmetics and Non Food Products). Opinion concerning SCCNFP (Scientific Committee on Cosmetics and Non Food Products). Opinion concerning the use of Benzoyl Peroxide (BPO) Hydroquinone (HQ), Hydroquinone Methylether (MEHQ) in artificial nail systems, 4 June 2002, SCCNFP/0486/01. Available at: http://ec.europa.eu/health/archive/ph_risk/committees/sccp/documents/out167_en.pdf

28   Schwensen JF, Johansen JD, Veien NK, Funding AT, Avnstorp C, Østerballe M, et al. Occupational contact dermatitis in hairdressers: an analysis of patch test data from the Danish Contact Dermatitis Group, 2002–2011. Contact Dermatitis 2014;70:233-237

29   Uter W, Gefeller O, John SM, Schnuch A, Geier J. Contact allergy to ingredients of hair cosmetics – a comparison of female hairdressers and clients based on IVDK 2007–2012 data. Contact Dermatitis 2014;71:13-20

30   O'Connell RL, White IR, McFadden JP, White JML. Hairdressers with dermatitis should always be patch tested regardless of atopy status. Contact Dermatitis 2010;62:177-181

31   Katugampola RP, Statham BN, English JSC, Wilkinson MM, Foulds IS, Green CM, Ormerod AD, et al. A multicentre review of the hairdressing allergens tested in the UK. Contact Dermatitis 2005;53:130-132

32   George ND, Srinivas CR, Balachandran C, Shenoi SD. Sensitivity to various ingredients of topical preparations following prolonged use. Contact Dermatitis 1990;23:367-368

33   Jow T, Hantash B. Hydroquinone-induced depigmentation: Case report and review of the literature. Dermatitis 2014;25:e1–e5

34   Halder RM, Richards GM. Topical agents used in the management of hyperpigmentation. Skin Therapy Lett 2004;9:1-3

35   Davis EC, Callender CD. Postinflammatory hyperpigmentation: A review of the epidemiology, clinical features, and treatment options in skin of color. J Clin Aesthet Dermatol 2010;3: 20-31

36   Grimes PE. Management of hyperpigmentation in darker racial ethnic groups. Semin Cutan Med Surg 2009;28:77-85

37   Ortonne JP, Passeron T. Melanin pigmentary disorders: treatment update. Dermatol Clin 2005;23:209-226

38   Levin CY, Maibach H. Exogenous ochronosis. An update on clinical features, causative agents and treatment options. Am J Clin Dermatol 2001;2:213-217

39   Levitt J. The safety of hydroquinone: a dermatologist's response to the 2006 Federal Register. J Am Acad Dermatol 2007;57:854-872

40   Halder RM, Nandekar MA, Neal KW. Pigmentary disorders in pigmented skins. In: Halder RM, ed. Dermatology and Dermatological Therapy of Pigmented Skins. Boca Raton, FL: CRC/Taylor & Francis, 2006:91-114

41   Badreshia-Bansal S, Draelos ZD. Insight into skin lightening cosmeceuticals for women of Color. J Drugs Dermatol 2007;6:32-39

42 Spencer MS. Topical use of hydroquinone for depigmentation. JAMA 1965;194:962-964

43 Arndt KA, Fitzpatrick TB. Topical use of hydroquinone as a depigmenting agent. JAMA 1965;194:965

44 Anderson B. Corneal and conjunctival pigmentation among workers engaged in manufacture of hydroquinone. Arch Ophthal 1947;38:812-826

45 Ahuja B. Berufsschädigung des Auges bei Arbeitern in Hydrochinon-Betreiben: Sitzungsbericht, April 26, 1947. Klin Monatsbl Augenk 1948;113:177 (article in German) (data cited in ref. 43)

46 Jirasek L, Kalensky J. Kontakni alergicky ekzema z Krmnychsmesi v zivocisne vyrobe. Csekoslovenskti Dermatologie 1975; 50:217 (article in Czech) (data cited in ref. 47)

47 Van der Walle HB, Delbressine LPC, Seutter K. Concomitant sensitization to hydroquinone and p-methoxyphenol in the guinea pig; inhibitors in acrylic monomers. Contact Dermatitis 1982;8:147-154

48 Tse TW. Hydroquinone for skin lightening: safety profile, duration of use and when should we stop? J Dermatolog Treat 2010;21:272-275

49 Ruocco V, Florio M. Fish-odor syndrome: An olfactory diagnosis. Int J Dermatol 1995;34:92-93

50 Olumide YM, Akinkugbe AO, Altraide D, Mohammed T, Ahamefule N, Ayanlono S, et al. Complications of chronic use of skin lightening cosmetics. Int J Dermatol 2008;47:344-353

51 Siak KT, Chee SS, Chee LG. Hydroquinone-induced exogenous ochronosis in Chinese – Two case reports and a review. Int J Dermatol 2008;47:639-640

52 Charlín R, Barcaui CB, Kac BK, Soares DB, Rabello Fonseca R, Azulay-Abulafia L. Hydroquinone-induced exogenous ochronosis: A report of four cases and usefulness of dermoscopy. Int J Dermatol 2008;47:19-23

53 Ladizinski B, Mistry N, Kundu RV. Widespread use of toxic skin lightening compounds: medical and psychosocial aspects. Dermatol Clin 2011;29:111-123

54 O'Donoghue JL. Hydroquinone and its analogues in dermatology – a risk–benefit viewpoint. J Cosmet Dermatol 2006;5:196-203

55 Van Ketel WG. Sensitization to hydroquinone and the monobenzyl ether of hydroquinone. Contact Dermatitis 1984;10:253

56 Bentley-Phillips B, Bayles MAH. Cutaneous reactions to topical application of hydroquinone. S Afr Med J 1975;49:1391-1395

57 Mann RJ, Harman RR. Nail staining due to hydroquinone skin-lightening creams. Br J Dermatol 1983;108:363-365

58 Garcia RL, White JW Jr, Willis WF. Hydroquinone nail pigmentation. Arch Dermatol 1978;114:1402-1403

59 Barrientos N, Ortiz-Frutos J, Gómez E, Iglesias L. Allergic contact dermatitis from a bleaching cream. Am J Cont Derm 2001;12:33-34

60 Smith TL. Depigmentation from 2% hydroquinone cream. The Shoch Letter 1981;31:48

61 Desmedt B, Van Hoeck E, Rogiers V, Courselle P, De Beer JO, De Paepe K, Deconinck E. Characterization of suspected illegal skin whitening cosmetics. J Pharm Biomed Anal 2014;90:85-91

62 Karamagi C, Owino E, Katabira ET. Hydroquinone neuropathy following use of skin bleaching creams: Case report. East African Medical Journal 2001;78:223-224

63 Nordlund JJ, Grimes PE, Ortonne JP. The safety of hydroquinone. J Eur Acad Dermatol Venereol 2006;20:781-787

64 Naumann G. Corneal damage in hydroquinone workers. Arch Ophthalmol 1966;76:189-194

65 DeCaprio AP. The toxicology of hydroquinone – relevance to occupational and environmental exposure. Crit Rev Toxicol 1999;29:283-330

66 Toombs EL. Hydroquinone – What is its future? Dermatol Ther 2007;20:149-156

67 Parlak AH, Aydogan I, Kavak A. Discolouration of fingernails from using hydroquinone skin lightening cream. J Cosmet Dermatol 2003;2:199-201

68 Ozluer SM, Muir J. Nail staining from hydroquinone cream. Australas J Dermatol 2000;41:255-256

69 Glazer A, Sofen BD, Gallo ES. Nail discoloration after use of hydroquinone. JAAD Case Rep 2016;2:57-58

70 Mishra SN, Dhurat RS, Deshpande DJ, Nayak CS. Diagnostic utility of dermatoscopy in hydroquinone-induced exogenous ochronosis. Int J Dermatol 2013;52:413-417

71 Andersen FA, Bergfeld WF, Belsito DV, Hill RA, Klaassen CD, Liebler DC, Marks JG Jr, Shank RC, Slaga TJ, Snyder PW. Final amended safety assessment of hydroquinone as used in cosmetics. Int J Toxicol 2010;29(6 Suppl.):274S-287S

72 Ly F, Kane A, Déme A, Ngom NF, Niang SO, Bello R, et al. First cases of squamous cell carcinoma associated with cosmetic use of bleaching compounds. Ann Dermatol Venereol 2010;137:128-131 (article in French).

73 Moche MJ, Glassman SJ, Modi D, Grayson W. Cutaneous annular sarcoidosis developing on a background of exogenous ochronosis: a report of two cases and review of the literature. Clin Exp Dermatol 2010;35:399-402

74 Jacyk WK. Annular granulomatous lesions in exogenous ochronosis are a manifestation of sarcoidosis. Am J Dermatopathol 1995;17:18-22

75 Thomas P, Schuh A, Eben R, Thomsen M. Allergy to bone cement components. Orthopäde 2008;37:117-120 (Article in German)

76 Eben R, Dietrich KA, Nerz C, Schneider S, Schuh A, Banke IJ, Mazoochian F, Thomas P. Contact allergy to metals and bone cement components in patients with intolerance of arthroplasty. Dtsch Med Wochenschr 2010;135:1418-1322 (article in German)

77 Barbaud A, Reichert-Penetrat S, Trechot P, Granel F, Schmutz JL. Sensitization to resorcinol in a prescription verrucide preparation: unusual systemic clinical features and prevalence. Ann Dermatol Venereol 2001;128:615-618 (article in French)

78 Kanerva L, Jolanki R, Alanko K, Estlander T. Patch-test reactions to plastic and glue allergens. Acta Derm Venereol 1999;79:296-300

79 Fisher AA. Differential diagnosis of idiopathic vitiligo from contact leukoderma. Part II: Leukoderma due to cosmetics and bleaching creams. Cutis 1994;53:232-234

80 Das M, Tandon A. Occupational vitiligo. Contact Dermatitis 1988;18:184-185

81 Choudat D, Neukirch F, Brochard P, Barrat G, Marsac J, Conso F, Philbert M. Allergy and occupational exposure to hydroquinone and to methionine. Br J Ind Med 1988;45:376-380

82 Cinotti E, Labeille B, Douchet C, Cambazard F, Perrot JL; groupe imagerie cutanée non invasive de la Société Française de Dermatologie. Role of dermoscopy and reflectance confocal microscopy as an aid in the diagnosis of exogenous ochronosis. Ann Dermatol Venereol 2016;143:318-320 (article in French)

83 Bhattar PA, Zawar VP, Godse KV, Patil SP, Nadkarni NJ, Gautam MM. Exogenous ochronosis. Indian J Dermatol 2015;60:537-543

84 Simmons BJ, Griffith RD, Bray FN, Falto-Aizpurua LA, Nouri K. Exogenous ochronosis: a comprehensive review of the diagnosis, epidemiology, causes, and treatments. Am J Clin Dermatol 2015;16:205-212

85 Nagler A, Hale CS, Meehan SA, Leger M. Exogenous ochronosis. Dermatol Online J 2014;20(12). pii: 13030/qt0v91k51s

86 Liu WC, Tey HL, Lee JS, Goh BK. Exogenous ochronosis in a Chinese patient: use of dermoscopy aids early diagnosis and selection of biopsy site. Singapore Med J 2014;55:e1-3

87 Gandhi V, Verma P, Naik G. Exogenous ochronosis after prolonged use of topical hydroquinone (2%) in a 50-year-old Indian female. Indian J Dermatol 2012;57:394-395

88 Martins VM, Sousa AR, Portela Nde C, Tigre CA, Gonçalves LM, Castro Filho RJ. Exogenous ochronosis: case report and literature review. An Bras Dermatol 2012;87:633-636

89 Ribas J, Schettini AP, Cavalcante Mde S. Exogenous ochronosis hydroquinone induced: a report of four cases. An Bras Dermatol 2010;85:699-703

90 Tan SK. Exogenous ochronosis-a diagnostic challenge. J Cosmet Dermatol 2010;9:313-317

91 Tan SK. Exogenous ochronosis in ethnic Chinese Asians: a clinicopathological study, diagnosis and treatment. J Eur Acad Dermatol Venereol 2011;25:842-850

92 Gil I, Segura S, Martínez-Escala E, Lloreta J, Puig S, Vélez M, Pujol RM, Herrero-González JE. Dermoscopic and reflectance confocal microscopic features of exogenous ochronosis. Arch Dermatol 2010;146:1021-1025

93 Merola JF, Meehan S, Walters RF, Brown L. Exogenous ochronosis. Dermatol Online J 2008;14(10):6

94 Tan SK, Sim CS, Goh CL. Hydroquinone-induced exogenous ochronosis in Chinese--two case reports and a review. Int J Dermatol 2008;47:639-640

95 Charlín R, Barcaui CB, Kac BK, Soares DB, Rabello-Fonseca R, Azulay-Abulafia L. Hydroquinone-induced exogenous ochronosis: a report of four cases and usefulness of dermoscopy. Int J Dermatol 2008;47:19-23

96 Ndoye Roth PA, Ly F, Kane H, Bissang AA, Wane AM, Sow AS, et al. Ocular lesions of artificial depigmentation. J Fr Ophtalmol 2015;38:493-496 (article in French)

2.239   HYDROXYDECYL UBIQUINONE

IDENTIFICATION

Description/definition	: Hydroxydecyl ubiquinone is the organic compound that conforms to the formula shown below
Chemical class(es)	: Alcohols; ethers; ketones
Chemical/IUPAC name	: 2-(10-Hydroxydecyl)-5,6-dimethoxy-3-methylcyclohexa-2,5-diene-1,4-dione
Other names	: Idebenone
CAS registry number (s)	: 58186-27-9
Merck Index monograph	: 6199
Function(s) in cosmetics	: EU: antioxidant. USA: antioxidants
Patch testing	: 1% pet. (1); 0.5% pet. (2,3,4); neither concentration is irritant
Molecular formula	: $C_{19}H_{30}O_5$

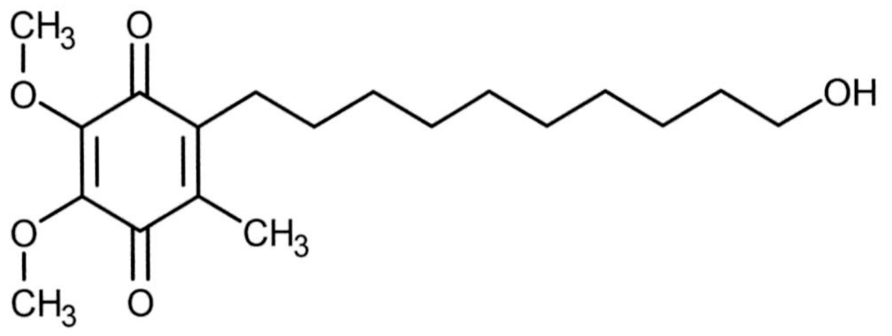

GENERAL

Hydroxydecyl ubiquinone (idebenone), a potent antioxidant, is a synthetic analogue of coenzyme Q10. It has been shown to inhibit lipid peroxidation, to maintain mitochondrial electron transport, and to stimulate nerve growth factor. It has been used orally in the treatment of Alzheimer's disease, Friedreich's ataxia, cerebrovascular disease, and liver disease. Hydroxydecyl ubiquinone-containing cosmeceuticals may claim to reduce wrinkles and other signs of aging by quenching free radicals in the epidermis (2).

CONTACT ALLERGY

Case reports and case series

A woman went to a beauty salon and received a facial treatment with an 'anti-aging' cream. Within 24 hours, she developed a severe, edematous and vesicular dermatitis of the face, ears, and neck. Patch testing was performed three months later with the North American Contact Dermatitis Group standard series and with the antimicrobials /vehicles/cosmetics series and the cream itself. The only reaction was to the anti-aging cream. The manufacturer provided a patch testing kit, with the individual ingredients of the cream premixed in petrolatum at the concentration used in the finished product. One ingredient was positive, which was idebenone, tested 0.5% pet. No reaction was observed in 20 control subjects tested with the same ingredient (2). Three similar patients with allergic contact dermatitis from hydroxydecyl ubiquinone in an anti-ageing cream (all of the same brand) were reported soon after this first publication of (1,3,4,5 [refs. 4 and 5 present the same patient]) and at least one more case was reported to the manufacturer (2).

Presence in cosmetic products and chemical analyses

In the USA, in April 2017, hydroxydecyl ubiquinone was present in zero of 56,714 cosmetic products of which the composition is known in FDA's Voluntary Cosmetic Registration Program (VCRP) (data obtained from FDA, May 2017). In March 2017, hydroxydecyl ubiquinone was present in 4 of 65,351 cosmetic products of which the composition is known in EWG's Skin Deep Cosmetics Database, USA (http://www.ewg.org/skindeep/).

LITERATURE

1   McAleer MA, Collins P. Allergic contact dermatitis to hydroxydecyl ubiquinone (idebenone) following application of anti-ageing cosmetic cream. Contact Dermatitis 2008;59:178-179

2   Sasseville D, Moreau L, Al-Sowaidi. Allergic contact dermatitis to idebenone used as an antioxidant in an anti-wrinkle cream. Contact Dermatitis 2007;56:117-118

3   Natkunarajah J, Ostlere L. Allergic contact dermatitis to idebenone in an over-the-counter anti-aging cream. Contact Dermatitis 2008;58:239

4   Fleming JD, White JML, White IR. Allergic contact dermatitis to hydroxydecyl ubiquinone: a newly described contact allergen in cosmetics. Br J Dermatol 2007;157 (Suppl. 1): 82–83

5   Fleming JD, White JML, White IR. Allergic contact dermatitis to hydroxydecyl ubiquinone: a newly described contact allergen in cosmetics. Contact Dermatitis 2008;58:245

2.240   HYDROXYETHYL ACRYLATE*
Not an INCI name

IDENTIFICATION

Description/definition : Hydroxyethyl acrylate is the organic compound that conforms to the formula shown
                         below
Chemical class(es)   : Esters
INCI name USA   : Neither in CosIng nor in the Personal Care Products Council Ingredient Database
Chemical/IUPAC name   : 2-Hydroxyethyl prop-2-enoate
CAS registry number (s) : 818-61-1
EC number(s)   : 212-454-9
Patch testing   : 0.1% pet. (Chemotechnique, SmartPracticeEurope, SmartPracticeCanada)
Molecular formula   : $C_5H_8O_3$

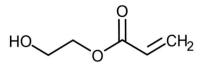

GENERAL

Discussion of contact allergy to (meth)acrylates *from non-cosmetic sources* is considered to fall outside the scope of this book. Therefore, only contact allergy from their presence in cosmetics is presented, which virtually always is from artificial nails. There are many reports of contact allergy to artificial nails, but the specific sensitizers have rarely been identified and – consequently - such publications are not presented in this and other acrylate and methacrylate monographs. Discussion is limited to publications in which the culprit (meth)acrylates have been identified, e.g., from information found in Material Data Safety Sheets, data obtained from the manufacturer or from chemical analyses.

Patients often react to many (meth)acrylates on patch testing. Primary sensitization to methacrylates may result in both methacrylate and acrylate cross-sensitization. Conversely, patients sensitized to acrylates are unlikely to show cross-sensitization to methacrylates (4).

General aspects of acrylates and methacrylates are presented in Chapter 2.219 HEMA (hydroxyethyl methacrylate). A discussion of general aspects of artificial nails, contact allergy to these products, the clinical picture of allergic contact dermatitis and other side effects of sculptured nails can also be found there. A very useful review of contact sensitization to allergens in nail cosmetics, with emphasis on acrylic manicures, was published in 2017 (10).

CONTACT ALLERGY

Patch testing in groups of patients
Studies in which consecutive patients suspected of contact dermatitis have been tested with hydroxyethyl acrylate (routine testing) and studies testing groups of selected patients are planned to be discussed in a future publication.

Case reports and case series
Hydroxyethyl acrylate was stated to be the (or an) allergen in 2 patients in a group of 603 individuals suffering from cosmetic dermatitis, seen in the period 2010-2015 in Leuven, Belgium (7). In the period 1996-2013, in a tertiary referral center in Valencia, Spain, 5419 patients were patch tested. Of these, 628 individuals had allergic contact dermatitis to cosmetics. Hydroxyethyl acrylate was the responsible allergen in 14 cases (8). Hydroxyethyl acrylate was responsible for 1 out of 959 cases of non-fragrance cosmetic allergy where the causal allergen was identified, Belgium, 2000-2010 (1). A group of 55 female patients presenting with hand eczema, who had contact with artificial nails, were patch tested with a series of acrylates in one center in Israel, 2001-2004. Twenty-one had one or more positive reactions, of who 14 were professional beauticians specializing in nail sculpturing. All reactions, including 8 to hydroxyethyl acrylate, were stated to be of current relevance (2). Because of the general lack of information on the composition of artificial nail materials, the fact that the author did no analyses of these products and the frequent occurrence of cross-reactivity among acrylates, one may wonder whether this statement can be accepted as entirely correct.

Six women who had experienced adverse reactions from an UV-cured nail polish had positive patch tests to its ingredient 'urethane acrylates'. This was described as a mixed isocyanate - acrylate polymer, containing hydroxyethyl acrylate (6). For more details see Chapter 2.490 Urethane acrylates. One patient had allergic contact dermatitis from an 'anti-cellulite'/'intense firming' cream; she reacted to the cream, hydroxyethyl acrylate, and various methacrylates (3). The cream did not list hydroxyethyl acrylate as a component, but hydroxyethyl acrylate/sodium acryloyldimethyltaurate copolymer was a component. The authors suggest, that this copolymer contained enough acrylate monomer to be responsible for the allergy, but chemical analysis could not be performed (3). A cosmetician teaching other cosmeticians how to make artificial nails developed occupational contact dermatitis of the hands and face from contact allergy to hydroxyethyl acrylate in UV-curing nail gel (5). Gas chromatography – mass spectrometry (GC-MS) showed the product to contain 2% hydroxyethyl acrylate (5).

Patch test sensitization
Two patients became sensitized from a patch test with 2-hydroxyethyl acrylate 0.5% pet. (9).

Presence in cosmetic products and chemical analyses
In the USA, in April 2017, 2-hydroxyethyl acrylate was present in 3 of 56,714 cosmetic products of which the composition is known in FDA's Voluntary Cosmetic Registration Program (VCRP) (data obtained from FDA, May 2017). In February 2017, hydroxyethyl acrylate was present in 8 of 64,480 cosmetic products of which the composition is known in EWG's Skin Deep Cosmetics Database, USA (http://www.ewg.org/skindeep/).

LITERATURE
1   Travassos AR, Claes L, Boey L, Drieghe J, Goossens A. Non-fragrance allergens in specific cosmetic products. Contact Dermatitis 2011;65:276-285
2   Lazarov A. Sensitization to acrylates is a common adverse reaction to artificial fingernails. J Eur Acad Derm Venereol 2007;21:169-174
3   Lucidarme N, Aerts O, Roelandts R, Goossens, A. Hydroxyethyl acrylate: a potential allergen in cosmetic creams?. Contact Dermatitis 2008;59:321-322
4   Aalto-Korte K, Henriks-Eckerman M-L, Kuuliala O, Jolanki R. Occupational methacrylate and acrylate allergy – cross-reactions and possible screening allergens. Contact Dermatitis 2010;63:301-312
5   Kanerva L, Lauerma A, Estlander T, Alanko K, Henriks-Eckerman ML, Jolanki R. Occupational allergic contact dermatitis caused by photobonded sculptured nails and a review of (meth) acrylates in nail cosmetics. Am J Contact Dermatitis 1996;7:109-115
6   Dahlin J, Berne B, Dunér K, Hosseiny S, Matura M, Nyman G, et al. Several cases of undesirable effects caused by methacrylate ultraviolet-curing nail polish for non-professional use. Contact Dermatitis 2016;75:151-156
7   Goossens A. Cosmetic contact allergens. Cosmetics 2016, 3, 5; doi:10.3390/cosmetics3010005
8   Zaragoza-Ninet V, Blasco Encinas R, Vilata-Corell JJ, Pérez-Ferriols A, Sierra-Talamantes C, Esteve-Martínez A, de la Cuadra-Oyanguren J. Allergic contact dermatitis due to cosmetics: A clinical and epidemiological study in a tertiary hospital. Actas Dermosifiliogr 2016;107:329-336
9   Kanerva L, Estlander T, Jolanki R. Sensitization to patch test acrylates. Contact Dermatitis 1988;18:10-15
10   Chou M, Dhingra N, Strugar TL. Contact sensitization to allergens in nail cosmetics. Dermatitis 2017;28:231-240

2.241   2-HYDROXYETHYLAMINO-5-NITROANISOLE

IDENTIFICATION

Description/definition   : 2-Hydroxyethylamino-5-nitroanisole is the substituted aromatic compound that
                             conforms to the formula shown below
Chemical class(es)   : Amines; color additives - hair
Chemical/IUPAC name   : 2-(2-Methoxy-4-nitroanilino)ethanol
Other names   : 2-[(2-Methoxy-4-nitrophenyl)amino]ethanol; ethanol, 2-((2-methoxy-4-nitrophenyl)
                             amino)-
CAS registry number (s)   : 66095-81-6
EC number(s)   : 266-138-0
Function(s) in cosmetics   : EU: hair dyeing. USA: hair colorants
EU cosmetic restrictions   : Regulated in Annex III/236 of the Regulation (EC) No. 1223/2009
Patch testing   : 0.06% alc. 95% / water (50/50) (1)
Molecular formula   : $C_9H_{12}N_2O_4$

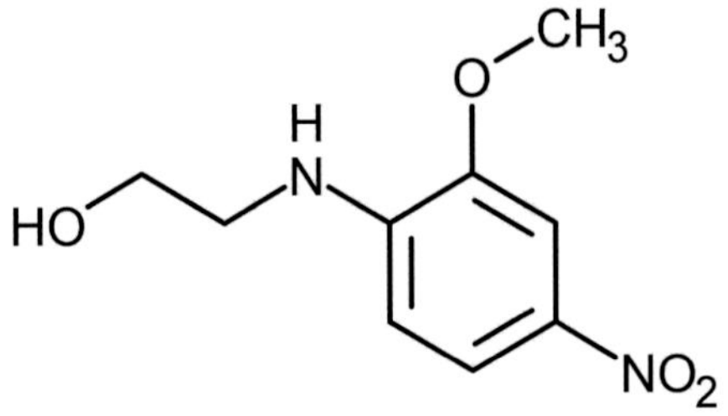

GENERAL

2-Hydroxyethylamino-5-nitroanisole belongs to the amine class coloring substances and is used in semi-permanent non-oxidative hair dying products. Its color is yellow (1).

CONTACT ALLERGY

Case reports and case series

A woman presented with an edema of the face and eczema of the scalp, which had been present for 6 days and had started two days after the use of a semi-permanent hair coloring preparation. The edema was more pronounced on the left side of the face. She had presented a similar episode 6 months before, after a coloration at her hairdresser. Patch tests were negative to the European standard series (including *p*-phenylenediamine) and to the hairdressing series. A semi-open test with the hair dye as is was positive. The patient was then patch tested with the components of the hair dye obtained from the manufacturer, which were diluted in ethanol 95% and water (50/50). A positive test was obtained with 2-hydroxyethylamino-5-nitroanisole 0.06%. Ten controls were negative (1).

Presence in cosmetic products and chemical analyses

In the USA, in April 2017, 2-hydroxyethylamino-5-nitroanisole was present in zero of 56,714 cosmetic products of which the composition is known in FDA's Voluntary Cosmetic Registration Program (VCRP) (data obtained from FDA, May 2017). In March 2017, 2-hydroxyethylamino-5-nitroanisole was present in one older product of 64,983 cosmetic products of which the composition is known in EWG's Skin Deep Cosmetics Database, USA (http://www. ewg.org/skindeep/).

LITERATURE

1   Dejobert Y, Piette F, Thomas P. Contact dermatitis to 2-hydroxyethylamino-5-nitroanisole and 3-nitro-p-
    hydroxyethyl aminophenol in a hair dye. Contact Dermatitis 2006;54:217-218

2.242   N,N-BIS(2-HYDROXYETHYL)-P-PHENYLENEDIAMINE SULFATE

IDENTIFICATION

Description/definition   : *N,N*-bis(2-Hydroxyethyl)-*p*-phenylenediamine sulfate is the substituted aromatic amine that conforms to the formula shown below

Chemical class(es)   : Amines; color additives - hair

Chemical/IUPAC name   : 2-[4-Amino-*N*-(2-hydroxyethyl)anilino]ethanol;sulfuric acid

Other names   : (*p*-Ammoniophenyl)bis(2-hydroxyethyl)ammonium sulphate

CAS registry number (s)   : 54381-16-7; 57524-61-5; 58262-44-5

CIR review(s)   : J Am Coll Toxicol 1992;11:129-143 (access: www.cir-safety.org/ingredients)

SCCS opinion(s)   : SCCP/0983/06 (2); SCCS/1572/16 (14)

Function(s) in cosmetics   : EU: hair dyeing. USA: hair colorants

EU cosmetic restrictions   : Regulated in Annex III/I/253 of the Directive 2012/21/EU

Patch testing   : 1% pet. (5)

Molecular formula   : $C_{10}H_{18}N_2O_6S$

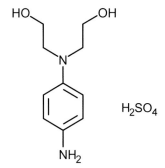

H_2SO_4

GENERAL

N,N-bis(2-Hydroxyethyl)-*p*-phenylenediamine sulfate is used in oxidative hair dying products. The chemistry of oxidative hair dying is discussed in Chapter 2.359 *p*-Phenylenediamine

CONTACT ALLERGY

Patch testing in groups of patients

In 2007-2008, in 3 European countries, 847 consecutive patients suspected of contact dermatitis were patch tested with *N,N*-bis(2-hydroxyethyl)-*p*-phenylenediamine sulfate 1% pet. (routine testing) and two patients had a positive patch test reaction. The relevance of these reactions was not mentioned (5). In 2012-2014, in Japan, 194 patients suspected of allergic contact dermatitis from hair dyes or perming solutions, of who 13% were hairdressers, were tested and 4 (2.1%) reacted to *N,N*-bis(2-hydroxyethyl)-*p*-phenylenediamine sulfate. All were hairdressers, but the relevance of the observed positive patch test reactions was not mentioned (13).

Case reports and case series

bis(Hydroxyethyl)-*p*-phenylenediamine sulfate was stated to be the (or an) allergen in one patient in a group of 603 individuals suffering from cosmetic dermatitis, seen in the period 2010-2015 in Leuven, Belgium (1).

Cross-reactions, pseudo-cross-reactions and co-reactions

N,N-bis(2-Hydroxyethyl)-*p*-phenylenediamine sulfate may cross-react with structurally related chemicals, notably those with a para-structure. Cross-reactivity between para-compounds is discussed in Chapter 2.359 *p*-Phenylenediamine.

Presence in cosmetic products and chemical analyses

In the USA, in April 2017, *N,N*-bis(2-hydroxyethyl)-*p*-phenylenediamine sulfate was present in 417 of 56,714 cosmetic products of which the composition is known in FDA's Voluntary Cosmetic Registration Program (VCRP) (data obtained from FDA, May 2017). In April 2017, *N,N*-bis(hydroxyethyl)-*p*-phenylenediamine sulfate was present in 73 of 66,485 cosmetic products of which the composition is known in EWG's Skin Deep Cosmetics Database, USA (http://www.ewg.org/skindeep/). In 2016, in Sweden, the labels of 26 oxidative hair dye products advertised with the signal words organic, natural or similar, or sold/used at a hair dressing salon advertised with the same terminology, were screened for the presence of known contact allergens. *N,N*-bis(2-Hydroxyethyl)-*p*-phenylenediamine sulfate was present in 1 (4%) product (4). In 2013-2014, labeled ingredient information from 252 home use and professional hair dye products (210 permanent and 42 non-permanent dyes) from 48 brands sold in Bangkok, Thailand, was collected to identify the type and frequency of potent contact sensitizers. *N,N*-bis(2-Hydroxyethyl)-*p*-phenylenediamine sulfate was present in 31 (12.3%) products (3).

In southern Germany, in 2013-2014, the labels of 924 permanent oxidative hair dyes were checked for the presence of hair dye components. There were 334 retail products (of seven different brands) and 590 professional products (of six different brands). The 924 products analyzed revealed a total of 58 different hair dye components, with retail products containing 32 and professional products 52. *N,N*-bis(2-Hydroxyethyl)-*p*-phenylenediamine sulfate was present in 3.7% of the 924 products (7). In 2013, in Korea, the labels of 99 oxidative hair dyes produced by Korean domestic manufacturers were examined for potent skin sensitizers. *N,N*-bis(2-Hydroxyethyl)-*p*-phenylenediamine sulfate was found to be present in 3(3%) of the hair dyes (9). In the USA, in 2012, ingredient labels of 107 different consumer oxidative hair dyes from 10 different companies were assessed in stores across the city of Phoenix, Arizona. *N,N*-bis(2-Hydroxyethyl)-*p*-phenylenediamine (as free base, sulfate, or HCl) was present in 41% of the products (8).

In 2011, labels and other information on 365 hair dye products (282 permanent dyes, 79 semi-permanent dyes, 4 direct dyes) available on the Danish market (159 hair dyes for private use, 206 for professional use by hairdressers) were collected to identify the presence of sensitizers. *N,N*-bis(2-Hydroxyethyl)-*p*-phenylenediamine sulfate was present in 24 (7%) products (6). In April 2010, in Spain, 111 consumer-available oxidative hair dye products of 19 brands were purchased to check the labeling for sensitizers. A systematic selection of products to be purchased from each hair dye brand was applied, including the darkest blonde shade available, one 'regular' light brown shade, one 'regular' dark brown shade, one 'regular' black shade, and two further shades with different colours (red, blue, purple, etc.). In this group of 111 hair dyes, *N,N*-bis(2-hydroxyethyl)-*p*-phenylenediamine sulfate was present in 18% of the products (11). In August - October 2008, the labels of 122 oxidative hair dye products on the Swedish market were examined for the presence of hair dye substances categorized as potent skin sensitizers. *N,N*-bis(2-Hydroxyethyl)-*p*-phenylenediamine sulfate was present in 13 of these products (10).

LITERATURE

1   Goossens A. Cosmetic contact allergens. Cosmetics 2016, 3, 5; doi:10.3390/cosmetics3010005
2   SCCP (Scientific Committee on Consumer Products). Opinion on *N,N*-bis(2-hydroxyethyl)-*p*-phenylenediamine sulfate, SCCP/0983/06
3   Boonchai W, Bunyavaree M, Winayanuwattikun W, Kasemsarn P. Contact sensitizers in commercial hair dye products sold in Thailand. Contact Dermatitis 2016;74:222-229
4   Thorén S, Yazar K. Contact allergens in 'natural' hair dyes. Contact Dermatitis 2016;74:302-304
5   Søsted H, Rustemeyer T, Gonçalo M, Bruze M, Goossens A, Giménez-Arnau AM, et al. Contact allergy to common ingredients in hair dyes. Contact Dermatitis 2013;69:32-39
6   The Danish Environmental Protection Agency. Survey and occurrence of PPD, PTD and other allergenic hair dye substances in hair dyes. Copenhagen, Denmark: The Danish Environmental Protection Agency, 2013 (ISBN 978-87-92903-92-1). Available at: http://www2.mst.dk/Udgiv/publications/2013/02/978-87-92903-92-1.pdf
7   Kirchlecher S, Hübner A, Uter W. Survey of sensitizing constituents of oxidative hair dyes (retail and professional products) in Germany. J Dtsch Dermatol Ges 2016;14:707-715
8   Hamann D, Yazar K, Hamann CR, Thyssen JP, Lidén C. p-Phenylenediamine and other allergens in hair dye products in the United States: a consumer exposure study. Contact Dermatitis 2014;70:213-218
9   Kim H, Kim K. Prevalence of potent skin sensitizers in oxidative hair dye products in Korea. Cutan Ocul Toxicol 2016;35:204-207
10   Yazar K, Boman A, Lidén C. Potent skin sensitizers in oxidative hair dye products on the Swedish market. Contact Dermatitis 2009;61:269-275
11   Yazar K, Boman A, Lidén C. *p*-Phenylenediamine and other hair dye sensitizers in Spain. Contact Dermatitis 2012;66:27-32
12   Ito A, Nishioka K, Kanto H, Yagami A, Yamada S, Sugiura M, et al. A multi-institutional joint study of contact dermatitis related to hair colouring and perming agents in Japan. Contact Dermatitis 2017;77:42-48
13   Ito A, Nishioka K, Kanto H, Yagami A, Yamada S, Sugiura M, et al. A multi-institutional joint study of contact dermatitis related to hair colouring and perming agents in Japan. Contact Dermatitis 2017;77:42-48
14   SCCS (Scientific Committee on Consumer Safety). Opinion on *N,N'*-Bis-(2-hydroxyethyl)-2-nitro-*p*-phenylenediamine, SCCS/1572/16, September 2016. Available at: https://ec.europa.eu/health/scientific_committees/consumer_safety/docs/sccs_o_196.pdf

2.243 HYDROXYPROPYL METHACRYLATE

IDENTIFICATION

Description/definition	: Hydroxypropyl methacrylate is the organic compound that conforms to the formula shown below
Chemical class(es)	: Alcohols; esters
Chemical/IUPAC name	: 2-Hydroxypropyl 2-methyl-2-propenoate
Other names	: 2-Propenoic acid, 2-methyl-, monoester with 1,2-propanediol
CAS registry number (s)	: 27813-02-1; 923-26-2
EC number(s)	: 248-666-3
CIR review(s)	: Int J Toxicol 2005;24(Suppl.5):53-100 (access: www.cir-safety.org/ingredients)
Function(s) in cosmetics	: EU: film forming. USA: artificial nail builders
Patch testing	: 2.0% pet. (Chemotechnique, SmartPracticeEurope, SmartPracticeCanada)
Molecular formula	: $C_7H_{12}O_3$

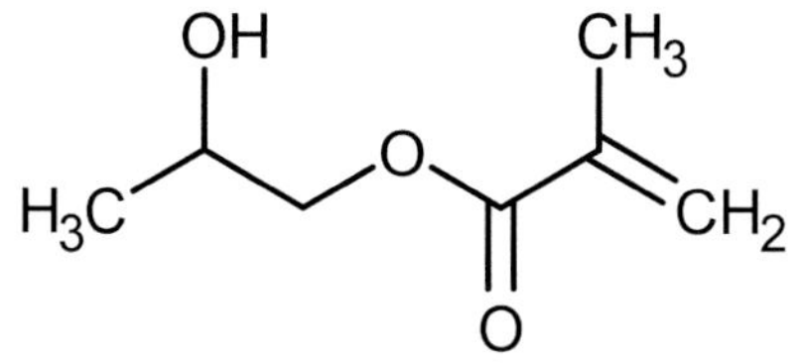

GENERAL

Discussion of contact allergy to (meth)acrylates *from non-cosmetic sources* is considered to fall outside the scope of this book. Therefore, only contact allergy from their presence in cosmetics is presented, which virtually always is from artificial nails. There are many reports of contact allergy to artificial nails, but the specific sensitizers have rarely been identified and – consequently - such publications are not presented in this and other acrylate and methacrylate monographs. Discussion is limited to publications in which the culprit (meth)acrylates have been identified, e.g., from information found in Material Data Safety Sheets, data obtained from the manufacturer or from chemical analyses.

Patients often react to many (meth)acrylates on patch testing. Primary sensitization to methacrylates may result in both methacrylate and acrylate cross-sensitization. Conversely, patients sensitized to acrylates are unlikely to show cross-sensitization to methacrylates (3).

General aspects of acrylates and methacrylates are presented in Chapter 2.219 HEMA (hydroxyethyl methacrylate). A discussion of general aspects of artificial nails, contact allergy to these products, the clinical picture of allergic contact dermatitis and other side effects of sculptured nails can also be found there. A very useful review of contact sensitization to allergens in nail cosmetics, with emphasis on acrylic manicures, was published in 2017 (7).

CONTACT ALLERGY

Patch testing in groups of patients

Studies in which consecutive patients suspected of contact dermatitis have been tested with hydroxypropyl methacrylate (routine testing) and studies testing groups of selected patients are planned to be discussed in a future publication.

Case reports and case series

Hydroxypropyl methacrylate was stated to be the (or an) allergen in 3 patients in a group of 603 individuals suffering from cosmetic dermatitis, seen in the period 2010-2015 in Leuven, Belgium (4). In the period 1996-2013, in a tertiary referral center in Valencia, Spain, 5419 patients were patch tested. Of these, 628 individuals had allergic contact dermatitis to cosmetics. Hydroxypropyl methacrylate was the responsible allergen in 18 cases (5).

A group of 55 female patients presenting with hand eczema and who had contact with artificial nails, were patch tested with a series of acrylates in one center in Israel, 2001-2004. Twenty-one had one or more positive reactions, of who 14 were professional beauticians specializing in nail sculpturing. All reactions, including 17 to hydroxypropyl methacrylate, were stated to be of current relevance (1). Because of the general lack of information on the composition of artificial nail materials, the fact that the author did no analyses of these products and the frequent occurrence of cross-reactivity among acrylates, one may wonder whether this statement can be accepted as entirely correct.

Between 2013 and 2016, in 4 dermatology departments in Spain, forty-three patients were diagnosed with ACD caused by (meth)acrylates in long-lasting nail polish. All were female, and all had hand dermatitis. Patients were mostly less than 40 years old and had an occupational cause of their dermatitis (93%, beauticians), which developed ~10 months after they had started to use the technique of applying long-lasting nail polish in their clients. The most frequently reacting patch test allergens were 2-hydroxypropyl methacrylate (41/43 [95%]), 2-hydroxyethyl methacrylate (HEMA) (39/43 [91%]), and tetrahydrofurfuryl methacrylate (31/39 [79%]). These three allergens were also the (meth)acrylate compounds most frequently identified on the labels of the patients' products (8).

One patient had allergic contact dermatitis from hydroxypropyl methacrylate in a nail liquid for making artificial nails (2). A manicurist had occupational, partly airborne, allergic contact dermatitis from hydroxypropyl methacrylate in a nail liquid, nail strengthener and a UV-cured nail gel (2).

Patch test sensitization
A patch test with 2-hydroxypropyl methacrylate 2% pet. sensitized one patient (6).

Presence in cosmetic products and chemical analyses
In August 2017, hydroxypropyl methacrylate was present in 63 of 70,693 cosmetic products of which the composition is known in EWG's Skin Deep Cosmetics Database, USA (http://www.ewg.org/skindeep/). In the USA, in April 2017, hydroxypropyl methacrylate was present in 113 of 56,714 cosmetic products of which the composition is known in FDA's Voluntary Cosmetic Registration Program (VCRP) (data obtained from FDA, May 2017).

LITERATURE

1   Lazarov A. Sensitization to acrylates is a common adverse reaction to artificial fingernails. J Eur Acad Derm Venereol 2007;21:169-174
2   Erdmann SM, Sachs B, Merk HF. Adverse reactions to sculptured nails. Allergy 2001;56:581-582
3   Aalto-Korte K, Henriks-Eckerman M-L, Kuuliala O, Jolanki R. Occupational methacrylate and acrylate allergy – cross-reactions and possible screening allergens. Contact Dermatitis 2010;63:301-312
4   Goossens A. Cosmetic contact allergens. Cosmetics 2016, 3, 5; doi:10.3390/cosmetics3010005
5   Zaragoza-Ninet V, Blasco Encinas R, Vilata-Corell JJ, Pérez-Ferriols A, Sierra-Talamantes C, Esteve-Martínez A, de la Cuadra-Oyanguren J. Allergic contact dermatitis due to cosmetics: A clinical and epidemiological study in a tertiary hospital. Actas Dermosifiliogr 2016;107:329-336
6   Kanerva L, Estlander T, Jolanki R. Active sensitization caused by 2-hydroxyethyl methacrylate, 2-hydroxypropyl methacrylate, ethyleneglycol dimethacrylate and N,N-dimethylaminoethyl methacrylate. J Eur Acad Derm Venereol 1992;1:165-169
7   Chou M, Dhingra N, Strugar TL. Contact sensitization to allergens in nail cosmetics. Dermatitis 2017;28:231-240
8   Gatica-Ortega ME, Pastor-Nieto MA, Mercader-García P, Silvestre-Salvador JF. Allergic contact dermatitis caused by (meth)acrylates in long-lasting nail polish - are we facing a new epidemic in the beauty industry? Contact Dermatitis 2017 Jun 27. doi: 10.1111/cod.12827. [Epub ahead of print]

2.244   HYDROXYPROPYL TETRAHYDROPYRANTRIOL

IDENTIFICATION

Description/definition	: Hydroxypropyl tetrahydropyrantriol is the organic compound that conforms to the formula shown below
Chemical class(es)	: Ethers; polyols
Chemical/IUPAC name	: (2S,3R,4S,5R)-2-(2-Hydroxypropyl)oxane-3,4,5-triol
Other names	: L-Gluco-octitol, 1,5-anhydro-6,8-dideoxy-, (7XI)-; Pro-xylane®
CAS registry number (s)	: 439685-79-7
Function(s) in cosmetics	: EU: skin conditioning. USA: skin-conditioning agents - miscellaneous
Patch testing	: 9% alcohol /water (50:50)
Molecular formula	: $C_8H_{16}O_5$

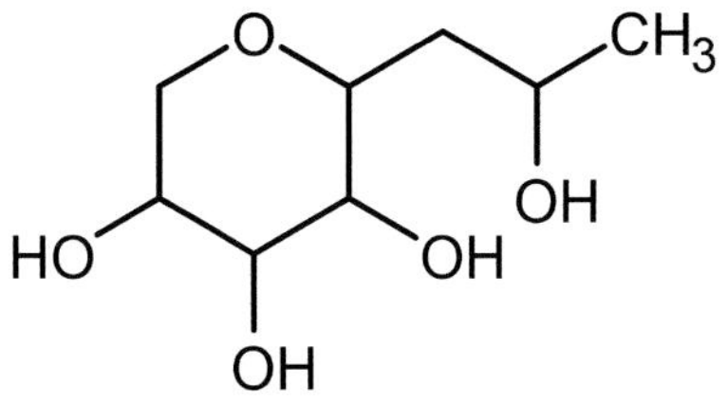

GENERAL

Hydroxypropyl tetrahydropyrantriol (Pro-Xylane®) has been used in cosmetics since 2006 as a 'natural' anti-ageing agent derived from beech wood (1). It is a sugar-protein hybrid made from xylose, a sugar found abundantly in beech trees. In a reconstructed skin model, it was shown to stimulate the production of glycosaminoglycans and heparan sulfate proteoglycan expression, to induce higher deposition of basement membrane and dermal -epidermal junction (DEJ) proteins, and to increase collagen VII gene expression. Based on this, it is supposed to have beneficial effects in aged skin by restoring DEJ integrity and by increasing the firmness of the skin (1).

CONTACT ALLERGY

Case reports and case series

A woman had suffered from two episodes of eyelid contact dermatitis related to anti-ageing creams. Patch tests were performed with the European baseline and a cosmetics series, but not with the implicated products (which she had thrown away) showed only a benzophenone allergy, which was not relevant. A few months later, the patient suffered from a third flare-up of dermatitis, after the application of a serum. Patch tests with the product and its ingredients gave positive reactions to the serum and to hydroxypropyl tetrahydropyrantriol 9% in a mixture of alcohol and water (50:50). Five control patients were negative. This ingredient was considered to be the culprit, because it was also contained in the two previously incriminated anti-ageing creams (1).

Presence in cosmetic products and chemical analyses

In July 2017, hydroxypropyl tetrahydropyrantriol was present in 29 of 69,548 cosmetic products of which the composition is known in EWG's Skin Deep Cosmetics Database, USA (http://www.ewg.org/skindeep/).

LITERATURE

1   Assier H, Wolkenstein P, Chosidow O. First case of contact dermatitis caused by hydroxypropyl tetrahydropyrantriol used in an anti-ageing cream. Contact Dermatitis 2017;77:60-61

2.245   HYDROXYSTEARIC ACID

IDENTIFICATION

Description/definition	: Hydroxystearic acid is the fatty acid that conforms generally to the formula shown below
Chemical class(es)	: Fatty acids
Chemical/IUPAC name	: 12-Hydroxyoctadecanoic acid
Other names	: 12-Hydroxystearic acid
CAS registry number (s)	: 106-14-9; 1330-70-7
EC number(s)	: 203-366-1; 215-545-1
CIR review(s)	: Int J Toxicol 1999;18(Suppl.1):1-10 (access: www.cir-safety.org/ingredients)
Function(s) in cosmetics	: EU: cleansing; emulsifying; surfactant. USA: surfactants - cleansing agents
Patch testing	: 10% pet. (2)
Molecular formula	: $C_{18}H_{36}O_3$

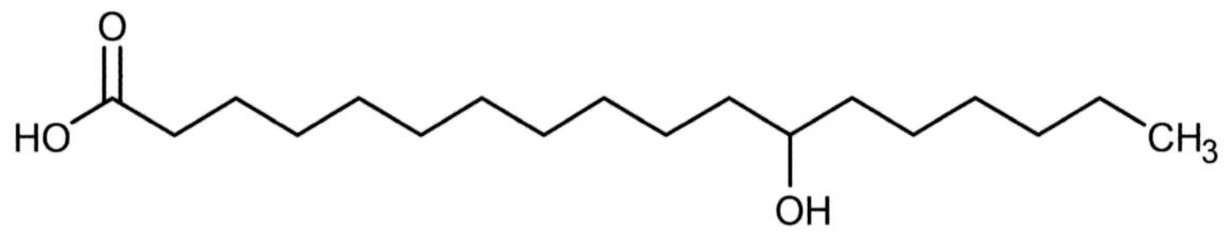

CONTACT ALLERGY

Case reports and case series

Hydroxystearic acid was responsible for 1 out of 959 cases of non-fragrance cosmetic allergy where the causal allergen was identified, Belgium, 2000-2010 (1). A woman was seen with pruritic edematous erythema and scaling on her lips. This had started 3 months after she used about 30 new cosmetic products. Positive patch test reactions were seen to 3 of her lip glosses, tested as is. She was then patch tested with 21 ingredients of these lip glosses and reacted to hydroxystearic acid 10% pet., which was present in all 3 lip products (2).

A man developed allergic contact cheilitis from a lip balm containing 4% bis-diglycerylpolyacyladipate-2 and 7%12-hydroxystearic acid. Patch testing was positive with bis-diglycerylpolyacyladipate-2 at 5% pet. and with 99.7% pure 12-hydroxystearic acid in serial dilution patch testing from 10% to 0.001% pet. There was also a positive patch test reaction to hydrogenated castor oil, in which hydroxystearic acid is the principal fatty acid. Bis-diglycerylpoly-acyladipate-2 is a partial ester of diglycerin with several fatty acids, including 10-30% adipic acid, 20-50% stearic acid, 5-10% 12-hydroxystearic acid, and 1-10% each of caprylic, capric, palmitic and isostearic acids. Patch testing in this patient was negative with glycerin and with capric, palmitic and stearic acids, which led the authors to conclude that their patient's positive patch test reaction to bis-diglycerylpolyacyladipate-2 could be explained by the 12-hydroxystearic acid that it contains (3,4).

Cross-reactions

Not to stearic acid (2,3); possibly to glyceryl stearate (2). In the text of one article it is mentioned that the patient co-reacted to stearic acid; in the table, however, the reaction was indicated as negative (2).

Presence in cosmetic products and chemical analyses

In the USA, in April 2017, hydroxystearic acid was present in 121 of 56,714 cosmetic products of which the composition is known in FDA's Voluntary Cosmetic Registration Program (VCRP) (data obtained from FDA, May 2017). In March 2017, hydroxystearic acid was present in 18 of 65,351 cosmetic products of which the composition is known in EWG's Skin Deep Cosmetics Database, USA (http://www.ewg.org/skindeep/).

LITERATURE

1   Travassos AR, Claes L, Boey L, Drieghe J, Goossens A. Non-fragrance allergens in specific cosmetic products. Contact Dermatitis 2011;65:276-285
2   Kimura M, Kawada A, Ogino M, Murayama Y. Simultaneous contact sensitivity to hydroxystearic acid and C18-36 acid triglyceride in lip glosses. Contact Dermatitis 2002;47:115
3   Shaw DW. Allergic contact dermatitis caused by bis-diglycerylpolyacyladipate-2 (Softisan® 649) owing to its 12-hydroxystearic acid content. Contact Dermatitis 2011;65:369-370
4   Shaw DW. Allergic contact dermatitis from 12-hydroxystearic acid and hydrogenated castor oil. Dermatitis 2009;20:E16-20 (cannot be found on-line)

2.246   IMIDAZOLIDINYL UREA

IDENTIFICATION

Description/definition	: Imidazolidinyl urea is the heterocyclic substituted urea that conforms to the formula shown below
Chemical class(es)	: Amides; heterocyclic compounds
Chemical/IUPAC name	: *N*,*N*'-Methylenebis[*N*'-[3-(hydroxymethyl)-2,5-dioxoimidazolidin-4-yl]urea]
Other names	: Imidurea; Germall® 115
CAS registry number (s)	: 39236-46-9
EC number(s)	: 254-372-6
Merck Index monograph	: 6227
CIR review(s)	: J Environ Pathol Toxicol 1980;4:133-146 (103) (access: www.cir-safety.org/ingredients)
Function(s) in cosmetics	: EU: preservative. USA: preservatives
EU cosmetic restrictions	: Regulated in Annex V/27 of the Regulation (EC) No. 1223/2009
Patch testing	: 2.0% pet. (Chemotechnique, SmartPracticeEurope, SmartPracticeCanada); 2.0% water (Chemotechnique); there have been reports of false-negative reactions to imidazolidinyl urea in petrolatum (77,78); however, in the NACDG studies, the petrolatum-based imidazolidinyl urea test material was significantly more sensitive than imidazolidinyl urea in an aqueous base (100)
Molecular formula	: $C_{11}H_{16}N_8O_8$

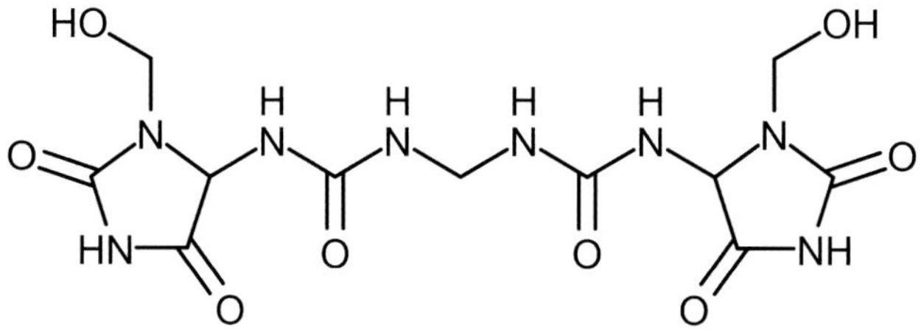

GENERAL

Imidazolidinyl urea is a widely used preservative, which is compatible with almost all cosmetic ingredients and is colorless, odorless, and tasteless. At typical use-levels of 0.3%, it is more active against bacteria than against yeasts and molds. The preservative acts synergistically with other preservatives, especially parabens. Imidazolidinyl urea is a formaldehyde-releaser, which releases formaldehyde through decomposition. In cosmetics and patch test materials, the major decomposition products are allantoin, (4-hydroxymethyl-2,5-dioxo-imidazolidine-4-yl)-urea (HU), (3,4-bis-hydroxymethyl-2,5-dioxo-imidazolidine-4-yl)-urea (3,4-BHU), and 3-hydroxymethyl-2,5-dioxo-imidazolidine-4-yl)-urea (11). Although it is often stated that contact allergy to imidazolidinyl urea may result from sensitization to the parent molecule *per se*, sensitization to its decomposition products is more likely. Of course, contact allergy may also occur from the formaldehyde released by this preservative. Virtually all cases of sensitization are from its presence in cosmetic products (9). The chemistry of imidazolidinyl urea has been discussed (11,26). The literature on formaldehyde-releasers in cosmetic products including imidazolidinyl urea up to 2009-2010 has been reviewed by the author (82,83). The literature up to 1990 has been reviewed in refs. 30 and 31. Other useful preservative allergy reviews have appeared in 2014 (115) and 2004 (116).

CONTACT ALLERGY

Patch testing in the general population and subgroups

In a study in five European countries, performed between 2008 and 2011, a random sample (n=3119) of the general population aged 18-74 was patch tested with imidazolidinyl urea (TRUE test). The total prevalence was 0.2% (women 0.2%, men 0.1%). The prevalence per country ranged from 0 to 0.2% (55). Of 201 healthy volunteer students from China aged 19-30 years, 1 (0.5%) reacted to imidazolidinyl urea 2% pet. (104).

Patch testing in groups of patients

Results of testing imidazolidinyl urea in consecutive patients suspected of contact dermatitis (routine patch testing) back to 1989 are shown in table 2.246.1. Results of patch testing in groups of *selected* patients (e.g., patients with eyelid dermatitis or individuals suspected of cosmetic allergy) back to 1994 are shown in table 2.246.2.

Patch testing in consecutive patients suspected of contact dermatitis: routine testing
Imidazolidinyl urea is not routinely tested in Europe (it has been added to the Spanish standard patch test series in 2016 [94]), but has been part of the screening series of the North American Contact Dermatitis Group (NACDG) for over 25 years. Their results have been published biannually (table 2.246.1). Since 1992, the preservative has been tested in a concentration of 2% both in petrolatum and in water. The petrolatum-based imidazolidinyl urea test material was statistically significantly more sensitive than the same allergen in an aqueous base (100); in the more recent NACDG studies (19,20,105), the water-based preparation has not been tested anymore. In these NADG studies, frequencies of sensitization (to the petrolatum-based material) have ranged from 1.6% to 3.2%, with a gradual but steady decline from 3.0% in the period 2001-2002 to 1.6% in the 2011-2012 and 2013-2014 study periods, probably from a decrease of its use in cosmetic products (19.105). Similar results were obtained in other US centers (7,36,41,52).

Table 2.246.1 Patch testing in groups of patients: Routine testing

Years and Country	Test conc. & vehicle	Number of patients tested | positive (%)		Selection of patients (S); Relevance (R); Comments (C)	Ref.
2013-14 USA, Canada	2% pet.	4859	76 (1.6%)	R: definite + probable relevance: 28%	105
2011-12 USA, Canada	2% pet.	4232	69 (1.6%)	R: definite + probable relevance: 29%	19
2009-2012, 12 European countries [b]	2% pet.	23,336	(0.6%) [a]	R: not stated; C: range per country 0-1.0%	110
2009-10 USA, Canada	2% pet.	4305	95 (2.2%)	R: definite + probable relevance: 33%	20
2006-2010 USA	2% pet.	3091	(2.5%)	R: 56%	52
	2% water	3069	(1.7%)	R: 47%	
2001-2010 Australia	2% pet.	5134	102 (2.0%)	R: 46%	96
2007-2008 8 European countries [b]	2% pet.	14,817	95 (0.6%) [a]	R: not stated; prevalences ranged from 0.4% (Netherlands) to 1.3% (Finland)	1
2007-8 USA, Canada	2% pet.	5082	(2.4%)	R: definite + probable relevance: 32%	15
	2% water	5082	(1.5%)	R: definite + probable relevance: 35%	
2005-6 USA, Canada	2% pet.	4438	(2.8%)	R: definite + probable relevance: 51%	14
	2% water	4447	(1.3%)	R: definite + probable relevance: 45%	
1993-2006 Australia	2% pet.	6845	(1.9%)	R: 46%	71
2004-2005 UK	2% pet.	6958	(0.9%)	R: not stated; C: prevalence 1.0% in women, 0.7% in men	32
2000-2005 USA	2% pet.	3819	(2.8%)	R: 74%	7
	2% water	3843	(2.1%)	R: 76%	
2003-4 USA, Canada	2% pet.	5139	151 (2.9%)	R: not stated	16
	2% water	5143	81 (1.6%)	R: not stated	
2002-4 USA, Canada	2% water	5784	(1.3%)	R: not stated	34
	2% pet.	5784	(2.5%)	R: not stated; C: the test preparation was found to contain 3.1% imidazolidinyl urea	
2001-2 USA, Canada	2% pet.	4897	(3.0%)	R: definite + probable relevance: 26%	33
	2% water	4909	(1.8%)	R: definite + probable relevance: 30%	
2000-2002 Finland	2% pet.	11,794	(0.8%)	R: not stated	35
2000 United Kingdom	2% pet.	3063	(0.5%)	R: 90% (in one center current + past relevance)	38
2000 Sweden	2% pet.	3790	(1.4%)	R: not stated	39
1998-2000 USA	2% pet.	1321	(3.3%)	R: not stated	36
	2% water	1322	(1.7%)	R: not stated	
1998-00 USA, Canada	2% pet.	5821	(2.0%)	R: definite + probable relevance: 27%	37
	2% water	5784	(2.5%)	R: definite + probably relevance: 21%	
1996-8 USA, Canada	2% pet.	4094	(3.2%)	R: definite + probable + possible relevance : 92%	40
	2% water	4101	(2.5%)	R: definite + probable + possible relevance: 86%	
1988-1997 USA	2% pet.	927	(1.9%)	R: not stated	41
1994-1996 USA	2% pet.	3080	(3.1%)	R: definite + probable relevance: 45%	42
	2% water	3101	(2.6%)	R: definite + probable relevance: 47%	
1992-1994 USA	2% pet.	3482	(2.6%)	R: definite + probable relevance: 58%	43
	2% water	3523	(1.9%)	R: definite + probable relevance: 54%	
1992-1993 Austria	2% pet.	11,516	(0.3%)	R: not stated	44
1989-90 Switzerland	2% pet.	2295	(1.0%)	R: not stated	45
1988-1989 Italy	2% pet.	934	6 (0.6%)	R: not stated	27

[a] age-standardized and sex-standardized proportions
[b] study of the ESSCA (European Surveillance System on Contact Allergy' network)

In European countries, prevalences have been consistently lower, ranging from 0.3% to 1.4%, mostly being below 1% (1,27,35,38, 39,44,45,110). In an Australian study, a frequency of sensitization of 1.9% was found in 6845 patients seen in the period 1993-2006 (71) and a virtually identical percentage of 2.0 in patients seen in the period 2001-2010 (96). In many investigations, no relevance figures were provided. In the NACDG studies, 'definite' + 'probable' relevance has ranged from 26% to 58% (mean 39% [2013-2014 period not included]). The incriminated products were never mentioned, but contact allergy to imidazolidinyl urea is nearly always the result of its presence in cosmetic products.

Patch testing in groups of selected patients
Data on patch testing with imidazolidinyl urea in groups of selected patients back to 1994 are summarized in table 2.246.2. Despite selection for possible reactions to cosmetics, a high prevalence rate has been observed in one investigation only. This was a small study of 57 patients with proven facial allergic contact dermatitis, of who 3 (5%) reacted to imidazolidinyl urea (54). Relevance data were lacking or unspecified in all but three (4,50,54) publications. In one study from the USA, all 17 and 22 positive patch test reactions were scored as relevant, but this included 'questionable' and 'past' relevance (4).

Table 2.246.2 Patch testing in groups of patients: Selected patient groups

Years and Country	Test conc. & vehicle	Number of patients tested	positive (%)	Selection of patients (S); Relevance (R); Comments (C)	Ref.
1996-2013 Netherlands	2% pet.	438	3 (0.7%)	S: children aged 0-17 years; R: not stated;	111
1994-2013 USA		342	13 (3.8%)	S: patients with atopic dermatitis as subgroup of 2453 successive patients suspected of contact dermatitis; R: not stated; C: in the non-atopic group, the frequency was only 1.9%; it was significantly higher in atopic dermatitis patients	97
2010-2011 Korea	2% pet.	584	17 (2.9%)	S: patients suspected of allergic cosmetic dermatitis; R: not stated	49
2006-2011 Singapore	2% pet.	350	2 (0.6%)	S: not specified; R: not stated; C: prevalence in men was 0%, in women 0.6%	53
2006-2011 IVDK	2% pet.	6981	(0.7%)	S: patients suspected of cosmetic intolerance and tested with a preservative series; R: not stated	107
2006-2010 USA	2% pet.	100	2 (2%)	S: patients with eyelid dermatitis; R: not stated	17
1994-2010 USA, Canada	2% pet.	432	? (?)	S: hairdressers/cosmetologists; R: in the group of 187 patients who had at least one relevant occupationally related reaction, 6 (3.2%) reacted to imidazolidinyl urea	108
2005-2009 Spain	2% water	3900	41 (1.1%)	S: patients allergic to formaldehyde or quaternium-15, or suspected of cosmetic or industrial contact dermatitis; R: not specified	2
1996-2009 IVDK	2% pet.	78,670	479 (0.6%) [a]	S: not specified; R: not specified	9
2000-2007 USA	2% pet.	941	22 (2.3%)	S: patients tested with a supplemental cosmetic screening series; R: 100% (for both test substances) C: weak study: a. high rate of macular erythema and weak reactions; b. relevance figures included 'questionable' and 'past' relevance	4
	2% water	943	17 (1.8%)		
2001-2002 Sweden		1075	(1.1%)	S: patients referred for routine testing willing to participate in a study on cosmetic use and adverse reactions; R: not stated	10
1990-1999 Belgium	2% pet.	1179	22 (1.9%)	S: patients suspected of cosmetic or iatrogenic dermatitis; R: not stated, probably 2 were from its presence in a corticosteroid preparation	22
1994-1998 UK	2% pet.	232	4 (1.7%)	S: patients with eyelid dermatitis; R: all were currently relevant	50
1995-1997 USA		57	3 (5%)	S: patients with facial allergic contact dermatitis; R: only relevant reactions were mentioned	54
1995-1996 Finland	2% pet.	1954	(1.1%)	S: patients suspected of cosmetic dermatitis; R: not stated	35
1993-5 Netherlands	2% pet.	1019	14 (1.4%)	S: not specified; R: not specified, but 3 patients reacted to imidazolidinyl urea in various products of a brand of 'hypoallergenic' cosmetics	72
1992-1995 IVDK [b]	2% pet.	17,327	(0.6%)	S: not specified, selected from 35,062 patients; R: not stated	46
1990-1994 IVDK [b]	2% pet.	11,452	(0.6%)	S: not specified, selected from 28,349 patients; R: not stated	47

[a] age-standardized and sex-standardized proportions
[b] it may be assumed that there is an overlap in the patient populations in these IVDK studies
IVDK: Information Network of Departments of Dermatology, Germany, Austria, Switzerland

Case reports and case series

Case series

Imidazolidinyl urea was stated to be the (or an) allergen in 16 patients in a group of 603 individuals suffering from cosmetic dermatitis, seen in the period 2010-2015 in Leuven, Belgium (51). Imidazolidinyl urea was responsible for 22 out of 959 cases of non-fragrance cosmetic allergy where the causal allergen was identified in the same clinic in Belgium, 2000-2010 (3). In the period 1996-2013, in a tertiary referral center in Valencia, Spain, 5419 patients were patch tested. Of these, 628 individuals had allergic contact dermatitis to cosmetics. Imidazolidinyl urea was the responsible allergen in one case (106). In a group of 2193 patients (1582 women, 611 men) with (presumed) cosmetic allergy, 134 reactions (6%) were caused by imidazolidinyl urea in a study of the NACDG, 2001-2004, imidazolidinyl urea ranking 10th in the list of most frequent allergens; their relevance was not mentioned (8). In a group of 46 patients with allergic contact dermatitis of the eyelids seen in Kansas City, USA, between 1994 and 2004, two cases (4%) were caused by contact allergy to imidazolidinyl urea (source not mentioned) (48). In a group of 119 patients with allergic contact dermatitis from cosmetics, investigated in The Netherlands in 1986-1987, two cases were caused by imidazolidinyl urea in skin care products (58,59).

In a group of 75 patients allergic to cosmetic products, seen in a private practice in The Netherlands in the period 1981-1986, one case was caused by imidazolidinyl urea in a skin care product (60, same patient as in ref. 61). In 3 clinics in Belgium, in the period 1978-1985, 279 patients with allergic contact dermatitis exclusively caused by cosmetics were seen. In this group, there were 3 reactions to imidazolidinyl urea. It was implied that this was the cause of the allergic reaction. One patient, who was allergic to a glycerin hand cream, was described in detail (76). Imidazolidinyl urea was responsible for 21 out of 399 cases of cosmetic allergy where the causal allergen was identified in a study of the NACDG, USA, 1977-1983 (5). Six cases of cosmetic ingredient related allergic contact dermatitis involving imidazolidinyl urea were reported to the Food and Drug Administration (FDA) by dermatologists in the North American Contact Dermatitis Group. These cases were observed following examination of over 2000 contact dermatitis cases from November 15, 1976, through November 15, 1977 (cited in ref. 103).

Case reports

One patient had allergic contact dermatitis from imidazolidinyl urea in a shampoo (18). Another individual reacted to imidazolidinyl urea in baby moist toilet tissue (21). An unknown number of patients had reactions to imidazolidinyl urea in sunscreen products (23). Two patients had positive patch tests to imidazolidinyl urea and to diazolidinyl urea, but were negative to formaldehyde (27). In one, the relevance was uncertain, the other patient had used cosmetics preserved with both imidazolidinyl urea and diazolidinyl urea (27). A woman had allergic contact dermatitis from a leave-on product containing imidazolidinyl urea; she also reacted to formaldehyde and to diazolidinyl urea, which was a constituent of other cosmetic products used by her (28). Another female patient reacted to imidazolidinyl urea in a moisturizing lotion and a liquid eyeliner (29). One patient had allergic cosmetic dermatitis from formaldehyde released from imidazolidinyl urea present in a skin care product (61). One individual had relevant positive patch test reactions to a moisturizer and to its ingredient imidazolidinyl urea (65). Another patient had allergic contact derma-titis from formaldehyde in imidazolidinyl urea present in a moisturizing cream and a body lotion (69). In a Finnish occupational contact dermatitis clinic, in a period of 6.5 years, a production worker was seen with occupational allergic contact dermatitis from imidazolidinyl urea in a hand cream and a hairdresser was investigated who proved to be allergic to this preservative in shampoos (70).

Three patients had allergic contact dermatitis from imidazolidinyl urea in various products of one particular brand of 'hypoallergenic' cosmetics; two of them also reacted to cosmetics containing diazolidinyl urea (72,101). Another patient reacted to imidazolidinyl urea in unspecified cosmetics of a 'hypoallergenic' brand, probably the same brand used only in The Netherlands (77). One patient had allergic contact dermatitis from a mascara preserved with imidazolidinyl urea (101). A girl had allergic contact dermatitis from 3 cosmetic creams of the same brand. She had probably been sensitized previously to a cream containing diazolidinyl urea and later also reacted to another cream preserved with imidazolidinyl urea from cross-reactivity (74). One individual had allergic contact dermatitis from imidazolidinyl urea in a moisturizing lotion, another from the presence of this preservative in a liquid eyeliner (first reports of contact allergy) (75). Two women had allergic contact dermatitis of the face from imidazolidinyl urea present in moisturizing creams (78). A woman had developed allergic contact dermatitis of the arms and legs from the preservative in a sunscreen. Four years later, she received ultrasound therapy for a painful shoulders and reacted to the ultrasound gel, which proved to contain imidazolidinyl urea (79). One patient reacted to imidazolidinyl urea in a sunscreen, a second to the preservative in a moisturizer and a foundation and a third to a foundation (102).

Contact allergy to imidazolidinyl urea in non-cosmetic products

Two patients reacted to imidazolidinyl urea in a corticosteroid preparation (22). A woman had allergic contact dermatitis from imidazolidinyl urea in an ultrasound gel; she had previously been sensitized to the preservative in a sunscreen product (79). Two patients had positive patch tests to some hydrogels used to treat leg ulcers, imidazolidinyl urea and diazolidinyl urea. Because the patients did not react to propylene glycol, the usual allergen in such gels, the authors suggested imidazolidinyl urea and/or diazolidinyl urea to be the allergenic culprit. However, the composition of the gels was unknown to them (98).

Cross-reactions, pseudo-cross-reactions and co-reactions

Imidazolidinyl urea is a formaldehyde-releaser. In a number of patients, contact allergy to the preservative is the result of sensitivity to formaldehyde. In these cases, pseudo-cross-reactions may be observed to formaldehyde and to other formaldehyde-releasers including diazolidinyl urea, DMDM hydantoin, quaternium-15, and − to a lesser degree − 2-bromo-2-nitropropane-1,3-diol (9,99,117). This subject is summarized in Chapter 2.188 Formaldehyde and discus-sed in detail in a review article by the author (82).

Cross-reactions to and from diazolidinyl urea *independent* of formaldehyde allergy are also seen frequently (27,76,117). This may in a number of cases be the result of the presence of two common (decomposition) compounds: (4-hydroxymethyl-2,5-dioxo-imidazolidine-4-yl)-urea (HU) and (3,4-bis-hydroxymethyl-2,5-dioxoimi-dazolidine-4-yl)-urea (3,4-BHU) (11). Contact allergies to imidazolidinyl urea and to the preservatives methyl-dibromoglutaronitrile and methylchloroisothiazolinone/methylisothiazolinone have been observed to be significantly associated. This probably results from concomitant or successive sensitization to these chemicals in the same or different products rather than from cross-reactivity (81).

Provocation tests

A positive reaction to a stay-on cosmetic preserved with 0.3% imidazolidinyl urea (containing approximately 300 ppm free formaldehyde) in a ROAT lasting 1 week was observed in one of three patients allergic to both formaldehyde and imidazolidinyl urea (84). In 20 patients with allergy to formaldehyde but negative patch test reactions to imidazolidinyl urea, the ROAT produced some follicular papules in 5 of 20. These were considered to be a mild allergic reaction, as none of the controls subjects had any reaction at all (84). Indeed, it may be assumed that prolonging the ROAT to 2-4 weeks would have resulted in more and stronger allergic reactions.

Presence in cosmetic products

In July 2017, imidazolidinyl urea was present in 251 of 69,545 cosmetic products of which the composition is known in EWG's Skin Deep Cosmetics Database, USA (http://www.ewg.org/skindeep/). In the USA, in April 2017, imidazolidinyl urea was present in 1958 of 56,714 cosmetic products of which the composition is known in FDA's Voluntary Cosmetic Registration Program (VCRP) (data obtained from FDA, May 2017). Imidazolidinyl urea was present in 53 of 4737 (1.1%) commonly used cosmetic products of which the full composition was known in 2016 in The Contact Allergen Management Program (CAMP) database of the American Contact Dermatitis Society (112). In 2014, in Thailand, the labels of 1000 cosmetic products (593 leave-on, 407 rinse-off products) were examined for the presence of preservatives. These were partly purchased in shops and on markets and partly brought in by patients. Imidazolidinyl urea was present in 33 products (3.3%); in the leave-on products, the percentage was 3 and in the rinse-off products 3.7 (113). Of 179 emollients available in Poland in 2014, 7 (3.9%) contained imidazolidinyl urea (114).

In 2013, 60 cosmetic products manufactured and purchased in Israel (40 stay-on and 20 rinse-off products) were investigated for preservatives. According to the labelling, 7 (12%) cosmetics contained imidazolidinyl urea. In the stay-on products (hand and body creams), the percentage was 18, whereas none of the 20 shampoos and soaps was preserved with imidazolidinyl urea (73). In 2009, in the USA, the ingredient lists of 1591 facial cosmetics from one company were screened for the presence of imidazolidinyl urea. The preservative was present in 0% of 132 blushers and 38 bronzers, in 0% of 90 concealers, in 0% of 174 eyeliners, in 0% of 304 eyeshadows, in 2% of 457 foundations, in 5% of 140 loose and pressed powders, and in 11% of 256 mascaras (66). In 2009, in the USA, the ingredient lists of 796 hair products from one company were screened for the presence of imidazolidinyl urea. Imidazolidinyl urea was present in 2% of 279 shampoos, in 0% of 231 conditioners, and in 0% of 286 styling products (67). In 2009, in the USA, the ingredient lists of 657 miscellaneous cosmetics from one company were screened for the presence of imidazolidinyl urea. Imidazolidinyl urea was present in 0% of 195 antiperspirants/deodorants, in 0% of 41 powders, in 2% of 167 shaving products, in 1% of 201 sun blocks, and in 0% of 53 wipes (68).

Imidazolidinyl urea was present in 102 of 3541 (2.7%) randomly sampled leave-on cosmetic products in Germany, 2006-2009 (12). In Germany, in 2006-2009, the labels of 4680 cosmetic products were screened for the presence of preservatives. Imidazolidinyl urea was present in 2.9% of the products, according to labelling information (109). The preservative was present in 5% of 204 cosmetic products (92 shampoos, 61 hair conditioners, 34 liquid soaps, 17 wet tissues) in Sweden, 2008 (13). In 2008, 19.5% of 33,212 cosmetics and toiletries registered in the USA Food and Drug Administration (FDA) Voluntary Cosmetic Registration Database contained a formaldehyde-releaser. They were more frequently used in rinse-off products (27.3%) than in stay-on cosmetics (16.9%). Imidazolidinyl urea was present in 7.0% of all products; in stay-on cosmetics, the percentage was 7.8 and in rinse-off products 4.7 (24). In the same period, in The Netherlands, of 496 stay-on cosmetic products present in a local drugstore and investigated by checking the ingredient labelling, 41 products (8.3%) proved to contain this preservative. Any formaldehyde-releaser was found in 122 (25%) of this group of stay-on products (24).

Of 38 cosmetic products marketed for babies in the UK in 2007, 7 (18%) contained imidazolidinyl urea (57). Of 23 brands of moist toilet paper marketed in 2006 in Italy, 4 (17%) were found to contain imidazolidinyl urea (62). Imidazolidinyl urea was present in 193 of 1774 (10.9%) cosmetics and toiletries in 2002 resp. in 184 of 1170 (15.7%) such products in 2005, filed in the Danish Product Register Database (PROBAS) (63). In 1998, 100 moisturizers sold in Sweden were analyzed for the presence and amount of preservatives. Thirty-five products contained a formaldehyde-releaser, 23 (23%) contained imidazolidinyl urea (56). In 1996, in the USA, imidazolidinyl urea was present in 3.0% of approximately 20,000 formulae voluntarily registered by cosmetic companies in the FDA Voluntary Cosmetic Registration Database (25).

Amounts of free formaldehyde released by imidazolidinyl urea and chemical analyses

Imidazolidinyl urea is prepared from 3 mole of formaldehyde and 2 mole of allantoin. From each molecule of imidazolidinyl urea, two formaldehyde molecules can be released (2 mole formaldehyde/mole imidazolidinyl urea) (91). Only about 75% of this theoretical amount of formaldehyde in imidazolidinyl urea will be released upon complete hydrolysis (91). The actual amounts of free formaldehyde released by imidazolidinyl urea in products depend on its concentration, the pH of the product, the temperature (the higher the temperature the more formaldehyde is present in solution after constant time) (86,95), the age of the product (upon storage increased levels of formaldehyde will be released [95]), the level of microbial contamination, and the other constituents of the products preserved with imidazolidinyl urea (46,86,87,88).

The pH may greatly influence the release of formaldehyde. Imidazolidinyl urea in lower concentrations is stable in a low pH (acidic) environment, but with increasing pH the amount of free formaldehyde also increases (89,90). The presence of protein in shampoo significantly decreased the amount of free formaldehyde compared to the same shampoo without protein (table 2.246.3), indicating that free formaldehyde was complexed by the protein introduced (85). Examples of reports of free formaldehyde concentrations in products containing imidazolidinyl urea are shown in table 2.246.3. Results of analysis of free formaldehyde in imidazolidinyl urea patch test preparations are presented in Chapter 2.188 Formaldehyde (6). A 2% aqueous solution prepared by a supplier of patch test materials at pH 5.0 contained 0.054% (540 ppm) free formaldehyde (6). In recent experiments, imidazolidinyl urea in cosmetics released about the same amount of formaldehyde as quaternium-15 and DMDM hydantoin, less than paraformaldehyde and diazolidinyl urea, but more than methenamine and 2-bromo-2-nitropropane-1,3-diol (95).

Table 2.246.3 Reports of free formaldehyde released from products containing imidazolidinyl urea (adapted from [82])

Product	Conc. of imidazolidinyl urea	Free formaldehyde (ppm)	Ref.
Shampoo containing protein	0.1%	17	85
	0.2%	36	
	0.4%	74	
	0.8%	117	
Shampoo *not* containing protein	0.1%	92	85
	0.2%	140	
	0.4%	230	
	0.8%	270	
Diluted cream	0.02%	30	92
	0.08%	80	
	0.16%	120	
	0.24%	160	
Shampoo	0.1%	8	86
Milky cleanser	0.3%	100	86
Cleansing cream	0.4%	92	86
Mascara	0.4%	7	86
Night cream	0.5%	131	86
Preservative saline solution	1.0%	1400	93
Preservative buffer solution	0.1%	100	90
Oil-in-water emulsion	0.3%	300	84

Other information

In an experimental study (80), the presence of around 200 ppm formaldehyde in a topical corticosteroid cream prolonged or prevented healing of experimentally induced allergic contact dermatitis from nickel in patients allergic to both formaldehyde and nickel. It was concluded that such creams should not be used on dermatitis in individuals allergic to formaldehyde (80).

OTHER SIDE EFFECTS

Immediate-type reactions
Of 50 individuals who had open tests with imidazolidinyl urea 2% in water on the forearm, 9 showed local macular erythema after 45 minutes, termed 'contact urticaria' by the authors (64).

LITERATURE
1   Uter W, Aberer W, Armario-Hita JC, , Fernandez-Vozmediano JM, Ayala F, Balato A, et al. Current patch test results with the European baseline series and extensions to it from the 'European Surveillance System on Contact Allergy' network, 2007-2008. Contact Dermatitis 2012;67:9-19

2   Latorre N, Borrego L, Fernández-Redondo V, García-Bravo B, Giménez-Arnau AM, Sánchez J, et al. Patch testing with formaldehyde and formaldehyde-releasers: multicenter study in Spain (2005-2009). Contact Dermatitis 2011;65:286-292

3   Travassos AR, Claes L, Boey L, Drieghe J, Goossens A. Non-fragrance allergens in specific cosmetic products. Contact Dermatitis 2011;65:276-285

4   Wetter DA, Yiannias JA, Prakash AV, Davis MD, Farmer SA, el-Azhary RA, et al. Results of patch testing to personal care product allergens in a standard series and a supplemental cosmetic series: an analysis of 945 patients from the Mayo Clinic Contact Dermatitis Group, 2000-2007. J Am Acad Dermatol 2010;63:789-798

5   Adams RM, Maibach HI, Clendenning WE, Fisher AA, Jordan WJ, Kanof N, et al. A five-year study of cosmetic reactions. J Am Acad Dermatol 1985;13:1062-1069

6   Emeis D, De Groot AC, Brinkmann J. Determination of formaldehyde in formaldehyde-releaser patch test preparations. Contact Dermatitis 2010;63:57-62

7   Davis MD, Scalf LA, Yiannias JA, Cheng JF, El-Azhary RA, Rohlinger AL, et al. Changing trends and allergens in the patch test standard series. Arch Dermatol 2008;144:67-72

8   Warshaw EM, Buchholz HJ, Belsito DV et al. Allergic patch test reactions associated with cosmetics: Retrospective analysis of cross-sectional data from the North American Contact Dermatitis Group, 2001-2004. J Am Acad Dermatol 2009;60:23-38

9   Schnuch A, Lessmann H, Geier J, Uter W. Contact allergy to preservatives. Analysis of IVDK data 1996-2009. Br J Dermatol 2011;164:1316-1325

10 Lindberg M, Tammela M, Bostrom A, Fischer T, Inerot A, Sundberg K, et al. Are adverse skin reactions to cosmetics underestimated in the clinical assessment of contact dermatitis? A prospective study among 1075 patients attending Swedish patch test clinics. Acta Derm Venereol 2004;84:291-295

11 Doi T, Takeda A, Asada A, Kajimura K. Characterization of the decomposition of compounds derived from imidazolidinyl urea in cosmetics and patch test materials. Contact Dermatitis 2012;67:284-292

12 Schnuch A, Mildau G, Kratz E-M, Uter W. Risk of sensitization to preservatives estimated on the basis of patch test data and exposure, according to a sample of 3541 leave-on products. Contact Dermatitis 2011;65:167-174

13 Yazar K, Johnsson S, Lind M-L, Boman A, Lidén C. Preservatives and fragrances in selected consumer-available cosmetics and detergents. Contact Dermatitis 2011;64:265-272

14 Zug KA, Warshaw EM, Fowler JF Jr, Maibach HI, Belsito DL, Pratt MD, et al. Patch-test results of the North American Contact Dermatitis Group 2005-2006. Dermatitis 2009;20:149-160

15 Fransway AF, Zug KA, Belsito DV, Deleo VA, Fowler JF Jr, Maibach HI, et al. North American Contact Dermatitis Group patch test results for 2007-2008. Dermatitis 2013;24:10-21

16 Warshaw EM, Belsito DV, DeLeo VA, Fowler JF Jr, Maibach HI, Marks JG, et al. North American Contact Dermatitis Group patch-test results, 2003-2004 study period. Dermatitis 2008;19:129-136

17 Wenk KS, Ehrlich AE. Fragrance series testing in eyelid dermatitis. Dermatitis 2012;23:22-26

18 Blondeel A. Contact allergy to the mild surfactant decylglucoside. Contact Dermatitis 2003;49:304-305

19 Warshaw EM, Maibach HI, Taylor JS, Sasseville D, DeKoven JG, Zirwas MJ, et al. North American Contact Dermatitis Group patch test results: 2011-2012. Dermatitis 2015;26:49-59

20 Warshaw EM, Belsito DV, Taylor JS, Sasseville D, DeKoven JG, Zirwas MJ, et al. North American Contact Dermatitis Group patch test results: 2009 to 2010. Dermatitis 2013;24:50-59

21 Timmermans A, De Hertog S, Gladys K, Vanacker H, Goossens A. 'Dermatologically tested' baby toilet tissues: a cause of allergic contact dermatitis in adults. Contact Dermatitis 2007;57:97-99

22 Goossens A, Huygens S, Matura M, Degreef H. Fluticasone propionate: a rare contact sensitizer. Eur J Dermatol 2001;11:29-34

23 Cook N, Freeman S. Report of 19 cases of photoallergic contact dermatitis to sunscreens seen at the Skin and Cancer Foundation. Austral J Dermatol 2001;42:257-259

24 De Groot AC, Veenstra M. Formaldehyde-releasers in cosmetics in the USA and in Europe. Contact Dermatitis 2010;62:221-224

25 Steinberg D. Frequency of use of preservatives in the United States. Paper given at Preservatech, Paris, 1996. www.creative-developments.co.uk/papers/Preservatives%201999.htm (last accessed 20-3-2009).

26 Lehmann SV, Hoeck U, Breinholdt J, Olsen CE, Kreilgaard B. Characterization and chemistry of imidazolidinyl urea and diazolidinyl urea. Contact Dermatitis 2006;54:50-58

27 Tosti A, Ristanti S, Lanzarini M. Contact sensitization to diazolidinyl urea: report of 3 cases. Contact Dermatitis 1990;22:127-128

28 De Groot AC, Bruynzeel DP, Jagtman BA, Weyland JW. Contact allergy to diazolidinyl urea (Germall II®). Contact Dermatitis 1988;18:202-205

29 Mandy SH. Contact dermatitis to substituted Imidazolidinyl urea – a common preservative in cosmetics. Arch Dermatol 1974;110:463

30 Fransway AF. The problem of preservation in the 1990s: I. Statement of the problem. Solution(s) of the industry, and the current use of formaldehyde and formaldehyde-releasing biocides. Am J Contact Dermatitis 1991;2:6-23

31 Fransway AF, Schmitz NA. The problem of preservation in the 1990s: II. Formaldehyde and formaldehyde-releasing biocides: incidences of cross-reactivity and the significance of the positive response to formaldehyde. Am J Contact Dermatitis 1991;2:78-88

32 Jong CT, Statham BN, Green CM, King CM, Gawkrodger DJ, Sansom JE, et al. Contact sensitivity to preservatives in the UK 2004–2005: results of a multicenter study. Contact Dermatitis 2007;57:165-168

33 Pratt MD, Belsito DV, DeLeo VA, Fowler JF Jr, Fransway AF, Maibach HI, et al. North American Contact Dermatitis Group patch-test results, 2001–2002 study period. Dermatitis 2004;15:176-183

34 Rietschel RL, Bruze M, Gruvberger B, Zug KA, Warshaw EM, Taylor JS, et al. The relationship of vehicle and concentration of imidazolidinylurea, with attention to formaldehyde status. Dermatitis 2006;17:48-49

35 Hasan T, Rantanen T, Alanko K, Harvima RJ, Jolanki R, Kalimo K, et al. Patch test reactions to cosmetic allergens in 1995–1997 and 2000–2002 in Finland –a multicentre study. Contact Dermatitis 2005;53:40-45

36 Wetter DA, Davis MDP, Yiannias JA, Cheng JF, Connolly SM, el-Azhary RA, et al. Patch test results from the Mayo Contact Dermatitis Group, 1998–2000. J Am Acad Dermatol 2005;53:416-421

37 Marks JG Jr, Belsito DV, DeLeo VA, Fowler JF Jr, Fransway AF, Maibach HI, et al. North American Contact Dermatitis Group patch-test results, 1998–2000. Am J Contact Dermat 2003;14:59-68

38 Britton JE, Wilkinson SM, English JSC, Gawkrodger DJ, Ormerod AD, Sansom JE, et al. The British standard series of contact dermatitis allergens: validation in clinical practice and value for clinical governance. Br J Dermatol 2003;148:259-264

39 Lindberg M, Edman B, Fischer T, Stenberg B. Time trends in Swedish patch test data from 1992 to 2000. A multi-centre study based on age- and sex-adjusted results of the Swedish standard series. Contact Dermatitis 2007;56:205-210

40 Marks JG Jr, Belsito DV, DeLeo VA, Fowler JF Jr, Fransway AF, Maibach HI, et al. North American Contact Dermatitis Group patch test results, 1996–1998. Arch Dermatol 2000;136:272-273

41 Albert MR, Chang Y, Gonzalez E. Concomitant positive patch test reactions to allergens in a patch testing standard series from 1988–1997. Am J Contact Dermat 1999;10:219-223

42 Marks JG Jr, Belsito DV, DeLeo VA, Fowler JF Jr, Fransway AF, Maibach HI,et al. North American Contact Dermatitis Group patch test results for the detection of delayed-type hypersensitivity to topical allergens. J Am Acad Dermatol 1998;38:911-918

43 Marks JG, Belsito DV, DeLeo VA, Fowler JF, Fransway AF, Maibach HI,et al. North American Contact Dermatitis Group standard tray patch test results 1992 through 1994. Am J Contact Dermatitis 1995;6:160-165

44 Kränke B, Szolar-Platzer C, Aberer W. Reactions to formaldehyde and formaldehyde releasers in a standard series. Contact Dermatitis 1996;35:192-193

45 Perrenoud D, Bircher A, Hunziker T, Suter H, Bruckner-Tuderman L, Stäger J, et al. Frequency of sensitization to 13 common preservatives in Switzerland. Contact Dermatitis 1994;30:276-279

46 Geier J, Lessmann H, Schuch A, Fuchs Th. Kontaktallergien durch formaldehydabspaltende Biozide. Allergologie 1997;20:215-224 (article in German)

47 Schnuch A, Geier J, Uter W, Frosch PJ. Patch testing with preservatives, antimicrobials and industrial biocides. Results from a multicentre study. Br J Dermatol 1998;138:467-476

48 Amin KA, Belsito DV. The aetiology of eyelid dermatitis: a 10-year retrospective analysis. Contact Dermatitis 2006;55:280-285

49 Lee SS, Hong DK, Jeong NJ, Lee JH, Choi YS, Lee AY, et al. Multicenter study of preservative sensitivity in patients with suspected cosmetic contact dermatitis in Korea. J Dermatol 2012;39:677-681

50 Cooper SM, Shaw S. Eyelid dermatitis: an evaluation of 232 patch test patients over 5 years. Contact Dermatitis 2000: 42;291-293

51 Goossens A. Cosmetic contact allergens. Cosmetics 2016, 3, 5; doi:10.3390/cosmetics3010005

52 Wentworth AB, Yiannias JA, Keeling JH, Hall MR, Camilleri MJ, Drage LA, et al. Trends in patch-test results and allergen changes in the standard series: a Mayo Clinic 5-year retrospective review (January 1, 2006, to December 31, 2010). J Am Acad Dermatol 2014;70:269-275

53 Cheng S, Leow YH, Goh CL, Goon A. contact sensitivity to preservatives in Singapore: frequency of sensitization to 11 common preservatives 2006–2011. Dermatitis 2014;25:77-82

54 Katz AS, Sherertz EF. Facial dermatitis: Patch test results and final diagnoses. Am J Cont Dermat 1999;10:153-156

55 Diepgen TL, Ofenloch RF, Bruze M, Bertuccio P, Cazzaniga S, Coenraads P-J, et al. Prevalence of contact allergy in the general population in different European regions. Br J Dermatol 2016;174:319-329

56 Gruvberger B, Bruze M, Tammela M. Preservatives in moisturizers on the Swedish market. Acta Derm Venereol 1998;78:52-56

57 White JML, McFadden JP. Exposure to haptens/contact allergens in baby cosmetic products. Contact Dermatitis 2008;59:176-177

58 De Groot AC, Bruynzeel DP, Bos JD, van der Meeren HL, van Joost T, Jagtman BA, Weyland JW. The allergens in cosmetics. Arch Dermatol 1988;124:1525-1529

59 De Groot AC. Adverse reactions to cosmetics. PhD Thesis, University of Groningen, The Netherlands: 1988, chapter 3.4, pp.105-113

60 De Groot AC. Contact allergy to cosmetics: Causative ingredients. Contact Dermatitis 1987;17:26-34

61 De Groot AC, Weyland JW. Hidden contact allergy to formaldehyde in imidazolidinyl urea. Contact Dermatitis 1987;17:124-125

62 Zoli V, Tosti A, Silvani S, Vincenzi C. Moist toilet papers as possible sensitizers: review of the literature and evaluation of commercial products in Italy. Contact Dermatitis 2006;55:252-254

63 Flyvholm, MA. Preservatives in registered chemical products. Contact Dermatitis 2005;53:27-32

64 Emmons WW, Marks JG. Immediate and delayed reactions to cosmetic ingredients. Contact Dermatitis 1985;13:258-265

65 Held E, Johansen JD, Agner T, Menné T. Contact allergy to cosmetics: testing with patients' own products. Contact Dermatitis 1999;40:310-315

66 Scheman A, Jacob S, Katta R, Nedorost S, Warshaw E, Zirwas M, et al. Part 1 of a 4 part series. Facial cosmetics: trends and alternatives. Data from the American Contact Alternative Group. J Clin Aesthet Dermatol 2011;4:25-30

67 Scheman A, Jacob S, Katta R, Nedorost S, Warshaw E, Zirwas M, et al. Part 2 of a 4 part series. Hair cosmetics: trends and alternatives. Data from the American Contact Alternative Group. J Clin Aesthet Dermatol 2011;4:42-46

68 Scheman A, Jacob S, Katta R, Nedorost S, Warshaw E, Zirwas M, et al. Part 4 of a 4 part series. Miscellaneous products: trends and alternatives in deodorants, antiperspirants, sunblocks, shaving products, powder, and wipes. Data from the American Contact Alternative Group. J Clin Aesthet Dermatol 2011;4:35-39

69 Mestach L, Goossens A. Allergic contact dermatitis and nail damage mimicking psoriasis caused by nail hardeners. Contact Dermatitis 2016;74:112-114

70 Aalto-Korte K, Kuuliala O, Suuronen K, Alanko K. Occupational contact allergy to formaldehyde and formaldehyde releasers. Contact Dermatitis 2008;59:280-289

71 Chow ET, Avolio AM, Lee A, Nixon R. Frequency of positive patch test reactions to preservatives: The Australian experience. Australas J Dermatol 2013;54:31-35

72 Okkerse A, Beursen-Reitsma AM, van Joost Th. Contact allergy to methyldibromoglutaronitrile and certain other preservatives. Contact Dermatitis 1996;34:151

73 Horev L, Isaksson M, Engfeldt M, Persson L, Ingber A, Bruze M. Preservatives in cosmetics in the Israeli market conform well to the EU legislation. J Eur Acad Dermatol Venereol 2015;29:761-766

74 García-Gavín J, González-Vilas D, Fernández-Redondo V, Toribio J. Allergic contact dermatitis in a girl due to several cosmetics containing diazolidinyl-urea or imidazolidinyl-urea. Contact Dermatitis 2010;63:49-50

75 Fisher AA. Allergic contact dermatitis from Germall 115, a new cosmetic preservative. Contact Dermatitis 1975;1:126

76 Dooms-Goossens A, de Boulle K, Dooms M, Degreef H. Imidazolidinyl urea dermatitis. Contact Dermatitis 1986;14:322-324

77 Van Neer PAFA, van der Kley AMJ. Imidazolidinyl urea (Germall 115) should be patch tested in water. Contact Dermatitis 1991;24:302

78 Foussereau J, Cavelier C. Water versus petrolatum for testing imidazolidinyl urea. Contact Dermatitis 1989;21:54-55

79   Ando M, Ansotegui IJ, Munoz D, Fernandez de Corres L. Allergic contact dermatitis from imidazolidinyl urea in an ultrasonic gel. Contact Dermatitis 2000;42:109

80   Isaksson M, Gruvberger B, Goon AT-J, Bruze M. Can an imidazolidinyl urea-preserved corticosteroid cream be safely used in individuals hypersensitive to formaldehyde? Contact Dermatitis 2006;54:29-34

81   Statham BN, Smith EV, Bodger OG, Green CM, King CM, Ormerod AD, et al. Concomitant contact allergy to methylchloroisothiazolinone/ methylisothiazolinone and formaldehyde-releasing preservatives. Contact Dermatitis 2010;62:56-57

82   De Groot AC, White IR, Flyvholm M-A, Lensen G, Coenraads P-J. Formaldehyde-releasers in cosmetics: relationship to formaldehyde contact allergy. Part 2. Patch test relationship to formaldehyde contact allergy, experimental provocation tests, amount of formaldehyde released and assessment of risk to consumers allergic to formaldehyde. Contact Dermatitis 2010;62:18-31

83   De Groot AC, White IR, Flyvholm M-A, Lensen G, Coenraads P-J. Formaldehyde-releasers: relationship to formaldehyde contact allergy. II. Formaldehyde-releasers used in cosmetics. Part 1. Characterization, frequency and relevance of sensitization, and frequency of use in cosmetics. Contact Dermatitis 2010;62:2-17

84   Flyvholm M A, Hall B M, Agner T, Tiedemann E, Greenhill P, Vanderveken W, et al. Threshold for occluded formaldehyde patch test in formaldehyde sensitive patients. Relationship to repeated open application test with a product containing formaldehyde releaser. Contact Dermatitis 1997;36:26-33

85   Rosen M, McFarland A. Free formaldehyde in anionic shampoos. J Soc Cosmet Chem 1984;35:157-169

86   Engelhardt H, Klinkner R. Determination of free formaldehyde in the presence of donators in cosmetics by HPLC and post-column derivation. Chromatographia 1985;20:559-565

87   Geier J, Lessmann H, Schnuch A, Uter W. Contact sensitizations in metalworkers with occupational dermatitis exposed to water-based metalworking fluids: results of the research project 'FaSt'. Int Arch Occup Environ Health 2004;77:543-551

88   Geier J, Lessmann H, Becker D, et al. Formaldehydabspalter. Dermatol Beruf Umwelt 2008;56:34-36 (article in German)

89   Emeis D, Anker W, Wittern K-P. Quantitative 13C NMR spectroscopic studies on the equilibrium of formaldehyde with its releasing preservatives. Anal Chem 2007;79:2096-2100

90   Kijami K, Takeda M, Okaya Y, et al. A study on release of formaldehyde from its donor-type preservatives. Anal Sci 1991;7(Suppl): 913-916

91   Johansen M, Bundgaard H. Kinetics of formaldehyde release from the cosmetic preservative Germall 115. Arch Pharm Chem Sci Ed 1981;9:117-122

92   Karlberg A-T, Skare L, Lindberg I, Nyhammer E. A method for quantification of formaldehyde in the presence of formaldehyde donors in skin-care products. Contact Dermatitis 1998;38:20-28

93   Andersen KE, Boman A, Hamann K, Wahlberg JE. Guinea pig maximization tests with formaldehyde releasers. Results of two laboratories. Contact Dermatitis 1984;10:257-266

94   Hervella-Garcés M, García-Gavín J, Silvestre-Salvador JF; en representación del Grupo Español de Investigación en Dermatitis de Contacto y Alergia Cutánea (GEIDAC). The Spanish standard patch test series: 2016 update by the Spanish Contact Dermatitis and Skin Allergy Research Group (GEIDAC). Actas Dermosifiliogr 2016;107:559-566

95   Lv C, Hou J, Xie W, Cheng H. Investigation on formaldehyde release from preservatives in cosmetics. Int J Cosm Sci 2015;37:474-478

96   Toholka R, Wang Y-S, Tate B, Tam M, Cahill J, Palmer A, Nixon R. The first Australian Baseline Series: Recommendations for patch testing in suspected contact dermatitis. Australas J Dermatol 2015;56:107-115

97   Shaughnessy CN, Malajian D, Belsito DV. Cutaneous delayed-type hypersensitivity in patients with atopic dermatitis: reactivity to topical preservatives. J Am Acad Dermatol 2014;70:102-107

98   Carvalho R, Maio P, Amaro C, Santos R, Cardoso J. Hydrogel allergic contact dermatitis and imidazolidinyl urea/diazolidinyl urea. Cutan Ocul Toxicol 2011;30:331-332

99   Landeck L, González E, Baden L, Neumann K, Schalock P. Positive concomitant test reactions to allergens in the standard patch test series. Int J Dermatol 2010;49:517-519

100 Rietschel RL, Warshaw EM, Sasseville D, Fowler JF Jr, DeLeo VA, Belsito DV, Taylor JS, et al; North American Contact Dermatitis Group. Sensitivity of petrolatum and aqueous vehicles for detecting allergy to imidazolidinylurea, diazolidinylurea, and DMDM hydantoin: a retrospective analysis from the North American Contact Dermatitis Group. Dermatitis 2007;18:155-162

101 Okkerse A, Thijssen-Vermijs ME, Geursen-Reitsma AM, van Joost T. Sensibilisatie voor hypoallergene cosmetica. [Sensitization to hypoallergenic cosmetics]. Ned Tijdschr Geneeskd 1994;138:2377-2380 (article in Dutch)

102 O'Brien TJ. Imidazolidinyl urea (Germall 115) causing cosmetic dermatitis. Australas J Dermatol 1987;28:36-37

103 Expert Panel of the Cosmetic Ingredient Review (CIR). Final report of the safety assessment for imidazolidinyl urea. J Environ Pathol Toxicol 1980;4:133-146

104 Zhao J, Li LF. Contact sensitization to cosmetic series of allergens in a general population in Beijing. J Cosmet Dermatol 2014;13:68-71

105 DeKoven JG, Warshaw EM, Belsito DV, Sasseville D, Maibach HI, Taylor JS, et al. North American Contact Dermatitis Group Patch Test Results: 2013-2014. Dermatitis. Dermatitis 2017;28:33-46

106 Zaragoza-Ninet V, Blasco Encinas R, Vilata-Corell JJ, Pérez-Ferriols A, Sierra-Talamantes C, Esteve-Martínez A, de la Cuadra-Oyanguren J. Allergic contact dermatitis due to cosmetics: A clinical and epidemiological study in a tertiary hospital. Actas Dermosifiliogr 2016;107:329-336

107 Dinkloh A, Worm M, Geier J, Schnuch A, Wollenberg A. Contact sensitization in patients with suspected cosmetic intolerance: results of the IVDK 2006-2011. J Eur Acad Dermatol Venereol 2015;29:1071-1081

108 Warshaw EM, Wang MZ, Mathias CGT, Maibach HI, Belsito DV, Zug KA, et al. Occupational contact dermatitis in hairdressers/cosmetologists; retrospective analysis of North American Contact Dermatitis Group data, 1994 to 2010. Dermatitis 2012;23:258-268

109 Uter W, Yazar K, Kratz EM, Mildau G, Lidén C. Coupled exposure to ingredients of cosmetic products: II. Preservatives. Contact Dermatitis 2014;70:219-226

110 Giménez-Arnau AM, Deza G, Bauer A, Johnston GA, Mahler V, Schuttelaar ML, et al. Contact allergy to preservatives: ESSCA* results with the baseline series, 2009-2012. J Eur Acad Dermatol Venereol 2017;31:664-671

111 Lubbes S, Rustemeyer T, Sillevis Smitt JH, Schuttelaar ML, Middelkamp-Hup MA. Contact sensitization in Dutch children and adolescents with and without atopic dermatitis - a retrospective analysis. Contact Dermatitis 2017;76:151-159

112 Beene KM, Scheman A, Severson D, Reeder MJ. Prevalence of preservatives across all product types in the Contact Allergen Management Program. Dermatitis 2017;28:81-87

113 Bunyavaree M, Kasemsarn P, Boonchai W. Cosmetic preservative labelling on the Thai market. Contact Dermatitis 2016;74:217-221

114 Osinka K, Karczmarz A, Krauze A, Feleszko W. Contact allergens in cosmetics used in atopic dermatitis: analysis of product composition. Contact Dermatitis 2016;75:241-243

115 Yim E, Baquerizo Nole KL, Tosti A. Contact dermatitis caused by preservatives. Dermatitis 2014;25:215-231

116 Sasseville D. Hypersensitivity to preservatives. Dermatol Ther 2004;17:251-263

117 Lynch MD, White JM, McFadden JP, Wang Y, White IR, Banerjee P. A dynamic landscape of allergen associations in delayed-type cutaneous hypersensitivity. Br J Dermatol 2017;176:184-196

2.247   IODOPROPYNYL BUTYLCARBAMATE

IDENTIFICATION

Description/definition	: Iodopropynyl butylcarbamate is the organic compound that conforms to the formula shown below
Chemical class(es)	: Amides; esters; halogen compounds
Chemical/IUPAC name	: 3-Iodoprop-2-ynyl *N*-butylcarbamate
Other name(s)	: IPBC
CAS registry number (s)	: 55406-53-6
EC number(s)	: 259-627-5
Merck Index monograph	: 6382
SCCS opinion(s)	: SCCNFP/0826/04 (60); SCCNFP, 23 June 1999 (61)
CIR review(s)	: Int J Toxicol 1998;17:1-37 (access: www.cir-safety.org/ingredients)
Function(s) in cosmetics	: EU: preservative. USA: pesticides; preservatives
EU cosmetic restrictions	: Regulated in Annex V/56 of the Regulation (EC) No. 1223/2009
Patch testing	: 0.2% pet. (Chemotechnique, SmartPracticeEurope, SmartPracticeCanada); 0.5% pet. (SmartPracticeCanada); the concentration of 0.2% is already marginally irritant (15,20)
Molecular formula	: $C_8H_{12}INO_2$

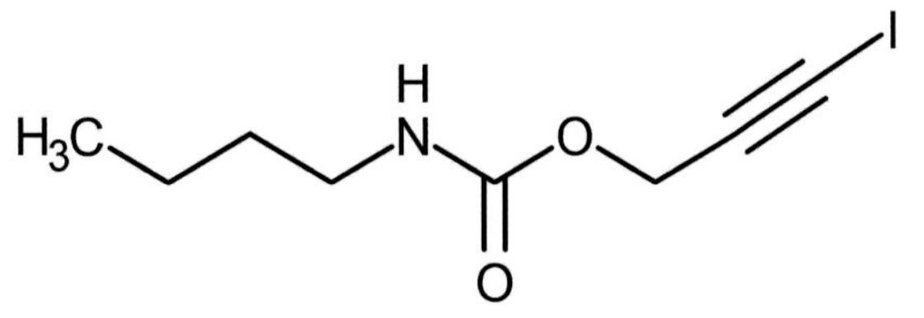

GENERAL

Iodopropynyl butylcarbamate (IPBC) is an organo-iodine preservative that acts as a wide-spectrum fungicide, bactericide, and acaricide. It is often combined with formaldehyde-releasers to complement the predominantly fungicidal activity of IPBC with antibacterial activity, e.g., against *Pseudomonas aeruginosa* (46). Originally developed for industrial use in the 1970s, IPBC was first and is still used as a fungicide for paint and as wood preservative in concentrations ranging from 0.02-4%. It has progressively been introduced into other industrial applications, such as paints, metalworking fluids, cooling water, inks, paper, adhesives and plastics, into household products, other consumer products such as contact lenses and a variety of cosmetic products (15,18,23,46).

According to current legislation, the maximum authorized concentrations in cosmetics marketed within the EU are 0.02% in rinse-off products, 0.01% in leave-on products, and 0.0075% in deodorants and antiperspirants. It should not be used in children under 3 years of age (except in bath products), in oral hygiene and lip care products, or in body lotions and creams intended to be applied on a large part of the body, given its iodine content and possible systemic absorption (19).

IPBC is a small lipophilic molecule that may penetrate the skin and cause contact allergy. Although it is often considered to be of low allergenic potential (17,36,37), IPBC has also been classified as a moderate (40) or moderate-to-strong sensitizer (41) in animal and local lymph node studies. Some authors suggest that iodopropynyl butylcarbamate can pose a high risk of sensitization, particularly in leave-on formulations (6).

Since the first publication on allergic contact dermatitis from IPBC in 1997 (20), several authors have reported on contact allergy to this preservative in cosmetic products (15,21,34,50,64), sanitary wipes/moist toilet paper/baby wipes (8,9,22,23), hand cleansers (15,51) and non-cosmetic products including adhesives (23), paper product (23), topical corticosteroid preparation (23), health devices/aids (23) and industrial products such as metalworking fluids (15,23,24), lubricant and preserving oil (15), paint (15), wood paint (26), wood preservative (25) and concentrated IPBC solution (20).

The literature on contact allergy to iodopropynyl butylcarbamate and other preservatives has been reviewed in 2004 (53) and 2014 (30).

CONTACT ALLERGY

Patch testing in groups of patients

Results of routine patch testing (testing in consecutive patients suspected of contact dermatitis) iodopropynyl butylcarbamate back to 1996 are shown in table 2.247.1. Results of testing in groups of *selected* patients (e.g., painters, hairdressers, patients with stasis dermatitis / leg ulcers, metalworkers suspected of contact dermatitis from metalworking fluids) back to 2002 are shown in table 2.247.2.

Patch testing in consecutive patients suspected of contact dermatitis: routine testing

Iodopropynyl butylcarbamate has been included in the screening tray of the North American Contact Dermatitis Group (NACDG) since 1998, and consequently, there are many data on iodopropynyl butylcarbamate contact allergy available from the USA + Canada, where the NACDG publishes their patch test results biannually. A major problem has been to determine the correct patch test concentration. Test concentrations used have included 0.1% pet., 0.2% pet. and 0.5% pet. The test concentration of 0.1% pet. is too low and results in false-negative reactions (38), whereas the test concentration of 0.5% is too high and causes many irritant reactions (15,16,23). However, also with the currently available test material of 0.2% in petrolatum, some false-positives, but also false-negatives may be expected (16). As the concentration currently used by the NACDG is 0.5%, it may be assumed that the high frequencies of sensitization of 4.2% and 4.7% recently found (33,65) can partly be explained by false-positive, irritant patch test reactions. In fact, in the 2011-2012 NACDG study, the group of 178 'positive' reactions included 44 ?+ (macular erythema only) reactions (33).

Table 2.247.1 Patch testing in groups of patients: Routine testing

Years and Country	Test conc. & vehicle	Number of patients tested	positive (%)	Selection of patients (S); Relevance (R); Comments (C)	Ref.
2013-14 USA, Canada	0.5% pet.	4859	229 (4.7%)	R: definite + probable relevance: 35%	65
2000-2013 Australia	?	5427	30 (0.6%)	R: not stated	51
2011-2012 USA, Canada	0.5% pet.	4231	178 (4.2%)	R: definite 3%, probable 37%; C: the group of 178 positives included 44 ?+ reactions	33
2009-2012, 12 European countries [b]	0.1% pet.	7956	(0.1%) [a]	R: not stated; C: range per country: one country only	69
	0.2% pet.	12,360	(1.2%) [a]	R: not stated; C: range per country 0.3-3.8%	
2000-2011 Denmark	0.1% pet. later 0.2%	9755	54 (0.6%)	R: in 26 positive patients seen in 2006-2011, 10 were relevant (n=8) or possibly relevant; products included cosmetics (n=6), paints (n=2), hand cleanser (n=1), metal-working fluid (n=1) and lubricant and preserving oil (n=1); significant association with male sex, hand eczema, and positive reactions to the thiuram-mix	15
2009-10 USA, Canada	0.5% pet.	4304	(4.3%)	R: definite 4%, probable 37%	29
2006-2010 USA	0.2% pet.	118	(3.4%)	R: 50%	56
	0.1% pet.	1229	(1.0%)	R: 25%	
2007-8 USA, Canada	0.5% pet.	5082	(3.1%)	R: definite + probable relevance: 33%	11
2007-2008, 5 European countries [b]	0.2% pet.	4039	(0.9%) [a]	R: not stated; C: frequencies of sensitization ranged from 0% to 1.7%	1
1998-2008 USA, Canada	0.1% and/or 0.5% pet.	25,321	329 (1.3%)	R: <6% of weak reactions and <11% of strong reactions were definitely relevant; most were possibly relevant, mostly from personal care products, rarely (<6%) from occupational exposure; C: allergic reactions to 0.1% ranged from 0.3-0.5%, to 0.5% from 2.3-3.1%; only 14/113 patients reacting to either 0.1% or 0.5% reacted to both concentrations; it was stated that a number of the 0.5% reactors may have been irritant	23
1996-2008 Denmark	0.5% pet.	10,085	41 (0.4%)	R: not stated	39
2005-6 USA, Canada	0.5% pet.	4435	106 (2.4%)	R: definite + probable relevance: 23%	10
	0.1% pet.	4433	22 (0.5%)	R: definite + probable relevance: 35%	10
2003-4 USA, Canada	0.1% pet.	5137	24 (0.5%)	R: not stated	12
2001-2 USA, Canada	0.1% pet.	4897	15 (0.3%)	R: definite + probable relevance 8%	47
1998-2000 USA, Canada	0.1% pet.	5770	23 (0.4%)	R: definite + probable relevance: 19%	32
1998-1999 IVDK	0.1% pet.	4483	16 (0.3%)	R: 25%, products not specified (probably cosmetics or topical drugs); C: 0.6% irritant or doubtful reactions; test concentration considered to be too low	38
1996-1999 Denmark	0.1% pet.	3168	7 (0.2%)	R: two patients used a skin lotion containing IPBC, in 2 the relevance was uncertain and 3 patients with occupational contact dermatitis were reported previously (20)	34
1996 Denmark	0.1% pet.	311	3 (1.0%)	R: 1/3 (33%) from a compound containing 30% IPBC solution in a paint producing factory	20

[a] age-standardized and sex-standardized proportions
[b] study of the ESSCA (European Surveillance System on Contact Allergy' network)
IVDK: Information Network of Departments of Dermatology, Germany, Austria, Switzerland

In groups tested with iodopropynyl butylcarbamate 0.1% pet., frequencies of sensitization have ranged from 0.1% to 1%. In groups tested with 0.2% pet., frequencies ranged from 0.9% to 3.4% (3.4% from a clinic where ?+ reactions are usually counted as positive [56]) and the 0.5% pet. concentration scored from 0.4% to 4.7% positive reactions. Relevance rates were usually quite low. In the NACDG studies, for example, 'definite' relevance was never more than 6% and 'definite' or 'probable' relevance ranged from 8% to 35%. Most reactions may have been caused by cosmetic products (15,23,34).

Patch testing in groups of selected patients

Results of testing in groups of *selected* patients (e.g., painters, hairdressers, patients with stasis dermatitis / leg ulcers, metalworkers suspected of contact dermatitis from metalworking fluids) back to 2002 are shown in table 2.247.2. In 13 investigations, frequencies of sensitization have ranged from 0.5% to 2.4%, but 10/13 had rates of 1.1% or lower. The highest frequency of 2.4% was found in a group of female hairdressers with current or previous occupational contact dermatitis, but the relevance of the positive reactions was not mentioned (67). In fact, the issue of relevance was addressed in 2 studies only; in one, only 11% of the reactions were relevant (62), in the other the rate was 100%, but this study had certain weaknesses (3). Culprit products were never mentioned (table 2.247.2).

Table 2.247.2 Patch testing in groups of patients: Selected patient groups

Years and Country	Test conc. & vehicle	Number of patients tested	positive (%)		Selection of patients (S); Relevance (R); Comments (C)	Ref.
2003-2014 IVDK	0.2% pet.	<5202		(1.1%)	S: patients with stasis dermatitis/ chronic leg ulcers; R: not stated; C: percentage of reactions not significantly higher than in a control group of routine testing	71
1996-2013 Netherlands	0.2% pet.	339	3	(0.9%)	S: children aged 0-17 years; R: not stated;	70
2007-2012 IVDK	0.2% pet.	653	14	(2.4%)	S: female hairdressers with current or previous occupational contact dermatitis; R: not stated	67
		1389	16	(1.2%)	S: female patients, clients of hairdressers, in who hair cosmetics were regarded as a cause of dermatitis, and who had never worked as hairdressers; R: not stated	
2003-2012 IVDK		1697	32	(1.9%)	S: nurses with occupational contact dermatitis; R: not stated	14
2011 China	0.2% pet.	201	1	(0.5%)	S: healthy student volunteers 19-30 years; R: not stated	63
2010-2011 Korea	0.1% pet.	584	3	(0.5%)	S: patients suspected of allergic cosmetic dermatitis; R: not stated	54
2006-2011 IVDK	0.2% pet.	6974		(1.1%)	S: patients suspected of cosmetic intolerance and tested with a preservative series (selection procedure not stated); R: not stated	66
2001-2010 Denmark	?	155	3	(1.9%)	S: painters; R: not stated	45
2001-2010 Australia	0.2% pet.	4258	28	(0.7%)	S: not stated; R: 11%	62
2003-2009 IVDK	0.2% pet.	40,772	389	(0.9%) [a]	S: not stated; R: not stated; C: most cases appear to be from occupational (non-cosmetic) sources; increase in prevalence of sensitization	4
2000-2007 USA	0.1% pet.	871	6	(0.7%)	S: patients tested with a supplemental cosmetic screening series; R: 100%; C: weak study: a. high rate of macular erythema and weak reactions; b. relevance figures included 'questionable' and 'past' relevance	3
2002-2003 IVDK	0.1% or 0.2% pet.	181	1	(0.5%)	S: metalworkers suspected of contact dermatitis from metalworking fluids; R: not stated	42
2000-2002 IVDK	0.1% pet.	228	2	(0.9%)	S: metalworkers with contact dermatitis working with metalworking fluids; R: not stated	44

[a] age-standardized and sex-standardized proportions
IVDK: Information Network of Departments of Dermatology, Germany, Austria, Switzerland

Case reports and case series

Iodopropynyl butylcarbamate was stated to be the (or an) allergen in 2 patients in a group of 603 individuals suffering from cosmetic dermatitis, seen in the period 2010-2015 in Leuven, Belgium (55). Iodopropynyl butylcarbamate was responsible for 2 out of 959 cases of non-fragrance cosmetic allergy where the causal allergen was identified, Belgium, 2000-2010 (2).

A man developed severe perianal and palmar contact dermatitis caused by sensitization to iodopropynyl butylcarbamate in moist sanitary wipes (8). A woman had allergic contact dermatitis of the face and neck and a man had ACD at the contact site of a prosthesis with the skin of a leg amputation stump from IPBC in baby wipes. One co-reacted to 2-bromo-2-nitropropane-1,3-diol, the other to MCI/MI and fragrances, which were also components of the causative baby wipes (9). A woman had papular dermatitis of the face from contact allergy to IPBC in a cosmetic cream (21). Three patients developed florid scalp dermatitis, associated with alopecia, after using a hair mousse containing IPBC from contact allergy to this preservative (50). An unspecified number of patients had ACD from iodopropynyl butylcarbamate in sunscreens (64). Two women had allergic contact dermatitis from IPBC in a skin lotion of the same brand, one of the hands, the other had widespread involvement (34). Six patients, five women and one man, had ACD from IPBC in emollient creams (n=3), a shaving foam (n=1), a facial moisturizer (n=1) and 'various cosmetic products' (n=1) (15).

In the period 2011-2014, 79 patients with a positive patch test reaction to an allergen identified with a wet wipe source were identified by the members of the NACDG. Iodopropynyl butylcarbamate was the (or an) allergen in 12% of the cases. Patients with wipe allergy were 15 times more likely to have anal/genital dermatitis compared with those without wipe allergy (75). A punching/stamping press machine operator had allergic contact dermatitis of the hands from IPBC present in wet wipes he used to clean his hands with (75).

Contact allergy to iodopropynyl butylcarbamate in non-cosmetic products

In a clinic in Denmark, in the period 2006-2011, 26 patients were found to be allergic to IPBC. Eight reactions were definitely relevant, two possibly, four of which were caused by non-cosmetic products. There were 2 painters who had occupational allergic hand dermatitis from IPBC in paint, a metalworker with hand dermatitis from hand cleansers and possibly from IPBC in metalworking fluids, and a packer with hand dermatitis from lubricant preserving oil (15). In a study of the NACDG, performed in 1998-2008, 25,321 patients were tested with IPBC 0.1% and/or 0.5% pet. and there were 329 allergic reactions (23). Definite relevance was very low with <11%, most reactions being of possible relevance. Cosmetics were the most frequent causative products. Non-cosmetic products which were incriminated included (each n=1) 'adhesives, glues, bonding agents', 'solvents, oils, lubricants, fuels', 'metalworking fluids, cutting oils' (n=2), 'machinery, vehicles', 'building materials', 'paper products and supplies', 'topical corticosteroids', 'tapes, adhesive bandages, adhesive aids', 'medical and miscellaneous health devices', and 'miscellaneous health aids' (23). It should be realized that seven of these patients had weak reactions to the 0.5% pet. IPBC test substance, which frequently induces irritant patch test reactions. An atopic female medical specialist practitioner had hand dermatitis from IPBC in a hand cleanser (51). A female production worker at a paint factory developed dermatitis on air-exposed skin areas (airborne contact dermatitis). Patch testing showed a strongly positive reaction to the preservative IPBC 0.01% in petrolatum. The compound was used as a preservative in wood treatment products manufactured at her work place (26).

A male patient had hand dermatitis lasting for 6 months. The patient had for 18 months been working in a paint manufacturing plant mixing the different ingredients in the paint. Patch tests showed a positive reaction to IPBC. The patient had been working daily with a compound containing IPBC in a 30% solution. Following replacement in the factory to avoid direct as well as indirect contact with IPBC, the hand dermatitis improved. A ROAT with a cream containing 0.1% IPBC was positive after 4 days (20). In a clinic in The Netherlands, in the period 1995-1999, 23 metalworkers with dermatitis were referred for patch testing, 5 of whom were positive to IPBC present in metalworking fluids. It should be mentioned that 4 out of 5 only reacted to high concentrations of IPBC (0.5% - 2.5% olive oil), which may obviously be irritant. Nevertheless, in the three patients who could avoid contact with the incriminated metalworking products, hand dermatitis cleared in 2 and improved in the third patient (24). A man working in a window frame-manufacturing plant, feeding softwood window frames into a painting and drying machine, developed occupational allergic contact dermatitis of the hands from IPBC present as a wood preservative in a water-based acrylic primer (25).

Cross-reactions, pseudo-cross-reactions and co-reactions

There is a statistically significant overrepresentation of positive patch test reactions to the thiuram-mix in IPBC-allergic patients (34) and *vice versa* (15). Iodopropynyl butylcarbamate and carbamates used as rubber accelerators (tested in the NACDG screening series as the carba-mix) have a carbonyl group in their structure; therefore it is theoretically possible that there is structural cross-reactivity between IPBC and carbamates. This has been investigated in a study of the NACDG (27,28). In a group of 25,398 patients patch tested in the USA in the period 1998-2008, there were 1131 allergic reactions to carba-mix and 332 positive reactions to IPBC (either 0.1% and/or 0.5% pet). Fifty-two patients reacted to both. Approximately 5% of patients who had allergic reactions to carba-mix also had allergic reactions to IPBC, whereas approximately 15% of patients who had allergic reactions to IPBC also had allergic reactions to carba mix, indicating a statistically significant association between positivity to carbamates and IPBC. However, the authors conclude that concomitant reactions to IPBC and carbamates are most likely due to the borderline irritant nature of both of these allergen preparations rather than true co-reactivity or structural cross-reactivity (28).

Presence in cosmetic products and chemical analyses

In the USA, in April 2017, iodopropynyl butylcarbamate was present in 1338 of 56,714 cosmetic products of which the composition is known in FDA's Voluntary Cosmetic Registration Program (VCRP) (data obtained from FDA, May 2017). In January 2017, iodopropynyl butylcarbamate (IPBC) was present in 718 of 64,655 cosmetic products of which the composition is known in EWG's Skin Deep Cosmetics Database, USA (http://www.ewg.org/skindeep/). IPBC was present in 41 (23%) of 178 facial wipes for which ingredient information was obtained online and from retail stores, USA, 2016 (72). IPBC was present in 22 (41%) of 54 personal hygiene wet wipes for which ingredient information was obtained online and from retail stores, USA, 2016 (73). Iodopropynyl butylcarbamate was present in 192 of 4737 (4.1%) commonly used cosmetic products of which the full composition was known in 2016 in The Contact Allergen Management Program (CAMP) database of the American Contact Dermatitis Society (74).

In the USA, in 2015-2016, 63 diaper wipes and 41 topical diaper preparations from a large retailer were screened for the presence of potential sensitizers. IPBC was found in 13/63 (21%) disposable diaper wipes and in none of 41 topical diaper preparations (52). Of 60 different Israeli brand cosmetics, including shampoos, liquid soaps, body creams and hand creams, randomly selected in 2015, nine (15%) contained IPBC (49). In 2009, in the USA, the ingredient lists of 796 hair products from one company were screened for the presence of iodopropynyl butylcarbamate. IPBC was present in 9% of 279 shampoos, in 0% of 231 conditioners, and in 0% of 286 styling products (58). In 2009, in the USA, the ingredient lists of 657 miscellaneous cosmetics from one company were screened for the presence of iodopropynyl butylcarbamate. IPBC was present in 0% of 195 antiperspirants / deodorants, in 0% of 41 powders, in 0% of 167 shaving products, in 2% of 201 sunblocks, and in 60% of 53 wipes (59).

Iodopropynyl butylcarbamate was present in 2.3% of 4133 stay-on products and in 3.7% of 1261 rinse-off products purchased in Germany, 2006-2009 (5). In another, possibly overlapping 2006-2009 German study, IPBC was present in 92/3541 (2.5%) randomly sampled leave-on cosmetic products (6). In a third, possibly also overlapping study from Germany, in 2006-2009, the labels of 4680 cosmetic products were screened for the presence of preservatives. IPBC was present in 3.1% of the products, according to labelling information (68). In 2008, in Sweden, IPBC was found in 0.5 % of 204 cosmetic products (92 shampoos, 61 hair conditioners, 34 liquid soaps, 17 wet tissues) (7). IPBC was identified in 9/17 (53%) samples of metalworking fluids purchased in Finland, 2008; the highest concentration was 0.09% (43). Of 179 shampoos commercially available at Walgreens pharmacies in the USA, 2008, 10 (5.5%) contained IPBC (31). Of 276 moisturizers sold in the USA in 2007, 45 (16%) contained iodopropynyl butylcarbamate (13). Of 23 brands of moist toilet paper marketed in 2006 in Italy, 4 (17%) contained IPBC (57).

In the US, companies can voluntarily register the use of cosmetic ingredients with the Food and Drug Administration (FDA). In 1996, 122 cosmetic products out of 19,150 were reported to contain IPBC (0.6%), and in 2001, 170 products out of 16687 (1.0%) were so reported (48). According to the FDA register, IPBC was the preservative in cosmetics with the fastest growth in use in that 5-year time period (35).

LITERATURE

1   Uter W, Aberer W, Armario-Hita JC, , Fernandez-Vozmediano JM, Ayala F, Balato A, et al. Current patch test results with the European baseline series and extensions to it from the 'European Surveillance System on Contact Allergy' network, 2007-2008. Contact Dermatitis 2012;67:9-19

2   Travassos AR, Claes L, Boey L, Drieghe J, Goossens A. Non-fragrance allergens in specific cosmetic products. Contact Dermatitis 2011;65:276-285

3   Wetter DA, Yiannias JA, Prakash AV, Davis MD, Farmer SA, el-Azhary RA, et al. Results of patch testing to personal care product allergens in a standard series and a supplemental cosmetic series: an analysis of 945 patients from the Mayo Clinic Contact Dermatitis Group, 2000-2007. J Am Acad Dermatol 2010;63:789-798

4   Schnuch A, Lessmann H, Geier J, Uter W. Contact allergy to preservatives. Analysis of IVDK data 1996-2009. Br J Dermatol 2011;164:1316-1325

5   Mildau G. INCI labelling of fragrances and preservatives on 5451 randomly selected cosmetic products in Germany, 2006 to 2009. Karlsruhe: Chemisches und Veterinär-Untersuchungsamt, 2010

6   Schnuch A, Mildau G, Kratz E-M, Uter W. Risk of sensitization to preservatives estimated on the basis of patch test data and exposure, according to a sample of 3541 leave-on products. Contact Dermatitis 2011;65:167-174

7   Yazar K, Johnsson S, Lind M-L, Boman A, Lidén C. Preservatives and fragrances in selected consumer-available cosmetics and detergents. Contact Dermatitis 2011;64:265-272

8   Schöllnast R, Kränke B, Aberer W. Anal and palmar contact dermatitis caused by iodopropynyl butylcarbamate in moist sanitary wipes. Hautarzt 2003;54:970-974

9   Fields KS, Nelson T, Powell D. Contact dermatitis caused by baby wipes. J Am Acad Dermatol 2006;54:S230-S232

10   Zug KA, Warshaw EM, Fowler JF Jr, Maibach HI, Belsito DL, Pratt MD, et al. Patch-test results of the North American Contact Dermatitis Group 2005-2006. Dermatitis 2009;20:149-160

11 Fransway AF, Zug KA, Belsito DV, Deleo VA, Fowler JF Jr, Maibach HI, et al. North American Contact Dermatitis Group patch test results for 2007-2008. Dermatitis 2013;24:10-21

12 Warshaw EM, Belsito DV, DeLeo VA, Fowler JF Jr, Maibach HI, Marks JG, et al. North American Contact Dermatitis Group patch-test results, 2003-2004 study period. Dermatitis 2008;19:129-136

13 Zirwas MJ, Stechschulte SA. Moisturizer allergy. Diagnosis and management. J Clin Aesthetic Dermatol 2008;1:38-44

14 Molin S, Bauer A, Schnuch A, Geier J. Occupational contact allergy in nurses: results from the Information Network of Departments of Dermatology 2003–2012. Contact Dermatitis 2015;72:164-171

15 Martin-Gorgojo A, Johansen JD. Contact dermatitis caused by iodopropynyl butylcarbamate in Denmark. Contact Dermatitis 2013;69:78-85

16 Brasch J, Schnuch A, Geier J, Aberer W, Uter W; German Contact Dermatitis Research Group; Information Network of Departments of Dermatology. Iodopropynylbutyl carbamate 0.2% is suggested for patch testing of patients with eczema possibly related to preservatives. Br J Dermatol 2004;151:608-615

17 Lanigan RS. Final report on the safety assessment of iodopropynyl butylcarbamate (IPBC). Int J Toxicol 1998;17(Suppl. 5):1-37

18 Rossmoore HW. Handbook of biocide and preservative use. Glasgow, UK: Blackie Academic and Professional, 1995

19 The Scientific Committee on Cosmetic Products and Non-Food Products (SCCNFP). Intended For Consumers opinion concerning iodopropynyl butylcarbamate. 2004. Available at: http://ec.europa.eu/health/ph_risk/committees/sccp/documents/out288_en.pdf

20 Bryld L E, Agner T, Rastogi S C, Menné T. Iodopropynyl butylcarbamate: a new contact allergen. Contact Dermatitis 1997;36:156-158

21 Pazzaglia M, Tosti A. Allergic contact dermatitis from 3-iodo-2-propynyl-butylcarbamate in a cosmetic cream. Contact Dermatitis 1999;41:290

22 Natkunarajah J, Osborne V, Holden C. Allergic contact dermatitis to iodopropynyl butylcarbamate found in a cosmetic cleansing wipe. Contact Dermatitis 2008;58:316-317

23 Warshaw EM, Boralessa Ratnayake D, Maibach HI, Sasseville D, Belsito DV, Zug KA, et al. Positive patch-test reactions to iodopropynyl butylcarbamate: retrospective analysis of North American Contact Dermatitis Group data, from 1998 to 2008. Dermatitis 2010;21:303-310

24 Majoie IM, van Ginkel CJ. The biocide iodopropynyl butylcarbamate (IPBC) as an allergen in cutting oils. Contact Dermatitis 2000;43:238-240

25 Davis RF, Johnston GA. Iodopropynyl butylcarbamate contact allergy from wood preservative. Contact Dermatitis 2007;56:112

26 Jensen CD, Thormann J, Andersen KE. Airborne allergic contact dermatitis from 3-iodo-2-propynyl-butylcarbamate at a paint factory. Contact Dermatitis 2003;48:155-157

27 Warshaw EM, Srihari Raju MS. Cross-reactivity between carba mix and iodopropynyl butylcarbamate: retrospective analysis from the North American Contact Dermatitis Group, 1998-2008. Dermatitis 2011;22:175

28 Warshaw EM, Raju S, DeKoven JG, Belsito DV, Zug KA, Zirwas MJ. Positive Patch Test Reactions to Carba Mix and Iodopropynyl Butylcarbamate: Data From the North American Contact Dermatitis Group, 1998–2008. Dermatitis 2013;24:241-245

29 Warshaw EM, Belsito DV, Taylor JS, Sasseville D, DeKoven JG, Zirwas MJ, et al. North American Contact Dermatitis Group Patch Test Results: 2009 to 2010. Dermatitis 2013;24:50-59

30 Yim E, Baquerizo Nole KL, Tosti, A. Contact dermatitis caused by preservatives. Dermatitis 2014;25:215-231

31 Zirwas M, Moennich J. Shampoos. Dermatitis 2009;20:106-110

32 Marks JG Jr, Belsito DV, DeLeo VA, Fowler JF Jr, Fransway AF, Maibach HI. North American Contact Dermatitis Group patch-test results, 1998 to 2000. Am J Cont Derm 2003;14:59-62

33 Warshaw EM, Maibach HI, Taylor JS, Sasseville D, DeKoven JG, Zirwas MJ. North American Contact Dermatitis Group Patch Test Results: 2011–2012. Dermatitis 2015;26::49-59

34 Bryld L, Agner T, Menné T. Allergic contact dermatitis from 3-iodo-2-propynyl-butylcarbamate (IPBC)—an update. Contact Dermatitis 2001;44:276-278

35 Steinberg D. Frequency of use of preservatives 2001. Cosmetics & Toiletries 2002;177:41-44

36 Johnson RS. Iodopropynyl butylcarbamate (IPBC). Final Report. Washington, Cosmetic Ingredient Review, 1996:1-29

37 Yamano T, Shimizu M, Noda T. Relative elicitation potencies of seven chemical allergens in the guinea pig maximization test. J Health Sci 2001;47:123–128

38 Schnuch A, Geier J, Brasch J, Uter W. The preservative iodopropynyl butylcarbamate: frequency of allergic reactions and diagnostic considerations. Contact Dermatitis 2002;46:153-156

39 Thyssen JP, Engkilde K, Lundov MD, Carlsen BC, Menné T, Johansen JD. Temporal trends of preservative allergy in Denmark (1985–2008). Contact Dermatitis 2010;62:102-108

40 Zissu D. The sensitizing potential of various biocides in the guinea pig maximization test. Contact Dermatitis 2002;46:224-227

41 Siebert J. The sensitizing potential of iodopropynyl butylcarbamate in the local lymph node assay. Contact Dermatitis 2004;51:318

42 Geier J, Lessmann H, Dickel H, Frosch PJ, Koch P, Becker D. Patch test results with the metalworking fluid series of the German Contact Dermatitis Research Group (DKG). Contact Dermatitis 2004;51:118-130

43 Henriks-Eckerman ML, Suuronen K, Jolanki R. Analysis of allergens in metalworking fluids. Contact Dermatitis 2008;59:261-267

44 Geier J, Lessmann H, Frosch PJ, Pirker C, Koch P, Aschoff R, et al. Patch testing with components of water-based metalworking fluids. Contact Dermatitis 2003;49:85-90

45 Mose AP, Lundov MD, Zachariae C, Menné T, Veien NK, Laurberg G, et al. Occupational contact dermatitis in painters – an analysis of patch test data from the Danish Contact Dermatitis Group. Contact Dermatitis 2012;67:293-297

46 Badreshia S, Marks J. Iodopropynyl butylcarbamate. Am J Contact Dermatitis 2002;13:77-79

47 Pratt MD, Belsito DV, DeLeo VA, Fowler JF Jr, Fransway AF, Maibach HI, et al. North American Contact Dermatitis Group patch-test results, 2001–2002 study period. Dermatitis 2004;15:176-183

48 Steinberg DC. Iodopropynyl butylcarbamate as a preservative. Am J Cont Dermatitis 2002;13:207-208

49 Horev L, Isaksson M, Engfeldt M, Persson L, Ingber A, Bruze M. Preservatives in cosmetics in the Israeli market conform well to the EU legislation. J Eur Acad Dermatol Venereol 2015;29:761-766

50 Hallai N, Stone NM, Hughes TM, Goodwin R. Shocking reactions to 'Shock-waves' hair mousse: allergic contact dermatitis to 3-iodo-2-propynylbutylcarbamate. Br J Dermatol 2004;151 (Suppl.68):111

51 Toholka R, Nixon R. Suspected allergic contact dermatitis to iodopropynyl butylcarbamate in an alcohol hand rub commonly used in Australian health-care settings. Australas J Dermatol 2014;55:70-71

52 Yu J, Treat J, Chaney K, Brod B. Potential allergens in disposable diaper wipes, topical diaper preparations, and disposable diapers: under-recognized etiology of pediatric perineal dermatitis. Dermatitis 2016;27:110-118

53 Sasseville D. Hypersensitivity to preservatives. Dermatol Ther 2004;17:251-263

54 Lee SS, Hong DK, Jeong NJ, Lee JH, Choi YS, Lee AY, et al. Multicenter study of preservative sensitivity in patients with suspected cosmetic contact dermatitis in Korea. J Dermatol 2012;39:677-681

55 Goossens A. Cosmetic contact allergens. Cosmetics 2016, 3, 5; doi:10.3390/cosmetics3010005

56 Wentworth AB, Yiannias JA, Keeling JH, Hall MR, Camilleri MJ, Drage LA, et al. Trends in patch-test results and allergen changes in the standard series: a Mayo Clinic 5-year retrospective review (January 1, 2006, to December 31, 2010). J Am Acad Dermatol 2014;70:269-275

57 Zoli V, Tosti A, Silvani S, Vincenzi C. Moist toilet papers as possible sensitizers: review of the literature and evaluation of commercial products in Italy. Contact Dermatitis 2006;55:252-254

58 Scheman A, Jacob S, Katta R, Nedorost S, Warshaw E, Zirwas M, et al. Part 2 of a 4 part series. Hair cosmetics: trends and alternatives. Data from the American Contact Alternative Group. J Clin Aesthet Dermatol 2011;4:42-46

59 Scheman A, Jacob S, Katta R, Nedorost S, Warshaw E, Zirwas M, et al. Part 4 of a 4 part series. Miscellaneous products: trends and alternatives in deodorants, antiperspirants, sunblocks, shaving products, powder, and wipes. Data from the American Contact Alternative Group. J Clin Aesthet Dermatol 2011;4:35-39

60 SCCNFP (Scientific Committee on Cosmetics and Non Food Products). Opinion concerning iodopropynyl butylcarbamate, 1 July 2004, SCCNFP/0826/04. Available at: http://ec.europa.eu/health/archive/ph_risk/committees/sccp/documents/out288_en.pdf

61 SCCNFP (Scientific Committee on Cosmetics and Non Food Products). Opinion concerning 3-Iodo-2-propynyl-butylcarbamate (IPBC), 23 June 1999. Available at: http://ec.europa.eu/health/scientific_committees/consumer_safety/opinions/sccnfp_opinions_97_04/sccp_out96_en.htm

62 Toholka R, Wang Y-S, Tate B, Tam M, Cahill J, Palmer A, Nixon R. The first Australian Baseline Series: Recommendations for patch testing in suspected contact dermatitis. Australas J Dermatol 2015;56:107-115

63 Zhao J, Li LF. Contact sensitization to cosmetic series of allergens in a general population in Beijing. J Cosmet Dermatol 2014;13:68-71

64 Higgins C, Nixon R. Contact dermatitis caused by sunscreens: a cross-sectional study in a Victorian patch-test population. Contact Dermatitis 2016;75(Suppl.1):49

65 DeKoven JG, Warshaw EM, Belsito DV, Sasseville D, Maibach HI, Taylor JS, et al. North American Contact Dermatitis Group Patch Test Results: 2013-2014. Dermatitis 2017;28:33-46

66 Dinkloh A, Worm M, Geier J, Schnuch A, Wollenberg A. Contact sensitization in patients with suspected cosmetic intolerance: results of the IVDK 2006-2011. J Eur Acad Dermatol Venereol 2015;29:1071-1081

67 Uter W, Gefeller O, John SM, Schnuch A, Geier J. Contact allergy to ingredients of hair cosmetics – a comparison of female hairdressers and clients based on IVDK 2007–2012 data. Contact Dermatitis 2014;71:13-20

68 Uter W, Yazar K, Kratz EM, Mildau G, Lidén C. Coupled exposure to ingredients of cosmetic products: II. Preservatives. Contact Dermatitis 2014;70:219-226

69 Giménez-Arnau AM, Deza G, Bauer A, Johnston GA, Mahler V, Schuttelaar ML, et al. Contact allergy to preservatives: ESSCA* results with the baseline series, 2009-2012. J Eur Acad Dermatol Venereol 2017;31:664-671

70 Lubbes S, Rustemeyer T, Sillevis Smitt JH, Schuttelaar ML, Middelkamp-Hup MA. Contact sensitization in Dutch children and adolescents with and without atopic dermatitis - a retrospective analysis. Contact Dermatitis 2017;76:151-159

71 Erfurt-Berge C, Geier J, Mahler V. The current spectrum of contact sensitization in patients with chronic leg ulcers or stasis dermatitis - new data from the Information Network of Departments of Dermatology (IVDK). Contact Dermatitis 2017;77:151-158

72 Aschenbeck KA, Warshaw EM. Allergenic ingredients in facial wet wipes. Dermatitis 2017 Mar 23. doi: 10.1097/DER.0000000000000268. [Epub ahead of print]

73 Aschenbeck KA, Warshaw EM. Allergenic ingredients in personal hygiene wet wipes. Dermatitis 2017 Mar 23. doi: 10.1097/DER.0000000000000275. [Epub ahead of print]

74 Beene KM, Scheman A, Severson D, Reeder MJ. Prevalence of preservatives across all product types in the Contact Allergen Management Program. Dermatitis 2017;28:81-87

75 Warshaw EM, Aschenbeck KA, Zug KA, Belsito DV, Zirwas MJ, Fowler JF Jr, Taylor JS, et al. Wet wipe allergens: Retrospective analysis from the North American Contact Dermatitis Group 2011-2014. Dermatitis 2017;28:64-69

2.248 IRON OXIDES*

* Not a EU INCI name

IDENTIFICATION

Description/definition	: Iron oxides is an inorganic compound consisting of any one or combinations of synthetically prepared iron oxides, including the hydrated forms
Chemical class(es)	: Color additives; inorganics
INCI name USA	: Iron oxides; the European Union (EU) INCI names are CI 77489, CI 77491, CI 77492 or CI 77499
Other names	: Black iron oxide; brown iron oxide; CI 77489; CI 77491; CI 77492; CI 77499; diiron trioxide; ferric oxide; ferrous oxide; iron hydroxide oxide yellow; pigment black 11; pigment brown 6,7; pigment red 101,102; pigment yellow 42,43; red iron oxide; triiron tetraoxide; yellow iron oxide
CAS registry number (s)	: 1309-37-1 (Fe_2O_3); 1309-38-2; 1317-61-9 (Fe_3O_4); 1332-37-2; 1345-25-1 (FeO); 12227-89-3; 20344-49-4; 51274-00-1; 52357-70-7; 64294-91-3
EC number(s)	: 215-168-2; 215-277-5; 215-570-8; 215-721-8; 235-442-5; 257-870-1
Merck Index monograph	: 5325 (Ferric oxide); 5337 (Ferrosoferric oxide); 5349 (Ferrous oxide); 5322 (Ferric hydroxide)
Function(s) in cosmetics	: EU: cosmetic colorant. USA: colorants
EU cosmetic restrictions	: Regulated in Annexes IV/134 (CI 77489), IV/135 (CI 77491), IV/136 (CI 77492) and IV/137 (CI 77499) of the Regulation (EC) No. 1223/2009
Patch testing	: 0.8% yellow iron oxide in pet. (1); 5% pet. black iron oxide (2).

CONTACT ALLERGY

Case reports and case series

A non-atopic woman had a one month history of bilateral upper and lower eyelid erythema, treated unsuccessfully with corticosteroid eye drops and a topically applied sulfonamide. At the time of the eruption, she wore an eyeliner and liquid mascara. Patch tests gave a positive reaction to the liquid mascara. Later, she was tested with its ingredients, obtained from the manufacturer, and she now reacted to yellow iron oxide 1.2% pet. Ten controls were negative to the test substance. Analysis showed that the substance actually contained 0.8% yellow iron oxide, which was 99.1% pure (1).

Another woman had a 10-month history of periorbital and eyelid dermatitis. Patch tests with the standard series, cosmetic series, steroid series, and her personal products yielded a strong reaction to her mascara. Later, she was tested with the ingredients of the mascara, obtained from the manufacturer, and the patient now reacted strongly to 5% black iron oxide in petrolatum. Ten controls had negative reactions to the test material (2).

Presence in cosmetic products and chemical analyses

In May 2017, iron oxides was present in 8115 of 64,655 cosmetic products of which the composition is known in EWG's Skin Deep Cosmetics Database, USA (http://www.ewg.org/skindeep/). In the USA, in April 2017, iron oxides was present in 11901 of 56,714 cosmetic products of which the composition is known in FDA's Voluntary Cosmetic Registration Program (VCRP) (data obtained from FDA, May 2017).

Other side effects

A man developed a widespread, pruritic maculopapular rash one week after the dosage of enalapril had been increased from 5 to 10 mg once daily. It appeared that the 10 mg preparation contained a coloring agent, whereas the 5 mg tablet did not. The eruption disappeared after taking only the color-free tablets. A woman presented with a painful, extensive eczematous rash. She said the rash had started two to three days after her enalapril dosage had been changed from 5 mg twice a day to a single 20 mg dose, the latter of which contains coloring agents. When she was given four 5 mg tablets instead of one 20 mg tablet the rash resolved within three days. The coloring agents common to the 10 mg and 20 mg preparations of enalapril were mapico red and mapico yellow, which are iron oxides. Patch tests were not performed, nor were provocation tests done. Hence, neither contact allergy to iron oxides nor its causal role was established (3).

LITERATURE

1 Zugerman C. Contact dermatitis to yellow iron oxide. Contact Dermatitis 1985;13:107-109
2 Saxena M, Warshaw E, Ahmed DDF. Eyelid allergic contact dermatitis to black iron oxide. Am J Cont Derm 2001;12:38-39
3 Gracey-Whitman L, Ell S. Artificial colourings and adverse reactions. BMJ 1995;310:1204

2.249 ISOAMYL P-METHOXYCINNAMATE

IDENTIFICATION

Description/definition	: Isoamyl p-methoxycinnamate is the ester of isoamyl alcohol and p-methoxycinnamic acid, which conforms generally to the formula shown below
Chemical class(es)	: Esters
Chemical/IUPAC name	: 3-Methylbutyl (E)-3-(4-methoxyphenyl)prop-2-enoate
Other names	: Amiloxate; isopentyl p-methoxycinnamate
CAS registry number (s)	: 71617-10-2
EC number(s)	: 275-702-5
SCCS opinion(s)	: SCCNFP, 24 June 1997 (32)
Function(s) in cosmetics	: EU: UV-absorber; UV-filter. USA: light stabilizers
EU cosmetic restrictions	: Regulated in Annex VI/14 of the Regulation (EC) No. 1223/2009
Patch testing	: 10.0% pet. (Chemotechnique, SmartPracticeCanada)
Molecular formula	: $C_{15}H_{20}O_3$

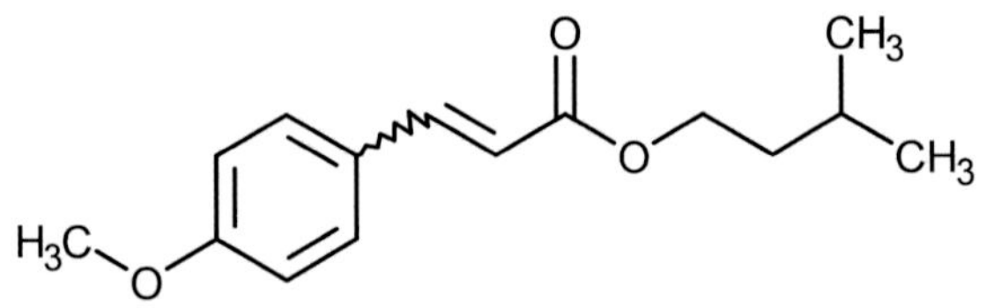

GENERAL

Isoamyl p-methoxycinnamate is a UVB filter with UV absorbance maximum (λ_{max}) at 308 nm, that has been used in Europe since 1976 (19,38). The literature on adverse reactions to sunscreens has been reviewed in several recent and older publications (25-30,40). A review of photocontact allergy to sunscreens was published in 2010 (37).

CONTACT ALLERGY

Patch testing in groups of patients

There are no studies in which consecutive patients suspected of contact dermatitis have been tested with isoamyl p-methoxycinnamate. Results of testing in groups of *selected* patients (e.g., patients suspected of photosensitivity, patients with dermatitis affecting mainly light-exposed skin or with a history of a sunscreen skin reaction) back to 1996 are shown in table 2.249.1. Frequencies of sensitization have been invariably low, ranging from 0.1% to 1.1%. In 3 of 5 studies, relevance was either not mentioned or not specified for isoamyl p-methoxycinnamate. The one positive reaction in a Colombian study was not relevant (35) and of 4 positive patch test reactions in a 2000-2002 study performed in Ireland, the UK and The Netherlands, 2 out of 4 reactions were relevant, and one was of past relevance (1).

Table 2.249.1 Patch testing in groups of patients: Selected patient groups

Years and Country	Test conc. & vehicle	Number of patients tested | positive (%)		Selection of patients (S); Relevance (R); Comments (C)	Ref.
2011-2013 Colombia	10% pet.	112	1 (0.9%)	S: dermatitis affecting mainly light-exposed skin, a history of a sunscreen or a topical NSAID skin reaction; R: not relevant	35
2008-2011 12 European countries	10% pet.	1031	2 (0.2%)	S: patients with exposed site dermatitis or history of a reaction to a sunscreen or topical NSAID; R: not specified	14
2000-2002; UK, I, NL	10% pet.	1155	4 (0.4%)	S: patients suspected of photosensitivity or reaction to a sunscreen; R: current relevance 2, unknown 1, past 1	1
1983-1998 UK	10% pet.	2715	3 (0.1%)	S: patients suspected of photosensitivity or with (a history of) dermatitis at exposed sites; R: not stated	2
1981-1996 Germany	10% pet. or undiluted	355	4 (1.1%)	S: patients suspected of clinical photosensitivity; R: not stated	5

I: Ireland; NL: Netherlands; UK: United Kingdom

Case reports and case series

Isoamyl p-methoxycinnamate was stated to be the (or an) allergen in 2 patients in a group of 603 individuals suffering from cosmetic dermatitis, seen in the period 2010-2015 in Leuven, Belgium (31). In the period 1996-2013, in a tertiary referral center in Valencia, Spain, 5419 patients were patch tested. Of these, 628 individuals had allergic contact dermatitis to cosmetics. Isoamyl *p*-methoxycinnamate was the responsible allergen in four cases (36, overlap with ref. 33). In the period 2000-2007, 202 patients with allergic contact dermatitis caused by cosmetics were seen in Valencia, Spain. In this group, one individual reacted to isoamyl-*p*-methoxycinna-mate from its presence in a sunscreen (33, overlap with ref. 36).

In the period 1981-1989, 56 patients (43 women, 13 men) were diagnosed with contact allergy or photocontact allergy to UV-filters in one center in Germany. There were 3 allergic reactions to isoamyl *p*-methoxycinnamate. All reactions were relevant and all 46 patients who could be (photo)patch tested with their own sunscreens (and a few of them with other cosmetics) had one or more positive (photo)patch tests to these products (39, overlap with refs. 5 and 7).

Cross-reactions, pseudo-cross-reactions and co-reactions (including photoreactions)

(Photo) cross-reactivity may occur with other cinnamates: ethylhexyl methoxycinnamate (7, article not read), cinoxate, cinnamal, cinnamic acid (13), *Myroxylon pereirae* (balsam of Peru, contains cinnamal and other cinnamates) (12), benzyl cinnamate, methyl cinnamate, cinnamyl alcohol (5). It has been suggested that methoxycinnamates may show cross-reactions with other cinnamates that can be found in perfumes, topical remedies, cosmetics, and food flavoring agents such as cinnamic acid, cinnamal, cinnamon extract and balsam of Peru, and that sensitized patients should be advised to avoid such products (20). However, there were no positive patch or photopatch tests to ethylhexyl methoxycinnamate or isoamyl *p*-methoxycinnamate in 18 patients allergic to cinnamon or cinnamate chemicals such as cinnamal, cinnamic acid, cinnamyl alcohol or *Myroxylon pereirae* resin (balsam of Peru), which contains various cinnamates (21).

Presence in cosmetic products and chemical analyses

In June 2017, isoamyl *p*-methoxycinnamate was present in 1 of 68,866 cosmetic products of which the composition is known in EWG's Skin Deep Cosmetics Database, USA (http://www.ewg.org/skindeep/). It should be realized that sunscreen products containing UV-filters are classified as drugs in the USA, not as cosmetics; the number mentioned here, therefore, is that of cosmetics containing the UV-filter, but it does *not* include their presence in sunscreens. In the USA, in April 2017, isoamyl *p*-methoxycinnamate was present in 27 of 56,714 cosmetic products of which the composition is known in FDA's Voluntary Cosmetic Registration Program (VCRP) (data obtained from FDA, May 2017).

In 2012, in Switzerland, 116 cosmetics from seven widely used leave-on product categories (19 lip care products, 8 lipsticks, 29 face creams, 11 liquid makeup foundations, 3 aftershaves, 7 hand creams and 39 sunscreens) were investigated to determine the frequency of occurrence and concentrations of 22 organic UV filters in these products. Isoamyl *p*-methoxycinnamate was found in only one of the products in a concentration of 7.05% (34). In a sample of 337 sunscreens marketed in the UK in 2010, isoamyl *p*-methoxycinnamate was present in 0.9% (24). Isoamyl *p*-methoxycinnamate was present in 4.1% of 4447 cosmetic products collected in Germany, 2006-2009 (15). Isoamyl *p*-methoxycinnamate was present in 4 of 75 (5%) sunscreen creams and lotions from 30 European and US producers purchased in Denmark in 2001 in a concentration range of 2.6-4.1% (17).

OTHER SIDE EFFECTS

Photosensitivity

Photopatch testing in groups of patients

Results of photopatch testing isoamyl *p*-methoxycinnamate in groups of selected patients (e.g., patients suspected of photosensitivity, patients with dermatitis affecting mainly light-exposed skin or with a history of a sunscreen skin reaction) back to 1994 are shown in table 2.249.2. In 11 studies, frequencies of photosensitization have ranged from 0.1% to 3.6%, but were 1% or lower in 7/11 investigations (table 2.249.2). In many studies, relevance was either not mentioned or specified for isoamyl *p*-methoxycinnamate , but in the studies that provided relevance data, 40-100% of the positive photopatch tests were considered to be relevant (1,11,18,35,).

Case reports and case series

A child had photoallergic CD from isoamyl *p*-methoxycinnamate in sunscreens (10). One patient reacted to a sunscreen used for polymorphic light eruption (12). Another individual suffered from photoallergic contact dermatitis caused by isoamyl *p*-methoxycinnamate in a sunscreen (22). In the period 1981-1989, 56 patients (43 women, 13 men) were diagnosed with contact allergy or photocontact allergy to UV-filters in one center in Germany. There were 3 photoallergic reactions to isoamyl *p*-methoxycinnamate. All reactions were relevant and all 46 patients who could be (photo)patch tested with their own sunscreens (and a few of them with other cosmetics) had one or more positive (photo)patch tests to these products (39, overlap with refs. 5 and 7). One patient had photoallergic contact dermatitis from isoamyl *p*-methoxycinnamate (6, article not read).

Several centers have reported positive photopatch tests to isoamyl *p*-methoxycinnamate, but without specifying their relevance (8,23).

Table 2.249.2 Photopatch testing in groups of patients

Years and Country	Test conc. & vehicle	Number of patients tested | positive (%)		Selection of patients (S); Relevance (R); Comments (C)	Ref.
2011-2013 Colombia	10% pet.	112	1 (0.9%)	S: dermatitis affecting mainly light-exposed skin, a history of a sunscreen or a topical NSAID skin reaction; R: relevant	35
2008-2011 12 European countries	10% pet.	1031	10 (1.0%)	S: patients with exposed site dermatitis or history of a reaction to a sunscreen or topical NSAID; R: 44% current and 11% past relevance for all photoallergens together	14
2000-2011 UK	10% pet.	157	1 (0.6%)	S: children <18 years suspected of photosensitivity; R: the reaction was caused by a sunscreen product	18
2003-2007 Portugal	10% pet.	83	1 (1.2%)	S: patients with suspected photoaggravated facial dermatitis or systemic photosensitivity; R: all sunscreen photopatch tests were of current or past relevance	16
2004-2006 Italy	10% pet.	1082	4 (0.4%)	S: patients with histories and clinical features suggestive of photoallergic contact dermatitis; 1/4 were cases of photoaugmented contact allergy; R: 100%	11
2000-2002 UK, I, NL	10% pet.	1155	14 (1.2%)	S: patients suspected of photosensitivity or reaction to a sunscreen; R: current relevance 5, unknown 8, cross-reaction 1	1
1994-1999 NL	10% pet.	55	2 (3.6%)	S: patients suspected of photosensitivity disorders; R: not stated	9
1983-1998 UK	10% pet.	2715	2 (0.1%)	S: patients suspected of photosensitivity or with (a history of) dermatitis at exposed sites; R: 37% for all photoallergens together	2
1991-97 Ger, Au, Swi		1261	5 (0.4%)	S: patients suspected of photosensitivity; R: not stated	3
1981-1996 Germany	10% pet. or undiluted	355	10 (2.8%)	S: patients suspected of clinical photosensitivity; R: not stated	5
1985-1994 Italy		1050	3 (0.3%)	S: patients with histories or clinical pictures suggestive of allergic contact photodermatitis; R: 97% for all sunscreens together	4

Au: Austria; Ger: Germany; I: Ireland; NL: Netherlands; UK: United Kingdom; Swi: Switzerland

LITERATURE

1   Bryden A, Moseley H, Ibbotson S, Chowdhury MM, Beck MH, Bourke J, et al. Photopatch testing of 1155 patients: results of the U.K. multicentre photopatch test study group. Brit J Dermatol 2006;155:737-747

2   Darvay A, White I, Rycroft R, Jones AB, Hawk JL, McFadden JP. Photoallergic contact dermatitis is uncommon. Br J Dermatol 2001;145:597-601

3   Neumann NJ, Hölzle E, Plewig G, Schwarz T, Panizzon RG, Breit R, et al. Photopatch testing: The 12-year experience of the German, Austrian and Swiss Photopatch Test Group. J Am Acad Dermatol 2000;42:183-192

4   Pigatto PD, Legori A, Bigardi AS, Guarrera M, Tosti A, Santucci B, et al. Gruppo Italiano recerca dermatiti da contatto ed ambientali Italian multicenter study of allergic contact photodermatitis: epidemiological aspects. Am J Contact Dermatitis 1996;17:158-163

5   Schauder S, Ippen H. Contact and photocontact sensitivity. Review of a 15-year experience and of the literature to suncreens. Contact Dermatitis 1997;37:221-232

6   Fagerlund VL, Kalimo K, Jansen CH. Valonsurjaaineet fotokontaktallergien aiheuttajin. Duodecim 1983;99:146-150

7   Schauder S. Kontaktekzem durch Lichtfilterhaltige Lichtschutzmittel und Kosmetika. Aktuelle Dermatologie 1991;17:47-57

8   Cook N, Freeman S. Report of 19 cases of photoallergic contact dermatitis to sunscreens seen at the Skin and Cancer Foundation. Austral J Dermatol 2001;42:257-259

9   Bakkum RS, Heule F. Results of photopatch testing in Rotterdam during a 10-year period. Br J Dermatol 2002;146:275-279

10   Cook N, Freeman S. Photosensitive dermatitis due to sunscreen allergy in a child. Australas J Dermatol 2002;43:133-135

11   Pigatto PD, Guzzi G, Schena D, Guarrera M, Foti C, Francalanci S, et al. Photopatch tests: an Italian multicentre study from 2004 to 2006. Contact Dermatitis 2008;59:103-108

12   Ghazavi MK, Johnston GA. Photo-allergic contact dermatitis caused by isoamyl *p*-methoxycinnamate in an 'organic' sunscreen. Contact Dermatitis 2011;64:115-116

13 Fisher AA. Sunscreen dermatitis: part II – the cinnamates. Cutis 1992;50:253-254

14 The European Multicentre Photopatch Test Study (EMCPPTS) Taskforce. A European multicentre photopatch test study. Br J Dermatol 2012;166:1002-1009

15 Uter W, Gonçalo M, Yazar K, Kratz E-M, Mildau G, Lidén C. Coupled exposure to ingredients of cosmetic products: III. Ultraviolet filters. Contact Dermatitis 2014;71:162-169

16 Cardoso J, Canelas MM, Gonçalo M, Figueiredo A. Photopatch testing with an extended series of photoallergens: a 5-year study. Contact Dermatitis 2009;60:325-329

17 Rastogi SC. UV filters in sunscreen products – a survey. Contact Dermatitis 2002;46:348-351

18 Haylett AK, Chiang YZ, Nie Z, Ling TC, Rhodes LE. Sunscreen photopatch testing: a series of 157 children. Br J Dermatol 2014;171:370-375

19 Kerr A, Ferguson J. Photoallergic contact dermatitis. Photodermatol Photoimmunol Photomed 2010;26:56-65

20 Fisher AA. Sunscreen dermatitis: Part II-The cinnamates. Cutis 1992;50:253-254.

21 Pentinga SE, Kuik DJ, Bruynzeel DP, Rustemeyer T. Do 'cinnamon-sensitive' patients react to cinnamate UV filters? Contact Dermatitis 2009;60:210-213

22 Monzón S, Abós T, Sáenz D, Pérez-Cinto N, Montijano R, Solano AM. Photoallergic contact dermatitis due to isoamyl-p-methoxycinnamate. J Invest Allergol Clin Immunol 2009;19:415-416

23 Collaris E, Frank J. Photoallergic contact dermatitis caused by ultraviolet filters in different sunscreens. Int J Dermatol 2008;47:35-37

24 Kerr AC. A survey of the availability of sunscreen filters in the U.K. Clin Exp Dermatol 2011;36:541-543

25 Heurung AR, Raju SI, Warshaw EM. Adverse reactions to sunscreen agents: epidemiology, responsible irritants and allergens, clinical characteristics, and management. Dermatitis 2014;25:289-326

26 Heurung AR, Raju SI, Warshaw EM. Contact allergen of the year. Benzophenones. Dermatitis 2014;25:3-10 (contains many mistakes; Erratum in Dermatitis 2014;25:92-95)

27 Avenel-Audran M. Sunscreen products: finding the allergen. Eur J Dermatol 2010;20:161-166

28 Scheuer E, Warshaw E. Sunscreen allergy: a review of epidemiology, clinical characteristics, and responsible allergens. Dermatitis 2006;17:3-11

29 Funk JO, Dromgoole SH, Maibach HI. Sunscreen intolerance: contact sensitization, photocontact sensitization, and irritancy of sunscreen agents. Dermatol Clin 1995;13:473-481

30 Dromgoole SH, Maibach HI. Sunscreening agent intolerance: Contact and photocontact sensitization and contact urticaria. J Am Acad Dermatol 1990;22:1068-1078

31 Goossens A. Cosmetic contact allergens. Cosmetics 2016, 3, 5; doi:10.3390/cosmetics3010005

32 SCCNFP (Scientific Committee on Cosmetics and Non Food Products). Opinion concerning concerning isopentyl-p-methoxycinnamate, 24 June 1997. Available at: http://ec.europa.eu/health/scientific_committees/consumer_safety/opinions/sccnfp_opinions_97_04/sccp_out06_en.htm

33 Laguna C, de la Cuadra J, Martín-González B, Zaragoza V, Martínez-Casimiro L, Alegre V. Allergic contact dermatitis to cosmetics. Actas Dermosifiliogr 2009;100:53-60

34 Manová E, von Goetz N, Hauri U, Bogdal C, Hungerbühler K. Organic UV filters in personal care products in Switzerland: A survey of occurrence and concentrations. Int J Hyg Environ Health 2013;216:508-514

35 Valbuena Mesa MC, Hoyos Jiménez EV. Photopatch testing in Bogota (Colombia): 2011–2013. Contact Dermatitis 2016;74:11-17

36 Zaragoza-Ninet V, Blasco Encinas R, Vilata-Corell JJ, Pérez-Ferriols A, Sierra-Talamantes C, Esteve-Martínez A, de la Cuadra-Oyanguren J. Allergic contact dermatitis due to cosmetics: A clinical and epidemiological study in a tertiary hospital. Actas Dermosifiliogr 2016;107:329-336

37 Shaw T, Simpson B, Wilson B, Oostman H, Rainey D, Storrs F. True photoallergy to sunscreens is rare despite popular belief. Dermatitis 2010;21:185-198

38 Shaath NA. Ultraviolet filters. Photochem Photobiol Sci 2010;9:464-469

39 Schauder S. Adverse reactions to sunscreening agents in 58 patients (part 3). Z Hautkr 1991;66:294-318 (article in German)

40 Schauder S. Survey of the literature on adverse reactions to preparations containing UV filters (1947-1989) (Literaturübersicht über Unverträglichkeitsreaktionen auf lichtfilterhaltige Produkte von 1947 bis 1989). Z Hautkr 1990;65:982-998 (article in German)

2.250   ISOBUTYL METHACRYLATE

IDENTIFICATION

Description/definition	: Isobutyl methacrylate is the organic compound that conforms to the formula shown below
Chemical class(es)	: Esters
Chemical/IUPAC name	: 2-Methylpropyl 2-methylprop-2-enoate
Other names	: 2-Propenoic acid, 2- methyl-, 2-methylpropyl ester
CAS registry number (s)	: 97-86-9
EC number(s)	: 02-613-0
CIR review(s)	: Int J Toxicol 2005;24(Suppl.5):53-100 (access: www.cir-safety.org/ingredients)
Function(s) in cosmetics	: EU: film forming. USA: artificial nail builders
Patch testing	: 2% pet.
Molecular formula	: $C_8H_{14}O_2$

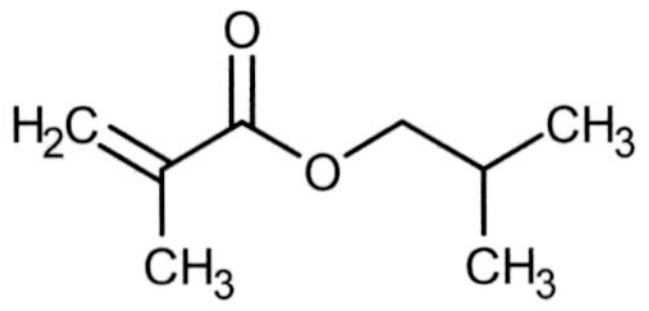

GENERAL

Discussion of contact allergy to (meth)acrylates *from non-cosmetic sources* is considered to fall outside the scope of this book. Therefore, only contact allergy from their presence in cosmetics is presented, which virtually always is from artificial nails. There are many reports of contact allergy to artificial nails, but the specific sensitizers have rarely been identified and – consequently - such publications are not presented in this and other acrylate and methacrylate monographs. Discussion is limited to publications in which the culprit (meth)acrylates have been identified, e.g., from information found in Material Data Safety Sheets, data obtained from the manufacturer or from chemical analyses.

Patients often react to many (meth)acrylates on patch testing. Primary sensitization to methacrylates may result in both methacrylate and acrylate cross-sensitization. Conversely, patients sensitized to acrylates are unlikely to show cross-sensitization to methacrylates (2).

General aspects of acrylates and methacrylates are presented in Chapter 2.188 HEMA (hydroxyethyl methacrylate). A discussion of general aspects of artificial nails, contact allergy to these products, the clinical picture of allergic contact dermatitis and other side effects of sculptured nails can also be found there. A very useful review of contact sensitization to allergens in nail cosmetics, with emphasis on acrylic manicures, was published in 2017 (3).

CONTACT ALLERGY

Patch testing in groups of patients

Studies in which consecutive patients suspected of contact dermatitis have been tested with isobutyl methacrylate (routine testing) and studies testing groups of selected patients are planned to be discussed in a future publication.

Case reports and case series

One patient had painful onychia and paronychia from contact allergy to isobutyl methacrylate in a nail extender (cold-curing artificial nail) (1).

Presence in cosmetic products and chemical analyses

In the USA, in April 2017, isobutyl methacrylate was present in 5 of 56,714 cosmetic products of which the composition is known in FDA's Voluntary Cosmetic Registration Program (VCRP) (data obtained from FDA, May 2017). In August 2017, isobutyl methacrylate was present in zero of 70.693 cosmetic products of which the composition is known in EWG's Skin Deep Cosmetics Database, USA (http://www.ewg.org/skindeep/).

LITERATURE

1 Fisher AA. Cross reactions between methyl methacrylate monomer and acrylic monomers presently used in acrylic nail preparations. Contact Dermatitis 1980;6:345-347

2 Aalto-Korte K, Henriks-Eckerman M-L, Kuuliala O, Jolanki R. Occupational methacrylate and acrylate allergy – cross-reactions and possible screening allergens. Contact Dermatitis 2010;63:301-312

3 Chou M, Dhingra N, Strugar TL. Contact sensitization to allergens in nail cosmetics. Dermatitis 2017;28:231-240

2.251   ISOBUTYL PABA*
Not an INCI name

IDENTIFICATION

Description/definition	: Isobutyl PABA is the ester of isobutyl alcohol and *p*-aminobenzoic acid, which conforms generally to the formula shown below
Chemical class(es)	: PABA derivatives
INCI name USA	: Neither in CosIng nor in the Personal Care Products Council Ingredient Database
Chemical/IUPAC name	: Isobutyl 4-aminobenzoate
Other names	: Isobutamben
CAS registry number (s)	: 94-14-4
EC number(s)	: 202-308-2
Patch testing	: 5% pet.
Molecular formula	: $C_{11}H_{15}NO_2$

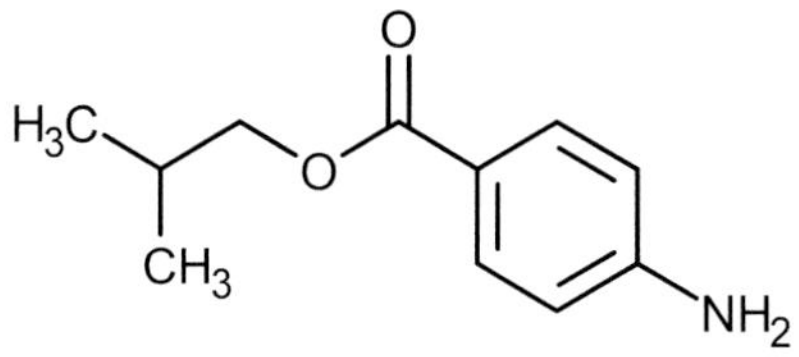

GENERAL
Isobutyl PABA (isobutamben) is cited as being used as local anesthetic in topical compositions and methods for treating pain, as a sunscreen and in other cosmetics (6). However, the chemical is not official in any pharmacopeia, and has no INCI name (neither present in CosIng nor in the Personal Care Products Council Ingredient Database). Moreover, in February 2017, isobutyl PABA was present in not a single of 64,480 cosmetic products of which the composition is known in EWG's Skin Deep Cosmetics Database, USA (http://www.ewg.org/skindeep/).

CONTACT ALLERGY

Case reports and case series
In the period 1978-1991, there were 12 relevant (related to sunscreens or other cosmetics) patch test reactions to isobutyl PABA in one center in Leuven, Belgium (1). In a 4-month-period in 1996, 475 patients with contact allergy to 'cosmetic ingredients' were collected in 5 centers in Belgium, UK and Germany. There were 4 reactions to isobutyl PABA; relevance was not stated (2). In France, among 67 patients photopatch tested, there are two positive patch test reactions to isobutyl PABA, relevance unknown (3).

Cross-reactions, pseudo-cross-reactions and co-reactions
In the period 1978-1991, there were 54 non-relevant positive patch test reactions to PABA and/or isobutyl PABA (not further specified) in Leuven, Belgium. Forty sensitizations represented a cross-reaction to chemically-related para-substituted compounds, particularly *p*-phenylenediamine, benzocaine, diaminodiphenylmethane and sulfanilamide (1). Cross-reaction to methyl *m*-amino-*p*-hydroxybenzoate (old orthoform) (5). Cross-reactivity between para-compounds is discussed in Chapter 2.359 *p*-Phenylenediamine.

Presence in cosmetic products and chemical analyses
In May 2017, isobutyl PABA was present in zero of 66,975 cosmetic products of which the composition is known in EWG's Skin Deep Cosmetics Database, USA (http://www.ewg.org/skindeep/). In the USA, in April 2017, isobutyl PABA was present in zero of 56,714 cosmetic products of which the composition is known in FDA's Voluntary Cosmetic Registration Program (VCRP) (data obtained from FDA, May 2017).

OTHER SIDE EFFECTS

Photosensitivity
One phototoxic reaction to isobutyl PABA was observed in France (3).

LITERATURE
1   Theeuwes M, Degreef H, Dooms-Goossens A. Para-aminobenzoic acid (PABA) and sunscreen allergy. Am J Cont Derm 1992;3:206-207

2   Goossens A, Beck MH, Haneke E, McFadden JP, Nolting S, Durupt G, Ries G. Adverse cutaneous reactions to cosmetic allergens. Contact Dermatitis 1999;40:112-113

3   Jeanmougin M. Determination du pouvoir photosensibilisant d'un medicament par la méthode des photopatch tests. Nouv Dermatol 1986;5(Suppl.3):204-208 (incomplete data, cited in ref. 4)

4   De Groot AC, Weyland JW, Nater JP. Unwanted effects of cosmetics and drugs used in dermatology, 3rd Edition. Amsterdam – London – New York – Tokyo: Elsevier, 1994

5   Lane CG, Luikart R II. Dermatitis from local anesthetics with a review of one hundred and seven cases from the literature. JAMA 1951;146:717-720

6   Schmidt AC. Structural characteristics and crystal polymorphism of three local anaesthetic bases crystal polymorphism of local anaesthetic drugs: part VII. Int J Pharm 2005;298:186-197

2.252 ISOHEXADECANE

IDENTIFICATION

Description/definition	: Isohexadecane is a branched chain aliphatic hydrocarbon with 16 carbons
Chemical class(es)	: Hydrocarbons
Chemical/IUPAC name	: 2,2,4,4,6,8,8-Heptamethylnonane
Other names	: Heptamethylnonane
CAS registry number (s)	: 93685-80-4; 4390-04-9; 60908-77-2
EC number(s)	: 297-628-2; 224-506-8
CIR review(s)	: Int J Toxicol 2012;31(Suppl.3):269-295 (access: www.cir-safety.org/ingredients)
Function(s) in cosmetics	: EU: emollient; skin conditioning; solvent. USA: skin-conditioning agents - emollient; solvents
Patch testing	: 10% alc. (1)
Molecular formula	: $C_{16}H_{34}$

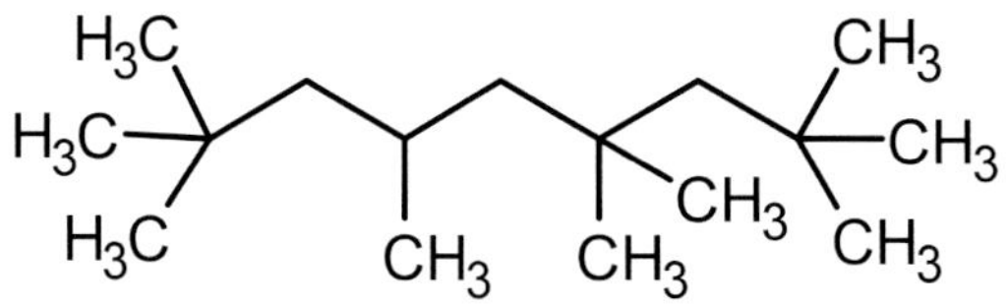

It is doubtful whether the three CAS numbers given by the Personal Care Products Council Ingredient Database all refer to the same chemical.

GENERAL

Isohexadecane is a mixture containing more than 99% C_{16} isoparaffins. It is found in cosmetics, surface coatings, floor polishes, shoe creams, car polishes and protective waxes and insecticide solutions (1).

CONTACT ALLERGY

Case reports and case series

A woman presented with a history of an eczematous rash after the application of a commercially available sunscreen with SPF 50. The rash had appeared after 3 days of application of the sunscreen over the face, neck and limbs and had been very pruritic. Patch tests with the European standard series gave positive reactions to formaldehyde, quaternium-15, imidazolidinyl urea and diazolidinyl urea. The ingredients of the sunscreen that she had used were obtained from the manufacturer, and were patch tested on the patient. There was a positive reaction to isohexadecane 10% alcohol at D2 and D4. Twenty controls tested negatively to this substance (1).

Presence in cosmetic products and chemical analyses

In the USA, in April 2017, isohexadecane was present in 1248 of 56,714 cosmetic products of which the composition is known in FDA's Voluntary Cosmetic Registration Program (VCRP) (data obtained from FDA, May 2017). In March 2017, isohexadecane was present in 549 of 65,351 cosmetic products of which the composition is known in EWG's Skin Deep Cosmetics Database, USA (http://www.ewg.org/skindeep/).

LITERATURE

1   Bharati A, King CM. Allergic contact dermatitis from isohexadecane and isopropyl myristate. Contact Dermatitis 2004;50:256-257

2.253   ISONONYL ISONONANOATE

IDENTIFICATION

Description/definition	: Isononyl isononanoate is the ester of a branched chain nonyl alcohol with a branched chain nonanoic acid. It conforms generally to the formula shown below
Chemical class(es)	: Esters
Chemical/IUPAC name	: 3,5,5-Trimethylhexyl 3,5,5-trimethylhexanoate
Other names	: Hexanoic acid, 3,5,5-trimethyl-, 3,5,5-trimethylhexyl ester
CAS registry number (s)	: 59219-71-5; 42131-25-9
EC number(s)	: 261-665-2
CIR review(s)	: Int J Toxicol 2011;30(Suppl.3):228-269; Final report, March 2013 (access: www.cir-safety.org/ingredients)
Function(s) in cosmetics	: EU: antistatic; emollient; skin conditioning. USA: skin-conditioning agents - emollient
Patch testing	: 5% alcohol (2)
Molecular formula	: $C_{18}H_{36}O_2$

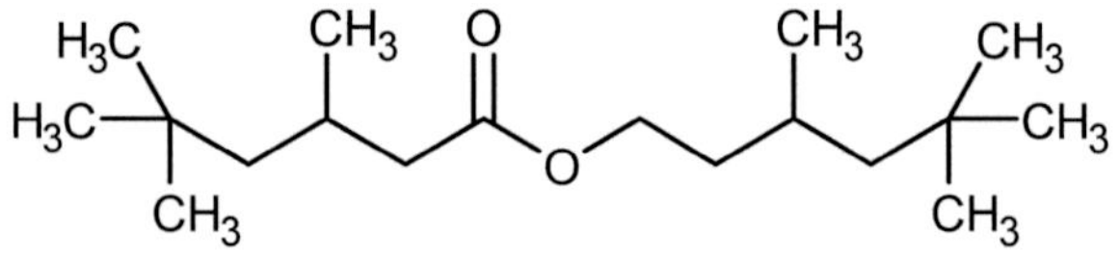

GENERAL

Isononyl isononanoate is the ester of a branched chain nonyl alcohol with a branched chain nonanoic acid, used as an emollient and skin conditioning agent in, e.g., lipsticks, foundations, skin care products, body and hand preparations, and make-up bases. In the cosmetic database in Leuven, Belgium, it was also found to be present in sunscreens, self-tanning and cleansing products, deodorants, face powders, as well as in creams to treat pregnancy marks (2).

CONTACT ALLERGY

Case reports and case series

Isononyl isononanoate was responsible for 2 out of 959 cases of non-fragrance cosmetic allergy where the causal allergen was identified, Belgium, 2000-2010 (1). A non-atopic woman, with a history of a reaction to an 'anticellulite' cream, presented with contact cheilitis following the application of a lipstick. Patch testing with the European baseline series and a cosmetics series was negative, but positive reactions were observed to 2 lipsticks and the anticellulite cream. The ingredients were not tested. Five years later, the patient presented again with a severe contact dermatitis on the eyelids due to a new lipstick, which she had applied to the eyelids, assuming it to be an eyeshadow. Patch testing was now performed with the ingredients of the lipstick, which resulted in a positive reaction to isononyl isononanoate. Later, additional patch testing with the ingredients were performed. This showed strong (vesicular) positive reactions to all 5 tested alcoholic dilutions of isononyl isononanoate, tested on the forearm, ranging from 1% to 20%. At D7, the patient developed severe edema of the whole test site area. A 5% preparation in pet. remained negative. Testing with isononyl isononanoate 5% alcohol was negative in 20 control subjects. The patient has remained symptom free since avoiding contact with cosmetics containing the allergens, which was also present in the anticellulite cream (2). She was probably one of the two allergic individuals mentioned in ref. 1.

Presence in cosmetic products and chemical analyses

In the USA, in April 2017, isononyl isononanoate was present in 1023 of 56,714 cosmetic products of which the composition is known in FDA's Voluntary Cosmetic Registration Program (VCRP) (data obtained from FDA, May 2017). In March 2017, isononyl isononanoate was present in 311 of 65,351 cosmetic products of which the composition is known in EWG's Skin Deep Cosmetics Database, USA (http://www.ewg.org/skindeep/).

LITERATURE

1   Travassos AR, Claes L, Boey L, Drieghe J, Goossens A. Non-fragrance allergens in specific cosmetic products. Contact Dermatitis 2011;65:276-285
2   Goossens A, Verbruggen K, Cattaert N, Boey L. New cosmetic allergens: isononyl isononanoate and trioleyl phosphate. Contact Dermatitis 2008;59:320-321

2.254   ISOPROPYL ALCOHOL

IDENTIFICATION

Description/definition	: Isopropyl alcohol is the aliphatic alcohol that conforms to the formula shown below
Chemical class(es)	: Alcohols
Chemical/IUPAC name	: Propan-2-ol
Other names	: Isopropanol; 2-hydroxypropane; 2-propanol
CAS registry number (s)	: 67-63-0
EC number(s)	: 200-661-7
CIR review(s)	: Int J Toxicol 2012;31(Suppl.4):112-136 (access: www.cir-safety.org/ingredients)
Merck Index monograph	: 6524
Function(s) in cosmetics	: EU: antifoaming; perfuming; solvent; viscosity controlling. USA: antifoaming agents; fragrance ingredients; solvents; viscosity decreasing agents
Patch testing	: pure (2); this test concentration is considered by some to cause irritant reactions (3); 10% water (16)
Molecular formula	: C_3H_8O

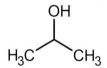

GENERAL

Isopropyl alcohol (isopropanol) is a secondary alcohol, a structural isomer of propanol, that can be produced by combining water and propene. It is a clear and flammable liquid that has a moderate evaporation rate and is completely miscible with most solvents. It is widely used as an industrial solvent and cleaning fluid, and is present in many products, such as lacquers, inks, and thinners, as well as in household products and cosmetics. Because of its antimicrobial activity (including multidrug-resistant pathogens, *Mycobacterium tuberculosis*, non-envelope viruses, and a variety of fungi), isopropyl alcohol is highly valued as a preservative and as an antiseptic in the clinical environment, being included in many solutions, gels and foams for this purpose (2).

CONTACT ALLERGY

General

Contact allergy to isopropyl alcohol in cosmetics and other products is usually considered to be rare, most cases being caused by its presence in swabs used to disinfect the skin before venepuncture. However, in a large series, there were 3% positive reactions, most of which were considered to be relevant (2). Other authors, however, stipulate that most of these reactions must have been irritant from the use of pure isopropyl alcohol for patch testing (3).

Patch testing in groups of patients

In the period 1992 to 2011, in Belgium, 1450 patients who had been in contact with isopropyl alcohol were patch tested with pure isopropyl alcohol and there were 44 (3.0%) positive reactions. In 37 patients (84%), the reaction was considered to be relevant from contact with topical drugs and disinfectants. Four cases were occupational, all presenting with hand dermatitis: a mechanic who had used isopropyl alcohol to degrease metals, and three nurses who had developed dermatitis following the use of medicinal products containing it (2).

Case reports and case series

Six positive patch test reactions to isopropyl alcohol were ascribed to cosmetic allergy (1). A female employee working in the laboratory of a cosmetic company manufacturing hair cosmetics had a positive patch test reaction from isopropyl alcohol in a hair lotion. However, she had not used the lotion herself, but participated as a paid volunteer in a patch testing program, the objective of which was to prove the safety of a hair lotion. Presumably, she had become sensitized to isopropyl alcohol from her work at the laboratory (8).

Contact allergy to isopropyl alcohol in non-cosmetic products

Case reports of single patients allergic to isopropyl alcohol in disinfectant swabs have been reported several times (4,5,6). A laboratory assistant had occupational allergic contact dermatitis from disinfectant swabs (7). Occupational contact allergy developed in a laboratory employee of a cosmetics producer (8). One patient had allergic contact dermatitis from isopropyl alcohol, the source of sensitization is unknown (10, article not read). A patient had contact allergy to isopropyl alcohol present in a gauze used for electrocardiography instead of a gel (11).

Another individual had eczematous dermatitis in the cubital fossae and on the back on one hand, where a venapuncture had been performed. A 'crude' patch test to the swab containing isopropyl alcohol was positive, but there was no reaction to another swab sample from which isopropyl alcohol had been allowed to evaporate (9). It should be realized that in a number of these reports, isopropyl alcohol itself was not patch tested, but the swab instead (4,9), or only a ROAT was performed with the swab (18). This is important, as some swabs contain other chemicals in addition to isopropyl alcohol, for example propylene oxide, which can also cause allergic contact dermatitis (7, also postulated in refs. 15 and 17). Additionally, a swab may produce a positive reaction, whereas patch testing with its ingredients is negative (14,19,22,23,24), which has been ascribed to compound allergy (the formation of a new chemical by interaction of other chemicals) (14,19,22), to the formation of a new chemical by gamma irradiation used to sterilize the product (23), or to a chemical compound or contaminant that is used or acquired during the manufacturing of the swabs or foils (24).

Cross-reactions, pseudo-cross-reactions and co-reactions
Cross-reactivity *from* ethyl alcohol (literature cited in ref. 8). Cross-reactivity to 1-propanol (propyl alcohol), 1-butanol (butyl alcohol) and 2-butanol (*sec*-butyl alcohol) (8). Ethyl alcohol; propylene glycol (2). Not to 1-propanol (21).

Presence in cosmetic products and chemical analyses
In the USA, in April 2017, isopropyl alcohol was present in 2419 of 56,714 cosmetic products of which the composition is known in FDA's Voluntary Cosmetic Registration Program (VCRP) (data obtained from FDA, May 2017). In April 2017, isopropyl alcohol was present in 1558 of 66,223 cosmetic products of which the composition is known in EWG's Skin Deep Cosmetics Database, USA (http://www.ewg.org/skindeep/).

OTHER SIDE EFFECTS

Immediate-type reactions
One author has stated that he has seen allergic contact urticaria due to ethyl and isopropyl alcohol (13). Contact urticarial reactions in 2 healthy volunteers to an extract of a cleansing tissue were unconvincingly ascribed to isopropyl alcohol (20).

LITERATURE
1   Kohl L, Blondeel A, Song M. Allergic contact dermatitis from cosmetics: retrospective analysis of 819 patch-tested patients. Dermatology 2002;204:334-337
2   Garcia-Gavin J, Lissens R, Timmermans A, Goossens A. Allergic contact dermatitis caused by isopropyl alcohol: a missed allergen? Contact Dermatitis 2011;65:101-106
3   Löffler H, Kampf G, Lachenmeier D, Diepgen TL, John SM. Allergic or irritant contact dermatitis after patch testing with alcohol – that is the point. Contact Dermatitis 2012;67:386-387
4   Vujevich J, Zirwas M. Delayed hypersensitivity to isopropyl alcohol. Contact Dermatitis 2007;56:287
5   Kwon JA, Lee MS, Kim MY, Park YM, Kim HO, Kim CW. Allergic contact dermatitis from dodecyldiaminoethylglycine and isopropyl alcohol in a commercial disinfectant swab. Contact Dermatitis 2003;48:339-340
6   Wasilewski C. Allergic contact dermatitis from isopropyl alcohol. Arch Dermatol 1968;98:502
7   Jensen O. Contact allergy to propylene oxide and isopropyl alcohol in a skin disinfectant swab. Contact Dermatitis 1981;7:148-150
8   Ludwig E, Hausen BM. Sensitivity to isopropyl alcohol. Contact Dermatitis 1977;3:240-244
9   McInnes A. Skin reaction to isopropyl alcohol. Br Med J 1973: 10: 357
10 Kurwa A R. Contact dermatitis from isopropyl alcohol. Contact Dermatitis Newsletter 1970;8:168
11 Fisher AA. Dermatologic hazards of electrocardiography. Cutis 1977;20:686 (further pages unknown)
12 McInnes A. Skin reaction to isopropyl alcohol. British Medical Journal 1973;1(5849):357
13 Fisher AA. Contact dermatitis: The noneczematous variety. Cutis 1968;4:567-571
14 Leow YH, Freeman S. Acute allergic contact dermatitis from Medi-swabs, with negative patch tests to the individual ingredients, including isopropyl alcohol. Contact Dermatitis 1995;33:125-126
15 Bateman PR. Contact dermatitis to alcohol swabs. Med J Aust 1977;2:841
16 De Groot AC. Patch Testing, 3rd Edition. Wapserveen, The Netherlands: acdegroot publishing, 2008 (ISBN 978-90-813233-1-4)
17 Richardson DR, Caravati JCM, Weary PE. Allergic contact dermatitis to alcohol swabs. Cutis 1969;5:1115-1118

18 Storer E, Marshman G, Kupa A. Contact dermatitis to alcohol swabs masquerading as vaccine allergy. Australas J Dermatol 2004;45:149-150

19 Tan B, King C. Allergic contact dermatitis from Steret® swabs. Contact Dermatitis 1996;34:62-63

20 Devos SA, van der Valk PG. Dermatitis around tracheostomies due to cleansing tissues. Contact Dermatitis 2001;44:111-112

21 Bosker HM, Politiek K, Urgert MC, Flach PA, Coenraads PJ, Schuttelaar ML. Occupational allergic contact dermatitis caused by 1-propanol in a hand disinfectant. Contact Dermatitis 2017;76:241-243

22 Lai-Kwon J, Ly L, Su JC, Nixon R, Tam MM. Unsuspected allergic contact dermatitis to alcohol swabs following neurosurgery. Australas J Dermatol 2014;55:296-298

23 Firoz EF, Turnbull RK, Loomis CA, Brownell I. Allergic contact dermatitis to gamma-irradiated WEBCOL alcohol prep pads. Pediatr Dermatol 2013;30:e281-282

24 Taylor J, Erkek E, Leow YH, Jacobsen D. Contact allergy to a commercial alcohol prep swab. Contact Dermatitis (ESCD Abstracts) 2004;50:155

2.255 ISOPROPYL DIBENZOYLMETHANE

IDENTIFICATION

Description/definition	: Isopropyl dibenzoylmethane is the organic compound that conforms to the formula shown below
Chemical class(es)	: Ketones
Chemical/IUPAC name	: 1-Naphthalen-2-ylpiperidine
Other names	: 1-[4-(1-Methylethyl)phenyl]-3-phenylpropane-1,3-dione; Eusolex® 8020; with 4-methylbenzylidene camphor in Eusolex® 8021
CAS registry number (s)	: 63250-25-9
EC number(s)	: 264-043-9
Function(s) in cosmetics	: EU: UV-absorber. USA: light stabilizers
Patch testing	: 2% pet.
Molecular formula	: $C_{18}H_{18}O_2$

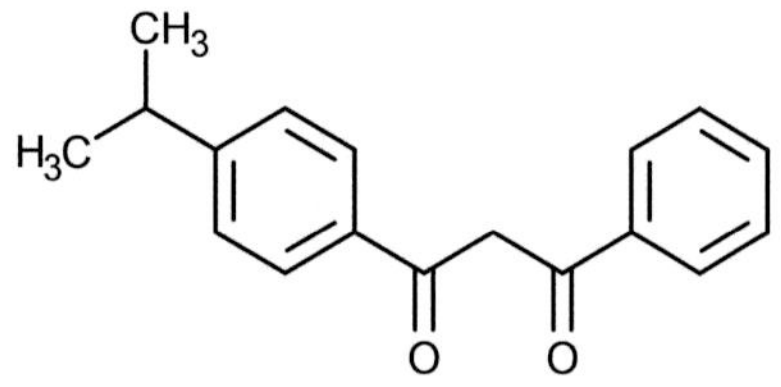

GENERAL

Isopropyl dibenzoylmethane is a UVA-absorber which has been used in Europe from 1979 to 1993 (39). It was the most frequent (photo)sensitizer in the 1980s and the 1990s. Isopropyl dibenzoylmethane was voluntarily removed from the market in 1993 and is not produced anymore. The UV-absorber was combined with 4-methylbenzylidene camphor in the commercial sunscreen Eusolex® 8021. Concomitant sensitization to the camphor-derivative was not infrequent in patients (photo)sensitized to isopropyl dibenzoylmethane. After withdrawal of the latter, however, contact allergy to 4-methylbenzylidene camphor became infrequent.

The literature on adverse reactions to sunscreens has been reviewed in several recent and older publications (42-47,57). A review of photocontact allergy to sunscreens was published in 2010 (57).

CONTACT ALLERGY

Patch testing in groups of patients

There are no studies in which isopropyl dibenzoylmethane has been patch tested in consecutive patients suspected of contact dermatitis (routine testing). Results of testing in groups of *selected* patients (e.g., patients suspected of

Table 2.255.1 Patch testing in groups of patients: Selected patient groups

Years and Country	Test conc. & vehicle	Number of patients tested	positive (%)	Selection of patients (S); Relevance (R); Comments (C)	Ref.
1993-2000 Australia	2% pet.	149	3 (2.0%)	S: patients suspected of photosensitivity; R: of 17 patient who had contact or photocontact reactions to a panel of 10 sunscreens, 10 were considered to have relevant reactions	35
1983-1998 UK	2% pet.	2715	4 (0.1%)	S: patients suspected of photosensitivity or with (a history of) dermatitis at exposed sites; R: not stated	1
1990-1996 Sweden	2% pet.	355	4 (1.1%)	S: patients suspected of photosensitivity; R: not stated	37
1981-1996 Germany	5 or 10% pet.	402	30 (7.5%)	S: patients suspected of clinical photosensitivity; R: not stated	5
1994-1999 Nether-lands	10% pet.	55	1 (1.8%)	S: patients suspected of photosensitivity disorders; R: not stated	16
1990-1994 France	2% or 10% pet.	370	7 (1.9%)	S: patients with suspected photodermatitis; R: not specified, 72% of all reactions in the study were considered relevant	12
1989-1991 UK	2% pet.	99	2 (2%)	S: 45 patients with photosensitivity dermatitis/actinic reticuloid syndrome, 54 with polymorphic light eruption; R: not specified	6
1989-1990 France	2% pet.	54	1 (2%)	S: patients suspected of photosensitivity; R: the reaction was relevant	23

photosensitivity, patients with dermatitis affecting mainly light-exposed skin or with a history of a sunscreen skin reaction) back to 1990 are shown in table 2.255.1. In 8 studies, frequencies of sensitization have ranged from 0.1% to 7.5%; all but one investigation scored 2% or lower. In 7/8 studies, relevance was either not mentioned or specified for isopropyl dibenzoylmethane. The one positive reaction in a French 1989-1990 study was relevant (23).

Case reports and case series
In the period 1978-1991, there were 3 relevant patch test reactions to isopropyl dibenzoylmethane in one center in Leuven, Belgium (34). In the period 1981-1989, 56 patients (43 women, 13 men) were diagnosed with contact allergy or photocontact allergy to UV-filters in one center in Germany. There were 16 contact allergic, 7 photoaggravated contact allergic and 22 photoallergic reactions to isopropyl dibenzoylmethane. All reactions in the 56 individuals were relevant and all 46 patients who could be (photo)patch tested with their own sunscreens (and a few of them with other cosmetics) had one or more positive (photo)patch tests to these products (52, overlap with refs. 5,13,14).

In a group of 119 patients with allergic contact dermatitis from cosmetics, investigated in The Netherlands in 1986-1987, two cases were caused by isopropyl dibenzoylmethane in lipsticks with UV-filter (48,49). In a group of 75 patients allergic to cosmetic products, seen in a private practice in The Netherlands in the period 1981-1986, one case was caused by isopropyl dibenzoylmethane in a lipstick with UV-absorber (50, same patient as in ref. 15).

Sunscreens
The first report of contact allergy to isopropyl dibenzoylmethane stems from 1986 and described 4 patients with allergic contact dermatitis from the presence of the UV-filter in sunscreens (14). Nine cases of allergic contact dermatitis from isopropyl dibenzoylmethane in sunscreens were soon thereafter reported by the same German authors (13; some of these had already been described in ref. 14); the authors mentioned five more cases (13, note added in proof). Nine individuals had allergic contact dermatitis from isopropyl dibenzoylmethane in sunscreen products, of which 5 were lipsticks; a tenth patient was allergic to the sunscreen in cosmetic products (15). Five of these ten also reacted to 4-methylbenzylidene camphor, the other UV-absorber in the commercial sunscreen Eusolex® 8021 (15).

Two patients had allergic contact dermatitis from isopropyl dibenzoylmethane in sunscreens (25). Of 280 patients tested with sunscreens in London, 1985-1987, two had ACD from isopropyl dibenzoylmethane in sunscreen preparations (38). Several authors have presented single case reports of patients allergic to isopropyl dibenzoylme-thane in sunscreen creams/lotions (7,19,20,24,33,53,55) and sunscreen lipsticks (21,31). A male patient had allergic contact dermatitis from isopropyl dibenzoylmethane (and 4-methylbenzylidene camphor) in a sunscreen cream; the presence of the UV-absorbers was established by chemical analysis (29).

Other cosmetics
One patient was allergic to isopropyl dibenzoylmethane in cosmetic products (15). One positive patch test reaction to isopropyl dibenzoylmethane was ascribed to cosmetic allergy (17). One patient had ACD from isopropyl dibenzoylmethane in a lip salve (18), another from a moisturizing cream (30). One individual had allergic contact dermatitis from isopropyl dibenzoylmethane in emollient creams (31). Of 280 patients tested with UV-absorbers in London, 1985-1987, two had ACD from isopropyl dibenzoylmethane in cosmetic creams (38).

Contact allergy to Eusolex® 8021 (combination with 4-methylbenzylidene camphor)
One individual reacted to Eusolex® 8021 in a moisturizing cream, containing isopropyl dibenzoylmethane and 4-methylbenzylidene camphor, which could not be tested separately (8). Another two patients also suffered from ACD to Eusolex® 8021, present in a sunscreen; the 2 components were not tested separately (32,56).

Other reports
In a group of 46 New Zealand farmers with dermatitis, investigated in one center in 1994-1997, one had occupational contact allergy to isopropyl dibenzoylmethane; the culprit product was not mentioned (41). Several centers have reported positive patch tests to isopropyl dibenzoylmethane, but without specifying their relevance (9,11).

Cross-reactions, pseudo-cross-reactions and co-reactions (including photoreactions)
(Photo)cross-reactions to butyl methoxydibenzoylmethane (5,16,26,52); cross-reactivity from butyl methoxydibenzoylmethane (27). In many cases, patients both reacted to isopropyl dibenzoylmethane and to 4-methylbenzylidene camphor, which were combined in the commercial sunscreen Eusolex® 8021 (concomitant sensitization) (14,15,29,31,36,52).

OTHER SIDE EFFECTS

Photosensitivity

Photopatch testing in groups of patients
Results of photopatch testing isopropyl dibenzoylmethane in groups of selected patients (e.g., patients suspected of photosensitivity, patients with dermatitis affecting mainly light-exposed skin or with a history of a sunscreen skin reaction) back to 1985 are shown in table 2.255.2. In 10 studies, frequencies of photosensitization have ranged from 0.1% to 8% (table 2.255.2). The high percentage of 8% was seen in Germany by authors who also described the first patients with (photo)contact allergy to isopropyl dibenzoylmethane in literature and who investigated many such patients (5). In not a single study was the relevance of the observed positive photopatch test reactions specified.

Table 2.255.2 Photopatch testing in groups of patients

Years and Country	Test conc. & vehicle	Number of patients tested | positive (%)		Selection of patients (S); Relevance (R); Comments (C)	Ref.
1991-2001 France		2076	31 (1.5%)	S: patients suspected of photoallergy; R: ? (article not read)	22
1993-2000 Australia	2% pet.	149	5 (3.4%)	S: patients suspected of photosensitivity; R: of 17 patient who had contact or photocontact reactions to a panel of 10 sunscreens, 10 were considered to have relevant reactions	35
1994-1999 NL	10% pet.	55	1 (1.8%)	S: patients suspected of photosensitivity disorders; R: not stated; C: many concomitant (cross-?) reactions to butyl methoxydibenzoylmethane	16
1983-1998 UK	2% pet.	2715	6 (0.2%)	S: patients suspected of photosensitivity or with (a history of) dermatitis at exposed sites; R: 37% for all photoallergens together	1
1991-97 Ger, Au, Swi	10% pet.	1261	7 (0.6%)	S: patients suspected of photosensitivity; R: not stated	2
1990-1996 Sweden	2% pet.	355	8 (2.2%)	S: patients suspected of photosensitivity; R: not stated	37
1981-1996 Germany	5 or 10% pet.	402	32 (8.0%)	S: patients suspected of clinical photosensitivity; R: not stated	5
1990-1994 France	2% or 10% pet.	370	11 (3.0%)	S: patients with suspected photodermatitis; R: not specified, 72% of all reactions in the study were considered relevant	12
1985-1993 Italy		1050	1 (0.1%)	S: patients suspected of photoallergic contact dermatitis; R: not specified (97% for all sunscreens together)	3
1980-85 Ger, Au, Swi	5% pet.	1129	10 (0.9%)	S: patients suspected of photoallergy, polymorphic light eruption, phototoxicity and skin problems with photo-distribution; R: not stated	4

Au: Austria; Ger: Germany; NL: Netherlands; Swi: Switzerland

Case reports and series
The first report of photocontact allergy to isopropyl dibenzoylmethane stems from 1986 and described 3 patients with photoallergic contact dermatitis from the presence of the UV-filter in sunscreens (14). Twelve cases of photoallergic contact dermatitis from isopropyl dibenzoylmethane in sunscreens were soon thereafter reported by the same German authors (13; some of these had already been described in ref. 14); the authors mentioned six more cases (13, note added in proof). Two patients (25) and another two (54) had photoallergic contact dermatitis from isopropyl dibenzoylmethane in sunscreens. Two other individuals had photoallergic contact dermatitis from isopropyl dibenzoylmethane, one from its presence in a sunscreen, the other from a cosmetic cream (28). In a 1-year-period (1996-1997), 3 patients had positive photopatch tests to isopropyl dibenzoylmethane in one center in Italy. Two had photoallergic contact dermatitis from facial cosmetics and one reaction was of past relevance from sunscreens. In 2 there was photo-co-reactivity to 4-methylbenzylidene camphor, the other ingredient of Eusolex® 8021 (36).

In the period 1981-1989, 56 patients (43 women, 13 men) were diagnosed with contact allergy or photocontact allergy to UV-filters in one center in Germany. There were 16 contact allergic, 7 photoaggravated contact allergic and 22 photoallergic reactions to isopropyl dibenzoylmethane. All reactions in the 56 individuals were relevant and all 46 patients who could be (photo)patch tested with their own sunscreens (and a few of them with other cosmetics) had one or more positive (photo)patch tests to these products (52, overlap with refs. 5,13,14).

Of 280 patients tested with sunscreens in London, 1985-1987, one had photoallergic contact dermatitis from cosmetic creams and two from sunscreens (38). One case of photoallergic contact dermatitis was reported (10, article not read). Another individual had photoallergic contact dermatitis from isopropyl dibenzoylmethane in a suntan lotion (26).

Several centers have reported positive photopatch tests to isopropyl dibenzoylmethane, but without specifying their relevance: n=1 (11), n=3 (9), n=21 (13). In a group of 2067 patients photopatch tested in 13 photobiology centers in France in 1991-2001, there were 31 cases of photocontact allergy to isopropyl dibenzoylmethane (relevance unknown, article not read) (40).

Immediate-type reactions
One patient had photocontact urticaria from isopropyl dibenzoylmethane in a sunscreen (28).

LITERATURE

1   Darvay A, White I, Rycroft R, Jones AB, Hawk JL, McFadden JP. Photoallergic contact dermatitis is uncommon. Br J Dermatol 2001;145:597-601

2   Neumann NJ, Hölzle E, Plewig G, Schwarz T, Panizzon RG, Breit R, et al. Photopatch testing: The 12-year experience of the German, Austrian and Swiss Photopatch Test Group. J Am Acad Dermatol 2000;42:183-192

3   Pigatto PD, Legori A, Bigardi AS, Guarrera M, Tosti A, Santucci B, et al. Gruppo Italiano recerca dermatiti da contatto ed ambientali Italian multicenter study of allergic contact photodermatitis: epidemiological aspects. Am J Contact Dermatitis 1996;17:158-163

4   Hölzle E, Neumann N, Hausen B, Przybilla B, Schauder S, Hönigsmann H, et al. Photopatch testing: the 5-year experience of the German, Austrian and Swiss Photopatch Test Group. J Am Acad Dermatol 1991;25:59-68

5   Schauder S, Ippen H. Contact and photocontact sensitivity. Review of a 15-year experience and of the literature to suncreens. Contact Dermatitis 1997;37:221-232

6   Bilsland D, Ferguson J. Contact allergy to sunscreen chemicals in photosensitivity dermatitis/actinic reticuloid syndrome (PD/AR) and polymorphic light eruption. Contact Dermatitis 1993;29:70-73

7   English JSC, White IR. Allergic contact dermatitis from isopropyl dibenzoylmethane. Contact Dermatitis 1986;15:94

8   Woods B. Dermatitis from Eusolex 8021 sunscreen agent in a cosmetic. Contact Dermatitis 1981;7:168

9   Trevisi P, Vincenzi C, Chieregato C, Guerra L, Tosti A. Sunscreen sensitization: a three-year study. Dermatology 1994;189:55-57

10   Jacobi H, Pinzer B. Photoallergic contact eczema caused by 4-isopropyldibenzoylmethane. Dermatol Monatsschr 1990;176:669-672

11   Marguery MC, Rakotondrazafy J, el Sayed F, Bayle-Lebey P, Journe F, Bazex J. Contact allergy to 3-(4'-methylbenzylidene) camphor and contact and photocontact allergy to 4-isopropyl dibenzoylmethane. Photodermatol Photoimmunol Photomed 1996;11:209-212

12   Journe F, Marguery M-C, Rakotondrazafy J, El Sayed F, Bazex J. Sunscreen sensitization: a 5-year study. Acta Derm Venereol (Stockh) 1999;79:211-213

13   Schauder S, Ippen H. Photoallergic and allergic contact eczema caused by dibenzoylmethane compounds and other sunscreening agents. Hautarzt 1988;39:435-440

14   Schauder S, Ippen H. Photoallergic and allergic contact dermatitis from dibenzoylmethanes. Photodermatol 1986;3:140-147

15   De Groot AC, van der Walle HB, Jagtman BA, Weyland JW. Contact allergy to 4-isopropyl-dibenzoylmethane and 3(4-methylbenzylidene) camphor in sunscreen Eusolex 8021. Contact Dermatitis 1987;16:249-254

16   Bakkum RS, Heule F. Results of photopatch testing in Rotterdam during a 10-year period. Br J Dermatol 2002;146:275-279

17   Kohl L, Blondeel A, Song M. Allergic contact dermatitis from cosmetics: retrospective analysis of 819 patch-tested patients. Dermatology 2002;204:334-337

18   Rodriguez-Serna M, Velasco M, Miquel J, de la Cuadra J, Aliaga A. (1999). Photoallergic contact dermatitis from Zovirax® cream. Contact Dermatitis 1999;41:54-55

19   Buckley DA, O'Sullivan D, Murphy GM. Contact and photocontact allergy to dibenzoylmethanes and contact allergy to methylbenzylidene camphor. Contact Dermatitis 1993;29:47

20   Goldermann R, Vardarman E, Neumann N, Scharffetter-Kochanek K, Goerz G. Contact dermatitis from UV-A and UV-B filters in a patient with erythropoietic protoporphyria. Contact Dermatitis 1993;28:300-301

21   Baes H, van Hecke E. Contact dermatitis from Zovirax cream. Contact Dermatitis 1990;23:200-201

22   Leonard F, Adamski H, Bonnevalle A, Bottlaender A, Bourrain JL, Goujon-Henry C, et al. The prospective multicenter study on standard photopatch tests by the French Society of Photodermatology from 1991-2001. Ann Dermatol Venereol 2005;132:313-320 (article in French)

23   Lenique P, Machet L, Vaillant L, Bensaid P, Muller C, Khallouf R, Lorette G. Contact and photocontact allergy to oxybenzone. Contact Dermatitis 1992;26:177-181

24   Haussmann A, Kleinhans D. Allergisches Kontaktekzem durch UV-Strahlenfilter in Sonnenschutzcremes - Zwei Fallbeobachtungen. Z Hautkr 1986;61:1654-1656

25   Gonçalo M, Ruas E, Figueiredo A, Gonçalo S. Contact and photocontact sensitivity to sunscreens. Contact Dermatitis 1995;33:278-280

26 Motley RJ, Reynolds AJ. Photocontact dermatitis due to isopropyl and butyl methoxy dibenzoylmethanes (Eusolex 8020 and Parsol 1789). Contact Dermatitis 1989;21:109-110

27 Crowe MJ, Banks SL, Guin JD. Photoallergic and allergic contact dermatitis to butyl-methoxydibenzoylmethane. Am J Cont Derm 1992;3:33-34

28 Murphy GM, White IR, Cronin E. Immediate and delayed photocontact dermatitis from isopropyl dibenzoylmethane. Contact Dermatitis 1990;22:129-131

29 Foussereau J, Cavelier C, Protois JC. Contact dermatitis from Eusolex 8021 elucidated by chemical analysis. Contact Dermatitis 1989;20:311-312

30 Garioch JJ, Forsyth A. Allergic contact dermatitis from 4-isopropyl-dibenzoylmethane in a light moisturising cream. Contact Dermatitis 1989;20:312-313

31 Alomar A, Cerda MT. Contact allergy to Eusolex® 8021. Contact Dermatitis 1989;20:74-75

32 Roberts DL. Contact allergy to Eusolex 8021. Contact Dermatitis 1988;18:302-303

33 Azón-Masoliver A, Vilaplana J, Romaguera C. Allergic contact dermatitis to Eusolex 8020. Am J Cont Derm 1993;4:229-230

34 Theeuwes M, Degreef H, Dooms-Goossens A. Para-aminobenzoic acid (PABA) and sunscreen allergy. Am J Cont Derm 1992;3:206-207

35 Crouch RB, Foley PA, Baker CS. The results of photopatch testing 172 patients to sunscreening agents at the photobiology clinic, St Vincent's Hospital, Melbourne. Australas J Dermatol 2002;43:74

36 Ricci C, Pazzaglia M, Tosti A. Photocontact dermatitis from UV filters. Contact Dermatitis 1998;38:343-344

37 Berne B, Ross AM. 7 years experience of photopatch testing with sunscreen allergens in Sweden. Contact Dermatitis 1998;38:61-64

38 English JSC, White IR, Cronin K. Sensitivity to sunscreens. Contact Dermatitis 1987;17:159-162

39 Kerr A, Ferguson J. Photoallergic contact dermatitis. Photodermatol Photoimmunol Photomed 2010;26:56-65

40 Leonard F, Adamski H, Bonnevalle A, Bottlaender A, Bourrain JL, Goujon-Henry C, et al. The prospective multicenter study on standard photopatch tests by the French Society of Photodermatology from 1991-2001. Ann Dermatol Venereol 2005;132:313-320 (in French)

41 Rademaker M. Occupational contact dermatitis among New Zealand farmers. Australas J Dermatol 1998;39:164-167

42 Heurung AR, Raju SI, Warshaw EM. Adverse reactions to sunscreen agents: epidemiology, responsible irritants and allergens, clinical characteristics, and management. Dermatitis 2014;25:289-326

43 Heurung AR, Raju SI, Warshaw EM. Contact allergen of the year. Benzophenones. Dermatitis 2014;25:3-10 (contains many mistakes; Erratum in Dermatitis 2014;25:92-95)

44 Avenel-Audran M. Sunscreen products: finding the allergen. Eur J Dermatol 2010;20:161-166

45 Scheuer E, Warshaw E. Sunscreen allergy: a review of epidemiology, clinical characteristics, and responsible allergens. Dermatitis 2006;17:3-11

46 Funk JO, Dromgoole SH, Maibach HI. Sunscreen intolerance: contact sensitization, photocontact sensitization, and irritancy of sunscreen agents. Dermatol Clin 1995;13:473-481

47 Dromgoole SH, Maibach HI. Sunscreening agent intolerance: Contact and photocontact sensitization and contact urticaria. J Am Acad Dermatol 1990;22:1068-1078

48 De Groot AC, Bruynzeel DP, Bos JD, van der Meeren HL, van Joost T, Jagtman BA, Weyland JW. The allergens in cosmetics. Arch Dermatol 1988;124:1525-1529

49 De Groot AC. Adverse reactions to cosmetics. PhD Thesis, University of Groningen, The Netherlands: 1988, chapter 3.4, pp.105-113

50 De Groot AC. Contact allergy to cosmetics: Causative ingredients. Contact Dermatitis 1987;17:26-34

51 Shaw T, Simpson B, Wilson B, Oostman H, Rainey D, Storrs F. True photoallergy to sunscreens is rare despite popular belief. Dermatitis 2010;21:185-198

52 Schauder S. Adverse reactions to sunscreening agents in 58 patients (part 3). Z Hautkr 1991;66:294-318 (article in German)

53 Kleinhans D. Kontaktallergie gegen UV-Filtersubstanzen in Lichtschutzpräparaten. Derm und Kosm 1988;29:28-34 (article in German)

54 Köster W, Juratli A. Verlauf von persistierender Lichtreaktion und aktinischem Retikuloid nach PUVA-Therapie – Eine Kasuistiek. Akt Dermatol 1989;15:167-173 (article in German)

55 Lübben U. Kontaktallergie auf Lichtschutzmittel. Z Hautkr 1987;62:1233 (article in German) A woman had ACD from isopropyl dibenzoylmethane in a sunscreen ().

56 Kimmig W. Allergische Kontaktdermatitis durch Lichtschutzmittel. Z Hautkr 1987;62:73 (article in German)

57 Schauder S. Survey of the literature on adverse reactions to preparations containing UV filters (1947-1989) (Literaturübersicht über Unverträglichkeitsreaktionen auf lichtfilterhaltige Produkte von 1947 bis 1989). Z Hautkr 1990;65:982-998 (article in German)

2.256   ISOPROPYL HYDROXYPALMITYL ETHER[*]
Not an INCI name

IDENTIFICATION

Description/definition : Isopropyl hydroxypalmityl ether is the fatty alcohol derivative that conforms to the structural formula shown below
Chemical class(es) : Ethers; fatty alcohols
INCI name USA : Neither in CosIng nor in the Personal Care Products Council Ingredient Database
Chemical/IUPAC name : 1-(1-Methylethoxy)-2-hexadecanol
Other names : 1-Isopropoxy-2-hexadecanol
CAS registry number (s) : 119655-66-2
Patch testing : Parent emulsifier 2.5% water, containing both DEA-dihydroxypalmityl phosphate and isopropyl hydroxypalmityl ether (1)
Molecular formula : $C_{19}H_{40}O_2$

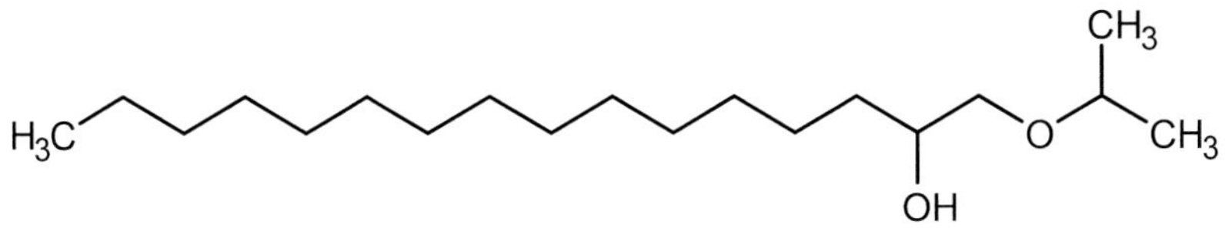

GENERAL

The emulsifier mentioned under Case reports and case series is an anionic oil-in-water emulsifier containing DEA-dihydroxypalmityl phosphate and isopropyl hydroxypalmityl ether and is available only as a mixture. It is (or at least was at the time of publication, the end of the 1980s) used in concentrations of 2% to 5% in cosmetics such as day and night creams, hand preparations, body lotions, aftershave emulsions, liquid make-up products, and sunscreens. Previous predictive testing had revealed no sensitizing potential (2).

CONTACT ALLERGY

Case reports and case series

A non-atopic woman had a one month history of acute itchy dermatitis on the face with edema of the eyelids. She was patch test positive to a facial beauty lotion which the patient had suspected. The manufacturer provided the component mixtures in the same concentrations as in the final product. Patch testing gave a positive reaction to the water phase, which was a mixture of propylene glycol (3%) and an emulsifier. The emulsifier, tested at 2.5% water, produced a positive reaction after 3 days; propylene glycol gave no reaction. The emulsifier proved to be a mixture of isopropyl hydroxypalmityl ether and DEA-dihydroxypalmityl phosphate. The chemicals were not tested separately (1).

Another woman had an itchy erythematosquamous eruption on both eyelids that had appeared after a month's use of the same facial beauty lotion. She had not used any other such cosmetics. Patch tests were positive to the facial beauty lotion, the water phase of the beauty lotion and the emulsifier of the beauty product. A repeated open application test (ROAT) (1x/day) with the emulsifier 2.5% water on the right upper arm gave a slight eczematous response after 3 days. The emulsifier in the same concentration produced no skin reactions in 10 control subjects. It proved to be a mixture of isopropyl hydroxypalmityl ether and DEA-dihydroxypalmityl phosphate. The chemicals were not tested separately (1). A third female patient allergic to the same cosmetic product and to the emulsifier was mentioned in the article (personal communication in ref. 1).

Presence in cosmetic products and chemical analyses

In January 2017, was present in zero of 64,655 cosmetic products of which the composition is known in EWG's Skin Deep Cosmetics Database, USA (http://www.ewg.org/skindeep/). In the USA, in April 2017, isopropyl hydroxylpalmityl ether was present in 2 of 56,714 cosmetic products of which the composition is known in FDA's Voluntary Cosmetic Registration Program (VCRP) (data obtained from FDA, May 2017).

LITERATURE

1 Dooms-Goossens A, Debusschere K, Gladys K, Degreef H. Contact allergy to an emulsifier in a cosmetic lotion. Contact Dermatitis 1988;18:249-250
2 Fiedler HP. Lexikon der Hilfsstoffe für Pharmazie, Kosmetik und angrenzende Gebiete, 2nd Edition. Aulendorf, Germany: Editio Cantor Verlag GmbH, 1981:320

2.257   ISOPROPYL MYRISTATE

IDENTIFICATION

Description/definition	: Isopropyl myristate is the ester of isopropyl alcohol and myristic acid, which conforms generally to the formula shown below
Chemical class(es)	: Esters
Chemical/IUPAC name	: Propan-2-yl tetradecanoate
Other names	: Isopropyl tetradecanoate
CAS registry number (s)	: 110-27-0
EC number(s)	: 203-751-4
CIR review(s)	: J Am Coll Toxicol 1982;1:55-80; Int J Toxicol 2005;24(Suppl.1):1-102; Int J Toxicol 2010;29(Suppl.3):162-186; Final report, March 2013 (access: www.cir-safety.org/ingredients)
Merck Index monograph	: 6531
Function(s) in cosmetics	: EU: binding; emollient; perfuming; skin conditioning; solvent. USA: binders; fragrance ingredients; skin-conditioning agents – emollient
Patch testing	: 20.0% pet. (Chemotechnique); 10% pet. (SmartPracticeEurope, SmartPracticeCanada); Isopropyl myristate 20% pet. may cause irritant reactions (6)
Molecular formula	: $C_{17}H_{34}O_2$

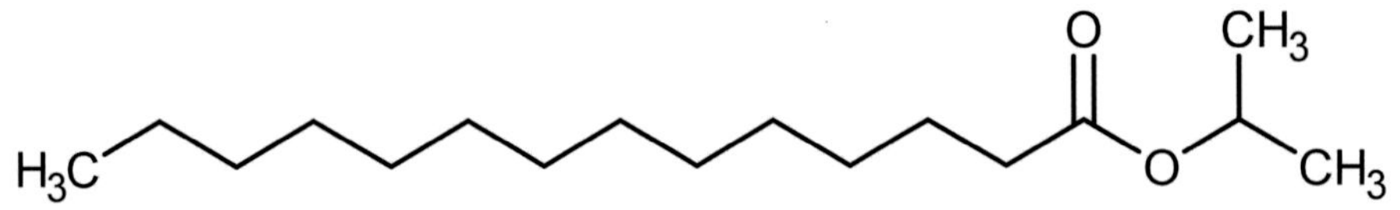

GENERAL

Isopropyl myristate, an ester of isopropyl alcohol and myristic acid, is a solvent with emollient and lubricating properties, and is found in a number of creams, lotions, and oils. It improves the texture of consumer products with a high oil content, and increases transdermal penetration – a desirable property in topical medicaments and emollients used in the management of dermatitis (34).

CONTACT ALLERGY

Patch testing in groups of patients
Results of studies patch testing isopropyl myristate in consecutive patients suspected of contact dermatitis (routine testing) and in groups of selected patients are shown in table 2.257.1. In routine testing, frequencies of sensitization have ranged from 0.1% to 2%, but in several other studies, not one positive reaction was found (12,13,14,15). Relevance ranged from 0% to 100%, but in all studies, the number of positive patients was small. In groups of *selected* patients (patients with leg ulcers, patients tested with a 'topicals series', patients suspected of cosmetic contact dermatitis), rates of sensitization were even lower (0.1%-1.2%). Relevance was – with one exception -either not mentioned or not specified for isopropyl myristate, causative products were not mentioned. In a study from the USA, all 4 positive patch test reactions were scored as relevant, but this included 'questionable' and 'past' relevance (2).

Case reports and case series
Isopropyl myristate was responsible for 5 out of 959 cases of non-fragrance cosmetic allergy where the causal allergen was identified, Belgium, 2000-2010 (1). In the period 2000-2007, 202 patients with allergic contact dermatitis caused by cosmetics were seen in Valencia, Spain. In this group, three individuals reacted to isopropyl myristate from its presence in sunscreens (28). A woman had allergic contact dermatitis from isopropyl myristate in a feminine hygiene spray (4). Another woman had allergic contact dermatitis of the face, neck, arms and legs from isopropyl myristate in a sunscreen preparation (19). Two women had ACD from isopropyl myristate in moisturizers 934). In the 1960s, two British dermatologists saw an unknown number of patients allergic to isopropyl myristate in spray deodorants (21,22).

Table 2.257.1 Patch testing in groups of patients

Years and Country	Test conc. & vehicle	Number of patients tested	positive (%)		Selection of patients (S); Relevance (R); Comments (C)	Ref.
Routine testing						
2006-2010 USA	20% pet.	3086		(0.2%)	R: 50%	26
2005-2006 Turkey		93	2	(2%)	R: the reactions were considered to be relevant	29
2000-2005 USA	20% pet.	3844		(0.2%)	R: 11%	3
2003-2005 China		599	8	(1.3%)	R: not stated	25
1998–2000 USA	2% pet.	710		(0.1%)	R: not stated	23
<1969 UK	pure	133	2	(1.5%)	R: no relevance found	17
	50% pet.	124	1	(0.8%)	R: no relevance found	
Testing in groups of selected patients						
2004-2008 France	10% pet.	423	2	(0.5%)	S: patients with leg ulcers; R: not stated	24
2000-2007 USA	20% pet.	944	4	(0.4%)	S: patients tested with a supplemental cosmetic screening series; R: 100%; C: weak study: a. high rate of macular erythema and weak reactions; b. relevance figures included 'questionable' and 'past' relevance	2
1992-2001 IVDK	20% pet.	8117	8	(0.1%)	S: patients tested with a 'topicals series'; R: in 6/16 relevan-	6
	10% pet.	4554	8	(0.2%)	ce was postulated but not proven; C: both concentrations, especially the 20% test material, may cause irritant reactions	
1997-2000 Israel		244	3	(1.2%)	S: patients suspected of cosmetic dermatitis; R: 64% of all patch test reactions in the cosmetic series was relevant	27
1990-1999 Belgium	10% alc.	344	4	(1.2%)	S: patients suspected of cosmetic or iatrogenic allergy; R: not specified, one probably reacted to a corticosteroid preparation	16

IVDK: Information Network of Departments of Dermatology, Germany, Austria, Switzerland

Contact allergy to isopropyl myristate in non-cosmetic products
One patient was allergic to isopropyl myristate in ketoconazole cream (5). Six patients had allergic contact dermatitis from isopropyl myristate an antibiotic-steroid spray (8). Another individual reacted to isopropyl myristate in a corticosteroid preparation (16).

Cross-reactions, pseudo-cross-reactions and co-reactions
Of 51 patients allergic to lanolin alcohol, 11 (22%) co-reacted to isopropyl myristate 10% in alcohol (18). In a larger study, such an association could not be confirmed (6). Possibly to isopropyl palmitate (34).

Presence in cosmetic products and chemical analyses
In May 2017, isopropyl myristate was present in 795 of 66,658 cosmetic products of which the composition is known in EWG's Skin Deep Cosmetics Database, USA (http://www.ewg.org/skindeep/). In the USA, in April 2017, isopropyl myristate was present in 1602 of 56,714 cosmetic products of which the composition is known in FDA's Voluntary Cosmetic Registration Program (VCRP) (data obtained from FDA, May 2017). Isopropyl myristate was present in 2246 of 19,000 cosmetic formulations on file at the US Food and Drug Administration (FDA) in 1980 (7).

Other information
Experimental data have shown no evidence of a noteworthy sensitizing potential of isopropyl myristate (9,10,11). Clinical studies of various sizes reporting patch test results with isopropyl myristate found no positive reactions (12,13,14,15).

OTHER SIDE EFFECTS

Other non-eczematous contact reactions
In (somewhat) older literature, isopropyl myristate has been suspected of being comedogenic in 'people with more sensitive complexions or acne-prone problems', based on rabbit ear assays (30,31,32). In more recent rabbit assays, isopropyl myristate was again scored as comedogenic (33).

LITERATURE

1   Travassos AR, Claes L, Boey L, Drieghe J, Goossens A. Non-fragrance allergens in specific cosmetic products. Contact Dermatitis 2011;65:276-285

2   Wetter DA, Yiannias JA, Prakash AV, Davis MD, Farmer SA, el-Azhary RA, et al. Results of patch testing to personal care product allergens in a standard series and a supplemental cosmetic series: an analysis of 945 patients from the Mayo Clinic Contact Dermatitis Group, 2000-2007. J Am Acad Dermatol 2010;63:789-798

3   Davis MD, Scalf LA, Yiannias JA, Cheng JF, El-Azhary RA, Rohlinger AL, et al. Changing trends and allergens in the patch test standard series. Arch Dermatol 2008;144:67-72

4   Fisher AA. Allergic reactions to feminine hygiene sprays. Arch Dermatol 1973;108:801-802

5   Guidetti MS, Vincenzi C, Guerra L, Tosti A. Contact dermatitis due to imidazole antimycotics. Contact Dermatitis 1995;33:282

6   Uter W, Schnuch A, Geier J, Lessmann H. Isopropyl myristate recommended for aimed rather than routine patch testing. Contact Dermatitis 2004;50:242-244

7   Maibach HI, Akerson JM, Marzulli FN, Wenninger J, Greif M, Hjorth N, Andersen KE, Wilkinson DS. Test concentrations and vehicles for dermatological testing of cosmetic ingredients. Contact Dermatitis 1980;6:369-404

8   Calnan CD. Isopropyl myristate sensitivity. Contact Dermatitis Newsletter 1968;3:41

9   Anonymous. Final report on the safety assessment of myristyl myristate and isopropyl myristate. J Am Coll Toxicol 1982;1: 55- 80

10 Klecak G. The Freund's complete adjuvant test and the open epicutaneous test. A complementary test procedure for realistic assessment of allergenic potential. Curr Probl Dermatol 1985;14:152-171

11 Ryan CA, Gerberick GF, Cruse LW et al. Activity of human contact allergens in the murine local lymph node assay. Contact Dermatitis 2000;43:95-102

12 Penchalaiah K, Handa S, Lakshmi SB, Sharma VK, Kumar B. Sensitizers commonly causing allergic contact dermatitis from cosmetics. Contact Dermatitis 2000;43:311-313

13 Meneghini CL, Rantuccio F, Lomuto M. Additives, vehicles and active drugs of topical medicaments as causes of delayed-type allergic dermatitis. Dermatologica 1971;143:137-147

14 Fregert S, Hjorth N. Results of standard patch tests with substances abandoned. Contact Dermatitis Newsletter 1969;5:85- 86

15 Schnuch A, Arnold R, Bahmer F, et al. Epikutantestung mit der Salbengrundlagenreihe. Ergebnisse des "Informationsverbundes. Derm Beruf Umwelt 1993;41:176-183

16 Goossens A, Huygens S, Matura M, Degreef H. Fluticasone propionate: a rare contact sensitizer. Eur J Dermatol 2001;11:29-34

17 Wilkinson DS. Isopropyl myristate. Contact Dermatitis Newsletter 1969;6:144

18 Auth R, Pevny I, Gernot P. Ein Beitrag zur Wollwachsalkohol-Allergie. Akt Dermatol 1984;10:215- 220

19 Bharati A, King CM. Allergic contact dermatitis from isohexadecane and isopropyl myristate. Contact Dermatitis 2004;50:256-257

20 Van Ketel WG. Allergic contact dermatitis from propellants in deodorant sprays in combination with allergy to ethyl chloride. Contact Dermatitis 1976;2:115-119

21 Calnan CD. Isopropyl myristate sensitivity Personal communication, 1969 (cited in ref. 20)

22 Wilkinson DS. Isopropyl myristate. Personal communication, 1969 (cited in ref. 20)

23 Wetter DA, Davis MDP, Yiannias JA, Cheng JF, Connolly SM, el-Azhary RA, et al. Patch test results from the Mayo Contact Dermatitis Group, 1998–2000. J Am Acad Dermatol 2005;53:416-421

24 Barbaud A, Collet E, Le Coz CJ, Meaume S, Gillois P. Contact allergy in chronic leg ulcers: results of a multicentre study carried out in 423 patients and proposal for an updated series of patch tests. Contact Dermatitis 2009;60:279-287

25 Li L-F, Liu G, Wang J. Patch test in Chinese patients with cosmetic allergic contact dermatitis to common cosmetic allergens from a European cosmetic series. Contact Dermatitis 2007;57:50-54

26 Wentworth AB, Yiannias JA, Keeling JH, Hall MR, Camilleri MJ, Drage LA, et al. Trends in patch-test results and allergen changes in the standard series: a Mayo Clinic 5-year retrospective review (January 1, 2006, to December 31, 2010). J Am Acad Dermatol 2014;70:269-275

27 Trattner A, Farchi Y, David M. Cosmetics patch tests: first report from Israel. Contact Dermatitis 2002;47:180-181

28 Laguna C, de la Cuadra J, Martín-González B, Zaragoza V, Martínez-Casimiro L, Alegre V. Allergic contact dermatitis to cosmetics. Actas Dermosifiliogr 2009;100:53-60

29 Ada S, Seçkin D. Patch testing in allergic contact dermatitis: is it useful to perform the cosmetic series in addition to the European standard series? J Eur Acad Dermatol Venereol 2010;24:1192-1196

30 Fulton JE Jr, Pay SR, Fulton JE 3rd. Comedogenicity of current therapeutic products, cosmetics, and ingredients in the rabbit ear. J Am Acad Dermatol 1984;10:96-105

31 Kligman AM, Mills OH. Acne cosmetica. Arch Dermatol 1972;106:843-850

32 Kligman AM, Kwong T. An improved rabbit ear model for assessing comedogenic substances. Br J Dermatol 1979;100:699-702

33 Nguyen SH, Dang TP, Maibach HI. Comedogenicity in rabbit: some cosmetic ingredients/vehicles. Cutan Ocul Toxicol 2007;26:287-292

34 Tong PL, Chow ET. Isopropyl myristate contact allergy: could your moisturizer be the culprit? Contact Dermatitis 2017;77:184-185

2.258   ISOSTEARAMIDOPROPYL MORPHOLINE LACTATE

IDENTIFICATION

Description/definition   : Isostearamidopropyl morpholine lactate is the lactic acid salt of isostearamidopropyl morpholine
Chemical class(es)   : Amines; organic salts
Chemical/IUPAC name   : 2-Hydroxypropanoic acid;16-methyl-N-(3-morpholin-4-ylpropyl)heptadecanamide
Other names   : Propanoic acid, 2-hydroxy-, compd. with N-(3-(4-morpholinyl)propyl)isooctadecanamide (1:1); 16-methyl-N-[3-(morpholin-4-yl)propyl]heptadecanamide; lactic acid
CAS registry number (s) : 72300-24-4; 133651-38-4
CIR review(s)   : Int J Toxicol 1999;18(Suppl.3):51-56
Function(s) in cosmetics : EU: antistatic. USA: antistatic agents
Patch testing   : 0.5% and 1% water (1); it is highly likely that these concentrations (or at least the higher one) may cause many irritant patch test reactions
Molecular formula   : $C_{28}H_{56}N_2O_5$

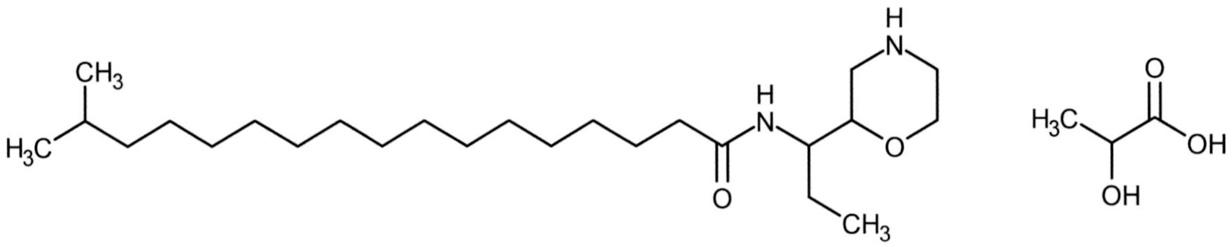

CONTACT ALLERGY

Patch testing in groups of patients

In 2015-2016, in the USA, 47 patients previously reacting to one or more surfactants present in the NACDG screening series were tested with isostearamidopropyl morpholine lactate 0.5% and 1% in water and 11 (23%) had a positive reaction. The relevance of these reactions was not mentioned. In addition to the 11 positive reactions, there were 21 doubtful reactions (3). This makes it highly likely that these concentrations (or at least the higher one) may cause many irritant reactions.

Case reports and case series

Two women had hand dermatitis from contact allergy to isostearamidopropyl morpholine lactate in a liquid hand cleanser; one of them, a massage therapist, had occupational ACD. The semi-open test with the cleanser pure was positive in both individuals on two occasions. Both patients were tested with the ingredient isostearamidopropyl morpholine lactate 0.1%, 0.5% and 1% in water. One reacted to the 0.5% and 1% concentrations, the other only to the highest concentration. Though this may cast some doubt on the allergic nature of the latter reaction, 10 controls tested with the same materials were negative (1). The massage therapist was probably again presented one year later in an Abstract (2).

Cross-reactions, pseudo-cross-reactions and co-reactions

Sodium lauroyl sarcosinate (1,3); disodium lauroamphodiacetate (1,3); oleamidopropyl dimethylamine (1,3); cocamidopropyl betaine (1,3); cocamidopropyl dimethylamine [amidoamine] (3). The authors suggested cross-sensitivity. However, another likely explanation is pseudo-cross-reactivity to common ingredients in these amide-type surfactants.

Presence in cosmetic products and chemical analyses

In the USA, in April 2017, isostearamidopropyl morpholine lactate was present in an unknown number of 56,714 cosmetic products of which the composition is known in FDA's Voluntary Cosmetic Registration Program (VCRP) (data accidentally not requested from FDA). In April 2017, isostearamidopropyl morpholine lactate was present in 30 of 65,434 cosmetic products of which the composition is known in EWG's Skin Deep Cosmetics Database, USA (http://www.ewg.org/skindeep/).

LITERATURE

1   Hanson JL, Warshaw EM. Contact allergy to surfactants in a hypoallergenic liquid cleanser. Dermatitis 2015;26:284-286

2   Hanson JL, Warshaw EM. Contact allergy to surfactants in a liquid cleanser. Dermatitis 2016;27(5):e2

3   Grey KR, Hanson J, Hagen SL, Hylwa SA, Warshaw EM. Epidemiology and co-reactivity of novel surfactant allergens: a double-blind randomized controlled study. Dermatitis 2016;27:348-354

2.259   ISOSTEARYL ALCOHOL

IDENTIFICATION

Description/definition   : Isostearyl alcohol is a mixture of branched chain 18 carbon aliphatic alcohols
Chemical class(es)   : Alcohols
Chemical/IUPAC name   : 16-Methylheptadecan-1-ol
Other names   : Isooctadecanol
CAS registry number (s)   : 27458-93-1; 41744-75-6
EC number(s)   : 248-470-8; 255-529-1
CIR review(s)   : J Am Coll Toxicol 1988;7:359-413 (access: www.cir-safety.org/ingredients)
Function(s) in cosmetics   : EU: emollient; skin conditioning; viscosity controlling. USA: skin-conditioning
                              agents – emollient; viscosity increasing agents - nonaqueous
Patch testing   : 5% alc.; 10% water; pure (4)
Molecular formula   : $C_{18}H_{38}O$

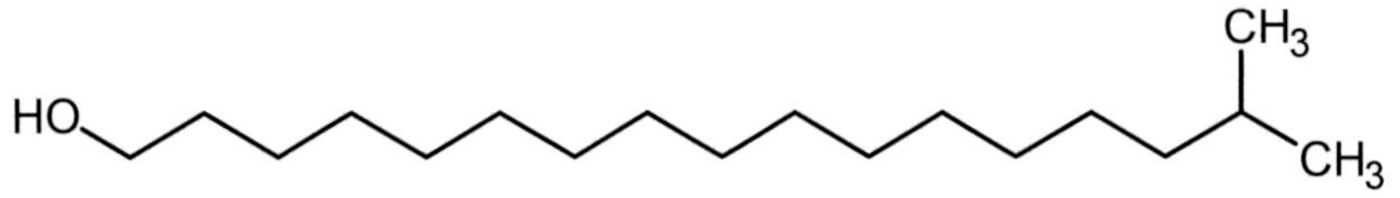

CONTACT ALLERGY

Case reports and case series
A female patient had allergic contact cheilitis from 2 lipsticks. She was patch test positive to the lipsticks, to glyceryl diisostearate in both lipsticks and to diisostearyl malate in one. Glyceryl diisostearate from the manufacturer was investigated by gas chromatography and proved to have the following composition: glyceryl diisostearate 66%, glyceryl triisostearate 29%, glyceryl (mono)isostearate 0.43%, isostearic acid 0.21% and unknown 4%. The commercial diisostearyl malate was also analyzed and proved to contain diisostearyl malate 93.3%, isostearyl alcohol 3.91% and unknown 2.79%. Later, the patient was patch tested with all these chemicals including purified glyceryl diisostearate and diisostearyl malate. The patient now reacted to all chemicals except isostearic acid. However, the purified glyceryl diisostearate and isosteary malate only had weak positive reactions when tested undiluted, whereas glyceryl (mono)isostearate 0.01% pet. and isostearyl alcohol 0.25% pet. showed strongly positive patch test reactions. It was concluded that these impurities were the most important sensitizers in the lipstick(s) (1). Contact allergy to isostearyl alcohol has been reported before from its presence in a pump spray deodorant, but these sensitizations were the result of human repeated insult patch testing (2).

Cross-reactions, pseudo-cross-reactions and co-reactions
See under Case reports

Presence in cosmetic products and chemical analyses
In the USA, in April 2017, isostearyl alcohol was present in 197 of 56,714 cosmetic products of which the composition is known in FDA's Voluntary Cosmetic Registration Program (VCRP) (data obtained from FDA, May 2017). In March 2017, isostearyl alcohol was present in 88 of 65,351 cosmetic products of which the composition is known in EWG's Skin Deep Cosmetics Database, USA (http://www.ewg.org/skindeep/).

Other non-eczematous contact reactions
In (somewhat) older literature, isostearyl alcohol has been suspected of being comedogenic, based on the rabbit ear assay (3).

LITERATURE
1   Hayakawa R, Matsunaga K, Suzuki M, Arima Y, Ohkido Y. Lipstick dermatitis due to C18 aliphatic compounds. Contact Dermatitis 1987;16:215-219
2   Aust LB, Maibach HI. Incidence of human skin sensitization to isostearyl alcohol in two separate groups of panelists. Contact Dermatitis 1980;6:269-271
3   Lanzet M. Comedogenic effects of cosmetic raw materials. Cosmetics & Toiletries 1986;101:63-72
4   De Groot AC. Patch Testing, 3rd Edition. Wapserveen, The Netherlands: acdegroot publishing, 2008 (ISBN 978-90-813233-1-4)

2.260 KOJIC ACID

IDENTIFICATION

Description/definition : Kojic acid is the heterocyclic compound that conforms to the formula shown below
Chemical class(es) : Heterocyclic compounds; ketones; phenols
Chemical/IUPAC name : 5-Hydroxy-2-(hydroxymethyl)pyran-4-one
Other names : 5-Hydroxy-2-(hydroxymethyl)-4*H*-pyran-4-one
CAS registry number (s) : 501-30-4
EC number(s) : 207-922-4
Merck Index monograph : 6635
CIR review(s) : Int J Toxicol 2010;29(Suppl.4):244-273 (access: www.cir-safety.org/ingredients)
SCCS opinion(s) : SCCS/1481/12 (6); SCCP/11182/08 (7)
Function(s) in cosmetics : EU: antioxidant. USA: antioxidants
Patch testing : 5% water, the test concentration is not irritant (2); 1% water (3); 0.5%-3% pet. (4)
Molecular formula : $C_6H_6O_4$

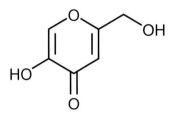

GENERAL

Kojic acid is a fungal metabolite produced by some species of *Aspergillus*, *Penicillium* and *Acetobacter*. It was first isolated from *Aspergillus* in 1907. It is a transparent crystalline particulate, highly soluble in water, ethanol and acetone. Kojic acid of high purity (> 99%) is obtained from *Aspergillus*, and is being used for topical application as skin lightening agent. The mode of action of kojic acid is inhibition of tyrosinase (9). It is also used in foods (e.g., bean paste, soy and sake) in some countries, particularly in Japan (2).

CONTACT ALLERGY

Patch testing in groups of patients

In 1992-1993, in Japan, 220 female patients suspected of cosmetic dermatitis were patch tested with kojic acid 5% in water. Of the 220 patients, 8 used at least one skin care product containing kojic acid, 5 of who reacted to kojic acid as well as to one or more of their own products containing 1% kojic acid, but not to their other products not containing it. The 5 kojic acid-sensitive women developed facial dermatitis 1-12 months after starting the application of kojic acid-containing products. Ingestion of foods containing kojic acid did not cause relapse of dermatitis, or any other adverse effects (2).

Case reports and case series

In the period 1996-2013, in a tertiary referral center in Valencia, Spain, 5419 patients were patch tested. Of these, 628 individuals had allergic contact dermatitis to cosmetics. Kojic acid was the responsible allergen in one case (8). Five women developed facial dermatitis from kojic acid in one or more cosmetic products (2). A woman had undergone sclerotherapy for varicose veins, after which she developed hyperpigmentation. A cream containing urea, hydroquinone, lactic acid, kojic acid and other ingredients was prescribed. After applying this cream for 4 months, she noted no improvement and therefor another pharmaceutical preparation was added. A few weeks later, the patient developed an eczematous eruption on and around the hyperpigmented areas. Patch tests were positive to the cream containing hydroquinone and kojic acid. Later, all ingredients were tested and the patient now reacted to kojic acid 1% and 5% in water. Twenty controls tested with these two kojic acid solutions were negative (3).

Another female patient developed acute dermatitis of the face and neck after applying a makeup product that she used for pigmented areas for 3 days. Two years before, the patient had developed an eczematous eruption after the use of an (unknown) product for 2 months over hyperpigmented areas caused by sclerotherapy for varicose veins. Patch tests were positive to the product and its ingredient kojic acid, tested 0.5%, 1% and 3% pet. (4). Two more patients had allergic contact dermatitis from kojic acid, but details are unknown (5).

Presence in cosmetic products and chemical analyses
In the USA, in April 2017, kojic acid was present in 49 of 56,714 cosmetic products of which the composition is known in FDA's Voluntary Cosmetic Registration Program (VCRP) (data obtained from FDA, May 2017). In April 2017, kojic acid was present in 17 of 66,223 cosmetic products of which the composition is known in EWG's Skin Deep Cosmetics Database, USA (http://www.ewg.org/skindeep/).

OTHER SIDE EFFECTS

Other non-eczematous contact reactions
One patient developed pigmentation from a skin lightening agent cream containing kojic acid. The pigmentation was reproduced with a (negative) patch test at D4 and D7 to both the cream and kojic acid 1% in water and persisted for a month (1). A case of chemical vitiligo after accidental spillage of 30% kojic acid has been reported (10).

LITERATURE
1 García-Gavín J, González-Vilas D, Fernández-Redondo V, Toribio J. Pigmented contact dermatitis due to kojic acid. A paradoxical side effect of a skin lightener. Contact Dermatitis 2010;62:63-64
2 Nakagawa M, Kawai K, Kawai K. Contact allergy to kojic acid in skin care products. Contact Dermatitis 1995;32:9-13
3 Serra-Baldrich E, Tribó MJ, Camarasa JG. Allergic contact dermatitis from kojic acid. Contact Dermatitis 1998;39:86-87
4 Mata TL, Sanchez JP, De La Cuadra Oyanguren J. Allergic contact dermatitis due to kojic acid. Dermatitis 2005;16:89
5 Hosono K. Two cases of contact dermatitis due to kojic acid. Environ Dermatol 1997:4:38–42 (in Japanese).
6 SCCS (Scientific Committee on Consumer Safety). Opinion on kojic acid, 26-27 June 2012, SCCS/1481/12. Available at: http://ec.europa.eu/health/scientific_committees/consumer_safety/docs/sccs_o_098.pdf
7 SCCP (Scientific Committee on Consumer Products). Opinion on kojic acid, 30 September 2008, SCCP/11182/08. Available at: http://ec.europa.eu/health/archive/ph_risk/committees/04_sccp/docs/sccp_o_148.pdf
8 Zaragoza-Ninet V, Blasco Encinas R, Vilata-Corell JJ, Pérez-Ferriols A, Sierra-Talamantes C, Esteve-Martínez A, de la Cuadra-Oyanguren J. Allergic contact dermatitis due to cosmetics: A clinical and epidemiological study in a tertiary hospital. Actas Dermosifiliogr 2016;107:329-336
9 Kim H, Choi HR, Kim DS, Park KC. Topical hypopigmenting agents for pigmentary disorders and their mechanisms of action. Ann Dermatol 2012;24:1-6
10 Iurassich S, Santoro M, Rossi E. A case of chemical vitiligo due to kojic acid. G Ital Dermatol Venereol 1997;132:443-444

2.261 LANOLIN

IDENTIFICATION

Description/definition : Lanolin is a refined derivative of the unctuous fat-like sebaceous secretion of sheep. It consists of a highly complex mixture of esters of high molecular weight, aliphatic, steroid or triterpenoid alcohols and fatty acids

Chemical class(es) : Lanolin and lanolin derivatives

Other names : Adeps lanae; wool wax; wool fat; lanolin, anhydrous

CAS registry number (s) : 8006-54-0

EC number(s) : 232-348-6

CIR review(s) : J Environ Pathol Toxicol 1980;4:63-92 (access: www.cir-safety.org/ingredients)

Merck Index monograph : 6679

Function(s) in cosmetics : EU: antistatic; emollient; emulsifying; hair conditioning; skin conditioning; surfactant. USA: emulsion stabilizers; hair conditioning agents; skin protectants; skin-conditioning agents – emollient; surfactants – emulsifying agents

Patch testing : 30% pet. (SmartPracticeEurope, SmartPracticeCanada); in virtually all centers, lanolin alcohol 30% pet., present in routine series, is used to detect contact allergy to lanolin

GENERAL

The term 'lanolin' stems from the Latin words for wool (lana) and oil (oleum) (54). Lanolin is derived from wool grease, a fatlike substance exuded by the sebaceous glands of sheep. This lubricant protects the wool of the sheep from the effects of weathering (sun, wind, rain, etc.) and constitutes from 5% to 25% of the weight of the sheared greasy wool (15). Lanolin is an amber-yellow, tenacious, unctuous mass with pronounced emollient properties, and has a slight and characteristic odor.

Although appearing to be a fat or a grease, chemically lanolin is classified as a wax. Raw lanolin consists of 75-90% (wt./wt.) wax esters (esters and polyesters of high molecular weight alcohols and fatty acids), 6-12% free alcohols, 1-8% free fatty acids, 1-5% water, 0.1-2% insoluble particulates, 0.2-2% lipid-soluble salts, 0.1-0.2% water-soluble salts, 0.1-1% detergent residues, 25-100 ppm pesticide residues and 0.1-0.5 ppm polycyclic aromatic hydrocarbons (54). Pharmaceutical grade lanolin contains a higher percentage of wax esters (97%), whereas free alcohols are lowered to a maximum of 2.5%, free fatty acids to 0.3% and water to 0.05%; other components have become negligible with the exception of detergent residues (0.02%) (54).

Lanolin has strong emulsifying and absorbent properties and blends and combines well with practically all other materials used in cosmetics and pharmaceuticals. In addition to its water binding and emulsifying qualities, it owes its importance to the ease with which it is absorbed onto human skin and hair. Its adhesive and tackifying properties make it an excellent plasticizer in adhesives and resins. Lanolin has unusual cleansing, soothing, and lubricating values. Because of these properties, lanolin is used in the medicinal field as a base (or vehicle) in the formulation of ointments, salves, creams, lotions, etc.. It is also used in adhesive bandages, surgical dressings, dermatological preparations and cosmetic products (15). Lanolin is also used for industrial purposes. It has been applied to metallic surfaces to prevent corrosion, added to ink to prevent crystallization, incorporated into furniture polish and shoe creams, and even applied to leather to enhance pliability and water resistance (54). Sheep wool and even wool clothing are also important sources of exposure to lanolin (54).

Lanolin derivatives with special qualities may be obtained by physical or chemical modification processes including hydrogenation (hydrogenated lanolin), acetylation (acetylated lanolin), ethoxylation (polyoxyethylene lanolins, PEG-lanolins), transesterification or hydrolysis (lanolin alcohol) (15).

Allergic contact dermatitis from exposure to lanolin has been known for almost 90 years: the first patch test-positive case of allergic contact dermatitis from lanolin stems from 1929 (56). A few case reports of lanolin allergy were published during the 1930s (51,57,58), but it was not until the 1950s, when several studies verifying the prevalence of lanolin sensitivity in dermatologic patients were published (59,60), that lanolin allergy became widely recognized (54). Yet, lanolin is a weak sensitizer (36). Most cases of contact allergy are caused by the use of lanolin-containing pharmaceutical products on diseased skin, especially for stasis dermatitis and leg ulcers (36) and for anogenital dermatitis (4). In cosmetics, which are applied to intact skin, it is relatively safe. Many patients shown to be allergic to lanolin alcohol by patch testing can tolerate lanolin-containing products, which is termed the lanolin paradox (3,5).

The allergens in lanolin are unknown, but are probably present in the alcoholic fraction, and attempts to isolate and identify them have proved difficult (2,54). Confirmation has been obtained that reducing the content of natural free alcohols in lanolin to below 3%, particularly in the absence of detergent residues, strongly reduces the frequency of positive patch test reactions amongst selected lanolin-sensitive skin patients (13,18). Lanolin alcohol 30% in petrolatum has been included in the European standard series since 1969, and can be considered the preferred patch test reagent, though testing with additional lanolin derivatives, especially Amerchol L 101®, will detect more sensitized patients (16,49). Both test preparation may, however, induce some irritant reactions (3).

In literature, the distinction between lanolin and lanolin alcohol is not always clear and it cannot be excluded that some cases of contact allergy to the product 'lanolin', presented in this chapter, were in fact caused by lanolin alcohol. Conversely, in some case reports presented as contact allergic reactions to lanolin alcohol (in the lanolin alcohol chapter), the culprit products may in fact have contained lanolin.

See also Chapter 2.262 Lanolin alcohol, Chapter 2.264 Lanolin oil and Chapter 2.263 Lanolin alcohol (and) paraffinum liquidum (better known as Amerchol® L 101). A review of the (very) early literature on lanolin allergy was published in 1983 (36), a more recent – very useful – review article on the subject of lanolin allergy appeared in 2008 (54).

CONTACT ALLERGY

Patch testing in groups of patients

In Japan, in 1972-1973, 756 consecutive patients suspected of contact dermatitis were patch tested with pure anhydrous lanolin and 21 (2.8%) had a positive reaction. The relevance of these reactions was not mentioned. There were far more reactions to hydrogenated lanolin (19).

From 1969 on, in Europe and many other countries, lanolin *alcohol* was used to detect lanolin allergy. The literature on testing with lanolin itself from the 1960s and before has been reviewed in refs. 36 and 54.

Case reports and case series

In a group of 119 patients with allergic contact dermatitis from cosmetics, investigated in The Netherlands in 1986-1987, one case was caused by lanolin in a herbal cosmetic (23,24). Lanolin was responsible for 15 out of 399 cases of cosmetic allergy where the causal allergen was identified in a study of the NACDG, USA, 1977-1983 (1). Seven patients reacted to lanolin in skin care products in an early publication from London (26). Four wool alcohol-sensitive subjects developed generalized eczema after using soap that contained lanolin (30). Four patients allergic to wool alcohols (positive patch tests to lanolin alcohol or Amerchol® L 101) had used different products containing lanolin, of which one was a moisturizing cream containing anhydrous lanolin (39).

Two children had ACD from lanolin in a moisturizing ointment (21). Two patients suffered from allergic contact dermatitis of the hands and wrists from lanolin in various ointments (51). One female patient developed ACD of the face from lanolin in facial makeup (25). Two other patients reacted to lanolin in a hand lotion (27,28). One patient had contact allergy to lanolin present in a moisturizing cream (9), another individual reacted to lanolin in an after-sun preparation (which may in fact have contained lanolin alcohol, considering the trade name) (38). One patient reacted to lanolin in a moisturizing cream used in the treatment of leg ulcers (40). A woman had ACD of the face from lanolin in the same moisturizing cream (41).

One patient had dermatitis around an eye operation site after application of a lanolin-containing ointment (10). Another individual suffered from cheilitis, which was (probably) caused by lanolin in a lipstick (42). A woman had allergic contact cheilitis from many contact allergens, including lanolin in two lip balms (45). Two other female patients suffered from allergic contact cheilitis caused by lanolin in lipsticks (29,50). A man had occupational allergic hand dermatitis from lanolin in a hand cream (37).

Contact allergy to lanolin in non-cosmetic products

Topical pharmaceutical products

In a group of 31 patients allergic to a topical pharmaceutical product, lanolin was the allergen or one of the allergens in 5 of these individuals (8). Seven patients had allergic contact dermatitis from adeps lanae (lanolin) in a topical pharmaceutical product for leg ulcers and thrombophlebitis (22). Two patients reacted to lanolin in topical pharmaceutical preparations (12,17). A woman developed acute allergic contact dermatitis from lanolin in unguentum aquosum BP (26). Another woman had ACD from lanolin (wool wax) in a topical pharmaceutical preparation to treat actinic keratoses (43).

A patient had allergic contact cheilitis from many contact allergens, including lanolin in a medicated lip ointment (45). A man and a woman, allergic to lanolin, both had episodes of allergic contact dermatitis when in contact with topical pharmaceuticals containing lanolin (50). A man developed allergic contact dermatitis of the penis after having had intercourse with his wife, who was treated for *Candida* vulvovaginitis with an anti-candidal cream containing lanolin ('consort' or 'connubial' contact dermatitis (53).

Other products

Lanolin used as a protective coating for metal may have caused or contributed to allergic contact dermatitis in a mechanical inspector (14). A forklift driver developed occupational hand dermatitis progressing to erythroderma from contact allergy to lanolin in a wax used to lubricate the steering wheel of the forklift (20). Lanolin in an adhesive plaster caused ACD in a man after sclerotherapy of varicose veins (44). An unknown number of patients had contact allergy to lanolin in adhesive tape (46). Two patients had positive patch tests to a herbal ointment and to its ingredient lanolin; the relevance of the reactions was uncertain (48). A young female figure skater had recalcitrant allergic contact dermatitis of the ankles from lanolin in protection gel pads inside her skates (55).

Cross-reactions, pseudo-cross-reactions and co-reactions
Pseudo-cross-reactions to lanolin alcohol (11,12). Acetylated lanolin (12,18); cetearyl alcohol (10,11); cetyl alcohol (10,11); hydrogenated lanolin (12,18,19); PPG-2 lanolin alcohol ether (12).

Presence in cosmetic products and chemical analyses
In August 2017, lanolin was present in 345 of 70,654 cosmetic products of which the composition is known in EWG's Skin Deep Cosmetics Database, USA (http://www.ewg.org/skindeep/). In the USA, in April 2017, lanolin was present in 714 of 56,714 cosmetic products of which the composition is known in FDA's Voluntary Cosmetic Registration Program (VCRP) (data obtained from FDA, May 2017). In the USA, in 2015-2016, 63 diaper wipes and 41 topical diaper preparations from a large retailer were screened for the presence of potential sensitizers. Lanolin was found in 5 (8%) disposable diaper wipes and in 14 (33%) topical diaper preparations (47).

In 2009, in the USA, the ingredient lists of 1591 facial cosmetics from one company were screened for the presence of lanolin. Lanolin was present in 2% of 132 blushers and 38 bronzers, in 10% of 90 concealers, in 11% of 174 eyeliners, in 24% of 304 eyeshadows, in 0% of 457 foundations, in 0% of 140 loose and pressed powders, and in 0% of 256 mascaras (31). In 2009, in the USA, the ingredient lists of 796 hair products from one company were screened for the presence of lanolin. Lanolin was present in 3% of 279 shampoos, in 4% of 231 conditioners, and in 14% of 286 styling products (32).

In 2009, in the USA, the ingredient lists of 730 lip cosmetics and dental care products from one company were screened for the presence of lanolin. Lanolin was present in 13% of 31 lip liners, in 44% of 429 lipsticks, in 42% of 92 lip moisturizers, in 0% of 153 toothpastes, and in 0% of 25 mouth washes (33). In 2009, in the USA, the ingredient lists of 657 miscellaneous cosmetics from one company were screened for the presence of lanolin. Lanolin was present only in 28% of 53 wipes (34). Of 276 moisturizers sold in the USA in 2007, 26 (10%) contained lanolin (6). Lanolin was present in 10 out of 166 (6%) corticosteroid preparations collected in 2007, USA (52).

OTHER SIDE EFFECTS

Other non-eczematous contact reactions
In (somewhat) older literature, lanolin (anhydrous) has been suspected of being comedogenic in 'people with more sensitive complexions or acne-prone problems', based on rabbit ear assays (35).

LITERATURE

1   Adams RM, Maibach HI, Clendenning WE, Fisher AA, Jordan WJ, Kanof N, et al. A five-year study of cosmetic reactions. J Am Acad Dermatol 1985;13:1062-1069
2   Fregert S, Dahlquist I, Trulsson L. An attempt to isolate and identify allergens in lanolin. Contact Dermatitis 1984;10:16-19
3   Kligman AM. The myth of lanolin allergy. Contact Dermatitis 1998;39:103-107
4   Wakelin SH, Smith H, White IR, Rycroft RJ, McFadden JP. A retrospective analysis of contact allergy to lanolin. Br J Dermatol 2001;145:28-31
5   Wolf R. The lanolin paradox. Dermatology 1996;192:198-202
6   Zirwas MJ, Stechschulte SA. Moisturizer allergy. Diagnosis and management. J Clin Aesthetic Dermatol 2008;1:38-44
7   Warshaw EM, Nelsen DD, Maibach HI, Marks JG Jr, Zug KA, Taylor JS, et al. Positive patch test reactions to lanolin: cross-sectional data from the North American Contact Dermatitis Group, 1994 to 2006. Dermatitis 2009;20:79-88
8   Pecegueiro M, Brandao M, Pinto J, Concalo S. Contact dermatitis to Hirudoid® cream. Contact Dermatitis 1987:17:290-293
9   Batten, TL, Wakeel RA, Douglas WS, Evans C, White MI, Moody R, Ormerod AD. Contact dermatitis from the old formula E45 cream. Contact Dermatitis 1994;30:159-161
10 Van Ketel, WG. Allergy to cetylalcohol. Contact Dermatitis 1984;11:125-126
11 Van Ketel, WG, Wemer J. Allergy to lanolin and "lanolin-free" creams. Contact Dermatitis 1983;9:420
12 Giorgini S, Melli MC, Sertoli A. Comments on the allergenic activity of lanolin. Contact Dermatitis 1983;9:425-426

13 Clark EW, Blondeel A, Cronin E, Oleffe JA, Wilkinson DS. Lanolin of reduced sensitizing potential. Contact Dermatitis 1981;7:80-83

14 Calnan CD. Lanolin in protective metal coatings. Contact Dermatitis 1979;5:267-268

15 Schlossman ML, McCarthy JP. Lanolin and derivatives chemistry: Relationship to allergic contact dermatitis. Contact Dermatitis 1979;5:65-72

16 Mortensen T. Allergy to lanolin. Contact Dermatitis 1979;5:137-139

17 Calnan CD. Oxypolyethoxydodecane in an ointment. Contact Dermatitis 1978;4:168-169

18 Clark EW, Cronin E, Wilkinson DS. Lanolin with reduced sensitizing potential A preliminary note. Contact Dermatitis 1977;3:69-74

19 Sugai T, Higashi J. Hypersensitivity to hydrogenated lanolin. Contact Dermatitis 1975;1:146-157

20 Carter ZA, Gordon K, Cruz PD. Erythroderma due to unwitting exposure to an unobvious allergen source. Dermatitis 2015;26:291

21 Jacob SE, Matiz C, Herro EM. Compositae-associated allergic contact dermatitis from bisabolol. Dermatitis 2011;22:102-105

22 Prins FJ, Smeenk G. Contacteczeem door Hirudoid zalf. Ned T Geneesk 1971;115:1935-1938

23 De Groot AC, Bruynzeel DP, Bos JD, van der Meeren HL, van Joost T, Jagtman BA, Weyland JW. The allergens in cosmetics. Arch Dermatol 1988;124:1525-1529

24 De Groot AC. Adverse reactions to cosmetics. PhD Thesis, University of Groningen, The Netherlands: 1988, chapter 3.4, pp.105-113

25 Cronin E. Contact dermatitis from cosmetics. J Soc Cosm Chem 1967;18:681-691

26 Cronin E. Lanolin dermatitis. Br J Derm 1966;78:167-174

27 Epstein E. The detection of lanolin allergy. Arch Dermatol 1972;106:678-681

28 Jordan WP. Allergic contact dermatitis in hand eczema. Arch Dermatol 1974;110:567-569

29 Cronin E. Contact Dermatitis. Edinburgh: Churchill Livingstone, 1980:147

30 Pecquet C, Bayrou O, Artigou C, et al. Eczéma de contact à la lanoline contenue dans des savons: quatre observations. Lettre du GERDA 1994;11:69-70

31 Scheman A, Jacob S, Katta R, Nedorost S, Warshaw E, Zirwas M, et al. Part 1 of a 4 part series. Facial cosmetics: trends and alternatives. Data from the American Contact Alternative Group. J Clin Aesthet Dermatol 2011;4:25-30

32 Scheman A, Jacob S, Katta R, Nedorost S, Warshaw E, Zirwas M, et al. Part 2 of a 4 part series. Hair cosmetics: trends and alternatives. Data from the American Contact Alternative Group. J Clin Aesthet Dermatol 2011;4:42-46

33 Scheman A, Jacob S, Katta R, Nedorost S, Warshaw E, Zirwas M, et al. Part 3 of a 4 part series. Lips and common Dental Care products: trends and alternatives. Data from the American Contact Alternative Group. J Clin Aesthet Dermatol 2011;4:50-53

34 Scheman A, Jacob S, Katta R, Nedorost S, Warshaw E, Zirwas M, et al. Part 4 of a 4 part series. Miscellaneous products: trends and alternatives in deodorants, antiperspirants, sunblocks, shaving products, powder, and wipes. Data from the American Contact Alternative Group. J Clin Aesthet Dermatol 2011;4:35-39

35 Fulton JE Jr, Pay SR, Fulton JE 3rd. Comedogenicity of current therapeutic products, cosmetics, and ingredients in the rabbit ear. J Am Acad Dermatol 1984;10:96-105

36 Kligman AM. Lanolin allergy: crisis or comedy. Contact Dermatitis 1983;9:99-107

37 Goossens A, Baret I, Swevers A. Allergic contact dermatitis caused by tetrahydroxypropyl ethylenediamine in cosmetic products. Contact Dermatitis 2011;64:161-164

38 Parry EJ, Bilsland D, Morley WN. Photocontact allergy to 4-tert,buty-4'-methoxy-dibenzoylmethane (Parsol 1789). Contact Dermatitis 1995;32:251-252

39 Henderson CA, Highet AS, Shamy HK. The frequency of lanolin contact allergy. Contact Dermatitis 1995;32:52

40 Kulozik M, Powell SM, Cherry G, Ryan T J. Contact sensitivity in community-based leg ulcer patients. Clin Exp Dermatol 1988;13:82-84

41 Hann S, Hughes TM, Stone NM. Flexural allergic contact dermatitis to benzalkonium chloride in antiseptic bath oil. Br J Dermatol 2007;157:795-798

42 Lim JTE, Ng SK, Goh CL. Contact cheilitis in Singapore. Contact Dermatitis 1992;27:263-264

43 Sams WM. Untoward response with topical fluorouracil. Arch Dermatol 1968;97:14-22

44 O'Donnell BF, Hodgson C. Allergic contact dermatitis due to lanolin in an adhesive plaster. Contact Dermatitis 1993;28:191-192

45 Fraser K, Pratt M. Polysensitization in recurrent lip dermatitis. J Cutan Med Surg 2015;19:77-80

46 Calnan CD. Diethyldithiocarbamate in adhesive tape. Contact Dermatitis 1978;4:61

47 Yu J, Treat J, Chaney K, Brod B. Potential allergens in disposable diaper wipes, topical diaper preparations, and disposable diapers: under-recognized etiology of pediatric perineal dermatitis. Dermatitis 2016;27:110-118

48 Bruynzeel DP, van Ketel WG, Young E, van Joost Th, Smeenk G. Contact sensitization by alternative topical medicaments containing plant extracts. Contact Dermatitis 1992;27:278-279

49 Miest RY, Yiannias JA, Chang Y-HH, Singh NRN. Diagnosis and prevalence of lanolin allergy. Dermatitis 2013;24:119-123

50 Sulzberger MB, Lazar MP, Furman D. A study of the allergenic constituents of lanolin (wool fat). J Invest Dermatol 1950;15:453-458

51 Sulzberger MB, Morse JL. Hypersensitiveness to wool fat—Report of 2 cases. JAMA 1931;96:2099-2100

52 Coloe J, Zirwas MJ. Allergens in corticosteroid vehicles. Dermatitis 2008;19:38-42

53 Pauluzzi P, Rizzi GM. Contact dermatitis to wool alcohols: an unusual manifestation. Am J Cont Dermat 1994;5:113-114

54 Lee B, Warshaw E. Lanolin allergy: History, epidemiology, responsible allergens, and management. Dermatitis 2008;19:63-72

55 Mandell JA, Tlougan BE, Cohen DE. Bunga Pad-induced ankle dermatitis in a figure skater. Dermatitis 2011;22:58-9

56 Ramirez M, Eller JJ. The patch test in contact dermatitis. Allergy 1929;1:489

57 Sézary A. Intolerance cutaneé à la lanoline. Presse Med 1936;93:1880 (cited in ref. 54)

58 Bonnevie P. Aetiologie und Pathogenese der Ekzemkrankheiten. In: Busck A, editor. Copenhagen: Nyt Nordisk Forlag, 1939 (cited in ref. 54)

59 Sulzberger MB, Warshaw T, Herman F. Studies of hypersensitivity to lanolin. J Invest Dermatol 1953;20:33-44

60 Baer RL, Serri F, Weissenbach-Vial C. Studies on allergic sensitization to certain topical therapeutic agents. AMA Arch Derm 1955;71:19-23

2.262   LANOLIN ALCOHOL

IDENTIFICATION

Description/definition	: Lanolin alcohol is a complex mixture of organic alcohols obtained by the hydrolysis of lanolin
Chemical class(es)	: Alcohols; lanolin and lanolin derivatives; sterols
Other names	: Wool wax alcohols; alcohols, lanolin; eucerin; lanolin alcohols; wool alcohols; alcoholes adipis lanae
CAS registry number (s)	: 8027-33-6
EC number(s)	: 232-430-1
CIR review(s)	: J Environ Pathol Toxicol 1980;4:63-92 (access: www.cir-safety.org/ingredients)
Merck Index monograph	: 6680
Function(s) in cosmetics	: EU: antistatic; binding; emollient; emulsifying; hair conditioning; viscosity controlling. USA: binders; emulsion stabilizers; hair conditioning agents; viscosity increasing agents - nonaqueous
Patch testing	: 30% pet. (Chemotechnique, SmartPracticeEurope, SmartPracticeCanada); this concentration may be slightly irritant (11)

GENERAL

Lanolin alcohol is a complex mixture of organic alcohols obtained by the hydrolysis of lanolin. For a general introduction to lanolin, its derivatives and applications see Chapter 2.261 Lanolin. Both lanolin and lanolin alcohol may be components of cosmetics, topical creams, household products, leather, furs, textile finishing and furniture-polishing materials, shoe polish, papers, and print colors (15). The allergens in lanolin are unknown, but are probably present in the alcoholic fraction, and attempts to isolate and identify them have proved difficult (10).

Lanolin alcohol (wool alcohols) 30% in petrolatum has been included in the European standard series since 1969, and can be considered the preferred patch test reagent. However, it does not detect all cases of sensitization (99) and reproducibility of a positive patch test is only 40-60% (20,103,104).

Lanolin and lanolin alcohol are weak sensitizers (11,97). Most cases of contact allergy are caused by the use of lanolin (alcohol) containing therapeutic products on damaged skin, especially for stasis dermatitis and leg ulcers (11,12,54,91,93,95,97) and for anogenital dermatitis (12,17). In cosmetics, which are applied to intact skin, lanolin alcohol is relatively safe. Many patients shown to be sensitive to lanolin (alcohol) by patch testing with lanolin alcohol can tolerate lanolin (alcohol) containing products; this is termed the lanolin paradox (11,13).

In literature, the distinction between lanolin and lanolin alcohol is not always clear and it cannot be excluded that some cases of contact allergy to the product 'lanolin alcohol', presented in this chapter, were in fact caused by lanolin (but, in that case, still the alcoholic part). Conversely, in case reports presented as contact allergic reactions to lanolin (in the lanolin chapter), the culprit products may in fact have contained lanolin alcohol.

See also Chapter 2.261 Lanolin, Chapter 2.264 Lanolin oil and Chapter 2.263 Lanolin alcohol (and) paraffinum liquidum (better known as Amerchol® L 101). A review of the (very) early literature on lanolin allergy was published in 1983 (97), a more recent – very useful – review of the subject of lanolin allergy in 2008 (102).

CONTACT ALLERGY

General population and subgroups

There have been investigations in several European countries (notably Denmark), in which random samples of the population of certain age groups have been patch tested with lanolin alcohol (table 2.262.1). Frequencies of sensitization were consistently low, ranging from 0% to 0.4% (63,65,66,67,68). In three Danish studies, the patch tests were read only at day 2, which may have resulted in underestimation of the actual rate of sensitization (65,66,68).

In subgroups of the general population, a higher rate of sensitization to lanolin alcohol has been observed of 1.4% (women 1.9%, men 1.0%) in adults aged 28-78 years, comprising a large percentage (>50%) of atopic individuals (70,72). In this study, the use of moisturizers applied to atopic dermatitis or otherwise mildly damaged atopic skin, may have resulted in the increased rate of sensitization (70,72).

Estimates of the 10-year prevalence of contact allergy to lanolin alcohol in the general population of Denmark based on the CE-DUR method ranged from 0.16% to 0.22% (61). In a similar study from Germany, the estimated prevalence in the general population in the period 1992-2000 ranged from 0.6% to 1.4% (16,62).

Table 2.262.1   Contact allergy in the general population and subgroups

Year and country	Selection and number tested	Prevalence of contact allergy			Comments	Ref.
		Total	Women	Men		
General population						
2008-11 five Euro-pean countries	general population, random sample, 18-74 years, n=3119	0.4%	0.5%	0.4%		63
2008 Denmark	general population, random sample, 15-41 years, n=469		0%	0.5%	patch tests were read on day 2 only	68
2006 Denmark	general population, random sample, 18-69 years, n=3460	0%	0%	0%	patch tests were read on day 2 only	65
2005 Norway	general population, random sample, 18-69 years, n=1236	0.1%	0.1%	0%		67
1990 Denmark	general population, random sample, 18-69 years, n=543	0.2%	0%	0.4%	patch tests were read on day 2 only; data from 15-17 years old excluded in the data presented here	66
Subgroups						
2010 Denmark	unselected population of 8th grade schoolchildren in Den-mark, 15 years later; n=442	0.2%	0.4%	0%	follow-up study	64
1997-1998 Germany	adults 28-78 year, with a large percentage (>50%) of atopic individuals, n=1141	1.4%	1.9%	1.0%		70, 72
1995-1996 Denmark	8th grade school children, 12-16 years, n=1146	0.3%	0.5%	0%		69, 71

Patch testing in groups of patients
Results of studies testing lanolin alcohol in consecutive patients suspected of contact dermatitis (routine testing) back to 1996 are shown in table 2.262.2. Results of testing in groups of *selected* patients (e.g., children with dermatitis, hairdressers with contact dermatitis, individuals with periorbital dermatitis or chronic cheilitis, patients suspected of intolerance to cosmetics, leg ulcer patients) back to 1989 are shown in table 2.262.3.

Patch testing in consecutive patients suspected of contact dermatitis: routine testing
As lanolin alcohol 30% pet. is included in the European Baseline Series, the screening tray of the North American Contact Dermatitis Group (NACDG) and most other national series routinely tested in consecutive patients suspected of contact dermatitis, there are many data on lanolin alcohol contact allergy available, notably from European countries and from the USA + Canada, where the NACDG publishes their patch test results biannually. However, from 2011 on, lanolin alcohol 30% pet. has been replaced by the NACDG with Amerchol® L 101 50% pet. (100,101). This has given an increase in positive reactions to 'lanolin alcohol' from 2-2.5% to 4.6% in the period 2011-2012 (101) and even 5.4% in 2013-2014 (100), which most likely harbors a number of false-positive, irritant reactions (see Chapter 2.263 Lanolin alcohol and paraffinum liquidum).

In 26 studies in which routine testing with lanolin alcohol was performed, rates of sensitization have ranged from 0.4% to 6.8% (table 2.262.2). In 18/26 investigations, rates were 2.5% or lower. In studies of the ESSCA (European Surveillance System on Contact Allergy network), with many participating centers in 9-12 European countries, there was also a wide range of 0% to 8.4% positive reactions between the centers (1,8,9,50,86). In the USA, prevalence rates decreased from 3.7% in 1994-1996 to 1.8% in 2005-2006 (41).

In many reports, no relevance data were provided. In the NACDG studies, 'definite' or 'probably' relevance was scored in 25-52% of the positive reactions. In the other studies, 21-80% of positive patch tests were considered to be relevant. Specific products were never mentioned. In a 1996-2006 USA study, relevant reactions were mostly caused by cosmetics (41). In a Belgian study, the relevant reactions were (partly?) ascribed to topical medicaments (7).

Table 2.262.2 Patch testing in groups of patients: Routine testing

Years and Country	Test conc. & vehicle	Number of patients tested | positive (%)		Selection of patients (S); Relevance (R); Comments (C)	Ref.
2013-2014 12 Euro-pean countries, 46 departments [b]	30% pet.	26,178	(1.9%)	R: not stated; C: results of 6 occupational dermatology clinics and one pediatric clinic not included in these figures; range of positive reactions: 0%-6.5%	9
2009-2012 12 Euro-pean countries [b]	30% pet.	56,435	(1.7%)	R: not specified	86
2009-10 USA, Canada	30% pet.	4306	108 (2.5%)	R: definite + probable relevance: 43%	22

Table 2.262.2 Patch testing in groups of patients: Routine testing (*continued*)

Years and Country	Test conc. & vehicle	Number of patients tested	positive (%)	Selection of patients (S); Relevance (R); Comments (C)	Ref.
2008-2010 USA	30% pet	591	23 (3.9%)	R: not stated; C: significant association with Amerchol® L 101 and with sorbitan sesquioleate	21
2006-2010 USA	30% pet.	3032	(2.4%)	R: 52%	56
2001-2010 Australia	30% pet.	5137	219 (4.2%)	R: 21%	83
2007-2008, 11 European countries [b]	30% pet.	23,883	312 (1.3%) [a]	R: not stated; prevalences ranged from 0.4% (Finland) to 2.9% (Germany)	1
2007-8 USA, Canada	30% pet.	5079	(2.1%)	R: definite + probable relevance: 52%	18
2005-06 USA, Canada	30% pet.	4451	(1.8%)	R: definite + probable relevance: 46%	14
1994-06 USA, Canada	30% pet.	25,811	634 (2.5%)	R: definite + probable relevance: 37%, mostly caused by cosmetics; C: decrease in the rate of positive reactions from 3.7% in 1994-1996 to 1.8% in 2005-2006	41
2000-2005 USA	30% pet.	3842	(1.9%)	R: 58%	5
2004, 11 European countries [b]	30% pet.	9377	209 (2.2%) [a]	R: not stated; C: range positives: 0.1%- 8.4%	8
2003-4 USA, Canada	30% pet.	5145	113 (2.2%)	R: not stated	19
2000-04 Switzerland		4094	147 (3.6%)	R: not stated	23
1998-2004 Israel	20% pet.	2156	11 (0.5%)	R: not stated	48
1992-2004 Turkey	30% pet.	1038	5 (0.4%)	R: not stated; C: prevalence in women 0.5%, in men 0.3%	49
2002-2003, 9 European centres [b]	30% pet.	9415	(3.0%)	R: not stated; C: prevalence range per centre (n=17) 0.0% - 7.3%	50
2001-2 USA, Canada	30% pet.	4908	(2.2%)	R: definite + probable relevance: 27%	43
2000-2002 Finland		11,810	(0.7%)	R: not stated	47
1997-2001 Czech Rep.	30% pet.	12,058	360 (3.0%)	R: not stated; C: prevalence in men 3.1%, in women 3.0%	51
2000 United Kingdom	30% pet.	3063	(3.3%)	R: 80% (current and past relevance in one centre)	46
1998-00 USA, Canada	30% pet.	5834	(2.4%)	R: definite + probable relevance: 26%	44
1998–2000 USA	30% pet.	738	(1.6%)	R: not stated	45
1996-2000 Europe	30% pet.	26,210	(2.9%)	R: not stated; C: prevalence in women 3.1%, in men 2.6%; C: ten centres, seven countries, EECDRG study	52
1998-1999 Belgium	30% pet.	819	56 (6.8%)	R: not specified, ascribed (partly?) to topical medicaments	7
1982-1996 UK	30% pet.	24,449	(1.7%)	R: not stated; C: range positives per annum 0.9%-2.3%; prevalence significantly higher in women; most frequent primary sites: lower legs and anogenital	12

[a] age-standardized and sex-standardized proportions
[b] study of the ESSCA (European Surveillance System on Contact Allergy network)
EECDRG: European Environmental and Contact Dermatitis Research Group

Patch testing in groups of selected patients
Results of testing lanolin alcohol in groups of selected patients (e.g., children with dermatitis, hairdressers with contact dermatitis, individuals with periorbital dermatitis or chronic cheilitis, patients suspected of intolerance to cosmetics, leg ulcer patients) back to 1989 are shown in table 2.262.3. In 16 investigations, frequencies of sensitization have ranged from 1.3% to 23%. As expected, the highest rates were found in groups of patients with leg ulcers / stasis dermatitis: 23% (54), 9% (95), 8% (91) and 7.8% (93). In two investigations patch testing children, high frequencies of sensitization were observed: 6.2% (92) and 4.9% (96). The most likely explanation is that these groups harbor many patients with atopic dermatitis, who have become sensitized to lanolin alcohol from the use of moisturizers on dermatitis and slightly damaged atopic skin. Indeed, in one study, the prevalence of sensitization was higher in atopic children than in non-atopics (92). However, there are also studies in groups of children with low sensitization rates: 1.5% (73) and 1.6% (33).

In general, selection on the basis of suspicion of cosmetic reactions (including cheilitis and periorbital dermatitis), did not result in prevalences higher than in routine testing (3,24,80,85,89). The only exception was a small group of patients with facial allergic contact dermatitis, in which 4/57 patients (7%) reacted to lanolin alcohol; in the total group of 85 patients with facial dermatitis (of any diagnosis), the percentage was 4.7 (60). Hairdressers and their clients had no increased sensitization rates (87,88).

Table 2.262.3 Patch testing in groups of patients: Selected patient groups

Years and Country	Test conc. & vehicle	Number of patients tested	positive (%)	Selection of patients (S); Relevance (R); Comments (C)	Ref.
2013-2015 USA		1109	54 (4.9%)	S: children 0-18 years suspected of contact dermatitis; R: 70%	96
2003-2014 IVDK	30% pet.	5202	(7.8%)	S: patients with stasis dermatitis / chronic leg ulcers; R: not stated; C: percentage of reactions significantly higher than in a control group of routine testing	93
2002-2013 Italy	30% pet.	2614	40 (1.5%)	S: children younger than 11 suspected of contact dermatitis; R: 20 (50%)	73
1996-2013 Netherlands	30% pet.	1009	63 (6.2%)	S: children aged 0-17 years; R: not stated; C: higher prevalence in atopic than in non-atopic children	92
2007-2012 IVDK	30% pet.	708	10 (1.3%)	S: female hairdressers with current or previous occupational contact dermatitis; R: not stated	88
		1900	33 (1.7%)	S: female patients, clients of hairdressers, in who hair cosmetics were regarded as a cause of dermatitis, and who had never worked as hairdressers; R: not stated	
2006-2011 IVDK	30% pet.	10,124	246 (2.6%)	S: patients suspected of cosmetic intolerance; R: not stated; C: the frequency of sensitization was significantly higher than in a control group	85
2002-2011 Denmark		399	5 (1.3%)	S: hairdressers with contact dermatitis; R: not stated	87
2000-2010 IVDK		4380	92 (2.1%)	S: patients with periorbital dermatitis; R: not stated; 42 (84%) also reacted to Amerchol® L 101, when tested later	24
2000-2007 USA	30% pet.	942	17 (1.8%)	S: patients tested with a supplemental cosmetic screening series; R: 94%; C: weak study: a. high rate of macular erythema and weak reactions; b. relevance figures included 'questionable' and 'past' relevance	3
2001-2006 Italy	30% pet.	129	3 (2.3%)	S: patients with chronic cheilitis; R: 2 reactions were relevant	89
1995-2004 UK	30% pet.	500	8 (1.6%)	S: children 0-16 years referred for patch testing; R: all reactions were relevant	33
<2004 USA, Canada	30% pet.	54	5 (9%)	S: patients with leg ulcers; R: 100% probable relevance	95
2000-2002 Serbia	30% pet.	75	6 (8%)	S: patients with venous leg ulcers and dermatitis of the surrounding skin; R: not stated	91
1995-1999 IVDK	30% pet.	971	(2.8%)	S: patients with allergic periorbital contact dermatitis; R: not stated	80
1995-1997 USA		57	4 (7%)	S: patients with facial allergic contact dermatitis; R: only relevant reactions were mentioned	60
1988-1989 UK		81	19 (23%)	S: patients with leg ulcers; R: not specified	54

IVDK: Information Network of Departments of Dermatology, Germany, Austria, Switzerland

Case reports and case series

Case series

Lanolin alcohol was stated to be the (or an) allergen in 14 patients in a group of 603 individuals suffering from cosmetic dermatitis, seen in the period 2010-2015 in Leuven, Belgium (55). In the period 1996-2013, in a tertiary referral center in Valencia, Spain, 5419 patients were patch tested. Of these, 628 individuals had allergic contact dermatitis to cosmetics. Lanolin alcohol was the responsible allergen in eleven cases (84). Lanolin alcohol was responsible for 29 out of 959 cases of non-fragrance cosmetic allergy where the causal allergen was identified, Belgium, 2000-2010 (2). In a group of 83 patients with cheilitis, seen in Bologna, Italy in the period 2001-2005, one reacted to lanolin alcohol in (unspecified) cosmetics (79).

In a group of 2193 patients (1582 women, 611 men) with (presumed) cosmetic allergy, 112 reactions (5%) were caused by lanolin alcohol in a study of the NACDG, 2001-2004, lanolin alcohol ranking 12th in the list of most frequent allergens (6). In a group of 60 patients with allergic contact cheilitis seen by the members of the NACDG between 2001 and 2004 and mostly from cosmetics, 4 (6.7%) cases were caused by lanolin alcohol (57). In a group of 46 patients with allergic contact dermatitis of the eyelids seen in Kansas City, USA, between 1994 and 2004, two cases (4.3%) were caused by contact allergy to lanolin alcohol (source not mentioned) (53). In a group of 146 patients patch tested for cheilitis in Amersham, UK, between 1982 and 2001, there were two positive patch test reactions to lanolin alcohol considered to be relevant for the lip dermatitis. Over half of the reactions in the entire group were ascribed to lipsticks and lip salves (42).

In a group of 119 patients with allergic contact dermatitis from cosmetics, investigated in The Netherlands in 1986-1987, one case was caused by Eucerit® (a purified lanolin alcohol plus cholesterol emulsifier) in a skin care product (74,75). In a group of 75 patients allergic to cosmetic products, seen in a private practice in The Netherlands in the period 1981-1986, four cases were caused by Eucerit® (a purified lanolin alcohol plus cholesterol emulsifier) and one case by lanolin alcohol in skin care products (77). Lanolin alcohol was responsible for 12 out of 399 cases of cosmetic allergy where the causal allergen was identified in a study of the NACDG, USA, 1977-1983 (4). Seven patients with dermatitis of the face allergic to lanolin mentioned exacerbation of eczema from products containing lanolin alcohol (cosmetic cream) or lanolin (pharmaceutical base) (26).

Case reports
A woman had allergic contact dermatitis of the face from lanolin alcohol in propolis cream (15). One patient had ACD from lanolin alcohol in a moisturizing cream (39). A woman with cheilitis had contact allergy to lanolin alcohol in lanolin cream, two others reacted to lanolin alcohol in lipsticks (59). Two patients reacted to lanolin alcohol in lipsticks and three to the material in the absorption base in eye cosmetics (78). Three other individuals had allergic contact dermatitis from lanolin alcohol present in an emollient used post-surgically to cover clean surgical wounds (27). A male child had worsening of atopic dermatitis from contact allergy to lanolin alcohol in a moisturizer (31). Two children with atopic dermatitis reacted to lanolin alcohol in the same moisturizer (34).

Contact allergy to lanolin alcohol in non-cosmetic products
One or more patients reacted to lanolin alcohol in paste bandage (25). A man had chronic anogenital dermatitis from lanolin alcohol in a pharmaceutical ointment (58). Another male patient had periorbital dermatitis from lanolin alcohol present in a concentration of 0.2% in a lubricant eye ointment (ocular topical pharmaceutical) (105). Three patients suffered from allergic contact dermatitis from lanolin alcohol in 'a commonly used product' (details unknown, article not read) (76).

Cross-reactions, pseudo-cross-reactions and co-reactions
Pseudo-cross-reactions to Amerchol® L 101 (21,24,29). Almost all patients reacting to lanolin alcohol co-react to Amerchol® L 101 (24), but far fewer patients reacting to Amerchol® L 101 co-react to lanolin alcohol in the baseline series (30). Patients reacting to lanolin alcohol 30% in petrolatum hardly ever react to lanolin purified by removal of detergent, biocide residues and natural free fatty alcohols (35).

Acetylated lanolin alcohol (38); Amerchol® CAB (petrolatum [and] lanolin alcohol) (82); cetearyl alcohol (36,37); cetyl alcohol (36,37); ethoxylated lanolin (98); hydrogenated lanolin (38); hydroxylated lanolin (38); lanolin (36,37,38); lanolin acids (38); oleyl alcohol (106); PPG-2 lanolin alcohol ether (38); sorbitan sesquioleate (21). *Not* to hydrogenated lanolin (40); not to Eucerin® (32); no cross-reactivity *from* primary hydrogenated lanolin sensitization (28).

Presence in cosmetic products and chemical analyses
In August 2017, lanolin alcohol was present in 149 of 70,678 cosmetic products of which the composition is known in EWG's Skin Deep Cosmetics Database, USA (http://www.ewg.org/skindeep/). In the USA, in April 2017, lanolin alcohol was present in 629 of 56,714 cosmetic products of which the composition is known in FDA's Voluntary Cosmetic Registration Program (VCRP) (data obtained from FDA, May 2017). Lanolin (derivatives) were present in 11 (20%) of 54 personal hygiene wet wipes for which ingredient information was obtained online and from retail stores, USA, 2016 (94). Of 179 emollients available in Poland in 2014, 25 (14.0%) contained lanolin alcohol (32).

Other information
Of 50 patients with a weak-positive (+) reaction to lanolin alcohol 30% pet., 8 (16%) had a positive ROAT with a lanolin alcohol-containing skin care product (concentration not mentioned). As 42 were negative, the authors concluded that patients with a weak positive reaction can safely use products containing lanolin alcohol, when applied to non-eczematous skin. However, the ROAT was performed for only one week, which is too short according to current knowledge and apart from that, one in every 6 patients was positive to the ROAT (29).

OTHER SIDE EFFECTS

Immediate-type reactions
In a group of 664 patch tested patients, there were 6 (0.9%) immediate contact reactions to lanolin alcohol as shown by 'well distinguished erythema' after 30 minutes (81). A woman had to give up her profession as a hairdresser because of urticarial skin eruptions following contact with substances used during working. An 'open patch test' after 30 minutes showed urticarial reactions to permanent wave solution, fixation solution, *p*-aminodiphenylamine, lanolin alcohol and clioquinol. The relevance of the reaction to lanolin alcohol is unknown (article not read) (107).

Other non-eczematous contact reactions

In (somewhat) older literature, lanolin alcohol has been suspected of being comedogenic in 'people with more sensitive complexions or acne-prone problems', based on rabbit ear assays (90).

LITERATURE

1   Uter W, Aberer W, Armario-Hita JC , Fernandez-Vozmediano JM, Ayala F, Balato A, et al. Current patch test results with the European baseline series and extensions to it from the 'European Surveillance System on Contact Allergy' network, 2007-2008. Contact Dermatitis 2012;67:9-19

2   Travassos AR, Claes L, Boey L, Drieghe J, Goossens A. Non-fragrance allergens in specific cosmetic products. Contact Dermatitis 2011;65:276-285

3   Wetter DA, Yiannias JA, Prakash AV, Davis MD, Farmer SA, el-Azhary RA, et al. Results of patch testing to personal care product allergens in a standard series and a supplemental cosmetic series: an analysis of 945 patients from the Mayo Clinic Contact Dermatitis Group, 2000-2007. J Am Acad Dermatol 2010;63:789-798

4   Adams RM, Maibach HI, Clendenning WE, Fisher AA, Jordan WJ, Kanof N, et al. A five-year study of cosmetic reactions. J Am Acad Dermatol 1985;13:1062-1069

5   Davis MD, Scalf LA, Yiannias JA, Cheng JF, El-Azhary RA, Rohlinger AL, et al. Changing trends and allergens in the patch test standard series. Arch Dermatol 2008;144:67-72

6   Warshaw EM, Buchholz HJ, Belsito DV et al. Allergic patch test reactions associated with cosmetics: Retrospective analysis of cross-sectional data from the North American Contact Dermatitis Group, 2001-2004. J Am Acad Dermatol 2009;60:23-38

7   Kohl L, Blondeel A, Song M. Allergic contact dermatitis from cosmetics: retrospective analysis of 819 patch-tested patients. Dermatology 2002;204:334-337

8   ESSCA Writing Group. The European Surveillance System of Contact Allergies (ESSCA): results of patch testing the standard series, 2004. J Eur Acad Dermatol Venereol 2008;22:174-181

9   Uter W, Amario-Hita JC, Balato A, Ballmer-Weber B, Bauer A, Belloni Fortina A, et al. European Surveillance System on Contact Allergies (ESSCA): results with the European baseline series, 2013/14. J Eur Acad Dermatol Venereol 2017 Jun 19. doi: 10.1111/jdv.14423. [Epub ahead of print]

10 Fregert S, Dahlquist I, Trulsson L. An attempt to isolate and identify allergens in lanolin. Contact Dermatitis 1984;10:16-19

11 Kligman AM. The myth of lanolin allergy. Contact Dermatitis 1998;39:103-107

12 Wakelin SH, Smith H, White IR, Rycroft RJ, McFadden JP. A retrospective analysis of contact allergy to lanolin. Br J Dermatol 2001;145:28-31

13 Wolf R. The lanolin paradox. Dermatology 1996;192:198-202

14 Zug KA, Warshaw EM, Fowler JF Jr, Maibach HI, Belsito DL, Pratt MD, et al. Patch-test results of the North American Contact Dermatitis Group 2005-2006. Dermatitis 2009;20:149-160

15 Fellinger C, Hemmer W, Wantke F, Wöhrl S, Jarisch R. Severe allergic dermatitis caused by lanolin alcohol as part of an ointment base in propolis cream. Contact Dermatitis 2013;68:59-61

16 Brasch J, Becker D, Aberer W, Bircher A, Kränke B, Denzer-Fürst S, et al. Contact Dermatitis. J Dtsch Dermatol Ges 2007;5:943-951

17 Barbaud A, Collet E, Le Coz CJ, Meaume S, Gillois P. Contact allergy in chronic leg ulcers: results of a multicentre study carried out in 423 patients and proposal for an updated series of patch test. Contact Dermatitis 2009;60:279-287

18 Fransway AF, Zug KA, Belsito DV, Deleo VA, Fowler JF Jr, Maibach HI, et al. North American Contact Dermatitis Group patch test results for 2007-2008. Dermatitis 2013;24:10-21

19 Warshaw EM, Belsito DV, DeLeo VA, Fowler JF Jr, Maibach HI, Marks JG, et al. North American Contact Dermatitis Group patch-test results, 2003-2004 study period. Dermatitis 2008;19:129-136

20 Carmichael AJ, Foulds IS, Bransbury DS. Loss of lanolin patch-test positivity. Br J Dermatol 1991;125:573-576

21 Cressey BD, Kumar N, Scheinman PL. Contact allergy to sorbitans: A follow-up study. Dermatitis 2012;23:158-161

22 Warshaw EM, Belsito DV, Taylor JS, Sasseville D, DeKoven JG, Zirwas MJ, et al. North American Contact Dermatitis Group patch test results: 2009 to 2010. Dermatitis 2013;24:50-59

23 Janach M, Kühne A, Seifert B, French LE, Ballmer-Weber B, Hofbauer GFL. Changing delayed-type sensitizations to the baseline series allergens over a decade at the Zurich University Hospital. Contact Dermatitis 2010;63:42-48

24 Landeck L, John SM, Geier J. Periorbital dermatitis in 4779 patients – patch test results during a 10-year period. Contact Dermatitis 2014;70:205-212

25 Kulozik M, Powell SM, Cherry G, Ryan T J. Contact sensitivity in community-based leg ulcer patients. Clin Exp Dermatol 1988;13:82-84

26 Cronin E. Lanolin dermatitis. Br J Dermatol 1966;78:167-174

27 Nguyen JC, Chesnut G, James WD, Saruk M. Allergic contact dermatitis caused by lanolin (wool) alcohol contained in an emollient in three postsurgical patients. J Am Acad Dermatol 2010;62:1064-1065

28 Vollum DI. Sensitivity to hydrogenated lanolin. Arch Dermatol 1969;100:774

29 Trummer, M, Aberer W and Kränke B. Clinical relevance of + patch test reactions to lanolin alcohol. Contact Dermatitis 2002;46:118

30 Matthieu L, Dockx P. Discrepancy in patch test results with wool wax alcohols and Amerchol® L-101. Contact Dermatitis 1997;36:150-151

31 Jacob SE, Hsu JW. Reactions to Aquaphor: is bisabolol the culprit? Pediatr Dermatol 2010;27:103-104

32 Osinka K, Karczmarz A, Krauze A, Feleszko W. Contact allergens in cosmetics used in atopic dermatitis: analysis of product composition. Contact Dermatitis 2016;75:241-243

33 Clayton TH, Wilkinson SM, Rawcliffe C, Pollock B, Clark SM. Allergic contact dermatitis in children: should pattern of dermatitis determine referral? A retrospective study of 500 children tested between 1995 and 2004 in one U.K. centre. Br J Dermatol 2006;154:114-117

34 Jacob SE, Matiz C, Herro EM. Compositae-associated allergic contact dermatitis from bisabolol. Dermatitis 2011;22:102-105

35 Edman B, Möller H. Testing a purified lanolin preparation by a randomized procedure. Contact Dermatitis 1989;20:287-290

36 Van Ketel, WG. Allergy to cetylalcohol. Contact Dermatitis 1984;11:125-126

37 Van Ketel, WG, Wemer J. Allergy to lanolin and "lanolin-free" creams. Contact Dermatitis 1983;9:420

38 Giorgini S, Melli MC, Sertoli A. Comments on the allergenic activity of lanolin. Contact Dermatitis 1983;9:425-426

39 Calnan CD. Lanolin in protective metal coatings. Contact Dermatitis 1979;5:267-268

40 Mortensen T. Allergy to lanolin. Contact Dermatitis 1979;5:137-139

41 Warshaw EM, Nelsen DD, Maibach HI, Marks JG Jr, Zug KA, Taylor JS, et al. Positive patch test reactions to lanolin: cross-sectional data from the North American Contact Dermatitis Group, 1994 to 2006. Dermatitis 2009;20:79-88

42 Strauss RM, Orton DI. Allergic contact cheilitis in the United Kingdom: a retrospective study. Am J Contact Dermat 2003;14:75-77

43 Pratt MD, Belsito DV, DeLeo VA, Fowler JF Jr, Fransway AF, Maibach HI, et al. North American Contact Dermatitis Group patch-test results, 2001–2002 study period. Dermatitis 2004;15:176-183

44 Marks JG Jr, Belsito DV, DeLeo VA, Fowler JF Jr, Fransway AF, Maibach HI, et al. North American Contact Dermatitis Group patch-test results, 1998–2000. Am J Contact Dermat 2003;14:59-62

45 Wetter DA, Davis MDP, Yiannias JA, Cheng JF, Connolly SM, el-Azhary RA, et al. Patch test results from the Mayo Contact Dermatitis Group, 1998–2000. J Am Acad Dermatol 2005;53:416-421

46 Britton JE, Wilkinson SM, English JSC, Gawkrodger DJ, Ormerod AD, Sansom JE, et al. The British standard series of contact dermatitis allergens: validation in clinical practice and value for clinical governance. Br J Dermatol 2003;148:259-264

47 Hasan T, Rantanen T, Alanko K, Harvima RJ, Jolanki R, Kalimo K, et al. Patch test reactions to cosmetic allergens in 1995–1997 and 2000–2002 in Finland –a multicentre study. Contact Dermatitis 2005;53:40-45

48 Lazarov A. European Standard Series patch test results from a contact dermatitis clinic in Israel during the 7-year period from 1998 to 2004. Contact Dermatitis 2006;55:73-76

49 Akyol A, Boyvat A, Peksari Y, Gurgey E. Contact sensitivity to standard series allergens in 1038 patients with contact dermatitis in Turkey. Contact Dermatitis 2005;52:333-337

50 Uter W, Hegewald J, Aberer W, Ayala F, Bircher AJ, Brasch J, et al. The European standard series in 9 European countries, 2002/2003 –First results of the European Surveillance System on Contact Allergies. Contact Dermatitis 2005;53:136-145

51 Machovcova A, Dastychova E, Kostalova D, et al. Common contact sensitizers in the Czech Republic. Patch test results in 12,058 patients with suspected contact dermatitis. Contact Dermatitis 2005;53:162-166

52 Bruynzeel DP, Diepgen TL, Andersen KE, Brandão FM, Bruze M, Frosch PJ, et al (EECDRG). Monitoring the European Standard Series in 10 centres 1996–2000. Contact Dermatitis 2005;53:146-152

53 Amin KA, Belsito DV. The aetiology of eyelid dermatitis: a 10-year retrospective analysis. Contact Dermatitis 2006;55:280-285

54 Wilson CC, Cameron J, Powell SM, Cherry G, Ryan TJ. High incidence of contact dermatitis in leg ulcer patients – implications for management. Clin Exp Dermatol 1991;16:250-253

55 Goossens A. Cosmetic contact allergens. Cosmetics 2016, 3, 5; doi:10.3390/cosmetics3010005

56 Wentworth AB, Yiannias JA, Keeling JH, Hall MR, Camilleri MJ, Drage LA, et al. Trends in patch-test results and allergen changes in the standard series: a Mayo Clinic 5-year retrospective review (January 1, 2006, to December 31, 2010). J Am Acad Dermatol 2014;70:269-275

57 Zug KA, Kornik R, Belsito DV, DeLeo VA, Fowler JF Jr, Maibach HI, et al. Patch-testing North American lip dermatitis patients: Data from the North American Contact Dermatitis Group, 2001 to 2004. Dermatitis 2008;19:202-208

58 Leysen J, Goossens A, Lambert J, Aerts O. Polyhexamethylene biguanide is a relevant sensitizer in wet wipes. Contact Dermatitis 2014: 70: 323-325

59 Freeman S, Stephens R. Cheilitis: Analysis of 75 cases referred to a contact dermatitis clinic. Am J Cont Dermat 1999;10:198-200

60 Katz AS, Sherertz EF. Facial dermatitis: Patch test results and final diagnoses. Am J Cont Dermat 1999;10:153-156

61 Thyssen JP, Uter W, Schnuch A, Linneberg A, Johansen JD. 10-year prevalence of contact allergy in the general population in Denmark estimated through the CE-DUR method. Contact Dermatitis 2007;57:265-272

62 Schnuch A, Uter W, Geier J, Gefeller O (for the IVDK study group). Epidemiology of contact allergy: an estimation of morbidity employing the clinical epidemiology and drug-utilization research (CE-DUR) approach. Contact Dermatitis 2002;47:32-39

63 Diepgen TL, Ofenloch RF, Bruze M, Bertuccio P, Cazzaniga S, Coenraads P-J, et al. Prevalence of contact allergy in the general population in different European regions. Br J Dermatol 2016;174:319-329

64 Mortz CG, Bindslev-Jensen C, Andersen KE. Prevalence, incidence rates and persistence of contact allergy and allergic contact dermatitis in The Odense Adolescence Cohort Study: a 15-year follow-up. Brit J Dermatol 2013;168:318-325

65 Thyssen JP, Linneberg A, Menné T, Nielsen NH, Johansen JD. Contact allergy to allergens of the TRUE-test (panels 1 and 2) has decreased modestly in the general population. Br J Dermatol 2009;161:1124-1129

66 Nielsen SH, Menné T. Allergic contact sensitization in an unselected Danish population. The Glostrup Allergy Study, Denmark. Acta Derm Venereol 1992;72:456-460

67 Dotterud LK, Smith-Sivertsen T. Allergic contact sensitization in the general adult population: a population-based study from Northern Norway. Contact Dermatitis 2007;56:10-15

68 Nielsen NH, Linneberg A, Menné T, Madsen F, Frølund L, Dirksen A, et al. Allergic contact sensitization in an adult Danish population: two cross-sectional surveys eight years apart (the Copenhagen Allergy Study). Acta Derm Venereol 2001;81:31-34

69 Mortz CG, Lauritsen JM, Bindslev-Jensen C, Andersen KE. Contact allergy and allergic contact dermatitis in adolescents: prevalence measures and associations. Acta Derm Venereol 2002;82:352-358

70 Schäfer T, Böhler E, Ruhdorfer S, Weigl L, Wessner D, Filipiak B, et al. Epidemiology of contact allergy in adults. Allergy 2001;56:1192-1196

71 Mortz CG, Lauritsen JM, Bindslev-Jensen C, Andersen KE. Prevalence of atopic dermatitis, asthma, allergic rhinitis, and hand and contact dermatitis in adolescents. The Odense Adolescence Cohort Study on Atopic Diseases and Dermatitis. Br J Dermatol 2001;144:523-532

72 Uter W, Ludwig A, Balda BR, Schnuch A, Pfahlberg A, Schäfer T, Wichmann HE, Ring J. The prevalence of contact allergy differed between population-based data and clinic–based data. J Clin Epidemiol 2004;57:627-632

73 Belloni Fortina A, Fontana E, Peserico A. Contact sensitization in children: A retrospective study of 2,614 children from a single center. Pediatr Dermatol 2016;33:399-404

74 De Groot AC, Bruynzeel DP, Bos JD, van der Meeren HL, van Joost T, Jagtman BA, Weyland JW. The allergens in cosmetics. Arch Dermatol 1988;124:1525-1529

75 De Groot AC. Adverse reactions to cosmetics. PhD Thesis, University of Groningen, The Netherlands: 1988, chapter 3.4, pp.105-113

76 Schulze-Dirks A, Frosch PJ. Contact allergy to dexpanthenol. Hautarzt 1988;39:375-377 (Article in German)

77 De Groot AC. Contact allergy to cosmetics: Causative ingredients. Contact Dermatitis 1987;17:26-34

78 Schorr WF. Lip gloss and gloss type cosmetics. Cont Derm Newsletter 1973;14:408-409

79 Zoli V, Silvani S, Vincenzi C, Tosti A. Allergic contact cheilitis. Contact Dermatitis 2006;54:296-297

80 Herbst RA, Uter W, Pirker C, Geier J, Frosch PJ. Allergic and non-allergic periorbital dermatitis: patch test results of the Information Network of the Departments of Dermatology during a 5-year period. Contact Dermatitis 2004;51:13-19

81 Katsarou A, Armenaka M, Ale I, Koufou V, Kalogeromitros, D. Frequency of immediate reactions to the European standard series. Contact Dermatitis 1999;41:276-279

82 Bojs G, Bruze M, Svensson Å. Contact allergy to the lanolin derivative Amerchol CAB. Am J Cont Derm 1992;3:83-85

83 Toholka R, Wang Y-S, Tate B, Tam M, Cahill J, Palmer A, Nixon R. The first Australian Baseline Series: Recommendations for patch testing in suspected contact dermatitis. Australas J Dermatol 2015;56:107-115

84 Zaragoza-Ninet V, Blasco Encinas R, Vilata-Corell JJ, Pérez-Ferriols A, Sierra-Talamantes C, Esteve-Martínez A, de la Cuadra-Oyanguren J. Allergic contact dermatitis due to cosmetics: A clinical and epidemiological study in a tertiary hospital. Actas Dermosifiliogr 2016;107:329-336

85   Dinkloh A, Worm M, Geier J, Schnuch A, Wollenberg A. Contact sensitization in patients with suspected cosmetic intolerance: results of the IVDK 2006-2011. J Eur Acad Dermatol Venereol 2015;29:1071-1081

86   Uter W, Spiewak R, Cooper SM, Wilkinson M, Sánchez Pérez J, Schnuch A, Schuttelaar M-L. Contact allergy to ingredients of topical medications: results of the European Surveillance System on Contact Allergies (ESSCA), 2009-2012. Pharmacoepidemiol Drug Saf 2016;25:1305-1312

87   Schwensen JF, Johansen JD, Veien NK, Funding AT, Avnstorp C, Østerballe M, et al. Occupational contact dermatitis in hairdressers: an analysis of patch test data from the Danish Contact Dermatitis Group, 2002–2011. Contact Dermatitis 2014;70:233-237

88   Uter W, Gefeller O, John SM, Schnuch A, Geier J. Contact allergy to ingredients of hair cosmetics – a comparison of female hairdressers and clients based on IVDK 2007–2012 data. Contact Dermatitis 2014;71:13-20

89   Schena D, Fantuzzi F, Girolomoni G. Contact allergy in chronic eczematous lip dermatitis. Eur J Dermatol 2008;18:688-692

90   Fulton JE Jr, Pay SR, Fulton JE 3rd. Comedogenicity of current therapeutic products, cosmetics, and ingredients in the rabbit ear. J Am Acad Dermatol 1984;10:96-105

91   Jankićević J, Vesić S, Vukićević J, Gajić M, Adamic M, Pavlović MD. Contact sensitivity in patients with venous leg ulcers in Serbia: comparison with contact dermatitis patients and relationship to ulcer duration. Contact Dermatitis 2008;58:32-36

92   Lubbes S, Rustemeyer T, Sillevis Smitt JH, Schuttelaar ML, Middelkamp-Hup MA. Contact sensitization in Dutch children and adolescents with and without atopic dermatitis - a retrospective analysis. Contact Dermatitis 2017;76:151-159

93   Erfurt-Berge C, Geier J, Mahler V. The current spectrum of contact sensitization in patients with chronic leg ulcers or stasis dermatitis - new data from the Information Network of Departments of Dermatology (IVDK). Contact Dermatitis 2017;77:151-158

94   Aschenbeck KA, Warshaw EM. Allergenic ingredients in personal hygiene wet wipes. Dermatitis 2017 Mar 23. doi: 10.1097/DER.0000000000000275. [Epub ahead of print]

95   Saap L, Fahim S, Arsenault E, Pratt M, Pierscianowski T, Falanga V, Pedvis-Leftick A. Contact sensitivity in patients with leg ulcerations: a North American study. Arch Dermatol 2004;140:1241-1246

96   Goldenberg A, Mousdicas N, Silverberg N, Powell D, Pelletier JL, Silverberg JI, et al. Pediatric Contact Dermatitis Registry inaugural case data. Dermatitis 2016;27:293-302

97   Kligman AM. Lanolin allergy: crisis or comedy. Contact Dermatitis 1983;9:99-107

98   Oleffe JA, Blondeel A, Boschmans S. Patch testing with lanolin. Contact Dermatitis 1978;4:233-234

99   Miest RY, Yiannias JA, Chang Y-HH, Singh NRN. Diagnosis and prevalence of lanolin allergy. Dermatitis 2013;24:119-123

100 DeKoven JG, Warshaw EM, Belsito DV, Sasseville D, Maibach HI, Taylor JS, et al. North American Contact Dermatitis Group Patch Test Results: 2013-2014. Dermatitis 2017;28:33-46

101 Warshaw EM, Maibach HI, Taylor JS, Sasseville D, DeKoven JG, Zirwas MJ, et al. North American Contact Dermatitis Group patch test results: 2011-2012. Dermatitis 2015;26:49-59

102 Lee B, Warshaw E. Lanolin allergy: History, epidemiology, responsible allergens, and management. Dermatitis 2008;19:63-72

103 Edman B, Moller H. Testing a purified lanolin preparation by a randomized procedure. Contact Dermatitis 1989;20:287-290

104 Brasch J, Henseler T, Aberer W, Bäuerle G, Frosch PJ, Fuchs T, et al. Reproducibility of patch tests: a multicenter study of synchronous left-versus right-sided patch tests by the German Contact Dermatitis Research Group. J Am Acad Dermatol 1994;31:584-591

105 Higgins CL, Nixon RL. Periorbital allergic contact dermatitis caused by lanolin in a lubricating eye ointment. Australas J Dermatol 2016;57:68-69

106 Tan BB, Noble AL, Roberts ME, Lear JT, English JS. Allergic contact dermatitis from oleyl alcohol in lipstick cross-reacting with ricinoleic acid in castor oil and lanolin. Contact Dermatitis 1997;37:41-42

107 Von Liebe V, Karge HJ, Burg G. Contact urticaria. Hautarzt 1979;30:544-546 (article in German)

2.263   LANOLIN ALCOHOL (AND) PARAFFINUM LIQUIDUM

IDENTIFICATION

Description/definition   : Lanolin alcohol (and) paraffinum liquidum is a product containing lanolin alcohols obtained from hydrolysis of lanolin and paraffinum liquidum. It is often used for patch testing, as it is said to identify contact allergy to lanolin alcohol better than lanolin alcohol itself (9,34)

INCI name USA   : Neither in CosIng nor in the Personal Care Products Council Ingredient Database
Other name(s)   : Amerchol® L 101
CAS registry number (s)   : 8029-05-8
Patch testing   : 50% pet. (Chemotechnique, SmartPracticeEurope, SmartPracticeCanada); this concentration may cause irritant reactions

GENERAL

Amerchol® L 101 may be used in cosmetics, pharmaceuticals, topical drugs, furniture polish, leather, metal corrosion prevention products, paper, inks, textiles, furs, cutting oils, and waxes (www.smartpracticecanada.com and several other patch test materials providers' websites). It should be appreciated that lanolin alcohol (and) paraffinum liquidum is mentioned neither in the EU nor in the USA INCI system (which in itself does not mean that it may not be used in cosmetics in the EU). Also, the material cannot be found in the EWG's Skin Deep Cosmetics Database, USA (http://www.ewg.org/skindeep/) and was (probably, as the name could not be found in their 9-digits numbers list of cosmetic ingredients) not present in any of the 56,714 cosmetics on file with FDA in the voluntary cosmetic registration program in April 2017.

In addition, in not one single case report of cosmetic allergy (allegedly) caused by Amerchol® L 101, was the presence of lanolin alcohol (and) paraffinum liquidum confirmed by the manufacturer and tested in the patient (with the possible exception of ref. 4). From these data, it seems doubtful that Amerchol® L 101 / lanolin alcohol (and) paraffinum liquidum is actually used in cosmetics, or at least to a considerable extent.

Patch testing with Amerchol® L 101 yields (far) higher rates of sensitization than testing with lanolin alcohol. In a number of studies (table 2.263.1, table 2.263.2), the preparation has been tested pure. It should be realized that very few individuals reacting to the 100% preparation also react to Amerchol® L 101 50% in pet. (the concentration in the current commercial patch test materials) (9). This, together with unlikely high prevalences of sensitization of up to 16% in routine testing (9) and very limited co-reactivity to lanolin alcohol in the baseline series, suggests that the undiluted preparation has irritant properties in patch testing. However, the commercial 50% preparation may also be a marginal irritant and cause false-positive reactions.

See also Chapter 2.264 Lanolin alcohol and Chapter 2.334 Paraffinum liquidum.

CONTACT ALLERGY

Patch testing in groups of patients

Results of routine patch testing (testing in consecutive patients suspected of contact dermatitis) with Amerchol® L 101 are shown in table 2.263.1. Results of testing in groups of *selected* patients (e.g., patients with leg ulcers, patients with periorbital dermatitis, patients suspected of contact allergy to topical preparations) are shown in table 2.263.2.

Patch testing in consecutive patients suspected of contact dermatitis: routine testing

Amerchol® L 101 is currently included in the screening tray of the North American Contact Dermatitis Group (NACDG) but not in the European baseline series. In routine testing with Amerchol® L 101 50% pet., rates of positive patch tests ranging from 0.7% to 7.6% have been observed. In only a few studies was relevance mentioned. In two NACDG studies, 42% and 46% of the reactions were of 'definite' or 'probable' relevance (8,27). In an Australian study, only 18% of the reactions were considered to be relevant (25). Causative products were not mentioned in any study.

Patch testing in groups of selected patients

Data on patch testing with Amerchol® L 101 in groups of selected patients (e.g., patients with leg ulcers, patients with periorbital dermatitis, patients suspected of contact allergy to topical preparations or suspected of cosmetic allergy) are summarized in table 2.263.2. In studies where patients were patch tested with the 50% pet. substance, frequencies of sensitization ranged from 0.9% to 19.6%. The highest frequencies were – as expected – in groups of patients with leg ulcers (16,19,32), who quite frequently become sensitized to lanolin alcohol. The sensitization rate was also high in children in a Dutch study (8.8%), notably in atopic children (33). Relevance was rarely mentioned. In

Table 2.263.1 Patch testing in groups of patients: Routine testing

Years and Country	Test conc. & vehicle	Number of patients tested	positive (%)	Selection of patients (S); Relevance (R); Comments (C)	Ref.
2015 Italy	50% pet.	310	11 (3.5%)	R: not stated	26
2013-14 USA, Canada	50% pet.	4859	260 (5.4%)	R: definite + probable relevance: 42%	27
2011-12 USA, Canada	50% pet.	4235	194 (4.6%)	R: definite + probable relevance: 46%	8
2008-2010 USA	50% pet.	591	31 (5.2%)	R: not stated; C: significant association with lanolin alcohols and with sorbitan sesquioleate	5
2001-2010 Australia	50% pet.	4794	219 (4.6%)	R: 18%	25
2009 Sweden	50% pet.	3112	(0.7%)	R: not stated	16
2003-2005 China		599	18 (3.9%)	R: not stated	17
1999-2001 Sweden	50% pet.	3790	(1.1%)	R: not stated; C: prevalence in women 1.6 %, in men 0.8% (standardized prevalences)	13
1998-1999 Belgium	50% pet.	819	62 (7.6%)	R: not specified, ascribed (partly?) to topical medicaments and cosmetics	2
1991-1993 Sweden	50% pet.	3680	(2.9%)	R: not stated; C: prevalence in women 4.6%, in men 2.7% (standardized prevalences)	13
1991-1992 Belgium	100%	393	56 (16.3%)	R: not stated	9
	50% pet.	223	6 (2.7%)		
<1983 Sweden	pure	2980	75 (2.5%)	R: not stated; C: the authors suggested that some reactions may have been irritant	10

a group of 7 patients with positive reactions, 2 were caused by cosmetics and 3 by topical medicaments (21). In a USA study, 96% of 26 positive patch tests were scored as relevant, but these included 'questionable' and 'past' relevance' (1). In two studies, 2/3 (3) to all (21) patch test positive patients also reacted to lanolin alcohol.

Table 2.263.2 Patch testing in groups of patients: Selected patient groups

Years and Country	Test conc. & vehicle	Number of patients tested	positive (%)	Selection of patients (S); Relevance (R); Comments (C)	Ref.
2003-2014 IVDK	50% pet.	4756	(9.7%)	S: patients with stasis dermatitis/ chronic leg ulcers; R: not stated	32
1996-2013 Netherlands	50% pet.	339	30 (8.8%)	S: children aged 0-17 years; R: not stated; C: higher prevalence in atopic than in non-atopic children	33
2003-2012 IVDK	50% pet.	1728	47 (2.7%)	S: nurses with occupational contact dermatitis; R: not stated	7
2006-2011 IVDK	50% pet.	7716	(4.1%)	S: patients suspected of cosmetic intolerance and tested with an ointment base series; R: not stated	29
2006-2010 USA	50% pet.	100	3 (3%)	S: patients with eyelid dermatitis; R: not stated	6
2004-2008 France	50% pet.	423	83 (19.6%)	S: patients with leg ulcers; R: not stated	15
2002-2008 UK	pure	110	7 (6.4%)	S: children 2-18 years old; R: all reactions were relevant; C: testing pure induces irritant reactions; there were few (not specified but certainly <3) reactions to lanolin alcohol	31
2000-2007 USA	50% pet.	935	26 (2.8%)	S: patients tested with a supplemental cosmetic screening series; R: 96%; C: weak study: a. high rate of macular erythema and weak reactions; b. relevance figures included 'questionable' and 'past' relevance	1
1993-2003 IVDK	50% pet.	735	16 (2.2%)	S: patients with scalp dermatitis; R: not stated	18
2000-2002 Finland		3446	(1.6%)	S: patients tested with a cosmetic series; R: not stated	14
1995-1999 IVDK	50% pet.	724	(4.0%)	S: patients with allergic periorbital contact dermatitis; R: not stated	22
1995-1996 Finland		1195	(2.8%)	S: patients tested with a cosmetic series; R: not stated	14
1982-1996 UK	50% pet. or 100%	2227	133 (6.0%)	S: patients tested with a 'medicament series'; R: 71% current relevance; C: 91/133 allergic patients (68%) also reacted to lanolin alcohols 30% pet.	3
<1990 India	pure	69	12 (19%)	S: patients with features suggestive of allergic contact dermatitis and histories of prolonged use of numerous topical preparations, or of exacerbation or spread of dermatitis following the use of such preparations; R: not stated	30
1988-1989 UK		81	12 (15%)	S: patients with leg ulcers; R: not specified	19
1986-1989 Italy	50% pet.	737	7 (0.9%)	S: patients with contact dermatitis apparently related to the use of topical preparations; R: 7 reactions were relevant, of which 2 from cosmetics and 3 from topical medicaments; C: all 7 positive patients co-reacted to lanolin alcohol	21

IVDK: Information Network of Departments of Dermatology, Germany, Austria, Switzerland

Case reports and case series

Amerchol® L 101 was stated to be the (or an) allergen in 14 patients in a group of 603 individuals suffering from cosmetic dermatitis, seen in the period 2010-2015 in Leuven, Belgium (20). In the period 1996-2013, in a tertiary referral center in Valencia, Spain, 5419 patients were patch tested. Of these, 628 individuals had allergic contact dermatitis to cosmetics. Amerchol® L 101 was the responsible allergen in 6 cases (28). In a group of 146 patients patch tested for cheilitis in Amersham, UK, between 1982 and 2001, there were two positive patch test reactions to Amerchol® L 101 considered to be relevant for the lip dermatitis. Over half of the reactions in the entire group were ascribed to lipsticks and lip salves (12). One case of contact allergy to Amerchol® L 101 in an atopic child from its presence in an emollient has been presented (4). Two patients had positive patch test reactions to moisturizers and to Amerchol® L 101, which reactions were considered to be relevant (23).

Cross-reactions, pseudo-cross-reactions and co-reactions

Pseudo-cross-reactions to lanolin alcohol (3,5,9,21). Almost all patients reacting to lanolin alcohol co-react to Amerchol® L 101, but far fewer patients reacting to Amerchol® L 101 co-react to lanolin alcohol in the baseline series (9).

Presence in cosmetic products and chemical analyses

In the USA, in April 2017, lanolin alcohol (and) paraffinum liquidum was present in zero of 56,714 cosmetic products of which the composition is known in FDA's Voluntary Cosmetic Registration Program (VCRP) (data obtained from FDA, May 2017). In April 2017, lanolin alcohol (and) paraffinum liquidum was present in 0 of 66,647 cosmetic products of which the composition is known in EWG's Skin Deep Cosmetics Database, USA (http://www.ewg.org/skindeep/).

LITERATURE

1 Wetter DA, Yiannias JA, Prakash AV, Davis MD, Farmer SA, el-Azhary RA, et al. Results of patch testing to personal care product allergens in a standard series and a supplemental cosmetic series: an analysis of 945 patients from the Mayo Clinic Contact Dermatitis Group, 2000-2007. J Am Acad Dermatol 2010;63:789-798

2 Kohl L, Blondeel A, Song M. Allergic contact dermatitis from cosmetics: retrospective analysis of 819 patch-tested patients. Dermatology 2002;204:334-337

3 Wakelin SH, Smith H, White IR, Rycroft RJ, McFadden JP. A retrospective analysis of contact allergy to lanolin. Br J Dermatol 2001;145:28-31

4 Mailhol C, Lauwers-Cances V, Rancé F, Paul C, Giordano-Labadie F. Prevalence and risk factors for allergic contact dermatitis to topical treatment in atopic dermatitis: a study in 641 children. Allergy 2009:64:801-806

5 Cressey BD, Kumar N, Scheinman PL. Contact allergy to sorbitans: A follow-up study. Dermatitis 2012;23:158-161

6 Wenk KS, Ehrlich AE. Fragrance series testing in eyelid dermatitis. Dermatitis 2012;23:22-26

7 Molin S, Bauer A, Schnuch A, Geier J. Occupational contact allergy in nurses: results from the Information Network of Departments of Dermatology 2003–2012. Contact Dermatitis 2015;72:164-171

8 Warshaw EM, Maibach HI, Taylor JS, Sasseville D, DeKoven JG, Zirwas MJ, et al. North American Contact Dermatitis Group patch test results: 2011-2012. Dermatitis 2015;26:49-59

9 Matthieu L, Dockx P. Discrepancy in patch test results with wool wax alcohols and Amerchol® L-101. Contact Dermatitis 1997;36:150-151

10 Fregert S, Dahlquist I, Trulsson L. An attempt to isolate and identify allergens in lanolin. Contact Dermatitis 1984;10:16-19

11 Miest RY, Yiannias JA, Chang YH, Singh N. Diagnosis and prevalence of lanolin allergy. Dermatitis 2013;24:119-23

12 Strauss RM, Orton DI. Allergic contact cheilitis in the United Kingdom: a retrospective study. Am J Contact Dermat 2003;14:75-77

13 Lindberg M, Edman B, Fischer T, Stenberg B. Time trends in Swedish patch test data from 1992 to 2000. A multi-centre study based on age- and sex-adjusted results of the Swedish standard series. Contact Dermatitis 2007;56:205-210

14 Hasan T, Rantanen T, Alanko K, Harvima RJ, Jolanki R, Kalimo K, et al. Patch test reactions to cosmetic allergens in 1995–1997 and 2000–2002 in Finland –a multicentre study. Contact Dermatitis 2005;53:40-45

15 Barbaud A, Collet E, Le Coz CJ, Meaume S, Gillois P. Contact allergy in chronic leg ulcers: results of a multicentre study carried out in 423 patients and proposal for an updated series of patch tests. Contact Dermatitis 2009;60:279-287

16 Fall S, Bruze M, Isaksson M, Lidén C, Matura M, Stenberg B, Lindberg M. Contact allergy trends in Sweden – a retrospective comparison of patch test data from 1992, 2000, and 2009. Contact Dermatitis 2015;72:297-304

17 Li L-F, Liu G, Wang J. Patch test in Chinese patients with cosmetic allergic contact dermatitis to common cosmetic allergens from a European cosmetic series. Contact Dermatitis 2007;57:50-54

18 Hillen U, Grabbe S, Uter W. Patch test results in patients with scalp dermatitis: analysis of data of the Information Network of Departments of Dermatology. Contact Dermatitis 2007;56:87-93

19 Wilson CC, Cameron J, Powell SM, Cherry G, Ryan TJ. High incidence of contact dermatitis in leg ulcer patients – implications for management. Clin Exp Dermatol 1991;16:250-253

20 Goossens A. Cosmetic contact allergens. Cosmetics 2016, 3, 5; doi:10.3390/cosmetics3010005

21 Tosti A, Guerra L, Morelli R, Bardazzi F. Prevalence and sources of sensitization to emulsifiers: a clinical study. Contact Dermatitis 1990;23:68-72

22 Herbst RA, Uter W, Pirker C, Geier J, Frosch PJ. Allergic and non-allergic periorbital dermatitis: patch test results of the Information Network of the Departments of Dermatology during a 5-year period. Contact Dermatitis 2004;51:13-19

23 Held E, Johansen JD, Agner T, Menné T. Contact allergy to cosmetics: testing with patients' own products. Contact Dermatitis 1999;40:310-315

24 Bojs G, Bruze M, Svensson Å. Contact allergy to the lanolin derivative Amerchol CAB. Am J Cont Derm 1992;3:83-85

25 Toholka R, Wang Y-S, Tate B, Tam M, Cahill J, Palmer A, Nixon R. The first Australian Baseline Series: Recommendations for patch testing in suspected contact dermatitis. Australas J Dermatol 2015;56:107-115

26 Corazza M, Virgili A, Ricci M, Bianchi A, Borghi A. Contact sensitization to emulsifying agents: an underrated issue? Dermatitis 2016;27:276-281

27 DeKoven JG, Warshaw EM, Belsito DV, Sasseville D, Maibach HI, Taylor JS, et al. North American Contact Dermatitis Group Patch Test Results: 2013-2014. Dermatitis 2017;28:33-46

28 Zaragoza-Ninet V, Blasco Encinas R, Vilata-Corell JJ, Pérez-Ferriols A, Sierra-Talamantes C, Esteve-Martínez A, de la Cuadra-Oyanguren J. Allergic contact dermatitis due to cosmetics: A clinical and epidemiological study in a tertiary hospital. Actas Dermosifiliogr 2016;107:329-336

29 Dinkloh A, Worm M, Geier J, Schnuch A, Wollenberg A. Contact sensitization in patients with suspected cosmetic intolerance: results of the IVDK 2006-2011. J Eur Acad Dermatol Venereol 2015;29:1071-1081

30 George ND, Srinivas CR, Balachandran C, Shenoi SD. Sensitivity to various ingredients of topical preparations following prolonged use. Contact Dermatitis 1990;23:367-368

31 Moustafa M, Holden CR, Athavale P, Cork MJ, Messenger AG, Gawkrodger DJ. Patch testing is a useful investigation in children with eczema. Contact Dermatitis 2011;65:208-212

32 Erfurt-Berge C, Geier J, Mahler V. The current spectrum of contact sensitization in patients with chronic leg ulcers or stasis dermatitis - new data from the Information Network of Departments of Dermatology (IVDK). Contact Dermatitis 2017 Feb 14. doi: 10.1111/cod.12763. [Epub ahead of print]

33 Lubbes S, Rustemeyer T, Sillevis Smitt JH, Schuttelaar ML, Middelkamp-Hup MA. Contact sensitization in Dutch children and adolescents with and without atopic dermatitis - a retrospective analysis. Contact Dermatitis 2017;76:151-159

2.264   LANOLIN OIL

IDENTIFICATION

Description/definition   : Lanolin oil is the liquid fraction of lanolin
Chemical class(es)   : Lanolin and lanolin derivatives
CAS registry number (s)   : 70321-63-0; 8038-43-5
EC number(s)   : 274-559-6
CIR review(s)   : J Environ Pathol Toxicol 1980;4:63-92 (access: www.cir-safety.org/ingredients)
Merck Index monograph : 6679 (Lanolin)
Function(s) in cosmetics : EU: antistatic; binding; emollient; emulsifying; hair conditioning; solvent. USA: hair
                            conditioning agents; skin-conditioning agents - emollient
Patch testing   : 30% pet.; pure (4)

CONTACT ALLERGY

Patch testing in groups of patients
In the period 2009,2011, in the USA, 286 consecutive patients were patch tested with lanolin oil 30% pet. and there was one (0.3%) positive reaction; its relevance was 'questionable' (5).

Case reports and case series
Lanolin oil was responsible for 2 out of 399 cases of cosmetic allergy where the causal allergen was identified in a study of the NACDG, USA, 1977-1983 (1). In a group of 119 patients with allergic contact dermatitis from cosmetics, investigated in The Netherlands in 1986-1987, one case was caused by lanolin oil in a lipstick with UV-filter (2,3).

Presence in cosmetic products and chemical analyses
In the USA, in April 2017, lanolin oil was present in 500 of 56,714 cosmetic products of which the composition is known in FDA's Voluntary Cosmetic Registration Program (VCRP) (data obtained from FDA, May 2017). In March 2017, lanolin oil was present in 213 of 65,351 cosmetic products of which the composition is known in EWG's Skin Deep Cosmetics Database, USA (http://www.ewg.org/skindeep/).

LITERATURE

1   Adams RM, Maibach HI, Clendenning WE, Fisher AA, Jordan WJ, Kanof N, et al. A five-year study of cosmetic reactions. J Am Acad Dermatol 1985;13:1062-1069
2   De Groot AC, Bruynzeel DP, Bos JD, van der Meeren HL, van Joost T, Jagtman BA, Weyland JW. The allergens in cosmetics. Arch Dermatol 1988;124:1525-1529
3   De Groot AC. Adverse reactions to cosmetics. PhD Thesis, University of Groningen, The Netherlands: 1988, chapter 3.4, pp.105-113
4   De Groot AC. Patch Testing, 3rd Edition. Wapserveen, The Netherlands: acdegroot publishing, 2008 (ISBN 978-90-813233-1-4)
5   Miest RY, Yiannias JA, Chang Y-HH, Singh NRN. Diagnosis and prevalence of lanolin allergy. Dermatitis 2013;24:119-123

2.265 LAURAMIDE DEA

IDENTIFICATION

Description/definition	: Lauramide DEA is a mixture of ethanolamides of lauric acid. It conforms generally to the formula shown below
Chemical class(es)	: Alkanolamides
Chemical/IUPAC name	: *N,N*-bis*(2*-Hydroxyethyl)dodecanamide
Other names	: Lauric acid diethanolamide
CAS registry number (s)	: 120-40-1
EC number(s)	: 204-393-1
CIR review(s)	: J Am Coll Toxicol 1986;5:415-454; Int J Toxicol 2013;32(Suppl.1):36-58 (access: www.cir-safety.org/ingredients)
Function(s) in cosmetics	: EU: antistatic; foam boosting; surfactant; viscosity controlling. USA: surfactants – foam boosting; viscosity increasing agents - aqueous
EU cosmetic restrictions	: Regulated in Annex III/60 of the Regulation (EC) No. 1223/2009
Patch testing	: 1% pet.
Molecular formula	: $C_{16}H_{33}NO_3$

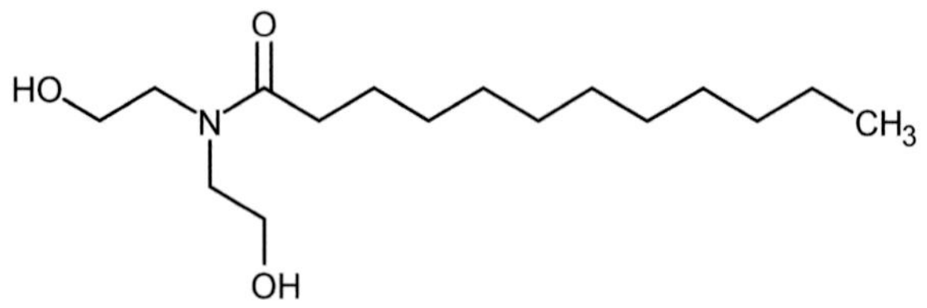

Case reports and case series

Eight positive patch test reactions to lauramide DEA were ascribed to cosmetic allergy (1); considering this large number in a small unselected patch test population (n=819), the test concentration, which was not mentioned, must certainly have been (mildly) irritant. In a group of 119 patients with allergic contact dermatitis from cosmetics, investigated in The Netherlands in 1986-1987, one case was caused by lauramide DEA in a shampoo (3,4, same patient as in ref. 2, described below).

A man noticed worsening of his scalp psoriasis and itching; in addition, a dermatitis developed on his eyelids. He suspected an anti-dandruff shampoo, which he had used for a year without ill-effects, of being the cause. Avoidance of the shampoo and topical corticosteroids cleared the itching and the dermatitis (and to a lesser extent also his psoriasis) within a week. The patient bought a different shampoo, but one day after using it for the first time, the symptoms returned. He was patch tested with the European Standard Series and the 2 shampoos; positive reactions were found to epoxy resin and both shampoos, tested 1% in water. Several months later, the patient was retested with the cosmetics and their individual ingredients. Shampoo no. 1 was positive, as was the ingredient cocamide DEA (0.5% pet). The second shampoo also elicited a positive patch test reaction, as did its ingredient, lauramide DEA 1% pet. Fifteen controls tested with lauramide DEA 1% pet. were negative (2).

Cross-reactions, pseudo-cross-reactions and co-reactions
Cocamide DEA (2).

Presence in cosmetic products and chemical analyses
In the USA, in April 2017, lauramide DEA was present in 251 of 56,714 cosmetic products of which the composition is known in FDA's Voluntary Cosmetic Registration Program (VCRP) (data obtained from FDA, May 2017). In March 2017, lauramide DEA was present in 51 of 65,351 cosmetic products of which the composition is known in EWG's Skin Deep Cosmetics Database, USA (http://www.ewg.org/skindeep/).

LITERATURE

1   Kohl L, Blondeel A, Song M. Allergic contact dermatitis from cosmetics: retrospective analysis of 819 patch-tested patients. Dermatology 2002;204:334-337
2   De Groot AC, de Wit FS, Bos JD, Weyland JW. Contact allergy to cocamide DEA and lauramide DEA in shampoos. Contact Dermatitis 1987;16:117-118
3   De Groot AC, Bruynzeel DP, Bos JD, van der Meeren HL, van Joost T, Jagtman BA, Weyland JW. The allergens in cosmetics. Arch Dermatol 1988;124:1525-1529
4   De Groot AC. Adverse reactions to cosmetics. PhD Thesis, University of Groningen, The Netherlands: 1988, chapter 3.4, pp.105-113

2.266 LAURAMINE OXIDE

IDENTIFICATION

Description/definition	: Lauramine oxide is the tertiary amine oxide that conforms generally to the formula shown below
Chemical class(es)	: Amine oxides
Chemical/IUPAC name	: *N,N*-Dimethyldodecan-1-amine oxide
Other names	: Dodecyldimethylamine oxide; lauryl dimethyl amine oxide; Ammonyx® LO
CAS registry number (s)	: 1643-20-5
EC number(s)	: 216-700-6
CIR review(s)	: J Am Coll Toxicol 1994;13:231-245 (access: www.cir-safety.org/ingredients)
Function(s) in cosmetics	: EU: antistatic; cleansing; foam boosting; hair conditioning; hydrotrope; perfuming; surfactant; viscosity controlling. USA: fragrance ingredients; hair conditioning agents; surfactants - cleansing agents; surfactants – foam boosters; surfactants - hydrotropes
Patch testing	: 1% water (2); 3.7% in water is mildly irritant (3,4)
Molecular formula	: $C_{14}H_{31}NO$

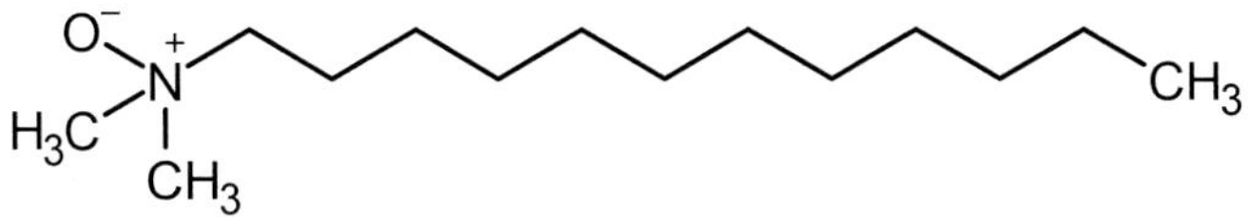

GENERAL

Lauramine oxide is a surface-active agent, often used to enhance the production of foam in industrial and household products, such as dishwashing liquids, and also in shampoos and bath foam preparations (2).

CONTACT ALLERGY

Case reports and case series

Lauramine oxide was responsible for 1 out of 959 cases of non-fragrance cosmetic allergy where the causal allergen was identified, Belgium, 2000-2010 (1).

Contact allergy to lauramine oxide in non-cosmetic products

Eight patients had allergic contact dermatitis from lauramine oxide in a surgical scrub (2). One patient (3) and two individuals (4) had allergic reactions to the same scrub. One of the latter two co-reacted to chlorhexidine, the active ingredient in the scrub (4).

Presence in cosmetic products and chemical analyses

In the USA, in April 2017, lauramine oxide was present in 128 of 56,714 cosmetic products of which the composition is known in FDA's Voluntary Cosmetic Registration Program (VCRP) (data obtained from FDA, May 2017). In March 2017, lauramine oxide was present in 16 of 65,351 cosmetic products of which the composition is known in EWG's Skin Deep Cosmetics Database, USA (http://www.ewg.org/skindeep/).

LITERATURE

1 Travassos AR, Claes L, Boey L, Drieghe J, Goossens A. Non-fragrance allergens in specific cosmetic products. Contact Dermatitis 2011;65:276-285
2 Dooms-Goossens A, Blockeel I. Allergic contact dermatitis and photoallergic contact dermatitis due to soaps and detergents. Clin Dermatol 1996;14: 67-76
3 Muston HL, Boss JM, Summerly R. Dermatitis from Ammonyx LO, a constituent of a surgical scrub. Contact Dermatitis 1977;3:347-348
4 Roberts DL, Summerly R, Byrne JPH. Contact dermatitis due to the constituents of Hibiscrub. Contact Dermatitis 1981;7:326-8

2.267   LAURETH-2

IDENTIFICATION

Description/definition	: Laureth-2 is the polyethylene glycol ether of lauryl alcohol that conforms to the formula shown below, where n has an average value of 2
Chemical class(es)	: Alkoxylated alcohols
Chemical/IUPAC name	: 2-[2-(Dodecyloxy)ethoxy]ethanol
Other names	: Diethylene glycol monododecyl ether; decyldiglycol; dodecyldiglycol; PEG-2 lauryl ether; polyethylene glycol 100 lauryl ether; polyoxyethylene (2) lauryl ether
CAS registry number (s)	: 3055-93-4; 9002-92-0; 68439-50-9
EC number(s)	: 221-279-7; 500-002-6; 500-213-3
CIR review(s)	: Int J Toxicol 2012;31(Suppl.2):169-244 (access: www.cir-safety.org/ingredients)
Function(s) in cosmetics	: EU: cleansing; emulsifying; surfactant. USA: surfactants - emulsifying agents
Patch testing	: No data available; suggested: 5-10% water
Molecular formula	: $CH_3(CH_2)_{11}(OCH_2CH_2)_nOH$

CONTACT ALLERGY

Case reports and case series

An atopic female patient was investigated for suspected hair dye allergy. In the past, she had dyed her hair with no adverse effects; however, 2 days after using a hair dye, she developed eczema of her scalp, face and neck, which subsequently spread to the rest of her body. The rash required treatment with oral prednisolone. A subsequent attempt at dying hair with a short contact treatment only resulted in a milder form of the same eczematous rash. The patient purchased a 'Dry Scalp Shampoo' as a milder alternative to regular shampoo. Less than 12 hr after using the shampoo, she developed an eczematous eruption over the scalp and extending down the neck to the abdomen. Later, the patient was patch tested with the British Contact Dermatitis Society (BCDS) standard, hairdressing, cosmetic and medicament series and personal products, which included perfume and the shampoo, diluted to 10% water. Positive reactions were observed to p-phenylenediamine, p-aminophenol and to the shampoo. The individual constituents of the shampoo were supplied by the manufacturer and tested in a similar method. The patient now reacted to polidocanol (laureth-9) 3% pet. on D4 and to another ingredient, laureth-2 (test concentration and vehicle not mentioned) (1).

Cross-reactions, pseudo-cross-reactions and co-reactions

Laureth-9 (polidocanol) (1).

Presence in cosmetic products and chemical analyses

n the USA, in April 2017, laureth-2 was present in 330 of 56,714 cosmetic products of which the composition is known in FDA's Voluntary Cosmetic Registration Program (VCRP) (data obtained from FDA, May 2017). In March 2017, laureth-2 was present in 56 of 65,351 cosmetic products of which the composition is known in EWG's Skin Deep Cosmetics Database, USA (http://www.ewg.org/skindeep/).

LITERATURE

1   Grills CE, Cooper SM. Polidocanol: a potential contact allergen in shampoo. Contact Dermatitis 2007;56:178

2.268 LAURETH-4

IDENTIFICATION

Description/definition	: Laureth-4 is the polyethylene glycol ether of lauryl alcohol. It conforms to the formula shown below, where n has an average value of 4
Chemical class(es)	: Alkoxylated alcohols
Chemical/IUPAC name	: 2-[2-[2-(2-Dodecoxyethoxy)ethoxy]ethoxy]ethanol
Other names	: 3,6,9,12-Tetraoxatetracosan-1-ol; dodecyltetraethylene glycol monoether; PEG-4 lauryl ether; polyethylene glycol 200 lauryl ether; polyoxyethylene (4) lauryl ether
CAS registry number (s)	: 5274-68-0; 9002-92-0; 68439-50-9
EC number(s)	: 226-097-1; 500-002-6; 500-213-3
CIR review(s)	: J Am Coll Toxicol 1983;2:1-15; Int J Toxicol 2012;31(Suppl.2):169-244 (access: www.cir-safety.org/ingredients)
Function(s) in cosmetics	: EU: antistatic; emulsifying; masking; surfactant. USA: surfactants – emulsifying agents
Patch testing	: 0.1% and 1% alc. (1)
Molecular formula	: $CH_3(CH_2)_{11}(OCH_2CH_2)_nOH$

CONTACT ALLERGY

Case reports and case series
In a 4-month-period in 1996, 475 patients with contact allergy to 'cosmetic ingredients' were collected in 5 centers in Belgium, UK and Germany. There was one reaction to laureth-4, but its relevance was not mentioned (2).

Contact allergy to laureth-4 in non-cosmetic products
A girl had eczematous lesions on her cheeks. For 2 months, she had treated a mild acne vulgaris of her face with an anti-acne stick and ointment. During this therapy, she had developed the eczematous lesions. The patient was patch tested with the ICDRG standard series and the two topical drugs. She had strong positive reactions to Amerchol ® L 101 and to the stick, but not to the ointment. Later, she was patch tested with the ingredients of the stick and she showed strongly positive patch test reactions to laureth-4 1% and 0.1% alc. Twenty controls tested with laureth-4 1% alc. were negative. Later, ten patients with strong positive reactions to Amerchol L ® 101 were tested with laureth-4 1%, 0.1% and 0.01% alc. Of these, one had strong reactions to laureth-4 1% and 0.1% alc. and a weak reaction to laureth-4 0.01% alc. This patient appeared not to use any skin preparations containing laureth-4 and the relationship to Amerchol sensitivity remained uncertain (1).

Presence in cosmetic products and chemical analyses
In the USA, in April 2017, laureth-4 was present in 768 of 56,714 cosmetic products of which the composition is known in FDA's Voluntary Cosmetic Registration Program (VCRP) (data obtained from FDA, May 2017). In March 2017, laureth-4 was present in 343 of 65,351 cosmetic products of which the composition is known in EWG's Skin Deep Cosmetics Database, USA (http://www.ewg.org/skindeep/).

OTHER SIDE EFFECTS

Other non-eczematous contact reactions
In (somewhat) older literature, laureth-4 has been suspected of being comedogenic in 'people with more sensitive complexions or acne-prone problems', based on rabbit ear assays (3).

LITERATURE
1   Svensson Å. Allergic contact dermatitis to laureth-4. Contact Dermatitis 1988;18:113-114
2   Goossens A, Beck MH, Haneke E, McFadden JP, Nolting S, Durupt G, Ries G. Adverse cutaneous reactions to cosmetic allergens. Contact Dermatitis 1999;40:112-113
3   Fulton JE Jr, Pay SR, Fulton JE 3rd. Comedogenicity of current therapeutic products, cosmetics, and ingredients in the rabbit ear. J Am Acad Dermatol 1984;10:96-105

2.269   LAURETH-7

IDENTIFICATION

Description/definition	: Laureth-7 is the polyethylene glycol ether of lauryl alcohol. It conforms to the formula shown below, where n has an average value of 7
Chemical class(es)	: Alkoxylated alcohols
Chemical/IUPAC name	: 2-[2-[2-[2-[2-[2-(2-Dodecoxyethoxy)ethoxy]ethoxy]ethoxy]ethoxy]ethoxy]ethanol
Other names	: 3,6,9,12,15,18,21-Heptaoxatritriacontanol; polyoxyethylene (7) lauryl ether; PEG-7 lauryl ether; polyethylene glycol (7) lauryl ether; dodecylheptaglycol
CAS registry number (s)	: 3055-97-8; 68439-50-9; 9002-92-0
EC number(s)	: 221-283-9; 500-213-3; 500-002-6
CIR review(s)	: Int J Toxicol 2012;31(Suppl.2):169-244 (access: www.cir-safety.org/ingredients)
Function(s) in cosmetics	: EU: emulsifying; surfactant. USA: surfactants - emulsifying agents
Patch testing	: 1% pet. (1)
Molecular formula	: $CH_3(CH_2)_{11}(OCH_2CH_2)_nOH$

CONTACT ALLERGY

Case reports and case series

A young woman was seen because of pruritic follicular papules on her face. She had started using 7 different cosmetics about 2 months previously. She began to notice papules and erythema on her face a few days before presentation. Almost all of the papules were follicular in location. The rash completely resolved 5 days after she stopped using the cosmetics and while being treated with a topical corticosteroid. Patch tests with the 7 cosmetic products revealed a positive reaction consisting of follicular papules to a liquid foundation at D3. Later, the 27 ingredients of this product were patch tested. Laureth-7 (described as polyoxyethylene lauryl ether 1% with 7 EO [an addition polymer of lauryl alcohol and 7 units of ethylene oxide]) showed papules at D3 and prominent follicular papules at D4. Six controls were negative. A use test with laureth-7 1% pet. produced follicular papules at D7. The authors suggest this to be an allergic reaction, but a biopsy to confirm this was refused by the patient (1).

Presence in cosmetic products and chemical analyses

In the USA, in April 2017, laureth-7 was present in 1389 of 56,714 cosmetic products of which the composition is known in FDA's Voluntary Cosmetic Registration Program (VCRP) (data obtained from FDA, May 2017). In March 2017, laureth-7 was present in 643 of 65,351 cosmetic products of which the composition is known in EWG's Skin Deep Cosmetics Database, USA (http://www.ewg.org/skindeep/).

LITERATURE

1   Kimura M, Kawada A. Follicular contact dermatitis due to polyoxyethylene laurylether. J Am Acad Dermatol 2000;42:879-880

2.270   LAURETH-9

IDENTIFICATION

Description/definition	: Laureth-9 is the polyethylene glycol ether of lauryl alcohol that conforms to the formula shown below, where n has an average value of 9
Chemical class(es)	: Alkoxylated alcohols
Chemical/IUPAC name	: 3,6,9,12,15,18,21,24,27-Nonaoxanonatriacontan-1-ol
Other names	: Dodecan-1-ol, ethoxylated; polidocanol; hydroxypolyethoxydodecane; dodecylnonaoxyethylene glycol monoether
CAS registry number (s)	: 3055-99-0; 9002-92-0; 68439-50-9
EC number(s)	: 221-284-4; 500-002-6; 500-213-3
CIR-review(s)	: Int J Toxicol 2012;31(Suppl.2):169-244 (access: www.cir-safety.org/ingredients)
SCCS opinion(s)	: SCCS/1457/11 (10); SCCP/1130/07 (11)
Merck Index monograph	: 8945
Function(s) in cosmetics	: EU: emulsifying. USA: surfactants - emulsifying agents
Patch testing	: 3% pet. (SmartpracticeEurope, SmartPracticeCanada)
Molecular formula	: $CH_3(CH_2)_{11}(OCH_2CH_2)_nOH$

GENERAL

Laureth-9 is an addition polymer of lauryl alcohol and an average of 9 units of ethylene oxide. It is soluble in lipids and water and thus widely used as an emulsifier and surfactant in cosmetics and cleaning products. It is also used as a topical anaesthetic and antipruritic and injected as a varicose vein sclerosant (1). In this chapter, only side effects of laureth-9 from topical application are discussed, thereby excluding complications of sclerotherapy including urticaria (6) and anaphylaxis (12).

CONTACT ALLERGY

Patch testing in groups of patients

Results of studies testing laureth-9 in consecutive patients suspected of contact dermatitis (routine testing) and in groups of selected patients are shown in table 2.270.1. In an older German study, routine testing with laureth-9 yielded 1.5% positive reactions. However, the test concentration is unknown and the relevance of the positive patch tests was not stated (9). In patients tested with a topical drugs series, rates of 1.2% to 2.1% positive reactions were found, depending on the test concentration and vehicle. Over half of the reactions were of current or past relevance. Many positive individuals had lower leg dermatitis and co-reactions to other topical drugs (3).

Table 2.270.1 Patch testing in groups of patients

Years and Country	Test conc. & vehicle	Number of patients tested | positive (%)		Selection of patients (S); Relevance (R); Comments (C)	Ref.
Routine testing					
<1970 Germany	?	2551	38 (1.5%)	R: not stated (data cited in ref. 8)	9
Testing in groups of selected patients					
1992-1999 IVDK	0.5% water	3186	(1.2%)	S: patients tested with a topical drug patch test series;	3
	3% pet.	6202	(2.1%)	R: 53% had current or past relevance; C: high frequency in elderly people with lower leg dermatitis and other topical drugs as co-sensitizers	

Case reports and case series

An atopic woman had suffered from dermatitis of her scalp, face and neck, which subsequently spread to the rest of her body, 2 days after dying her hair. A subsequent attempt at dying hair with a short contact treatment only resulted in a milder form of the same eczematous rash. The patient started to use a new mild shampoo. Less than 12 hours after using it for the first time, she developed an eczematous eruption over the scalp extending down the neck. Patch tests revealed positive reactions to p-phenylenediamine, p-aminophenol and the shampoo tested 10% water. When tested with its ingredients, there were positive reactions to laureth-9 3% and to laureth-2 (test concentration and vehicle not mentioned) (1). One patient had allergic contact dermatitis from laureth-9 in a cosmetic itch relief cream (4).

A woman, known to be allergic to nickel and fragrance, had a one-year history of work-related dermatitis of the hands, spreading to the arms, face, neck and V of the neck. Her eczema had relapsed and she then started using a perfume-free moisturizing lotion several times a day, which worsened the condition. Patch tests gave a positive reaction to the lotion only. Discontinuing the use of this cosmetic product resulted in clearance of the dermatitis after 3 weeks. A repeated open application test (ROAT) with the lotion was positive at D2 already. When tested with its ingredients, the patient had a ?+ reaction to laureth-9 3% in water. Patch testing with a dilution series of laureth-9 at 0.3%, 3%, and 10% resulted in positive reactions to all three concentrations, which were negative in 20 controls (5).

Contact allergy to laureth-9 in non-cosmetic products

Sixteen patients with positive patch test reactions to laureth-9 (polidocanol) were observed in Germany. The majority of the patients suffered from chronic dermatitis and had further contact sensitizations to antibiotics and to vehicle constituents. The clinical relevance of positive reactions to polidocanol remained unclear in many cases. A positive reaction was reproduced in only two of six patients at a follow-up examination (2).

One patient had ACD from laureth-9 in a topical pharmaceutical product for treatment of a leg ulcer. She had previously been treated with the chemical for varicose veins; after injection, she had felt pain and nearly collapsed (probably unrelated to allergy) (7). One patient was allergic to laureth-9 (termed oxypolyethoxydodecane) in a topical pharmaceutical preparation (8).

Cross-reactions, pseudo-cross-reactions and co-reactions

Co-reaction to laureth-2, which was present in the same product (1).

Presence in cosmetic products and chemical analyses

In the USA, in April 2017, laureth-9 was present in 223 of 56,714 cosmetic products of which the composition is known in FDA's Voluntary Cosmetic Registration Program (VCRP) (data obtained from FDA, May 2017). In April 2017, laureth-9 was present in 160 of 66,223 cosmetic products of which the composition is known in EWG's Skin Deep Cosmetics Database, USA (http://www.ewg.org/skindeep/).

LITERATURE

1   Grills CE, Cooper SM. Polidocanol: a potential contact allergen in shampoo. Contact Dermatitis 2007;56:178
2   Frosch PJ, Schulze-Dirks A. Contact allergy caused by polidocanol. Hautarzt 1989;40:146-149
3   Uter W, Geier J, Fuchs T. Contact allergy to polidocanol, 1992 to 1999. J Allergy Clin Immunol 2000;106:1203-1204
4   Fairhurst D,Wilkinson M. Independent sensitization to polidocanol and trometamol or glycerol within same product. Contact Dermatitis 2007;56:179
5   Gallo R, Basso M, Voltolini S, Guarrera M. Allergic contact dermatitis from laureth-9 and polyquaternium-7 in a skin-care product. Contact Dermatitis 2001;45:356-357
6   Henriquez-Santana A, Fernandez-Guarino M, González de Olano D, Gonzalez-Cervera J, Huertas-Barbudo B, Aldanondo I. Urticaria induced by Etoxisclerol (polidocanol). J Eur Acad Dermatol Venereol 2008;22:261-262
7   Huber-Riffeser G. Allergic contact dermatitis to polidocanol (Thesit). Contact Dermatitis 1978;4:245
8   Calnan CD. Oxypolyethoxydodecane in an ointment. Contact Dermatitis 1978;4:168-169
9   Hartung J, Rudolph PO. Z Haut- und Geschlechtskrankheiten 1970;45:457 (data cited in ref. 8)
10   SCCS (Scientific Committee on Consumer Safety). Opinion on polidocanol. Addendum to the SCCP opinion on polidocanol (SCCP/1130/07), 13-14 December 2011, SCCS/1457/11. Available at: http://ec.europa.eu/health/scientific_committees/consumer_safety/docs/sccs_o_076.pdf
11   SCCP (Scientific Committee on Consumer Products). Opinion on Polidocanol (Laureth-9), 2 October 2007, SCCP/ /1130/07. Available at: http://ec.europa.eu/health/archive/ph_risk/committees/04_sccp/docs/sccp_o_113.pdf
12   Stricker BH, van Oijen JA, Kroon C, Ovink AH. Anaphylaxis following use of polidocanol. Ned Tijdschr Geneeskd 1990;134:240-242 (article in Dutch)

2.271 LAURETH-12

IDENTIFICATION

Description/definition	: Laureth-12 is the polyethylene glycol ether of lauryl alcohol that conforms to the formula shown below, where n has an average value of 12
Chemical class(es)	: Alkoxylated alcohols
Chemical/IUPAC name	: 2-[2-[2-[2-[2-[2-[2-[2-[2-[2-[2-(2-Dodecoxyethoxy)ethoxy]ethoxy]ethoxy]ethoxy]ethoxy]ethoxy]ethoxy]ethoxy]ethoxy]ethanol
Other names	: 3,6,9,12,15,18,21,24,27,30,33,36-Dodecaoxaoctatetracontan-1-ol; PEG-12 lauryl ether; dodecyl dodeca(oxyethylene) ether; polyoxyethylene (12) lauryl ether; polyethylene glycol 600 lauryl ether
CAS registry number (s)	: 3056-00-6; 9002-92-0; 68213-23-0; 68439-50-9
EC number(s)	: 221-286-5
CIR review(s)	: Int J Toxicol 2012;31(Suppl.2):169-244 (access: www.cir-safety.org/ingredients)
Function(s) in cosmetics	: EU: emulsifying; surfactant. USA: surfactants - emulsifying agents
Patch testing	: No data available; suggested: 5-10% water (1)
Molecular formula	: $CH_3(CH_2)_{11}(OCH_2CH_2)_nOH$

CONTACT ALLERGY

Case reports and case series

A woman presented with a history of recurrent facial swelling and scalp irritation after using hair dyes. Patch testing to the British Contact Dermatitis Society (BCDS) standard series and the hairdressing series was negative. Subsequent patch testing to constituents of her hair product, in addition to the bases, preservatives, and cosmetics series, showed positive reactions to laureth-12, which was a constituent of the hair dye. The test concentration and vehicle were not mentioned and neither was patch testing in control subjects (1).

Presence in cosmetic products and chemical analyses

In the USA, in April 2017, laureth-12was present in 304 of 56,714 cosmetic products of which the composition is known in FDA's Voluntary Cosmetic Registration Program (VCRP) (data obtained from FDA, May 2017). In March 2017, laureth-12 was present in 62 of 65,351 cosmetic products of which the composition is known in EWG's Skin Deep Cosmetics Database, USA (http://www.ewg.org/skindeep/).

LITERATURE

1   Field S, Hazelwood E, Bourke B, Bourke JF. Allergic contact dermatitis from tertiary-butylhydroquinone and Laureth 12 in a hair dye. Contact Dermatitis 2007;56:116

2.272   LAUROYL COLLAGEN AMINO ACIDS

IDENTIFICATION

Description/definition	: Lauroyl collagen amino acids is the product obtained by the condensation of lauric acid chloride with collagen amino acids
Chemical class(es)	: Amino acids
Other names	: Amino acids, collagen, 1-oxododecyl derivatives
CAS registry number (s)	: 68920-59-2
CIR review(s)	: Final report, January 2014 (access: www.cir-safety.org/ingredients)
Function(s) in cosmetics	: EU: antistatic; cleansing; hair conditioning. USA: hair conditioning agents; surfactants – cleansing agents
Patch testing	: No data available

CONTACT ALLERGY

Case reports and case series
Lauroyl collagen amino acids were responsible for 1 out of 959 cases of non-fragrance cosmetic allergy where the causal allergen was identified, Belgium, 2000-2010 (1).

Presence in cosmetic products and chemical analyses
In the USA, in April 2017, lauroyl collagen amino acids was present in 1 of 56,714 cosmetic products of which the composition is known in FDA's Voluntary Cosmetic Registration Program (VCRP) (data obtained from FDA, May 2017). In March 2017, lauroyl collagen amino acids was present in zero of 65,431 cosmetic products of which the composition is known in EWG's Skin Deep Cosmetics Database, USA (http://www.ewg.org/skindeep/).

LITERATURE
1   Travassos AR, Claes L, Boey L, Drieghe J, Goossens A. Non-fragrance allergens in specific cosmetic products. Contact Dermatitis 2011;65:276-285

2.273   LAURUS NOBILIS LEAF EXTRACT

IDENTIFICATION

Description/definition	: Laurus nobilis leaf extract is an extract of the leaves of the laurel, *Laurus nobilis* L., Lauraceae
Chemical class(es)	: Botanical products and botanical derivatives
Other names	: Bay laurel extract; sweet bay extract
CAS registry number (s)	: 84603-73-6
EC number(s)	: 283-272-5
Merck Index monograph	: 6707 (Laurel)
Function(s) in cosmetics	: EU: masking; refreshing; tonic. USA: flavoring agents; fragrance ingredients; oral care agents; skin-conditioning agents - miscellaneous; skin-conditioning agents - occlusive
Patch testing	: No data available

CONTACT ALLERGY

Case reports and case series

A man presented with a one-year history of recurrent dermatitis of the face, notably of the eyelids, cheeks and perioral region. The patient, a metalworker, related the outbreaks to iron and cutting fluids used in his workplace. However, patch tests with cutting fluids and other products used in his work were negative. The patient was then tested with the standard series, and a positive reaction was obtained to the sesquiterpene lactone-mix at D4. A further patch test with Helenin (commercialized preparation containing alantolactone and isoalactolactone) was also positive and resulted in an eczematous reaction at D10. As sesquiterpene lactones are present in the Compositae family of plants (with which he had no contact) and many cosmetic products contain Compositae plant extracts, cosmetic allergy was suspected. However, the patient denied using any cosmetics himself. Therefore, he was tested with his girlfriend's cosmetics. Now, there was a positive reaction a deodorant containing *Laurus nobilis* and *Anthemis nobilis* and to several other products.

The patient was diagnosed as having allergic contact dermatitis due to sesquiterpene lactones present in his girlfriend's cosmetics. After avoiding contact with these products and others containing Compositae plant extracts, the patient has remained symptom-free. It should be appreciated that the ingredients of the deodorant were not tested separately, and therefore it is unknown whether the allergens were present in the Laurus nobilis extract or in the Anthemis nobilis extract. As the allergic reaction was caused by his girlfriend's cosmetics, this was a case of 'consort' or 'connubial' allergic contact dermatitis (1).

Presence in cosmetic products and chemical analyses

In the USA, in April 2017, Laurus nobilis leaf extract was present in 21 of 56,714 cosmetic products of which the composition is known in FDA's Voluntary Cosmetic Registration Program (VCRP) (data obtained from FDA, May 2017). In March 2017, Laurus nobilis leaf extract was present in 10 of 65,431 cosmetic products of which the composition is known in EWG's Skin Deep Cosmetics Database, USA (http://www.ewg.org/skindeep/).

LITERATURE

1   Bernedo N, Audicana MT, Uriel O, Velasco M, Gastaminza G, Fernández E, Muñoz D. Allergic contact dermatitis from cosmetics applied by the patient's girlfriend. Contact Dermatitis 2004;50:252-253

2.274   LAURYL ALCOHOL

IDENTIFICATION

Description/definition	: Lauryl alcohol is the fatty alcohol that conforms generally to the formula shown below
Chemical class(es)	: Fatty alcohols
Chemical/IUPAC name	: Dodecan-1-ol
Other names	: Dodecyl alcohol; alcohol C-12; 1-hydroxydodecane
CAS registry number (s)	: 112-53-8
EC number(s)	: 203-982-0
Merck Index monograph	: 4721
Function(s) in cosmetics	: EU: emollient; emulsifying; emulsion stabilizing; viscosity controlling. USA: emulsion stabilizers; fragrance ingredients; skin-conditioning agents - emollient; surfactants – foam boosters; viscosity increasing agents – aqueous; viscosity increasing agents – nonaqueous
Patch testing	: 10% pet. (2,3)
Molecular formula	: $C_{12}H_{26}O$

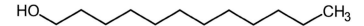

CONTACT ALLERGY

Case reports and case series

Lauryl alcohol was responsible for 3 out of 959 cases of non-fragrance cosmetic allergy where the causal allergen was identified, Belgium, 2000-2010 (1). In a 4-month-period in 1996, 475 patients with contact allergy to 'cosmetic ingredients' were collected in 5 centers in Belgium, UK and Germany. There was one reaction to lauryl alcohol; its relevance was not mentioned (5).

Contact allergy to lauryl alcohol in non-cosmetic products

Lauryl alcohol was the allergen or one of the allergens in a tissue accompanying a depilatory wax in 9 patients with contact dermatitis from the wax and/or the tissue (2,3).

Cross-reactions, pseudo-cross-reactions and co-reactions

Lauryl alcohol can be present in technical grade cetyl alcohol, used in cosmetics (4).

Presence in cosmetic products and chemical analyses

In the USA, in April 2017, lauryl alcohol was present in 138 of 56,714 cosmetic products of which the composition is known in FDA's Voluntary Cosmetic Registration Program (VCRP) (data obtained from FDA, May 2017). In April 2017, lauryl alcohol was present in of 66,223 cosmetic products of which the composition is known in EWG's Skin Deep Cosmetics Database, USA (http://www.ewg.org/skindeep/).

OTHER SIDE EFFECTS

Other non-eczematous contact reactions

In (somewhat) older literature, lauryl alcohol has been suspected of being comedogenic, based on rabbit ear assays (6,7).

LITERATURE

1   Travassos AR, Claes L, Boey L, Drieghe J, Goossens A. Non-fragrance allergens in specific cosmetic products. Contact Dermatitis 2011;65:276-285
2   Goossens A, Armingaud P, Avenel-Audran M et al. An epidemic of allergic contact dermatitis due to epilating products. Contact Dermatitis 2002;46:67-70
3   Goossens A. An epidemic of allergic contact dermatitis due to epilating products. Contact Dermatitis 2001;45:360
4   Komamura H, Dor T, Inui S, Yoshikawa K. A case of contact dermatitis due to impurities of cetyl alcohol. Contact Dermatitis 1997;36:44-46

5   Goossens A, Beck MH, Haneke E, McFadden JP, Nolting S, Durupt G, Ries G. Adverse cutaneous reactions to cosmetic allergens. Contact Dermatitis 1999;40:112-113

6   Kligman AM, Mills OH. Acne cosmetica. Arch Dermatol 1972;106:843-850

7   Kligman AM, Kwong T. An improved rabbit ear model for assessing comedogenic substances. Br J Dermatol 1979;100:699-702

2.275   LAURYL GLUCOSIDE

IDENTIFICATION

Description/definition	: Lauryl glucoside is the product obtained by the condensation of lauryl alcohol with glucose
Chemical class(es)	: Carbohydrates; ethers
Other names	: D-Glucopyranose, oligomeric, C10-16 alkyl glycosides; dodecyl D-glucoside
CAS registry number (s)	: 110615-47-9; 27836-64-2
EC number(s)	: 248-685-7
CIR review(s)	: Int J Toxicol 2013;32(Suppl.3):22-48 (access: www.cir-safety.org/ingredients)
Function(s) in cosmetics	: EU: cleansing; surfactant. USA: surfactants - cleansing agents
Patch testing	: 3% pet. (SmartPracticeCanada)
Molecular formula	: $C_{18}H_{36}O_6$ (CAS 27836-64-2); unspecified (CAS 110615-47-9)

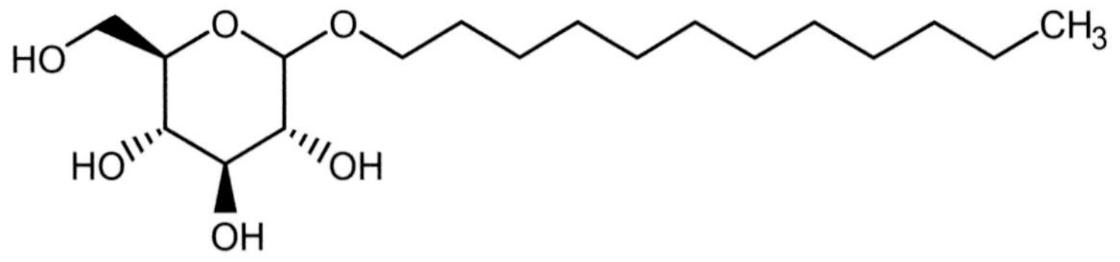

GENERAL

Lauryl glucoside is one of the alkyl glucosides, a family of organic molecules of vegetal origin. They are produced by the condensation of a sugar, usually a cyclic form of glucose (D-glucopyranose), with a fatty alcohol composed of a linear side chain ranging from 2 to 22 carbons. Fatty alcohol is extracted from palm, coconut, or rapeseed oil, and glucose can be obtained from corn, wheat starch, and potato. The average number of carbon atoms composing the alcohol side chain determines the name of the alkyl glucoside. Members of the alkyl glucoside family include butyl, caprylyl, decyl, lauryl, coco-, cetearyl, undecyl, myristyl, hexadecyl, octadecyl, arachidyl, and caprylyl/capryl glucoside, C10-16, C12-18, C12-20, and C20-22 alkyl glucosides, branched isostearyl glucoside, and octyldodecyl glucoside.

Most of the alkyl glucosides are primarily used as mild non-ionic surfactants in cosmetics and cleansing products for human skin, mostly as a mixture of several alkyl glucosides, as it is difficult to obtain individual glucosides at high purity. They can also sometimes function as emulsion stabilizers in sunscreens, skin and hair cleansing agents, and humectants. They can be found in certain baby products such as wipes and cleansers and in antiseptic solutions (2). Other alkyl glucosides which have caused cosmetic allergy include arachidyl glucoside, cetearyl glucoside, coco-glucoside, decyl glucoside and myristyl glucoside. These are discussed in their respective chapters. A comprehensive review of contact allergy to alkyl glucosides has been published in 2017 (15,16).

CONTACT ALLERGY

Patch testing in consecutive patients suspected of contact dermatitis: routine testing

In 2008, lauryl glucoside 5% pet. was added to the baseline series of the members of the Groupe d' Etudes et de Recherches en Dermato-Allergologie (GERDA) in France, Belgium, and Switzerland. Since 2012, the positivity rate for lauryl glucoside has always been more than 1.5% (2% in 2012, 1.6% in 2013, and 2.6% in 2014). These numbers were deemed considerable by the investigators and they concluded that lauryl glucoside should be part of the baseline patch testing series because it is a common, emerging, allergen (17).

Patch testing in groups of selected patients

The results of testing lauryl glucoside in groups of selected patients (e.g., patients tested with a cosmetics and vehicle series, patients tested with a facial series, patients tested with an 'additional series') are shown in table 2.275.1. In four studies, rates of sensitization ranged from 0.5% to 0.9%. In the most recent study from Canada, the frequency of sensitization to lauryl glucoside and/or decyl glucoside rose to 2.2% in the first 6 months of 2016 (16). In that study, all 15 reactions were considered to be relevant. Over 70% were women who mostly had dermatitis of the face and hands; moisturizers and hand creams were most frequently implicated (16).

Case reports and case series

Lauryl glucoside was stated to be the (or an) allergen in 8 patients in a group of 603 individuals suffering from cosmetic dermatitis, seen in the period 2010-2015 in Leuven, Belgium (12). Lauryl glucoside was responsible for 3 out of 959 cases of non-fragrance cosmetic allergy where the causal allergen was identified, Belgium, 2000-2010 (1).

Table 2.275.1 Patch testing in groups of patients: Selected patient groups

Years and Country	Test conc. & vehicle	Number of patients tested	positive (%)		Selection of patients (S); Relevance (R); Comments (C)	Ref.
2009-2016 Canada		1628	15	(0.9%)	S: patients tested with a cosmetics and vehicles series; R: all reactions were relevant; C: >70% were women who mostly had dermatitis of the face and hands; moisturizers and hand creams were most frequently implicated; the frequency of sensitization to lauryl glucoside and/or decyl glucoside rose to 2.2% in the first 6 months of 2016	16
2012 UK	3% pet.	157	1	(0.6%)	S: patients tested with a facial series; R: not found	10
2011 China	3% pet.	201	1	(0.5%)	S: healthy student volunteers 19-30 years; R: not stated	13
2004 France	3% pet.	?	?	(0.5%)	S: patients tested with an 'additional series'; R: not stated; C: casually cited in ref.8	8

During a 19-year period (1993-2012), of 11,842 patients with suspected contact dermatitis patch tested in Leuven, Belgium, 30 patients (24 women and 6 men) presented with a positive reaction to one or more alkyl glucosides. The causal products were shampoos (n=12), skin-cleansing products (n=12, among which were wipes for intimate hygiene), sunscreen products (n=5), skin-care products (n=4), and a deodorant (n=1). Reactions to lauryl glucoside were seen in 23/30 (77%) of the patients. Co-reactions to other glucosides were as follows: coco-glucoside 18 (78%), decyl glucoside 15 (65%), and ceteraryl glucoside 3 (13%). Twenty-five of the 30 patients who reacted to alkyl glucosides also had positive test results with non-related chemicals; 16 of these even had multiple sensitivities, defined as three or more contact allergies (11).

A patient was predictively tested with 6 different shower gels (semi-open, to determine their irritant potential), and reacted positively to all products tested. The common ingredient in 5 was lauryl glucoside. When tested with their ingredients, the patient showed positive reactions to both lauryl glucoside and coco-glucoside (4). A woman had ACD of the hands from lauryl glucoside and coco-glucoside in a body lotion and a sunscreen that she applied to her child's skin (4). Two women, of who one was an apprentice hairdresser, had allergic contact dermatitis of the hands from lauryl glucoside in shampoos (6). A patient known to be allergic to decyl glucoside in Tinosorb® M had positive patch test reactions to his facial cosmetics containing lauryl glucoside (3). A man suffered from ACD of the back of his arms caused by lauryl glucoside in a sunscreen (19).

Contact allergy to lauryl glucoside in non-cosmetic products
A nurse had ACD of the hands from contact allergy to coco-glucoside and lauryl glucoside in a lotion she used for cleaning her hands (4).

Cross-reactions, pseudo-cross-reactions and co-reactions
Other glucosides such as coco-glucoside, decyl glucoside, myristyl glucoside and cetearyl glucoside (3,4,5,6,8,9,11, 16). Possibly to methyl glucose dioleate (6). In commercial batches of decyl, coco- and lauryl glucoside about 500 ng/g isobornyl acrylate was found as an impurity. It has been suggested, that this chemical may play a role in the simultaneous reactions to various alkyl glucosides (14). Often, a mixture of several alkyl glucosides is present in cosmetic products, as it is very difficult to obtain individual glucosides of high purity (7). Because of this and of their chemical similarity, concomitant reactivity or cross-reactions may occur with the various glucosides (3).

Presence in cosmetic products and chemical analyses
In the USA, in April 2017, lauryl glucoside was present in 713 of 56,714 cosmetic products of which the composition is known in FDA's Voluntary Cosmetic Registration Program (VCRP) (data obtained from FDA, May 2017). In QAugust 2017, lauryl glucoside was present in 439 of 70,693 cosmetic products of which the composition is known in EWG's Skin Deep Cosmetics Database, USA (http://www.ewg.org/skindeep/). Lauryl glucoside was present in 10 (6%) of 178 facial wipes for which ingredient information was obtained online and from retail stores, USA, 2016 (18).

LITERATURE
1 Travassos AR, Claes L, Boey L, Drieghe J, Goossens A. Non-fragrance allergens in specific cosmetic products. Contact Dermatitis 2011;65:276-285
2 Fiume MM, Heldreth B, Bergfeld WF, Belsito DV, Hill RA, Klaassen CD, et al. Safety assessment of decyl glucoside and other alkyl glucosides as used in cosmetics. Int J Toxicol 2013;32(Suppl.5):22S-48S
3 Pereira N, Coutinho I, Andrade P, Gonçalo M. The UV filter Tinosorb M, containing decyl glucoside, is a frequent cause of allergic contact dermatitis. Dermatitis 2013;24:41-43
4 Goossens A, Decraene T, Platteaux N, Nardelli A, Rasschaert V. Glucosides as unexpected allergens in cosmetics. Contact Dermatitis 2003;48:164-166

5   Andrade P, Gonçalo M, Figueiredo A. Allergic contact dermatitis to decyl glucoside in Tinosorb® M. Contact Dermatitis 2010;62:119-120

6   Blondeel A. Contact allergy to the mild surfactant decylglucoside. Contact Dermatitis 2003;49:304-305

7   Le Coz CJ, Meyer MT. Contact allergy to decyl glucoside in antiseptic after body piercing. Contact Dermatitis 2003;48:279-280

8   Krehic M, Avenel-Audran M. Allergic contact dermatitis from decyl glucoside in an antiseptic lotion. Contact Dermatitis 2009;61:349-350

9   Liuti F, Borrego L. Contact dermatitis caused by Tinosorb® M: the importance of patch testing with pure methylene bis-benzotriazolyl tetramethylbutylphenol. Contact Dermatitis 2015;73:192-193

10 Shanmugam S, Wilkinson M, Kirk S. Pitfalls of patch testing with glucosides. Contact Dermatitis 2014;71:108-109

11 Gijbels D, Timmermans A, Serrano P, Verreycken E, Goossens A. Allergic contact dermatitis caused by alkyl glucosides. Contact Dermatitis 2014;70:175-182

12 Goossens A. Cosmetic contact allergens. Cosmetics 2016, 3, 5; doi:10.3390/cosmetics3010005

13 Zhao J, Li LF. Contact sensitization to cosmetic series of allergens in a general population in Beijing. J Cosmet Dermatol 2014;13:68-71

14 Foti C, Romita P, Rigano L, Zimerson E, Sicilia M, Ballini A, et al. Isobornyl acrylate: an impurity in alkyl glucosides. Cutan Ocul Toxicol 2016;35:115-119

15 Loranger C, Alfalah M, Ferrier Le Bouedec M-C, Sasseville Denis. Alkyl glucosides in contact dermatitis: a systematic review. Dermatitis Dermatitis 2017;28:5-13

16 Alfalah M, Loranger C, Sasseville D. Contact allergen of the year. Alkyl glucosides. Dermatitis 2017;28:3-4

17 Castelain M, Castelain F. Les ajouts à la batterie standard: utiles ou inutiles? In: Tennstedt D, Goossens A, Baeck M, eds. Progrès en Dermato-Allergologie: Bruxelles 2015. Montrouge, France: John Libbey Eurotext, 2015:275-286

18 Aschenbeck KA, Warshaw EM. Allergenic ingredients in facial wet wipes. Dermatitis 2017 Mar 23. doi: 10.1097/DER.0000000000000268. [Epub ahead of print]

19 Martínez-González MI, González-Pérez R, García-Rio I, Heras-González S. Allergic contact dermatitis caused by benzoic acid and lauryl glucoside in a sunscreen. Contact Dermatitis 2017;77:186-187

2.276 LAURYLPYRIDINIUM CHLORIDE

IDENTIFICATION

Description/definition : Laurylpyridinium chloride is the quaternary ammonium compound that conforms generally to the formula shown below

Chemical class(es) : Heterocyclic compounds; quaternary ammonium compounds

Chemical/IUPAC name : 1-Dodecylpyridin-1-ium chloride

CAS registry number (s) : 104-74-5

EC number(s) : 203-232-2

Function(s) in cosmetics : EU: antimicrobial; antistatic; deodorant; surfactant. USA: antistatic agents; cosmetic biocides; deodorant agents

Patch testing : 0.1% water; this concentration may cause irritant reactions (1)

Molecular formula : $C_{17}H_{30}ClN$

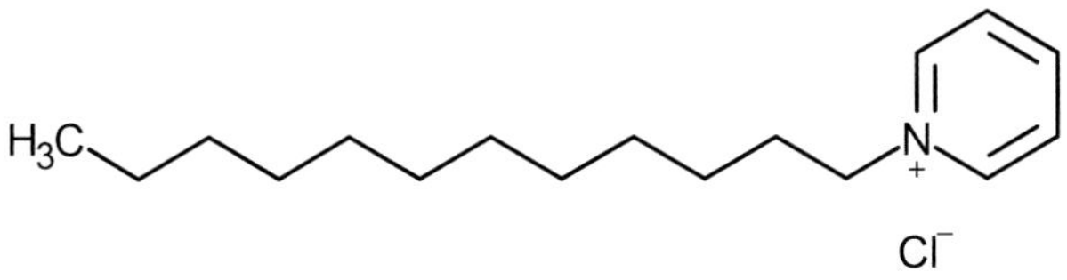

CONTACT ALLERGY

Case reports and case series

In a group of 119 patients with allergic contact dermatitis from cosmetics, investigated in The Netherlands in 1986-1987, one case was caused by laurylpyridinium chloride in a hair conditioner (2,3, same patient as in ref. 1, discussed below).

A man had recurrent itchy dermatitis on the left side of the chest and adjacent area of the arm, where his wife usually rested her head when sleeping. He had noticed that the eruption always developed after his wife had used a particular hair conditioner. Patch tests with the European standard series and the conditioner, tested undiluted, showed a positive reaction to the conditioner at D2 and D3. Later, its ingredients were tested separately. A positive reaction was found to laurylpyridinium chloride 0.1% water, but not to 0.01% water. No reactions were observed to an additional series of quaternary ammonium compounds: domiphen bromide, toloconium methyl sulfate, benzalkonium chloride, cetrimonium bromide, cetalkonium chloride, cetylpyridinium chloride (all 0.05% water) and benzoxonium chloride (0.02% water). Of 23 controls tested with laurylpyridinium chloride 0.1% water, 16 were negative, 6 had a ?+, and one a + reaction. Since his wife stopped using the hair conditioner, the patient has had no recurrence of his dermatitis (1). As the allergic eruption was caused by a product used by the patient's wife, this was a case of 'connubial' or 'consort' contact dermatitis.

Cross-reactions, pseudo-cross-reactions and co-reactions

Not to other quaternary ammonium compounds: domiphen bromide, benzoxonium chloride, benzalkonium chloride, cetylpyridinium chloride, cetrimonium bromide, cetalkonium chloride, toloconium methyl sulfate (1).

Presence in cosmetic products and chemical analyses

In the USA, in April 2017, laurylpyridinium chloride was present in 8 of 56,714 cosmetic products of which the composition is known in FDA's Voluntary Cosmetic Registration Program (VCRP) (data obtained from FDA, May 2017). In March 2017, laurylpyridinium chloride was present in one of 65,431 cosmetic products of which the composition is known in EWG's Skin Deep Cosmetics Database, USA (http://www.ewg.org/skindeep/).

LITERATURE

1 Bruynzeel DP, de Groot AC, Weyland JW. Contact dermatitis to lauryl pyridinium chloride and benzoxonium chloride. Contact Dermatitis 1987;17:41-42

2 De Groot AC, Bruynzeel DP, Bos JD, van der Meeren HL, van Joost T, Jagtman BA, Weyland JW. The allergens in cosmetics. Arch Dermatol 1988;124:1525-1529

3 De Groot AC. Adverse reactions to cosmetics. PhD Thesis, University of Groningen, The Netherlands: 1988, chapter 3.4, pp.105-113

2.277   LAWSONE

IDENTIFICATION

Description/definition	: Lawsone is the substituted naphthoquinone that conforms to the formula shown below
Chemical class(es)	: Color additives – hair; phenols
Chemical/IUPAC name	: 4-Hydroxynaphthalene-1,2-dione
Other names	: 2-Hydroxy-1,4-naphthoquinone; CI 75480; CI natural orange 6
CAS registry number (s)	: 83-72-7
EC number(s)	: 201-496-3
SCCS opinion(s)	: SCCNFP/0798/04 (15); SCCNFP/0583/02 (16); SCCNFP/0562/02 (17); SCCNFP/0385/00 (18)
Merck Index monograph	: 6718
Function(s) in cosmetics	: EU: hair dyeing. USA: colorants; sunscreen agents
Patch testing	: 5% pet. (2,3)
Molecular formula	: $C_{10}H_6O_3$

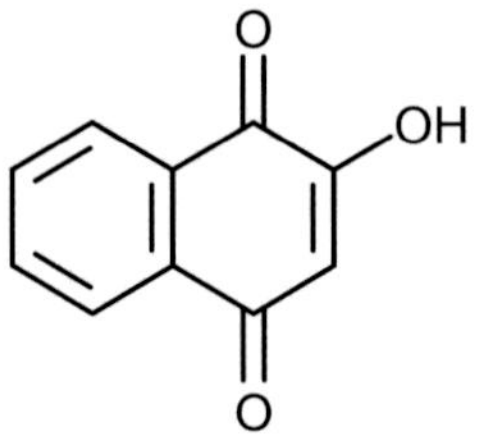

GENERAL

Lawsone is the coloring material in henna (Chapter 2.221 Henna). Lawsone is typically present in a concentration of <2% in henna leaves and natural red henna preparations (1,2). Side effects of red henna and black henna (the combination of red henna with p-phenylenediamine; see Chapter 2.220 Henna, black) have been reviewed in 2013 (19).

CONTACT ALLERGY

Case reports and case series

A 9-year old boy developed generalized dermatitis two weeks after a black henna tattoo was applied. Patch tests were positive to p-phenylenediamine (PPD), benzocaine, N-isopropyl-N'-phenyl-p-phenylenediamine and lawsone 10% pet. The allergy to lawsone was considered to be provoked by the reaction to PPD; control tests with lawsone were not performed (1). A 50-year-old woman had three episodes of acute palpebral dermatitis after dying her hair with henna. Patch tests were positive to henna powder 10% pet. and to lawsone 5% pet; control tests were negative and there was no reaction to p-phenylenediamine (2).

A man with allergic reactions to CI 12150 and CI 12010 in a sunscreen also had a positive patch test to lawsone 5% pet. on two occasions; control tests were negative. The relevance of this contact allergy remained unexplained (3). A 13-year-old girl had recurring dermatitis after applying commercial henna powder or a paste of fresh henna leaves to the back of the hands. She had strongly positive patch test reactions to commercial henna, henna leaves made into a past, and lawsone; the test concentrations were not mentioned and no control tests were performed (4).

Presence in cosmetic products and chemical analyses

In May 2017, lawsone was present in zero of 66,658 cosmetic products of which the composition is known in EWG's Skin Deep Cosmetics Database, USA (http://www.ewg.org/skindeep/). In the USA, in April 2017, lawsone was present in zero of 56,714 cosmetic products of which the composition is known in FDA's Voluntary Cosmetic Registration Program (VCRP) (data obtained from FDA, May 2017). In 2011, labels and other information on 365 hair dye products (282 permanent dyes, 79 semi-permanent dyes, 4 direct dyes) available on the Danish market (159 hair dyes for private use, 206 for professional use by hairdressers) were collected to identify the presence of sensitizers. Lawsone was present in 2 (0.5%) products (19).

The amounts of lawsone were investigated by high-performance liquid chromatography in three products used by henna tattoo artists, 11 commercially available henna preparations for hair dying and tattoos and a batch of henna leaves. The henna leaves contained 1.85-1.87% lawsone. Only one of the three preparations used by tattoo artists contained lawsone (0.21-0.35%). Of the 11 commercial henna preparations analysed, nine contained lawsone

(1-2%) (13). The lawsone content in eight commercial henna powders and two collected henna leaves ranged from 0.004 up to 0.608 wt%, indicating that some samples were almost devoid of lawsone (probably black henna) (14).

In 2013, 25 commercial black henna tattoo samples were collected from 15 tattoo shops in 5 cities in Turkey to analyse them for the presence of *p*-phenylenediamine, lawsone and heavy metals. Lawsone was detected with high-performance liquid chromatography in 21 of the 25 samples in concentrations ranging from 0.002 to 88.2% (20).

OTHER SIDE EFFECTS

Immediate-type reactions
Immediate contact reactions to lawsone-containing henna are discussed in Chapter 2.221 Henna. It is not certain that lawsone is the allergen in such reactions.

Systemic side effects
The structure and redox potential of lawsone (2-hydroxy-1,4-naphthoquinone) is similar to that of 1,4-naphtho-quinone, a metabolite of naphthalene and potent oxidant of glucose-6-phosphate dehydrogenase (G6PD) deficient cells. Topical application of henna may therefor cause life threatening hemolysis in children with G6PD deficiency. Signs and symptoms may include pallor, lethargy, vomiting, jaundice, anemia, tachycardia, poor peripheral perfusion, shock and even death (5,7,8,9,10,11,12; see also Chapter 2.221 Henna).

LITERATURE

1   Jung P, Sesztak-Greinecker G, Wantke F, Götz M, Jarisch R, Hemmer W. The extent of black henna tattoo's complications are not restricted to PPD-sensitization. Contact Dermatitis 2006;55:57
2   Perez RG, Gonzalez R, Gonzalez M, Soloeta R. Palpebral eczema due to contact allergy to henna used as a hair dye. Contact Dermatitis 2003;48:238
3   Wantke F, Götz M, Jarisch R. Contact dermatitis due to henna, solvent red 1 and solvent red 3. A case report. Contact Dermatitis 1992;27:346-347
4   Gupta BN, Mathur AK, Agarwal C, Singh A. Contact sensitivity to henna. Contact Dermatitis 1986;15:303-304
5   Raupp P, Hassan JA, Varughese M, Kristiansson B. Henna causes life threatening haemolysis in glucose-6-phosphate dehydrogenase deficiency. Arch Dis Child 2001;85:411-412
6   The Danish Environmental Protection Agency. Survey and occurrence of PPD, PTD and other allergenic hair dye substances in hair dyes. Copenhagen, Denmark: The Danish Environmental Protection Agency, 2013 (ISBN 978-87-92903-92-1). Available at: http://www2.mst.dk/Udgiv/publications/2013/02/978-87-92903-92-1.pdf
7   Kandil HH, al-Ghanem MM, Sarwat MA, al-Thallab FS. Henna (*Lawsonia inermis* Linn.) inducing haemolysis among G6PD-deficient newborns. A new clinical observation. Ann Trop Paediatr 1996;16:287-291
8   Zinkham WH, Oski FA. Henna: a potential cause of oxidative hemolysis and neonatal hyperbilirubinemia. Pediatrics 1996;97:707-709
9   Kök AN, Ertekin MV, Ertekin V, Avci B. Henna (*Lawsonia inermis* Linn.) induced haemolytic anaemia in siblings. Int J Clin Pract 2004;58:530-532
10 Ozsoylu S. Henna intoxication. Lancet 1996;348:1173
11 McMillan DC, Sarvate SD, Oatis JE Jr, Jollow DJ. Role of oxidant stress in lawsone-induced hemolytic anemia. Toxocol Sci 2004;82:647-655
12 Katar S, Devecioglu C, Ozbeck MN, Ecer S. Henna causes life-threatening hyperbilirubinaemia in glucose-6-phosphate dehydrogenase deficiency. Clin Exp Dermatol 2007;32:235-236
13 Almeida PJ, Borrego L, Pulido-Melián E, González-Díaz O. Quantification of *p*-phenylenediamine and 2-hydroxy-1,4-naphthoquinone in henna tattoos. Contact Dermatitis 2011;66:33-37
14 El-Shaer NS, Badr JM, Aboul-Ela MA, Gohar YM. Determination of lawsone in henna powders by high performance thin layer chromatography. J Sep Sci 2007;30:3311-3315
15 SCCNFP (Scientific Committee on Cosmetics and Non Food Products). Opinion concerning lawsone, 16 February 2004, SCCNFP/0798/04. Available at:
    http://ec.europa.eu/health/archive/ph_risk/committees/sccp/documents/out254_en.pdf
16 SCCNFP (Scientific Committee on Cosmetics and Non Food Products). Opinion concerning lawsone, 17 September 2002, SCCNFP/0583/02. Available at:
    http://ec.europa.eu/health/archive/ph_risk/committees/sccp/documents/out177_en.pdf

17   SCCNFP (Scientific Committee on Cosmetics and Non Food Products). Opinion concerning lawsone, 27 February 2002, SCCNFP/0562/02. Available at:
http://ec.europa.eu/health/archive/ph_risk/committees/sccp/documents/out159_en.pdf

18   SCCNFP (Scientific Committee on Cosmetics and Non Food Products). Opinion concerning lawsone, 13 March 2001,SCCNFP/0385/00. Available at:
http://ec.europa.eu/health/archive/ph_risk/committees/sccp/documents/out139_en.pdf

19   De Groot AC. Side-effects of henna and semi-permanent 'black henna' tattoos: a full review. Contact Dermatitis 2013;69:1-25

20   Aktas Sukuroglu A, Battal D, Burgaz S. Monitoring of lawsone, p-phenylenediamine and heavy metals in commercial temporary black henna tattoos sold in Turkey. Contact Dermatitis 2017;76:89-95

2.278 LEAD ACETATE

IDENTIFICATION

Description/definition : Lead acetate is the inorganic salt that conforms to the formula shown below
Chemical class(es) : Color additives – hair; organic salts
Chemical/IUPAC name : Lead(2+) diacetate
Other names : Lead diacetate
CAS registry number (s) : 301-04-2; 15347-57-6
EC number(s) : 206-104-4; 239-379-4
SCCS opinion(s) : SCCNFP/0832/04 (2)
Merck Index monograph : 6722
Function(s) in cosmetics : EU: formerly used for hair dyeing; delisted in 2005. USA: hair colorants
EU cosmetic restrictions : Regulated in Annex II/289 of the Regulation (EC) No. 1223/2009 (prohibited)
Patch testing : Lead(II)acetate trihydrate 0.5% water (Chemotechnique)
Molecular formula : $C_4H_6O_4Pb$

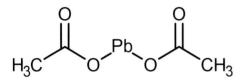

GENERAL
Side effects of lead acetate other than in cosmetics is considered to fall outside the scope of this book.

CONTACT ALLERGY

Case reports and case series
One patient had allergic contact dermatitis from lead acetate in a hair dye (1).

Presence in cosmetic products and chemical analyses
In the USA, in April 2017, lead acetate was present in 5 of 56,714 cosmetic products of which the composition is known in FDA's Voluntary Cosmetic Registration Program (VCRP) (data obtained from FDA, May 2017). In March 2017, lead acetate was present in 5 of 65,431 cosmetic products of which the composition is known in EWG's Skin Deep Cosmetics Database, USA (http://www.ewg.org/skindeep/).

LITERATURE
1   Edwards EK Jr, Edwards EK. Allergic contact dermatitis to lead acetate in a hair dye. Cutis 1982;30:629-630
2   SCCNFP (Scientific Committee on Cosmetics and Non Food Products). Opinion concerning lead acetate, 1 July 2004, SCCNFP/0832/04. Available at:
    http://ec.europa.eu/health/archive/ph_risk/committees/sccp/documents/out286_en.pdf

2.279 LONICERA JAPONICA (HONEYSUCKLE) FLOWER EXTRACT

IDENTIFICATION

Description/definition	: Lonicera japonica flower extract is an extract of the flowers of the Japanese honeysuckle, *Lonicera japonica*, Caprifoliaceae
Chemical class(es)	: Botanical products and botanical derivatives
INCI name USA	: Lonicera japonica (honeysuckle) flower extract
Other names	: Honeysuckle (flower) extract
CAS registry number (s)	: 223749-79-9
Function(s) in cosmetics	: EU: skin conditioning. USA: skin-conditioning agents - miscellaneous
Patch testing	: 2% and 5% water (1).

GENERAL

Lonicera japonica extract is the aqueous extract from the flowers of the Japanese honeysuckle, and is a popular remedy in traditional Chinese medicine. It may have anti-inflammatory and antimicrobial activity, the latter possibly attributable to a mixture of esters of lonicerin and natural *p*-hydroxybenzoic acid. Because of these combined properties, Lonicera japonica extract is used in cosmetic products for sensitive/allergic skin, where chemical preservatives are increasingly being replaced by natural antimicrobial ingredients (1).

CONTACT ALLERGY

Case reports and case series

A woman presented with generalized treatment-resistant dermatitis. The eruption had started on her legs after use of post-epilation soothing remedies, and had become worse following applications of a body lotion for 'sensitive/ allergic skin'. Patch testing with the SIDAPA baseline series, a cosmetic series, and her own products revealed positive reactions to formaldehyde, fragrance mix, and to three of her own products. Two of these contained formaldehyde releasers and fragrances, whereas the third product, the body lotion, did not. A ROAT with this product was positive after 2 applications already. When tested with the ingredients of the lotion, supplied by its manufacturer, there were positive results to Lonicera japonica flower extract tested 2% and 5% in water. Fifteen controls were negative.

When patch testing was performed, the Lonicera extract sample was odorless, but 5 months later it had a pungent formaldehyde odor. Analytical investigation confirmed the presence of formaldehyde in the extract but it was not present in the body lotion. According to its safety data sheet, the Lonicera extract could leach trace amounts of hexamine and other formaldehyde releasers from epoxy or phenolic-based plastic packaging. As the patch test with the extract 2% in water was positive, the extract must have extracted quite a lot of formaldehyde from its plastic container. The package of the patient's body lotion was made of high-density polyethylene, a material that is not related to formaldehyde, and GC/MS analysis did not detect formaldehyde in it. Therefore, the nature of the allergen(s) in the body lotion remained obscure (1).

Presence in cosmetic products and chemical analyses

In the USA, in April 2017, Lonicera japonica (honeysuckle) flower extract was present in 116 of 56,714 cosmetic products of which the composition is known in FDA's Voluntary Cosmetic Registration Program (VCRP) (data obtained from FDA, May 2017). In March 2017, Lonicera japonica (Japanese honeysuckle) flower extract was present in 154 of 65,431 cosmetic products of which the composition is known in EWG's Skin Deep Cosmetics Database, USA (http://www.ewg.org/skindeep/).

LITERATURE

1   Gallo R, Paolini S, Salis A, Cinotti E, Parodi A. Positive patch test reaction to *Lonicera japonica* extract in a patient sensitized to formaldehyde. Contact Dermatitis 2012;66:47-49

2.280 MACADAMIA TERNIFOLIA SEED OIL

IDENTIFICATION

Description/definition : Macadamia ternifolia seed oil is the fixed oil obtained from the nuts of the bushnut,
Macadamia ternifolia, Proteaceae. It consists primarily of the glycerides of fatty acids
Chemical class(es) : Fats and oils
Other names : Macadamia nut oil
CAS registry number (s) : 128497-20-1; 129811-19-4
Function(s) in cosmetics : EU: emollient. USA: skin-conditioning agents - occlusive
Patch testing : unknown; suggested: 30% pet.

CONTACT ALLERGY

Case reports and case series
A woman had allergic contact cheilitis from macadamia nut oil in a lipstick. It was not stated how the material was tested (undiluted?) nor whether control tests have been performed. The picture of the positive patch test 'reactions' (only one was shown, but the patient also reacted to diisostearyl malate) was not quite convincing in showing a classic positive allergic patch test reaction (1).

LITERATURE

1   Sugiura K, Sugiura M. Di-isostearyl malate and macademia nut oil in lipstick caused cheilitis. J Eur Acad Dermatol Venereol 2009;23:606-607

2.281   MAGNOLIA GRANDIFLORA BARK EXTRACT

IDENTIFICATION

Description/definition	: Magnolia grandiflora bark extract is the extract of the bark of the *Magnolia grandiflora* L., Magnoliaceae
Chemical class(es)	: Botanical products and botanical derivatives
CAS registry number (s)	: 85085-47-8
EC number(s)	: 285-376-6
Function(s) in cosmetics	: EU: antimicrobial; antioxidant; skin conditioning. USA: antimicrobial agents; antioxidants; skin-conditioning agents - miscellaneous
Patch testing	: No data available

CONTACT ALLERGY

Case reports and case series

Magnolia grandiflora bark extract was stated to be the (or an) allergen in 2 patients in a group of 603 individuals suffering from cosmetic dermatitis, seen in the period 2010-2015 in Leuven, Belgium (1).

Presence in cosmetic products and chemical analyses

In the USA, in April 2017, Magnolia grandiflora bark extract was present in 13 of 56,714 cosmetic products of which the composition is known in FDA's Voluntary Cosmetic Registration Program (VCRP) (data obtained from FDA, May 2017). In March 2017, Magnolia grandiflora bark extract was present in 8 of 65,431 cosmetic products of which the composition is known in EWG's Skin Deep Cosmetics Database, USA (http://www.ewg.org/skindeep/).

LITERATURE

1   Goossens A. Cosmetic contact allergens. Cosmetics 2016, 3, 5; doi:10.3390/cosmetics3010005

2.282 MAGNOLIA OFFICINALIS BARK EXTRACT

IDENTIFICATION

Description/definition : Magnolia officinalis bark extract is an extract of the bark of *Magnolia officinalis*, Magnoliaceae
Chemical class(es) : Botanical products and botanical derivatives
Function(s) in cosmetics : EU: antimicrobial; skin conditioning. USA: antimicrobial agents; skin-conditioning agents - miscellaneous
Patch testing : 0.5% pet. (1,2,3)

GENERAL

Magnolia officinalis is native to the mountains and valleys of China. Magnolia bark, obtained from its dried stem, root or branch, has been used for centuries in traditional Asian medicine for the treatment of anxiety, sleeping disorders, and allergic diseases. Its main active ingredients are magnolol and honokiol, two polyphenolic compounds. Various alleged beneficial pharmacological properties have been found, including anti-inflammatory, antioxidant, anticancer, antidepressant and hepatoprotective effects. The extract can be found in dietary supplements and has been proposed for use in chewing gum and mints for its breath-freshening effect. In addition, Magnolia officinalis bark extract has been used as a cosmetic ingredient for some years in recommended concentrations of 0.1-0.5%, especially in 'anti-ageing' cosmetic products for the face, 'protective formulas', and 'anti-redness skin care' products (1,2).

CONTACT ALLERGY

Case reports and case series

A woman presented with acute vesicular, edematous and pruritic dermatitis of the face a few days after applying a new 'anti-ageing' day care cream on her face. She had used a similar cream for night care a few months earlier, but had stopped using it after 3 months because of redness and itching. Patch tests gave positive reactions to the anti-ageing cream, tested as is. A ROAT was strongly positive on D3. When tested with the ingredients, the patient had a positive response to M. officinalis bark extract 0.5% pet.; the material tested in 10 controls gave only negative reactions (2). In a virtually identical case report, a female individual had ACD of the face from Magnolia officinalis bark extract in a 'volume-filler' day and night cream (same brand as the previous patient). A ROAT was strongly positive after already 1 day and when she was patch tested with the constituents of the cream that she had previously reacted to, there was a positive patch test to Magnolia officinalis bark extract at 0.5% pet. only (3).

In one clinic in Leuven, Belgium, specialized in cosmetic allergy, 3 patients reacting to the extract in 'anti-aging' creams were seen in the period May 2014 to February 2015 (1). Two of them used a day or night cream of the same brand as the patients in refs. 2 and 3, the third used an anti-age day cream SPF 15 of another brand, but from the same manufacturer. All three had dermatitis of the face and reacted to their suspected cosmetic products and to the ingredient Magnolia officinalis bark extract, tested at 0.5% pet. Two of the three also had positive patch tests to the related Magnolia *grandiflora* bark extract 0.05% pet. (1).

Cross-reactions, pseudo-cross-reactions and co-reactions

Magnolia grandiflora bark extract (1).

Presence in cosmetic products and chemical analyses

In the USA, in April 2017, Magnolia officinalis bark extract was present in 14 of 56,714 cosmetic products of which the composition is known in FDA's Voluntary Cosmetic Registration Program (VCRP) (data obtained from FDA, May 2017). In March 2017, Magnolia officinalis bark extract was present in 44 of 65,431 cosmetic products of which the composition is known in EWG's Skin Deep Cosmetics Database, USA (http://www.ewg.org/skindeep/).

LITERATURE

1 Ghys K, De Palma A, Vandevenne A, Werbrouck J, Goossens A. *Magnolia officinalis* bark extract, a recently identified contact allergen in 'anti-ageing' cosmetics. Contact Dermatitis 2015;73:130-132
2 Raison-Peyron N, Césaire A, Du-Thanh A, Dereure O. Allergic contact dermatitis caused by *Magnolia officinalis* bark extract in a facial anti-ageing cream. Contact Dermatitis 2015;72:416-417
3 Nilausen TD, Johansen JD, Thyssen JP. Allergic contact dermatitis of the face caused by *Magnolia officinalis* bark extract. Contact Dermatitis 2016;75:385-387

2.283   MALEATED SOYBEAN OIL

IDENTIFICATION

Description/definition : Maleated soybean oil is a modified soybean oil in which some of the unsaturation has been converted to a cyclic dicarboxylic acid generally conforming to the formula shown below, where R represents the unreacted residual soybean oil
Chemical class(es) : Fats and oils
Other names : Soybean oil, maleated; Ceraphyl® GA (or Ceraphyl® GA-D, deodorized and antioxidant-treated); the commercial products are no longer available
CAS registry number (s) : 68648-66-8
EC number(s) : 272-000-0
Function(s) in cosmetics : EU: emollient; skin conditioning. USA: skin-conditioning agents – miscellaneous
Patch testing : 20% acetone (4)

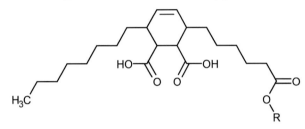

GENERAL

Maleated soybean oil, the fumaric acid adduct of soybean oil, is an amber-yellow, viscous, oily liquid that was used in the textile industry and was introduced in the 1990s in cosmetics, since it penetrates the stratum corneum and alters the structure of epidermal lipids. It softens the skin and improves the water-resistance of sunscreens. After receiving complaints from French dermatologists, the producer of the maleated soybean oil had already performed a molecular distillation, eliminating shorter-chain fatty acids. Since this 'purified' form had been substituted in cosmetics, the company had had no more complaints, suggesting the purified form to be less sensitizing. However, 4 patients allergic to the crude substance also reacted to the 'purified' form (2,4). Shortly thereafter, the producer stopped delivering the substance for commercial purposes (2). Maleated soybean oil is a complex mixture, and the precise identity of the allergen is unknown (4).

CONTACT ALLERGY

Case reports and case series

Maleated soybean oil was responsible for 1 out of 959 cases of non-fragrance cosmetic allergy where the causal allergen was identified, Belgium, 2000-2010 (1). One patient had allergic contact dermatitis from maleated soybean oil in a facial moisturizer (2). In another case, cosmetic allergy was ascribed (not certain) to maleated soybean oil (3). Four patients were seen in a 9-months period in 1993 in a clinic in Leuven, Belgium, who had allergic contact dermatitis from the same 'skin repair' cosmetic product; they all reacted to pure maleated soybean oil and later to 'purified', oxidized and irradiated soybean oils at 20% acetone and some to 10% acetone (4).

Presence in cosmetic products and chemical analyses

In the USA, in April 2017, soybean oil, maleated was present in 13 of 56,714 cosmetic products of which the composition is known in FDA's Voluntary Cosmetic Registration Program (VCRP) (data obtained from FDA, May 2017). In April 2017, maleated soybean oil was present in 17 of 66,223 cosmetic products of which the composition is known in EWG's Skin Deep Cosmetics Database, USA (http://www.ewg.org/skindeep/).

LITERATURE

1   Travassos AR, Claes L, Boey L, Drieghe J, Goossens A. Non-fragrance allergens in specific cosmetic products. Contact Dermatitis 2011;65:276-285
2   Le Coz C-J, Lefèbre C. Contact dermatitis from maleated soybean oil: last gasps of an expiring cosmetic allergen. Contact Dermatitis 2000;43:118-119
3   Wantke F, Hemmer W, Gotz M, Jarisch R. Contact dermatitis from jojoba oil and myristyl lactate/maleated soybean oil. Contact Dermatitis 1996;34:1-72
4   Dooms-Goossens A, Buyse L, Stals H. Maleated soybean oil, a new cosmetic allergen. Contact Dermatitis 1995;32:49-51

2.284 MANDELIC ACID

IDENTIFICATION

Description/definition : Mandelic acid is the organic acid that conforms to the formula shown below
Chemical class(es) : Carboxylic acids
Chemical/IUPAC name : 2-Hydroxy-2-phenylacetic acid
Other names : Benzeneacetic acid, α-hydroxy-; phenylglycolic acid; almond acid; amygdalic acid
CAS registry number (s) : 90-64-2
EC number(s) : 202-007-6
Merck Index monograph : 7051
Function(s) in cosmetics : EU: antimicrobial. USA: not reported
Patch testing : 5% pet. (1)
Molecular formula : $C_8H_8O_3$

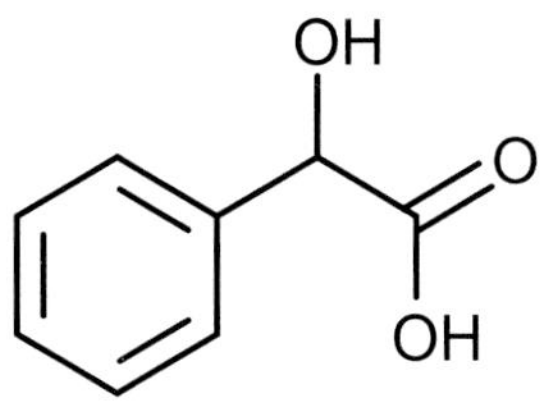

GENERAL

Mandelic is an α-acetoxy acid, that may be present in lip salves used for the prevention of recurrent herpes labialis, as it allegedly increases stratum corneum thickness by enhancing corneocyte cohesion (1).

CONTACT ALLERGY

Case reports and case series

A woman had recurrent herpes simplex infections of the lips for 3 years in relationship to solar exposure. Her recurrences were treated with an acyclovir antiviral cream and, as a preventive measure, a lip salve. At one point, while the patient was using the lip product, she developed an edematous desquamative cheilitis. As she believed this to be a fresh recurrence of the herpes, she began to treat herself with the antiviral cream, which resulted in an intense worsening of the cheilitis within a few hours. Patch tests were performed later, showing positive reactions to 2 antiviral creams, their constituent acyclovir, and (probably) to the lip salve. All ingredients of this cosmetic product were tested later, and only mandelic acid reacted at 5% pet. Eighteen controls were negative (1).

Presence in cosmetic products and chemical analyses

In the USA, in April 2017, mandelic acid was present in 40 of 56,714 cosmetic products of which the composition is known in FDA's Voluntary Cosmetic Registration Program (VCRP) (data obtained from FDA, May 2017). In March 2017, mandelic acid was present in 7 of 65,431 cosmetic products of which the composition is known in EWG's Skin Deep Cosmetics Database, USA (http://www.ewg.org/skindeep/).

LITERATURE

1   Aguirre A, Manzano D, Izu R, Gardeazabal J, Pérez JLD. Allergic contact cheilitis from mandelic acid. Contact Dermatitis 1994;31:133-134

2.285   MENTHOXYPROPANEDIOL

IDENTIFICATION

Description/definition	: Menthoxypropanediol is the organic compound that conforms to the formula shown below
Chemical class(es)	: Alcohols
Chemical/IUPAC name	: 3-(5-Methyl-2-propan-2-ylcyclohexyl)oxypropane-1,2-diol
Other names	: 3-{[5-Methyl-2-(1-methylethyl)cyclohexyl]oxy}-; 3-l-menthoxypropane-1,2-diol; L-menthylglyceryl ether
CAS registry number (s)	: 87061-04-9
EC number(s)	: 289-296-2
Function(s) in cosmetics	: EU: masking; refreshing. USA: flavoring agent; fragrance ingredient
Patch testing	: 5% pet. (1)
Molecular formula	: $C_{13}H_{26}O_3$

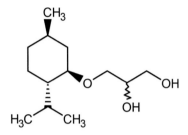

GENERAL
Menthoxypropanediol is a synthetic derivative of menthol.

CONTACT ALLERGY

Case reports and case series
A woman presented with perioral erythema and scaling. She had been using several lip cosmetics including a 'medicated' lip balm. Patch testing with the European baseline series, a cosmetic series, and her own cosmetics, showed a positive patch test reaction to the lip balm, tested undiluted. A repeated open application test (ROAT) with the incriminated product caused an itchy erythematous and papular reaction after a few days. Later, all ingredients of the lip balm were tested separately and the patient reacted only to menthoxypropanediol 5% pet.; menthol 5% pet. was negative. Menthoxypropanediol was present in the lip balm in a concentration of 0.4%. Later, the patient was tested with a dilution series of this chemical. The reaction to 5% pet. was strong, to 2% positive on day 3 only and to 0.5% negative on D2 and ?+ on D3. Testing with menthoxypropanediol 5% pet. was negative in five controls (1).

Cross-reactions, pseudo-cross-reactions and co-reactions
Not to menthol (1).

Presence in cosmetic products and chemical analyses
In the USA, in April 2017, Menthoxypropanediol was present in 162 of 56,714 cosmetic products of which the composition is known in FDA's Voluntary Cosmetic Registration Program (VCRP) (data obtained from FDA, May 2017). In March 2017, menthoxypropanediol was present in 34 of 65,431 cosmetic products of which the composition is known in EWG's Skin Deep Cosmetics Database, USA (http://www.ewg.org/skindeep/).

LITERATURE
1   Franken L, de Groot A, Laheij-de Boer A-M. Allergic contact dermatitis caused by menthoxypropanediol in a lip cosmetic. Contact Dermatitis 2013;69:377-378

2.286   METHENAMINE

IDENTIFICATION

Description/definition   : Methenamine is the organic amine that conforms to the formula shown below
Chemical class(es)   : Amines
Chemical/IUPAC name   : 1,3,5,7-Tetraazatricyclo[3.3.1.1(3,7)]decane
Other names   : Hexamethylenetetramine; hexamine; urotropin
CAS registry number (s)   : 100-97-0
EC number(s)   : 202-905-8
CIR review(s)   : J Am Coll Toxicol 1992;11:531-558 (access: www.cir-safety.org/ingredients)
Merck Index monograph : 7308
Function(s) in cosmetics : EU: preservative. USA: cosmetic biocides; preservatives
EU cosmetic restrictions : Regulated in Annex V/30 of the Regulation (EC) No. 1223/2009
Patch testing   : 2.0% pet. (Chemotechnique); 1% pet. (SmartPracticeEurope, SmartPracticeCanada)
Molecular formula   : $C_6H_{12}N_4$

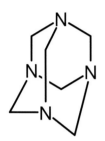

GENERAL

Methenamine is a quaternary ammonium compound with formaldehyde-releasing capacity, often used as preservative. The chemical does not itself have antimicrobial activity, which is derived from the formaldehyde released under hydrolytic conditions in an acidic environment (6). Methenamine is manufactured by the reaction of formaldehyde and ammonia in the liquid phase in a closed system (15). It is very infrequently used as a preservative in cosmetics and other products applied topically. Its main use is in the plastics industry for curing processes of phenol-formaldehyde resins (resols, novolaks) or the manufacture of binders for core sand. It is also employed in the rubber industry as (secondary) vulcanization accelerator or together with resorcinol and silica as adhesion promoter. Further applications are diverse chemical syntheses, the manufacture of nitrilotriacetic acid, explosives or fuel tablets (4,5,6,15). Methenamine was formerly used as a urinary tract anti-infective drug (6).

CONTACT ALLERGY

Testing in groups of patients

Results of studies patch testing methenamine in consecutive patients suspected of contact dermatitis (routine testing) and in groups of selected patients are shown in table 2.286.1. In routine testing (one study only), the frequency of sensitization was 1% in a very small study from Turkey (14). In three studies patch testing groups of *selected* patients (healthy student volunteers, patients tested with a cosmetic series, patients allergic to formaldehyde or quaternium-15), rates of sensitization ranged from 0.3% to 2.1% (table 2.286.1). In a group of 931 patients allergic to formaldehyde or quaternium-15, or suspected of cosmetic or industrial contact dermatitis, there were – surprisingly – only 3 (0.3%) positive reactions. This may be related to the fact that – under certain conditions – methenamine was shown to release little formaldehyde compared to other formaldehyde-releasers (9) and to the fact that no hydrolysis of formaldehyde is possible in a petrolatum base. If the authors would have tested with methenamine 1% in water (which at pH 6.5 may contain 0.37% (3700 ppm) free formaldehyde [3]), the results might have been drastically different.

In 2/3 studies, no relevance data were provided. In a study from the USA, all 18 positive patch test reactions were considered to be relevant (2). However, relevance figures included 'questionable' and 'past' relevance and causative products were not mentioned. It was not stated how many co-reactions there were to formaldehyde (2).

Table 2.286.1 Patch testing in groups of patients

Years and Country	Test conc. & vehicle	Number of patients tested | positive (%)		Selection of patients (S); Relevance (R); Comments (C)	Ref.
Routine testing					
2005-2006 Turkey		93	1 (1%)	R: the reaction was considered to be relevant	14
Testing in groups of selected patients					
2011 China	2% pet.	201	3 (1.5%)	S: healthy student volunteers 19-30 years; R: not stated	13
2005-2009 Spain	2% pet.	931	3 (0.3%)	S: patients allergic to formaldehyde or quaternium-15, or suspicion of cosmetic or industrial contact dermatitis; R: not specified	1
2000-2007 USA	2% pet.	870	18 (2.1%)	S: patients tested with a supplemental cosmetic screening series; R: 100%; C: weak study: a. high rate of macular erythema and weak reactions; b. relevance figures included 'questionable' and 'past' relevance	2

Case reports and case series
One patient had allergic contact dermatitis from formaldehyde released by methenamine in an antiperspirant spray (4).

Contact allergy to methenamine in non-cosmetic products
One patient had occupational allergic contact dermatitis from methenamine in core molding, not related to formaldehyde allergy (5). In several instances, people who developed ACD from formaldehyde in antiperspirants experienced persisting axillary dermatitis due to the use of rubber dress shields that contained methenamine (7). Formerly, patients sensitized by external exposure to formaldehyde have developed systemic contact dermatitis ('eczematous contact-type dermatitis medicamentosa') by ingesting medicines that contain methenamine (8). In early years, methenamine was a frequent sensitizer in the rubber industry (10,16,17).

In the 1980s, sensitization to methenamine had become rare except from its presence in textile adhesives (10). Two workers in a plant producing methenamine had to be transferred because of skin problems. One had dermatitis of the face, the other suffered from generalized redness, itching, dermatitis and conjunctivitis. Later, they were patch tested and both reacted to methenamine 1% and 2% in water (15).

Cross-reactions, pseudo-cross-reactions and co-reactions
As methenamine is a formaldehyde-releaser, pseudo-cross-reactions may be expected to formaldehyde (12) and other formaldehyde-releasers including quaternium-15, imidazolidinyl urea and DMDM hydantoin (1,4). A group of 32 patients allergic to quaternium-15 was tested with methenamine 1% pet. and 11 (34%) had positive patch tests. As both chemicals are formaldehyde-releasers, this co-reactivity could be interpreted as being caused by formaldehyde sensitivity (pseudo-cross-reactivity). However, approximately the same proportion, 1/3, of both formaldehyde-positive and formaldehyde-negative quaternium-15 sensitive patients also reacted to methenamine. These results suggest, according to the author, that the simultaneous reactions to quaternium-15 and methenamine can also be related to their related chemical structure: both are quaternary ammonium compounds, quaternium-15 being a chloroallyl derivative of methenamine (11). However, in a Spanish study, some patients allergic to methenamine also reacted to formaldehyde, DMDM hydantoin, 2-bromo-2-nitropropane-1,3-diol and imidazolidinyl urea, which are not structurally related to methenamine. Thus, these co-reactivities were almost certainly caused by formaldehyde sensitivity (1).

Presence of methenamine in cosmetic products
In May 2017, methenamine was present in 4 of 66,658 cosmetic products of which the composition is known in EWG's Skin Deep Cosmetics Database, USA (http://www.ewg.org/skindeep/). In the USA, in April 2017, methenamine was present in 5 of 56,714 cosmetic products of which the composition is known in FDA's Voluntary Cosmetic Registration Program (VCRP) (data obtained from FDA, May 2017).

Amounts of free formaldehyde released by methenamine and chemical analyses
A 1% aqueous solution prepared by a supplier of patch test materials at pH 6.5 contained 0.37% (3700 ppm) free formaldehyde (3). In recent experiments, methenamine in cosmetics, after 2-bromo-2-nitropropane-1,3-diol, released the lowest amount of formaldehyde of all formaldehyde-releasers investigated (paraformaldehyde, diazolidinyl urea, DMDM hydantoin, quaternium-15 , imidazolidinyl urea, methenamine, 2-bromo-2-nitropropane-1,3-diol (9).

OTHER SIDE EFFECTS

Irritant contact dermatitis
Irritant contact dermatitis of the hands may develop in subjects with high exposure to methenamine (15).

Miscellaneous side effects
Occupational asthma caused by methenamine has been reported (18).

LITERATURE

1   Latorre N, Borrego L, Fernández-Redondo V, García-Bravo B, Giménez-Arnau AM, Sánchez J, et al. Patch testing with formaldehyde and formaldehyde-releasers: multicenter study in Spain (2005-2009). Contact Dermatitis 2011;65:286-292

2   Wetter DA, Yiannias JA, Prakash AV, Davis MD, Farmer SA, el-Azhary RA, et al. Results of patch testing to personal care product allergens in a standard series and a supplemental cosmetic series: an analysis of 945 patients from the Mayo Clinic Contact Dermatitis Group, 2000-2007. J Am Acad Dermatol 2010;63:789-798

3   Emeis D, De Groot AC, Brinkmann J. Determination of formaldehyde in formaldehyde-releaser patch test preparations. Contact Dermatitis 2010;63:57-62

4   González-Pérez R, González-Hermosa R, Aseginolaza B, Luis Díaz-Ramón J, Soloeta R. Allergic contact dermatitis from methenamine in an antiperspirant spray. Contact Dermatitis 2003;49:266

5   Hayakawa R, Arima Y, Hirose O, Takeuchi Y. Allergic contact dermatitis due to hexamethylenetetramine in core molding. Contact Dermatitis 1988;18:226-228

6   Expert Panel of the Cosmetic Ingredient Review. Final report on the safety assessment of methenamine. J Am Coll Toxicol 1992;11:531-558

7   Fisher AA. Current contact news - Dermatitis due to formaldehyde-releasing agents in cosmetics and medicaments. Cutis 1978;22:655, 658, 662, 664, 708

8   Sulzberger MB. Dermatologic Allergy. Springfield, IL, USA: Charles C. Thomas, 1940:380 (cited in ref. 6)

9   Lv C, Hou J, Xie W, Cheng H. Investigation on formaldehyde release from preservatives in cosmetics. Int J Cosm Sci 2015;37:474-478

10 Taylor JS. Rubber. In: Fisher AA, Ed. Contact Dermatitis, 3rd edition. Philadelphia: Lea & Febiger, 1986: 637

11 Aalto-Korte K. Simultaneous allergic reactions to quaternium-15 and methenamine. Contact Dermatitis 2000;42:365

12 Aalto-Korte K, Kuuliala O, Suuronen K, Alanko K. Occupational contact allergy to formaldehyde and formaldehyde releasers. Contact Dermatitis 2008;59:280-289

13 Zhao J, Li LF. Contact sensitization to cosmetic series of allergens in a general population in Beijing. J Cosmet Dermatol 2014;13:68-71

14 Ada S, Seçkin D. Patch testing in allergic contact dermatitis: is it useful to perform the cosmetic series in addition to the European standard series? J Eur Acad Dermatol Venereol 2010;24:1192-1196

15 Merget R, Topcu M, Friese K, Vormberg R, Fuchs T, Raulf-Heimsoth M, Breitstadt R. A cross-sectional study of workers in the chemical industry with occupational exposure to hexamethylenetetramine. Int Arch Occup Environ Health 1999;72:533-538

16 Schwartz L, Tulipan L, Birmingham DJ. Occupational diseases of the skin, 3rd ed. Philadelphia, USA: Lea & Febiger, 1957

17 Williams TM, Hickey JLS, Bishop CC. Health hazard evaluation report no HETA-83-196-1492, Goodyear Tire and Rubber Company, Gadsden, Alabama. Health and Human Services, Cincinatti (cited in ref. 15)

18 Gelfand HH. Respiratory allergy due to chemical compounds encountered in the rubber, lacquer, shellac, and beauty culture industries. J Allergy 1963;34:374-381

2.287   METHOXY PEG-17/DODECYL GLYCOL COPOLYMER

IDENTIFICATION

Description/definition   : Methoxy PEG-17/dodecyl glycol copolymer is the polymer that conforms generally to the formula shown below, where x has an average value of 17 and y has an average value of 1

Chemical class(es)   : Alkoxylated alcohols; synthetic polymers

Other names   : Oxirane, decyl-, polymer with oxirane, monomethyl ether (17 mol EO, 1 mol decyl oxirane, average molar ratios)

CAS registry number (s)   : 88507-00-0

Function(s) in cosmetics : EU: emulsifying; skin conditioning. USA: dispersing agents – nonsurfactant; emulsion stabilizers; skin-conditioning agents – miscellaneous; viscosity increasing agents – nonaqueous

Patch testing   : 10% pet. (3)

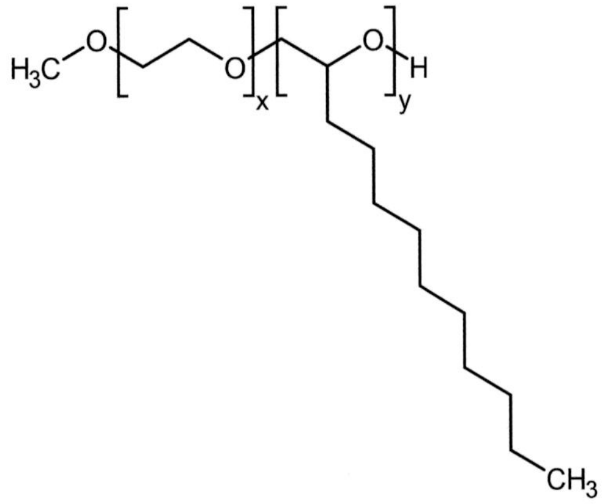

GENERAL

Copolymers are important ingredients in cosmetics, added because of their antistatic, film-forming, binding, suspending, viscosity-increasing, skin-conditioning, and emulsion-stabilizing properties. Copolymers have been underestimated for a long time as to their sensitizing capacities because of their large structures and high molecular weights. Allergic contact dermatitis to copolymers in cosmetics, however, does occur, but the exact nature of the hapten is still unknown. The copolymers are not likely to be haptens themselves in view of their large molecular weights. The sensitizer could be an additive, an impurity, a product that forms during polymerization, a residual monomer, or a degradation product (4).

CONTACT ALLERGY

Case reports and case series

A woman with no past history of dermatitis was seen with acute dermatitis of the legs and forearms, which had developed within 24 hours of applying a new moisturizing milk. The dermatitis cleared within 2 weeks by avoiding the cosmetic and applying topical corticosteroids. Patch tests were performed with a standard series, some additional allergens and the patient's cosmetic products. There was a positive reaction to the milk at D2. Next, a repeated open application test (ROAT) was performed with the milk, which resulted in a vesicular eczematous reaction within 3 days. Later, patch testing was carried out with the ingredients of the cosmetic and again with the milk, which confirmed the contact allergy to the milk and gave a positive reaction to its ingredient methoxy PEG-17/dodecyl glycol copolymer tested as is and 10% pet.; there was no reaction to the copolymer 1% pet. A ROAT in the antecubital fossa with the chemical 'as is' was already beginning to be positive after 2 days. Methoxy PEG-17/dodecyl glycol copolymer was present in the moisturizing milk at a concentration of 2% (3).

The authors suggested that the hapten is likely to be an alkyl epoxide used for polymerization, a by-pass product occurring during polymerization, or some impurity like 1,4-dioxane, obtained from dimerization of ethylene oxide and inherent to all PEGs (polyethylene glycols) (3).

Cross-reactions, pseudo-cross-reactions and co-reactions

Methoxy PEG-22/dodecyl glycol copolymer (1,2)

Presence in cosmetic products and chemical analyses

In the USA, in April 2017, methoxy PEG-17 dodecyl glycol copolymer was present in zero of 56,714 cosmetic products of which the composition is known in FDA's Voluntary Cosmetic Registration Program (VCRP) (data obtained from FDA, May 2017). In March 2017, methoxy PEG-17/dodecyl glycol copolymer was present in zero of 65,431 cosmetic products of which the composition is known in EWG's Skin Deep Cosmetics Database, USA (http://www.ewg.org/skindeep/).

LITERATURE

1 Goossens A, Armingaud P, Avenel-Audran M, Begon-Bagdassarian I, Constandt L, Giordano-Labadie F, et al. An epidemic of allergic contact dermatitis due to epilating products. Contact Dermatitis 2002;46:67-70

2 Goossens A. An epidemic of allergic contact dermatitis due to epilating products. Contact Dermatitis 2001;45:360

3 Le Coz C-J, Heid E. Allergic contact dermatitis from methoxy PEG-17/dodecyl glycol copolymer (Elfacos® OW 100). Contact Dermatitis 2001;44:308-309

4 Quartier S, Garmyn M, Becart S, Goossens A. Allergic contact dermatitis to copolymers in cosmetics – case report and review of the literature. Contact Dermatitis 2006;55:257-267